FUNDAMENTALS

OF

AQUACULTURE

"The book is highly readable and comprehensive in scope. It represents a lifetime experience of a teacher and scientist and will be a most welcome contribution to the development of aquaculture worldwide."

Rafael D. Guerrero III, Ph.D., executive director of the Philippine Council for Aquatic and Marine Research Development; aquaculture advisor International Foundation of Science, member Philippine National Academy for Science and Technology.

"Its (book) coverage is worldwide, with extensive documentation of practices in Southeast Asia. The writing is clear and very readable. I believe that the book can best be summarized as an aquaculture book for all aquaculturists."

Lo-chai Chen, Ph.D., professor Department of Biology, San Diego State University; author of the book "Aquaculture in Taiwan."

"Jim Avault has written a wonderfully authoritative, understandable, and comprehensive text on aquaculture. (It is) one to be savored by the neophyte as well as the experienced culturist."

Joseph P. McCraren, late executive director of the National Aquaculture Association and of the U.S. Trout Farmers Association; past president of the Fish Culture Section of the American Fisheries Society, cited by the U.S. Joint Subcommittee on Aquaculture.

"Professor Avault has done a masterful job in authoring the Fundamentals of Aquaculture. This book covers a wide scope of relevant topics ranging from the whys and hows of aquaculture to marketing and financial considerations. It is well illustrated with numerous high-quality photographs, and each of the 17 chapters is richly referenced. Those who are seriously interested in or presently engaged in aquaculture should acquire this book."

Donovan D. Moss, Ph.D., professor emeritus Department of Fisheries and Allied Aquacultures Auburn University; past president of the Fish Culture Section of the American Fisheries Society, inductee Fish Culture Hall of Fame.

"This book should be read by everyone thinking about entering the field of aquaculture. If I were a banker financing fish farmers, I would require all loan applicants to read this book before I would read their loan applications. This book is not only a wealth of knowledge about fish farming, it is interesting to read. Student, potential fish farmer, fish farmer, or banker, this is the first book on aquaculture they should read. It will be mandatory that all employees of Fish Breeders of Idaho Inc. read this book."

Leo E. Ray, Fish Breeders of Idaho Inc.; past president of the Catfish Farmers of America and of the U.S. Trout Farmers Association.

FUNDAMENTALS OF AQUACULTURE

A Step-by-Step Guide to Commercial Aquaculture

By James W. Avault, Jr., Ph.D.
School of Forestry, Wildlife, and Fisheries
Louisiana Agricultural Experiment Station
Louisiana State University Agricultural Center

AVA Publishing Company Inc.
Baton Rouge, Louisiana
United States of America

Fundamentals of Aquaculture
A Step-by-Step Guide to
Commercial Aquaculture

By James W. Avault, Jr., Ph.D.

Published by:
AVA Publishing Company Inc.
Post Office Box 84060
Baton Rouge, Louisiana 70884-4060 USA

ISBN 0-9649549-0-7

Cover created by Barbara Corns
Art work by Alyson Gonzalez
Copy editing by Jane Honeycutt

Printed in the United States of America

10 9 8 7 6 5 4 3 2 1

DEDICATION

This book is dedicated to my parents, James and Eleanor Avault.

ABOUT THE AUTHOR

James W. Avault, Jr. was born 20 May 1935 in East St. Louis, Illinois. He developed a love of agriculture and of the outdoors as a young man. After an honorable discharge from the U.S. Navy in 1957, he entered the University of Missouri. He pursued a bachelor of science degree in agriculture with emphasis in wildlife conservation. To learn more about wildlife, he sought summer employment between semesters. No jobs in wildlife *per se* were available at that time, but he got a job at the national fish hatchery in Welaka, Florida. This experience opened new opportunities. Here was a chance to combine the outdoors and agriculture through fish husbandry. He later worked at two other national fish hatcheries, in Natchitoches, Louisiana and in Frankfort, Kentucky. In 1961 he entered Auburn University, Auburn, Alabama. He received the Master of Science degree in 1963 and the Ph. D. in 1966, both in aquaculture. After this, he joined the faculty at Louisiana State University where he began teaching and conducting research in aquaculture. Through research, he played a role in developing the emerging aquaculture industry, particularly crawfish farming. He was the architect of the State Aquaculture Plan for Louisiana. The Plan became the blueprint for the aquaculture program of the LSU Agricultural Center.

Dr. Avault has been active in professional organizations, and he has served as president of the World Mariculture (Aquaculture) Society, the Fish Culture Section of the American Fisheries Society, and the International Association of Astacology. Avault is recognized as one of the founding fathers of the World Aquaculture Society (WAS) and the International Association of Astacology. The WAS home office is located on the campus of Louisiana State University.

Dr. Avault has served as a consultant or advisor in more than 20 countries on five continents. This plus his other broad experiences make him well qualified to write the book "Fundamentals of Aquaculture."

CHAPTERS

CONTENTS

PREFACE

This book is written as a text at the college level and as a guide for the beginning fish farmer or aquaculturist. It also serves as a reference for someone who is established in aquaculture. The book attempts to cover all aspects of commercial aquaculture from A to Z. The book, however, is not a how-to-do-it book nor does it provide cook-book directions for commercial aquaculture. Rather it is meant to serve as a step-by-step guide for someone contemplating commercial aquaculture or for someone already engaged in commercial aquaculture. The book will aid you in asking all of the right questions and how and where to get the answers.

The book outlines and discusses the fundamentals of commercial aquaculture. In doing so, a discipline approach is taken rather than a species approach. By understanding the fundamentals of aquaculture, you should be able to culture any species, assuming the knowledge base and infrastructure are present. For example, in Louisiana rainbow trout (*Oncorhynchus mykiss*) and marine shrimp are not cultured commercially. However, the author has a former student who owns and operates a trout farm in Virginia and another student who has managed a shrimp farm in Ecuador. The book has attempted to cover all aspects of commercial aquaculture to provide the student with the fundamentals of aquaculture. Some readers will note that certain chapters may not be of interest to them. For example, a trout farmer who uses raceways may have less interest in the chapter on fertilization, liming, and pond muds. Some instructors, too, may wish to use certain portions of the book to meet the particular needs of their students. Therefore, each chapter has been written to stand alone. For example, when a species is first mentioned in a new chapter, its scientific name is given even though it may have been given in a previous chapter.

Since this book is designed as a text for the student and as a guide for someone in commercial aquaculture, every attempt is made to make the book as readable as possible. At the beginning of each chapter, the purpose of that chapter is stated. Each chapter is organized in outline form and is divided into many subheadings and numerical points. In certain chapters problems are presented, and mathematical solutions are given. At the end of each chapter, study questions are given that review major points. A comprehensive reference section is presented at the end of each chapter for further reading.

ACKNOWLEDGMENTS

The author wishes to acknowledge the late H.S. Swingle, and T.V.R. Pillay for their helpful suggestions on the book outline.

The following people helped in typing the book: Sebell Jones typed many of the original chapters that were used as mimeograph handouts in class. Kim Miller typed a number of the chapters in draft form. Others who assisted with revisions included Tammy Baum, Jeannine de la Bretonne, and Jean Doquet. Craig Lilystrom, Mark Lamon, and Paul Medley gave helpful advice on use of the word processor. Mike Pursley spent many hours assisting the author in formatting the book. Cathy Macmurdo is appreciated for her help in secretarial matters.

A number of colleagues read drafts of chapters and offered suggestions. They include Claude E. Boyd, G.L. Schroeder, Tom Lovell, Robert P. Romaire, Bruce McGoogan, Lynn Dellenbarger, Terry Tiersch, Jill Jenkins-Tiersch, Karim Belhadjali, Dudley Culley, Jack Snow, Jay Huner, Roger Miller, Don Moss, Harold Webber, Wayne Swingle, Rex Caffey, Jimmy Avery, John Bennett, and Addie Cormie. John Hargreaves read drafts of many chapters and made a significant contribution for improving the book. Students offered many helpful suggestions. The author learned much from them.

Kelly Harle and Barbara Corns, graphic design; Ms. Frankie Gould, art direction; and Alyson Gonzalez, illustrator, are greatly appreciated for their advice on the art work in this book. The line drawings were done by Ms. Gonzalez. Nimje Rinaldi de Oliver developed in the dark room many of the photographs that are used in this book. The book cover was created by artist Barbara Corns. Andy Bishop is thanked for advice on printing the book.

Jane Honeycutt spent many hours copy editing drafts of the manuscript. She played a major role in putting the book together. Her professional advice and counsel were indispensable.

Richard Gallagher and Gregory Gallagher of Aquaculture Magazine receive special thanks. Some of the material in this book was printed in Aquaculture Magazine. Their encouragement in the preparation of the book is most appreciated.

A number of people served as an inspiration to the author: An uncle, Edward Marlin, fostered in the author a love of the outdoors. Ubaldo Cossio played a major role in development of the aquaculture facility of the LSU Agricultural Center. His never-ending enthusiasm and friendship, especially during the early years, are particularly appreciated. H. Rouse Caffey was always there to offer encouragement and support. He played a major role in the development of the aquaculture program of the LSU Agricultural Center. This leadership carried over to the private sector, making Louisiana a major aquaculture state. There were many colleagues from whom so much was learned; they gave freely of their knowledge. To such colleagues as the late Larry de la Bretonne, Jr., Robert P. Romaire, W. Guthrie Perry, Jr., and many others the author owes much.

Tables and parts of tables copyrighted by the National Academy of Sciences are reprinted with permission through the courtesy of the National Academy Press, Washington, D.C. as follows: Nutrient requirement of trout, salmon, and catfish, copyrighted 1977. (page 9 table 3; page 11 table 5 in part; page 18 table 6; page 19 table 7 in part; page 68 table B-5; page 69 table B-6.) Nutrient requirement of warmwater fishes and shellfishes, copyrighted 1983. (page 4 table 3 in part; page 16 table 16 in part; page 50 table 17.) Nutrient requirements of fish, copyrighted 1993. (page 100 table A-3 in part.)

Round pond design copyrighted 1991, page 86 figure 6.2 in The Oceanic Institute Shrimp Manual-- Intensive Shrimp Production Technology is reprinted with permission. Funding was provided by the United States Department of Agriculture through the Gulf Coast Research Laboratory Consortium to the Oceanic Institute under contract numbers CSRS-2-2537 and 88-38808-3320.

The following material copyrighted by John Wiley & Sons is reprinted with permission: Fish and Invertebrate Culture by Stephen H. Spotte copyrighted 1970. (page 4 figure 1 the nitrogen cycle; page 10 figure 3 water circulation through a subgravel filter by the airlift method; page 11 figure 4 operating principles of an airlift; page 54 figure 22 direct-current airstripping device.)

The American Fisheries Society is acknowledged for use of the following material: table 3 from Bonn, E.W. and B.J. Follis. 1967. Effects of hydrogen sulfide on channel catfish, *Ictalurus punctatus*. Transactions of the American Fisheries Society 96(1): 31-36; figure 5, from Boyd, C.E. et al. 1978. Predicting early morning dissolved oxygen concentrations in channel catfish ponds. Transactions of the American Fisheries Society 107(3):484-492; table 1, from Meyer, F.P. 1970. Seasonal fluctuations in the incidence of disease on fish farms, pages 21-29 in S.F. Snieszko, editor. A symposium of diseases of fishes and shellfishes. American Fisheries Society Special Publication No. 5; table 1, from McDaniel, D., editor. 1979. Procedures for the detection and identification of certain fish pathogens. The American Fisheries Society, Fish Health Section, Bethesda, Maryland.

The following material copyrighted by the Interstate Printers and Publishers, Inc. Danville, Illinois is used with permission: Lee, J.S. Commercial Catfish Farming (figures 5.4 and 5.5, respectively on pages 61 and 63.)

DISCLAIMER

This book is designed to provide information on the subject matter covered. It is sold with the understanding that neither the publisher nor the author are engaged in rendering legal, accounting, or other professional services. Every effort has been made to make this book as complete and as accurate as possible. However, there may be mistakes both typographical and in content. The material in this book has in part been obtained from other sources believed to be reliable, but the author and publisher are not responsible for any errors or omissions. Always seek the services of a competent professional before acting on any of the material in this book.

CHAPTER 1
GETTING STARTED

Getting started in commercial aquaculture -- how do you begin? In the first chapter, we define aquaculture and related terms, discuss briefly the history of aquaculture, and tell how to make a start and where to get help. In subsequent chapters, a chronology of topics takes you step-by-step through the development of commercial aquaculture. In the last chapter, we discuss preparation of your business plan.

SOME DEFINITIONS

A commercial fisher paddles a pirogue through the swamps of the Atchafalaya Basin in southern Louisiana. Channel catfish (*Ictalurus punctatus*) are removed from set-hooks baited the night before. Meanwhile, a farmer harvests channel catfish by draining a pond constructed near Baton Rouge, Louisiana. In the first instance, the commercial fisher is catching what nature has provided (capture fisheries). The fish farmer, however, is harvesting a crop that has been stocked and managed (culture fisheries). A person may catch fish just for the fun of it rather than for a profit (sport fisheries) (Figure 1.1).

Figure 1.1 J.C. Tyson with channel catfish he caught in a sportfishing pond.

1

Culture fisheries, usually termed aquaculture, is the commercial growing or farming of plants and animals in fresh, brackish, or saline water. Aquaculture, as defined here, is a type of farming where predictable crops can be managed and grown in waters owned or leased. Desirable numbers of a culture species are stocked or confined in a given area, and waters may be fertilized or the culture species fed. Undesirable environmental factors may be controlled, and the crop is harvested and sold. Thus, the aquatic crop is grown as most any other agricultural crop. Aquaculture may mean culture of channel catfish for food, culture of koi (*Cyprinus carpio*) for ornamental purposes (Figure 1.2), culture of largemouth bass (*Micropterus salmoides*) to stock fee-fishing lakes, culture of golden shiners (*Notemigonus crysoleucas*) as bait fish, growing of seaweed for food additives, or the culture of other species for sundry purposes.

Figure 1.2 James W. Avault III with koi pond he designed and constructed.

Aquaculture may be termed extensive or intensive. Extensive aquaculture is defined as growing a culture species corresponding to natural productivity or productivity from low-quality inputs such as fertilizers. Intensive aquaculture refers to growing a maximum quantity in limited space. A channel catfish farmer stocks 1,250 fingerlings per hectare (500/ac) and fertilizes the water. No feed is given, and fish live on natural organisms produced in the water. This is an example of extensive aquaculture, when the fish grown correspond to the productivity of the pond. Intensive aquaculture involves denser stocking rates, such as 25,000 fingerlings per hectare (10,000/ac), use of formulated feed, and use of mechanical aeration to obtain higher production. Growing a culture species in raceways involving extremely high stocking rates, high feeding rates, and the lavish use of flowing water is an example of a highly intensive culture system. Fish Breeders of Idaho Inc. has stocked fingerling channel catfish at rates up to 32 to 64 kg/m^3 (2 to 4 lb/ft^3) of space. There are many nuances to these definitions. For example, in the Philippines shrimp farming has been defined as: extensive, less than 30,000 stocked per hectare (12,000/ac); semi-intensive, 30,000 to 100,000/ha (12,000 to 40,000/ac); and intensive, greater than 100,000/ha (Avault 1988a). In Taiwan, highly intensive stocking rates for shrimp have reached 600,000/ha (240,000/ac).

An aquaculture operation may be termed complete or incomplete. A complete operation may involve spawning of brood stock to obtain eggs, nursery production of larvae or fingerlings, and eventual production of a food product for the consumer. A complete aquaculture operation, sometimes called vertical integration, also may be involved in manufacture of feeds, processing, and marketing. An incomplete operation involves only a few of these procedures. For example, a shrimp hatchery may specialize in production of postlarval shrimp to sell to growers. In Taiwan, there has been a high degree of specialization. Some workers specialize in capturing and selling mother shrimp (gravid females). The resulting nauplii, first larval stage, are handled by a nauplius broker, who sells to a hatchery. The nauplii are then grown in indoor tanks until they reach the early postlarval stage (PL-10 to PL-12). Once this stage is reached, larvae are sold to a nursery through a broker who stocks the PLs into small outdoor ponds and grows them to PL-20 to PL-35. Another broker sells this stage to farmers for grow-out.

There are other terms to describe aquaculture. Aquiculture is used by some to mean the same thing as aquaculture. Although not a widely accepted term, some prefer its use because its spelling is akin to agriculture. Mariculture falls under aquaculture and is a term denoting farming in saline water. There is a host of other terms: brackishwater aquaculture, fish farming, fish culture, pisciculture, shellfish culture, crustacean culture, marine farming, freshwater fish culture, warmwater fish culture, coldwater fish culture, catfish farming, and hydroponics -- to name a few. Fish farming and fish culture are restricted to fish, sometimes referred to as finfish, and may include such species as rainbow trout (*Oncorhynchus mykiss*), channel catfish, and bigmouth buffalo (*Ictiobus cyprinellus*). Shellfish culture is concerned with oysters, mussels, clams, and other mollusks. Crustacean culture is concerned with crawfish, shrimp, lobsters, and crabs. Marine farming means the growing of culture species in the ocean, the farming of salmon in floating net-pens for example. Warmwater fish culture deals with fish species that live in warm waters. For example, temperatures between 21° and 30°C (70° and 86°F) appear most suitable for channel catfish. Coldwater fish culture includes fish normally found in cold waters, such as rainbow trout that grow best at temperatures between 7° and 16° C (45° and 61°F). Sometimes we refer to the farming of a single species, such as catfish farming.

Hydroponics involves growing plants in water without soil. The plants may not always be aquatic. Tomatoes are being grown on rafts suspended in water. The plants may obtain nutrients from waste products of fish grown in the same waters. The term aquaculture is an umbrella. It includes all types of aquatic culture, be it finfish, crustaceans, mollusks, or plants.

HISTORY OF AQUACULTURE

The beginning of aquaculture is open to conjecture. Fish are thought to have invaded inundated land. When waters receded, some fish remained stranded in potholes. Since they were trapped, they could be removed and eaten when needed. Some fish escaped detection and spawned while stranded. The stock could thus be perpetuated from this lesson in fish culture. The next step was the deliberate stocking of ponds with young fishes. It was probably reasoned that fish were animals and would therefore grow if fed. An array of feedstuffs was introduced into ponds, mainly whatever scraps and wastes were available. Another theory has it that aquaculture began as an extension of rice farming.

Indo-Pacific Region

Aquaculture is ancient, particularly in the Indo-Pacific Region. This region includes territories situated between Pakistan in the West, Japan in the North, and Australia in the South. Earliest records come from China, whose civilization began about 5,000 years ago. The artificial hatching of fish was practiced in China in 2000 B.C. The first treatise on culture of common carp (*Cyprinus carpio*) was written by Fan Lai in 475 B.C. Early aquaculture of carp closely followed the manufacture of silk. The silkworm pupae and feces were used to feed fish. Since silkworm culture dates back to 2700 B.C. in China, one can see the possible antiquity of aquaculture.

Hora and Pillay (1962) gave a good account of the early history of aquaculture. They wrote that in A.D. 1243 Chow Mit of the Sung Dynasty described in his book "Kwei Sin Chak Shik" how carp fry were transported in bamboo baskets. Heu in A.D. 1639 wrote in "A Complete Book of Agriculture" how carp were collected from rivers and reared in ponds. During the 6th century, eating common carp in China posed a problem (Ling 1977). It seemed that the Tang Dynasty Emperor's name "Lee" was also the name of the common carp in Chinese. The name Emperor Lee was considered sacred. It was therefore inconceivable that Lee could be cultured and harvested for eating. So other species of fish were sought for culture. Since fry of riverine carps were difficult to separate after capture, a mixture of carp species was stocked; this is believed to have given rise to polyculture.

Over the centuries the Chinese passed down traditional fish culture to each succeeding generation. Those Chinese who migrated to Taiwan, Thailand, Malaya, Indonesia, and elsewhere in the Indo-Pacific Region brought with them knowledge of fish culture. They soon inspired local people to take up fish culture, and the culture of new species was begun. In Taiwan, more than 50 different species are cultured today (Chen 1990). The milkfish (*Chanos chanos*) has been cultured in brackish water on a large scale in Taiwan, the Philippines, and Indonesia (Figure 1.3). More than 180,000 ha (450,000 ac) have been devoted to milkfish farming in the Philippines alone, and on the island of Java in Indonesia there have been milkfish ponds as far as the eye can see along the north coast. Milkfish culture probably originated in Java during the 15th century.

Figure 1.3 Milkfish ponds in the Philippines.

Elsewhere in the Indo-Pacific Region, Siluroid fishes in Cambodia have been cultured in bamboo enclosures held in running water. This innovation was a forerunner of cage culture as we know it today. In Thailand the catfish *Pangasius* sp. was cultured in ancient days. The use of the Java tilapia (*Oreochromis mossambicus*) in 1939 by Pak Mudjair opened a new world to aquaculture in the Indo-Pacific Region (Figure 1.4). This hardy fish thrived under almost any condition and was grown in both fresh and brackish waters. It was soon introduced to a number of countries. Fish culture in India and Pakistan is ancient in certain provinces. In India, Kautilya wrote about it in 300 B.C. Tripathi (1990), reviewing freshwater aquaculture in India, reported that about 75 species of carps, catfishes, perches, and prawns are suitable for culture in ponds where the minimum water temperatures are above 15°C (59°F) most of the year.

Figure 1.4 Various species of tilapia are important for aquaculture.

Japan is notable for aquaculture, with the culture of clams recorded as early as A.D. 745. Today this country cultures a variety of species on an intensive scale. At one time or another virtually every edible aquatic species has been screened for aquaculture. Some of the more important species cultured today include mullet (*Mugil* spp.), yellowtail (*Seriola quinqueradiata*), common carp, eel (*Anguilla japonica*), rainbow trout, shrimp (*Penaeus* spp.), and the oyster (*Crassostrea gigas*). The culture of shrimp and yellowtail is especially noteworthy in Japan. Shrimp culture techniques began in 1934 when Motosaku Fujinaga was successful in spawning and the partial rearing of the kuruma shrimp (*Penaeus japonicus*). In 1959 he set up a pilot hatchery, and by 1967 some 20 operators, using his methods, produced 4,000 mt (4,410 tons) of shrimp from 8,500 ha (21,250 ac) of water. The yellowtail is cultured intensively in floating net-pens. Production went from 300 mt (330 tons) in 1958 to more than 30,000 mt (33,075 tons) by 1968 (Figure 1.5). Kafuku and Ikenoue (1983) described modern methods of aquaculture in Japan.

In Hawaii and Australia there is a great deal of interest in aquaculture. Milkfish culture in Hawaii has a long history; the freshwater prawn (*Macrobrachium rosenbergii*) has been cultured, and the mullet has been farmed in ponds. In Australia, oyster farming is the oldest form of aquaculture. It was practiced in New South Wales late last century, and today is one of the most important fisheries. By 1969, more than 6,533 mt shell weight (7,203 tons) of rock oysters (*Crassostrea commercialis*) valued at $3.4 million were farmed. Australia is also conducting research with other species. The farming of marron crawfish (*Cherax tenuimanus*) has been investigated.

More recently, the redclaw crawfish (*C. quadricarinatus*) has piqued interest. Both rainbow trout and brown trout (*Salmo trutta*) have been introduced into the southern part of that country. Tasmania has some saltwater trout farms, and aquaculture of the giant freshwater crawfish (*Astacopsis gouldi*), which may reach 3.6 kg (8 lb), has intrigued aquaculturists.

Figure 1.5 Net-pen culture of yellowtail near Kyoto, Japan.

For many years, particularly after World War II, the focus in Taiwan, the Philippines, and elsewhere in the Indo-Pacific Region was on production of fish protein for the domestic market. Various carps, tilapias, and mollusks -- capable of giving high yields with relatively low inputs -- were cultured. The decade of the 1980s, however, witnessed a new era, with emphasis on production of high-value species such as shrimp for hard currency (Figures 1.6, 1.7). As emphasis changed from production of fish protein toward production of high-value species, so did culture techniques, from a mainly extensive type of aquaculture to a more intensive system. High density stocking, use of formulated diets, and continuous aeration became the norm (Figure 1.8). Where possible, extensive grow-out facilities were converted to intensive culture, and in the Philippines and Indonesia suitable milkfish ponds have been converted to ponds for culture of the black tiger shrimp (*Penaeus monodon*). Indonesia has become the second most important producer of cultured shrimp in the world, behind China. Production reached an estimated 70,000 mt (77,175 tons) in 1988. The Philippines produced an estimated

8

50,000 mt (55,125 tons) of shrimp in 1989, accounting for about 8% of the world farmed shrimp harvest (Wildman et al. 1992).

Chua (1986), Maclean et al. (1986) and Joseph (1990) reviewed aquaculture development in Asia. The publication "World Aquaculture," published by the World Aquaculture Society, has given reviews on aquaculture development in various countries.

Figure 1.6 Ponds being constructed in China for shrimp culture.

Figure 1.7 Shrimp ponds along the South China Sea Coast.

Figure 1.8 Shrimp farm in Taiwan that used continuous aeration. Notice that the ponds go up to the house.

Near and Middle East

In the Near and Middle East region, aquaculture historically has not been of great importance except in Israel. This region is predominantly arid and is bordered on the West by the Mediterranean Sea and on the East by Afghanistan and Pakistan. Israel is highly advanced in aquaculture; the common carp is the major species cultured. Tilapia, mullet, and other carps are cultured in various combinations with the carp. Sarig (1972) gave figures for 1971. There were 84 farms with a total area of 4,868 ha (12,170 ac). A total of 12,533 mt (13,818 tons) was marketed, of which 85% was carp. From 1977 to 1987 the number of fish farms decreased from 79 to 57, a decrease of 28%. The pond area also decreased from 4,153 ha (10,383 ac) to 2,951 ha (7,378 ac) (Sarig 1987). The yield, however, has gone up from 4.33 mt/ha (3.87 tons/ac) in 1977 to 6.01 mt/ha (5.37 tons/ac) in 1986. In Israel and elsewhere in the Near and Middle East, water is especially precious, and fish crops must compete with other water uses. Until about 1975, Israel centered on monoculture of common carp with formulated diets. Since then polyculture of common carp, other Chinese carps, mullet, and tilapia, along with use of organic fertilizers, has gained importance. Hepher and Pruginin's book (1981) described commercial fish farming in Israel.

Huet (1970) told of experimental aquaculture stations in the Sudan, Syria, Iraq, the United Arab Republic (Egypt), Iran, and Lebanon. The common carp was the most important species, followed by various species of tilapias.

Egypt has tested several Indian carps (*Labeo rohita, Cirrhina mrigala, Catla catla*) and a Chinese carp (*Hypophthalmichthys molitrix*). Huet (1970) further mentioned that localized aquaculture exists. The sturgeon (*Acipenser* spp.) is cultured in Iran, eels in Egypt, catfish (*Clarias lazera*) in Syria, certain species of *Barbus* in Iraq, and *Heterotis* in the Sudan. In the decade of the 1980s some countries, such as Egypt, began showing interest in aquaculture of shrimp and other high-value species. In the Kingdom of Saudi Arabia, 19 commercial fish farms were in operation in 1992 (Siddiqui and Najada 1992). Tilapia, marine shrimp, the rabbit fish (*Siganus* spp.), and the prawn (*Macrobrachium rosenbergii*) are some of the culture species being tested (Figure 1.9).

Figure 1.9 Feisal A. Bukhari of the Fish Farming Center near Jeddah, Ministry of Agriculture and Water, examines tilapia at a private fish farm near Riyadh, Kingdom of Saudi Arabia.

Europe

In Europe aquaculture is fairly widespread. Perhaps the oldest history comes from the Romans who cultured oysters more than 2,000 years ago. Young oysters were collected near the mouth of the Adriatic Sea and moved to selected waters where they were fattened. In Central and Occidental Europe, fish culture developed during the Middle Ages. Most fish culture then was concerned with the common carp (Figure 1.10). Carp were bred and cultured in the monasteries. Their culture spread throughout Europe, especially in Germany, Poland, Czechoslovakia, Hungary, Yugoslavia, and Romania. Later the rainbow trout was cultured, and the brown trout and brook trout (*Salvelinus fontinalis*) to a lesser degree.

Figure 1.10 Harvest of common carp in Austria.

In the 14th century, trout culture was stimulated when a French monk fertilized trout eggs artificially, and by the 15th century carp culture was quite specialized. In the 16th century, Bohemia and Moravia, both Czechoslovakian provinces, had about 180,113 ha (450,283 ac) of fish ponds. Fish culture became firmly established in England about A.D. 1400 to A.D. 1500. Today England has turned its attention to culture of marine flatfish, plaice (*Pleuronectes platessa*), Dover sole (*Solea solea*), and the turbot (*Scophthalmus maximus*). Scotland has become a major producer of salmon, producing 41,000 mt (45,202 tons) in 1991 (Folsom et al. 1992).

Eel culture has gained importance, and several countries have been involved including Czechoslovakia, Hungary, and Spain. In southern Spain the young eels invade rice fields where they are captured and put into fattening ponds. Young eels are also bought from commercial fishers and grown in ponds.

Crawfish culture has generated much interest in Europe. The native crawfish, principally *Astacus astacus*, have been devastated by a fungal disease called the crawfish plague. Crawfish have been introduced into a number of European countries, particularly Scandinavian countries, Austria, and Poland. The signal crawfish (*Pacifastacus leniusculus*) from California has been introduced into cool European waters, and the Louisiana red swamp crawfish (*Procambarus clarkii*) has been introduced into warmer waters. Both species are supposedly less affected by the plague. The red swamp crawfish was successfully introduced into southern Spain in 1973. In Scandinavian countries, salmonid culture is well established. Fish farming in Norway began in the 1950s. By 1972 about 70 to 80 fish farms were in operation, producing approximately 1,500 mt (1,654 tons) of salmon and trout. Net-pen culture of the Atlantic salmon (*Salmo salar*) is especially important, and by 1988 approximately 74,000 mt (81,585 tons) were cultured. In 1991, Norway produced 154,000 mt (169,785 tons), making this country the world leader (Folsom et al. 1992).

Denmark is well known for the culture of trout, and as early as 1972 more than 600 trout farms were in operation. More than 90% of the marketable trout, mostly rainbow trout, are exported. Brown trout are cultured to a lesser degree, mainly for egg production for exportation. Some trout farms make use of brackish waters of up to 10 ppt. Earthen ponds are used to culture the trout, and the nearby Baltic Sea and North Sea have provided an excellent source of trash fish for feed. Elsewhere in Europe trout are cultured in France and northern Italy.

Russia has large-scale pond systems, particularly in the regions of Pskov, Novgorod, and Leningrad. In 1970, Leningrad alone had more than 1,000 ha (2,500 ac) in carp ponds.

Africa

In Africa aquaculture has been on a very low scale. Bardach et al. (1972) presented a good survey. Most aquaculture in Africa consists of small family ponds. Tilapia, for example, are stocked at 1 to 2 per m^2 (0.8 to 1.6/yd^2) in ponds that are 100 to 600 m^2 (120 to 718 yd^2) in size, and fed agricultural byproducts (Figure 1.11). Africans have traditionally hunted and captured fishes and have not embraced aquaculture as have the people of the Indo-Pacific Region. Various tilapia species stocked into small ponds receive virtually no management, and they soon overcrowd with young. The African fish farmer, by adding a predatory fish such as *Hemichromis fasciatus*, can control excess tilapia young. In recent times, the common carp has been introduced into many areas of Africa. The raising of trout is practiced on a small scale in Morocco and Kenya. The status, potential, and constraints for aquaculture development in Africa were reviewed by FAO (1975) and by Shehadeh (1976).

Latin America

In Latin American countries, aquaculture historically has been of a very low intensity. Huet (1970) stated that in 1964 culture of the common carp in Mexico involved 12,500 ha (31,250 ac). Three species of tilapia and the grass carp (*Ctenopharyngodon idella*) have been introduced. Brown trout are being grown in Mexico and in Central America. In South America aquaculture is of some importance in Brazil. Carp have been farmed in the states of Sao Paulo and Parana. Various species of tilapia are being cultured.

Recently, Chile has emerged as a world leader in net-pen culture of Atlantic salmon. In 1991, it produced 34,000 mt (37,485 tons) (Folsom et al. 1992).

Figure 1.11 Feeding tilapia rice byproducts in family pond, Liberia.

Figure 1.12 Shrimp pond in Nicaragua showing sluice gate.

Latin American countries have a real potential for aquaculture, and during the 1970s and 1980s shrimp farming burgeoned. Ecuador, Panama, Peru, and Honduras have developed commercial shrimp farms, and other countries are beginning. Ecuadorean growers have carried out a massive pond construction program, building more than 100,000 ha (250,000 ac) (Weidner et al. 1992). Belize had approximately six shrimp farms in developmental stages in 1989, and Nicaragua began shrimp farming in 1990 (Figure 1.12). Though more than 20 species have been mentioned for culture worldwide, *Penaeus vannamei* and *P. stylirostris* are the species of choice in Latin America.

North America

In North America aquaculture had its beginning not much more than a century ago. In the United States, Benson (1970), Dicks and Harvey (1989), and Parker (1989) reviewed the history of aquaculture development. Oysters and trout received early attention in the United States. In the beginning, oysters were caught from public beds with primitive tools such as hand tongs. They were gathered, not farmed. During the 1840s and 1850s commercial fishers from the Adriatic seacoast of Yugoslavia arrived in Louisiana. They brought with them knowledge of farming oysters. They noticed that in certain locations oysters grew fatter and tastier. Oysters from these preferred areas were soon depleted. When small oysters were moved to these preferred water bottoms, the farming of oysters was begun in a crude sense. This occurred in the late 1850s.

Theodatus Garlick read published works of European fish culture and in 1853 succeeded in artificially fertilizing eggs of brook trout (Benson 1970). This feat, amazing for its day and age, sparked others into fish culture. E.C. Kellogg and D.W. Chapman followed by hatching eggs of brook trout in 1855. In 1857 Garlick published his treatise on artificial propagation and pisciculture, which further stimulated salmon and trout breeding. The most noted of the trout breeders was Seth Green who began in 1864, just before the end of the Civil War. He was most successful and gave lessons in fish culture at $10 per day. He also raised eggs and fry of brook trout for sale. These early efforts, however, were primarily concerned with stocking natural waters. Private hatcheries made most of their money selling eggs and fry. Seth Green, for instance, intended to raise brook trout for market, but the high profit for eggs and fry diverted him from raising many fish for the table. Prices per thousand for brook trout then were: eggs $8 to $10, fingerlings $30 to $40, and 2-year-old fish $250. Table trout sold for $2.20/kg ($1.00/lb). The demand for trout as food eventually proved lucrative. During the period 1950 to 1960, annual commercial trout production was estimated at between 817 and 1,234 mt (900 and 1,360 tons). By 1968 it was 7,410 to 8,234 mt

(8,170 to 9,078 tons). Early trout farms were scattered among several states (Figure 1.13). By 1973 more than 90% of the nation's dressed trout were produced in the Snake River area of southern Idaho, and this trend continues. Three of the largest farms, all within a radius of 170 km (105 miles), had the combined potential to produce in excess of 5,898 mt (6,500 tons) of trout.

Figure 1.13 Trout raceways in North Carolina. Note demand feeders.

Going back to 1870, fish culture was practiced in 19 of 37 states plus the territories of Colorado and Kansas. More than 100 people were engaged in fish culture either as a hobby or as a business. In addition to brook trout, state fish commissions began propagation of Atlantic salmon, American shad (*Alosa sapidissima*), lake trout (*Salvelinus namaycush*), yellow perch (*Perca flavescens*), largemouth bass, and other species. The goal was to set up hatcheries for the purpose of restocking natural waters, and little thought was given to improvement of the environment.

The federal government became involved in aquaculture in 1871 when the U.S. Commission of Fish and Fisheries was formed. It continued the theme of the state fish commissions. Millions of young shad, haddock (*Melanogrammus aeglefinus*), sheepshead (*Archosargus probatocephalus*), and lobsters (*Homarus* sp.) were hatched and released into natural waters. This practice continued for many years.

Other events are worth noting during this early era of aquaculture. In 1870 a meeting of practical fish culturists was held in New York, and the American Fish Culturists Association was established. Over the years the organization grew, became active in federal policy regarding fisheries, and eventually was renamed the American Fisheries Society. Also in 1870 Congress spent its first federal funds ($100) for fish investigations at Woods

Hole, Massachusetts. In 1915 Congress approved the appointment of a full-time pathologist, H.S. Davis, who ultimately published the book "Culture and Diseases of Game Fishes" in 1929. This book replaced the "Manual of Fish Culture" published in 1898.

Commercial culture of warmwater fish began in the late 1920s and early 1930s. Attention was focused on production of bait minnows for sportfishing. Culture of bait minnows proved lucrative, particularly after World War II; by 1971 more than 32,400 ha (81,000 ac) were devoted to minnows. In the 1950s the burgeoning industry expanded to include other species -- crappie (*Pomoxis* spp.), largemouth bass, and buffalo. The bigmouth buffalo was grown in Arkansas, Louisiana, and Mississippi, but the market price and production per hectare (224 to 784 kg/ha or 200 to 700 lb/ac) were not encouraging.

Commercial catfish farming had a modest beginning in the late 1950s. By 1960 less than 200 ha (500 ac) were devoted to catfish production in the United States. By 1963 approximately 960 ha (2,400 ac) were in catfish ponds, and in 1969 the figure climbed to nearly 16,000 ha (40,000 ac). By 1973 a total of 22,000 ha (55,000 ac) of water was devoted to production of marketable catfish in the United States (Figures 1.14, 1.15). The total harvest amounted to 21,778 mt (24,000 tons) valued at $26 million. By 1991 the United States had approximately 62,800 ha (157,000 ac) in production, of which 37,200 ha (93,000 ac) were in the state of Mississippi.

Several states are involved in the commercial fishery of crawfish. As early as 1970, approximately 20 commercial fishers trapped on the Sacramento River delta from May 18 through September 10. More than 37,642 kg (83,000 lb) of crawfish valued at $32,430 were landed at Courtland, California. Most crawfish caught on the West Coast are shipped to Sweden or France. Crawfish farming had modest beginnings in the 1970s in Missouri, Texas, Mississippi, North and South Carolina, and Arkansas. The major crawfish industry, however, is limited for the most part to Louisiana, and originally was limited almost exclusively to south Louisiana. The bulk of the Louisiana crawfish crop consists of the red swamp crawfish; a small percentage of white river crawfish (*P. zonangulus*) is mixed with the red swamp crawfish.

Crawfish farming in Louisiana began during the 1940s, possibly by accident. It is thought that a rice farmer flooded a field one fall, after the harvest of rice, to provide duck hunting habitat. Next spring the duck pond was teeming with crawfish. Duck hunters were transformed into crawfish trappers who harvested the unexpected crop.

The future of the crawfish industry looks promising, and the number of ponds devoted to crawfish farming is increasing. In Louisiana more than 4,800 ha (12,000 ac) were devoted to crawfish culture in 1969. The figure climbed in 1970 to 10,000 ha (25,000 ac), and in 1971 close to 16,000 ha (40,000 ac) were in crawfish ponds. By 1973 there were 334 managed crawfish ponds comprising 17,600 ha (44,000 ac), and by the mid-1980s close to 56,000 ha (140,000 ac) were in production.

Figure 1.14 Early channel catfish farm in Tennessee. Photo courtesy of Soil Conservation Service, U.S. Department of Agriculture.

Figure 1.15 Catfish harvest (Photo credit same as Figure 1.14).

Elsewhere in North America aquaculture is of importance in Canada and Alaska. In British Columbia aquaculture dates back to about 1912 when oyster seed (*Crassostrea gigas*) was first imported from Japan (Deegan 1988). Freshwater trout farming began in the 1950s, followed 2 decades later by salmon culture. Coho salmon (*Oncorhynchus kitsutch*), chinook salmon (*O. tshawytscha*), rainbow trout, and Atlantic salmon are the major salmonid species being cultured. In 1984 approximately 10 licensed salmon farms operated along the coast of British Columbia, and only 4 years later 178 farms, totaling 940 ha (2,350 ac), were in production. In 1988-89 more than 220 applications for salmon farming ventures were reviewed. The Atlantic salmon is the species of choice in most instances, even on the Pacific Coast.

TAKING THE FIRST STEP

The pros and cons of beginning commercial aquaculture were discussed by Wellborn (1985), Cacho et al. (1986), Harrell (1988), and Gordon (1989).

A soybean and rice farmer near Yazoo City, Mississippi, has idle land that can be to put into aquaculture. Yazoo City is in the Mississippi Delta region -- channel catfish country. So the choice seems logical, grow channel catfish. A landowner in south Louisiana has idle land and wants income from it. In this case farming crawfish seems an appropriate choice.

Suppose, however, that you wish to begin aquaculture, but own no land. You are open-minded regarding the species cultured. How do you make a start? Perhaps the first thing to realize is that aquaculture is a business, and like any business requires knowledge, capital, labor, and management. The next thought is that the culture or farming of an aquatic species has many things in common with the farming of traditional farm crops (Shell 1991). Simply put, aquaculture is agriculture. A simple comparison of steps involved in corn production and channel catfish farming is presented below:

Corn Production	Catfish Farming
(1) Secure funds to begin	(1) Secure funds and permits to begin if needed
(2) Plow ground	(2) Build ponds and get a source of water
(3) Plant seed	(3) Stock fingerlings
(4) Fertilize soil	(4) Fertilize pond water and/or feed fish, and maintain good water quality
(5) Control weeds and insects	(5) Control weeds, wild fish, and pests
(6) Control parasites and disease	(6) Control parasites and diseases
(7) Harvest, process, market	(7) Harvest, process, market

Once these concepts are understood, you must establish goals and preferably put them into writing. Do you want a small operation just to supplement your retirement income? If so, what size of operation will you require? Will you develop your incipient aquaculture operation into a full-time business? Will it be vertically integrated, or will you specialize in one particular area? Once you visualize short- and long-range goals, a feasibility study should be conducted. Begin with a checklist. A partial list might include: which species to culture, where to locate, any legal constraints, marketing potential, profit outlook, and other aspects. Finally a business plan must be prepared.

In choosing a species to culture, you should seriously consider the market. Is there a market for the aquatic crop being considered, and what is the market price? It would be foolhardy to invest money, grow a crop of fish, and then at harvest time look for a buyer. It is also foolish to grow a crop of fish for $1.00 a kg when the market will pay only 50 cents. Some species, such as shrimp, are readily accepted throughout much of the world and bring a relatively high price. Channel catfish, once limited to southern markets, is now being accepted elsewhere in the country and brings a good price. Tilapia, capable of tremendous production in ponds, was once generally unacceptable as food in the United States. The culture of tilapia is sound from a biological standpoint because the tilapia feeds low on the food chain, but from a business standpoint markets had been difficult to obtain. Now, however, tilapia is highly regarded as tablefare thanks to effective promotion. Historically, markets in the United States have been most interested in high-value species such as trout, salmon, catfish, shrimp, and oysters. Species such as carp and mullet have been overlooked. Markets now exist for carp and mullet. Carp are eaten in New York Asian markets, and mullet are eaten in Florida, Mississippi, and a few other places. There is a real potential for ethnic markets with a variety of aquatic species.

Second, in selecting a species to culture you must have a thorough knowledge of its biology and be able to obtain young or larva for stocking. The channel catfish is a freshwater species that grows best in warm water. It is only logical that a catfish farm be located in the South or in other warm climates to take advantage of the long growing season. Trout require cool water and have a high oxygen demand. Pompano (*Trachinotus carolinus*) begin to die when the water cools to 10°C (50°F), so this limits its distribution for culture. Oysters require brackish or saline water.

Sometimes we can alter certain biological requirements or even take advantage of a changing environment. In Louisiana freshwater species, such as blue (*Ictalurus furcatus*), channel, and white catfish (*I. catus*), have been successfully cultured in brackish waters up to 8 ppt. Parasites and diseases have posed virtually no threat, and spawning was controlled. Trout have been grown in the South during winter. Warmwater species have been grown in northern waters warmed from power plants.

Consider the location for the aquaculture operation and any legal and social problems that may arise. In 1972 the National Oceanographic and Atmospheric Agency published a synopsis of opinions on problems and priorities in aquaculture. Among other things, legal and regulatory restraints pertaining to water ownership and use were noted as the greatest single inhibition to commercial aquaculture in the United States. Legal and social problems can be a major stumbling block when public waters are sought for aquaculture. In Arkansas, cage culture of catfish was allowed in certain public waters. A portion of the fish harvested was released into open water as payment. Other states such as Louisiana generally prohibit cage culture in public waters; however, 10 permits were issued in 1989-90 in Louisiana. Net-pen culture of salmon off the coast of Washington has aroused the ire of some people who feel that the pens spoil the beauty of the area and pollute pristine waters. A final example is the leasing of Gulf of Mexico waters for shrimp culture. In the late 1960s, a large company began farming shrimp in the Gulf of Mexico off the Florida coast. The limiting factor that stopped the company for more than a year was the legal aspect of leasing public waters in the Gulf. The aquaculture operation called for enclosing an area with a net, thus restricting other uses. Landmark legislation was needed before the first shrimp could be stocked, but the public could not be excluded from the area. Culture of oysters may or may not pose a legal problem. In Louisiana, water bottoms have been leased to people for oyster production for many years. This kind of operation does not inhibit passage of boats, and the operation is out of public view. Off-bottom culture could pose problems.

WHERE TO GET HELP

There are numerous places to obtain information on aquaculture. We might categorize them into: (1) federal, (2) state, (3) universities, (4) the private sector, (5) various aquaculture organizations, and (6) books, journals, magazines, newsletters, and other publications.

Federal Agencies

Several federal agencies are involved with aquaculture. The U.S. Department of Agriculture (USDA), the lead agency for aquaculture at the federal level, has several divisions involved directly or indirectly in aquaculture. The Soil Conservation Service gives technical help for pond construction and watershed management. The Agricultural Research Service and the Cooperative State Research Service support some aquaculture research at land-grant institutions. The extension service has technical personnel who serve as liaisons between departmental research and the extension technical staffs at land-grant institutions. In 1987 four regional aquaculture research, development, and demonstration centers were established by the USDA in Hawaii, Massachusetts, Mississippi, and Washington. A total of $3 million was appropriated to initiate aquaculture programs at the four centers. A fifth center was later established in the Midwest. Each center allocates funds to other states within its jurisdiction.

The U.S. Fish and Wildlife Service (FWS) of the Department of the Interior has conducted fishery's research in three general areas: fish husbandry, pest control, and reservoir ecosystems. These collectively involved research in fish diseases, nutrition, fish biology and ecology, salmon culture, warmwater fish culture, fish control, pesticides, and reservoirs. All of this research has been conducted in more than 20 laboratories and stations throughout the United States. The FWS is responsible for sport fishes, though much information generated is applicable to aquaculture. For example, the FWS station at Stuttgart, Arkansas, has conducted research on catfish, bait minnows, and other species, and it has assisted fish farmers. The station at Marion, Alabama, has worked on nutrition, physiology, and genetics of catfish. Fish disease research has been conducted at Leetown, West Virginia, and Seattle, Washington. Salmon culture research has been conducted in Longview, Washington, and research on fish control has been conducted at LaCrosse, Wisconsin, and Warm Springs, Georgia.

The National Marine Fisheries Service (NMFS) of the Department of Commerce conducts marine research including aquaculture with fishes, shrimp, oysters, and other crustaceans and mollusks. The NMFS has a number of research stations. Aquaculture of oysters has been researched at Milford, Connecticut, and at Oxford, Maryland. Pompano and other finfishes have been studied for aquaculture at St. Petersburg, Florida. Pioneering research in spawning penaeid shrimp was conducted at Galveston, Texas.

The Office of Sea Grant, a component of the National Oceanic and Atmospheric Administration (NOAA), directs the National Sea Grant Program. This program, along with NOAA, is also in the Department of Commerce. It provides support for marine research and development, education, and advisory service programs, and it sponsors education of ocean scientists and other specialists at selected colleges and universities. The Sea Grant Program has sparked much of the aquaculture research at various colleges and universities. Many species are being studied for aquaculture with Sea Grant funds.

Other federal agencies are involved in aquaculture, some only in a regulatory manner. The Environmental Protection Agency regulates effluents from the draining of ponds and other aquaculture facilities into navigable waters. Its concern is the effect of aquaculture practices on the environment. The Food and Drug Administration (FDA) regulates the kind of chemicals used to control weeds in ponds and diseases in fish. More recently, the FDA has assisted processing plants in setting up safety and quality assurance standards. Its concern is the effect of aquaculture practices on our food. It also regulates the drugs and hormones that are incorporated into feeds.

The National Wildlife Federation (1995) publishes annually a conservation directory of addresses and phone numbers. The Joint Subcommittee on Aquaculture (JSA) is a collection of 17 federal agencies and organizations that promulgated a directory of government programs; responsibilities, addresses, and phone numbers are provided. The National Agricultural Library has an Aquaculture Information Center that serves as a focal point for those interested in obtaining literature. The address is Aquaculture Information Center National Agriculture Library, Room 111, Beltsville, MD 20705.

State Agencies

Each state has a department of agriculture and a department of conservation. The latter sometimes has a different title, such as wildlife and fisheries commission. In some states the department of agriculture is helpful to fish farmers. In Mississippi, for example, this department has been a great help to channel catfish farmers. The department of conservation also has excellent aquaculture programs in some states. For example, in Alabama the Marine Resources Laboratory has conducted aquaculture research with oysters, pompano, rainbow trout, and others. In the Louisiana Department of Wildlife and Fisheries, two divisions have been involved in aquaculture research. The Division of Oysters, Seafood, and Water Bottoms conducted some of the first research on shrimp aquaculture in the United States. Rockefeller Wildlife Refuge of the Refuge Division has one of the finest brackishwater pond facilities in the nation. More than 60 experimental ponds have been used to screen a host of species for aquaculture.

Universities

Countless universities are involved in aquaculture research. Virtually all began conducting research only during the last 2 or 3 decades. As examples, Auburn University, a land-grant university, is one of the most notable for its aquaculture research. H.S. Swingle pioneered aquaculture research in the United States with warmwater species beginning in the 1930s. Since then, Auburn's program has grown to include virtually every species of food value, both marine and freshwater, in all parts of the world. Other nations are assisted in setting up aquaculture programs. The Louisiana State University Agricultural Center has conducted aquaculture research since the mid 1960s with a variety of species, and it has pioneered crawfish farming (Figure 1.16).

Figure 1.16 Ponds of the Louisiana State University Agricultural Center, Baton Rouge, Louisiana.

Figure 1.17 The late Laurence W. de la Bretonne, Jr., (dip net) of the Louisiana Cooperative Extension Service with crawfish farmer.

The land-grant institutions and the USDA together have spelled success for agriculture in this nation. During the Civil War era, organized agricultural research was born. On 15 May, 1862, President Lincoln established the USDA. The counterpart of the USDA was established 2 July, 1862, with the Land Grant Act (Avault 1988b). The Land Grant Act provided land to states and territories for the purpose of establishing colleges to further agriculture and the mechanical arts. The idea of land-grant institutions was to provide higher education for working citizens. Today each state has a land-grant institution. Each land-grant institution has an agricultural experiment station that works closely with the USDA. Today there are more than 50 agricultural experiment stations in the United States and territories. For a list of state agricultural experiment stations, consult the conservation directory (National Wildlife Federation 1995).

Now attention is being focused on aquaculture. One of the most massive organized projects in aquaculture was begun in 1971. Twelve states joined in a regional project to research virtually every aspect of catfish farming. While the agricultural experiment station is charged with research duties, the cooperative extension service has the job of getting the research information out into the field (Figure 1.17). Each land-grant institution has an extension service, some of which assist in planning an aquaculture operation. For publications, videos, and other materials on aquaculture, contact the cooperative extension service.

Private Sector

During an entrepreneur's feasibility study, some fish farmers already in the business may volunteer helpful information. Many established farmers are members of an aquaculture organization or producer group.

Aquaculture Organizations

Various aquaculture organizations offer an opportunity to keep abreast of the latest technology, meetings, and related matters. The World Aquaculture Society, for example, founded in 1970, has more than 4,000 members representing 100 countries. The society holds an annual meeting and publishes a quarterly journal, magazine, and special publications. The home office is located at 143 J.M. Parker Coliseum, Louisiana State University, Baton Rouge, LA 70803 USA. The National Aquaculture Association, founded in the United States, addresses issues of national interest such as product inspection, therapeutic compounds, interstate and international commerce, and licensing and permitting. As another example, the Asian Fisheries Society offers aquaculturists access to technology with its biannual meetings, proceedings, and journal. There are organizations for people interested in a particular species or group of species -- International

Association of Astacology, Catfish Farmers of America, U.S. Trout Farmers Association, and Louisiana Crawfish Farmers Association, to name four.

Books, Journals, Magazines, Newsletters, Other Publications

At the end of each chapter, books and other references are listed for further reading. Members of aquaculture organizations usually receive valuable newsletters that keep them up-to-date on meetings, latest equipment, gear, and other matters. A number of independent newsletters are also available. Naga, for example, a quarterly published by ICLARM in Manila, Philippines, has given a good account of aquaculture in Asia. Various magazines, such as Aquaculture Magazine, have kept abreast of aquaculture matters pertinent to fish farmers. Aquaculture Magazine publishes dates and locations of coming meetings, research reports, and reviews of private fish farming. Its annual buyer's guide offers a wealth of information including a list of aquaculture businesses; international, national, regional, and state associations; universities offering aquaculture degrees; diagnostic services available, and other pertinent information.

STUDY QUESTIONS

1. Define, explain, or identify capture fisheries, culture fisheries, sport fisheries, aquaculture, extensive and intensive aquaculture, mariculture, complete aquaculture, and incomplete aquaculture.

2. Discuss the theory of how aquaculture began.

3. In outline form give a succinct review of the history of aquaculture in the Indo-Pacific Region, Europe, and the United States.

4. You are starting commercial aquaculture. Where would you seek help?

5. List those aquaculture organizations that would be of most interest to you.

6. List aquaculture publications you would consider subscribing to.

REFERENCES

Anonymous. 1991. Aquaculture books of special and general interest (a list of 497 aquaculture books). Aquaculture Magazine 17(5):57-86.

Avault, J.W., Jr. (editor). 1970-1985. Proceedings (Journal) of the World Mariculture Society. Louisiana: Louisiana State University Division of Continuing Education.

Avault, J.W., Jr. 1987. The tiger prawn in the Philippines. Aquaculture Magazine 13(6):51-52.

Avault, J.W., Jr. 1988a. The black tiger prawn in Taiwan. Aquaculture Magazine 14(6):53-54.

Avault, J.W., Jr. 1988b. The Hatch Act. World Aquaculture 19(3):19-20.

Avault, J.W., Jr. 1989. How will fish be grown in the future. Aquaculture Magazine 15(1):57-59.

Avault, J.W., Jr. 1989. Getting started in aquaculture -- where to get help. Aquaculture Magazine 15(6):63-66.

Avault, J.W., Jr. 1993. Ten requirements for culturing a "new" species: a checklist. Aquaculture Magazine 19(6):68-73.

Bardach, J.E., J.H. Ryther and W.O. McLarney. 1972. Aquaculture. New York: Wiley Interscience Press. 868 pp.

Benson, N.G. (editor). 1970. A Century of Fisheries in North America. American Fisheries Society. Special Publication No. 7. 330 pp.

Berge, L. 1969. Pondfish Farming in Norway (Damfisknaeringen I Norge). Translated by U.S. Joint Publications Research Service for Bureau of Commercial Fisheries. 121 pp.

Cacho, O., H. Kinnucan and S. Sindelar. 1986. Catfish farming risks in Alabama. Auburn University, Alabama Agricultural Experiment Station. Circular 287.

Chen, L.C. 1990. Aquaculture in Taiwan. Osney Mead-Oxford: Fishing News (Books), a Division of Blackwell Scientific Publications Ltd. 273 pp.

Chua, T.E. 1986. An overview of the fisheries and aquaculture industries in Asia. pp.1-8. In Proceedings of the First Asian Fisheries Forum, Manila, Philippines. 727 pp.

Coche, A.G. 1987. Selected aquaculture publications: serials, newsletters, meeting proceedings, and bibliographies/directories/glossaries. FAO Fisheries Circular No. 808.

Coche, A.G. (compiler). 1991. Aquaculture in fresh waters, a list of reference books and monographs, 1951-1991. Revision 4. FAO Fisheries Circular No. 724.

Davis, H.S. 1961. Culture and Diseases of Game Fishes. Berkeley and Los Angeles, California: University of California Press. 332 pp.

Deegan, R. 1988. Focus on British Columbia, the growth of an aquaculture industry. Aquaculture Today 1(1):37-40.

Dicks, M. and D. Harvey. 1989. Aquaculture situation and outlook. United States Department of Agriculture Economics Research. Research Aqua-2, March 1989.

FAO. 1971. A list of inland fishery workers in Europe. FAO Fisheries Technical Paper 15, Revision 2.

FAO. 1971. Directory of Fish Culture Research Institutions. FAO Fisheries Technical Paper No. 85 Revision 1.

FAO. 1975. Aquaculture planning in Africa. Organisation des nations pour L'alimentation et L'agriculture ADCP/REP/75/1.

Fish Farming International. 1973. London: Fishing News (Books) Ltd. Press. No. 1. 152 pp.

Fish Farming International. 1974. London: Fishing News (Books) Ltd. Press. No. 2. 148 pp.

Folsom, W., D. Altman, A. Manuar, F. Nielson, T. Revord, E. Sanborn, M. Wildman. 1992. World Salmon Culture: Europe, North and South America, and Pacific. National Marine Fisheries Service NOAA Technical Memorandum NMFS-F/SPO-3. 323 pp.

Gary, D.L. 1973. A Geographic Systems Analysis of the Commercial Crawfish Industry. Ph. D. Dissertation, Oregon State University. 123 pp.

Gordon, K.G. 1989. Starting an aquaculture business. Kevgor Aquasystems. P.O. Box 48851-595 Burrad St., Vancouver, B. C. V7X1A8 Canada.

Harrell, R.M. 1988. Fish culture in Maryland, weighing the pros and cons. Maryland Sea Grant Extension Program. Finfish Aquaculture Workbook Series.

Hepher, B. and Y. Pruginin. 1981. Commercial Fish Farming. New York, Chichester, Brisbane and Toronto: John Wiley & Sons. 261 pp.

Hickling, C.F. 1961. Tropical Inland Fisheries. New York: John Wiley & Sons Inc. 287 pp.

Hickling, C.F. 1962. Fish Culture. London: Faber and Faber Press. 295 pp.

Honna, A. 1971. Aquiculture in Japan. Tokyo: Japan FAO Association. 148 pp.

Hora, S.L. and T.V.R. Pillay. 1962. Handbook on Fish Culture in the Indo-Pacific Region. Rome: Food and Agriculture Organization of the United Nations. 204 pp.

Huet, M. 1970. Textbook of Fish Culture, Breeding and Cultivation of Fish. Translated by Henry Kahn. 4th edition, revised. Surrey, England: Fishing News (Books) Ltd. 436 pp.

Iverson, E.S. 1968. Farming the Edge of the Sea. Surrey, England: Fishing News (Books) Ltd. 301 pp.

Joint Subcommittes.e on Aquaculture. 1987. Aquaculture: a guide to federal government programs. Prepared by the JSA in cooperation with the National Agricultural Library and the U.S. Department of Agriculture. 34 pp.

Joint Subcommittee on Aquaculture. 1991 Aquaculture: a guide to federal government programs. Prepared by the JSA in cooperation with the National Agricultural Library and the U.S. Department of Agriculture. 38 pp.

Jones, W. 1972. How to get started. American Fish Farmer & World Aquaculture News 4(1):10.

Joseph, M.M. (editor). 1990. Aquaculture in Asia. Asian Fisheries Society, Indian Branch, College of Fisheries, University of Agricultural Sciences, Mangalore-- 575 002, Karnataka, India. 395 pp.

Kafuku, T. and H. Ikenoue. 1983. Modern Methods of Aquaculture in Japan. Amsterdam-Oxford-New York: Elsevier Science Publishing Company Inc. 216 pp.

Kirpichnikov, V.S. (editor). 1970. Selective breeding of carp and intensification of fish breeding in ponds. Translated from Russian. Bulletin State Scientific Research Institute of Lake and River Fisheries 61:1-249.

Larson, C.M. 1971. A world list of fishery limnologists. FAO Fisheries Technical Paper No. 108.

Ling, D.E. 1977. Aquaculture in Southeast Asia -- A historic review. Seattle: University of Washington Press.

Maar, A, M.A.E. Mortimer and I. Van der Lingen. 1966. Fish Culture in Central East Africa. Rome: Food and Agriculture Organization of the United Nations. 156 pp.

Maclean, J.L., L.B. Dizon and L.V. Hosillos (editors). 1986. The first Asian Fisheries Forum. Metro Manila, Philippines: Asian Fisheries Society MC P.O. Box 1501, Makati, Metro Manila, Philippines. 727 pp.

Meyer, F.P. , K.E. Sneed and P.T. Eschmeyer, (editors). 1973. Second Report to the Fish Farmers. Washington, D.C. : Bureau of Sport Fisheries and Wildlife Resource Publication 113. 123 pp.

28

Milne, P.H. 1972. Fish and Shellfish Farming in Coastal Waters. Surrey, England: Fishing News (Books) Ltd. 208 pp.

National Wildlife Federation. 1995. The Conservation Directory. Published by The Wildlife Federation, 1400 Sixteenth Street N.W., Washington, D.C. 20036-2266.

Parker, N.C. 1989. History, status, and future of aquaculture in the United States. Reviews in Aquatic Science 1(1):97-109.

Pillay, T.V.R. (editor). 1967-68. Proceedings of the World Symposium on Warm-Water Pond Fish Culture. Rome: Food and Agriculture Organization of the United Nations. FAO Fisheries Reports No. 44, 5 Volumes.

Pillay, T.V.R. 1990. Aquaculture: Principles and Practices. Osney Mead-Oxford: Fishing News (Books), a Division of Blackwell Scientific Publications Ltd. 575 pp.

Sarig, S. 1972. Fisheries and fish culture in Israel in 1971. Bamidgeh 24(3):55-75.

Sarig, S. 1987. Fisheries and fish culture in Israel in 1985 and 1986. Bamidgeh 39(4): 95-108.

Shapiro, S. (editor). 1971. Our Changing Fisheries. Washington, D.C.: Superintendent of Documents. 534 pp.

Shehadeh, Z.H. (editor). 1976. Report of the Symposium on Aquaculture in Africa. Accra, Ghana 30 September to 2 October 1975. CIFA Technical Report (4). 36 pp. and CIFA Technical Report Supplement 1. 791 pp.

Shell, E.W. 1991. Husbandry of animals on land and in water: similarities and differences. Presented at a symposium titled "Aquaculture in Animal Science" at the ASAS 82nd Annual Meeting, Ames, Iowa.

Shell, E.W. 1993. The Development of Aquaculture: An Ecosystems Perspective. Auburn University, Alabama Agricultural Experiment Station. 265 pp.

Siddiqui, A.Q. and A.R.A. Najada. 1992. Aquaculture in Saudi Arabia. World Aquaculture 23(2):6-9.

Tamura, T. 1970. Marine Aquaculture. Translated by Mary I. Watanabe. National Technical Information Service, U.S. Department of Commerce.

Tripathi, S.D. 1990. Freshwater aquaculture in India. pp. 191-222. In Aquaculture in Asia. Asian Fisheries Society, Indian Branch. c/o College of Fisheries, University of Agricultural Sciences, Mangalore-575 002, Karnataka, India.

U.S. Commission of Fish and Fisheries. 1898. A Manual of Fish Culture. U.S. Government Printing Office. 340 pp.

Weidner, D., T. Revord, R. Wells and A. Manuar. 1992. World Shrimp Culture. National Marine Service, NOAA Technical Memorandum NMFS-F/SPO-7, Volume 2 Latin Amercia.

Wellborn, T.L. 1985. Guide for prospective catfish farmers. Mississippi State University, Mississippi Cooperative Extension Service. Publication 1465.

Wildman, M., P. Niemeier, F. Nielsen, J. Beverly, T. Schneider, H. Riha, E. Sanborn, D. Weidner, D. Decker and B. Rosenberry. 1992. World Shrimp Culture: Africa, Asia, Europe, Middle East, North America. National Marine Fisheries Service NOAA. Technical Memorandum NMFS-F/SPO-4, Volume 1. 141 pp.

CHAPTER 2
AQUATIC FOOD PRODUCTION AND PEOPLE

Food, clothing, and shelter are basic material needs of people, but we sometimes take them for granted. The world population is increasing and farmland is decreasing. How much more will the world's population grow? Will there always be enough food? What role does capture fisheries play in providing food? What is the potential of aquaculture? In this chapter, we try to answer these questions.

A GROWING WORLD POPULATION
Population Growth

At the time of Christ the world population was estimated at 250 million. This population slowly expanded and by 1600 it doubled, reaching 500 million. It was around 1830 that the world population reached 1 billion. A century later there were 2 billion people. By 1960, only 30 years later, the world population reached 3 billion. In 1991 there were 5.4 billion people in the world. This population is growing by 86 million people each year and could increase by 96 million a year by the year 2000 (Table 2.1). Adding 86 million people a year is like creating another United States every 3 years. United Nations' demographic projections show the world population doubling before leveling off sometime late in the next century (Figure 2.1).

Table 2.1 World population growth by decade, 1950 to 1990, with projection.

Year	Population	Increase by decade	Average annual increase
	(billion)	(million)	
1950	2.515		
1960	3.019	504	50
1970	3.698	679	68
1980	4.450	752	75
1990	5.292	842	84
2000	6.251	959	96

Source: United Nations, Department of International Economic and Social Affairs, World Population Prospects 1988 (New York: 1989).

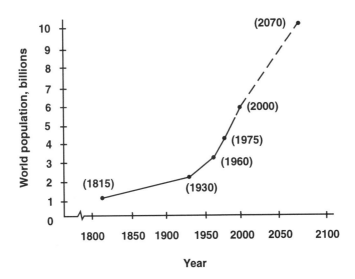

Figure 2.1 World population projected over time. U.N. Demographic Yearbook, 1992.

The most dramatic population increases will take place in Africa, with a 3% growth rate, and in Latin America, with a 2.1% growth rate (Table 2.2).

As a benchmark, a 2% growth rate means that for 1,000 people in a given population, 20 are added each year. Asia, with more than 3.1 billion people in 1991, contained well over half of the world's population, whereas Australia and New Zealand combined had only 27 million people.

Table 2.2 Population and population density for the world and for major areas.

	Population 1991	Birth rate	Death rate	Annual rate population increase	Population density per square km
	(000,000)	1985-90	1985-90	1985-90	1991
Major Area					
World	5385	27	10	1.7	39
Africa	662	45	15	3.0	22
Asia	3171	28	9	1.9	115
Europe	500	13	11	0.2	101
L. America	457	29	7	2.1	22
N. America	278	15	9	0.8	13
Oceania	26.9	19	8	1.5	3
U.S.S.R.	291	18	11	0.8	13

Source: U.N. Demographic Yearbook 1992.
Australia and New Zealand combined make up Oceania. 1 km = 0.621 miles.

In 1989 the population of India was 810 million. With a growth rate of 2.12%, this population increases by 15.2 million annually. India is expected to reach 1 billion by the turn of the century. China is already past the 1 billion mark and growing at an annual rate of 20 million per year (Unklesbay 1992).

Birth Rate, Death Rate, and Growth Rate

You must know birth rates, death rates, and growth rates to understand population growth. The birth rate is expressed as the number of births per thousand people per year. The total number of births for a given year is divided by the estimated population at midyear. For example, there were 3,453,000 live births in the United States in a year ending with 30 September 1968 (Ehrlich and Ehrlich 1970). The population on 31 March 1968, which was at midyear, was estimated at 198,400,000. The birth rate for that period was 3,453,000 ÷ 198,400,000 = 0.0174. There were 0.0174 births per person or 0.0174 x 1000 = 17.4 births per 1,000 people. On the other hand, there were 1,906,000 deaths during the same period, resulting in a death rate of 1,906,000 ÷ 198,400,000 = 0.0096 x 1,000 = 9.6 deaths per thousand people from 1 October 1967 to 30 September 1968.

The growth rate is obtained simply by subtracting the death rate from the birth rate, or in our example above 17.4 - 9.6 = 7.8 per thousand. In other words, during the year from 1 October 1967 to 30 September 1968, 7.8 people were added for each 1,000 people in the United States. This is the rate of natural increase, because immigration is not considered. Demographers express the growth rate as a rate per hundred rather than as a rate per thousand. From 1985 to 1990 the estimated world birth rate was 27 and the death rate was 10. The population growth rate was thus 27 - 10 = 17, or 1.7% (Table 2.2).

Another way to express growth rate is in terms of doubling time. This is the time needed for a population to double. In early years, a low growth rate was accompanied by a long doubling time. It took 230 years for the world population to double between the years of 1600 and 1830. It took 100 years for the population to double between 1830 and 1930. It took only 37 years for the population to double from 1950 to 1987. As a benchmark, a population with a growth rate of 1 will double its population in 70 years. A growth rate of 2 will require 35 years for the population to double. Look again at growth rates for various regions of the world (Table 2.2).

Births - Deaths x Per Capita Consumption

One way to express the well-being of a population is births - deaths x per capita consumption. Overpopulation is brought into balance by changing any or all of these factors. That is, there can be a decrease in the birth rate and per capita consumption, or there can be an increase in the death rate. It is unlikely that the death rate will be increased, barring some catastrophe; rather, it is decreasing slightly. Recorded in history are various crises that allowed the death rate to escalate. The bubonic plague killed an estimated 25% of Europe's population between 1348 and 1350. The Hundred Years' War (1337 to 1453) and the Thirty Years' War (1618 to 1648) inflated the death rates in Europe. Various famines have increased death rates. In recent years, famine has occurred in Bihar (India), Rwanda and Somali (Africa), and Bangladesh (Asia). Some famines, such as the one in Somali, are exacerbated by civil wars. More recently, Acquired Immunodeficiency Syndrome (AIDS) is so widespread in Africa that it could devastate entire populations. By the year 2000, a third of the people in Uganda could perish from AIDS (Unklesbay 1992).

After World War II a marked decline in the death rate occurred, particularly in developing countries. Modern drugs and public health programs were fostered. Malaria was assaulted with insecticides, and in Sri Lanka the death rate dropped dramatically. Control of yellow fever, smallpox, cholera, and other diseases further lowered the death rate.

Birth rates also have fluctuated. During the latter half of the 19th century, industrialization in western countries was accompanied by a relatively high birth rate and a decline in the death rate. For a while the growth rate in these developed countries was greater than the world average. In Western Europe this led to mass emigration. Gradually, as the industrial revolution progressed, birth rates began to decline in western countries. By the early 20th century the birth rate had dropped so that it neared the death rate in some countries. For instance, by the 1930s the combined death rate of Denmark, Norway, and Sweden was 12, and the birth rate had dropped to a low 16.

The birth rate has always been high in developing countries. Unlike in developed countries, the dramatic drop in the death rate has not been accompanied by a significant drop in the birth rate, and the growth rate soars. Children are a form of social security in many developing countries. A large family ensures the parents that they will be cared for in old age, and governments have been slow to encourage birth control.

The birth rate in the United States has shown interesting changes. In 1910 it was 30; it crashed to 18 during the depression years of the mid-1930s and leaped to 27 after World War II. Since then the birth rate has slowly declined and in 1971 stood at 17. By 1973 it dropped even lower. Only 1.9 children were born per couple.

If the population is to level off, zero growth must be obtained. This is simply when the birth rate of a population equals the death rate, discounting migration. This means that in North America the birth rate of 15 in 1991 would have to drop to 9 to stabilize the population. The birth rate would have to be lowered even more to allow for immigration. Most demographers agree that to obtain zero growth a couple in the United States should have no more than about two children. Even at two children per family, it will take several decades for the population to level off.

On a world scale, the relatively high birth rate of 27 and a death rate of 10 tell the story (Table 2.2). Even if the birth rate drops by 50%, the population will still continue to grow. The birth rate in Latin America is four times that of its death rate. Only a dramatic drop in the birth rate can stop the population from skyrocketing. Africa, with a birth rate of 45 and death rate of 15, must reduce its birth rate by more than 65% to reach zero growth.

The per capita consumption also affects the well-being of a population. Demands on foodstuffs have increased not only because there are more mouths to feed but also because of rising affluence in certain countries. People in developed countries are not only eating more, they are eating better, thus increasing per capita consumption. The average availability of grain in developing countries in 1973 was about 181 kg (400 lb) per person per year. This figure is trending downward. Such low quantities of grain are eaten directly. The average North American, on the other hand, uses about 907 kg (2,000 lb) of grain per year, of which only 68 kg (150 lb) is consumed directly in the form of bread and similar products. The rest is fed to animals and eaten indirectly as meat, eggs, and other animal products. The rule for converting grain into protein is 3.2 kg (7 lb) of grain per kg of beef, 1.8 kg (4 lb) for pork, and 1.4 kg (3 lb) for poultry.

In developed regions such as North America, per capita consumption of animal products has increased. In the United States per capita consumption of beef jumped from 25 kg (55 lb) in 1940 to more than 52 kg (114 lb) by 1972. In the 1980s and 1990s, beef consumption dropped, but poultry and fish consumption increased (Agricultural Statistics 1992). As countries become more affluent they include more animal products in their diet. This puts an even greater demand on the world supply of grain and may even put the price of grain out of reach to poor countries.

World demographers often link population growth and grain production in predicting the well-being of a country or region. Nick Ludington of the Associated Press summarized a report of the Union of Concerned Scientists (The Advocate, Baton Rouge, Louisiana 27 May 1994). Three scenarios were presented: A moderate view is that the world population reaches 10 billion and grain production increases 50% by the year 2050. Even so, world per capita grain consumption will decrease by 20%. Africa, China, and India with half the world's population by 2050 will face severe problems. A pessimistic view has world population reaching 13 billion by 2050, and per capita grain production dropping by 40%. An optimistic view has the world population stabilizing at 7.8 billion by 2050. Grain production would be adequate, assuming a near doubling of production.

Population Density

The population density of a country can be measured by the number of people per square kilometer. This is a better index than total population. The population density of North America was approximately 13 people per square kilometer in 1991 (Table 2.2), considerably less than Asia's 115 for the same period. Europe had a relatively high density of 101, whereas the former U.S.S.R. has only 13 people per square kilometer. Australia and New Zealand combined had 3. The population density for all countries and for all regions of the world must be viewed along with the area considered wasteland. In Australia, for example, most people live along the coastline. Much of the interior is considered uninhabitable.

Family Planning

Because of the growing concern for the rising world population, the United Nations held the first conference on world population in 1954. In 1967 the United Nations signed the U.N. Declaration on Population proclaiming family planning as a basic human right. By 1971 only 17% of the countries that were members of the United Nations had policies for limiting population growth, and the effectiveness of such programs is sometimes limited. In the United States, the National Commission on Population Growth and the National Future have studied the relationship between population growth and the quality of life. Landmark legislation, enacted by the U.S. Congress in 1970, extended family planning services throughout the United States. The United States has worked through the Agency for International Development (AID) to develop a worldwide program for population control and family planning.

China and Japan developed a resolve to curb their population growth. China adopted a one-child family goal; those families having more than one child suffered a decline in living standards. Between 1970 and 1976, China's population growth rate dropped from 2.6 to 1.3. After World War II, Japan realized that it must rely more on its own natural resources, and, to maintain an acceptable standard of living, the birth rate had to be lowered. Between 1949 and 1956, Japan lowered its population growth rate from 2.2 to about 1. In the 1990s, however, Japan had some concern that its lower birth rate is causing a shortage of labor for its economic development.

LAND TO GROW FOOD

Though the world's potential population seems infinite, land to grow food is finite. The world's land surface covers about 13.4 billion ha (33 billion ac).

In the early 1970s, 1.4 billion ha (3.5 billion ac) were considered arable land and land under permanent crops. Permanent meadow and pasture land accounted for 3 billion ha (7.4 billion ac). Land to grow food then amounted to roughly 33% of the total land area. This figure drops to about 30% if we discount land to grow non-edible crops such as cotton. During this same period, cropland in the United States occupied about 19% of the land, pastures 28%, forests 32%, and wasteland 13%. Cities occupied about twice as much land in 1973 as in 1950, amounting to 1.5% of the entire United States land area. Highways and airports, despite rapid expansion, took up only 1%. Land to grow food throughout the world continues to change and is depicted in Figure 2.2 for the year 1987.

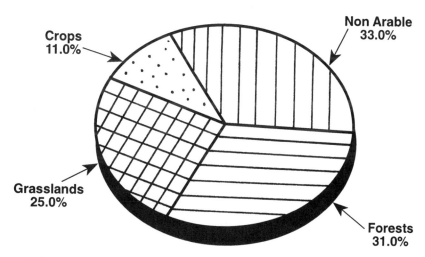

Figure 2.2 World land use. Source: Food and Agriculture Organization, 1988.

The distribution of arable land throughout the world is uneven. Some regions are blessed with arable land whereas others have been short-changed. Africa, with a total land area of more than 3 billion ha, can claim only 7% as arable. Latin America can classify only 6% of its land as arable. A few major regions are favored with large areas of arable land: continental Western Europe, continental United States east of the Rocky Mountains, and India.

The share of arable land varies greatly between countries of a geographic region. Close to 50% of the land in India is considered arable, but only 11% is considered arable in China. Within Western Europe roughly 65% of Denmark is arable but its neighbor, Norway, can cultivate only 2% to 3% of its land. In Latin American countries, only 2% of Brazil has been considered arable contrasted with 17% for Cuba. Canada has only 3% to 4% arable land.

By 1988, major detrimental land changes occurred (Brown et al. 1989). Perhaps the most significant change is the degradation or desertification of land by human activities. Each year, irreversible desertification occurs on approximately 6 million ha (15 million ac) worldwide. An additional 20 million ha (50 million ac) become so degraded that they are unprofitable to farm or graze. According to the United Nations Environment Programme (UNEP) in 1984, 4.5 billion ha (11.25 billion ac), or 35% of the earth's land surface, are threatened by desertification.

The four major causes of land degradation, according to Brown et al. (1989), are: (1) overgrazing on rangelands, (2) overcultivation of croplands, (3) water-logging and salinization of irrigated lands, and (4) deforestation. Overgrazing by cattle, sheep, goats, and camels, and over-cultivation leave the land exposed to the ravages of wind and rain. Agricultural land without vegetation, or land on steep slopes, is subject to erosion from wind and rain (Figure 2.3).

Figure 2.3 Unprotected land is subject to erosion.

When soils are overirrigated, the water table rises, enters the root zone, and damages crops. In dry regions salinization often accompanies waterlogging. The last major cause of land degradation, deforestation, results in erosion of soil, and it may interfere with the natural phenomena of the hydrological cycle. According to Brown et al. (1989), the U.N. Food and Agriculture Organization (FAO) estimates that each year 11.3 million ha (28.3 million ac) of tropical forests are lost to land clearing, and in the Brazilian Amazon alone approximately 8 million ha (20 million ac) of forests were cleared in 1987. Such deforestation can alter the hydrological cycle. More rainfall runs off, and less gets recycled back to the atmosphere to generate new rainfall. With the reduction of rainfall, ground water becomes increasingly more important (Figure 2.4).

Figure 2.4 Hand-dug water well, Sierra Leone.

Brown et al. (1989) reviewed strategies for combating land degradation to regain productivity. For example, the United States with the Conservation Reserve Plan hoped to idle 16 million ha (40 million ac) of highly erodible farmland to be planted in grass or trees. Farmers are compensated for the set-aside.

GROWING FOOD ON THE LAND
The World Picture

Grain production has been used as a barometer to measure a country's effort to keep ahead of population growth. Between 1934 and 1938 Latin America exported more grain than did North America. Only Western Europe imported grain. Africa, Asia, Eastern Europe, and the U.S.S.R. held their own in grain production. Changes occurred after World War II. The death rate dropped dramatically in developing countries, resulting in more mouths to feed. From 1948 to 1952 Latin America and Africa began slipping, although still producing a surplus of grain. Asia, however, began importing grain. Eventually all regions except North America, Western Europe, and Australia and New Zealand began importing again. Today the United States has emerged as the breadbasket of the world. In 1972, the United States exported 14.5 million mt (16 million tons) of grain to the former Soviet Union, the equivalent of nearly half the U.S. wheat crop. In the first 9 months of 1973, approximately 1.8 million mt (2 million tons) of wheat worth $184 million and $70 million of corn were shipped to China. During the 1980s, the United States exported roughly 40% of its crop production. In world trading, the United States has provided approximately 75% of all the corn and soybeans, 40% of the wheat, and 25% of the rice (Unklesbay 1992).

At the start of the 1987 harvest, world grain reserves totaled a record 459 million mt (506 million tons), enough to feed the world for 101 days (Brown et al. 1989). The drought in 1988, however, lowered carryover stocks to approximately 54 days of consumption, the lowest since 1972. As the world population continues to escalate, the significance of carryover stocks magnifies.

Increasing Food Production

Food production can be increased by farming additional land or by increasing yields on existing lands. The geographic regions classified as developed -- North America, Western Europe, the former Soviet Union, and Australia and New Zealand -- have been mostly dependent on increased yields from existing lands for the past quarter century. Developing geographic regions -- Asia, Africa, and Latin America -- have increased yields mainly by adding new land to cultivation. During the last two decades, however, Asia has become more dependent on increased yields rather than on expansion of farmland. Africa and Latin America have increased yields by bringing new lands under cultivation. Much of the land in these two regions has thin soil. A common practice in certain parts of these regions has been slash and burn. Trees and brush are cut and burned. Crops are planted for a few years. When the land "wears out," it is abandoned and allowed to grow back into natural vegetation (Figure 2.5).

Figure 2.5 Slash and burn agriculture in Liberia.

Increasing yields on farmland can be accomplished by multiple cropping, fertilization, irrigation, use of pesticides, use of improved plant varieties, and mechanization. Overriding all these factors is the technology or knowledge to make a particular piece of land productive.

Multiple cropping is a practice of growing two or more crops per year on the same land. In some areas of the United States, farmers plant winter wheat in the fall and harvest in late spring. This crop is followed by soybeans that are harvested in the fall. Multiple cropping requires more fertilizer, rainfall or irrigation when needed, and plant varieties with a shorter growing season. Multiple cropping then is limited to geographic areas with a sufficiently long growing season and water. More capital and labor also are required, particularly if fertilizer is used. The science of multiple cropping is well developed in Taiwan, Japan, Korea, and China. Tropical countries are well suited to multiple cropping since the growing season is yearlong.

Fertilizer assumes an important role in food production, especially as farmland becomes more scarce. Fertilizer can contribute significantly to increased yields in developing countries, assuming enough moisture is present. It has been estimated that in some developing countries production could be doubled by increasing usage of fertilizer. In the United States fertilizer is used liberally, and plant varieties are used that respond to heavy use of fertilizer.

Irrigation is widely practiced in some regions of the world. Asia depends on irrigation, as do India and China. Japan has more than half of its farmland under irrigation. The western United States has large areas under irrigation. Water for irrigation comes from two main sources, surface and underground. Rivers and streams furnish most of the water; wells and ponds are secondary sources. The costs of obtaining water for irrigation and water quality are important factors to consider. To obtain ground water and most surface water, pumps and fuel are required. Where food prices are high enough, these costs may be justified.

Pesticides are classified as insecticides, fungicides, or herbicides. Pests and diseases are usually controlled with insecticides and fungicides. Weeds may be controlled mechanically as well as with herbicides. Countries with high production have depended on pesticides.

Improved plant varieties imply improved yields. Yet seeds are often improved for a specific characteristic. This may mean a stronger stem to reduce lodging, a resistance to diseases, or a greater response to fertilizers. Some seeds are developed that mature early or require a shorter growing season. High-lysine corn and improved seeds of rice and wheat show promise for increasing food production. Biotechnology holds promise for improving crop yields. Agricultural scientists have developed plant cell cultures to propagate superior plants. Genes have been transferred from one plant to another to impart a favorable characteristic. A good example is the genetically engineered tomato to prevent mushiness during transit. Developing countries can benefit from use of improved seeds, but seeds must be used that are adaptable to the area. For example, seeds that respond to heavy use of fertilizer may not adapt to lands where little or no fertilizer is available.

Mechanization may be land saving and labor saving. Use of tractors instead of draft animals saves land. Land formerly used to produce feed for horses can now produce food. Mechanization saves labor. Tractors disc land, and airplanes may apply herbicides to control weeds. The use of mechanization in developing countries sounds easier than it is. Lack of capital, farming on a small scale, and century-old traditions retard mechanization. Almost all developing countries have more than one-half of their economically active population engaged in farming. Mechanization frightens some governments. What would be done if people are put out of work?

To increase food production, we must also maintain our soil and water base and protect our environment. In the mid 1980s the concept of sustainable agriculture was advanced (Edwards et al. 1990). Sustainable agriculture is the philosophy of increasing crop production without the loss of natural resources such as soil and water, and without damage to the environment.

We must protect our environment. Erosion and desertification must be reversed. Water must be used wisely, as in Israel with the practice of underground drip irrigation. Acid rain and the erosion of our ozone layer must be curtailed. The deterioration of the ozone layer allows more ultraviolet radiation from the sun to the earth. This greenhouse effect is thought to have resulted in the record heat wave in 1988. Pollution -- domestic, industrial, and agricultural -- must be lowered. Many problems, such as acid rain and reduction of the ozone layer, must be solved on a cooperative global effort.

FOOD REQUIREMENTS OF PEOPLE
The Demand for Food

The world's population increases by approximately 86 million each year. An additional 29 million mt (32 million tons) of food must be produced annually to feed them. More than 800 million people in developing countries are critically short of most of life's necessities, such as food, clothing, shelter, and fuel (Unklesbay 1992). The hungry nations are getting hungrier, and in many countries people merely eke out an existence. To get adequate food, a country must be able to grow its own, have money to buy it, or depend on donated food.

Caloric and Protein Needs

The recommended energy allowances, set by the Food and Nutrition Board of the National Academy of Sciences National Research Council, are the standards used in assessing caloric, protein, and other nutrient requirements for people in the United States. Various factors modify these values. For example, a 77-kg (170-lb) white-collar worker may need only 2,900 calories per day, whereas a blue-collar worker may need 3,700 calories. Pregnant women need a high caloric and protein intake.

The desired protein consumption should average about 70 g (2.5 oz) of total protein per capita per day. Certain developed countries greatly exceed this level. Most developing countries do not come near this amount. Haitians, for example, exist on 39 g (1.4 oz) of protein and 1,750 calories (Unklesbay 1992).

POTENTIAL SOURCES OF FOOD
Single-cell Protein

Microbial cells from algae, bacteria, and yeasts, collectively known as single-cell protein (SCP), are a source of protein. Substances for growing SCP range from carbon dioxide and light to sugarcane waste and petroleum. In addition to a carbon source, a nitrogen source is needed. Other elements such as calcium, phosphorus, magnesium, and iron also must be present.

Algal species cultured include *Chlorella* sp., *Scenedesmus* sp., and *Spirulina maxima*. Tribes in the Chad Republic have harvested *S. maxima* from shallow ponds for many years. Algae can be used for animal or human food. Protein content ranges from 50% to 60%, and amino acid profiles are good except for low methionine. Algae culture is limited by the need for sunlight most of the year and a continuous supply of carbon dioxide as a carbon source. For optimum growth, CO_2 must be provided since air contains only about 350 ppm of CO_2. Algae have been tolerated in human diets at amounts up to 100 g (3.5 oz) per day. Over this amount, gastrointestinal disorders may result.

Bacteria have high growth rates, 20- to 30-minute doubling time, as compared with 2 to 3 hours for yeast, and 16 hours or more for algae. Crude protein may reach 85%, and amino acid profiles show better balances of essential amino acids such as methionine, lysine, and tryptophan, than do those of algae or yeasts. Bacteria can use inexpensive industrial wastes as media for protein production. The bacterium *Cellulomonas* has converted cellulose of sugarcane waste to protein.

Yeast has probably the most favorable characteristics for use as a food supplement, followed by bacteria. More than 50% of the dry weight of yeast is protein. Members of the vitamin B complex group are plentiful.

There are advantages and disadvantages with the use of SCP. Key problems are: (1) potential danger of kidney stone formation or the development of gout, (2) adverse gastrointestinal reactions, (3) possible adverse skin reactions, and (4) possible presence of carcinogenic compounds. There are other problems, the most important of which are costs of producing, harvesting, and acceptability. With algae, large volumes of water must be handled. Cost of de-watering is high. Harvest of bacteria cells from the growth medium is difficult. The small size of bacteria (0.5 to 2 microns) as compared to yeast (5 to 6 microns) makes the centrifugation process costly for recovery of bacteria. Perhaps the major concern in use of SCP is its palatability and acceptability. It is important that taste, flavor, and texture be acceptable. One might think that SCP would be greedily accepted by hungry populations. This is not necessarily so. The hungriest people have the fewest food items in their diet and are slow to accept new foods.

There are several advantages of SCP. The potential to produce large volumes of protein using wastes is particularly appealing. Land is not a critical factor since little space is required. SCP can be used as human food and in animal feeds. SCP has been suggested for use as an extender in ground meat and frankfurters. In the United States the use of SCP in animal feeds is realistic, especially for poultry. Use of SCP in animal feeds in developing countries shows less promise because livestock and poultry are usually not able to consume SCP directly. Since SCP can constitute only 5% to 15% of the animal feed ration, other ingredients would be needed.

Fish Protein Concentrate

Fish protein concentrate (FPC) is defined as those products obtained from fish where the protein is more concentrated than the original raw product. The main advantage of FPC is that it is supposed to use stocks of fish that are largely unexploited. The disadvantage is that these species may be important in the food web of commercially important species. Further, some fish species considered for FPC are used for manufacture of fish oil and fish meal. FPC, which contains between 75% and 95% protein, may be prepared by several methods including chemical (solvent extraction) or biological (enzymatic and microbial) procedures.

Several species of fish have been used to make FPC. These include red hake (*Urophycis chuss*), Atlantic menhaden (*Brevoortia tyrannus*), Atlantic herring (*Clupea harengus harengus*), northern anchovy (*Engraulis mordax*), alewife (*Alosa pseudoharengus*), and ocean pout (*Macrozoarces americanus*).

Several manufacturing plants were constructed to produce FPC. In 1971 a plant was constructed in Aberdeen, Washington. The experimental plant was designed to process 45 mt (50 tons) of raw fish into 6.8 mt (7.5 tons) of FPC every 24 hours. Plants were also constructed in Nova Scotia, Canada; Agadir, Morocco; and New Bedford, Massachusetts.

FPC did show some promise as a food additive or extender in such products as meat, bread, pasta, and crackers. Marketing of FPC, like marketing of SCP, is difficult. Social, economic, and cultural considerations must be taken into account. Moreover, the U.S. Food and Drug Administration requirements for human food make it difficult for FPC manufacturing to be economical.

Hydroponics

Hydroponics is the growing of vegetables and other plants in water without the benefit of soil. Nutrients are put into solution, and some medium such as chipped pumice rock or vermiculite is used to support the plant; or plants are held in place with string. There is an interest in hydroponics for fish culture operations. Water chestnuts have been grown in pools containing fish. The plants removed nutrients produced from fish waste and uneaten feed.

FISH AS FOOD
Per Capita Consumption

Average annual world per capita consumption of fishery products (whole weight) for human food during 1982 to 1984 was about 12 kg (27 lb) (Dicks and Harvey 1988). Per capita consumption of fishery products, however, varies widely throughout the world. Europeans and Asians include fishery products in their diets with regularity. High per capita consumption of fishery products from 1982 to 1984 was found in Iceland, 89 kg (196 lb); Japan, 74 kg (164 lb); Hong Kong, 54 kg (118 lb); and Denmark, 52 kg (114 lb) (Dicks and Harvey 1988). In Latin America the picture is varied. Certain countries such as Brazil, Cuba, and Mexico have a relatively low per capita consumption. People in Panama, on the other hand, regularly consume fishery products. In the Near East, fish historically has been eaten rarely except in Israel where consumption is still relatively low. However, certain oil-rich countries now include high-value fishery products in their diets. In the Far East fish is eaten more often, and a number of countries such as Japan, Hong Kong, and Taiwan rely heavily on fish for animal protein. In most African countries fish is by no means eaten regularly, except perhaps in coastal countries (Figure 2.6). In Australia and New Zealand fish is eaten, but mainly as an alternative to other animal protein. For years much the same could be said for North America.

In the United States, beef, and pork to a lesser degree, is most important in the diet. Over the years the per capita consumption of meat has ranged from 67 kg (148 lb) in 1959 to 51 kg (112 lb) in 1991 (Agricultural Statistics 1973, 1992). Poultry also has increased, going from 16 kg (35 lb) to 23 kg

(50 lb) for the same period. Fish, on the other hand, has played a relatively minor role in the diet. During the years 1986 to 1991 per capita consumption of meat has trended downward, whereas consumption of poultry and fish has steadily increased (Table 2.3). In 1991, per capita consumption of fish in the United States was 6.7 kg (14.8 lb). The population increase in the United States of about 2 million each year also accounts for higher demand. Most fishery products eaten are from high-value species such as shrimp. They are eaten more for taste than for protein. However, a health-conscious population now consumes more fishery products.

Figure 2.6 Fish market in Sierra Leone.

Table 2.3 Per capita consumption, retail-weight equivalent, of edible meat, poultry, and fish in the United States 1983 to 1991.

Year	Meat[a] (pounds)	Poultry[b] (pounds)	Fish (pounds)	Total (pounds)
1983	123.9	42.6	13.3	179.8
1984	123.7	43.7	14.1	181.5
1985	124.9	45.2	15.0	185.1
1986	122.2	47.1	15.4	184.7
1987	117.4	50.7	16.1	184.2
1988	119.5	51.7	15.1	186.3
1989	115.9	53.6	15.6	185.1
1990	112.4	55.9	15.0	183.3
1991	112.0	50.1	14.8	184.9

Source: Agricultural Statistics 1992 [a] includes beef, veal, lamb, and mutton and pork
[b] chicken and turkey combined   Note: 2.205 lb = 1 kg.

Table 2.4 Nutritive value of selected raw animal products per 100 grams edible products. (Author's note: Animals with less fat are now being produced.)

Food	Protein (grams)	Fat (grams)	Carbohydrate (grams)	Energy (calories)
Beef[a]	18.0	21.0	0.0	266
Chicken[b]	18.6	4.9	0.0	124
Eggs	12.9	11.5	0.9	163
Milk[c]	3.5	3.5	4.9	65
Pork[a]	10.2	52.0	0.0	513
Trout (rainbow)	21.5	11.4	0.0	195

Source: USDA Agriculture Handbook No. 8 Composition of Foods 1963.
[a]carcass [b]whole chicken -- skin, flesh, giblets [c]whole milk Note: 1 lb = 454 g.

Fish Compared with Other Animal Products

Fish compares favorably with other animal products as a source of protein (Table 2.4). Generally it contains about the same protein content as beef and chicken but more than pork, milk, or eggs. The fat content of fish is much lower than most animal products except perhaps milk. Rainbow trout (*Oncorhynchus mykiss*), the example used in Table 2.4, contains more fat than most fish species. Generally a fat content of less than 5% is average. Carbohydrates are low in most animal products and are only noticeable in milk. Fish contains far fewer calories, 195 for 100 g of rainbow trout, than does beef at 266 calories or pork at 513 calories. The main reason is the low fat content of fish. In recent years, beef and pork are being produced which have less fat. This is due to development of new breeds and to a change in animal diets, such as relying more on grass and less on grain.

Fish a Health Food

Fish, crustaceans, and mollusks are 90% to 100% digestible. Compared with mammals, fishery products have a much greater ratio of muscle protein to connective tissue protein. Muscle protein is easier to digest. Because of its digestibility, fish is often included in the diets of people with digestive disorders, such as ulcers.

Fish is often recommended for heart patients because of the chemical nature of the fat and because of the relatively low cholesterol content. Fish is high in omega-3 polyunsaturated fatty acids which doctors recommend over saturated fatty acids. Cholesterol is a culprit in heart attacks. Fish contains relatively low quantities of cholesterol, compared with beef or poultry, generally less than 40 mg per 100 g (3.5 oz) of flesh. Shellfish, such as lobsters, contain slightly more cholesterol than other fishery products.

Fish is rich in certain vitamins and minerals. Fat-soluble vitamins, especially vitamins A and D, are found in fish liver oil. Many youngsters in past years were given cod liver oil. Four water-soluble vitamins, B_6, B_{12}, biotin, and niacin, can be found in fish and shellfish. The remaining four B vitamins are found in fishery products, but generally not in appreciable quantities. Fish is especially rich in minerals and contains phosphorous, potassium, and iron in large amounts. Fish contains more calcium, magnesium, and chlorine than does meat. Other minerals in fish include sulphur and sodium.

Fishery products are a storehouse for many trace minerals. Marine species are rich in iodine, which is important in preventing goiter. People in countries with a high fish diet usually have excellent teeth because of the fluoride in fish. Other trace minerals abundant in fish include copper, zinc, manganese, cobalt, molybdenum, and selenium. Oysters are a particularly good source of trace minerals.

Four Main Groups of Fish

Fish can be broken down into four main groups (Shapiro 1971): (1) low fat and high protein, including those species with less than 5% fat and more than 15% protein, such as channel catfish (*Ictalurus punctatus*), lobster (*Homarus* sp.), shrimp (*Penaeus* spp.), rainbow trout, and tuna (*Thunnus* spp.); (2) medium fat and high protein content, including those species with 5% to 15% fat and more than 15% protein, such as salmon (*Oncorhynchus* spp. and *Salmo salar*); (3) high fat and low protein content, including those fishes that contain more than 15% fat and less than 15% protein; only a few species fall into this group, including certain subspecies of lake trout (*Salvelinus namaycush*), herring (*Alosa* spp.), mackerel (*Scomber* spp.), and sardine (*Sardinella* spp. and *Sardinops sagax*) during particular seasons; (4) low fat and low protein, such as oysters (*Crassostrea* spp. and *Ostrea* spp.) and clams (*Mercenaria mercenaria* et al.) with a fat content of less than 5% and a protein content of less than 15%; the other major component is water, which accounts for about 80% of the weight.

Nutritional Composition of Selected Fishes

As noted earlier, fish are placed in one of four general groups based on protein and fat content. In Table 2.5 data are presented on selected finfishes, crustaceans, and mollusks, all of which are being cultured or which show potential for culture. It is interesting to compare the species on the basis of nutritive value. You might consider the protein content as a factor in selecting a species to culture. From this standpoint, the yellowfin tuna (*Thunnus albacares*) would be a good species to culture. By the same reasoning, the eel

(*Anguilla* spp.) should be the culture species to farm, if you were interested in as much energy (calories) as possible.

In the United States interests lie most with high-value species. Freshwater channel catfish is 18% protein; rainbow trout is 22% protein. Shrimp, 21% protein, and lobster, 20% protein, are highly regarded as gourmet items. Oysters are low in protein, but the quality of the protein is high.

Table 2.5 Composition of the edible portion of raw (fresh or frozen) crustacea, finfish, and mollusks for protein, fat, carbohydrate, and energy.

Species[a]	Protein %	Fat %	Carbohydrate %	Energy[b]
Carp, common	18.0	6.2	--	--
Catfish, freshwater	17.6	3.2	--	--
Crab, blue	16.1	1.0	1.25	81.5
Crayfish	18.7	1.7	--	--
Eels, freshwater	18.0	17.3	--	246.0
Lobsters	19.6	1.3	0.8	95.0
Mullet, striped	19.4	5.5	--	143.0
Oyster	6.9	1.5	3.3	--
Pompano	19.3	1.4	2.8	86.2
Prawns, freshwater	16.8	1.2	--	--
Salmon, coho	21.5	5.7	--	--
Scallop	17.2	0.7	--	--
Shrimp	20.5	1.1	2.2	88.3
Sole, Dover	15.0	0.8	--	--
Trout, rainbow	22.0	11.7	--	--
Tuna, yellowfin	24.3	2.2	--	--

Source: Adapted from Sidwell et al. 1974. Note 1 lb = 454 grams. [a]Scientific names are those accepted by the American Fisheries Society. [b]calories/100 grams.

THE WORLD FISHERIES PICTURE

Marine ecosystems encompass most of the earth's surface, or nearly 71%. Freshwater lakes and streams cover approximately 0.4% of the earth's surface, yet fishery products contribute only a tenth of the animal protein in our diets.

The World Catch

After World War II, the harvest from our oceans and fresh waters seemed to indicate that the resource was virtually unlimited. All that seemed necessary was to increase the harvesting effort and apply new technology (Figures 2.7 a, b, c).

48

(a)

(b)

(c)

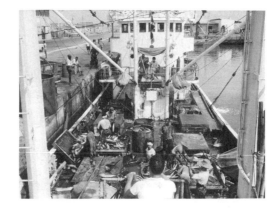

Figures 2.7 a, b, c Different levels of capture fisheries. (a) Fishers pulling a beach seine in Sumatra, Indonesia; (b) Artisanal fishers in Sri Lanka. Photo courtesy of Food and Agriculture Organization, by S. Bunnag; (c) Japanese tuna ship. Photo courtesy of Food and Agriculture Organization, by A. Dafever.

World landings during 1948 to 1952 averaged 21.9 million mt (24 million tons) (Table 2.6) and showed steady increases through the period 1963 to 1967. From 1968 on increases continued but at a slower rate. Eventually harvest of fishery products began to level off. In 1989, a record 100 million mt (110 million tons) were harvested. About 30% of that harvest was converted into fish meal and used in animal and pet feeds.

Table 2.6 Annual world landings of aquatic resources (million metric tons) (excluding mammals and seaweeds).

Period	Inland waters	Marine (less Anchoveta)	Anchoveta	Total (all species)
1948-52	2.5	19.4	0.0	21.9
1953-57	3.8	25.1	0.1	29.0
1958-62	5.8	30.3	3.7	39.8
1963-67	7.3	37.6	9.0	53.9
1968-72	8.9	48.2	10.0	67.1
1973-77	6.8	56.4	2.8	66.0
1978-82	7.7	63.8	1.4	72.9
1983-87	10.9	74.5	1.6	87.0
1988	13.4	82.1	3.6	99.1
1989	13.9	81.0	5.4	100.3
1990	14.5	79.0	3.8	97.3

Source: FAO Fisheries Circular No. 710, Revision 8, Part 1 FIRM/ C710 (Rev. 8, Part 1) (EN). 1992. Note: 1 mt = 1.1 tons.

The Potential World Catch

At first glance you might think that the vast oceans would be our salvation with respect to food problems, merely because of their immensity. The truth is that the open seas, which are biological deserts, constitute 90% of our oceans. The surface waters have enough light for photosynthesis but nutrients are in short supply. The most productive areas of our marine ecosystem are: (1) estuaries that act as traps for nutrients entering from freshwater flow, (2) upwelling areas where deep, cold water rich in nutrients is brought to the top, and (3) waters overlying the continental shelves.

How much then can our oceans yield? On the basis of productivity estimates from all marine ecosystems, Ryther (1969) suggested that harvestable fishery products from all ocean waters are between 200 and 250 million mt (220 and 276 million tons). We cannot, however, harvest this total production without serious disruption of various food chains. Therefore, Ryther's estimate is that the long-term sustainable harvest may be about 100 million mt (110 million tons).

Some experts estimate that upwards of 150 million mt (165 million tons) are conceivable. To exceed these levels we would have to move far down the food chain and use such planktonic animals as krill, and this is being done. Nevertheless, it may be wiser to let fish harvest krill and then harvest these animals.

To derive the greatest benefit of fishery products from our oceans year after year, we should try to obtain the optimum sustained yield. Unlike maximum sustained yield (harvest of a particular stock of fish over the years without causing the stock to increase or decrease in abundance) optimum sustained yield takes into account socio-economic, environmental, aesthetic, legal, and other factors. This unfortunately is often difficult to assess because so many countries with differing opinions are involved.

The Crisis of Ocean Fisheries

Jessica Mathews, in a special report to the Washington Post, wrote (20 March 1994, Baton Rouge Sunday Advocate) that the drastic overuse of ocean fisheries has caused a crisis. Thirteen of 17 major global fisheries are depleted or in serious decline. The other four are overexploited or fully exploited. All have reached or far exceeded sustainable yields. The global catch of preferred species has been declining since the mid 1980s. The rising tonnages are deceiving. While the annual harvest has flirted with the 100 million mt mark, much of the catch has shifted from valuable species such as flounder (*Paralichthys* spp.), haddock (*Melanogrammus aeglefinus*), Atlantic cod (*Gadus morhua*), and swordfish (*Xiphias gladius*) to much less edible ones, such as spiny dogfish (*Squalus acanthias*), skate (*Raja* spp.), and shark (various species). Already, marine scientists are concerned that overfishing is depleting shark populations. Whenever commercial fishers switch to a new, underutilized species, such as the shark, there is a lag time before management practices are put in place.

Tom Knudson wrote in the Wall Street Journal (22 March 1994) that he interviewed a number of chefs regarding the switch to less desirable species. One chef stated, all the popular species are dwindling. We are depleting our oceans. One restaurant serves grilled skate spareribs. Not long ago this fish was thrown overboard as a trash fish. Another restaurant in Cambridge no longer has cod available. Instead, it serves such dishes as deep-fried smelt, a sardine-like fish. Another newcomer, the ocean catfish, which is also known as wolffish, has been described as a sweet, good-tasting fish. People are getting used to eating it. In some places the pout is being eaten.

Jessica Mathews further wrote that nine of 12 Atlantic groundfish stocks have collapsed. The harvest of such species as cod, haddock, and flounder is down by 70% to 85%. Pacific salmon are nearing commercial biological extinction. In Seafood Business (March/April 1994) the "collapse" of global groundfish was noted. This fishery has gone from 12.1 million mt (13.3 million tons) in 1987 to 9.1 mt (10 tons) in 1991. In that period the Atlantic cod harvest has dropped 31% and Alaska pollock 25%. The overall groundfish catch outlook for 1994 indicates a further decline to around 8 million mt (8.8 million tons). In eastern Canada, five of eight areas have been closed to cod fishing altogether, while fishing in the other three areas has been seriously reduced. In the National Fisherman (April 1994) it was noted that most of the water from Nova Scotia to Newfoundland has been closed to fishing in an effort to bring back depleted groundfish stocks. In all, the closures have meant the loss of 40,000 jobs. Anthony (1993) gave an in-depth review on the state of groundfish resources from the northeastern United States.

What is Causing the Problem?

There are a number of reasons given for the crisis in our ocean fisheries. Ken Kelley (National Fisherman December 1993) wrote that it is the opinion of the Fisheries Conservation Council (FCC) that the changing environment and colder ocean waters have played a major role in the decline of groundfish stocks. The most extreme impacts have occurred off Newfoundland and Labrador where the FCC found "some stocks have virtually disappeared from parts of their normal range." The reason for the colder waters is arguable. Some theorize that global warming has resulted in some melting of the polar cap, with colder water flowing south. This impact of the colder water and ice cover in 1991 kept groundfish from coming near shore, and their fate has been a matter of conjecture.

Jessica Mathews feels that oil exploration caused the crisis on the Georges Bank in the Atlantic Ocean. She reported that in 1979, following a second oil-shortage crisis, the government explored for oil on the Georges Bank. This area was teeming with fish and had more fish per square meter than any place in the world. It served as a spawning ground for dozens of species fished there and elsewhere. Though no oil was found, the Georges Bank was nearly destroyed. After 350 years of continuous fishing, the area was stripped bare in a decade. Today, much of it is closed to fishing.

Overfishing is perhaps the most often heard reason for depletion of our ocean fisheries. In one instance, one small community on the Atlantic Coast had a modest fishing fleet (Avault 1994). As a method of economic development, the government offered incentives to expand the fishing effort. In a few years the fishing fleet increased significantly, and overfishing became a problem. Restrictions had to be placed on the harvest of certain fish stocks. At first, boats could only harvest so many fish per day. This meant that some boats had to dump excess overboard to comply with regulations. Later, regulations were amended. The commercial fishers had a single 24-hour period to harvest a particular stock of fish for the entire year's catch.

The National Fisherman magazine is replete with examples of overfishing. Advanced technology, including sonar, spotter planes, improved nets, and the sheer numbers of fishing vessels, greatly increased the harvest of fish from our oceans. Many countries, including the United States, subsidize commercial fishers when they come on hard economic times so they can make payments on their fishing vessels and get by until better times. Countries are sensitive to the needs of their citizens. This does not, however, solve the root problem. One of the overall problems is the fish in our oceans seem to belong to everyone, despite our 200-mile (322 km) zoning. The attitude is, if we don't catch the fish someone else will.

Some say our nursery areas are being destroyed. In Louisiana, for example, huge chunks of coastline are lost each year. To prevent flooding, water has been channeled out to the sea and not allowed to spill over onto the surrounding land to deposit silt. The silt, which for centuries was deposited to build new estuarine areas, was going straight out to sea. In some cases, aquaculture is the culprit for loss of nursery areas. Shell (1993) quoting others wrote that mangrove swamps are good areas for shrimp farming. With the escalation of shrimp farming, the mangroves have been eliminated in many areas. By 1985, Java had lost 70% of its mangroves, Sulawesi 49%, Sumatra 36%, the Philippines 45%, Thailand 27%, and Malaysia, 20%.

In the Pacific Northwest, Pacific salmon stocks have been reduced drastically. At least 106 stocks of salmon and steelhead trout (*O. mykiss*) have been lost (Boyle 1994). The Pacific Fishery Management Council halted salmon fishing entirely off the coast of Washington state for the first time ever. Strict limits were placed on sport and commercial fishing for Oregon and California. Blamed for the problem are hydropower dam operations, logging and grazing practices, and irrigation that diverts water. Overfishing, too, played a role in the decline of salmon populations.

There are no doubt other reasons for the decline of our ocean fisheries. We have not even mentioned pollution. And some blame El Nino. The United Nations will address the issues.

Implication for Aquaculture

The obvious implication is that the production shortfall from ocean fisheries -- coupled with increased population and per capita consumption -- enhances aquaculture production. And this is so. But there are two warning signs. One is overproduction of certain culture species, and the other is depletion of our natural resources. A good example is the glut on the market of salmon produced from aquaculture. In less than a decade we seemed to go from a modest production of salmon to overproduction. Many salmon growers in Norway and elsewhere have undergone hard economic times. A strong promotional effort will help solve the problem, especially in regions not known for eating salmon.

Depletion of our natural resources in the name of aquaculture is no reason to condone the practice. The loss of mangrove swamps, as pointed out by Shell (1993), destroys one resource while developing another. In developing aquaculture around the world, we must be careful to manage our natural resources, such as land and water, rather than use them up.

Channel catfish farmers in the United States are practicing conservation. For example, ponds in grow-out are seldom drained for harvesting fish, thus conserving water. Fish are partially harvested by seining; marketable fish are removed and smaller fish remain for further growth. Further, when pond water drops by 15 cm (6 in) because of evaporation or seepage, only 7.6 cm (3 in) are added back. This allows you to capture additional water when it rains. In the long-run, aquaculture will have to be practiced more "sustainable." This means there will not be a net loss of natural resources in production of the crop.

Increasing the Availability of Fishery Products

There are ways to increase the availability of fishery products from our oceans other than simply capturing more fish. Gorga and Ronsivalli (1988) listed them as: (1) use of underutilized species, (2) preservation of temporary oversupply, (3) improved efficiency of processing, and (4) quality assurance.

Several questions should be asked when considering a new species for market. Does it resemble a popular one already accepted by consumers? Is the stock of the species of sufficient size to support a fishery? The pollock (*Theragra chalcogramma*) was once considered a trash fish. It is similar to haddock but has darker flesh. A moderate effort to educate the industry and consumers paid off, and a market was established. The development of the red crab (*Cancer* sp.) industry came about when the demand for lobster meat increased significantly. The red crab meat appeared to have all of the organoleptic properties of the lobster, but there were two impediments. The first was inefficiency in extraction of meats. This was overcome with development of mechanized processing similar to that used for snow crabs (*Chionoecetes opilo*). The second impediment was that red crabs shed their legs shortly after harvest, thus making their harvest uneconomical. This problem was overcome by sectioning crabs at sea to obtain the highest possible yield.

Sometimes certain species are harvested in great abundance and a temporary oversupply exists. The fluctuation in the market price of a particular species because of oversupply can be high, as much as 100%. One solution is to store a part of the catch by freezing. Fish are often moved as a fresh product first since they are usually more valuable than frozen. Any surplus left over may be frozen, but by then the quality of the product has diminished. Thus certain frozen products are often perceived as being of poor quality. Nevertheless, high quality can be obtained by freezing fish shortly after harvest and maintaining them at about -29°C (-20°F).

The conventional methods of processing fish and shellfish often result in waste. When fillets are cut from fish, approximately 35% of the original weight is recovered; the other 65% is sold for use in fish meals or fertilizers, or is discarded. Waste also may occur when meats are separated from shellfish. Improved processing techniques, such as use of deboning machines, have increased yields for both finfish and shellfish. The National Marine Fisheries Service has researched recovery of meats from certain species. As a result the Atlantic red crab, formerly an underutilized species, is now a highly acceptable species in great demand. A market was also developed for simulated (surimi) blue crab (*Callinectes sapidus*) lump meat and other products. Minced fish added to hamburger or frankfurters did not detract from the organoleptic qualities of these products but enhanced their nutritional value. Gorga and Ronsivalli (1988) estimated that approximately 227 million kg (500 million lb) of edible meats potentially can be recovered and added to the U.S. food supply if deboning machines are used.

Some fishery products harvested at sea are eventually discarded because they spoil from improper handling. Spoilage may also occur at other levels before reaching the consumer. The greatest spoilage probably occurs in the supermarkets. The cumulative spoilage may be 10% or more of the original harvest.

ROLE OF AQUACULTURE
Production from World Aquaculture
During 1966 to 1967, annual world production from aquaculture was about 1 million mt (1.1 million tons) (President's Science Advisors Committee 1967). In 1970, a partial estimate based on 36 countries put world production at 2.6 million mt (2.9 million tons) (Pillay 1972a). In 1972, estimated production was more than 5 million mt (5.5 million tons) (Pillay 1973). His estimate, based on data from 42 countries, put production of finfish at 3.7 million mt (4.1 million tons) from 2.2 million ha (5.4 million ac), mollusks at about 1 million mt, and crustaceans at 14,000 mt (15,400 tons). Seaweeds also contributed 373,000 mt (411,000 tons), cultured mainly in Japan and Korea. In 1975, estimated production based on 60 countries exceeded 6 million mt (6.6 million tons) (Pillay 1979). In 1985, estimated production from 136 countries was 10.6 million mt (11.7 million tons) (Nash 1988) (Table 2.7). It should be noted, however, that all production estimates over the years have been just that, estimates. In 1991, aquaculture production

was placed at more than 15 million mt (16.5 million tons), based on 142 countries reporting (Food and Agriculture Organization 1994).

Table 2.7 World aquaculture production in 1985 (metric tons).

	Finfishes	Crustaceans	Mollusks	Seaweeds	Others
Africa	60,600	100	400	0	0
America, North	197,800	33,800	160,800	200	0
America, South	28,500	32,900	1,900	4,900	0
Asia	3,792,600	198,500	2,120,000	2,767,500	28,200
Europe	340,800	300	495,000	4,500	0
Oceania[a]	1,200	100	20,500	100	100
U.S.S.R.	296,000	0	0	0	0
Totals	4,717,500	265,700	2,798,600	2,777,200	28,300
Percentages (%)	4.5	2.5	26.5	26.2	0.3
Grand Total	10, 587,300 mt				

Source: Nash 1988. [a]Australia and New Zealand combined. Note: 1 mt = 1.1 tons.

Nash (1988) broke down aquaculture production according to leading countries (Table 2.8), environment -- fresh water, brackish water, and marine (Table 2.9), species (Table 2.10), and by culture system (Table 2.11).

Table 2.8 Aquaculture production of leading countries in 1985 (in metric tons).

Country	Total	Finfishes	Crustaceans	Mollusks	Seaweeds	Others
China	5,202,200	2,392,800	42,700	1,120,000	1,646,700	00,000
Japan	1,184,300	0,283,900	02,200	0,359,800	0,530,000	08,400
Korea	0,790,200	0,003,700	00,100	0,369,000	0,397,800	19,600
Philippines	0,494,400	0,243,700	29,900	0,037,900	0,182,900	00,000
USA	0,353,200	0,195,200	29,800	0,128,000	0,000,000	00,000
U.S.S.R.	0,296,000	0,296,000	NA	NA	0,000,000	00,000
Indonesia	0,309,900	0,271,900	38,000	0,000,000	0,000,000	00,200
France	0,215,800	0,034,000	00,200	0,181,600	0,000,000	00,000
VietNam	0,204,000	0,191,000	13,000	0,000,000	0,000,000	00,000

Source: Nash 1988. NA = not available.

His 1985 data (Table 2.8) listed 10 countries that each produced more than 200,000 mt (220,500 tons) per annum, including seaweeds. These top countries accounted for more than 88% of total aquaculture production in 1985. Since 1985, Indonesia had a 61% increase in aquaculture production (Figure 2.8); France, 31%; Republic of Korea, 24%; United States, 15%; China, 14%; Philippines, 12%, and Japan, 6% (Nash 1988). While some countries focus on high-value species, others also see aquaculture as a means of producing animal protein (Figure 2.9).

Figure 2.8 Fish farmer in Sukabumi, Java, holds brood carp.

Figure 2.9 Fish farmer displays fish produced in Orissa, India; training in fish farming given by FAO. Photo courtesy of Food and Agriculture Organization.

Regarding aquaculture by environment, 53% of the world's aquaculture production, excluding seaweeds, occurred in fresh water, 7% in brackish, and 40% in marine (Table 2.9).

Table 2.9 Aquaculture production by aquatic environment in 1985 (in metric tons, excluding seaweeds).

Region	Freshwater	Brackishwater	Marine	Total
Africa	59, 300	1,400	400	61,100
America , North	194,100	31,800	172,000	397,900
America, South	28,700	31,700	3,000	63,400
Asia	3,292,200	467,800	2,379,300	6,139,300
Europe	789,000	34,900	512,300	836,200
Oceania[a]	1,100	50	20,650	21,800
U.S.S.R.	285,500	10,500	0	296,000
Total (approx.)	4,149, 900	578,150	3,087,650	7,915,700
Percent (%)	53	7	40	100

Source: Nash 1988. [a] Australia and New Zealand combined. FAO 1987.
Note 1mt = 1.1 tons.

Aquaculture production by species included 186 genera and species under some form of culture. Species, used in a broad sense, included 102 finfish, 32 crustaceans, 44 mollusks, and 8 seaweeds (Table 2.10). Ponds dominated as the most important culture system (Table 2.11).

Some of these data from Nash (1988) can be updated. From 1985 onward, aquaculture production of pen-raised salmon, especially Atlantic salmon, has increased significantly (Table 2.12). For example in British Columbia, Canada, there were 10 licensed salmon farms in 1985 and 82 in 1986 on 283 ha (707 ac); there were 1,978 farms on 940 ha (2,350 ac) in 1988 (Deegan 1988). Production of salmon in Canada was estimated at 4,000 mt (4,410 tons) in 1987 and grew to 27,000 mt (29,768 tons) by 1991 (Folsom et al. 1992). Norway has been the largest producer of salmon. Chile has potential. Chilean salmon production, about 500 mt (551 tons) in 1985, reached 34,000 mt (37,485 tons) in 1991 (Harvey 1994).

Production of marine shrimp has also burgeoned since 1985 (Table 2.13). In 1993, world shrimp production from aquaculture reached approximately 609,000 mt (671,422 tons) (Rosenberry 1993).

The Food and Agriculture Organization (1994) gave further statistics on world production of aquaculture.

Table 2.10 Production of important aquaculture species in 1985 (in metric tons).

Bighead carp	850,800
Common carp	365,100
Grass carp	297,100
Silver carp	838,600
Nile tilapia	35,600
Mosambique tilapia	35,900
Tilapias others	123,000
Channel catfish	122,900
Rainbow trout	150,400
Atlantic salmon	37,600
Pink salmon	26,800
Coho salmon	8,900
Milkfish	329,000
Japanese eel	79,400
Japanese amberjack	152,300
Giant river prawn	6,000
Red swamp crawfish	29,500
Giant tiger prawn	39,900
Whiteleg shrimp	30,900
Banana prawn	14,600
European flat oyster	2,800
Pacific cupped oyster	684,100
American cupped oyster	124,500
"Other" cupped oysters	444,300
Manila clam	81,700
Blood cockle	152,200
Blue mussel	415,600
Green mussel	47,700
Mediterranean mussel	65,200
Sweetfish	11,000

Source: Nash 1988. Note 1 mt = 1.1 tons.

Table 2.11 Aquaculture production by farming practices in 1985 (percentage of total production, excluding seaweeds)

Ponds and tanks	41
Enclosures and pens	3
Cages	<1
Raceways and silos	1
Barrages	<1
Other methods	<1
Mollusks on bottom	18
Mollusks off bottom	7
Unspecified production	29

Source: Nash 1988

Table 2.12 Aquaculture production of salmon for leading countries, 1991.

Country	Metric tons	Country	Metric tons
Norway	154,000	Ireland	9,000
Scotland	41,000	United States	7,000
Chile	34,000	Iceland	3,000
Canada	27,000	Australia	2,700
Japan	27,000	New Zealand	2,000
Faroe Islands	16,000	France	1,400

Source: Folsom et al. 1992. Other countries with some production include Sweden, Spain, Finland, Korea, and Turkey. Note 1 mt = 1.1 tons.

Table 2.13 Estimated world shrimp production from aquaculture, live weight equivalent, for the years 1987-1991.

Region/country	1987	1988	1989	1990	1991	Change 1987-91
			1,000 metric tons			percent
Asia						
China	153	199	175	150	145	-5
Indonesia	73	96	97	120	140	92
Thailand	24	56	94	100e	110e	358
India	22	25	25	30	35e	59
Vietnam	20	22	22	30e	30e	50
Philippines	36	45	48	54	30e	-16
Taiwan	115	44	32	30	30e	-74
Other	23	25	29	35	38	65
Subtotal	466	513	522	549	558	20
Latin America						
Ecuador	69	70	64	70	100	45
Columbia	1	1	3	6	10	900
Mexico	4	6	5	8	9	125
Peru	2	2	4	5	6	200
Honduras	2	2	3	3	5	150
Other	5	8	8	10	9	80
Subtotal	83	89	87	102	139	67
Africa	1	1	1	Na	Na	–
Middle East	Negl.	Negl.	Negl.	Negl.	Negl.	–
Europe	Negl.	Negl.	Negl.	Negl.	Negl.	–
North America	1	1	1	1	2	100
Oceania	Na	Na	Na	Na	Na	Na
World Total	551	604	611	652	699	27

Source: Modified from Wildman et al. 1992, Rosenberry 1993. NA = not available. Author's note: Production from Ecuador dropped by an estimated 20% in 1993-94.

Production from the United States

Aquaculture production -- including food and non-food finfish, shellfish (crustaceans and mollusks), and aquatic plants -- has increased more than 20% annually from 1980 to 1988, making it one of the fastest growing sectors of agriculture in the United States (Dicks and Harvey 1988). Production of food fish and shellfish amounted to approximately 317 million kg (700 million lb) in 1987 and was close to $550 million at the farm gate, compared with 92 million kg (203 million lb) and $191 million in 1980. Also in 1987, non-food aquaculture production included among other culture species $71.5 million of baitfish and $23 million of tropical fish. In 1990, U.S. aquaculture production reached approximately 390 million kg (860 million lb) with a farm gate value of $760 million (Joint Subcommittee on Aquaculture 1993). In 1993, channel catfish alone sold to processors amounted to 208 million kg (449 million lb) (Harvey 1994). The U.S. aquaculture industry and ancillary businesses accounted for nearly 300,000 full-time jobs with an economic impact of $8 billion, rivaling that of commercial fisheries.

Major culture species include baitfish, catfish, clams, crawfish, freshwater prawns (*Macrobrachium rosenbergii*), mussels (*Mytilus* spp.), oysters, salmon, shrimp, tropical (ornamental) fish, and trout. These account for more than 85% of total production and value. A partial list of other potential species includes the alligator (*Alligator mississipiensis*), striped bass x white bass hybrid (female *Morone saxatilis* x male *M. chrysops*), various carps, eel, red drum (*Sciaenops ocellata*), northern pike (*Esox lucius*), sturgeon (*Acipenser* spp.), and the tilapias. Dicks and Harvey (1988) reviewed the status, potential, and constraints of aquaculture in the United States (See also Chapter 3 for species profiles).

Potential Expansion of World Aquaculture

Earlier we noted that the ultimate production of fishery products from natural waters may peak near 100 million mt (110 million tons) per year. But what is the ultimate production from aquaculture? This is more difficult to assess and will be affected by a number of factors.

Aquaculture production can be increased on existing operations and by expanding aquaculture to new areas (Avault 1980). Yields can be increased on existing operations by carefully selecting culture species with emphasis on species that feed low on the food chain. Production with species near the first link in the food chain, such as filter-feeding mollusks, is greater than that with species that feed further up the food chain. Polyculture uses all food niches in ponds. Yields of 10 mt per ha per year (4.4 tons per ac) have been achieved through polyculture in India and Israel (Avault 1980) (Figure 2.10). Intensive culture involving high-density stocking, feeding, and aeration has produced as much as 25 mt/ha (11 tons/ ac) per year. Now some operations are injecting pure oxygen into grow-out units. Chapter 14 details methods for increasing production.

Figure 2.10 Harvesting major carps grown in polyculture, Andhra Pradesh, India.

Aquaculture could be expanded to millions of hectares of land and water. In Asia, except for rice land, virtually none of this land can now be used to produce traditional land crops because of acid soils and other problems. There are 11 million ha (27 million ac) of swamps and floodlands, 936,000 ha (2,340,000 ac) of freshwater reservoirs, 85 million ha (213 million ac) of irrigated rice fields, and 1 million ha (2.5 million ac) of brackish and saltwater swamps in Asia that could be considered for aquaculture (Avault 1980). However, many countries keep certain lands in their natural state to serve as nursery grounds for wild species and to retard erosion.

Perhaps a major area for future expansion of aquaculture is in the ocean itself. The culture of mollusks can produce tremendous weights of meat in a relatively small area. Of more recent origin is pen-culture of salmon. Farming the ocean has its problems, however, including legal, social, and environmental. Nevertheless, salmon and other appropriate species could be farmed in huge quantities offshore, away from eyesight. Submerging pens would help avoid problems from rough seas.

When all factors are considered, the profit motive will fuel expansion of aquaculture most, and this especially means culture of high-value species such as shrimp and salmon. Both developed countries and developing countries are expanding efforts with high-value species. Developing countries such as the Philippines see foreign exchange as a strong incentive. Not only did the Philippines develop a shrimp farming industry almost overnight, but it is also converting suitable milkfish ponds into shrimp ponds. In 1987, 7% of the shrimp consumed in the world were grown in ponds. This percentage increased to 25% in less than a decade.

Aquaculture products have predictability and quality control. For example, trapping and consuming wild crawfish in Louisiana has a long tradition. Nevertheless, markets could not be firmly established because of the unpredictability of the harvest. With the arrival of farming, predictable crops could be produced year after year. Processing plants have been set up to cater to European markets. Before farming, this was difficult. Regarding quality control, a culture species can be grown to the required size, processed, and quick frozen for a superior product. In Central America, shrimp (*Penaeus vannamei*) can be grown to 20 g (0.7 oz) or to whatever size the market desires. One farm near Bacolod in the Philippines grows shrimp (*P. monodon*) to 32 g (1.1 oz) each for one particular customer. Many farms have capabilities to harvest shrimp and individually quick freeze (IQF) in a matter of minutes. Finfish, too, and mollusks can be grown tailor-made for specific markets.

How much production then can we forecast from aquaculture? Pillay (1990) felt that production of more than 26 million mt (28.7 million tons) can be obtained by the turn of the century if the current percentage rate of increase is maintained and if technical, financial, and policy supports are present. Larkin (1990) estimated that 25 million mt (27.5 million tons) are possible by 2000 and 50 million mt (55 million tons) could be reached before 2020. New (1991) reviewed the subject in-depth. He reported that the Food and Agriculture Organization (FAO), in its message for World Food Day 1990, stated that we should concentrate on the need for aquaculture rather than trying to forecast the future. The FAO would like to see a 30% increase in per capita fish consumption by the year 2025. If so, the per capita consumption would reach nearly 25 kg (55 lb). New (1991), in estimating need, took into account both population increase and per capita consumption. He calculated that the total harvest from capture fisheries and culture fisheries combined would need to be more than 162 million mt (179 million tons) in 2025 to maintain the 1989 per capita availability of fish. If per capita consumption were increased by 30%, nearly 209 million mt (230 million tons) would be required.

In summation, productivity from our oceans and other natural waters is finite. The demand for fishery products, however, will continue to increase because of more mouths to feed and because of increased per capita consumption. Aquaculture can help make up this shortfall. The ultimate production from aquaculture is more difficult to assess based on natural resources. The increasing demand for fish meal as an ingredient in fish feed could become a limiting factor. In the future, we may have to turn our attention more to the cultivation of species, such as carps, tilapia and crawfish, which use agricultural byproducts. Sustainable aquaculture will receive more emphasis as we husband our natural resources to increase aquaculture production. The profit motive, environmental concerns, and government incentives and constraints will be dominant factors affecting continued expansion of world aquaculture.

STUDY QUESTIONS

1. Describe the growth of the world population in terms of doubling time. What regions of the world have the fastest growing populations?

2. How are birth rate, death rate, and growth rate determined for a population? Use a hypothetical example to illustrate and show math.

3. Discuss the following factors that determine the well-being of a country: birth rate, death rate, growth rate, population density, and available arable land.

4. Discuss the ways in which our natural resources (land and water) are being degraded. How can this process be reversed?

5. Discuss the potential and constraints for use of single-cell protein and fish protein concentrate as sources of food.

6. Why are fish considered a health food? How do fish compare to beef, pork, and poultry?

7. What are the status, potential, and constraints of world capture fisheries?

8. What are the status, potential, and constraints of world aquaculture?

REFERENCES

Agricultural Statistics. 1973, 1987, 1992. USDA. Washington, D.C.: Superintendent of Documents.

Anthony, V.C. 1993. The state of groundfish resources off the Northeastern United States. Fisheries 18(3):12-17.

Avault, J.W., Jr. 1980. Aquaculture. pp. 379-411. In Fisheries Management. New York-Toronto: John Wiley & Sons Inc. 422 pp.

64

Avault, J.W., Jr. 1990. Aquaculture in the United States, the signs for the future. Keynote Address Fish Farming Expo III New Orleans, Louisiana, December 9, 1990. Aquaculture Magazine 16(2):59-64.

Avault, J.W., Jr. 1994. What is happening to our ocean fisheries and what is the implication for aquaculture? Aquaculture Magazine 20(4):82-87.

Bardach, J.E. 1968. The status and potential of aquaculture, particularly fish culture. Part III. Fish Culture. A.I.B.S., 2. 193 pp.

Bernard, B. 1969. Population control. Science 163:533-543.

Bhattacharjee, J.K. 1971. Population explosion and microorganisms as a potential source of food. The Biologist 53(1):22-28.

Borgstrom, G. (editor). 1962. Nutrition, sanitation, and utilization. In Fish as Food, Volume II. New York and London: Academic Press Inc. 777 pp.

Borgstrom, G. 1973. The Food and People Dilemma. California: Duxbury Press. 140 pp.

Boyd, C. 1968. Fresh-water plants: a potential source of protein. Economic Botany 22(4):359-368.

Boyle, R.H. 1994. Pacific salmon ban. Outdoor Life Magazine 194(1):32-35.

Brown, L.R. 1963. Man, land and food. Foreign Agricultural Economic Report No. 11, U.S.D.A. 153 pp.

Brown, L.R. 1973. We run the risk of empty meat counters. U.S. News and World Report, July 16, 1973.

Brown, L.R. 1973. The somber world food outlook. Wall Street Journal. March 26, 1973.

Brown, L.R. 1973. The need for a world food reserve. Wall Street Journal. October 10, 1973.

Brown, L.R., et al. 1989. State of the World. New York-London: W.W. Norton & Company Inc. 256 pp.

Brown, L.R. et al. 1994. State of the World. New York, London: W.W. Norton & Company Inc. 265 pp.

Carter, L.J. 1974. Law of the sea: fisheries plight poses dilemma for United States. Science 185 (4148):336-339.

Deegan, R. 1988. Focus on British Columbia. Aquaculture Today 1(1):37-40.

Dicks, M. and D. Harvey. 1988. Aquaculture situation and outlook. U.S. Department of Agriculture Economic Research Service. Aqua-1, October 1988.

Edwards, C.A., R. Lal, P. Madden, R.H. Miller and G. House (editors). 1990. Sustainable Agricultural Systems. Delray, Florida: St. Lucie Press. 696 pp.

Ehrlich, P.R. and A.H. Ehrlich. 1970. Population Resources Environment. California: W.H. Freeman and Company Inc. 383 pp.

Fisheries of the United States. 1973. Current Fishery Statistics. Washington, D.C. : Superintendent of Documents.

Folsom, W., D. Altman, A. Manuar, F. Nielson, T. Revord, E. Sanborn, M. Wildman. 1992. World Salmon Culture: Europe, North America and South America, and Pacific. National Marine Fisheries Service, NOAA. Technical Memorandum NMFS-F/SPO-3.

Food. 1959. The Yearbook of Agriculture. Washington, D.C.: U.S. Government Printing Office. 736 pp.

Food and Agriculture Organization. 1969. Provisional Indicative World Plan for Agriculture Development. Volumes 1 and 2. 672 pp.

Food and Agriculture Organization. 1971. Production Yearbook. 829 pp.

Food and Agriculture Organization. 1988. Share of earths surface that is land in crops, pasture, forest and other uses. Rome: FAO 1987 Production Yearbook.

Food and Agriculture Organization. 1989. Aquaculture Development and Coordination Program , aquaculture minutes, December 1989 No.6.

Food and Agriculture Organization. 1994. Aquaculture Production. FAO Circular No. 815 Revision 6.

Food and Agriculture Organization, Marine Resources Service Fishery Resources and Environment Division. 1987. Review of the state of world fishery resources. FAO Fisheries Circular (710) Revision 5. 64 pp.

Food and Nutrition Board. 1968. Recommended dietary allowances. 7th edition. Washington, D.C. : National Academy of Sciences.

Gorga, C. and L.J. Ronsivalli. 1988. Quality Assurance of Seafood. New York: An Avi Book Published by Van Nostrand Reinhold. 245 pp.

Hanson, J.A. (editor). 1974. Open Sea Mariculture. Pennsylvania: Dowden, Hutchinson & Ross, Inc. 410 pp.

Harvey, D. 1994. Aquaculture situation and outlook. U.S. Department of Agriculture Economic Research Service. AQS-12, March 1994.

Hearings before a subcommittee of the committee on government operations, House of Representatives. 1969. Effects of population growth on natural resources and the environment. Washington, D.C.: U.S. Government Printing Office. 256 pp.

Hickling, C.F. 1962. Fish Culture. London: Faber and Faber. 295 pp.

Holt, S.J. 1969. The food resources of the ocean. pp. 139-151. In Food. San Francisco: W.H. Freeman and Company.

Huxley, J. 1956. World population. Scientific America 194(3): 63-76.

Idyll, C.P. 1970. The Sea Against Hunger. New York: Thomas Y. Crowell Company. 221 pp.

Joint Subcommittee on Aquaculture. 1993. Aquaculture in the United States: status, opportunities, and recommendations. A Report to the Federal Coordinating Council on Science, Engineering, and Technology. 21 pp.

Kensler, C.B. 1989. A regional survey of the aquaculture sector in North America. United Nations Development Programme, Food and Agriculture Organization ADCP/REP/89/37.

Knobl, G.M. Jr., B.R. Stillings, W.E. Fox and M.B. Hale. 1971. Fish protein concentrates. Commercial Fisheries Review 33(7-8):54-63.

Larkin, P.A. 1990. From hunting fish to farming fish: trends in the transition. pp. 68-70. In Aquaculture International 1990 Proceedings, Vancouver, Canada.

Lipinsky, E.S. and J.H. Litchfield. 1970. Algae, bacteria, and yeasts as food or feed. CRC Critical Reviews in Food Technology 1(4):581-618.

Lipinsky, E.S. and J.H. Litchfield. 1974. Single-cell protein in perspective. Food Technology, May 1974.

Loyacano, H.A. 1973. Effects of Chinese waterchestnut in floating rafts on production of channel catfish in plastic pools. Proceedings Southeastern Association of Game and Fish Commissioners 27:470-473.

The Malthusian spectre: challenges of food and population. 1969. United States Air Force Academy. 33 pp.

Nash, C.E. 1988. A global overview of aquaculture production. Journal of the World Aquaculture Society 19(2):51-58.

New, M.B. 1991. Turn on the millennium: navigating troubled waters or riding crest of the wave? Keynote address presented at the Annual Meeting of the World Aquaculture Society, Puerto Rico. Mimeograph 86 pp.

Parker, N.C. 1989. History, status, and future of aquaculture in the United States. Reviews in Aquatic Sciences 1(1):97-109.

Patrick, R. 1987. Seafood for healthy eating. Louisiana Cooperative Extension Service. Publication 2332.

Pillay, T.V.R. (editor). 1972a. Coastal aquaculture in the Indo-Pacific Region. London: Indo-Pacific Fisheries Council and the Food and Agriculture Organization. 497 pp.

Pillay, T.V.R. 1972. Problems and priorities in aquaculture development. In Progress in Fishery and Food Science. University of Washington, College of Fisheries. Fiftieth Anniversary Celebration Symposium. University of Washington Publication Fisheries (New Service) 5:203-208.

Pillay, T.V.R. 1973. The role of aquaculture in fishery development and management. In Technical Conference on Fisheries Management and Development, Vancouver, Canada. 24 pp.

Pillay, T.V.R. 1979. Estimated world production through aquaculture in 1975. pp. 1-10. In Advances in Aquaculture. FAO Technical Conference on Aquaculture, Kyoto, Japan. 653 pp.

Pillay, T.V.R. 1990. Aquaculture Principles and Practices. Oxford, England: Fishing News Books (Blackwell Scientific Publications Ltd.) 575 pp.

Pillay, T.V.R., and W.A. Dill (editors). 1979. Advances in Aquaculture. Papers presented at the FAO Technical Conference on Aquaculture, Kyoto, Japan. 653 pp.

Population Program Assistance. 1972. Agency for International Development. Bureau for Population and Humanitarian Assistance Office of Population. 267 pp.

Presidents Science Advisory Committee Panel of the World Food Supply. 1967. The World Food Problem (3 Volumes). Washington, D.C.: Superintendent of Documents.

Production Yearbook. 1971. Food and Agriculture Organization of the United Nations.

Rosenberry, R. 1990, 1993. World Shrimp Farming. Aquaculture Digest.

Ryther, J.H. 1969. Photosynthesis and fish production in the sea. Science 166:72-76.

Ryther, J.H. and G.C. Matthiessen. 1969. Mariculture: its status and potential. Woods Hole Oceanographic Institute, Volume XIV, No. 4. 14 pp.

Shapiro, S. 1964. Fisheries of the World. pp. 161-177. In Farmer's World, The Yearbook of Agriculture.

Shapiro, S. (editor). 1971. Our Changing Fisheries. United States Department of Commerce, National Oceanic and Atmospheric Administration, National Marine Fisheries Service. Washington D.C.: U.S. Government Printing Office. 534 pp.

Shell, E.W. 1993. The Development of Aquaculture: An Ecosystems Perspective. Auburn University, Alabama Agricultural Experiment Station. 265 pp.

Sidwell, V.D., P.R. Foncannon, N.S. Moore and J.C. Bonnet. 1974. Composition of the edible portion of raw (fresh or frozen) crustaceans, finfish, and mollusks. 1. protein, fat, moisture, ash, carbohydrate, energy value, and cholesterol. Marine Fisheries Review 36(3):21-35.

Siegel, R.A. and R.S. Johntson. 1989. Economic and trade strategies in world fisheries. Marine Fisheries Review 51(1):1-2.

Stillings, B.R. and M.H. Thompson. 1971. Dietary role of fish and shellfish. pp. 40-55. In Our Changing Fisheries. Washington, D.C.: Superintendent of Documents. 534 pp.

Uchida, R.N. 1972. Review of recent progress in coastal aquaculture in the United States. In Coastal Aquaculture in the Indo-Pacific Region. London: Indo-Pacific Fisheries Council and the Food and Agriculture Organization.

UN, DIESA. 1989. World Population, 1988 Prospects. New York: 1989.

United Nations Demographic Yearbook. 43 rd edition. 1992.

Unklesbay, N. 1992. World Food Production and You. New York and London: The Haworth Press Inc. 444 pp.

U.S. Department of Commerce. 1993. Our Living Oceans, Report on the Status of U.S. Living Marine Resources, 1993. NOAA Technical Memorandum NMFS-F/SPOI-15.

Walker, W.H., R.O. Smitherman and J.W. Avault, Jr. 1967. Crawfish waste: a potential feed source for channel catfish. Louisiana Agriculture 10(2):14-15.

Watt, B.K. and A.L. Merrill. 1963. Composition of foods. Agriculture Handbook No. 8. USDA Washington, DC: Superintendent of Documents.

Wildman, M., P. Niemeier, F. Nielsen, J. Beverly, T. Schneider, H. Riha, E. Sanborn, D. Weidner, D. Decker, B. Rosenberry. 1992. World Shrimp Farming Volume I. Africa, Asia, Europe, Middle East, North America. National Marine Fisheries Service, National Oceanic and Atmospheric Administration. NOAA Technical Memo. NMFS/F/SPO-4.

Yearbook of Fishery Statistics. 1972. Volume 34, Food and Agriculture Organization of the United Nations.

CHAPTER 3
WHICH SPECIES TO CULTURE

One decision an entrepreneur makes, when contemplating commercial aquaculture, is which species to culture. Success or failure may hinge on the right choice. Though one species may have a high market demand, it may not be economical to culture. Another species may be hardy and thrive under culture conditions but be unacceptable in the marketplace. Still another species may meet most basic requirements, but seed or young may not be readily available.

A myriad of factors must be considered when selecting a species for culture, and few species meet all requirements (Avault 1986d, 1993; Gordon 1990; Iverson and Hale 1992). Technology must be well known for all facets of commercial aquaculture. The biological requirements for optimum growth and reproduction must be known. A species should be hardy and thrive under culture conditions. It should be readily accepted in the marketplace. Overlying all considerations, a species must be cultured at a profit. Jhingran and Gopalakrishnan (1974) listed approximately 465 species of plants and animals as cultured aquatic organisms. Pillay (1990) gave a checklist of 95 finfish, 32 crustaceans, 35 mollusks, and 19 species of aquatic plants.

In this chapter, we outline information needed when selecting a culture species. (Legal aspects are covered in Chapter 4.) A synopsis also is given for selected culture species. The species profiled are representatives of commercial aquaculture; some species with potential are included. Each species synopsis covers: status of the industry if established, culture methods, constraints, potential for expansion, and pertinent references.

BIOLOGICAL CONSIDERATIONS
Water Temperature and Water Quality

Most species have a relatively broad range of tolerance to water temperatures. A more narrow range within the broad tolerance provides for optimum growth, reproduction, and general well-being. For example, rainbow trout (*Oncorhynchus mykiss*), which is a coldwater fish, cannot tolerate water above 21°C (70°F). Conversely, certain species from tropical climates, such as *Oreochromis mossambicus*, cannot tolerate temperatures below 10°C (50°F). Various tilapias can, however, tolerate poor water quality, for example dissolved oxygen levels less than 1 ppm. Salmonids require oxygen-rich waters, above 5 ppm dissolved oxygen.

Each species has its own requirements for various water quality parameters, and these must be known if the species is to be cultured successfully. Remember, you are not looking for water quality that a culture species can tolerate. You are looking for ideal conditions so that a culture species will thrive.

Fresh, Brackish, Saltwater

Species such as *O. mossambicus* grow well in water ranging from fresh to saltwater (euryhaline). Most culture species, however, have a much narrower tolerance range, and we usually catalog them as freshwater, brackishwater, or saltwater species. The milkfish (*Chanos chanos*) is considered a brackish-water species. The prawn (*Macrobrachium* spp.) requires brackish water up to the postlarval stage and fresh water thereafter. Various eel (*Anguilla* spp.) species live in fresh water but spawn in salt water (catadromous). Striped bass (*Morone saxatilis*) live in salt water but spawn in fresh water (anadromous). Penaeid shrimp spawn offshore in salt water. Their larvae drift into brackish estuaries where they grow before migrating back offshore to reproduce. Penaeid shrimp species are grown in saltwater ponds, and yet some species such as *Penaeus monodon* grow faster if water is less than sea strength. Availability of fresh water is therefore a consideration.

You must understand not only tolerance ranges from fresh water to salt water but also the optimum levels for reproduction and culture. Sometimes a species is cultured in water where it does not normally occur. For example, the channel catfish (*Ictalurus punctatus*), a freshwater fish, grows well in brackish water up to 6 ppt. By growing this species in brackish water, off-flavor and certain parasites have not posed a problem, and there is no danger of an unplanned spawn in grow-out ponds.

Growth Rate

Ideally a culture species should exhibit rapid growth and reach market size quickly. The red swamp crawfish (*Procambarus clarkii*) is capable of reaching market size in 3 months from newly hatched young. The signal crawfish (*Pacifastacus leniusculus leniusculus*), however, requires 2 to 3 years to reach market size. This is because it grows in cold water. Nevertheless, its high value in Europe makes it economical to culture. The paddlefish (*Polyodon spathula*) grows very fast, as much as 1 kg (2.2 lb) per month. Grass carp (*Ctenopharyngodon idella*) may grow 500 g (1.1 lb) a month. The milkfish exhibits exceedingly fast growth initially, but its growth rate decreases once the fish reaches approximately 500 g. This is usually of no consequence since fish are harvested when 350 g (0.8 lb) to 500 g in size.

Feeding Habits

The feeding habits of a culture species must be known. Generally these can be broken down into two broad periods. The first extends from newly hatched young to a size for stocking grow-out ponds or other culture systems. The second is the period of grow-out to market size. There is sometimes an intermediate period if juveniles or fingerlings are produced.

Another consideration is the type of feed required. Some species, like the red swamp crawfish, grow well on detritus as a food substrate. The crawfish glean bacteria and other microorganisms from rice straw and other organic matter. Obviously, the feed cost is relatively low. Oysters and other mollusks, being filter feeders throughout life, use plankton. Larval prawns and shrimp use brine shrimp (*Artemia*) and other live foods, but past the postlarval stage formulated diets are normally used. Species such as trout, salmon, channel catfish, and shrimp are fed formulated diets.

Not all formulated diets are the same. The protein requirement reflects the culture species' food habits in nature. Trout and salmon have a higher protein requirement than channel catfish, and the catfish has a higher protein requirement than the tilapia. Various eel species require a very high protein diet because of their natural carnivorous food habits. There are even differences among various shrimp species, *Penaeus japonicus* having a high protein requirement. You might reason that to be on the safe side a diet high in protein should be used, but protein especially from animal sources (fishmeal) is costly. Diets must be developed for each culture species to provide optimum nutrition at the least possible cost.

Reproduction

Lack of a dependable seed supply has resulted in the failure of some aquaculture operations. Not all culture species used in commercial aquaculture spawn readily in captivity. Certain penaeid shrimps, for example, have been farmed by first obtaining wild seed from ocean bays. The huge milkfish farming industry has relied on wild-caught fry for years. Seed of riverine Chinese carps for centuries had to be obtained from the wild. However, spawning can now be achieved by injecting mature fish with hormones. Overall, quality seed must be available in quantities required and when needed for grow-out. Additionally, it is desirable that a culture species not reproduce while in grow-out. It is best that market size is reached before maturity is attained, so that most of the feed is used for growth of flesh and not for the formation of sex products.

Hardiness

In nature, many species reach the carrying capacity of their environment. Availability of natural food is often the limiting factor for further expansion in terms of numbers and weight. To make a profit, aquaculturists crowd culture species into ponds or other grow-out units where it is possible to provide a formulated feed. Feed, then, is no longer a limiting factor. Now a culture species must adapt to social crowding, to poorer water quality, and to handling, all of which may cause stress and disease. To be successful, a culture species must adapt to these conditions.

Productivity

Productivity of a pond-grown species is often expressed in terms of weight grown per surface area (kg/ha or lb/ac) in a certain period. With some species, such as raceway-grown trout, we express production in terms of weight grown per unit volume of water (kg/m^3 or lb/yd^3) or per flow rate of water (kg/liter/second, lb/ft^3/second, or lb/gpm). For species grown in floating cages and net-pens, we often use the expression weight grown per volume (kg/m^3 or lb/yd^3). Regardless of the species or culture system, to make a profit you must achieve high production of marketable animals.

MARKETING

Before you culture any species, the market must be thoroughly studied and specific buyer(s) targeted. Some species may have multiple marketing possibilities. For example, the channel catfish can be grown for sale as fingerlings, food fish, or as stockers for fee-fishing lakes. Brood stock may be sold to other fish farmers. Byproducts also have value. Catfish oil may serve as an attractant in crawfish baits, and the carcass and entrails can be incorporated back into feeds.

Though we usually think of food production, culture species also can be marketed for other purposes. Examples are alligators (*Alligator mississipiensis*) for hides, minnows (various species) as bait for sport fishing, tropical fish as ornamentals, largemouth bass (*Micropterus salmoides*) for sport fishing, grass carp, and certain species of tilapia for aquatic weed control, and various species for biological test animals.

ECONOMICS

In the final analysis, a species must be cultured for a profit in commercial aquaculture. This can be ascertained with a costs and returns analysis, cash flow projection, and other economic calculations.

FINFISH

Numerous species of finfish are cultured worldwide. Hora and Pillay (1962) listed 69 species cultured in the Indo-Pacific Region alone, and their list contained only a single species of tilapia, *O. mossambicus*.

Channel Catfish

The channel catfish is grown principally in the southeastern United States (Figure 3.1). There are more than 1,100 commercial growers in 15 states (National Aquaculture Development Plan 1983). In 1984, more than 68,182 mt (75,171 tons) of catfish were produced, and in 1985 a major fast-food restaurant chain added farm-raised catfish to its menu, requiring approximately 13,636 mt (15,034 tons) with the first order. Though there were problems with this specific order, other fast-food restaurants are exploring the use of farm-raised catfish.

Figure 3.1 Ronnie Bean with channel catfish.

The catfish farming industry expanded at an annual rate of almost 20% during the 1980s. In 1986, Mississippi alone had close to 33,185 ha (82,000 ac) in catfish production. Alabama, Arkansas, Louisiana, and California are other important catfish-producing states. In 1990, processing plants received 163,332 mt (180,000 tons) valued at $323 million, an increase of almost 20% above 1989 sales. Water area devoted to catfish farming reached 64,800 ha (162,000 ac) (Harvey 1991). In 1993, growers sold 208,163 mt (229,500 tons) of catfish to processing plants (Harvey 1994).

This freshwater species spawns readily in captivity when water temperature reaches a minimum of 21°C (70°F) (Jensen et al. 1983). However, it generally fails to spawn when held at year-round high temperatures. Channel catfish have been successfully cultured in brackishwater ponds at salinities ranging from 2 to 11 ppt (Perry and Avault 1968, 1969, 1973). Allen and Avault (1969, 1971) established salinity tolerances for blue (*I. furcatus*) and channel catfish.

Production of catfish is reviewed by Lee (1973, 1991), Avault (1980a), Bush et al. (1982), Tucker (1985), Tucker and Robinson (1990), and Tave and Tucker (1993). Fingerlings are stocked into grow-out ponds at rates ranging from 12,500 to 25,000/ha (5,000 to 10,000)/ac). Fish are fed daily with a formulated diet. A 15-cm (6-inch) fingerling will reach a market size of about 0.57 to 0.68 kg (1.25 to 1.5 lb) in approximately 210 growing days when the water temperature is above 18°C (65°F).

Fish are batch harvested or cull harvested. In batch harvesting, ponds are drained and fish harvested all at once. Most farmers, however, practice cull harvesting. In cull harvesting, marketable fish are selectively removed at about 3-week intervals. This process, called topping-off, involves seining marketable fish; smaller fish go through the mesh of the seine. Fingerlings are re-stocked to replace those fish removed. Some farmers re-stock one fingerling for each 454 g (1 lb) of marketable fish removed. This practice of topping-off allows for a more consistent supply. Moreover, it conserves water since ponds may go years without being drained.

Production of catfish averages around 11,200 kg/ha (10,000 lb/ac) per year. Catfish farmers traditionally have marketed fish to processing plants, local stores and restaurants, backyard sales, and live haulers who sell to others. Farmers also may use catfish in fee-fishing operations. Some specialize in hatchery production and sale of fingerlings and brood fish.

As production in ponds increases, water quality problems will intensify because of pollution from fish wastes. Examples are oxygen depletion, and high ammonia and nitrite levels. Diseases, such as enteric septicemia of catfish (ESC) and brown blood disease, along with off-flavor, are also of major concern. Bird predation, too, is a chronic problem.

Opportunities exist for new farmers, provided start-up capital is available. Land and suitable ground water can be found in a number of states. Economics and marketing are major considerations. Some years, prices paid to producers have dropped below break-even costs. You must have the reserves to hold out for better prices. Future emphasis of producers will focus on increasing total weight of fish grown per hectare while lowering production costs. With current practices, it appears that production per hectare has reached a maximum, although Plemmons and Avault (1980) produced more than 14,000 kg/ha (12,500 lb/ac) of fish with high stocking and feeding rates and with constant aeration. Genetics can play a major role for increasing production by making superior fish available to producers. The channel catfish is fast becoming a versatile product in the marketplace, and it is being promoted for fast-food restaurants, upscale restaurants, and for home use.

Other Catfish Species

The blue catfish and white catfish (*I. catus*) have been grown commercially but to a much lesser extent. The white catfish is hardy but is slower growing and develops a large head as it matures. This lessens the dressout percentage. The blue catfish has a relatively high dressout percentage; it is more than 60% meat for whole fish with entrails, skin, and head removed. It grows with less size variation at harvest than channel catfish. The blue catfish when spawning is more sensitive to disturbances, and it matures later than channel catfish. First-year growth is slower than that of channel catfish, but it will often outgrow channel catfish the second year in production ponds. This is particularly important since the market has shifted from a whole, dressed catfish to fillets. Larger fish are required for fillets. A female channel catfish crossed with a male blue catfish produces a faster growing fish than either parent. Methods need to be developed to cross the two species under commercial conditions.

Other Ictalurids, such as the yellow bullhead (*I. natalis*), brown bullhead (*I. nebulosus*), and flathead catfish (*Pylodictis olivaris*), have been pond tested. Growth of bullheads is slow. Flathead catfish are carnivorous, making it difficult to rear fingerlings.

Other species of catfish are being cultured throughout the world (Figure 3.2).

Figure 3.2 Various species of catfish are of importance throughout the world.

Clarias batrachus and *C. macrocephalus* are two highly valued species found throughout Southeast Asia, the Indian subcontinent, and Africa as well as parts of the Near East (Bardach et al. 1972). They are hardy and possess an accessory breathing organ that allows them to be cultured at extremely high densities. *C. batrachus* escaped in the United States and became known as the walking catfish. Both species spawn in captivity and grow well on ground trash fish mixed with rice byproducts. Hecht et al. (1988) reported that culture of the sharptooth catfish (*Clarias gariepinus*) is being practiced in southern Africa, on a subsistence level elsewhere in Africa, and in the Netherlands. They stated that commercial catfish farming is now entering an exponential growth phase.

Pangasius spp., particularly *P. sutchi* of Asia, have culture potential. In Thailand *Pangasius* sp. is polycultured with *O. niloticus.* Spawning naturally in rivers, wild fry are captured for stocking grow-out ponds. In Cambodia, *Pangasius* spp. are cultured in floating cages. Fry and fingerlings are stocked into floating bamboo cages at rates of 150 to 300/m^3 (115 to 230/yd^3) and fed ground trash fish plus boiled rice and rice bran. When 15 cm (6 in) long, the fish are stocked into larger cages. They reach 0.08 to 1 kg (0.18 to 2.2 lb) in 8 to 10 months (Bardach et al. 1972).

In Europe *Silurus glanis*, the sheatfish, has been used as a predator to control excess reproduction of other species. *Plotosus anguillaris, P. canius,* and *Tandanus tandanus* have been considered for culture in the Indo-Pacific Region. In Liberia, *Heterobrancus bidorsalis* is a highly prized species that is often grown in combination with *O. niloticus.* The Brazilian catfishes *Rhamdia quelen* and *R. hilarii* offer potential for aquaculture (Machado and Castagnolli 1979).

Rainbow Trout and Other Trout Species

Several species of trout being farmed include brook trout (*Salvelinus fontinalis*), brown trout (*Salmo trutta*), and rainbow trout (Avault 1980a) (Figure 3.3). In Europe trout have been farmed for more than 100 years. Denmark began growing rainbow trout for food around 1890. Japan is a major producer of rainbow trout (Kafuku and Ikenoue 1983). Trout biology is reviewed by Ade (1989) and Willers (1991), and trout culture by Sedgwick (1976), Leitritz and Lewis (1980), and Laird and Needham (1988).

Figure 3.3 Rainbow trout.

In the United States, brook trout received attention around 1890. Hatcheries generally produced fingerlings for stocking natural streams. Currently the rainbow trout dominates the industry as the major species cultured for the table. This species adapts well to domestication, is hardy, and grows rapidly. It is tolerant of a wide range of environments and will grow in fresh water up to full ocean salinity. It is easy to reproduce the rainbow trout in captivity; some farmers rely on hatchery specialists for seed to stock grow-out units.

In the United States, rainbow trout are produced mainly in Idaho, California, Wisconsin, Michigan, Colorado, North Carolina, and Pennsylvania. Of these, Idaho produces approximately 90% of the total rainbow trout cultured. The U.S. Department of Agriculture's Reporting Service showed that trout producers surveyed in 14 states sold 19,450 mt (21,444 tons) of trout during 1981. In 1989, there were 478 trout farmers. Sales of trout and trout eggs amounted to $72.6 million (Harvey 1990). In 1993, there were 457 firms in the United States involved with trout farming. Sale of fish totaled 24.8 million kg (54.6 million lb) (Harvey 1994).

The rainbow trout thrives in freshwater raceways at water temperatures around 14° to 15°C (57° to 59°F). Idaho's Snake River Valley furnishes ideal conditions. Gravity flow water is available at a constant 14° to 15°C. Farmers lease water from the state based on flow rate. Rainbow trout spawn readily in captivity. Mature fish are hand stripped of eggs and sperm. Fertilized eggs are incubated in hatcheries, and resulting fry are reared in tanks until they are ready for stocking into grow-out raceways. Five to 6 months after stocking, the fish are graded by size; tops (large) are moved to one raceway, and bottoms (smaller fish) are moved to another raceway (Figure 3.4). Several gradings may be made during the time fish are grown to market size.

Figure 3.4 Grading rainbow trout to size.

In 15°C water, it takes about 11 to 13 months to grow a 3.8 cm (1.5 in) fingerling to a 283 to 340 g (10 to 12 oz) market size. If water is 13°C (55°F), it takes 15 to 18 months. As a rule, approximately 160 to 240 kg of trout/liter/second of water flow (10,000 to 15,000 lb/ft^3/second or 22 to 33 lb/gpm) are grown. This production is possible with reuse of water.

In the United States, production increases of rainbow trout may have to come mainly by increasing output on existing farms. In the early 1950s, when trout farming in Idaho received recognition as an industry, farmers expanded output by adding new facilities and leasing additional water from the state. Virtually all water has been leased in the Snake River Valley of Idaho, but two methods have been used to increase output. First, water is reused. Instead of flowing through one culture unit and then being wasted, water flows through a series of culture units. Second, oxygen has been injected into water to improve its quality, and carrying capacity as high as 0.16 kg/liter (10 lb/ft^3) is now possible. Entrepreneurs may find it difficult to develop new trout production facilities unless spring water is used where available in other states. In some states fee-fishing in trout ponds has potential. Regarding problems, federal intervention and regulations are most often mentioned (Mackey 1994).

Salmon

A single species represents the Atlantic salmon group (*Salmo salar*), although a number of races occur. The Pacific salmon group all belong to the genus *Oncorhynchus* and include pink (*O. gorbuscha*), sockeye (*O. nerka*), coho or silver (*O. kisutch*), chum (*O. keta*), and spring or chinook (*O. tshawytscha*). The biology and farming of salmon were reviewed by Leitritz and Lewis (1980), Sedgwick (1982), Kafuku and Ikenoue (1983), Laird and Needham (1988), and Ade (1989). Childerhose and Trim (1981) and Pearcy (1992) covered ecology of Pacific salmonids. Shaw and Miur (1987) reviewed the economics and marketing of salmon. The journal "Salmon Farming" is published monthly by the Scottish Salmon Growers Association. Folsom et al. (1992) reviewed world salmon culture.

Salmon are anadromous coldwater species. They live in salt water and return to freshwater streams to spawn. Because salmon are considered a high-value sport and commercial species, much public support has gone into their study and propagation. On the Pacific Coast, public hatcheries in California, Oregon, Idaho, Washington, Alaska, and British Columbia have made massive releases of juvenile salmon into natural waters. By 1960, 72 facilities produced salmon on the Pacific Coast of the United States, and by 1976 the number of facilities increased to 154. Production of migrant fish increased from 152 million in 1960 to more than 600 million in 1982 (National Aquaculture Development Plan 1983). In British Columbia more than 30 facilities produced salmon in 1988. The Japanese began to operate hatcheries in 1888 in Hokkaido to replenish dwindling numbers of chum salmon. Soon after private hatcheries were established. Today commercial aquaculture of salmon occurs in Japan, Norway, Scotland, Ireland, Chile, Nova Scotia, the Pacific Coast, and elsewhere where salmon occur naturally.

Salmon are cultured by four basic techniques: pond culture, ocean ranching, net-pen culture, and raceways. Allen et al. (1980) discussed research on rearing Pacific salmon in saltwater ponds. This method previously has not been common. Ocean ranching involves handstripping and fertilization of eggs, hatching of eggs, feeding of young in tanks or pens, releasing of fish to the ocean where they graze on natural food, and the returning of fish to the hatchery when they are ready to spawn. Surplus fish not required as brooders are dressed and marketed. In 1982 Oregon had seven private salmon ranching operations that released 26 million young fish. Alaska had 17 private, non-profit, ocean-ranching operations that released 127 million fish. California had one operation. Washington did not allow private ocean ranching. British Columbia had significant releases. Pen culture of salmon involves handstripping of sex products, fertilization and hatching of eggs, growing fry in freshwater tanks, and then growing fish to market size in floating net-pens. Pen culture of coho salmon in Puget Sound is well established (Nyegaard 1973). Raceway culture is practiced in Nova Scotia where seawater is pumped to shore-based tanks. Meade (1974) discussed reuse of water for raceway systems.

Atlantic Salmon-- This salmon species, like many other salmon species, has been successfully spawned and reared in hatcheries for more than 100 years. Brood fish are stripped of eggs and milt, and fertilized eggs are hatched much like rainbow trout. Young fish spend the first part of their life in freshwater tanks and are known as parr. They are stocked into floating net-pens in fresh water and grown to the smolt stage. When smolts, they are ready to migrate to sea. The name smolt comes from the silvery sheen that scales develop. Once released into a freshwater stream, fish migrate to the ocean where post-smolts feed on natural fish food. They become piscivorous and very territorial in the ocean. Fish are in the grilse stage the first year at sea. Adults ultimately return to spawn and are recaptured.

The Atlantic salmon is a highly prized market fish. It has good potential for ocean ranching and is being cultured in floating net-pens in Norway, British Columbia, Chile, and elsewhere. In Norway, brood fish are spawned in hatcheries. When fry reach 30 to 50 mm (1 to 2 in) in length at the parr stage, they are stocked into outdoor tanks. After 1 to 2 years the smolt stage is reached, and fingerlings are stocked into floating net-pens. After an additional 1 to 2 years, a marketable fish of 2 to 6 kg (4.4 to 13 lb) is reached. Overall, the Atlantic salmon is the species of choice for most net-pen operations. This includes those on the Pacific Coast where legal. It takes well to handling and culture operations, and it grows rapidly.

Pink Salmon-- This species derives its name from having pink flesh rather than red. The fry in nature migrate to sea almost as soon as the yolk sacs are absorbed, omitting a lengthy parr stage in fresh water. It grows rapidly and may reach 2 to 3 kg (4.4 to 6.6 lb) in 2 years from the time of hatching.

Coho Salmon-- The coho or silver salmon domesticates well, is easy to handle, and thrives under culture conditions (Figure 3.5). It was the first salmon species used in net-pen culture on the Pacific Coast in the Puget Sound, and it is of interest for sea farming in Europe. This fish has been grown in pens to pan size of about 350 g (12 oz) in 6 to 8 months. It may mature early in the grilse stage if grown to 1.5 kg (3.3 lb) or larger. Early maturity is a reason for harvest when fish are still relatively small. As fish mature, more feed is converted to form sex products and less to form flesh. The development and use of select races with later maturity may offset this problem. Coho can mature in fresh water without transfer to the sea, thus expanding their culture potential.

Figure 3.5 Coho salmon.

Sockeye Salmon-- This salmon develops a deep red flesh in the ocean and is highly prized for canning. Freshwater races, called Kokanees, can live entirely in fresh water. The sockeye is the least piscivorous of the Pacific salmon, and though it can be spawned and reared in hatcheries, it has not been given as much attention as the coho and others. Virtually all wild populations are carriers of the IHN virus. Because this species matures late and can adapt to fresh water, it is a good candidate for culture.

Chum Salmon-- This species is not considered as high a quality fish in North America as are other salmon species. Japan and the former Soviet Union, however, are ranching chum salmon. Kafuku and Ikenoue (1983) gave a detailed account of chum culture in Japan.

Chinook Salmon-- This species is farmed in floating net-pens and is often preferred over coho, but there has at times been a smaller egg supply. It has been a major culture species off the coast of British Columbia. An advantage for culture is that chinook salmon can enter salt water at 5 g (0.2 oz) in size. It matures late and grows very large, both desirable culture traits.

Although salmon species vary, some generalizations can be made. Legal and social aspects are major considerations, particularly when public waters are involved. Salmon are highly prized fishes in the marketplace. Aquaculturists must consider market competition with wild-caught salmon, competition from culture operations in other countries, and the economics of culture. Around 1990, a glut of Norwegian salmon on the world market drove prices down, forcing some farmers out of business. The positive side of the low prices is that new markets opened at grocery stores. People who had never eaten salmon before now found the product at an attractive price.

Hatchery methods are well developed because of a long history of government-sponsored programs. A concern has been the timing of fry transfer from fresh water to salt water without stress and loss. Ideally, a salmon for culture should have a long tolerance time when transfer can be made from fresh water to salt water.

Diseases have plagued net-pen operations. In the 1980s *Vibrio* spp. caused much mortality with salmon. A vaccine was developed to fight against it. Around 1990 the salmon louse (*Gyrodactylus salaris*) created problems with Norwegian salmon. This is a parasite found on wild salmon that is normally of no consequence, but in high-density salmon pens it can be a serious pest. This small crustacean feeds on the flesh of salmon, causing unsightly blemishes. A compound is available for control of this parasite. Other problems include degradation of the environment, genetic pollution of wild salmon, red tides, and biofouling of net mesh.

In pen-culture, feed and feeding are of major importance. Species for culture must be selected which accept pelleted feed that does not require a high (50%) protein content. The species selected must be grown to a desirable market size before it becomes sexually mature. Upon processing, salmon must taste and look as good as wild-caught salmon. Pink or red flesh is essential in marketing cultured salmon.

Look for more deep-sea pens in the future. In some countries, such as Ireland and the Faroe Islands, deep-sea pens are common. Folsom et al. (1992) listed the advantages: (1) The constant water movement disperses wastes by ocean currents. (2) The constant motion of the water forces salmon to swim. This produces leaner and healthier fish. (3) Potential farm sites near shore are limited. Since deep-sea sites are well off shore, there is less objection from landowners and tourists. (4) Deep-sea operations allow farmers to expand more easily, thus generating savings from large-scale, cost-cutting measures. (5) Since there is more room, crowding is less of a problem. This puts less stress on the fish, and less medicated feed is needed. (6) Operations in the Faroe Islands indicate that they may be more efficient to operate.

Minnows and Other Baitfish

Commercial production of bait minnows was worth more than $100 million in 1983 (Dupree and Huner 1984). Arkansas accounts for about half the supply in the United States, and in 1982 had 22,800 ha (56,339 ac) in minnow production (National Aquaculture Development Plan 1983). In 1980, Minnesota had 731 farms totaling 6,480 ha (16,012 ac). Kansas, Louisiana, Mississippi, and Missouri each had more than 405 ha (1,000 ac) devoted to baitfish aquaculture. Production of minnows has averaged about 672 kg/ha (600 lb/ac), and net profit has been about $494 per ha ($200/ac) (National Aquaculture Development Plan 1983). Of about 100 species of fish used as sportfishing bait in the United States, only four are raised in quantity. The four, in order of importance, are golden shiner (*Notemigonus crysoleucas*), fathead minnow (*Pimephales promelas*), white sucker (*Catostomus commersoni*), and goldfish (*Carassius auratus*).

Golden Shiner-- This fish, which gets its name from a gold flashing appearance, is grown principally in the mid-South (Figure 3.6). One strain, with orange or red fins, has an exceedingly nervous temperament and leaps out of bait containers. An ovarian protozoan parasite (*Plistophora ovariae*) is a problem, but selecting young, 1-year-old brood stock helps to avoid the parasite. Brood stock becomes sexually mature at 1 year of age when about 6.4 cm (2.5 in) long. They readily spawn up to 10,000 eggs per female when the water temperature reaches 21°C (70°F). Spawning mats are set out to collect adhesive eggs. Egg-laden mats are removed and placed into nursery ponds for hatching. In grow-out, stocking rates vary from 123,550 to 494,200 fish/ha (50,000 to 200,000/ac). With feeding, production ranges from 672 to 896 kg/ha (600 to 800 lb/ac). At harvest, fish are graded to size.

Smaller sizes, up to 6.4 cm, are used for crappie (*Pomoxis* spp.) bait; larger sizes, up to 25 cm (10 in), are used as bait for largemouth bass and for catfish on trotlines.

Figure 3.6 Golden shiner.

Fathead Minnows-- This cylindrical fish, which seldom grows larger than 7.6 cm (3 in), is reared principally in Minnesota, the Dakotas, and Arkansas. Sexual maturity is reached at one year of age, and spawning begins at a water temperature of 18°C (65°F). Each female lays from 200 to 500 eggs per spawn. One female was reported to have produced more than 4,000 young from 12 spawns in an 11-week period. Adhesive eggs attach to the undersides of boards or other substrate. Fry are stocked at 123,550 to 741,300/ha (50,000 to 300,000/ac) in grow-out ponds. Some catfish farmers stock adult fatheads into brood ponds at a rate of 4,942/ha (2,000/ac) to provide winter forage.

White Sucker-- This species occurs naturally east of the Rocky Mountains from southern Canada south to Colorado, Missouri, and Georgia. It is produced as bait principally in the upper Midwest for crappie, muskellunge (*Esox masquinongy*), yellow perch (*Perca flavescens*), and northern pike (*Esox lucius*).

Goldfish-- The goldfish, with its many color variations, is well known as both an aquarium fish and baitfish. It normally begins spawning at 16°C (61°F). A female may lay 2,000 to 4,000 eggs during each of several spawns. The goldfish is cultured much like the golden shiner. It is not as widely accepted as the golden shiner for bait because it is sluggish. Nevertheless, it is very hardy and makes a good trotline bait. The goldfish is also grown to feed carnivorous tropical fish in aquaria.

Other Baitfish-- The bull minnow (*Fundulus grandis*) is used along the Gulf of Mexico for saltwater sportfishing. Suppliers of live bait rely almost exclusively on fish from the wild. Tatum and Helton (1977) produced up to 570 kg/ha (509 lb/ac) of bull minnows in about 3 months at stocking rates ranging from 61,775 to 123,550/ha (25,000 to 50,000/ac) in grow-out. Shang and Baldwin (1980) reported on pond culture of top minnows (*Poecilia vittata* and *P. mexicana*) as baitfish for skip jack tuna (*Katsuwonus pelamis*). Tilapia also have been used as baitfish for both freshwater and saltwater sportfishes.

Minnow farming has good potential as leisure time increases and people go fishing more often. Markets must be carefully studied and competition from artificial baits considered. A farmer should determine the market demand and then try to fill the void, rather than producing a product then looking for a market. Perhaps the best possibility for new markets is use of bait minnows in saltwater sportfishing. Like most aquaculture enterprises, farming bait minnows is capital intensive. Moreover, more labor is required than most other types of aquaculture because of grading and extra effort in shipping and delivering.

Buffalo

In the southeastern United States, particularly Arkansas, the freshwater buffalo (*Ictiobus* spp.) was grown in the early 1950s. Markets were not well established, and the buffalo later gave way to the channel catfish. Two species of buffalo and one hybrid have been tested as pond fish. Perry and Avault (1975) successfully grew bigmouth buffalo (*I. cyprinellus*), black buffalo (*I. niger*), and the female bigmouth buffalo x male black buffalo hybrid in brackish ponds with channel catfish. When buffalo were stocked at 247/ha (100/ac) with channel catfish stocked at rates up to 4,942/ha (2,000/ac), buffalo added up to 336 kg/ha (300 lb/ac) to total production with no adverse effects to catfish production. The fertilized eggs and fingerlings of these species and hybrid tolerated salinities up to 9 ppt (Hollander and Avault 1975).

Buffalo must reach 1.4 to 2.3 kg (3 to 5 lb) for the market. A 2-year grow-out period may be required, causing a concern for unwanted spawns. This is not a problem with the hybrid. The market for buffalo is limited because of annoying intermuscular y-bones. Even with the apparent drawbacks, this fish, especially the hybrid, shows good potential for grow-out with channel catfish. The buffalo is an excellent eating fish but does not have the widespread market appeal of the channel catfish.

Largemouth Bass, Bluegill, and Other Sunfishes

Though the carnivorous largemouth bass has been farmed for food in Taiwan on a limited scale, this freshwater species is mainly sought after as sport in areas where it occurs naturally or has been introduced. The fish has a wide distribution -- originally from southern Canada through the Great Lakes drainage and south into Mexico, and from Virginia to Florida on the Atlantic Coast. The Florida strain of the largemouth bass is especially sought after because it grows rapidly and reaches a large size -- making it a real trophy fish. Because of its popularity, state and national fish hatcheries have propagated the largemouth bass for decades. Fingerlings are stocked into public waters and have been distributed to private citizens.

The bluegill (*Lepomis macrochirus*) has also been produced at state and national hatcheries and is grown in combination with the largemouth bass. In new sportfishing ponds that are fertilized, bluegill fingerlings are stocked in the fall of the year at 3,707/ha (1,500/ac). The next spring largemouth bass are stocked at a rate of 247 fingerlings/ha (100/ac).

In most instances, when a culture species is grown for food, it is not desirable for it to reproduce in grow-out ponds. In largemouth bass-bluegill ponds, however, ponds may never be drained as long as there is good fishing. The pond owner, then, desires that both largemouth bass and bluegill spawn naturally (Swingle and Smith 1950). Bluegill are prolific and usually spawn the first summer after stocking. They may spawn as many as three to four times in one summer as long as water temperature remains above 27°C (80°F). Bass spawn once a year in the spring when water temperatures reach 21°C (70°F). The largemouth bass depends on bluegill young as food to realize maximum growth. By being thinned down, bluegill now have ample food available, and they also reach a desirable size for sportfishing. Both species expand in numbers and weight until the carrying capacity of the pond is reached. The fish population ultimately reaches a "balance."

Balance is determined by three factors:

(1) Both species must reproduce each year. This is usually determined by checking pond waters with a small-mesh seine in the summer after both species have had an opportunity to reproduce (Swingle 1956).

(2) Good fishing must exist. Though this may vary, generally one should be able to harvest each year up to 56 kg/ha (50 lb/ac) of largemouth bass and 224 kg/ha (200 lb/ac) of bluegill (Swingle 1949).

(3) The population of forage (F) species (bluegill) must be in a proper ratio by weight with the carnivorous (C) species (largemouth bass). Swingle (1950) determined that for a pond to be in balance the F/C ratio may range from 1.4 to 10.

Swingle (1956) described a method by seining to determine pond balance. In addition to use of a small-mesh seine to check for reproduction, a 15-m

(50-ft) long seine is used to determine the abundance of intermediate size (8- to 13-cm or 3- to 5-in) bluegill. A balance range has an average of 5 to 30 intermediates per quadrant seine haul. When below five, not enough bluegill are present; when above 30, bluegill are overcrowded.

A number of other sunfishes are popular sportfishes, most of which have been propagated at state and national hatcheries. The redear (*Lepomis microlophus*) has been stocked into largemouth bass-bluegill ponds to add fishing variety. It grows a little larger than the bluegill, but it is not prolific enough in most instances to be stocked alone with largemouth bass. Both the white crappie and black crappie (*Pomoxis annularis* and *P. nigromaculatus*) are good sportfishes that grow well in large reservoirs, more than 20 ha (50 ac), with largemouth bass, bluegill, and redear. In small farm ponds, crappie compete with these species for food and space, and all species may become stunted.

Entrepreneurs who wish to propagate or farm largemouth bass and other sunfishes for commercial purposes must consider competition with state and national hatcheries. Some states have not permitted farming of sportfish for food purposes. However, there are limited possibilities for private investors. Probably the best is development and operation of fee-fishing lakes where people pay for the opportunity to fish managed lakes. Fishing rights can be leased by the day or the year, or people are charged according to the weight of fish caught. Such operations, which are located near population centers, appeal to urban citizens.

Striped Bass and Hybrid Striped Bass

The striped bass is an important food and sportfish in the United States. Its original range extended along the Atlantic Coast from the St. Lawrence River, Canada, to the St. John's River in northern Florida. It is also found along the Gulf of Mexico from Florida to Louisiana. In 1879 and 1881, yearling striped bass were released into San Francisco Bay (National Aquaculture Development Plan 1983). The striped bass populations were devastated before the turn of the century because of commercial exploitation and environmental degradation. Landings from the Atlantic Coast plummeted from 6,700 mt (7,387 tons) in 1973 to 760 mt (838 tons) in 1983. Chesapeake Bay was formerly a major commercial source of this species.

In 1954 landlocked striped bass spawned in Santee Cooper Reservoir, South Carolina, and biologists saw the striped bass as a freshwater sportfish and as a predator of gizzard shad (*Dorosoma cepedianum*). The gizzard shad is considered a trash fish and often reaches large populations in reservoirs. In 1961 a striped bass hatchery was built in South Carolina. Later, other states and national hatcheries began research, and the successful use of hormone injections gave impetus to production of striped bass seed. In 1983,

36 states had 279 reservoirs with striped bass populations. Seed production of striped bass is well worked out and is summarized by Parker and Geiger (1984).

The striped bass is normally anadromous, living along coastlines in brackish or salt water and moving into fresh water to spawn. Wild gravid brood stock is taken during spawning migration when water temperatures range from 14° to 22°C (57° to 72°F). Brood fish receive hormone injections and are handstripped of sex products or are allowed to spawn in tanks. Ultimately fry are stocked into nursery ponds and grown to fingerling size on zooplankton produced by fertilization. Though a carnivorous fish, striped bass will take pelleted feeds while in the fry and fingerling stages. However, as they grow in size they may feed reluctantly on pelleted feeds, and forage fish are often required.

The hybrid fish -- female striped bass x male white bass (*M. chrysops*) -- is hardier than the striped bass in culture ponds and grows faster in the first year or two. Several commercial producers are attempting to culture both for the food market. Van Olst and Carlberg (1990) reviewed the status and potential of hybrid striped bass. McCraren (1984), and Hodson and Jarvis (1990) outlined procedures for farming the hybrid.

Aquaculture of striped bass and its hybrid for the food market has both potential and drawbacks. Seed production is well worked out, but feeding of striped bass in grow-out to market size poses a problem. Like most carnivorous species, striped bass require live forage fish as they grow out of the fingerling stage. The hybrid striped bass is a better fish to culture. In one trial at North Carolina State University 8,960 kg/ha (8,000 lb/ac) were produced under intensive management and constant aeration. The dependence upon wild brood stock could result in a shortage of seed certain years. The female striped bass is sometimes in short supply, whereas the white bass (both sexes) is usually more abundant. This has led some hatcheries to produce a reciprocal hybrid (female white bass x male striped bass). The reciprocal gives good performance. Domestication of brood stock also will help to alleviate seed shortages. Dormant markets are being re-awakened, particularly along the Atlantic Coast where citizens have had a tradition of eating striped bass.

Common Carp

No other species of finfish has been cultured longer or more widespread than the common carp (*Cyprinus carpio*). It has been farmed for at least 2,400 years in China, 1,900 years in Japan, and has been widely introduced throughout the world (Suzuki 1979). It is farmed as far north as the former Soviet Union where ponds freeze over in winter and as far south as the Philippines where it has been grown in rice fields. In Austria, and elsewhere in Europe, large Christmas carp is a cherished tradition, and in many Asian countries carp is an important source of animal protein. As far back as 1965, carp contributed approximately 210,000 mt (231,525 tons) to the world fish supply, not including production from China that exceeds production for all other countries combined. A total of 1.5 million mt (1.65 million tons) of common and Chinese carp was grown there in 1965, but this last estimate could be 50% low (Bardach et al. 1972).

Because of the carp's long history, strains have been developed over the centuries through selective breeding. Included are the leather carp with no scales, line carp with lines of scales along the dorsal area and lateral line, mirror carp with a few large, randomly located scales, and a fully scaled carp (Figure 3.7). The mirror carp and scaled carp have remained; the others have been discarded. Various countries have continued carp breeding, and the mirror carp in Israel is often referred to as the Israeli carp. In China, a fully scaled strain of common carp, known as the big-belly carp, evolved. It can withstand a harsh environment of crowding and poor water quality. Pillay (1990) discussed various strains of common carp and noted that this fish is probably one of the few culture species that can be considered domesticated.

Figure 3.7 Strain of common carp.

In 1877, the common carp was introduced into the United States, and it is now found in all 48 contiguous states. Though highly prized in Europe and Asia, the common carp was not accepted in the United States and is often considered a pest. It muddies the water while foraging the bottom, interferes with more desirable sportfish such as largemouth bass and bluegill, and its flesh contains many small bones. Certain states have had eradication programs to control carp populations in reservoirs. One method is to lower the water level to strand eggs just after carp spawning. Carp typically spawn in weed beds along shorelines; adhesive eggs stick to vegetation.

The common carp is very hardy, fast growing, will thrive under a variety of conditions, and readily reproduces in captivity. Though a freshwater fish, the common carp can tolerate up to 20 ppt salinity. It also tolerates alkaline or acid water, is not bothered by turbid water, and it will grow well on a variety of feeds including agricultural byproducts. Its biology, reproduction, and farming are very well known and are summarized by Sigler (1958), Bardach et al. (1972), and Pillay (1990).

The common carp is farmed in a variety of culture systems. In Poland, Szumiec (1979) reported on farming of common carp. His goal was to produce 1,000-g (2.2-lb) or larger fish. He varied stocking rates from 300 to 10,000/ha (121 to 4,047/ac). Feeds included pellets containing 25% protein mostly of plant origin, dough of the same composition, wheat used as a comparable carbohydrate feed, and super pellets containing 40% protein of mostly animal origin. Pond studies began at the end of April and lasted to the end of September. They were repeated for 4 years. Szumiec easily achieved >1,000-g fish in most of his ponds. Some fish reached 1,371 g (3 lb). Overall he concluded that ponds can produce 2,000 to 3,000 kg/ha (1,786 to 2,679 lb/ac) of carp with carbohydrate feeds and 3,000 to 6,000 kg/ha (2,679 to 5,358 lb/ac) with protein-rich pellets.

In Japan common carp production for 1973 totaled 26,344 mt (29,044 tons) and was derived as follows: from irrigation ponds 11,566 mt (12,752 tons), running-water raceways 5,534 mt (6,101 tons), small fish ponds 3,495 mt (3,853 tons), and floating net-pens 5,749 mt (6,338 tons) (Suzuki 1979).

In Israel common carp have been farmed intensively with use of pelleted feeds. Here, this species has constituted up to 85% of total production from aquaculture. Later other species were combined with the common carp and manuring strategies were used to develop pond organisms as fish food. In 1982, pondfish production from Israel consisted of common carp comprising 63% of the total, tilapia 20%, silver carp (*Hypophthalmichthys molitrix*) 8.2%, and mullet (*Mugil cephalus*) 6.8% (Sarig 1983).

In the Philippines the common carp has been grown in rice fields. Fingerlings are stocked in open trenches where they forage on natural organisms, or they may be fed. In one study from February to June, common carp stocked in rice fields grew from an average of 47 to 237 g (0.1 to 0.5 lb), and production was 208 kg/ha (186 lb/ac) (Grover 1979).

Without question the common carp ranks very high as the ideal pond fish to culture. It is hardy and adapts well to a variety of environments, adapts well to ponds and other culture systems, will eat a variety of foodstuffs, reproduces easily in captivity, and grows to a large size rapidly. Economic, market, and social considerations may, however, limit its culture in certain countries. In the United States this species is often overlooked, but it has potential for select markets where certain carp-eating groups are found. It has use in fee-fishing ponds because it grows very large quickly and provides youngsters with a big trophy. The meat of large carp can be scored with a knife, and very tiny bones will fry up crisp. Larger bones are easy to remove by hand. The common carp makes good fish bait, particularly on trotlines. Still another use of common carp is for aquatic weed control. The common carp is omnivorous, not herbivorous, but its rooting activities along the bottom dislodge weeds and muddy the water that shades out weeds. When stocked at 124/ha (50/ac), carp controlled filamentous algae and certain higher plants without detriment to fish populations present (Avault et al. 1968a).

Grass Carp and Other Chinese Carps

The grass carp, also known as white amur, is one of the largest species in the Cyprinidae family and may reach 45 kg (100 lb) (Figure 3.8). It is native to large rivers, such as the Yangtze and Amur in China and Siberia, respectively, which drain into the Pacific Ocean. It has been extensively cultured in China, Malaysia, Singapore, Borneo, Indonesia, Thailand, Taiwan, Hong Kong, the Philippines, and elsewhere (Hickling 1960).

Figure 3.8 Jay V. Huner of the University of Southwestern Louisiana with grass carp.

Pillay (1990) reviewed the culture of Chinese carps. The grass carp can withstand water temperatures from 0°C (32°F) to more than 32°C (90°F), oxygen concentrations as low as 0.5 ppm, and salinities up to 10 ppt. Spawning of this riverine species occurs from April to mid August at water temperatures above 20°C (68°F). A current of 61 to 152 cm (2 to 5 ft) per second, and a rising water level in excess of 122 cm (4 ft) within a 12-hour period are required for spawning. Seed from grass carp and other Chinese carp, with the exception of the common carp, had for centuries been collected wild in China.

As fish farmers moved from mainland China to Taiwan, seed had to be shipped in each year since there are virtually no natural rivers large enough to accommodate spawning. In 1962, induced spawning of Chinese carps by pituitary injection led to commercialization of seed production (Lin 1965). The grass carp feeds on aquatic plants in ponds and will readily accept terrestrial plants. In Malaysia, grass carp consume large quantities of napier grass. Hickling (1960) reported that about 22 kg (49 lb) of napier grass were required to produce each 0.45 kg (1 lb) of fish.

Around 1963 grass carp were introduced into Alabama and Arkansas for aquatic weed control. This species has since been introduced into other states. Grass carp controlled a wide variety of weeds when stocked at 49 to 99/ha (20 to 40/ac) (Avault et al. 1968a). There is concern that grass carp might become established in rivers and be detrimental to aquatic plants and native fish populations. For that reason, some states have banned their importation. The hybrid, female common carp x male grass carp, was evaluated for weed control purposes (Figure 3.9). It did not control weeds, nor was it sterile (Avault and Merkowsky 1978). A cross between the grass carp and the bighead carp (*Aristichthys nobilis*) produced a hybrid that also did not control weeds. The best prospect for weed control is use of triploid grass carp. This fish controls weeds and it will not reproduce.

Figure 3.9 Hybrid grass carp (common carp x grass carp).

Various Chinese carps have been grown in combination for centuries. Each species occupies a different food niche in the pond, thus allowing for production up to 8,000 kg/ha (7,144 lb/ac). The common carp, discussed earlier, forages on bottom-dwelling benthic organisms, such as chironomid worms. Silver carp, with sponge-like gill rakers, filters out phytoplankton of 10 microns or less. It occupies the upper strata of water. The bighead carp feeds on larger plankton organisms, principally zooplankton in the upper strata (Stone 1994) (Figure 3.10). Black carp (*Mylopharyngodon piceus*), with pharyngeal teeth like human molars, is well suited for grinding hard shells of snails. The mud carp (*Cirrhina molitorella*), an omnivore, feeds on still another trophic level, decaying vegetation and detritus on the bottom. Its feeding habits are similar to the common carp, but it does not muddy the water with its feeding activities like the common carp.

Figure 3.10 Bighead carp. Photo courtesy of John Wozniak, Louisiana Cooperative Extension Service.

In the United States, both the grass carp and bighead carp have been stocked into channel catfish ponds, where legal, to add to total production. Carp harvested are marketed to Oriental population centers in the United States. In Israel Chinese carp species, principally the silver carp, bighead carp, and grass carp, are stocked into production ponds as "sanitary species" along with a primary culture species (Cohen et al. 1983). They reduce plankton communities and macrophytic vegetation and thus prevent a plethora of nutrients from building up, that would result in poor water quality.

The usefulness of grass carp and other Chinese carps as food fish has been documented over centuries for Asia, especially in China. When high fish production is considered with low quality feed inputs, one thinks of Chinese carps stocked in combination. In the United States this author has conducted taste tests by cooking the grass carp and several native species. The grass carp ranked number one in virtually all tests. The major concern, however, is the presence of numerous floating bones. This species will probably prove most useful for controlling aquatic weeds, particularly with use of triploid fish.

Indian Carps

The major Indian carps include catla (*Catla catla*), rohu (*Labeo rohita*), and mrigal (*Cirrhinus mrigala*). Some people also include calbasu (*Labeo calbasu*) in this group. All carps are native to India and spawn naturally in rivers. They ingest a variety of phytoplankters, zooplankters, and higher plants. Catla prefers to feed on zooplankton near the surface. Rohu and mrigal both prefer to feed on plant matter including decaying vegetation. Rohu feeds in the water column whereas mrigal is a bottom feeder (Ranade and Kewalramani 1968). These species are the most important pond fishes in India, according to Hora and Pillay (1962) and Pillay (1990). The eastern states of India, particularly West Bengal, have a history of growing these three species together for food. The major carps are hardy, grow rapidly, reach a large size, and are readily accepted in the marketplace.

Bardach et al. (1972) described two methods for spawning these carps in captivity. In bund (pond) spawning, grass is grown during the dry season on a large flat piece of land. Brood fish are held in a pool within the bund that has a levee to separate it from the rest of the bund. During the monsoon season the levee is opened, allowing fish and water to flood the bund containing grass. Fish spawn, and eggs are collected with seines and placed into pits near the bund. The eggs hatch in 12 to 18 hours. The second method of producing seed is to induce spawning artificially with hormonal injections.

Chakrabarty et al. (1979) described grow-out techniques. They stocked a total of 6,000 fingerlings per ha (2,428/ac) in ponds with a species ratio of catla 3, rohu 4, and mrigal 3. Management involved fertilization with cow dung, urea, triple superphosphate, and ammonium sulphate. A mixture of ground nut oil cake and de-oiled rice polish was also fed. Top production approached 4,000 kg/ha (3,572 lb/ac), and the best average growth was 800 g (1.8 lb) per fish (catla). They concluded that a stocking rate of 5,000 fingerlings/ha (2,023/ac) may be better to produce a 1 kg (2.2 lb) fish and that a stocking ratio of catla, rohu, and mrigal should be 4:3:3. It appears that the combination of the three major carps in pond production does not fill all the food niches. Chakrabarty et al. (1979) suggested that production could reach 8,000 kg/ha (7,144 lb/ac) if the Chinese silver carp, grass carp, and common carp were added to the system.

The Indian major carps are well accepted in the marketplace where they are native. Seed production and culture techniques, though worked out, are not as advanced as those in China with Chinese carps. If seed is readily available, Chinese carps could be added to the system to increase production.

Tilapia

Tilapia perhaps have received more attention worldwide than any other group of fish (Figure 3.11). The genus *Tilapia* and *Oreochromis*, with about 100 known species, originated in Africa and now extends north to Israel and Jordan (Chimits 1955). Tilapia were introduced into the Philippines, Taiwan, Sri Lanka, Thailand, Puerto Rico, Hawaii, the continental United States, and elsewhere (Chen 1953; Atz 1954). The history of tilapia is ancient. The fish Saint Peter caught in the Sea of Galilee and those fed by Christ to the multitudes were tilapia. Egyptian tombs dated at 2,500 B.C. contain paintings of tilapia, suggesting possible culture (Bardach et al. 1972).

Today tilapia are farmed throughout the world in the tropics and sub-tropics. In the United States commercial farming occurs in Idaho, Mississippi, Alabama, California, Colorado, Florida, Hawaii, Utah, and other states (National Aquaculture Development Plan 1983). Tilapia farming is reviewed by Pullin et al. (1987) and Pillay (1990).

Figure 3.11 Tilapia.

The tilapia, like the common carp, seems to be the ideal fish to farm although there are some drawbacks. It is low on the food chain, feeding directly on algae, detritus, or plankton. Two herbivorous tilapia, *T. zilli* and *T.*

melanopleura, feed directly on higher or rooted plants. Tilapia also readily accept various agricultural byproducts as food. Tilapia are resistant to disease, grow rapidly, flourish under crowded conditions giving high production per hectare, tolerate very poor water quality, and grow in fresh or brackish water.

Tilapia have been cultured in just about every conceivable system. In Idaho, for example, *O. mossambicus* has been grown in raceways receiving heated artesian water. Channel catfish are grown in raceways ahead of tilapia. The tilapia thrives on waste feed and catfish wastes that wash down. For each 2 kg (4.4 lb) of catfish produced, 1 kg (2.2 lb) of tilapia has been produced (Avault 1981a). Tilapia are grown in sewage oxidation ponds, floating cages, rice fields, and they thrive when stocked into ponds with other species.

In Israel, *O. aureus* has been reared at high densities in monoculture with aeration. In one study, densities ranged from 22,000 to 100,000/ha (8,903 to 40,469/ac). Fish were fed pelleted feeds with 25% protein for up to 140 days. Best results were at a stocking density of 80,000/ha (32,376/ac) with production reaching 167 kg/ha/day (149 lb/ac/day) for 100 days. Total net production reached 16,750 kg/ha (14,958 lb/ac) (Tal and Ziv 1978). The hybrid, *O. niloticus* x *O. aureus*, is a commonly cultured fish in Israel. Tilapia are grown at the subsistence level in developing nations. Though techniques may vary, *O. niloticus* fingerlings 2.5 to 5 cm (1 to 2 in) in length are stocked at a rate of 1 to 2/m^2 (0.8 to 1.6/yd^2) in a 200 to 600 m^2 (239 to 718 yd^2) pond. Fish are fed rice bran, and in 6 months they reach 100 g (3.5 oz) each.

The main drawbacks of tilapia are that they may spawn when only 2 to 3 months old, will die when water temperatures get too low, and they do not have universal appeal in the marketplace. Tilapia, with the exception of *T. melanopleura* and *T. zilli,* are mouth brooders. The eggs are incubated in the mouth. This special care results in high survival of young. Since tilapia may reproduce every 30 days if water temperatures are suitable, a grow-out pond can soon become overpopulated with small fish. To overcome this problem fingerling tilapia can be hand sexed, and only faster growing males stocked. Females are usually discarded. Carnivorous fish, such as the largemouth bass, can be stocked into grow-out ponds to crop back fry, or tilapia can be grown in floating cages or in waters too saline for reproduction.

Much attention has been focused on use of monosex, all-male hybrids. Hybridization between certain tilapia species, such as female *O. niloticus* x male *O. hornorum*, may yield mostly males. Monosex populations of all males can be produced by incorporating either methyltestosterone or ethynyltestosterone into feed. Dosages of 30 and 60 mg/kg of feed are used, respectively. Daily rations are 10% to 12% of body weight for 3 to 4 weeks (Shelton and Jensen 1990). It is often difficult keeping species and strains of tilapia apart, and they readily cross without hormone injections (Avault and Shell 1968).

Different species of tilapia have different tolerances to low water temperatures. In laboratory studies, *O. mossambicus* fingerlings began dying at 12°C (54°F) and *O. aureus* at 7°C (45°F). Hybrids of the two species were intermediate in cold tolerance (Avault and Shell 1968). Thus in temperate countries, brood tilapia must be overwintered in heated water, and the cost must be considered (Avault et al. 1968b).

The market appeal of tilapia varies greatly, even in the same country. *O. mossambicus*, perhaps one of the hardiest species except for low water temperatures, is disdained by some because of its dark color and black peritoneum. *O. niloticus* and *O. aureus* are preferred in some countries because they grow larger than *O. mossambicus* and are attractive. The mutant red tilapia was discovered with *O. mossambicus* in Taiwan in 1969. Commercial strains were developed by hybridizing them with *O. niloticus* (Behrends and Smitherman 1990). Selective breeding has helped to improve growth rate, survival, and percentage of red progeny (Fitzgerald 1979). Smitherman and Stone (1982), however, reported that this hybrid may be very inbred since growth was 40% less than *O. niloticus*. In Asia, red often denotes joy and well-being, so the red tilapia is highly prized. In the United States, the red tilapia has been marketed as a cherry snapper or by other descriptive names. In Jamaica, farming red tilapia is a major industry (Figures 3.12, 3.13). Tilapia generally have been perceived as a fish to provide animal protein in developing countries. In recent years, however, tilapia have found their way to upscale restaurants. In one instance, *O. niloticus* has been cultured to a weight of 681 g (1.5 lb), purged in clean water with no feed for 3 days, filleted, and individually quick frozen to produce a quality product. This particular operation in Robert, Louisiana, cultures tilapia in a recirculating system (Figure 3.14).

Tilapia have potential in many parts of the world, including the United States. *O. niloticus* and *O. aureus* are probably the two best species to consider for culture in the United States for both food and sportfish. Because tilapia interbreed so easily, strains or races have developed. Not all are good performers, and it is sometimes difficult to find a "pure" strain of a given species. The Egyptian strain of *O. niloticus* is a good performer. Tilapia grow well in combination with channel catfish and other species, but unwanted spawning must be controlled. Tilapia are good as fish bait, but some states ban their introduction. *T. melanopleura* and *T. zilli* have good potential for aquatic weed control, but are not as good as the grass carp. When stocked into ponds as fingerlings at 4,942/ha (2,000/ac) in the spring/summer, they control a variety of weeds before they die in the winter. Certain tilapia have appeal as ornamentals.

Figure 3.12 Feeding red tilapia in Jamaica.

Figure 3.13 Same pond after feeding.

Figure 3.14 Steve Abernathy's recirculating system for tilapia, Robert, Louisiana.

Ornamental Fish

This group of fishes, used for aesthetic purposes, is also known as aquarium fish, hobby fish, or tropical fish. In the United States, commercial culture of ornamentals is centered in Florida, particularly around Tampa. Including marine and freshwater fishes, it has grossed approximately $200 million annually (National Aquaculture Development Plan 1983). In Florida alone 223 tropical fish farms, comprising more than 22,000 ponds, produced ornamentals in 1982. Ornamentals are also raised on a limited scale in other states. Tanks, vats, and small earthen ponds are used to culture ornamentals (Dupree and Huner 1984).

Species from at least seven different families of fish are cultured.
(1) The Poeciliidae or livebearers may eat their living young and should be separated from them with use of cages or cover for young. The mosquito fish (*Gambusia affinis*) is found in this family. Other representative species include sailfin molly (*Poecilia latipinna*), guppy (*P. reticulata*), swordtail (*Xiphophorus helleri*), and platy (*X. maculatus*).
(2) The Cyprinidae, carp and minnow family, contains the ornamental zebra danio (*Brachydanio rerio*), clown barb (*Puntus everetti*), and rasboras (*Rasbora* sp.). The common carp has many color variations, and one variation is known as Irogoi or koi carp in Japan. The goldfish is a common ornamental. Members in the Cyprinidae family may scatter their eggs on gravel or attach them to plants. There is no parental care.
(3) The killifishes, family Cyprinodontidae, have adhesive eggs, and there is no parental care. The blue gularis (*Aphyosemion coeruleum*) is an example. This family also contains several important baitfishes.
(4) The characins, family Characidae, have varied breeding habits. Some species have exacting water quality requirements. Family examples include black-winged hatchetfish (*Carnegiella marthae*), red-spotted copeina (*Copeina* gukttata), black tetra (*Gymnocorymbus ternetzi*), and glow-light tetra (*Hemigrammus erythrozonus*).
(5) The Cichlidae includes mouthbrooding tilapia, plus species with various other breeding habits. Three representatives are discus fish (*Symphysodon discus*), firemouth cichlid (*Cichlasoma meeki*), and angelfish (*Pterophyllum scalare*).
(6) The family Anabantidae (gouramies) contains species with air chambers in their heads. They require atmospheric oxygen. Males of some species build bubble nests at the surface for egg incubation, and they guard eggs and fry. The fighting fish (*Betta splendens*) and blue gourami (*Trichogaster trichopterus*) are representative species.
(7) The corydoras catfishes, family Callichthyidae, join belly to belly during mating. Eggs are extruded into a pocket created by the female's ventral fins during fertilization. Eggs are then deposited on plants. There is no parental

care of fry. The bronze catfish (*Corydoras aneneus*) is a representative species.

The United States imports most of its tropical fish. Ramsey (1985) noted that for the month of October 1971 the United States imported nearly 8 million live fishes from 35 countries. These included members of at least 582 species from 100 families. Freshwater fishes made up 63% of these species and 99% of the individuals. *Paracheirodon innesi*, primarily from Hong Kong, was the major species imported followed by *Paracheirodon axelrodi*, primarily wild-caught stocks from Brazil; *Pterophyllum scalare* from Hong Kong; *Poecilia reticulata* from Singapore; *Gyrinocheilus aymonieri* from Thailand; and species of hypostomine and ancistrine loricariid catfishes under the composite name *Hpostomus plecostomus* from Columbia. These species collectively made up 41% of total fish imported.

Culture of ornamentals in the United States is a viable industry. Still, 80% to 90% of the tropical fish sold are imported. Since virtually all ornamental fish are tropical, special arrangements must be made to bring them indoors during winter. Though tolerances vary, most tropicals are sensitive to water temperatures below 16°C (60°F). Ornamentals are normally shipped by air, so disease control and special handling are especially important.

Milkfish

The milkfish is an excellent fish for culture in brackishwater ponds. It has been cultured on a large scale in the Philippines, Indonesia, and Taiwan (Figure 3.15). In the Philippines alone, up to 180,000 ha (444,780 ac) have been devoted to milkfish culture. Formerly, you could go from one end of Java to the other and seldom lose sight of milkfish ponds. The milkfish is euryhaline, hardy and disease resistant, grows rapidly, feeds low on the food chain, and is readily accepted in the marketplace in countries where grown.

Figure 3.15 Milkfish being examined at the Tungkang Marine Laboratory, Taiwan.

Milkfish occur naturally in warm offshore waters of the Red Sea, the Indian Ocean from East Africa to southern Australia, the Pacific Ocean from southern Japan to Australia on the west, and San Francisco Bay to southern Mexico on the east (Bardach et al. 1972). In nature, milkfish spawn near the sea coast in about 25 m (82 ft) of water. Up to 5 million pelagic eggs are produced per female. Eggs hatch in about 24 hours, and fry drift into warm estuaries of at least 23°C (73°F) where they feed on plankton (Bardach et al. 1972).

Virtually all fry used in grow-out have been caught wild along sea coasts by fry collectors. Dealers buy from collectors and in turn sell to farmers. Spawning milkfish in captivity is not easily accomplished. Vanstone et al. (1977), Chaudhuri et al. (1978), Kuo et al. (1979), and Liao et al. (1979) reported on spawning milkfish under controlled conditions. Lee and Liao (1985), Lee et al. (1986), and Pillay (1990) reviewed reproduction and culture of milkfish.

Methods for grow-out, which vary from area to area and from country to country, are summarized by Bardach et al. (1972). Fry are stocked into nursery ponds containing a complex of blue-green algae, called lab-lab or lumut in the Philippines, which was nurtured from specialized fertilization techniques. Ultimately fingerlings are harvested and restocked into grow-out ponds (tambaks), or resold to farmers. There are variations and nuances to this procedure, and often many people are involved.

In some instances fry are stocked into a pond that interconnects with a second and third pond. Each succeeding pond is larger than the first. Fry feed in the first pond. Then several weeks later, when most of the natural food is depleted, they are allowed to enter the second pond, and later the third pond.

In Indonesia, ponds may be stocked at 2,000 to 10,000 fingerlings/ha (809 to 4,047/ac). Milkfish are grown to 300 to 800 g (0.7 to 1.8 lb) each by harvest. In the Philippines, milkfish are usually grown first in nursery ponds, then transition ponds, before stocking into grow-out ponds. Fish are grown to about 350 g (0.8 lb) at harvest (Figure 3.16).

In Taiwan, mixed sizes of milkfish have been grown together. Larger fish are harvested every few weeks and replaced with an equal number of fingerlings. With optimum management, ponds in Indonesia and the Philippines can produce up to 1,000 kg/ha (893 lb/ac), and in Taiwan production may reach 1,900 kg/ha (1,697 lb/ac). Though milkfish farmers often rely on naturally cultured food, some use supplemental feeds such as rice bran plus whatever else is available locally.

Figure 3.16 Milkfish ready for market.

Two other culture strategies are noteworthy, the plankton or deep-water method and pen culture. With the plankton method, ponds must be 75 to 100 cm (30 to 39 in) deep. Inorganic fertilizer is used to encourage plankton blooms, and milkfish fry are stocked at 3,000 to 5,000/ha (1,214 to 2,023/ac) (Anonymous 1974). Milkfish feed on plankton instead of lab-lab. Pen culture is a major culture technique in Laguna de Bay near Manila (Delmendo and Gedney 1976). The lake is highly productive because of domestic wastes from Manila. Bamboo poles are stuck into the bottom to form fish pens. Water passes through the pens, but fish do not. Milkfish stocked into pens subsist on phytoplankton and other natural organisms. Waters are not fertilized, and fish are not always fed.

The expansion of new milkfish ponds does not seem too likely. Although thousands of hectares of mangrove swamps have been identified as potential milkfish pond sites in the Indo-Pacific Region, destruction of natural habitat for pond construction does not justify the loss of natural fish production. The goal for milkfish-producing countries is to increase production in existing ponds. Though most milkfish are moved through domestic markets, there is potential for international export. Filipinos living in New York, for example, relish 500 g (1.1 lb) and larger fish. Some farmers feed supplemental diets to produce a larger fish.

A major problem in farming milkfish has been the undependable supply of fry. Some years there is a great shortage of fry and some ponds have gone unstocked, or other species are substituted. When milkfish seed is one day mass produced in captivity, then the industry will stabilize. Some milkfish farmers have converted to other species because of an unreliable supply of seed. Tilapia have been accepted in certain markets in the Philippines, and the red tilapia is achieving acceptance in many other parts of the world.

Penaeid shrimp may also replace milkfish as a culture species in some traditional milkfish ponds. Shrimp have been grown together with milkfish for years; wild-caught postlarval shrimp are stocked into milkfish ponds with the tide. Shrimp also may be monocultured. Such a conversion from milkfish to shrimp would require deeper ponds, more capital for seed and feed, availability of fresh water to dilute salinity for certain species such as *Penaeus monodon*, and more intensive management.

Mullet

The striped or grey mullet is one of the most widely distributed food fishes in the world, and it may be found in coastal waters throughout the tropics and subtropics (Figure 3.17). It is euryhaline and can live in fresh water and salt water past 35 ppt. Though preferring warm waters, it can withstand wide temperature ranges from near freezing up to 35°C (95°F). The mullet feeds low on the food chain by sucking up detritus on muddy bottoms or by grazing microalgae at the surface.

Figure 3.17 Mullet.

Though *M. cephalus* is the primary species of mullet in most countries, at least 12 other mullet species have some importance as food fish (Pillay 1990). Culture of mullet occurs in widely scattered countries including India, Taiwan, Hong Kong, Italy, Israel, and elsewhere. The mullet is important to some degree in the United States as a food fish but not as a cultured species. During the 1950s and 1960s, the annual United States wild harvest of mullet approximated 18,140 mt (20,000 tons) (Cato et al. 1976). Of this total, Florida usually accounts for 80%. In Florida the fish is popular, sold fresh in the round, but it does not always process well nor have a good shelf life. This is because of the presence of dark flesh as well as white flesh. The dark muscle found in some areas of the body is composed of lipids and heme protein that are susceptible to oxidation and rancidity.

Mugil spp. culture has been dependent on wild seed, even though mullet have been successfully spawned in captivity in Taiwan (Tang 1964; Liao 1969), Israel (Abraham et al. 1967), and Hawaii (Shehadeh and Norris 1972; Kuo et al, 1973). Futch (1976) described in detail the life history and natural spawning of striped mullet along the Florida coastline. Large schools migrate from estuaries to 8 to 32 km (5 to 20 miles) offshore from October through February. Eggs are shed and fertilized by several males. They hatch in 48 hours. Fry drift into shore where they migrate to grassy areas. They usually reach 19 cm (7 in) by one year and may enter the commercial fishery the second year.

The culture of mullet in most countries is usually in combination with other species. Perry and Avault (1972) reported on culture of mullet, tilapia, and channel catfish in polyculture. In some instances, mullet have been intensively cultured as the only species. Bardach et al. (1972) reported that in Hong Kong fed mullet produced 2,500 to 3,000 kg/ha (2,233 to 2,679 lb/ac) in a 300-day grow-out.

The mullet has many attributes for culture and is widely distributed. Next to the milkfish, it is probably the most important brackishwater species. However, seed availability and shelf life of the product are major considerations. In the contiguous 48 states, it will probably not be a preferred species except in very select markets in Florida and certain other Gulf Coast states.

Yellowtail

Production of yellowtail (*Seriola quinqueradiata*) has accounted for approximately 95% of the total marine finfish cultured in Japan. The yellowtail is a delicacy here and is sliced raw as sashimi and served with soy sauce and horseradish. It is also prepared in other specialty dishes.

The biology and culture of yellowtail are summarized by Fujiya (1979) and Kafuku and Ikenoue (1983). Yellowtail is a warmwater fish that is found from Hokkaido, Japan, in the north to Taiwan in the south where the warm Kuroshio current flows. Yellowtail produces pelagic eggs at spawning. Fertilized eggs hatch in 51 to 68 hours in water temperatures of 18° to 24°C (64° to 75°F). Fry move with the current and concentrate in drifting seaweeds along coastlines. Wild fry, called mojako, are collected by licensed fishers, sorted to size, and sold to fish farmers.

Since the yellowtail is carnivorous, care must be taken in sorting to at least three sizes. Three grow-out units have been used: ponds that allow seawater to exchange back and forth, net-enclosures built in the sea, and floating net-pens, the major culture unit. When fry are 5 to 10 cm (2 to 4 in) in length, they are stocked in floating net-pens at densities of 80 to 200/m^3 (61 to 153/yd^3), in net enclosures at 5 to 20/m^3 (4 to 15/yd^3), and in ponds at 1 to 2/m^3 (0.8 to 1.6/yd^3). Optimum conditions for growth are water temperatures of 24° to 29°C (75° to 84°F), salinity at 16 ppt, and dissolved oxygen above 5 ppm. Fish are fed a mixture of ground-up trash fish, with white-meated fish preferred. In net-pens fish are harvested at sizes of 2 to 3.5 kg (4.4 to 7.7 lb). It takes 2 years in grow-out for fish to reach the larger size, and this is done in southern Japan where the water temperature is higher.

Yellowtail culture is well established in Japan and began in the 1930s in Kagawa Prefecture. It should continue, but significant expansion is doubtful because of industrial pollution and because of pollution from the culture method itself. Culture grounds have become contaminated from fish feces and waste feed. When fish containing high fat content are used as yellowtail feed, the fat floats on the water surface and decreases water transparency. Neither Fujiya (1979) nor Kafuku and Ikenoue (1983) mentioned seed supply as a concern. Diseases, however, have become a problem because of high-density culture methods used.

Porgies

Twelve species of porgies, belonging to the family Sparidae, have been considered for aquaculture. Of these, the black porgy (*Acanthopagrus schlegeli*) and the red sea bream (*Pagrus major*) have received the most attention.

Black Porgy-- The black porgy is popular in Taiwan (Figure 3.18). It is protandrously hermaphroditic; fish are normally males first and later change to females. Depending on the age of the fish, brood stock may be predominantly male or female. In one report, 1- to 2-year-old fish were mostly males. Of 3-year-old fish, 39% were functional females; 11% of males were undergoing sex reversal (Chen 1990). Ovulation can be induced by hypophysation. Sex products are stripped from brood fish, and the dry method is used for fertilization. After yolk sac absorption, fry are fed brine shrimp nauplii and other live food.

In one study, black porgy averaging 3 cm (1.2 in) stocked into a concrete pond and fed daily on trash fish reached 180 g (6 oz) in 12 months (Chen 1990). In another study, 15-g (0.5-oz) fingerlings stocked into a net-pen reached market size of 300 to 400 g (11 to 14 oz) in about 12 months. Aquaculture of the black porgy should expand because it is a high-value species. Major concerns are a shortage of fingerlings to stock grow-out units and the need to develop a formulated feed.

Figure 3.18 Black porgy.

Red Sea Bream-- The red sea bream, also known as red porgy, is called "king of the ocean" in Japan. Its brilliant pink body denotes happiness and good fortune, and the fish is often served at celebrations and special occasions. The red sea bream had been temporarily held for market in tanks, ponds, and nets, but it was 1965 before commercial culture began (Kafuku and Ikenoue 1983).

Two methods are used to obtain seed. Eggs and sperm are obtained from wild stock by stripping mature fish immediately after landing by commercial fishers. In the second method, brood fish approximately 4 years old and 1 kg (2.2 lb) in size are spawned in tanks. The pelagic eggs are collected and hatched. Ideal conditions for spawning are water temperature 15° to 21°C (59° to 70°F), salinity above 16 ppt, and dissolved oxygen at 4.5 ppm. Fry are placed in tanks with green seawater or phytoplankton. Zooplankton such as nauplii and adult copepods are added later as forage, and eventually juvenile red sea bream are fed larger food animals. When the fish exceed 2 cm (0.8 in), minced shrimp or fish are fed. Fry are transferred to floating net-pens for grow-out at 6 to 8 kg/m^3 (10 to 14 lb/yd^3) (Fujiya 1979). Cut up trash fish are fed, and a formulated diet is used to a lesser degree.

Cultured red sea bream may be released back into natural waters or shipped alive to the market. Those shipped alive are fed a low-fat diet for about one month before shipping. To impart a vivid pink color to the fish, food containing carotenoids, such as shrimp meal, is also given to fish before shipping. Culture of the red sea bream, like culture of yellowtail, should not expand significantly in Japan because of a lack of physical space and because of pollution. There is, however, a type of ocean ranching that shows promise. The culture species is held in net-pens. At feeding a device is used to emit a sound and vibration in water that conditions the fish. Ultimately juvenile fish are released from pens into ocean waters. Feeding stations are established and fish are attracted to the sound as before. Up to 20% of the fish that were released have been recaptured. Seed production in captivity is well worked out and should expand. The availability of trash fish may have a bearing on expansion one day. The red tilapia, which is much easier to culture, may offer competition in some markets.

Sea Bass

Several species of sea bass are being cultured. The Japanese sea bass (*Lateolabrax japonicus*) is a euryhaline piscivorous fish of marine origin, but it can function in freshwater ponds (Chen 1990). It is sometimes used in polyculture systems to control wild fish. In nature this fish spawns in the sea during winter. Larvae drift toward river mouths. They ascend rivers in summer, return to sea in the fall, and re-enter rivers the next spring.

Seed has been gathered wild and produced in captivity. Brood fish mature in freshwater ponds, males at age 2 and females at age 3. An egg sample is taken from a gravid female with a vinyl suction tube inserted into the ovary through the oviduct. When a female gives rise to a 0.6 mm diameter or larger ova, ovulation can be induced by hypophysation. Injections are given 24 hours apart with HCG and homogenate of pituitary glands from common carp. Ovulation is accomplished approximately 95 to 97 hours after the first of three injections. Eggs are stripped from females and milt from males. The dry method is used to accomplish fertilization. Some hatcheries with larger, older brood stock have induced fish to spawn naturally without injections. Newly hatched fry live off the yolk sac for 4 to 5 days, after which live food such as rotifers and copepods are fed.

Growing fry must be graded to size because they are carnivorous even when young. Gradually live foods are supplemented with formulated feed. The nursery phase lasts about 3 months when fingerlings reach 8 cm (3 in) in length. The Japanese sea bass feeds actively when water is 18° to 27°C (64° to 81°F). In nature this fish feeds only on live food or food items suspended in the water column. In culture, it is trained to accept extruded pellets. A major limiting factor is seed availability.

Pillay (1990) discussed reproduction and culture of the European sea bass (*Dicentrarchus labrax*) and the Asian sea bass (*Lates calcarifer*). Copeland and Grey (1987) reviewed culture of sea bass (*Lates calcarifer*) in ponds and in floating net-pens. Both species have similar culture requirements as the Japanese sea bass.

The sea bass or barramundi (*Lates calcarifer*) is widely distributed in coastal and fresh waters throughout the Indo-West Pacific Region including India, Burma, Sri Lanka, Bangladesh, Malay Peninsula, Java, Borneo, Celebes,

Philippines, Papua New Guinea, northern Australia, southern China, and Taiwan (Copeland and Grey 1987). It has a complex life history, being a protandromus hermaphrodite. Fish reach sexual maturity as males when about 3 to 4 years of age and change into females when about 6 to 8 years old. Spawning occurs in brackish waters near the mouths of rivers, beginning in August or September through February. Maturation is triggered by a temperature increase near the end of the dry season. Spawning coincides with the tides, and fry enter the coastal swamps with the peak spring tides. As the wet season develops, swamps fill up with fresh water, producing an optimum nursery ground for young fish.

The high popularity for all species of sea bass has made them obvious choices for aquaculture. Their culture should expand. Wild seed has been collected for stocking grow-out units, and the fish has been induced to spawn with hormone injection and manipulation of the environment. Seed production, however, is sometimes a bottleneck and may be a limiting factor in production. Other considerations are development of feeds for sea bass. Being carnivorous, they require a high protein diet. Trash fish is used; formulated feeds are available and need further development. Cannibalism makes it imperative that fish of the same size are stocked together.

Eel

Eel farming began in 1894 in Japan, and by 1973 this country produced 24,000 mt (26,460 tons) per year (Usui 1974). Since then, Taiwan and Korea have adopted Japanese technology for farming eels (Matsui 1984). Eel farming is also important in France, Italy, and Spain. The life history of the eel has always been somewhat of a mystery. Eels are catadromous; they live in fresh water and spawn at sea. Eels breed at sea many kilometers from land, but it took a lifetime of research by Danish biologist Johannes Schmidt to discover that eels breed in the Sargasso Sea, virtually in the middle of the Atlantic Ocean (Usui 1974).

Of the 16 species of eels in the genus *Anguilla*, nine occur in the Indonesian archipelago. Eels also are found off most coasts in the world that receive warm currents. The most common species include *A. japonicus* or Japanese eel, *A. anguilla* European eel, *A. rostrata* American eel, and *A. australis* the Australian or New Zealand eel. Cremer (1976) discussed preliminary aquaculture research in the Philippines with *A. marmorata, A. celebesensis,* and *A. bicolor pacifica.* Usui (1974) listed distinguishing characteristics for separating eel species: mottled or plain color, number of vertebrae ranging from 103 to 116, long or short dorsal fins, and habitat in ponds or streams.

Though the life history of different eel species varies, a generalized account follows. While eels are still growing in fresh water, they are called brown- or yellow-stage because of their color. The freshwater stage may last from 2 to 30 years. Before migration to sea, eels enter the silver stage and cease to feed. They rely on their high fat content for energy. The fat content of European eels may reach as high as 28%. The migration to the Sargasso Sea is fantastic. The European eel may travel 6,500 km (4,037 miles) and take 1.5 years to complete the trip. The Japanese eel migrates to the Pacific Ocean and spawns at a depth of 400 to 500 m (1,314 to 1,641 ft) when water temperatures are 16° to 17°C (61° to 63°F) and salinity is above 35 ppt (Kafuku and Ikenoue 1983). The eggs hatch into leaf-shaped leptocephalus larvae, which drift toward the coast with the current. This stage ultimately settles to the bottom and develops into the elver stage.

Elvers collect at river mouths and begin migration up river, feeding on detritus. It is this stage that is captured with nets and stocked into grow-out units for culture. In Japan a detailed account of culture is given by (Usui 1974) and Kafuku and Ikenoue (1983). Elvers are stocked into 60 to 70 cm (24 to 28 in) deep concrete tanks at 30 to 50/m^2 (25 to 42/yd^2). Here they are acclimated to tank conditions for several days and then fed tubificid worms. Gradually formulated feed is used. This consists of powdered fish meal and a starch that is made into a dough ball with water. The feed is placed in a basket partly submerged in water, and young eels can move in and out. After several months, when eels are feeding exclusively on prepared feed, they are graded to size and restocked into tanks for final grow-out. The culture density of 10-g (0.35-oz) eels is 3 to 6 kg/m^2 (5.5 to 11 lb/yd^2) and for larger ones 9 to 21 kg/m^2 (17 to 39 lb/yd^2). Around the 5th month after initial stocking fastest growing eels are ready for harvest. They are approximately 100 to 200 g (3.5 to 7 oz) (Figure 3.19).

Figure 3.19 Processing eels near Kyoto, Japan.

Culture techniques vary in other countries. Earthen ponds have been used for culture in Spain, with chicken entrails fed. Some eel farmers in other countries use minced trash fish; others use pelleted diets.

Eating eels is very popular in Europe, Japan, and Taiwan. In Japan, for example, the eel is eaten in specialty dishes such as kabayaki. Biologically, the eel is not the ideal species to culture. Wild seed must be captured. Moreover, the eel is carnivorous and requires high-cost feed containing more than 50% protein. Nevertheless, the eel is so highly prized as food that consumers are willing to pay the price. The eel will always be considered a luxury dish unless seed can be produced in hatcheries and the cost of feed lowered.

Gourami and Other Labyrinth Fishes

The giant gourami (*Osphronemus goramy*), like other species in the family Anabantidae, has an accessory air-breathing organ, the labyrinth, which allows it to use atmospheric oxygen. This species, cultured in Southeast Asia, is a freshwater fish living in rivers, swamps, and lakes. It readily spawns in ponds by first constructing a nest out of grass and weeds about 30 cm (12 in) below the water surface (Hora and Pillay 1962). Females lay several thousand eggs that are fertilized in the nest. The buoyant eggs, containing oil globules, hatch in 30 to 36 hours. Beginning the 5th day, fry feed on microorganisms associated with the decomposing nest. Fry and fingerlings also feed on a variety of foods including white ants, grasshoppers, worms, and soft plants. In grow-out, the gourami grows best at water temperatures of 24° to 28°C (75° to 82°F). Though usually grown with other species, 200 kg/ha (179 lb/ac) of gourami have been produced in monoculture.

Sepat Siam-- The sepat siam (*Trichogaster pectoralis*) is of importance in Thailand, Malaya, Indonesia, Vietnam, and Cambodia. A freshwater fish, it lives in rivers and swamps. To spawn, the male prepares a frothy bubble nest and coaxes the female over to it. Fertilization occurs, and the male collects the eggs in his mouth and blows them into the nest. Overall, the biology is similar to the gourami. The sepat siam is of particular importance in the rice fields of Malaysia where it has constituted more than 70% of fish production from a total of four major fish species (Eng et al. 1973).

Kissing Gourami-- The kissing gourami (*Helostoma temmincki*) gets its name from kissing its own kind as well as animate and inanimate objects. Kissing gouramis are bred by stocking them in special ponds. After fertilization, free-floating eggs mix with vegetation that reduces predation by parents. Rearing ponds are fertilized, and fry are grown. After 30 days, they are stocked into grow-out ponds. The gourami and other labyrinth species are often grown incidentally in rice fields and in combination with other fish species. Seed can be obtained easily, and culture techniques are fairly well established. A major detriment to their culture in rice fields is the excessive use of pesticides.

Yellow Perch

The yellow perch is in high demand as a food fish in the Great Lakes states. The Lake Erie fishery has provided 80% to 88% of the fish consumed. This amounted to 15,000 mt (16,538 tons) in 1969, but it has now dropped by more than half. With well-established markets but a declining supply, aquaculture of yellow perch has gained interest. Early attempts in large aquaria demonstrated that 1- to 1.5-g (about 0.05 oz) fingerlings can be grown to market size of 150 g (5 oz) in 9 to 11 months. Optimum growing conditions are water temperatures of approximately $22^{\circ}C$ ($72^{\circ}F$) and a photoperiod of 16 hours (Calbert and Huh 1976). The yellow perch accepts commercial diets, can be spawned in captivity, and can be mechanically processed (Kayes and Calbert 1979).

Sturgeon

The United States sturgeon (*Acipenser* spp.) fishery for caviar began in 1855. By 1880 smoked and fresh meat and oil also became important on both the Atlantic and Pacific coasts (National Aquaculture Development Plan 1983). By 1915, sturgeon harvests plummeted because of overfishing, water pollution, and construction of dams that interfered with spawning runs. Landings on the East Coast of the United States for 1982 were about 120,000 kg (264,600 lb). This is quite small when compared to landings during peak harvests from 1880 to 1890 (3.5 million kg or 7.7 million lb) (Smith and Dingley 1984).

Former Soviet Union and Japanese scientists have established aquaculture centers for sturgeon, and in the United States research has begun in South Carolina and California. Smith and Dingley (1984) reported on the biology and culture of the Atlantic (*Acipenser oxyrhynchus*) and shortnose sturgeon (*A. brevirostrum*) on the Atlantic Coast, and Doroshev et al. (1983) have done likewise for the white sturgeon (*A. transmontanus*) on the Pacific Coast. Another sturgeon species of interest is the lake sturgeon (*A. fulvescens*).

Sturgeon are truly anadromous. Atlantic sturgeon spend up to 6 years in rivers and then migrate to sea for growth and maturity. At maturity fish return to rivers in a spawning migration. The shortnose sturgeon also migrates, but spends more time in fresh water. In South Carolina, female Atlantic sturgeon spawn for the first time when 11 years old (7 to 19 range). They re-spawn at 16 years (12 to 24 range). Males first spawn at 8 years (5 to 13 range) and re-spawn at 13 (7 to 21 range) (Smith and Dingley 1984).

Shortnose sturgeon exhibit a similar spawning cycle; they mature late and do not spawn each year. Sturgeon have been spawned in captivity with the aid of hormones, and preliminary trials have been conducted for pond culture. Because the sturgeon is such a valuable fish in the marketplace, research may ultimately make its culture economical. Incipient farmers in California are culturing the sturgeon.

Paddlefish

The paddlefish, like the bigmouth buffalo, is primarily a zooplankton feeder (Figure 3.20). There has been some interest in the culture of this species because it is low on the food chain and grows very rapidly. Dillard et al. (1986) reviewed the status, management, and propagation of paddlefish. Hanfman (1990) published a bibliography on paddlefish. In certain states, particularly those along the Mississippi River, a modest commercial fishery once existed. Swingle (1965) reported that paddlefish, when stocked into ponds containing other fish species, grew by as much as 0.9 kg (2 lb) a month. In other studies (Tuten and Avault 1981), paddlefish were stocked into replicated ponds containing crawfish (*Procambarus clarkii*), channel catfish, and bigmouth buffalo. Catfish held in cages were fed; other species were not. Paddlefish grew from 0.9 kg to 2.7 kg (2 to 6 lb) in 309 days. When dissolved oxygen became low in ponds, paddlefish became stressed before other species. The spawning of paddlefish in captivity, successful rearing of seed, and the use of roe as caviar have renewed interest in the culture of this fish.

Figure 3.20 Paddlefish.

Cachama or Pacu

The cachama or pacu (*Colossoma macropomum*) is a migratory characid of the subfamily Serrasalminae that also includes the piranha (*Serrasalmus* spp.) The cachama is a herbivore with large crushing teeth that feeds mainly on fruits, nuts, seeds, and leaves (Woynarovich 1986) (Figure 3.21).

A pelagic spawner, the cachama spawns annually when around 2 to 3 years of age. A 3.5 kg (7.7 lb) female produces almost 400,000 eggs. Young use the abundant nutrient sources of flooded forests and plains, later to return to rivers. Found in South America and introduced into Panama and elsewhere in Central America, *C. macropomum* and *C. bidens*, a similar species, have been gaining in popularity as aquaculture species. These species have been spawned in captivity with hormone injection. In Venezuela, growth of cachama from egg to about 1 kg (2.2 lb) in one year is possible with intensive cage culture. Cachama are resistant to low levels of dissolved oxygen because they can respire at the air-water interface.

Figure 3.21 Cachama

Red Drum

The red drum or red fish (*Sciaenops ocellatus*), an important sport and food fish, occurs from the Gulf of Maine to Key West, Florida, on the Atlantic Coast (Figure 3.22). It is also found in the Gulf of Mexico from Florida to Mexico. The biology of red drum is reviewed by Overstreet (1983) and Mercer (1984), and its food habits by Boothby and Avault (1971) and Bass and Avault (1975).

In nature, red drum males mature at age I+ and females at age II to III. Spawning has been accomplished in tanks with manipulation of photoperiod and water temperature (Arnold 1977). Fecundity is high, and in one study 52 red drum spawns produced 60 million eggs. Pursley (1988) found red drum reared in tanks grew significantly larger at a water chloride content of 500 ppm than at 150 ppm.

Figure 3.22 Red drum.

A number of preliminary studies on the culture of red drum are reviewed by Mercer (1984). Chamberlain et al. (1987) developed a manual on red drum culture. The red drum adapts well to culture conditions, may grow up to 2 kg/year (4.4 lb/year), and grows in near fresh water to saline waters.

There are two drawbacks to its culture in coastal states. It may die during exceptionally cold winters. For optimum growth, brackish water may be necessary. This presents two options: construct ponds along the coastline to grow fish, or construct ponds further inland and use water from saltwater wells. The first option would have coastal zone management regulations to be concerned with; the second option would have to deal with the discharge of saltwater effluents into freshwater ecosystems. In Louisiana, a limited number of permits have been issued for the culture of fish in floating net-pens in brackish water. In Texas, red drum farming has a start. Ponds can be constructed relatively close to the coastline without destruction of wetlands. The market demand for red drum has greatly increased since 1985 because of a popular dish called blackened red fish. However, periodic shortages of this fish mean other fish species have been substituted for red drum.

CRUSTACEANS

Three groups of crustaceans are cultured on a large commercial scale, namely freshwater crawfish, freshwater prawns, and marine shrimp. Lobsters and crabs also are cultured on a smaller scale. Crustacean farming was reviewed by McVey (1983), Chávez (1990), and Lee and Wickins (1992).

Red Swamp Crawfish

Aquaculture of freshwater crawfish is a major industry in the United States. In 1988, more than 58,681 ha (145,000 ac) were devoted to crawfish farming in Louisiana alone. Texas farmed close to 8,499 ha (21,000 ac). Mississippi, South Carolina, North Carolina, and California are farming crawfish. Although there are 284 species and subspecies of crawfish in North and Middle America (Hobbs 1972), the red swamp crawfish is the major species cultured for food (Figure 3.23). The white river crawfish (*P. zonangulus*) is often mixed with red swamp crawfish populations and may constitute 5% to 20% of the total.

Figure 3.23 Red swamp crawfish.

The biology and aquaculture of red swamp crawfish were reviewed by Avault (1974a, 1980c, 1981b), Avault and Huner (1985), Morales (1987), Holdich and Lowery (1988), de la Bretonne and Romaire (1989), Huner and Barr (1991), and Huner (1994). Hart and Clark (1989) published a bibliography of freshwater crawfishes.

Ponds for crawfish farming require only 46 to 61 cm (18 to 24 in) of water. Since crawfish are harvested by trapping and not seining, it is not essential that pond bottoms be perfectly smooth. Pond sizes vary, but 4 ha (10 ac) is an ideal size for economic construction, water management, and harvest. When pond construction is complete, the bottom is plowed, pond filled with water, and approximately 56 kg of brood crawfish are stocked per hectare (50 lb/ac) in May or June. Water is then removed over a week or two to encourage burrowing. Crawfish typically mate in late spring; the female retains the sperm in a seminal receptacle until late summer or early fall when eggs are normally produced and fertilized. Rice varieties that produce much foliage, such as Mars or Nortai, are planted and fertilized. Some farmers rely on natural vegetation for crawfish forage such as alligatorweed (*Alternanthera philoxeroides*).

114

During summer crawfish usually remain underground. In the fall, 15 September to 15 October in Louisiana, water is added back to the pond, and crawfish emerge from their burrows. Each female releases approximately 300 young that are attached to her tail. Young and adults begin feeding on bacteria, zooplankton, and other organisms associated with decomposition of rice forage. If rice is planted early enough, March or April, grain may be harvested.

Crawfish may be harvested several times a week from late November to the end of May. Baited hexagonal-mesh wire traps are used at 49 to 74/ha (20 to 30/ac). Romaire (1989) reviewed harvest techniques. By the end of May, remaining crawfish not harvested mate and burrow underground. Thus, it is not necessary to restock production ponds each year. Moreover, reproduction, hatching, and growth of young all occur in the same pond. Crawfish production varies greatly, but 1,344 kg/ha (1,200 lb/ac) can be achieved easily. Day and Avault (1984) reported that close to 4,500 kg/ha (4,019 lb/ac) of crawfish were produced with only rice forage as a food substrate. Crawfish are marketed live and as a peeled tail meat after blanching in boiling water.

Farming of red swamp crawfish and white river crawfish also occurs in the rice fields of southern Spain near Seville, but management techniques vary somewhat (Figure 3.24). Crawfish are harvested while rice is still growing. Small unbaited hoop nets with wings are placed in water supply ditches bordering rice fields. Crawfish follow the current into the traps.

Figure 3.24 Archduke Andreas-Salvador Habsburgo Lorena successfully introduced red swamp crawfish into southern Spain in 1973.

The red swamp crawfish has been introduced into other countries -- Costa Rica, Dominican Republic, Brazil, France, Zambia, Uganda, Kenya, and Japan -- and is of some commercial importance. In some countries like Japan, however, the crawfish is often considered a pest. With the exception of Spain and the United States, most countries have a low level of management and simply harvest from natural water bodies.

The potential for expansion of crawfish farming is excellent, particularly in temperate countries where rice is grown. In 1986-87 a major chain restaurant bought 317,460 kg (700,000 lb) of tail meat from Louisiana processors, and other large buyers are entering the market. Soft-shell crawfish, recently molted, have potential as both food and as bait in sportfishing (Figure 3.25). Huner and Avault (1976) reported on production of soft-shell crawfish, but it was not until Cain and Avault (1983) developed the electro-trawl that harvest of soft-crawfish became commercially feasible. Culley et al. (1985) later developed a system for shedding crawfish in tanks.

Figure 3.25 Rex Caffey examines soft-shell crawfish. Shedding tanks can be seen.

Several areas in crawfish farming require special attention. Harvesting crawfish with traps is very labor intensive and costly. Oxygen depletion is a particularly acute problem in the fall when ponds are flooded and again in the spring as water temperatures rise. Rice forage is an excellent food substrate, but it may become depleted before the harvest season is over. Special formulated diets may have a place after forages become depleted. Finally, marketing is paramount as with any aquaculture product.

Other Species of American Crawfish

Several other species of crawfish in the United States have some potential for aquaculture. The paper shell crawfish (*Orconectes immunis*), found in the

Midwest and Northeast, has been grown for fish bait. Both *O. rusticus* and *O. nais*, found in midwestern fish ponds, are harvested if economics are favorable. *O. virilis* is harvested for bait and food in Wisconsin. The signal crawfish (*Pacifastacus leniusculus*), native to the West Coast, is harvested as food from natural waters and sold primarily to Scandinavian countries (Figure 3.26). Three other species in the genus *Procambarus* may be suitable for culture -- *P. hayi*, *P. fallax*, and *P. troglodytes*. *P. hayi* is found in Mississippi and Tennessee, *P. fallax* in Florida and Georgia, and *P. troglodytes* in the southeastern United States.

Figure 3.26 Signal crawfish.

Australian Crawfish

Much attention has been given to aquaculture of Australian crawfish because some species grow to a very large size. *Astacopsis gouldi*, the world's largest crawfish, may reach 4 kg (9 lb) each. There are more than 100 known species of Australian crawfish, but *Cherax tenuimanus* (marron) and *C. destructor* (yabbie) have the most potential for aquaculture (Carroll 1980; Anonymous 1981; Matilda 1982; Merrick and Lambert 1991). Morrissy (1979, 1984) reported on pond production and artificial feeds for the marron.

The marron, found in southwestern Australia, is detritivorous but will accept a variety of feedstuffs including formulated crustacean diets, poultry diets, and pelleted plants such as alfalfa. Most "feeds" appear to serve as food substrate for microorganisms rather than being eaten directly by crawfish. When stocked into ponds at 5/m^2 (4/yd^2), crawfish reach 45 g (2 oz) each and produce 2,100 kg/ha (1,875 lb/ac) in one year and 120 g (4 oz) and 3,175 kg/ha (2,835 lb/ac) by the second year. Survival is about 50% by year two (Anonymous 1981).

The yabbie has the widest distribution of all Australian crawfish. It is found in south Australia, Victoria, New South Wales, Western Queensland, and the Northern Territory. Adults reach 140 g (5 oz) or more. Other Australian crawfish that have been considered for aquaculture include *Euastacus armatus* (the Murray River Cray), *E. valentulus*, *E. hystricosus*, and *A. gouldi*. Members of the genus *Euastacus* are very spiny and generally prefer cool, running water. Although these crawfish grow very large, growth is slow, and the percentage of edible meat is relatively small in proportion to overall size. Basic biological research for all species is still required along with market development.

In the late 1980s, the redclaw crawfish (*Cherax quadricarinatus*) was re-discovered while the crawfishes of Australia were being studied and re-cataloged nationwide (Austin 1986, 1987) (Figure 3.27). Jones (1989, 1990) followed with an in-depth study on the biology and aquaculture of the red claw crawfish. Rouse et al. (1991) reported on its aquaculture potential in Alabama and the southern United States. They concluded that the redclaw crawfish can grow up to 80 g (3 oz) in 6 months, has up to 30% tail meat, reproduces readily in captivity, and can tolerate harsh pond conditions. This species ceases feeding when water temperatures drop below 12°C (54°F), and it begins dying below 10°C (50°F).

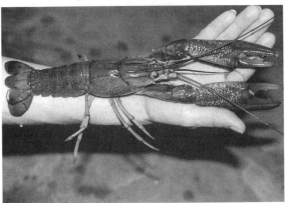

Figure 3.27 Redclaw crawfish.

European Crawfish

Crawfish culture in Europe is reviewed by Skurdal et al. (1989) and Ackefors and Lindqvist (1994). Unlike North America and Australia, Europe has relatively few crawfish species. Major native species include *Astacus astacus*, *Astacus leptodactylus*, *Austropotamobius pallipes*, and *Austropotamobius torrentium*. *Orconectes limosus*, *P. leniusculus*, *P. clarkii*, and *P. zonangulus* have been introduced into Europe from the United States. Catching and eating crawfish have been a tradition for centuries in Austria and elsewhere in Europe (Spitzy 1972). Crawfish have been plentiful in rivers and lakes of the Habsburg Empire. Emperor Maximilian I, and before him the Prince-Archbishops of Salzburg, drew up rules for catching crawfish. The minimum legal size was burnt into the oars of fishing boats.

In 1860, a fungal disease caused by *Aphanomyces astaci* first appeared in northern Italy and rapidly spread throughout France and central Europe and eventually into Russia, Finland, and elsewhere (Unestam 1972). The most important crawfish species, *A. astacus* (noble crawfish), was devastated. Crawfish, principally *P. leniusculus*, a coldwater species, were introduced into European waters (Figure 3.28). They are immune to the fungal plague. A private hatchery for *P. leniusculus* was developed near Blentarp, Sweden (Figure 3.29). Young are produced and sold to restock natural waters. Crawfish farming *per se*, except in southern Spain, has been of little importance previously, but interest is strong. Ready markets already exist, but basic research on culture techniques is required.

Crawfish culture takes two forms (Ackefors and Lindqvist 1994). Early or one-summer juveniles are produced for restoration of natural waters. Marketable crawfish, ranging in size from 9 to 10 cm (3.5 to 4 in) and larger, are grown within the culture facility.

Figure 3.28 Reinhard Spitzy of Hinterthal, Austria, examines crawfish. Spitzy played an important role in the revitalization of crawfish populations in Europe.

Figure 3.29 Stellan Karlsson of Simontorp Aquaculture AB, Blentarp, Sweden, with adult signal crawfish. Crawfish are brood stock used for spawning.

Freshwater Prawns

More than 100 species of freshwater prawns in the genus *Macrobrachium* occur worldwide. Of these, the giant freshwater prawn (*M. rosenbergii*) is the major species farmed commercially (Figure 3.30). Prawn culture is reviewed by Hanson and Goodwin (1977), New (1982, 1990), New and Singholka (1982), Huner and Brown (1985), Cange et al. (1986), and Lee and Wickins (1992). Other prawn species with culture potential include *M. americanum, M. carcinus,* and *M. acanthurus. M. rosenbergii* is native to the Indo-Pacific Region and has been introduced into almost every continent for farming. It is farmed to some degree in Thailand, Taiwan, the Philippines, Indonesia, Malaysia, Costa Rica, Honduras, Mexico, Dominican Republic, Puerto Rico, Zimbabwe, Israel, and elsewhere (Figure 3.31).

Figure 3.30 Freshwater prawn.

Figure 3.31 Harvesting prawns in Central America.

Prawn farming techniques may vary from country to country. Generally postlarval prawns, or juveniles, are stocked into ponds at rates varying from 50,000 to 250,000/ha (20,235 to 101,174/ac), fed a formulated feed daily, and harvested at an acceptable size. Prawns may be batch harvested all at once by seining and complete pond drainage or cull harvested by periodic pond seining to remove only large marketable prawns. In the latter method, smaller prawns remain for further growth, and a like number of postlarval or juvenile prawns may be restocked to replace the number of marketable prawns removed. Cull harvesting may be repeated every 3 or 4 weeks. Batch harvesting is practiced in temperate climates, whereas in tropical climates cull harvesting is the rule. In certain countries with a relatively short growing season, juvenile prawns, (PL-30), instead of postlarvae (PL-1), may be stocked into ponds. Growth must be maximized in summer because prawns may begin dying when water temperatures fall below 14°C (57°F). Stocking juvenile prawns usually increases survival and results in a larger prawn at harvest.

There are several considerations when contemplating prawn farming. First, the penaeid or saltwater shrimps may compete with the prawn in the market-place. You would have to market the prawn at a competitive price and perhaps produce a larger animal for a specialty market. The shelf life of prawns is not as good as shrimp. Most farmers chill-kill prawns in ice water, and some blanch in boiling water to retard deterioration of the product.

Regarding pond farming, several factors are of importance. When compared with penaeid shrimp, *M. rosenbergii* is relatively easy to mature and spawn in captivity. Many prawn farmers obtain gravid females from grow-out ponds after harvest. A shortage of seed or postlarvae, however, may be a temporary problem in isolated instances. *M. rosenbergii* farming on a large scale may be restricted to tropical countries. In subtropical and temperate regions, special strategies will have to be developed to farm this species. New research developments include polyculture with channel catfish (Miltner et al. 1983), rotation of prawns with crawfish (Granados et al. 1991), and development of soft-shell prawns for food (Caffey et al. 1993).

Size variation of prawns at harvest is a problem in prawn farming, though not in marine shrimp farming. *M. rosenbergii* develops a strong "pecking order" under pond culture conditions. This usually increases with stocking density. Possible solutions to overcome this include: (1) stocking at low rates (<25,000/ha or 10,117/ac) to decrease social interaction, (2) stocking at relatively high rates to break down the pecking order by crowding (i.e. 250,000/ha or 101,174/ac), (3) stocking with large, uniform-size juveniles that were first reared in outdoor nursery ponds, (4) stocking one sex in grow-out ponds, (5) developing a more docile strain of prawn, (6) providing substrate such as planted rice to lessen social contact, (7) harvesting by culling, and (8) developing marketing strategies for prawns of various sizes. For example, a 17-g (0.6 oz) prawn is the ideal size for soft-shell shedding systems. At this size prawns have not segregated into different social groups.

Overall, the prawn *M. rosenbergii* is a good species for farming in ponds. It is hardy, grows well in polyculture, can tolerate low levels of dissolved oxygen down to 1 ppm, and is a high-value species.

Marine Shrimp

World shrimp landings from capture fisheries increased steadily during the mid 1960s and reached 1.53 million mt (1.69 million tons) live weight in 1978. Since then landings have leveled off at about 1.36 million mt (1.5 million tons) (Chamberlain et al. 1985). Shrimp production in ponds reached 111,000 mt (122,378 tons) in 1984 or about 7% of total world landings; by 1991 pond-raised shrimp provided approximately 28% of the shrimp consumed (Weidner and Rosenberry 1992). More than 50 countries farm shrimp. Major shrimp farming countries include China, Indonesia, Ecuador, India, the Philippines, Taiwan, Thailand, and Japan. In 1991, world shrimp production from aquaculture was estimated at 697,145 mt (768,602 tons). About 1 million ha (2.5 million ac) of ponds yielded 725 kg/ha (647 lb/ac). The world has 4,756 shrimp hatcheries and 36,840 shrimp farms. The western hemisphere produces approximately 20% of the farm-raised shrimp and the eastern hemisphere 80% (Weidner and Rosenberry 1992).

Shrimp farming was reviewed by Hanson and Goodwin (1977), Lawrence et al. (1985), Taki et al. (1985), De Loach et al. (1991), Chamberlain et al.

(1992), and Fast and Lester (1992). Shigueno (1975, 1978) discussed shrimp farming in Japan, Liao (1985,1986) in Taiwan, and Sandifer (1991) in North America and the Caribbean. Mistakidis (1968) reviewed the basic biology and culture of shrimp. Main and Fulks (1990) examined cold-tolerant shrimp. The National Marine Fisheries Service (NMFS 1992) compiled information on world shrimp farming. Bob Rosenberry publishes a journal on world shrimp farming through his Aquaculture Digest (9434 Kearny Mesa Road, San Diego, California 92131). The digest reports on commercial shrimp farming.

Penaeus vannamei-- Although more than 20 species of shrimp have been farmed, only a handful are cultured on a large scale. *Penaeus vannamei* is the preferred species for pond culture in Latin America. A native of the Pacific West Coast from northern Peru to Sonora, Mexico, it is the major species cultured in Ecuador. It reaches 20 g (0.7 oz) in approximately 4 to 6 months when stocked as a PL-5 or PL-15 at 50,000 to 75,000/ha (20,235 to 30,352/ac) (Lawrence et al. 1985). Villalon (1991) developed a manual for semi-intensive culture, with *P. vannamei* in mind. Wyban and Sweeney (1991) reported on growing *P. vannamei* at super-high densities in round outdoor tanks. *P. vannamei* has excellent grow-out capabilities in ponds, but this species has been somewhat difficult to mature and spawn in captivity. *P. stylirostris*, with a similar range as *P. vannamei*, is easier to reproduce under captive conditions. Large numbers of postlarvae can be produced, but survival in ponds has often been poor.

P. monodon-- This shrimp is native to east and southeast Africa, Pakistan to Japan, the Malay Archipelago, and northern Australia. It is one of the largest shrimp species cultured (Figure 3.32).

Figure 3.32 *P. monodon.*

In 1989, it constituted 46% of total world production of all shrimp cultured in ponds (Rosenberry 1990). The biology and culture of *P. monodon* are reviewed by Motoh (1981) and SEAFDEC (1988). This species tolerates wide ranges of salinities. In 1988, Taiwan alone had more than 1,500 hatcheries that produced *P. monodon* larvae. In grow-out it takes approximately 4 to 6 months for 5- to 25-day-old postlarvae to reach 20- to 40-g (0.7- to 1.4- oz) market size at stocking densities of 50,000 to 250,000/ha (20,235 to 101,174/ac) (Lawrence et al. 1985). In the Philippines, PL-20 *P. monodon* can reach a 30-g (1 oz) size in 120 days or less, making it possible to grow up to two and a half crops a year under ideal conditions.

P. japonicus-- This species is native to the Red Sea, east and southeast Africa to Korea, Japan and the Malay Archipelago. It is the species of choice in Japan. It prefers sandy pond bottoms and a higher protein diet than other species. In grow-out, it reaches market size of 20 g in 5 to 6 months when stocked at 25,000 to 37,000/ha (10,117 to 14,974/ac) (Lawrence et al. 1985).

Other Shrimp Species-- A partial list of other shrimp species cultured includes *P. semisulcatus, P. orientalis, P. kerathurus, P. merguiensis, P. indicus*, and *P. setiferus. P. orientalis (= chinensis)* and *P. merguiensis* are major species cultured in China. Liao (1985) listed a total of 31 shrimp species that have been artificially propagated.

Although the basic biology of shrimp varies among species, a generalized account follows. Mature shrimp spawn off-shore where eggs are released into the open ocean. Eggs hatch within 18 to 24 hours at 28°C (82°F). Larval shrimp go through five naupliar stages, three protozoea stages, and three mysis stages before reaching the postlarval stage. In natural waters, postlarval shrimp migrate into estuaries for continued growth and migrate back to open waters when sexually mature.

Obtaining seed for culture purposes is not always easy. Some grow-out operations still rely on wild-caught seed from coastal waters, and depending on species, seed supply may be unpredictable. Shrimp have been spawned in captivity by placing gravid females caught off-shore in hatchery tanks. Maturation of shrimp in captivity is more difficult, but has had some success by manipulation of light and temperature. Eyestalk ablation facilitates maturation and spawning with some species. In ablation, an eye stalk is removed near the base by cutting, pinching with thumb and fingers, or searing with a red-hot pair of forceps.

Grow-out procedures for shrimp vary greatly. Extensive culture occurs where shrimp are stocked by hand or nature and receive little management. Production is low as are expenses. This type of culture has been practiced in much of Southeast Asia and to some degree in Latin America. In intensive culture systems in Japan and Taiwan, *P. japonicus* has been stocked in concrete ponds at very high rates, up to 160 juveniles/m^2 (134/yd^2). Production reaches 4.5 to 24 mt/ha (2 to 11 tons/ac) (Lawrence et al. 1985). *P. monodon*, semi-intensively cultured in Taiwan, has been stocked at 20 to 40/m^2 (16 to 32/yd^2), yielding 1.4 to 9.6 mt/ha (0.6 to 4.3 tons/ac).

The outlook for expansion of shrimp farming is good in many countries because of a strong market demand, yet the fantastic growth of the industry worldwide will affect market prices. New markets will have to be developed. Japan and the United States together capture close to 50% of the market (Weidner and Rosenberry 1992). European markets should be targeted.

Diseases, especially viral diseases, have devastated crops of *P. monodon* in Taiwan and elsewhere. Stress resulting from high stocking rates and from poor water quality has predisposed shrimp to disease. *P. vannamei* has had similar problems with viral diseases in some countries. Specific Pathogen Free postlarvae have been made available for some shrimp species.

The trend in shrimp farming has been ever higher stocking and feeding rates. Boyd (1992) suggested that stocking rates in excess of 20/m^2 for *P. monodon* will lead to serious problems. Higher stocking rates of *P. vannamei* are permissible because this species is harvested at a smaller size, and feeding rates are lower. Feeding rates above 100 to 150 kg/ha per day (89 to 134 lb/ac) cannot be used for long without serious deterioration of water quality and pond bottom soils.

In Ecuador, Indonesia, and elsewhere, pesticide pollution from agricultural practices has been blamed for massive shrimp die-offs. The water supply for shrimp farms should be carefully selected to avoid such problems. Further, some shrimp farms that are downstream from other farms may pump polluted water into their ponds.

Logistical problems in some countries (roads, supplies, communications) and the need for trained aquaculturists should be noted also. In the United States, shrimp have been farmed in Texas, South Carolina, and Hawaii. Shrimp farming has been considered in Louisiana, Florida, and Arizona. Major constraints have been restrictions from coastal zone management laws, a relatively short growing season, competition from other countries, and in some states restrictions on introductions of *P. vannamei* and other non-native shrimp species.

Other Crustaceans

The mud crab (*Scylla serrata*) traditionally has been polycultured in brackish water with milkfish and penaeid shrimp. Seed is collected from the wild (Liong 1994).

The blue crab (*Callinectes sapidus*) and two species of lobsters, *Homarus americanus* from North America and *H. gammarus* from Europe, have potential for aquaculture. Oesterling and Provenzano (1985) listed other possible aquaculture candidates for the United States: spiny lobster (*Panulirus* spp.), the spot prawn (*Pendalus platyceros*), cancroid crabs (*Cancer magister, C. irroratus, and C. borealis*), stone crabs (mainly *Menippe mercenaria*), tanner or snow crabs (*Chionoecetes bairdi* and *C. opilio*), and the king crab (*Paralithodes camtschatica*).

The blue crab is a highly prized gourmet food. Soft-shell crabs just molted bring up to ten times more money than hard-shell crabs. For decades, capture fishers have separated hard crabs from crabs about to molt. These latter crabs were held in floating cages and ultimately sold as soft crabs after ecdysis or molting. Oesterling (1976) summarized the life history in nature. Before mating, females move to lower salinity waters where they are cradled below males. While cradled, the females molt and mate. After mating, the male continues to cradle the female until her shell hardens. When hard, she is released by the male and migrates to higher salinity waters. From 700,000 to 2 million eggs are produced. After eggs are fertilized with stored sperm, they attach to swimmerets on the female's abdomen. Eggs hatch in 7 to 14 days to the planktonic zoea stage. After 31 to 49 days, crab zoea metamorphose to the benthic megalops stage that works its way back to the coast.

Aquaculture of crabs begins with the harvest of juveniles or adults in nature. Perry et al. (1979) described methods of harvest that include use of crab pots (traps), crab scrapes, peeler pounds, and jimmy or peeler pots. A crab scrape is a rectangular wire mesh frame with a bag that is pulled over grassy areas where "peeler" crabs congregate to seek protection. A peeler pound or crab fyke is a trap with wings to funnel in crabs in still waters where peelers concentrate. Jimmy pots are conventional crab pots seeded with males to attract females. Captured peeler crabs are then held in floats or brought indoors and stocked into shedding tanks. Avault (1986) summarized production of soft-shell crabs, and Oesterling (1984) provided a detailed step-by-step manual on shedding blue crabs.

Various methods such as eyestalk ablation have been tried to induce crabs to molt. Most crabbers simply observe crabs and sort them out at molting. Premolt crabs show recognizable signs of shedding. The last two segments of the swimming paddle show a white line just inside the edge of the paddle. White-line crabs should molt in 7 to 14 days, pink-line crabs in 3 to 6 days, and red-line crabs in 1 to 3 days. White-line crabs can be graded every 2 to 3 days, whereas red-line crabs should be checked every 3 to 4 hours.

When a split occurs across the back, the crab is called a buster or cracked crab. Once this split occurs, it takes up to 3 hours to complete the molt. The shell remains very soft for up to 5 hours, and this is the most desirable time to market the animal. The potential for expansion of shedding operations is good, provided wild-caught juveniles and adult crabs remain available.

Of the more than 160 species of lobsters, only two closely related species, *Homarus americanus* and *H. gammarus*, appear to have potential for aquaculture (D'Abramo and Conklin 1985). Most other lobster species have such complex and lengthy larval stages that commercial aquaculture seems impractical.

Aquaculture of the lobster begins with procurement of brood stock. Brood stock of *H. americanus* has been obtained from captured berried or egg-bearing females, particularly during summer. Special permits are required since berried females are protected by fishing regulations. Another source of brood stock is wild, mated female lobsters that have not extruded eggs. These females are recently molted and are shiny and clean. From 60% to 80% of them extrude eggs within a 7-month period (Schuur et al. 1976). Controlled matings of lobsters in the laboratory are well worked out. Reproductively mature lobsters are paired, placed together in isolation in the morning, and separated in late afternoon. The presence of a sperm plug in the seminal receptacle of the female is a sign of successful mating; however, this is not always an accurate indicator that insemination has occurred. Photoperiod can be controlled to favor egg extrusion.

D'Abramo and Conklin (1985) summarized hatchery and nursery techniques for larvae rearing. When eggs are about to hatch, individual females are isolated. At 20°C (68°F) larval development is complete in less than 2 weeks. Larvae may be fed a variety of diets including chopped fish and mollusks, *Artemia* nauplii, and formulated feeds. Grow-out of juvenile lobsters to market size of about 500 g (1.1 lb) requires approximately 2 years with water at 20°C. In nature about 6 years are required to produce a 500-g animal. Although hatchery and nursery systems for lobsters are well worked out, there is less knowledge for commercial grow-out systems.

Small-scale lobster farming (*Panulirus homarus*) occurs in Taiwan (Chen 1990) (Figure 3.33). Juveniles from capture fisheries are stocked in small ponds with numerous hides to avoid cannibalism. They are fed daily a diet of trash fish slightly below satiation. Grading to size is done every 2 to 3 months since growth rate is highly variable. Lobsters are harvested by seining when about 300 to 800 g (0.7 to 1.8 lb) in size. Fast growers reach 800 g in 18 months. In 1987, there were about 20 lobster farmers in Taiwan who produced approximately 400,000 lobsters. One of the largest farms has about 1.3 ha (3.25 ac) of water and produces about 150,000 marketable lobsters a year (Chen 1990). Although the market for lobster is insatiable, expansion of lobster culture is limited by seed supply.

Waddy (1989) reviewed lobster farming in intensive culture systems. Lobsters are isolated individually to avoid cannibalism and to lessen large differences in growth. Site selection for facilities is a major consideration. Although hatchery and nursery systems may use synthetic sea salts inland, larger water volumes are required for grow-out facilities. To obtain saline waters with ideal temperatures along the coastline may be difficult, because of coastal zone management laws in the United States. Use of heated effluents from power plants may work if effluents do not contain heavy metals or other pollutants. In spite of the difficulties facing lobster aquaculture, high market demand should continue to spur further research.

Figure 3.33 Small-scale lobster farmer in Taiwan.

MOLLUSKS

Three groups of mollusks are cultured on a large commercial scale, namely oysters, mussels, and clams. Abalone and scallops have potential and are farmed commercially. In 1991, world aquaculture production of mollusks was approximately 3.1 million mt (3.13 million tons), accounting for 18.7% of total aquaculture production (Food and Agriculture Organization 1993). Mollusk production is broken down to mussels, 35.2%; oysters, 29.1%; clams, 18.6%; scallops, 11.3%; and other mollusks, 5.8%. Chew (1990) summarized global introductions of mollusks. Aiken (1993a, b, c) edited a series of papers on bivalve culture.

Oysters

Oyster culture is ancient, dating back to at least 95 B.C. in the Roman Empire when Serigus Arata cultivated oysters on the bottom of Lake Lucsinus (Pausina 1970). Over time, the love of eating and growing oysters spread to other parts of the world. Pillay (1979) listed 16 countries that farm oysters in appreciable quantities. A partial list includes Japan, United States, France, Korea, Mexico, Thailand, Taiwan, and Australia.

Oysters belong to one of two basic types: flat or cup-shaped. The flat oysters, with both shells flattened, include species in the genus *Ostrea*. The cup-shaped oysters are represented by species belonging to the genus *Crassostrea*. The cup-shaped and flat oysters differ in their reproductive physiology. Male and female *Crassostrea* release sex products into the water where fertilization and development occur. *Ostrea* males expel sperm that are drawn in by an inhalent current made by the female. Eggs in *Ostrea* are held in the pallial cavity near the gills where fertilization and early development occur. Larvae are brooded in the pallial cavity for 8 to 10 days and then expelled as free swimming veligers. Aquaculture of oysters is treated at length by Bardach et al. (1972), Korringa (1976a, b), Morse et al. (1984), Burrell (1985), Quayle (1988), and Quayle and Newkirk (1989).

American Oyster-- The American oyster (*Crassostrea virginica*) is found along the Atlantic Coast of North America and all along the coast of the Gulf of Mexico (Figure 3.34). It also has been introduced into Hawaii and the Pacific Coast of California and Washington. The biology of the American oyster was reviewed by Galstoff (1964). In the United States, each state has its own management program for oyster farming.

Figure 3.34 American oyster.

In Louisiana, close to 121,408 ha (300,000 ac) of waterbottoms have been leased by the state to individuals (Perret et al. 1991). The state has provided oyster seed at no cost. Clam shells (*Rangia* sp.) are distributed on oyster spawning beds when veliger larvae are most abundant. The clam shells or "cultch" serves as a place of attachment for oyster larvae. The timing of cultch distribution is important. If too early, barnacles and other fouling organisms set on the cultch. If too late, a good set of oysters may be missed. Spawning begins when the water temperature reaches approximately 20°C (68°F). As many as 100 million eggs may be produced by a single female. Eggs hatch in only a few hours, and the free swimming veliger larvae drift about on currents for 2 to 3 weeks until they attach themselves by a muscular foot to a clean surface.

Beginning 1 September, Louisiana oyster farmers may obtain seed from state-managed beds. Harvested seed oysters are transported to more saline, leased water bottoms and distributed by hand with shovels or with high-pressure water hoses. Between 494 and 741 sacks are distributed per hectare (200 to 300/ac). (1 sack = 1.25 to 1.5 bushels. 1 bushel = 35.2 liters. 3 bushels = 1 barrel. 1 barrel = 210 pounds or 95 kg.) Planted oysters feed on plankton and are usually harvested about 6 months later by oyster luggers pulling dredges. Some farmers grow oysters longer, but they run the risk of losing the crop to predators. For each bushel planted, 2 to 3 bushels are harvested. Once harvested, oysters are transported to a shucking house where hand labor separates the oyster meat from the shell. A shucker can process 14 to 15 sacks in 5.5 hours. One sack yields about 3.8 liters (1 gal) of meat. Smaller oyster meats may be steam canned; larger meats are sold raw in 3.8-liter cans. Higher quality oysters are left whole for the counter trade. Shells are used for cesspools and roadbeds.

The American oyster is an excellent species for aquaculture. It is in high market demand, and because it is a filter feeder low on the food chain, no feed inputs are required by the farmer. Public waterbottoms, which must be leased from the state, are not always available. Water-bottoms once leased have been passed down through family generations.

Pollution, predators, and diseases pose a major threat to oysters. Because of these problems, production has dropped at an alarming rate over the years. Louisiana could probably double its area devoted to oyster farming if it were not for pollution. Polluted areas have been identified by checking the total bacteria count and fecal coliform count in waters. Oyster farming waters are closed if fecal coliform bacteria counts exceed health standards. Depuration of oysters will help alleviate contamination. Oysters are placed in tanks with uncontaminated water. After being held for several days, oysters purge themselves of microbial pathogens (Neilson et al. 1978).

Some years the shortage of oyster seed is a problem. This has spurred interest in establishment of shore-based hatcheries. Production of cultchless oysters is of particular interest. When oyster or clam shells are used as cultch on traditional spawning beds, overcrowding of oysters may occur on available cultch. Cultchless oysters are produced in land-based hatcheries by allowing larvae to set on small particles such as polished marble (Hidu et al. 1975). Individual oysters are ultimately produced that are rounder and better shaped than clustered oysters set on cultch. Moreover, the bulkiness of cultch need not be handled.

Japanese Oyster-- *Crassostrea gigas* is highly prized in Japan, and is eaten raw with vinegar. Annual production in Japan in 1982 was around 200,000 mt (220,500 tons) including shell weight (Kafuku and Ikenoue 1983). Seed is obtained on collectors made of oyster or scallop shells strung on wire. Strings of collectors are hung on bamboo racks in shallow seas. On the average, 25 oyster larvae attach to a cultch 10 cm (4 in) in length. Part of the seed is transferred directly to grow-out grounds and is cultured to market size in a year. Most seed, though, is "hardened" during autumn and winter for grow-out the next year. To harden, oyster larvae on collectors are placed at mean tide level so they are exposed to intermittent air and waves. Hardening stunts the seed temporarily and improves the ability to withstand shipping.

In Japan, oysters are grown out by one of several methods. A small quantity is grown on the water bottom. In rack culture, strings of cultch with young oysters are placed in shallow seas. The raft method and long-line methods are more commonly employed. In raft culture, strings of oyster-bearing cultch hang suspended from floating rafts. The long-line method is practiced in deeper waters, up to 30 m (98 ft) deep. Cultch strings are hung from long lines floating under buoys.

C. gigas seed is shipped to the Pacific West Coast of the United States. Cultch with attached seed is removed from strings and planted on the bottom for about 22 months. The oysters are then taken up, clusters broken, and the oysters replanted. Originally 24,710 to 34,594 oyster "spat" are planted per hectare (10,000 to 14,000/ac). Though bottom culture is the rule, limited raft culture and stake culture are practiced. Major considerations for *C. gigas* culture on the Pacific West Coast include market competition with imported food oysters from Japan, Korea, and the Gulf of Mexico in the United States. High production cost is also a consideration.

European Oyster-- The flat oyster (*Ostrea edulis*) is cultured in Europe and, to some degree, in Maine. In Maine, oyster farmers depend almost entirely on hatchery seed. The European oyster spawns at a water temperature of 15° to 18°C (59° to 64°F). Young oysters are grown in mesh trays in a nursery until they reach 10 to 25 mm (4 to 10 in) in length. Grow-out for market is off-bottom in trays or in nets that are suspended from rafts or long lines. As they grow, oysters are graded several times to size. Burrell (1985) reported that in Maine 27 producers grew 5.5 million oysters to market size in 1982. Off-bottom culture in Maine is expensive, but oysters bring a high enough price to make it economical to culture them for select markets.

Culture of the European oyster in France is especially important and is well documented by Bardach et al. (1972). Like many other oyster species, its spawning grounds are limited. Most seed production in Europe occurs in the Gulf of Moribihan on the southern coast of Brittany. Spat is obtained on semi-cylindrical ceramic tiles (similar to roof tiles) or with plastic mesh material. Spat collectors may remain out throughout the summer and fall. A good set is 30 to 50 seed oysters per tile. During winter, tiles containing seed are brought in, and young oysters are stripped off. Seed oysters are distributed evenly on water bottoms or "parcs," where they grow for 1.5 years. They are then taken up by hand and moved to deeper water for 2 years until market size is reached. Finally they are taken up and moved back to shallow intertidal areas for final fattening. Some producers fatten oysters in a "claire." This is a shallow, brackishwater pond about 0.1 to 0.2 ha (0.25 to 0.5 ac) which is rich in plankton. Fertilizer may be used to encourage plankton growth.

Olympia Oyster-- *Ostrea lurida* is a small species that reaches 5 cm (2 in) length. It is grown in Puget Sound, Washington, and in selected bays in Oregon. Spawning occurs at 13° to 16°C (55° to 61°F). Oyster shells or clam shells are used as cultch to collect oyster seed. Oyster seed is moved into impoundments located in the intertidal zone for grow-out to market size. Whole oysters are sold to wholesalers who shuck and pack them in jars for the restaurant trade. Farming of *O. lurida* is on a low scale; less than 450 kg (992 lb) were harvested in 1981 (Burrell 1985). Low availability of seed has resulted in farmers shifting to culture of *C. gigas*.

Pearl Oyster-- The pearl oyster (*Pinctada fucata*) is used in Japan to produce cultured pearls. A cultured pearl is produced by surgically placing a round nucleus of a freshwater shell inside a mother shell. The farming of mother oysters and production of cultured pearls are described by Kafuku and Ikenoue (1983). After the operation, oysters are placed in pearl nets and suspended from rafts. If the oyster is a successful recipient of the artificial nucleus, a pearl sac grows around the nucleus in 7 to 30 days. Fertility of the water, water temperature, water current, and other factors affect the pearl's quality. Fassler (1991a, b and 1992) and Balakrishna (1995) reviewed pearl culture throughout the world.

Other Oyster Species-- Several other important oyster species are farmed throughout the world. In France the Portuguese oyster (*Crassostrea angulata*) is cultured on water bottoms. It is a hardy species but less desirable in the marketplace because of its irregular shell. In Australia, the Sydney rock oyster (*C. commercialis*) is farmed, mostly by family operations. Oysters are grown in racks on oyster grounds leased from the government. In tropical countries oyster farming does not have a long history. The slipper oyster (*C. iredalei*) has some potential in the Philippines. The mangrove oyster (*C. rhizophorae*) is cultured in Cuba and Jamaica.

Mussels

The culture of mussels has a long history in France, Spain, the Netherlands, and Sweden. In the United States four private firms farmed the edible blue mussel (*Mytilus edulis*) in 1982 on about 100 ha (247 ac) (Lutz 1985). The annual combined production was 2,600 mt (2,867 tons) or 771 mt (850 tons) of wet meat valued at $1.9 million. The biology and culture of mussels were reviewed by Bardach et al. (1972), Lutz (1980, 1985), and Jamieson (1989). Virtually all of the world's commercial production of cultured mussels consists of the common edible blue mussel and the Mediterranean mussel (*M. galloprovincialis*). In the Philippines and Thailand, the green mussel (*Perna viridis*) (formerly known as *Mytilus smaragdinus*) is cultured (Figure 3.35).

The mussel, like the oyster, is a filter feeder. *M. edulis* reaches sexual maturity in one year and spawns with rising water temperature. Eggs and sperm are shed externally, and a single female may produce 25 million eggs at one time. Fertilized eggs hatch, and within 48 hours a fully developed shell forms at the veliger stage. The planktonic veliger stage lasts 2 to 4 weeks. Ultimately larval mussels attach to substratum or cultch by means of byssal threads that they secrete.

Mussels are farmed by one of four basic methods. Hurlburt and Hurlburt (1975) gave a good review.

(1) Bottom culture is practiced along the coastline of Germany and the Netherlands. Water bottoms are leased from the government. Mussel seed is dredged from natural spawning grounds and transplanted to growing waters 3 to 6 m (10 to 20 ft) deep. Dutch farmers can produce approximately 56,000 kg of live mussels per hectare per year (50,000 lb/ac/year), or about 6,811 kg/ha (6,081 lb/ac) of meat.

Figure 3.35 Mussels being harvested in the Philippines. Photo courtesy of Bureau of Fisheries and Aquatic Resources, Philippines.

(2) The bouchot method of culture is practiced along the Atlantic Coast of France, where mussel farming dates back to the year 1235 (Bardach et al. 1972). Water temperatures range from 4° to 21°C (39° to 70°F), and the salinity 29 to 34 ppt. Tides are tremendous and may exceed 15 m (49 ft). Oak poles are driven into the ocean bottom in rows spaced 1 m (3.3 ft) apart; the distance between rows is about 3 m. Seed mussels may be collected on ropes that are in turn wrapped around poles. As mussels grow in mass they are thinned down and placed in plastic net tubes that are re-wrapped around poles. It takes 12 to 18 months to produce a marketable mussel of 8 cm (3 in) long. Some farms may have as many as 75,000 poles. One pole will yield 9 to 11 kg (20 to 24 lb) of live mussels per year or about 4.5 kg (10 lb) of meat (Hurlburt and Hurlburt 1975). One hectare will yield about 11,200 kg (10,000 lb/ac) of live mussels or more than 1,800 kg of meat annually (1,607 lb/ac/year). In the Philippines, particularly around Cavite, the pole method for farming mussels began around 1960 (Yap et al. 1979). Bamboo poles are driven into the soft muddy bottom.

(3) Since 1970 new methods for growing mussels have evolved. In Spain, raft or rope culture is practiced on selected Galacian bays or rias. These areas are protected from turbulent weather by islands at the mouths. Mussels are grown on ropes suspended from rafts. They have to be thinned and transplanted several times during the growing season because their bulk would cause them to slip off the ropes. A 9-m (30-ft) long rope produces more than 114 kg (251 lb) of live mussels annually. A raft with 700 ropes produces 81,720 kg (180,193 lb) of live mussels or as much as 40,860 kg (90,096 lb) of drained meat annually (Hurlburt and Hurlburt 1975). One hectare of water can support 7 to 12 rafts, and when intensively cultivated one hectare of water can produce more than 280,503 kg (250,449 lb/ac) of pure meat per year. In Spain, depuration of harvested mussels is the rule. Seawater is pumped into holding tanks containing chlorine. Chlorine controls pathogenic organisms and eventually evaporates. Mussels are placed in the tanks for 48 hours, and the purified water is slowly recirculated. About 45% of the product is canned, 5% frozen, and the rest is sold fresh.

(4) The fourth and most recent method of culturing mussels is the long-line method practiced in Sweden. This method has potential for the United States (Lutz 1985). Like the raft culture of Spain, various types of substrates are hung vertically for both spat collection and grow-out. Unlike the Spanish method, however, no large rafts are used. Instead, buoyed floats are used to suspend horizontal ropes from which vertical ropes are suspended. In Sweden vertical ropes are about 6.5 m (21 ft) long to facilitate mechanization. In China, lines are made of straw or plastic ropes 50 to 60 m (55 to 65 yd) long. Glass floats suspend the ropes. Mussels are grown for 6 months to 1 year (Zhang 1984).

The culture of mussels is biologically sound. Because mussels are filter feeders low on the food chain, tremendous weights of mussels can be produced in a relatively small area. Mussel-growing areas are typically leased from the government by family-run operations, and new areas may be limited in some countries. The long-line method, however, may allow new areas to open. Figueras (1989) discussed problems and risks for mussel farming in Spain and France. In Spain, dinoflagellate blooms may bring in paralytic shellfish poisoning or diarrhetic shellfish poisoning. Mussels must be screened continuously. Fouling by algae, tunicates, and barnacles can occur. In France, the stingray (*Trygon pastinacea*) and various sea birds are predators. Storms may do some damage to bouchots.

In the United States, people generally prefer oysters to mussels, and domestic markets have been limited. Nevertheless, promotion and marketing efforts are paying off and markets are expanding. Mussels do not close their shells when removed from water and therefore do not ship well whole.

Clams

Historically clams have been cultured for centuries in Japan and elsewhere in the Indo-Pacific Region. In the United States the hard clam (*Mercenaria mercenaria*) is harvested wild in 16 states. It and five other species -- namely the surf clam (*Spisula solidissima*), soft-shell clam (*Mya arenaria*), ocean quahog (*Artica islandica*), Manila or Japanese clam (*Tapes japonica*), and *Saxidomus giganteus* -- are candidates for aquaculture in the United States (Figure 3.36) (Manzi 1985). In the United States, clam aquaculture has been practiced by about 15 companies (National Aquaculture Development Plan 1983). Six commercial hatcheries have produced 250 million to 500 million seed per year.

Figure 3.36 Clams are becoming more popular as a culture species.

Aquaculture of clams is reviewed by Bardach et al. (1972), Manzi (1985), and Manzi and Castagna (1989). Castagna and Kraeuter (1981) gave a particularly detailed account of farming the hard clam, and Anderson et al. (1982) presented a guide to farming the Manila clam.

Techniques for farming clams around the world are very similar and involve bottom culture. Seed may be obtained wild or from hatcheries. A brief account of hard clam culture follows: The hard clam may reach sexual maturity by 1 year of age. In hatchery troughs water temperature is raised to 28° to 30°C (82° to 86°F) then lowered to 22°C (72°F). This cycle can be repeated every 30 minutes until spawning is triggered (Castagna and Kraeuter 1981). Fertilized eggs are collected, counted, and moved to growing chambers with culture water. Development of eggs to larvae is best at salinities of 26 to 30 ppt and at water temperatures of 18°C (64°F) to 28°C. Larvae are free swimming for 8 to 10 days and then attach or "set" to the sides of the tank. They spend part of the time attached and part of the time swimming. In time, juvenile clams are introduced in grow-out pens; these are placed on water bottoms. Clam densities are 3,200 to 4,300 per m^2 (2,676 to 3,595/yd^2). Marketable clams are harvested about 24 months later.

Unlike oysters and mussels, clams do not require permanent cultch. Once clams in nursery plots reach 25 mm (1 in), usually after a year, they should be thinned and replanted. Placing growing clams in submersible cages helps to avoid predation. There are variations of these techniques where rafts and trays are used for nursery and grow-out. In some countries wild seed is obtained and planted on water bottoms. Techniques are simple and have varied little for centuries.

The prospectus for farming clams is mixed. In North America and Europe, clams are considered a luxury food, whereas in most Asian countries, they are considered a cheap source of protein. One clam farming operation in South Carolina is practicing strict quality assurance (Aiken 1993a). Water quality and clams are monitored for toxins routinely. Harvested clams are "sea polished" to remove grit and to purge the gut. Upscale restaurants are being targeted for marketing. Clam farmers must compete in the marketplace with wild-caught clams and with oysters (Bardach et al. 1972). On the plus side, a former abundance of wild clams has helped develop market demand. Farmed clams could fill the void as wild stocks decline. Niche marketing, as being done by the farm in South Carolina, is a good approach. Obtaining seed is fairly routine, and culture techniques are worked out. Predators and pests pose a problem, and government waters must usually be leased.

Abalone

The abalone (*Haliotis* spp.) is a large, herbivorous marine snail that is highly prized for the meat of its muscular foot. There are about 100 species worldwide. Major fisheries are found in Japan, Mexico, Australia, South Africa, Korea, and the United States. California and Hawaii are the states with a well-established fishery in the United States. Worldwide production of abalone from capture fisheries has been about 20,000 mt (22,050 tons) (Food and Agricultural Organization 1975). Principal species in the United States include red abalone (*H. rufescens*), pink abalone (*H. corrugata*), black abalone (*H. cracherodii*), green abalone (*H. fulgens*), pinto abalone (*H. kamtschatkana*), threaded abalone (*H. kamtschatkana assimilis*), white abalone (*H. sorenseni*), and flat abalone (*H. walallensis*) (Hooker and Morse 1985). Declining of natural fisheries has spurred interest in aquaculture, especially with the red and pink abalone in California. Abalone has been spawned in captivity. One California-based company produced abalone from seed to market size entirely in land-based raceways. The company preferred the red abalone (Svenson 1988). Growth to market size is slow, and it may take 2 to 5 years. Grow-out usually involves stocking ocean water bottoms. Predators, such as sea otters, may pose a major constraint. Hahn (1989) gave information for culture techniques.

Scallops

There are about 360 species of scallops throughout the world. Most species are unsuitable for aquaculture because of slow growth and small size. Swann (1989), Hardy (1991), and Shumway (1991) reviewed aquaculture of scallops. Japan is a leader in scallop farming, producing 200,000 mt (220,500 tons) in 1988. Most scallop farmers use Japanese technology with variations. The farming cycle of scallops involves the collection of wild seed or hatchery seed production, followed by grow-out. It requires about 2 years to raise the Japanese scallop (*Patinopectin yessoensis*) to market size from larval setting.

The culture site should allow for a minimum of environmental fluctuations. Scallops should not be exposed during low tides. Furthermore, wave action makes scallops sick, and they may stop feeding. The Japanese scallop grows well at water temperatures of 8° to 10°C (46° to 50°F). Minimum suitable temperature is 5°C (41°F) and maximum is 20°C (68°F). Salinity of 28 ppt or higher is desirable. Like most mullusks, scallops are subject to predators, and best results are to suspend growing scallops off-bottom.

REPTILES AND AMPHIBIANS

Alligators

The alligator occurs naturally in southern states and has been of particular interest in Louisiana and Florida. Declining populations resulted in the federal government placing the alligator on the endangered species list in 1973. This spurred research in Louisiana, Florida, and elsewhere with the goal of increasing natural populations. Alligator farming for both meat and hides grew from this (Avault 1985; Joanen and McNease 1987a, b).

The alligator reproduces in captivity. Louisiana studies noted that 40 to 45 eggs per clutch are laid in late June and hatch in 65 days (Figure 3.37). Young alligators are grown in tanks at 29° to 32°C (85° to 90° F) year-round. They grow at a rate of 5 cm (2 in) per month. When about 1 year old, alligators are stocked into outdoor pens at 11 animals/m² (9/yd²). They are later thinned to 4/m² (3/yd²) (Figure 3.38). Though pen sizes vary, a 3 x 5 m (10 x16 ft) chamber is common in Louisiana. This will accommodate 150 young alligators the first year. Animals are fed vitamin-enriched meat or a formulated diet. They reach 1.4 to 1.5 m (4.5 to 5 ft) in about 2 years. Animals are usually harvested when 3 years old at 1.5 m. In Louisiana, 101 farmers sold 122,789 skins in 1993 that were shipped to France, Japan, or were processed in the United States. The skins sold for $15/30 cm (1ft) for a total value of $7,183,157. A total of 245,578 kg (111,373 lb) deboned meat was sold for $2,401,753 (W. Guthrie Perry, Jr., personal communication, 1995).

Figure 3.37 Alligator eggs.

Figure 3.38 Young alligators being grown in a pen.

Turtles

Turtles, especially the green sea turtle (*Chelonia mydas*), have been considered for aquaculture. The green sea turtle grazes on aquatic plants and may reach 70 kg (154 lb) (Hendrickson 1974). In nature it reaches sexual maturity in about 6 years. Each female makes multiple nests on coastal shores with 100 or more eggs. Eggs develop alone in the sand, and newly hatched young make their way to the sea. Culture of these turtles has been attempted in Australia, the Bahamas, and Grand Cayman Island. A series of papers on the green sea turtle was published in the Proceedings of the World Mariculture Society (Avault 1974b). In Taiwan and elsewhere in the Orient, the soft-shell turtle (*Pelodiscina sinensis*) is cultured to some degree.

The snapping turtle (*Chelydra serpentina*) is a candidate species for aquaculture (Figure 3.39). The meat is sold primarily to restaurants for turtle soup. Little is known about culture requirements. Research is being conducted to determine culture methodology such as nutrient requirements. Preliminary research indicates that the snapping turtle readily accepts formulated feeds. Feed conversion and growth rate are comparable with other commercially grown warmwater species (Maxwell Mayeaux, personal communication, 1995).

Figure 3.39 Snapping turtle.

Frogs

The common bullfrog (*Rana catesbeiana*) is cultured on a limited scale in Japan, Brazil, and Taiwan. Culture has been attempted in the United States (Culley et al. 1981; Chen 1990). In most instances, so-called frog farming involves harvest of frogs from natural marsh areas. Mature frogs mate in the spring, and fertilized eggs float in a jelly-like mass on the water. Tadpoles feed on organic matter, but when the tail is lost and they metamorphose into adult frogs, live food is required. This has been a major constraint to frog farming. The Japanese have experimented with keeping dead food in motion. In Japan and in Brazil, waste meat is suspended over frog pens. Flies lay eggs on the meat, and resulting maggots are used as frog food. One commercial farm in Brazil had been successful in getting frogs to eat formulated feed by mixing feed with live food. In Taiwan, Chen (1990) reported that bullfrogs readily accept feed pellets without training although occasionally they are given live maggots.

SEAWEEDS

Seaweeds have been used since time immemorial as human food in the Indo-Pacific Region (Rao 1965; Doty 1977). A number of species has been used, but the three most commonly used seaweeds are kombu (*Laminaria* sp.), nori (*Porphyra* sp.), and wakame (*Undaria* spp.) (Hunter and Nyegaard 1974). Seaweeds have multiple uses besides food. Mannitol alcohol produced from seaweed is used in explosives; dusting powder, chewing gum, food binders and stabilizers, shoe polish, agar and algin, are examples of other products (Anonymous 1966). Aquaculture of seaweeds is reviewed by Iverson (1976), Abbott et al. (1980), and Hansen et al. (1981). Kafuku and Ikenoue (1983) discussed farming of wakame and nori.

STUDY QUESTIONS

1. List factors that must be considered when choosing a species for commercial aquaculture.

2. Discuss the importance of water temperature for production of channel catfish, rainbow trout, and tilapia.

3. Discuss the importance of salinity for production of shrimp and prawns, *Macrobrachium rosenbergii*.

4. Discuss the spawning cycle of penaeid shrimp in nature.

5. Discuss the steps for farming channel catfish and rainbow trout.

6. Discuss the steps for farming the oyster on water bottoms in the Gulf of Mexico.

7. Give the length of time to grow channel catfish, rainbow trout, and the shrimp *P. monodon* to marketable size. Assume the catfish will be grown to about 681 g (1.5 lb), trout to 340 g (12 oz), and the shrimp to 35 g (1.2 oz).

8. How is productivity expressed for pond-grown fish, such as channel catfish?

9. How is productivity expressed for raceway-grown fish, such as the rainbow trout?

10. List some of the important culture species for which seed has been obtained wild from natural waters.

11. Which culture species are most important in the United States? Why?

12. Describe methods for stocking and managing a sportfishing pond with largemouth bass and bluegill.

13. Most culture species are grown for food. List four examples of culture species that are cultured for other purposes.

14. Select a culture species you would like to farm. Now evaluate it according to the checklist you prepared in question one.

REFERENCES

Abbot, I.A., M.S. Foster and L.F. Eklund (editors). 1980. Pacific Seaweed Aquaculture. Proceedings of a Symposium. California Sea Grant, University of California, La Jolla.

Abraham, M., A. Yashouv and N. Blanc. 1967. Introduction experimentale de la ponte chez *Mugil capito* confine en eau douce. C.R. hebd. Seanc. Academy. Science Paris 265:818-821.

Ackefors, H, and O.V. Lindqvist. 1994. Cultivation of freshwater crayfishes in Europe. pp. 157-216. In Freshwater Crayfish Aquaculture. New York: Food Products Press, an imprint of The Haworth Press Inc. 312 pp.

Ade, R. 1989. The Trout and Salmon Handbook. New York-Oxford: Facts on File Inc. 122 pp.

Aiken, D. (editor). 1993a. Bivalve culture I. World Aquaculture Volume 24, No. 2. 112 pp.

Aiken, D. (editor). 1993b. Bivalve culture II. World Aquaculture Volume 24, No. 3. 96 pp.

Aiken, D. (editor). 1993c. Bivalve culture III. World Aquaculture Volume 24, No. 4. 96 pp.

Allen, G.H., J. Hedgepath, J. Pandozzi and M. Jennings. 1980. Rearing Pacific salmon in saltwater ponds fertilized with domestic waste water. Data report. Wastewater Aquaculture Project. Fisheries Department, Humbolt State University, Arcata, California 95521.

Allen, K.O. and J.W. Avault, Jr. 1969. Effects of salinity on growth and survival of channel catfish (*Ictalurus punctatus*). Proceedings Southeastern Association of Game and Fish Commissioners 23:319-331.

Allen, K.O. and J.W. Avault, Jr. 1971. Note on the relative salinity tolerance of channel and blue catfish. Progressive Fish-Culturist 33(3):135-137.

Anderson, G.J., M.B. Miller and K.K. Chew. 1982. A guide to Manila clam aquaculture in Puget Sound. Washington Sea Grant. Technical Report WSG 82-4. 45 pp.

Anonymous. 1966. Seaweeds are not weeds. Fish and Wildlife Service. Conservation Note 7.

Anonymous. 1974. Plankton method for raising bangus. Brackishwater Aquaculture Center, Leganes, Iloilo Philippines. Inland Fisheries Project No. NSDB-UP-CLSU 7103

Anonymous. 1981. Marron and marron farming. Extension and Publicity Section. Department of Fisheries and Wildlife, 108 Adelaide, Terrace Perth 6000.

Anonymous. 1987. Hybrid striped bass. U.S. Department of Agriculture, Office of Aquaculture. 8 pp.

Arnold, C.R. 1977. Laboratory spawning and larval rearing of red drum and southern flounder. Proceedings Southeastern Association of Fish and Wildlife Agencies 21: 437-440.

Arnold, C.R., G.J. Holt and P. Thomas (editors). 1988. Proceedings of a Symposium on the Culture of Red Drum and Other Warm Water Fishes. Contributions in Marine Science Supplement to Volume 30. University of Texas at Austin, Marine Science Institute, Port Aransas, Texas 78373-1267. 197 pp.

Atz, J.W. 1954. The peregrinating tilapia. Animal Kingdom 57(5):148- 155.

Austin, C.M. 1986. Electrophoretic and morphological systematic studies of the genus *Cherax* (Decapoda: Parastacidae) in Australia. Ph.D. Dissertation, Department of Zoology, University of Western Australia.

Austin, C.M. 1987. Diversity of Australian freshwater crayfishes increases potential for aquaculture. Australian Fisheries 46(5):30-31.

Avault, J.W., Jr. (editor). 1974a. Freshwater Crayfish-2. International Symposium on Freshwater Crayfish, Baton Rouge, Louisiana. 676 pp.

Avault, J.W., Jr. (editor). 1974b. Proceedings of the World Mariculture Society, Volume 5. 482 pp.

Avault, J.W., Jr. 1980a Management of aquatic species. pp. 658-674. In Animal Agriculture. San Francisco: W.H. Freeman and Company. 739 pp.

Avault, J.W., Jr. 1980b. Aquaculture. pp. 379-411. In Fisheries Management. New York-Toronto: John Wiley & Sons Inc. 422 pp.

Avault, J.W., Jr. 1980c. The bare bones of crawfish farming. Aquaculture Magazine 6(6):42-43.

Avault, J.W., Jr. 1981a. "Wastes" can be turned into cash. Aquaculture Magazine 7(3): 38-39.

Avault, J.W., Jr. 1981b. Double cropping rice and crawfish. Aquaculture Magazine 7(2):40-41.

Avault, J.W., Jr. 1983. Potpourri of research with tilapia. Aquaculture Magazine 10(5): 42-44.

Avault, J.W., Jr. 1984. Plan of research for Inland Fisheries Department of Central Agricultural Research Institute, Liberia. Mimeograph 42 pp.

Avault, J.W., Jr. 1985. The alligator story. Aquaculture Magazine 11(4):41-44.

Avault, J.W., Jr. 1986a. Soft shell crabs and crawfish. Aquaculture Magazine 12(2): 45-48.

Avault, J.W., Jr. 1986b. Seven years of pond research with the prawn *Macrobrachium rosenbergii* in Louisiana. Aquaculture Magazine 12(4):51-54.

Avault, J.W., Jr. 1986c. Aquaculture potential in the United States. Aquaculture Magazine 12(5):43-45.

Avault, J.W., Jr. 1986d. Which species to culture -- a checklist. Aquaculture Magazine 12(6):41-44.

Avault, J.W., Jr. 1987a Species profile -- tilapia. Aquaculture Magazine 13(1):47-49.

Avault, J.W., Jr. 1987b. Species profile -- minnows and other baitfish. Aquaculture Magazine 13(2):45-47.

Avault, J.W., Jr. 1987c. Species profile -- salmon. Aquaculture Magazine 13(4):65-66.

Avault, J.W., Jr. 1987d. Species profile -- mussels and clams. Aquaculture Magazine 13(5):56-58.

Avault, J.W., Jr. 1988. "New" species for aquaculture. Aquaculture Magazine 14(2): 53-55.

Avault, J.W., Jr. 1989. How will fish be grown in the future. Aquaculture Magazine 15(1):57-59.

Avault, J.W., Jr. 1990a. Species profile -- Chinese carps, common carp. Aquaculture Magazine 16(2):59-64.

Avault, J.W., Jr. 1990b. Species profile -- buffalo fish, mullet, paddlefish. Aquaculture Magazine 16(3):79-82.

Avault, J.W., Jr. 1990c. Culture species for aquaculture, why some succeed and others fail. Aquaculture Magazine 16(4):77-79.

Avault, J.W., Jr. 1992a. Future outlook for the catfish farming industry. Aquaculture Magazine 18(2):69-71.

Avault, J.W., Jr. 1992b. A review of world crustacean aquaculture. Part one. Aquaculture Magazine 18(3):84-93.

Avault, J.W., Jr. 1992c. A review of world crustacean aquaculture. Part two. Aquaculture Magazine 18(4):83-92.

Avault, J.W., Jr. 1993. Ten requirements for culturing a "new" species: a checklist. Aquaculture Magazine 19(6):68-73.

Avault, J.W., Jr. and E.W. Shell. 1968. Preliminary studies with hybrid tilapia, *Tilapia aurea* x *T. mossambica.* Proceedings of the World Symposium on Warm-Water Pond Fish Culture. FAO Fisheries Report No. 44, 4:237-242.

Avault, J.W., Jr. and A. Merkowsky. 1978. Evaluation of hybrid (common x grass) carp for weed control. In Symposium on Culture of Exotic Fishes, Auburn, Alabama. Fish Culture Section, American Fisheries Society 1978:144-155.

Avault, J.W., Jr. and J.V. Huner. 1985. Crawfish culture in the United States. pp. 1-62. In Crustacean and Mollusk Aquaculture in the United States. Westport, Connecticut: Avi Publishing Company Inc. 476 pp.

Avault, J.W., Jr., R.O. Smitherman and E.W. Shell. 1968a. Evaluation of eight species of fish for aquatic weed control. Proceedings of the World Symposium on Warm-Water Pond Fish Culture. FAO Fisheries Report No. 44, 5:109-122.

Avault, J.W., Jr., E.W. Shell and R.O. Smitherman. 1968b. Procedures for overwintering tilapia. Proceedings of the World Symposium on Warm-Water Pond Fish Culture. FAO Fisheries Report No. 44, 4:343-345.

Axelrod, H.R. 1973. Koi of the World, Japanese Colored Carp. Neptune City, New Jersey : T.F.H. Publications Inc. 239 pp.

Balakrishna, V.G. 1995. Pearl of the purest ray from dark fathomed oceans. Fisheries World Indiaqua '95 Special, Vijayawada, India. 58 pp.

Bardach, J.E., J.H. Ryther and W.O. McLarney. 1972. Aquaculture. New York-London-Sydney-Toronto: Wiley-Interscience, a Division of John Wiley & Sons Inc. 868 pp.

Bass, R.J. and J.W. Avault, Jr. 1975. Food habits, length-weight relationship, condition factor and growth of juvenile red drum, *Sciaenops occellata*, in Louisiana. Transactions of the American Fisheries Society 104(1):35-45.

Behrends, L.L. and R.O. Smitherman. 1990. Genetics and breeding of red tilapia. pp. 19-26. In Proceedings Auburn Symposium of Fisheries and Aquaculture. Auburn University, Auburn, Alabama. 365 pp.

Boothby, R.N. and J.W. Avault, Jr. 1971. Food habits, length-weight relationship and condition factor of the red drum, *Sciaenops ocellata*. Transactions of the American Fisheries Society 100 (2):290-295.

Boyd, C.E. 1992. Shrimp pond bottom soil and sediment management pp. 166-181. In Proceedings of the Special Session on Shrimp Farming. Baton Rouge, Louisiana: World Aquaculture Society. 301 pp.

Burrell, V.G. 1985. Oyster culture. pp. 235-273. In Crustacean and Mollusk Aquaculture in the United States. Westport, Connecticut : Avi Publishing Company Inc. 476 pp.

Bush, J.C., E.D. Norwood, Jr., E.E. Prather and S.F. Baima. 1982. Catfish farming. U.S. Department of Agriculture. U.S. Government Printing Office. Farmers Bulletin 2260. 29 pp.

Caffey, R.H., C.G. Lutz, J.W. Avault, Jr. and K.K. Higgins. 1993. Observations on production of soft-shell freshwater prawns, *Macrobrachium rosenbergii*, in commercial shedding facilities. Journal of Applied Aquaculture 2(2):93-102.

Cain, C.D. and J.W. Avault, Jr. 1983. Evaluation of a boat-mounted electro-trawl as a commercial harvesting system for crawfish. Aquaculture Engineering 2:101-118.

Calbert, H.E. and H.T. Huh. 1976. Culturing yellow perch (*Perca flavescens*) under controlled environmental conditions for the upper midwest market. Proceedings of the World Mariculture Society 7:137-144.

Cange, S.W., M.S. Lamon, J.W. Avault, Jr. and W.G. Perry, Jr. 1986. An overview of prawn culture research in Louisiana: 1979-1985. Louisiana Agriculture 29 (4):12-14.

Carroll, P.N. (editor). 1980. A yabbie potpourri. A collection of notes on Australian crayfish and native fish. Hawkesbury Agricultural College.

Castagna, M. and J.N. Kraeuter. 1981. Manual for growing the hard clam *Mercenaria*. Virginia Institute of Marine Science. Special Report No. 249.

Cato, J.C., P.B. Youngberg and R. Raulerson. 1976. Production, prices and marketing: an economic analysis of the Florida mullet fishery. pp. 15-64. In Economics, Biology, and Food Technology of Mullet. Florida Sea Grant Program. Report No. 15.

Chakrabarty, R.D., P.R. Sen, N.G.S. Rao and S.R. Ghosh. 1979. Intensive culture of Indian major carps. pp. 153-157. In Advances in Aquaculture. FAO Technical Conference on Aquaculture, Kyoto, Japan. 653 pp.

Chamberlain, G.W. 1985. Coastal Aquaculture. Texas A & M Agricultural Extension Service. 2 (1).

Chamberlain, G.W., M.G. Haby and R.J. Miget (editors). 1985. Texas shrimp farming manual. Texas A & M, Sea Grant College Program, and Central Power & Light.

Chamberlain, G.W., R.J. Miget and M.G. Haby (editors). 1987. Manual on red drum. Texas Agricultural Extension Service and Texas A & M University Sea Grant Program.

Chamberlain, G., J. Villalon and J. Wyban (editors). 1992. Proceedings of the Special Session on Shrimp Farming. Baton Rouge, Louisiana: World Aquaculture Society. 301 pp.

Chaudhuri, H., J.V. Juario, J.H. Primavera, R. Samson and R. Mateo. 1978. Observations on artificial fertilization of eggs and the embryonic and larval development of milkfish, *Chanos Chanos* (Forskal). Aquaculture 13(2):95-113.

Chávez, J.C. (editor). 1990. The Aquaculture of Shrimp, Prawn, and Crayfish in the World: Basics and Technologies. Tokyo, Japan: Midori Shobo Company Ltd. 380 pp. (in Japanese).

Chávez, J. and C. Cáceres. 1992. Scallop culture in the Northwest of Mexico. World Aquaculture 23(4):20-25.

Chen, T.P. 1953. The culture of tilapia in rice paddies in Taiwan. Chinese-American Joint Commission Rural Reconstruction Fisheries Service 2. 29 pp.

Chen, L.C. 1990. Aquaculture in Taiwan. Osney Mead-Oxford, England: Fishing News (Books), a division of Blackwell Scientific Publications Inc. 273 pp.

Chew, K.K. 1990. Global bivalve shellfish introductions (keynote address annual meeting of the World Aquaculture Society, 1990). World Aquaculture 21(3):9-22.

Childerhose, R.J. and M. Trim. 1981. Pacific Salmon and Steelhead Trout. Seattle, Washington: University of Washington Press. 158 pp.

Chimits, P. 1955. Tilapia and its culture. FAO Fisheries Bulletin 8 (1):1-33.

Cohen, D., Z. Ra'anan and A. Barnes. 1983. The production of freshwater prawn, *Macrobrachium rosenbergii*, in Israel, integration into fish polyculture systems. Aquaculture 31:67-76.

Copeland, J.W. and D.L. Grey (editors). 1987. Management of wild and cultured sea bass/ barramundi (*Lates calcarifer*). Australian Centre for International Agriculture Research G.P.O. Box 1571, Canberra, A.C.T. 2601 Australia. ACIAR Proceedings No. 20.

Cremer, M.C. 1976. Eel culture in the Philippines. Proceedings of the World Mariculture Society 7:129-136.

Culley, D.D., W. Baldwin and K. Roberts. 1981. The feasibility of mass culture of the bullfrog in Hawaii. Sea Grant No. LSU- 81-004.

Culley, D.D., M.Z. Said and E. Rejmankova. 1985. Producing soft crawfish, a status report. Louisiana Sea Grant College Program, LSU Center for Wetland Resources. 16 pp.

D'Abramo, L.R. and D.E. Conklin. 1985. Lobster aquaculture. pp. 159-201. In Crustacean and Mollusk Aquaculture of the United States. Westport, Connecticut : Avi Publishing Company Inc. 476 pp.

Day, C. and J.W. Avault, Jr. 1984. Crayfish, *Procambarus clarkii*, production in ponds receiving varying amounts of soybean stubble or rice straw as forage. In International Symposium on Freshwater Crayfish, Lund, Sweden 6:247-265.

de la Bretonne, L.W., Jr. and R.P. Romaire. 1989. Commercial crawfish cultivation practices: a review. Journal of Shellfish Research 8(1):267-275.

Delmendo, M.N. and R.H. Gedney. 1976. Laguna de Bay fish pen aquaculture development -- Philippines. Proceedings of the World Mariculture Society 7:257-263.

DeLoach, P.F., W.J. Dougherty and M.A. Davidson (editors). 1991. Frontiers of shrimp research. Amsterdam-Oxford-New York-Tokyo: Elsevier Science Publishing Company Inc. 294 pp.

Dillard, J.G., L.K. Graham and T.R. Russell (editors). 1986. The paddlefish: status, management and propagation. Proceedings of paddlefish -- a Threatened Resource. Held in conjunction with the 45th Midwest Fish and Wildlife Conference.

Doroshev, S.I., W.H. Clark, Jr., P.B. Lutes, R.L. Swallow, K.E. Beer, A.B. McGuire and M. D. Cochran. 1983. Artificial propagation of the white sturgeon, *Acipenser transmontanus.* Aquaculture 32:93-104.

Doty, M.S. 1977. Seaweed resources and their culture in the South China Sea Region. South China Sea Fisheries Development and Coordinating Programme SCS/77/WP/60.

Dupree, H.K. and J.V. Huner. 1984. Third Report to the Fish Farmer. U.S. Department of Interior, U.S. Fish and Wildlife Service, Washington, D.C. 270 pp.

Eng, T. C., C.B. Jock, S.H. Koon and T. Moulton. 1973. A report on paddy and paddyfield fish production in Krian, Perak. Ministry of Agriculture & Fisheries, Malaysia. Bulletin No. 128.

Fassler, C.R. 1991a. Farming jewels, the aquaculture of pearls. Aquaculture Magazine 17(5):34-51.

Fassler, C.R. 1991b. The return of the American pearl. Aquaculture Magazine 17(6): 63-78.

Fassler, C.R. 1992. Pearls: an update. Aquaculture Magazine 18(3):66-70.

Fast, A.W. and L.J. Lester (editors). 1992. Marine Shrimp Culture: Principles and Practices. Amsterdam-London-New York-Tokyo: Elsevier Science Publishers Inc. 862 pp.

Figueras, A.J. 1989. Mussel culture in Spain and France. World Aquaculture 20(4):8-17.

Fitzgerald, W.J. 1979. The red-orange tilapia. Fish Farming International 6(1):26-27.

Folsom, W., D. Altman, A. Manuar, F. Nielson, T. Revord, E. Sanborn and M. Wildman. 1992. World Salmon Culture. National Marine Fisheries Service, NOAA. Technical Memorandum NMFS-F/S PO3.

Food and Agriculture Organization. 1975. Yearbook of Fisheries Statistics. Volume 40. United Nations Food and Agriculture Organization.

Food and Agriculture Organization. 1993. Aquaculture production. FAO Circular No. 815 Revision 5.

Fujiya, M. 1979. Coastal culture of yellowtail (*Seriola quinqueradiata*) and red sea bream (*Pagrus major*) in Japan. pp. 453-458. In Advances in Aquaculture. FAO Technical Conference on Aquaculture, Kyoto, Japan. 653 pp.

Futch, C.R. 1976. Biology of striped mullet. pp. 65- 69. In Economics, Biology and Food Technology of Mullet. Florida Sea Grant Report No. 15.

Galstoff, P.S. 1964. The American oyster. U.S. Fish and Wildlife Service, Fishery Bulletin Volume 64.

Giudice, J.J., D.L. Gray and J.M. Martin. 1981. Manual for bait fish culture in the South. U.S. Fish and Wildlife Service and the University of Arkansas Cooperative Extension Service. Bulletin EC 550.

Gordon, K.G. 1990. How to choose your species. Kevgor Aquasystems P.O. Box 48851-595 Burrard Street, Vancouver, B.C. V7X 1A8 Canada. 56 pp.

Granados, A.E., J.W. Avault, Jr. and S.W. Cange. 1991. Double cropping Malaysian prawns, *Macrobrachium rosenbergii*, and red swamp crawfish, *Procambarus clarkii*. Journal of Applied Aquaculture 1(1):65-77.

Grover, J.G. 1979. Rice-fish culture and the green revolution. pp. 223-224. In Advances in Aquaculture. FAO Technical Conference on Aquaculture, Kyoto, Japan. 653 pp.

Hahn, K.O. (editor). 1989. Handbook of Culture of Abalone and other Marine Gastropods. Boca Raton, Florida: CRC Press Inc. 348 pp.

Hanfman, D.T. 1990. Paddlefish. National Agricultural Library, Beltsville, Maryland. AIC Series No. 2.

Hanson, J.A. and H.L. Goodwin (editors). 1977. Shrimp and Prawn Farming in the Western Hemisphere. Stroudsbourg, Pennsylvania: Dowden, Hutchinson, and Ross Inc. 439 pp.

Hansen, J.E., J.E. Packard and W.T. Doyle. 1981. Mariculture of red seaweeds. California Sea Grant. Report # 7-CSGCP-002.

Hardy, D. 1991. Scallop Farming. Osney Mead-Oxford, England: Fishing News (Books) Inc. 237 pp.

Hart, C.W. and J. Clark. 1989. An Interdisciplinary Bibliography of Freshwater Crayfishes. Washington and London: Smithsonian Institution Press. 498 pp.

Harvey, D. 1990. Aquaculture situation and outlook report. Commodity Economics Division, Economic Research Service, U.S. Department of Agriculture, March 1990, AQUA-4.

Harvey, D. 1991. Aquaculture situation and outlook report. Commodity Economics Division, Economic Research Service, U.S. Department of Agriculture, March 1991, AQUA-6.

Harvey, D. 1994. Aquaculture situation and outlook report. Commodity Economics Division, Economic Research Service, U.S. Department of Agriculture, March 1994. AQUA-12.

Hecht, T., W. Uys and P.J. Britz (editors). 1988. The culture of sharptooth catfish, *Clarias gariepinus*, in southern Africa. South African National Scientific Programmes Report No. 153. 133 pp.

Hendrickson, J.R. 1974. Marine turtle culture -- an overview. Proceedings of the World Mariculture Society 5:167-176.

Hickling, C.F. 1960. Observations on the growth rate of the Chinese grass carp *Ctenopharyngodon idellus*. Malayan Agricultural Journal 43 (1):49-53.

Hidu, H., S. Chapman and P.W. Soule. 1975. Cultchless setting of European oysters, *Ostrea edulis*, using polished marble. Proceedings of the National Shellfisheries Association 65:13-14.

148

Hobbs, H.H., Jr. 1972. Biota of freshwater ecosystems identification manual No. 9, crayfishes (Astacidae), of North and Middle America. Superintendent of Documents, U.S. Government Printing Office, Washington, D.C. Water Pollution Control Research Series 18050 ELDO 5/72.

Hodson, R.G. and J. Jarvis. 1990. Raising hybrid striped bass in ponds. UNC Sea Grant Publication NCRI-T-90-008.

Holdich, D.M. and R.S. Lowery (editors). 1988. Freshwater Crayfish: Biology, Management and Exploitation. London & Sydney: Croom Helm; Portland Oregon: Timber Press. 498 pp.

Holdich, D.M. and G.F. Warner (editors). 1993. Freshwater Crayfish-9. International Symposium on Freshwater Crayfish, Reading, England. 483 pp.

Hollander, E.E. and J.W. Avault, Jr. 1975. Effects of salinity on survival of buffalo fish eggs through yearlings. Progressive Fish-Culturist 37(1):47-51.

Hooker, N. and D. Morse. 1985. Abalone: The emerging development of commercial cultivation in the United States. pp. 365-414. In Crustacean and Mollusk Aquaculture in the United States. Westport, Connecticut: Avi Publishing Company Inc. 476 pp.

Hora, S.L. and T.V.R. Pillay. 1962. Handbook on fish culture in the Indo-Pacific Region. FAO Fisheries Biology. Technical Paper 14. 203 pp.

Huner, J.V. (editor). 1994. Freshwater Crayfish Aquaculture in North America, Europe, and Australia. New York-London-Norwood (Australia): Food Products Press of the Haworth Press Inc. 312 pp.

Huner, J.V. and J.W. Avault, Jr. 1976. Producing crawfish for fishbait. Louisiana State University, Center for Wetland Resources. Sea Grant Publication No. LSU-TI-76-001. 23 pp.

Huner, J.V. and E.E. Brown (editors). 1985. Crustacean and Mollusk Aquaculture in the United States. Westport, Connecticut: Avi Publishing Company Inc. 476 pp.

Huner, J.V. and J.W. Avault, Jr. 1990. Crawfish culture and its status in the United States and the world. pp. 275-290. In Aquaculture of Shrimp, Prawn and Crawfish in the World: Basics and Technologies. Midori Shobo Co., Ltd. Tokyo, Japan. (in Japanese)

Huner, J.V. and J.E. Barr. 1991. Red swamp crawfish, biology and exploitation. 3rd edition. Louisiana State University, Louisiana Sea Grant Program, Center for Wetland Resources. 128 pp.

Hunter, C.J. and C.W. Nyegaard. 1974. Seaweed farming in Puget Sound. Washington State University, College of Agriculture, Cooperative Extension Service. Extension Bulletin 654. 10 pp.

Hurlburt, C.G. and S.W. Hurlburt. 1975. Blue gold: mariculture of the edible blue mussel (Mytilus edulis). Marine Fisheries Review 37(10):10-18.

Iverson, E.S. 1976. Farming the Edge of the Sea. 2nd edition. Osney Mead-Oxford: Fishing News (Books) Ltd.

Iverson, E.S. and K.K. Hale. 1992. Aquaculture Sourcebook: A Guide to North American Species. New York: An Avi Book, published by Van Nostrand Reinhold. 308 pp.

Jamieson, G. (editor). 1989. Mussel culture. World Aquaculture 20(4):112 pp.

Jensen, J., R. Dunham and J. Flynn. 1983. Producing channel catfish fingerlings. Auburn University, Alabama Cooperative Extension Service. Circular ANR-327, 22 pp.

Jhingran, V.G. and V. Gopalakrishnan. 1974. Catalog of cultivated aquatic organisms. FAO Fisheries Technical Paper 130.

Joanen, T. and L. McNease. 1987a. The management of alligators in Louisiana, USA. pp. 33-42. In Wildlife Management: Crocodiles and Alligators. Surrey Beatty and Sons Pty Ltd in Association with the Conservation Commission of the Northern Territory.

Joanen, T. and L. McNease. 1987b. Alligator farming research in Louisiana. pp. 329-340. In Wildlife Management: Crocodiles and Alligators. Surrey Beatty and Sons Pty Ltd in Association with the Conservation Commission of the Northern Territory.

Jones, C.M. 1989. The biology and aquaculture potential of Cherax quadricarinatus. Queensland. Department of Primary Industries, Fisheries Branch, Research Station, Walkamin Q, Australia Project No. QDPI/8860.

Jones, C.M. 1990. The biology and aquaculture potential of the tropical freshwater crayfish Cherax quadricarinatus. Queensland Department of Primary Industries GPO Boc 46 Brisbane Q 4001. 110 pp.

Juliano, R.O., R.M. Arce, P.M. Fernandez, M.M. Lijauco and L.G. Handog. 1976. The Philippines recommendations for bangus. Philippine Council for Agricultural Resources. 41 pp.

Kafuku, T. and H. Ikenoue (editors). 1983. Modern Methods of Aquaculture in Japan. Amsterdam-Oxford-New York: Elsevier Science Publishing Company Inc. 216 pp.

Kayes, T.B. and J.E. Calbert. 1979. Effects of photoperiod and temperature on the spawning of yellow perch (Perca flavescens). Proceedings of the World Mariculture Society 10:306-316.

Korringa, P. 1976a. Farming the Cupped Oysters of the Genus Crassostrea. Amsterdam-Oxford-New York: Elsevier Science Publishing Company Inc. 224 pp.

Korringa, P. 1976b. Farming the Flat Oysters of the Genus Ostrea. Amsterdam-Oxford-New York: Elsevier Science Publishing Company Inc. 238 pp.

Kuo, C.M., C.E. Nash and Z. Shehadeh. 1973. The grey mullet (Mugil cephalus L.): induced breeding and larval rearing research. 1972-73. Volume II. Oceanic Institute, Waimanalo, Hawaii. National Sea Grant Program. Report No. 01-73-128.

Kuo, C.M., C.E. Nash and W.O. Watanabe. 1979. Induced breeding experiments with the milkfish, Chanos chanos (Forskal) in Hawaii. Aquaculture 18(2):95-105.

Laird, L. and T Needham. 1988. Salmon and Trout Farming. New York: John Wiley & Sons Inc. 271 pp.

Lawrence, A.L., J.P. McVey and J.V. Huner. 1985. Penaeid shrimp culture. pp. 127-157. In Crustacean and Mollusk Aquaculture in the United States. Westport, Connecticut: Avi Publishing Company Inc. 476 pp.

Lee, C.S. and I.C. Liao (editors). 1985. Reproduction and culture of milkfish. Proceedings for a Workshop Held at Tungkang Marine Laboratory, Taiwan. 226 pp.

Lee, C.S., M.S. Gordon and W.O. Watanabe (editors). 1986. Aquaculture of milkfish (Chanos chanos): state of the art. Oceanic Institute Makapuu Point Waimanalo, Hawaii 96795, USA. 284 pp.

Lee, J.S. 1973. Commercial Catfish Farming. Danville, Illinois: Interstate Printers and Publishers Inc. 263 pp.

Lee, J.S. 1991. Commercial Catfish Farming. 3rd edition. Danville, Illinois: Interstate Printers and Publishers Inc. 338 pp.

Lee, D.O and J.F. Wickins. 1992. Crustacean Farming. New York-Toronto: Halsted Press, an Imprint of John Wiley & Sons Inc. 392 pp.

Leitritz, E. and R.C. Lewis. 1980. Trout and salmon culture. California Department of Fish and Game. California Fish Bulletin 164. 19 pp.

Liao, I.C. 1969. Artificial propagation of grey mullet, *Mugil cephalus* Linnaeus. Joint Commission on Rural Reconstruction. Fisheries Series 8:10-20. (in Chinese, English abstract).

Liao, I.C. 1985. A brief review on the larval rearing techniques of penaeid prawns. pp. 65-78. In First International Conference on the Culture of Penaeid Prawns/Shrimps. Aquaculture Department, Southeast Asian Fisheries Development Center, Iloilo City, Philippines.

Liao, I.C. 1986. General introduction to the prawn pond system in Taiwan. Aquaculture Engineering 5:219-233.

Liao, I.C., J.V. Juario, S. Kumagai, H. Nakajima, H. Natividad and P. Buri. 1979. On the induced spawning and rearing of milkfish, *Chanos chanos* (Forskal). Aquaculture 18(2):75-93.

Lin, S.Y. 1965. Induced spawning of Chinese carps by pituitary injection in Taiwan. Chinese-American Joint Commission on Rural Reconstruction. Fisheries Series No. 5.

Liong, P.C. 1994. Crab culture -- present status, future prospects. Aqua International 2(4&5):4-11.

Lutz, R.A. (editor). 1980. Mussel Culture and Harvest: A North American Perspective. Amsterdam-Oxford-New York: Elsevier Science Publishing Company Inc. 350 pp.

Lutz, R.A. 1985. Mussel aquaculture in the United States. pp. 311-363. In Crustacean and Mollusk Aquaculture in the United States. Westport, Connecticut: Avi Publishing Company Inc. 475 pp.

Machado, C.R. and N. Castagnolli. 1979. Preliminary observations related to culture of *Rhamdia hilarii*, a Brazilian catfish. pp. 180-184. In Advances in Aquaculture. FAO Technical Conference on Aquaculture, Kyoto, Japan. 653 pp.

Mackey, P. 1994. Presidents message. Salmonid 18(1):2.

Main, K.L. and W. Fulks (editors). 1990. The culture of cold-tolerant shrimp: Proceedings of an Asian-U.S. Workshop on Shrimp Culture. The Oceanic Institute and the National Oceanic and Atmospheric Administration. 215 pp.

Manzi, J.J. 1985. Clam aquaculture. pp. 275 -310. In Crustacean and Mollusk Aquaculture in the United States. Westport, Connecticut: Avi Publishing Company Inc. 476 pp.

Manzi, J.J. and M. Castagna (editors). 1989. Clam Mariculture in North America. Amsterdam-Oxford-New York-Tokyo: Elsevier Science Publishing Company Inc. 461 pp.

Matilda, C.E. 1982. Annotated bibliography of the Australian freshwater crayfish (Family Parastacidae). Queensland Department of Primary Industries Bibliography Q G82001.

Matsui, I. 1984. Theory and Practice of Eel Culture. A.A. Balkema/Rotterdam. 133 pp. (translated from Japanese).

McCraren, J.P. (editor). 1984. The Aquaculture of Striped Bass. University of Maryland. Sea Grant College UM-SG-MAP-84-01.

McVey, J.P. (editor). 1983. Handbook of Mariculture, Volume 1 Crustacean Aquaculture. Boca Raton, Florida: CRC Press Inc. 442. pp.

Meade, T.L. 1974. The technology of closed system culture of salmonids. University of Rhode Island, Animal Science/NOAA Sea Grant. Marine Technical Report 30.

Mercer, L.P. 1984. A bibliography and fisheries profile of red drum, *Sciaenops ocellatus*. North Carolina Department of Natural Resources and Community Development Division of Marine Fisheries. Special Scientific Report No. 41.

Merrick, J.R. and C.N. Lambert. 1991. The Yabby, Marron, and Red Claw -- Production and Marketing. Artarmon, N.S.W., Australia: J.R. Merrick Publications. 180 pp.

Miltner, M.R., A.E. Granados, R.P. Romaire, J.W. Avault, Jr., Z. Ra'anan and D. Cohen. 1983. Polyculture of the prawn *Macrobrachium rosenbergii*, with fingerling and adult channel catfish, *Ictalurus punctatus*, and Chinese carps, *Hypophthalmichthys molitrix* and *Ctenopharyngodon* idella in earthen ponds in South Louisiana. Journal of the World Mariculture Society 14:127-134.

Mistakidis, M.E. (editor). 1968. Proceedings of the World Scientific Biological Culture of Shrimps and Prawns. FAO UN Fisheries Report No. 57, 2, 5.

Morales, J.C. 1987. Cria del Cangrejo De Rio. Barcelona, Spain: Editorial Hispano Europea, S.A. (in Spanish). 160 pp.

Morrissy, N.M. 1979. Experimental pond production of marron, *Cherax tenuimanus* (Smith) (Decapoda: Parastacidae). Aquaculture 16 (1979):319-344.

Morrissy, N.M. 1984. Assessment of artificial feeds for battery culture of a freshwater crayfish, marron (*Cherax tenuimanus*) (Decapoda: Parastacidae). Department of Fisheries and Wildlife, Western Australia. Report No. 63.

Morse, D.E., K.K. Chew and R. Mann (editors). 1984. Recent Innovations in Cultivation of Pacific Mollusks. Amsterdam-Oxford-New York-Tokyo: Elsevier Science Publishing Company Inc. 404 pp.

Motoh H. 1981. Studies on the fisheries biology of the giant tiger prawn, *Penaeus monodon*. Southeast Asian Fisheries Development Center, Tigbauan, Iloilo, Philippines. 128 pp.

National Aquaculture Development Plan. 1983. Joint Subcommittee on Aquaculture of the Federal Coordinating Council on Science, Engineering, and Technology. Washington, D.C. Volume II. 196 pp.

Neilson, B.J., D.S. Haven, F.D. Perkins, R. Morales-Almo and M.W. Rhodes. 1978. Bacterial depuration by the American oyster (*Crassostrea virginica*) under controlled conditions. Virginia Institute of Marine Science, Gloucester Point, Virginia. Special Scientific Report No. 88.

152

New, M.B. (editor). 1982. Giant Prawn Farming. Selected Papers Presented at "Giant Prawn 1980," an International Conference on Freshwater Prawn Farming. Bangkok, Thailand. Amsterdam-Oxford-New York: Elsevier Science Publishing Company Inc..

New , M.B. 1990. Freshwater prawn culture: a review. Aquaculture 88(1990):99-143.

New, M.B. and S. Singholka. 1982. Freshwater Prawn Farming. A manual for the culture of *Macrobrachium rosenbergii*. FAO Fisheries Technical Paper No. 225 FIRI/T225 (EN).

NMFS. 1992. World Shrimp Culture. Volumes 1 and 2. National Marine Fisheries Service. NOAA Silver Springs, Maryland.

Nyegaard, C.W. 1973. Coho salmon farming in Puget Sound. Washington State University, College of Agriculture, Cooperative Extension Service. Extension Bulletin 647.

Oesterling, M.J. 1976. Reproduction, growth and migration of blue crabs along Florida's Gulf Coast. Florida Sea Grant Publication SUSF-SG-76-003.

Oesterling, M.J. 1984 Manual for handling and shedding blue crabs (*Callinectes sapidus*). Virginia Institute of Marine Science. Special Report in Applied Marine Science and Ocean Engineering No. 271.

Oesterling, M.J. and A.J. Provenzano. 1985. Other Crustacean Species. pp. 203-234. In Crustacean and Mollusk Aquaculture of the United States. Westport, Connecticut: Avi Publishing Company Inc. 476 pp.

Overstreet, R.M. 1983. Aspects of the biology of the red drum, *Sciaenops ocellatus*, in Mississippi. Gulf Research Reports Supplement 1:45-68.

Parker, N.C. and J.G. Geiger. 1984. Production methods for striped bass. pp. 106-118. In Third Report to the Fish Farmers. U.S. Fish and Wildlife Service. 270 pp.

Pausina, B.V. 1970. Louisiana oyster culture. Proceedings of the World Mariculture Society 1:29-34.

Pearcy, W.G. 1992. Ocean Ecology of North Pacific Salmonids. University of Washington Press. Washington Sea Grant Program. 179 pp.

Perret, W.S., R.J. Dugas and M.F. Chatry. 1991. Louisiana oyster: enhancing the resource through shell planting. World Aquaculture 22(4):42-45.

Perry, H.M., J.T. Ogle and L.C. Nicholson. 1979. The fishery for soft crabs with emphasis on the development of a closed recirculating sea water system for shedding crabs. Proceedings Blue Crab Colloquium, October 18-19. Gulf States Marine Commission.

Perry, W.G., Jr. and J.W. Avault, Jr. 1968. Preliminary experiment on culture of blue, channel, and white catfish in brackish water ponds. Proceedings Southeastern Association of Game and Fish Commissioners 22:397-406.

Perry, W.G., Jr. and J.W. Avault, Jr. 1969. Culture of blue, channel, and white catfish in brackish water ponds. Proceedings Southeastern Association of Game and Fish Commissioners 23:592-604.

Perry, W.G., Jr. and J.W. Avault, Jr. 1972. Comparisons of striped mullet and tilapia for added production in caged catfish studies. Progressive Fish-Culturist 34(4):229-232.

Perry, W.G., Jr. and J.W. Avault, Jr. 1973. Influence of floating and sinking feeds and fingerling size on channel catfish production. Proceedings Southeastern Association of Game and Fish Commissioners 27:500-511.

Perry, W.G., Jr. and J.W. Avault, Jr. 1975. Polyculture studies with channel catfish and buffalo. Proceedings Southeastern Association of Game and Fish Commissioners 29: 91-98.

Pillay, T.V.R. 1979. The status of aquaculture. pp. 1-10. In Advances in Aquaculture. FAO Technical Conference on Aquaculture, Kyoto, Japan. 653 pp..

Pillay, T.V.R. 1990. Aquaculture: Principles and Practices. Surrey, Engalnd: Fishing News (Books) Inc. 575 pp.

Plemmons, B. and J.W. Avault, Jr. 1980. Six tons of catfish per acre with constant aeration. Louisiana Agriculture 23(4):6, 7, & 9.

Pullin, R.S.V., T. Bhukaswan, K. Tonguthai and J.L. Maclean (editors). 1987. The Second International Symposium on Tilapia in Aquaculture. Manila, Philip-pines. ICLARM Contribution No. 530. 623 pp.

Pursley, M.G. 1988. Effect of total water hardness and chlorides on survival, growth and feed conversion of juvenile red drum, *Sciaenops ocellatus* (Linnaeus). Louisiana State University, M.S. Thesis 61 pp.

Quayle, D.B. 1988. Pacific Oyster Culture in British Columbia. Canadian Bulletin of Fisheries and Aquatic Sciences. 218 pp.

Quayle, D.B. and G.F. Newkirk. 1989. Farming Bivalve Mollusks: Methods for Study and Development. Baton Rouge, Louisiana: World Aquaculture Society. 294 pp.

Ramsey, J.S. 1985. Sampling aquarium fishes imported by the United States. Journal of the Alabama Academy of Science 56(4):220-246.

Ranade, S.S. and H.G. Kewalramani. 1968. Studies on the rate of food passage in the intestine of *Labeo rohita* (Ham.), *Cirrhina mrigala* (Ham.), and *Catla catla* (Ham.). Proceedings of the World Symposium on Warm-Water Pond Fish Culture. FAO Fisheries Report No. 44, 5:109-122.

Rao, G.N. 1965. Use of seaweeds directly as human food. Indo-Pacific Fisheries Council. Regional Studies No. 2.

Rickards, W.L., W.R. Jones and J.E. Foster. 1978. Techniques for culturing the American eel. Proceedings of the World Mariculture Society 9:641-652.

Romaire, R.P. 1989. Overview of harvest technology used in commercial crawfish aquaculture. Journal of Shellfish Research 8(1):281-286.

Rosenberry, B. 1990. World Shrimp Farming. Aquaculture Digest 16(5): 24 pp.

Rosenberry, B. 1991. Directory, shrimp farming in the Western Hemisphere. Aqua-culture Digest. 48 pp.

Rouse, D.B., C.M. Austin and P.B. Medley. 1991. Progress toward profits, information on the Australian crayfish. Aquaculture Magazine 17(2):46-56.

Sandifer, P.A. (editor). 1991. Shrimp Culture in North America and the Caribbean. Baton Rouge, Louisiana: World Aquaculture Society. 235 pp.

Sarig, S. 1983. Fisheries and fish culture in Israel in 1982. Bamidgeh 35(4):95-108.

Schuur, A.M., W.S. Fisher, J.V. Olst, J. Carlberg, J.T. Hughes, R.A. Schleser and R. A. Ford. 1976. Hatchery methods for production of juvenile lobsters (*Homarus americanus*). University of California, La Jolla, California. Sea Grant Publication No. 48.

SEAFDEC. 1988. Biology and Culture of *Penaeus monodon*. Brackishwater Aquaculture Information System Aquaculture Department, Southeastern Asian Fisheries Development Center. 178 pp.

Sedgwick, S.D. 1976. Trout Farming Handbook. London: Seely, Service & Company. 163 pp.

Sedgwick, S.D. 1982. The Salmon Handbook. London: Andre Deutsch Limited. 242 pp.

Shang, Y.C. and W.J. Baldwin. 1980. Economic aspects of pond culture of topminnows (Family Poecilidae) in Hawaii as an alternative baitfish for skipjack tuna. Proceedings of the World Mariculture Society 11:592-595.

Shaw, S.A. and J.F. Muir. 1987. Salmon: Economics and Marketing. London and Sydney: Timber Press, Portland, Oregon. 270 pp.

Shehadeh, Z.H. and K.S. Norris. 1972. The grey mullet (*Mugil cephalus* L.): induced breeding and larval rearing research 1970-1972. Oceanic Institute. Waimanalo, Hawaii, National Sea Grant Program. Report No. 01-72-76-1.

Shelton, W.L. and G.L. Jensen. 1990. Control of unwanted reproduction of tilapia and carps. pp. 7-17. In Proceedings Auburn Symposium of Fisheries and Aquaculture. Auburn University, Alabama. 365 pp.

Shigueno, K. 1975. Shrimp Culture in Japan. Tokyo-Japan: Association for International Technical Promotion. 153 pp.

Shigueno, K. 1978. Problems in Prawn Culture. New Delhi: Amerind Publishing Company, Put. Ltd.

Shumway, S.E. (editor). 1991. Scallops: Biology, Ecology and Aquaculture. Amsterdam-Oxford- New York-Tokyo: Elsevier Science Publishing Company Inc. 1,095 pp.

Sigler, W.F. 1958. The ecology and use of carp in Utah. Utah State University, Utah Agricultural Experiment Station. Bulletin 405.

Skurdal, J., K. Westman and P.I. Bergan (editors). 1989. Crayfish in Europe. Report from the Workshop on Crayfish Culture 16 November 1987 Trondheim, Norway. 198 pp.

Smith, T.I.J. and E.K. Dingley. 1984. Review and biology of Atlantic, *Acipenser oxyrhynchus,* and shortnose sturgeon, *A. brevirostrum.* Journal of the World Mariculture Society 15:210-218.

Smitherman, R.O. and N.M. Stone. 1982. Breeding and culture of the red-gold color phase of tilapia. Journal of the World Mariculture Society 13:210-220.

Spitzy, R. 1972. Crayfish in Austria, history and actual situation. In International Symposium on Freshwater Crayfish, Hinterthal, Austria 1:10-14.

Stickney, R.R. 1986. Tilapia tolerance of saline waters: a review. Progressive Fish-Culturist 48(3):161-167.

Stone, N. 1994. Bighead carp. Aquaculture Magazine 20(4):12-26.

Suzuki, R. 1979. The culture of common carp in Japan. pp. 161-166. In Advances in Aquaculture. FAO Technical Conference on Aquaculture, Kyoto, Japan. 653 pp.

Svenson, G. 1988. Harvesting abalone on land. Aquaculture Magazine 14(1):31-33.

Swann. C. 1989. An introduction to scallop farming. Kevgor Aquasystems P.O. Box 48851-595 Burrard Street, Vancouver, B.C. V7X1A8, Canada. 56 pp.

Swingle, H.A. 1965. Growth rates of paddlefish receiving supplemental feeding in fertilized ponds. Progressive Fish-Culturist 27(4):220.

Swingle, H.S. 1949. Some recent developments in pond management. Transactions North American Wildlife Annual Conference. Wildlife Management Institute 14:295 -312.

Swingle, H.S. 1950. Relationships and dynamics of balanced and unbalanced fish populations. Alabama Polytechnic Institute, Alabama Agricultural Experiment Station. Bulletin No. 274.

Swingle, H.S. 1956. Appraisal of methods of fish population study- Part IV determination of balance in farm fish ponds. Transactions North American Wildlife Annual Conference. Wildlife Management Institute 21:299-322.

Swingle, H.S. and E.V. Smith. 1950. Factors affecting the reproduction of bluegill bream and largemouth black bass in ponds. Alabama Polytechnic Institute, Alabama Agricultural Experiment Station. Circular No. 87.

Szumiec, J. 1979. Some experiments on intensive farming of common carp in Poland. pp. 157-161. In Advances in Aquaculture. FAO Technical Conference on Aquaculture, Kyoto, Japan. 653 pp.

Taki, Y., J.H. Primavera and J.A. Llobrera (editors). 1985. Proceedings of the First International Conference on the Culture of Penaeid Prawns/Shrimps. Aquaculture Department, Southeast Asian Fisheries Development Center, Iloilo, Philippines. 197 pp.

Tal, S. and I. Ziv. 1978. Culture of exotic fishes in Israel. In Symposium on Culture of Exotic Fishes, Auburn, Alabama. Fish Culture Section, American Fisheries Society 1978:1-9.

Tamadachi, M. 1990. The Cult of Koi. Neptune City, New Jersey: T.F.H. Publications Inc. 288 pp.

Tang, Y.A. 1964. Induced spawning of striped mullet by hormone injection. Gyoruigaku Zasshi 12: 23-30.

Tatum, W.M. and R.F. Helton, Jr. 1977. Preliminary results of experiments on the feasibility of producing bull minnows (Fundulus grandis) for the live bait industry. Proceedings of the World Mariculture Society 8:49-54.

Tave, D. and C.S. Tucker. (editors). 1993. Recent Developments in Catfish Aquaculture. New York-London: The Haworth Press Inc. 389 pp.

Tucker, C.S. (editor). 1985. Channel Catfish Culture. Amsterdam-Oxford-New York-Tokyo: Elsevier Science Publishing Company Inc. 657 pp.

Tucker, C.S. and E.H. Robinson. 1990. Channel Catfish Farming Handbook. New York: An Avi Book published by Van Nostrand Reinhold. 454 pp.

Tuten, J.S. and J.W. Avault, Jr. 1981. Growing red swamp crayfish (Procambarus clarkii) and several North American fish species together. Progressive Fish-Culturist 43:97-99.

Unestam, T. 1972. Significance of diseases on freshwater crayfish. In International Symposium on Freshwater Crayfish, Hinterthal, Austria 1:135-150.

Usui, A. 1974. Eel culture. Surrey, England: Fishing News (Books) Ltd. 186 pp.

156

Van Olst, J.C. and J.M. Carlberg. 1990. Commercial culture of hybrid striped bass: status and potential. Aquaculture Magazine 16(1):49-57.

Vanstone, W.E., L.B. Tiro, Jr., A.C. Villaluz, D.C. Ramsingh, S. Kumagai, P.J. Dulduco, M.M.L. Barnes and C.E. Duenas. 1977. Induced spawning, artificial fertilization of eggs and larval rearing of the milkfish *Chanos chanos* (Forskal) in the Philippines. Southeast Asian Fisheries Development Center. Technical Report No. 3.

Villalobos, A. 1983. Crayfishes of Mexico. Published by the Smithsonian Institute Libraries, and the National Science Foundation, Washington, D.C. by Amerind Publishing Company Pvt. Ltd., New Delhi. 276 pp.

Villalon, J.R. 1991. Practical manual for semi-intensive commercial production of marine shrimp. Texas A & M Sea Grant Office. 104 pp.

Waddy, S.L. 1989. Farming the homarid lobsters: state of the art. World Aquaculture 19(4):63-71.

Weidner, D. and B. Rosenberry. 1992. World shrimp farming. pp. 1-21. In Proceedings of the Special Session on Shrimp Farming. Baton Rouge, Louisiana: World Aquaculture Society. 301 pp.

Willers, B. 1991. Trout Biology. New York: Lyons & Burford Publishers. 273 pp.

Woynarovich, E. 1986. Propagacao artificial e criacao de alevinos. Tambaqui e Pirapitinga. Programa Nacional de Irrigacao. Companhia de Desenvolvimento do vale do Sao Francisco. 68 pp.

Wyban, J.A. and J.N. Sweeney. 1991. The Oceanic Institute Shrimp Manual. Intensive shrimp production technology. Oceanic Institute Makapuu Point P.O. Box 25280 Honolulu, Hawaii, USA 956825.

Yap. W.G., A.L. Young, C.E.F. Orano and M.T. de Castro. 1979. Manual of mussel farming. Southeast Asian Fisheries Development Center, Tigbauan Iloilo, Philippines. Aquaculture Extension Manual No. 6

Zhang F. 1984. Mussel culture in China. pp. 1-10. In Recent Innovations in Cultivation of Pacific Mollusks. The Netherlands: Elsevier Science Publishing Company Inc. 404 pp.

CHAPTER 4
SOCIAL AND LEGAL CONSIDERATIONS

The choice of a site for aquaculture may involve social and legal matters, particularly if public waters are involved. A permit(s) to begin commercial aquaculture may be required. Laws regulate the species grown, water used and disposed, chemicals applied to culture systems, and the way in which a culture species is grown, harvested, processed, and marketed. International regulations must be considered when foreign countries are involved. In this chapter we address these issues.

SOCIO-CULTURAL CONSIDERATIONS

Aquaculture development has an effect on socio-cultural aspects of community life in both developed and developing nations. Some regions of the world such as Asia have a history of aquaculture development. Other regions, such as Africa and Latin America, do not. Countries and regions of the world with a heritage of aquaculture are more apt to accept aquaculture development.

Socio-cultural changes resulting from aquaculture development take place among several classes of people. Pollnac (1991) reviewed this subject with emphasis on the developing world. The working class of people that becomes involved in commercial aquaculture will have to adjust to a new way of life. Adoption of a new way to earn a living and a change in one's life style can have a profound impact on family life. A second class of people includes the investor or the entrepreneur. This may involve an individual, a cooperative, or companies of various sizes. Some do well financially; others may fail. A third class of people includes those who make up the business community that provides the goods and services to commercial aquaculture. The impact here is almost always beneficial. Another class of people includes the bystanders who have no involvement in aquaculture but who nevertheless are affected. These are usually people who are concerned with the use of natural resources and with the impact of aquaculture on the environment. Finally, aquaculture development may have an effect on the local, regional, or even national government. Below are some examples of aquaculture development on socio-cultural change, both negative and positive.

On the Negative Side

To most aquaculturists a series of raceways, a checkerboard grid of ponds, or neat rows of floating net-pens are a beautiful sight. However, some citizens, environmental groups, commercial fishers, and governmental agencies may view aquaculture differently. They are apt to point out perceived market competition, depletion of potable water supplies, pollution of the environment, despoiling of aesthetics, noise, bad smells, and interference with recreation and navigation.

Commercial fishers sometimes develop antagonism toward some forms of aquaculture. Stickney (1988), who examined problems emerging from net-pen culture of salmon (*Oncorhynchus* spp.), noted that some commercial fishers view net-pen aquaculture as a threat to their very existence. In 1967 the Louisiana Agricultural Experiment Station began a 5-year project on shrimp (*Penaeus setiferus*) farming near the Gulf of Mexico. Ponds were stocked with wild postlarval shrimp that came across weirs at high tide. The project was discontinued after 5 years because of the perceived loss of young shrimp from natural waters. Wild-caught channel catfish (*Ictalurus punctatus*) have been an important fishery in Louisiana and Florida, but this capture fishery has been replaced largely by farm-grown catfish.

Aquaculture can and does compete with communities and agriculture for potable water. In Taiwan the shrimp *Penaeus monodon* has been grown. Water from the sea is pumped into shore-based ponds. Fresh water, pumped from the ground, dilutes sea water to about 20 ppt salinity. Because of the lavish use of fresh water, land subsidence has been a serious problem in some communities. In certain Mississippi counties catfish farming has resulted in a serious drop of the water table.

Pollution from aquaculture can be a serious problem. Attention has been particularly focused on net-pen culture of salmon. The Seattle Post-Intelligence Newspaper (March 1989) had this to say: "A typical net-pen fish farming operation on Puget Sound produces pollutants equivalent to un-treated sewage from approximately 10,000 persons." The pollution comes from feces, urine, and uneaten feed. The newspaper report further stated that "100 fish farms would produce 55 mt (61 tons) of oxygen demanding wastes per day." The paper did not give the size of the average farm, and some fish farmers may take issue with the alleged amount of pollution. Nevertheless, what the public perceives often affects laws enacted and regulations.

Stickney (1994) listed issues that have been raised for net-pen culture in Puget Sound. Feces and waste feed settle to the bottom and develop sterile zones. Excess nutrients produced from net-pen culture create noxious algae blooms. Antibiotics in feed can lead to development of resistant strains of bacteria. Culture species can transfer diseases to native species and to humans. Culture species that escape can affect wild salmon runs. Net-pens interfere with navigation and recreation. Net-pen operations cause noxious odors and noises.

Sometimes pollution occurs inland. A number of retirees live in the Hagerman Valley of Idaho. This area, next to the Snake River, is in the heart of trout farming. Tremendous quantities of water flush fish wastes from raceways into the Snake River. Residents of Hagerman are concerned about the pollution.

Pollution of the environment can occur in other ways. An aquaculture operation in public waters can become an eyesore and cause loud noises and offensive smells, especially if processing is involved. This is particularly disturbing to residents of shoreline homes and vacation retreats. Recreation and navigation usually supersede aquaculture usage. Moreover, an upland property owner's riparian right of access to and from the property by water is protected by common law. In certain developing countries and even developed countries, however, priorities are rearranged. Aquaculture, a source of animal protein and foreign exchange, receives a higher priority than recreation and other activities. Pollution may receive more tolerance.

On the Positive Side

Aquaculture provides many benefits and opportunities. A partial list includes jobs, enhancement of ancillary businesses, overall economic enhancement, expansion of fishery markets, availability of quality products for consumers, and in some instances improved markets for commercial fisheries.

Aquaculture operations employ a varying number of people. In Louisiana, for each 4,000 ha (10,000 ac) of ponds devoted to crawfish farming approximately 420 jobs are created at the producer and processor level combined. Many ancillary businesses flourish, such as bait manufacturing and harvesting equipment. The farm-gate value of pond-grown crawfish in 1993 was $27.06 million; the value added was about $25 million, making this industry worth more than $50 million.

Sometimes aquaculture has a profound economic benefit for a community or region. In 1973, crawfish (*Procambarus clarkii*) were introduced from Louisiana into Seville, Spain. The native crawfish had been devastated by a fungal disease. This left a biological niche and a market niche open. At that time some of the local communities had depressed economies. Within 10 years, more than 32,000 ha (80,000 ac) were growing crawfish near Seville, and the economy improved significantly.

Another example is Bacolod on Negros Occidental in the Philippines. For years this community virtually depended on a single crop, sugarcane. When market prices became depressed, the economy plummeted, and by 1985 Negros Occidental was one of the most depressed provinces in the Philippines.

Shrimp (*Penaeus monodon*) farming developed, and the entire community benefited. The Negros economy had a 40% increase in beer sales, a 30% increase in soft drink consumption, a 20% rise in the volume of cargo transported, and a 15% increase in passenger traffic.

Aquaculture provides consumers with quality products. Culture species can be grown to a preferred market size, processed while in robust condition, and packaged to maintain wholesomeness. With the increasing demand for fishery products worldwide and the plateauing of the ocean harvest, aquaculture can help make up the shortfall. Domestic aquaculture in the United States provided 7% of all fishery products consumed in the United States in 1988, and this percentage is increasing.

Aquaculture can expand existing fishery markets, sometimes benefiting capture fisheries. In Louisiana, trappers of wild crawfish could not establish stable markets in other states or countries, because the wild crop is unpredictable. One year wild crawfish are plentiful; the next year they may not be. Production from pond-grown crawfish is more predictable year after year, and so international markets could be established. In 1988, six processing plants began to cater exclusively to European markets. Pond crawfish usually are available from November through May, whereas wild-caught crawfish typically enter the market after this, with some overlap in time.

Salmon from captive fisheries and culture fisheries on the West Coast of the United States can complement one another in the marketplace. Stickney (1988) noted that the commercial harvest of Pacific salmon in Alaska begins in summer, with a peak in July. Going down the coastline of Alaska, through British Columbia and into Washington and Oregon, the salmon run begins increasingly later in the year. By late fall it is mostly complete. Salmon farmers, however, usually do not market their product during natural spawning runs. Instead they market during winter when wild salmon are not available. Thus, between wild-caught and net-pen salmon the product is available for a longer time. A stronger market can be established, benefiting both commercial fishers and farmers.

Stock enhancement from aquaculture benefits commercial fishers as well as sport fisheries. In Texas shrimp and finfish have been spawned and young released into natural waters. Japan and Taiwan have had stock enhancement programs.

Fishery products play a major role in the trade deficit of the United States. This country has imported up to 70% of its fish consumed. In 1978, fishery products amounted to almost 10% of the national trade deficit and 28% of the deficit for non-petroleum products (Avault 1985). Much of this deficit was caused by importation of shrimp. In 1981, the value of edible fish imported was more than $3 billion. In 1993, imported shrimp alone amounted to 272 million kg (601 million lb) valued at $2.2 billion (Harvey 1994). Though these figures are constantly changing, the trend is clear; aquaculture can play and is playing a major role in offsetting the United States' trade deficit while providing wholesome food to consumers.

LEGAL CONSIDERATIONS

Historically, wildlife and fisheries have been regulated and monitored by the U.S. Fish and Wildlife Service at the federal level and by departments of wildlife and fisheries at the state level. At both levels laws and regulations have focused on wild populations of game and fish. As aquaculture developed in the United States, many of these laws were at odds with it. The cottage industry of aquaculture was put under the jurisdiction of federal and state agencies that historically regulated wild populations. In 1976, for example, the National Aquaculture Act recognized aquaculture as an emerging industry, but the Act placed the jurisdiction jointly with the U.S. Fish and Wildlife Service and the U.S. Department of Commerce. The U.S. Department of Agriculture was designated in a supporting role. Eventually the U.S. Department of Agriculture was designated lead agency for aquaculture, whereas at the state level the transition to state agriculture departments has been slower.

Williams et al. (1975) documented legal aspects of channel catfish and crawfish farming in Louisiana. Legal aspects of aquaculture also were reviewed for South Carolina (DeVoe and Whetstone 1987), California (Bowden 1981), Great Britain (Howarth 1990), and Canada (Wildsmith 1982; Anonymous 1990). In the United States, the Joint Subcommittee on Aquaculture (1992) promulgated federal regulations for drugs, biologicals, and chemicals used in aquaculture. The National Research Council of the National Academy of Sciences assessed marine aquaculture with emphasis on government policy (NRC 1992). Rubino and Wilson (1993) reviewed government regulations.

In the rest of this chapter, we take you step-by-step through the legal process of commercial aquaculture. You should keep in mind that regulations are constantly changing, and new ones are being added. Moreover, federal and state agencies administering regulations also change. For example, the Federal Wetlands Law has involved three different federal agencies -- each with its own manual on what constitutes wetlands. Of late, however, there has been a consolidation of these agencies to form a common policy on wetlands. No two state agencies have identical regulations regarding aquaculture. A good example is the way states view exotic species for commercial aquaculture.

Permits

A permit has been required for fish farming in many states. To raise domesticated fish for commercial markets in Louisiana, a farmer had to apply to the Louisiana Department of Wildlife and Fisheries. The fee was formerly $10 (Williams et al. 1975). In 1989 the fee was $15, but channel catfish and crawfish are now exempt.

If public waters are involved, the permit process can be elaborate and take months, even years, to complete and will involve numerous federal, state, and local agencies. There is no guarantee that the appropriate permits will be given. DeVoe and Whetstone (1987) developed a guide with flow charts for South Carolina to aid beginning aquaculturists with the permit process.

What is Fish Farming

Some states, such as Louisiana, legally define "fish farming." Louisiana law has defined "fish" as "all fish, shellfish, crustaceans, frogs, turtles and other aquaculture organisms that have a sport or economic value." "Agriculture" is defined including "the cultivating, growing, harvesting and/or marketing of domesticated fish." Fish farming is legally defined as "farming" or "agriculture," thus allowing for agricultural benefits, such as certain agricultural operational loans and disaster benefits.

Location of Aquaculture Facility

An aquaculture operation developed on privately owned land should meet with few legal constraints. There are some exceptions. In Louisiana, ponds constructed within the basin of a continuously flowing river, bayou, or other stream; or ponds that use lands of natural streams or natural lake beds have been subject to all laws and regulations that apply to the taking of fish in public waters. Such ponds fall outside the definition of privately owned waters, and fish raised in such ponds are not domesticated fish.

Some states, such as South Carolina, have zoned all land, and the permitting process varies from zone to zone. The state is zoned into the "critical areas" and "non-critical areas." The critical areas, as defined under the South Carolina Management Act of 1977, include the coastal waters, tidelands, beaches, and primary oceanfront sand dunes seaward of the critical area boundary line as determined by the South Carolina Coastal Council (DeVoe and Whetstone 1987). Non-critical areas of the state extend from the critical area boundary line inland.

Some privately owned land is affected by two federal laws. The Coastal Zone Management Act of 1972 was an attempt at a federal protection plan. It stated that "there is a national interest in the effective management, beneficial use, protection, and development of the coastal zone." It further stated that it is a national policy to "preserve, protect, develop, and where possible to restore or enhance the resources of the nation's coastal zone for this and succeeding generations." The Act, monitored by the Department of Commerce, encourages states to develop their own coastal zone management plans. Grants have been made available. The Federal Wetlands Law, under the Clean Water Act, is similar to the Coastal Zone Management Act. It protects and encourages enhancement of "wetlands." Wetlands refer to lowlands that are covered with shallow and sometimes temporary or intermittent waters. Wetlands need not be inundated at all times. Wetlands are designated according to: (1) type of soil, (2) type of vegetation present, and (3) the hydrology of the area. Such lands include marshes, swamps, bogs, wet meadows, potholes, sloughs, and flood-plain lands. Most of the nation's wetlands are located in estuaries, but lands much further inland have been designated wetlands.

Aquaculturists who wish to develop an aquaculture operation within officially designated wetlands or coastal zone will have to provide an environmental impact statement and seek a permit(s) from appropriate governmental agencies. Granting of a permit is not an automatic procedure. One entrepreneur in Louisiana was allowed to clear brush and trees from a designated wetland's area for construction of crawfish ponds. However, the permit stipulated that trees had to be replanted. Cypress (*Taxodium distichum*) trees were planted in the crawfish ponds.

Permits to use public lands and waters for aquaculture are far more difficult to obtain than permits to use private lands. In Louisiana permits for cage culture have been granted, but only on a trial basis. Initially a limit of 10 permits was authorized by the Louisiana Department of Wildlife and Fisheries. In Arkansas cage culture has been allowed with a permit. A portion of the harvest had to be released into the public waters that supported the cages. In Florida a shrimp farming company obtained a permit to use a public bay, but it took years of effort and there were many stipulations. The public could not be kept out, and navigation could not be impeded. Bottom culture of oysters requires a permit, but there are no major legal constraints, because this culture is historically old and accepted. Moreover, bottom culture is out of sight and does not hinder recreation or navigation. DeVoe and Mount (1989) reviewed leasing systems for 10 states. Pen culture of salmon in public waters involves numerous permits, and there are many stipulations if the permit is granted. The Coast Guard and Army Corps of Engineers, among other agencies, must be involved in the permit process because the culture facility may be a navigation hazard (Hampson 1975).

An abalone (*Haliotis* spp.) farming company in California needed 4 years to obtain all of the necessary permits (Staton 1989). Permits were required from numerous local agencies as well as from state and federal agencies. Moreover, several environmental groups, including the Sierra Club and

Audubon Society, became "informal regulators." Some of the regulators included county and city planning commissions, city councils, county boards of supervisors, California Coastal Commission, State Lands Commission, water quality control boards, fire and forestry departments, U.S. Fish and Wildlife Service, U.S. Army Corps of Engineers, and others (California Aquatic Farming April 1989).

Water Supply

In Chapter 6, various sources of water available for aquaculture are discussed. Some sources require a permit. If one uses groundwater on private property, there are usually no legal constraints. However in certain states, especially western states where water is typically scarce, there are restrictions. In Louisiana if a well produces in excess of 189,250 liters (50,000 gal) in any one day, it must be registered with the state Department of Public Works. In Louisiana, water from public streams may be pumped into land-based ponds if the water is screened to prevent destruction of fish. In Idaho a permit process is required to use spring water for trout farming in raceways. Once a permit is issued, the trout farmer must "prove up." That is, trout must be grown. The farmer cannot just enjoy the aesthetics of the water. In North Carolina it has been possible to own a stream, part of which is diverted to trout raceways.

Culture Species

In choosing a culture species to grow, there are various restrictions imposed by law. In some states, such as Louisiana, game or sport fish cannot be grown and sold as food. In this state game fish include largemouth bass (*Micropterus salmoides*), crappie (*Pomoxis* spp.), and others. However, a person may charge a fee for fishing game fish in a privately owned pond.

There are laws prohibiting the possession, sale, or transportation of certain fish species. The Lacey Act of 1900 gives the Department of Interior authority over any species that is taken illegally in any state or foreign nation and moved in interstate or foreign commerce. The Lacey Act and Lacey Act amendments of 1981 (Title 16, U.S.C. 3371) were enacted to protect indigenous species and prevent trade in endangered or threatened wildlife. The Black Bass Act of 1926 is similar to the Lacey Act. The question then is what is an illegally taken fish? Different states have different interpretations. In Georgia all fish have been considered "wildlife" and therefore the property of the state. A state violation is a misdemeanor, but if state lines are crossed the offense becomes a felony.

The use of exotic species can create many legal problems. An exotic species might be defined as not being native to the area. Thus the Atlantic salmon (*Salmo salar*), which is being farmed in British Columbia, is an exotic there. The Japanese oyster (*Crassostrea gigas*) is cultured in Europe and on the West Coast of North America. The grass carp (*Ctenopharyngodon idella*) is legally sold in Arkansas according to state law. In Louisiana it is illegal to stock, although sterile, triploid grass carp can be used if certified by the state. In Alabama and Arkansas, the bighead carp (*Aristichthys nobilis*) is grown together with channel catfish. In many states this carp is illegal to grow. In some states tilapia can be grown in ponds. In Louisiana, a permit is needed and tilapia must be grown in indoor recirculating systems. In some instances, a culture species such as the prawn (*Macrobrachium rosenbergii*) may be exotic, but it is perceived as so highly desirable that regulations are sometimes relaxed and permits are more easily obtained. The tropical or ornamental fish industry depends largely on exotic species, most of which are imported from other countries. Perhaps the culture species most highly regulated are those designated endangered or near extinction. Such species, including certain species of turtles, are protected by the Endangered Species Preservation Act.

Federal regulations have been developed to curtail introduction of exotic species. The 1990 the Aquatic Nuisance Prevention and Control Act (Public Law 101-646) was enacted, mainly because of zebra mussel introductions. Guidelines have been developed for introduction of exotic species by the International Council for the Exploration of the Seas (ICES), the American Fisheries Society, and the North Atlantic Salmon Conservation Organization (Rubino and Wilson 1993). The ICES guidelines are generally accepted. The procedure is as follows: (1) conduct comprehensive disease study in native habitat, (2) transfer species to closed system in recipient area, (3) maintain and study population in closed system, (4) develop brood stock in closed system, (5) grow isolated F_1 individuals and destroy original brood stock, and (6) introduce small lots to natural water and continue disease study.

There may be a legal limitation on the size of fish grown and sold. In Louisiana, for example, channel catfish could not be harvested (trapped) and sold unless they were a minimum of about 28 cm (11 in) long. At one time, fingerling producers in Louisiana broke the law whenever they harvested undersized fish and sold them to other farmers for grow-out. The law had wild populations of channel catfish in mind, but it affected fingerling producers of channel catfish. The rationale of the law was that channel catfish should be given an opportunity to reproduce at least once in nature, before being trapped, to perpetuate the species.

Sometimes a culture species may be native to a state, region, or country but it does not spawn readily in captivity. Young to stock grow-out ponds are captured from the wild. Regulations affect this capture. An example was the capture of pompano (*Trachinotus carolinus*) fingerlings in the Gulf of Mexico. For a while, some states such as Florida and Louisiana regulated beach seining of fingerling pompano for use in private ponds. The practice of capturing milkfish (*Chanos chanos*) fry in ocean bays in the Philippines and Indonesia is ancient. Elvers (*Anguilla* spp.) are caught at the mouths of rivers in Japan and elsewhere. Eel culture has a long tradition. Louisiana permits the removal of wild alligator (*Alligator mississipiensis*) eggs for aquaculture, but part of the juveniles produced must be released back into the wild. The process is monitored and regulated by the Louisiana Department of Wildlife and Fisheries. Shrimp hatcheries in many countries use wild-caught gravid females to produce seed in hatcheries. Hybrid striped bass culture relies on wild-caught brood stock of striped bass (*Morone saxatilis*) and white bass (*M. chrysops*). Whenever wild species are used in commercial aquaculture, there will be laws and regulations at the state and federal level.

Ownership and Theft

Some state laws have declared that all fish are owned by the state. In Louisiana an opinion by the Attorney General in 1940 stated that the state owns all fish, even those in private lakes. More recently, a trout farmer noted in 1989 that all fish were viewed as wildlife in Georgia, and that all wildlife is owned by the state. This leaves the fish farmer in a difficult position. Does he or she own the fish in ponds or not? What happens if someone takes fish without the farmer's permission? What if fish escape after a flood or storm into public waters -- can they be recovered? It may be necessary to distinguish genetically between domesticated fish and wild fish.

The problem of ownership is gradually being resolved through legislation as aquaculture gains more visibility. This problem is not unique to the United States. For example, when crawfish were first introduced into private farms in southern Spain, landowners could not keep the public from harvesting crawfish on private property. Some landowners did not fight this "right" of the public, but instead bought the crawfish and set up processing plants.

Certification of Fish and Eggs

Certain fish and eggs must be certified free of specific disease-causing organisms before they can be moved (sold). Viral diseases of trout are particularly being targeted for this special certification. The U.S. Fish and Wildlife Service has handled certification in the United States, but the USFWS has not had a mandate nor appropriate funding to handle this certification.

Government regulations involve certification of fish and fish eggs. The Lacey Act (Title 50 Code of Federal Regulations) prohibits importation of injurious wildlife species into the United States. As an example, the Lacey Act requires that salmonid eggs and fish be certified free of the protozoan parasite *Myxosoma cerebralis* and the virus causing viral hemorrhagic septicemia (Rubino and Wilson 1993). The federal Joint Subcommittee on Aquaculture developed a task force to identify methods for preventing introductions of foreign and domestic pathogens. States have various regulations. Washington and Alaska have certification and quarantine requirements for salmon eggs. Hawaii uses the ICES protocol to prevent introductions of IHHN and other viral pathogens with non-native shrimp. Varying regulations between states and the lack of a standard national policy make it difficult for the fish farmer. The Joint Subcommittee on Aquaculture has taken the lead role for developing uniform standards.

Use of Chemical Compounds and Drugs

Chemical compounds and drugs have been used in aquaculture to control fish diseases, predators and pests, and weeds. Two federal agencies regulate chemicals and drugs, the Food and Drug Administration (FDA) and the Environmental Protection Agency (EPA). The FDA regulates those chemicals and drugs that may be used on or in food for human consumption because of the possible harmful effect caused by residues in flesh. The EPA has promulgated regulations on use of chemicals that may be harmful to the environment.

Regulatory control includes all facets of development, distribution, and use. Control applies to the manufacturing process, bulk shipment, formulation, retail packaging, labeling, interstate shipment, applicators, application rates, use patterns, and the species on which the compound can be legally applied (Schnick et al. 1989). Permits are required by the FDA if aquaculturists produce their own medicated feeds using certain therapeutants. They must provide quality assurance data to prove that the product produced is consistent with permitted levels.

Before a candidate therapeutant can be registered for use in aquaculture, it must be studied according to regulations established by the FDA (U.S. Congress 1972; Schnick 1988). A major problem in the registration of a compound is the high cost. Companies need a worldwide market of $60 million annually per drug for each species to make a profit (Rubino and Wilson 1993). The total demand for chemicals and drugs in the United States is only $10 million annually (Schnick 1992). Few private companies are willing to go to the expense of conducting research needed to register a compound because only a relatively small quantity will be sold. Most companies would rather register compounds for agriculture, such as cotton farming, because of the large volume required. In the United States, the U.S. Department of Interior has charged the National Fisheries Research Center, LaCrosse, Wisconsin, with the primary responsibility for research to register fishery compounds. The U.S. Department of Agriculture also is involved in registration efforts through the Interregional Research Project Number 4, also known as the IR-4 project. State cooperative extension services also participate in the effort. Schnick et al. (1992) presented a list of chemicals needed for finfish culture, and Williams and Lightner (1988) did likewise for shrimp culture.

Predator and Pest Control

Predator and pest control, discussed in Chapter 11, may involve a number of species ranging from aquatic birds to fur animals. The Migratory Bird Conservation Act of 1929 protects certain bird species. If birds are eating fish in private ponds, this does not give the farmer authority to kill those birds. A permit must be obtained, and even then restrictions must be followed. Fur animals can be harvested (trapped) during the regular trapping season. Regulations have been developed in various states. During the off-season, a special permit is required from the State Department of Wildlife and Fisheries.

Draining Ponds and Other Culture Systems

Drainage and waste disposal deserve serious consideration by the pros-pective fish farmer. Feces and other wastes from culture species and uneaten feed deteriorate water quality, and the draining of polluting substances into natural streams is prohibited. Each state has an agency that regulates discharges into navigable streams. In Louisiana, it is the Department of Environmental Quality. At the federal level, it is the EPA.

The National Pollutant Discharge Elimination System (NPDES) is that part of federal law (Clean Water Act of 1977) which regulates discharges into navigable waters. Some aquaculture operations, such as catfish and crawfish, have been exempt if discharges of effluents from either a closed pond or raceway facility occur less frequently than 30 days each year. However, if the regional administrator of EPA or the state director decides otherwise, a NPDES permit is required.

A permit may be required by the EPA or delegated state agency prior to discharge of effluents. Facilities for coldwater species, such as salmon and trout, require permits if there is discharge at least 30 days per year. These facilities, however, are exempt if they produce less than 9,070 kg (20,000 lb) of fish per year and feed used is less than 2,268 kg (5,000 lb) during the calendar months of maximum feeding (Rubino and Wilson 1993). Facilities for warmwater species, such as channel catfish and minnows, require permits if there is discharge at least 30 days per year. These facilities, however, are exempt if they produce less than 45,351 kg (100,000 million lb) of fish per year, and if pond facilities discharge only during periods of excess runoff.

Regulations change, and it is best that an aquaculture operation develops a pollution control strategy from the start. Not all aquaculture operations, however, need be concerned with effluents. Bottom culture of oysters involves no manufactured feeds nor drainage. Pen-culture of salmon involves no effluents *per se*, but waters are polluted from the fish wastes and uneaten feed. As aquaculture continues to expand, aquaculturists must deal with pollution control from their facilities.

Harvesting

Some states may have harvesting regulations. In Louisiana, a fish farmer may harvest as many domesticated fish as wanted, at any time, and by any type of seine or tackle, as long as the method harvests the fish alive. Furthermore, fish farmers are allowed to transport all harvesting equipment, except electric shocking devices, on public roads and highways, thus exempting them from laws making possession of certain equipment unlawful. Any seines, tackle, or other devices used to harvest fish from fish ponds, if used in public waters, must meet legal requirements regarding harvesting equipment applicable to fishing in public waters.

In South Carolina, a shellfish harvesting permit is required from the state for gathering shellfish on state-owned lands. A harvesting equipment permit is required when using dredges, hydraulic escalators, patent tongs, or any other mechanically operated devices for taking shellfish from any bottoms.

The harvesting of oysters and other mollusks is very closely regulated because waters may become polluted, thus posing a human health problem. Public health control of mollusks became a national concern in the United States in the late 19th and early 20th century when illness was noted from eating raw oysters, clams, and other mollusks. This illness was noted also in other parts of the world, especially Europe. In 1925, the U.S. Surgeon General organized a conference to develop guidelines for sanitation control of the oyster industry. Participating were state and municipal health authorities, state conservation commissions, the Bureau of Chemistry (now the Food and Drug Administration), the Bureau of Commercial Fisheries (now the National Marine Fisheries Service), and the shellfish industry. Resolutions were recommended for the sanitary control of the oyster industry (FDA 1986 a, b). The National Shellfish Sanitation Program (NSSP), which developed from the meeting in 1925, relied on each state to carry out a program for the sanitary control of the shellfish industry. A manual was developed that promulgated guidelines (regulations) in two parts: part I, sanitation of shellfish-growing areas, and part II, sanitation of the harvesting and processing of shellfish (FDA 1986 a, b).

Pollution of growing waters for oysters and other mollusks is widespread throughout much of the world. In Louisiana, for example, approximately one-half of the productive oyster-growing waters may be closed at certain times of the year (Broutman and Leonard 1988). Pollution from raw sewage contains extremely high counts of *Escherichia coli*, a fecal coliform bacterium. A standard method for reporting the indication of pollution in growing waters and in shellfish has been the determination of most probable numbers (MPN) of fecal coliforms (American Public Health Association 1976, 1985; Association of Official Analytical Chemists 1984). These are considered "indicators" of the possible presence of more serious bacterial pathogens such as *Salmonella* spp. and enteric viruses such as Hepatitis A and Norwalk virus (Kilgen et al. 1988). Processed raw oysters must meet the wholesale market criteria of total aerobic plate counts of 500,000 or fewer microorganisms per gram of oyster meat, and oyster meat guidelines of 230 MPN fecal coliforms/100 grams (Kilgen et al. 1988). In growing waters, fecal coliforms must not exceed 14 MPN/100 ml. Kilgen et al. (1988), however, reported that standard fecal coliform bacterial indicators do not necessarily correlate with the presence of human viruses in shellfish and growing waters, and the whole subject is being reviewed.

Processing

The FDA and state health administrations set standards to ensure that food is fit for human consumption and that the processing, manufacturing, and packaging of fishery products are carried out under sanitary conditions and in conformity with good manufacturing practices. Detailed standards cover not only requirements for seafood processing but also each element of the various processes used. There are also set standards for plant and grounds, equipment and utensils, sanitary conditions and controls, and the various flavoring methods.

Federal inspection of fishery processing plants had been on an *ad hoc* basis. Upon request, the National Marine Fisheries Service inspected processing plants. The expense has been borne by the plant. In 1993, the FDA announced its plans to have the first mandatory fish-safety program in the United States. The plan is called "hazard analysis of critical control points" (HACCP). In essence, HACCP requires processors to look at the way in which they work to determine where and how something could go wrong relative to safety of food and personnel. HACCP plans are developed by the processing plant with oversight from the FDA.

Commercial processors must comply with EPA regulations on waste discharges from processing plants. Municipal regulations also must be checked. For example, one fish processing plant in Baton Rouge, Louisiana, had to be relocated because it is unlawful to slaughter livestock within the city limits.

Marketing

A special license(s) for marketing aquaculture products may be required by certain states. In some instances, the Lacey Act may affect the moving of illegally taken fish across state lines. The transport of exotics and endangered species is especially subject to scrutiny. When marketing a culture species, the correct name must be used. Creative names cannot be used. In the United States, the American Fisheries Society promulgated approved nomenclature for mollusks, crustaceans, and finfish (Turgeon 1988; Williams 1989; Robins 1991).

Laws in Foreign Countries

Each country has laws that must be taken into account. Not all laws are written. Some are only "understood." Further, laws are constantly being changed and modified. An aquaculture company may make an entry into a particular country under one set of conditions only to have them changed. In one South American country, for example, a company developed a profitable business in aquaculture, only to learn that a major percentage of the profit had to remain in the country. In Indonesia, the government agency Bandan Urusan Logistik (BULOG) sets the price on all commodities imported or exported, including fish feed and other aquaculture supplies and products. Many countries are now turning their attention to the effect of aquaculture on the environment. In 1990 Taiwan began a policy of zero growth in aquaculture. Canada (British Columbia), Norway, and other salmon-producing countries are moving toward a strict permitting process, principally to protect the environment.

STUDY QUESTIONS

1. List as many negative aspects of aquaculture as you can.
2. List as many positive aspects of aquaculture as you can.
3. List the federal agencies involved with aquaculture and discuss the role of each.
4. What are the Coastal Zone Management Act of 1972, Federal Wetlands Law, Lacey Act of 1900, Migratory Bird Conservation Act of 1929, National Pollutant Discharge Elimination System, and the National Shellfish Sanitation Program?

REFERENCES

American Public Health Association. 1976. Compendium of methods for the microbiological examination of foods. APHA. Washington, D.C. 702 pp.

American Public Health Association. 1985. Recommended procedures for the examination of seawater and shellfish. 5th edition. APHA Washington, D.C. 144 pp.

Anonymous (editor). 1975. Northwest mariculture laws. Papers and Presentations from a Symposium held at the Law Center, University of Oregon, Eugene, June 7, 1974.

Anonymous. 1988. Fish Farming: B.G.'s new venture on the coast. Alaska Sea Grant Program. Aquaculture Note # 13.

Anonymous. 1990. Aquaculture Act and Regulations. Chapter 18 of the revised statutes, 1989. Printed and published by the Queens Printer, Halifax.

Association of Official Analytical Chemists. 1984. Bacteriological Analytical Manual. Division of Microbiology. U.S. Food and Drug Administration. AOAC. Arlington, VA.

Avault, J.W., Jr. 1974. The EPA's proposed regulations affect cage culture in heated effluents. The Commercial Fish Farmer and World Aquaculture News 1(1):14-15.

Avault, J.W., Jr. 1985. Crustaceans. In Proceedings Role of the United States Government in Aquaculture. Nonfederal Perspectives, 73rd Annual Meeting of the International Association of Fish and Wildlife Agencies.

Bowden, G. 1981. Coastal Aquaculture Law and Policy, a Case Study of California. Boulder, Colorado: Western Press. 241 pp.

Broutman, M.A. and D.L. Leonard. 1988. The quality of shellfish growing waters in the Gulf of Mexico. National Oceanic and Atmospheric Administration, Strategic Assessment Branch, Ocean Assessment Division, Office of Oceanography and Marine Assessments, National Ocean Service, Washington, D.C. 43 pp.

DeVoe, M.R. and J.M. Whetstone. 1987. An interim guide to aquaculture permitting in South Carolina. South Carolina Sea Grant Consortium, SC-SG-TR-84-2.

DeVoe, M.R. and A.S. Mount. 1989. An analysis of ten state aquaculture leasing systems: issues and strategies. Journal of Shellfish Research 8(1):233-239.

Food and Drug Administration. 1980. Food and Drug Administration Acts. Federal Food, Drug, and Cosmetic Act as amended January 1980. Public Health Service Act, Biological Products. Radiation Control for Health and Safety Act. Fair Packaging and Labeling Act. Superintendent of Documents, U.S. Government Printing Office, Washington, D.C. 20402. 169 pp.

Food and Drug Administration. 1984. All about FDA, an orientation handbook. U.S. Department of Health and Human Services, Public Health Service.

Food and Drug Administration. 1986a. National shellfish sanitation program manual of operations. Part I, sanitation of shellfish growing areas. U.S. Department of Health and Human Services, Public Health Service.

Food and Drug Administration. 1986b. National shellfish sanitation program manual of operations. Part II, sanitation of the harvesting and processing of shellfish. U.S. Department of Health and Human Services, Public Health Service.

Hampson, A.A. 1975. Setting up a mariculture business: legal considerations. pp. 11-14. In Northwest Mariculture Laws. Papers and Presentations from a Symposium held at the Law Center, University of Oregon, Eugene, June 7, 1974.

Harvey, D. 1994. Aquaculture situation and outlook. Commodity Economics Division, Economic Research Service, U.S. Department of Agriculture, March AQS-12.

Howarth, W. 1990. The Law of Aquaculture. Fishing News (Books), a Division of Blackwell Scientific Publications Ltd. 271 pp.

Joint Subcommittee on Aquaculture. 1992. Federal regulations of drugs, biologicals, and chemicals used in aquaculture production. Aquaculture Information Center, National Agricultural Library, U.S. Department of Agriculture. 123 pp.

Kilgen, M.B., M.T. Cole and C.R. Hackney. 1988. Shellfish sanitation studies in Louisiana. Journal of Shellfish Research 7(3):527-530.

National Research Council. 1992. Marine Aquaculture, Opportunities for Growth. Washington, D.C.: National Academy Press. 290 pp.

Patterson, K.W., J. Lindsey and A.L. Bertrand. 1974. The human dimension of coastal zone development. LSU Agricultural Center, Louisiana Agricultural Experiment Station. Bulletin No. 679.

Pollnac, R.B. 1991. The role of sociocultural factors in aquaculture development projects. pp. 165-191. In Status and Potential of Aquaculture in the Caribbean. Advances in World Aquaculture, Volume 5. Baton Rouge, Louisiana: World Aquaculture Society. 274 pp.

Reitze, A.W., Jr. 1974. Environmental Planning: Law of Land and Resources. North American International, P. O. Box 28278, Washington, D.C. 20005.

Robins, C.R. (chair) et al. 1991. Common and Scientific Names of Fishes from the United States and Canada. 5th edition. American Fisheries Society. Special Publication 20.

Rubino, M.C. 1992. Wetland regulations and aquaculture. Aquaculture Magazine 18(1): 41-47.

Rubino, M.C. and C.A. Wilson. 1993. Issues in aquaculture regulations. National Oceanic and Atmospheric Administration. U.S. Department of Agriculture. 71 pp.

Schnick, R.A. 1988. The impetus to register new therapeutants for aquaculture. Progressive Fish-Culturist 50:190-196.

Schnick, R. 1992. Potential solution to crisis in aqua chemicals. The Aquaculture News, March, pp. 16, 22.

Schnick, R.A., F.P. Meyer and L.G. Gray. 1989. A guide to approved chemicals in fish production and fishery resource management. University of Arkansas Cooperative Extension Service and U.S. Fish and Wildlife Service P.O. Box 391, Little Rock, Arkansas 72203.

Sindermann, C.S. 1986. Strategies for reducing risks from introductions of aquatic organisms: a marine perspective. Fisheries 11(2):10-15.

State of Louisiana. 1986. Food, Drug & Cosmetic Laws and Regulations. Department of Health and Human Resources. Office of Preventive and Public Health Services.

Staton, H. 1989. Property rights and regulations. Aquatic Farming, Official publication of the California Aquaculture Association, April 1989.

Stickney, R.R. 1988. Commercial fishing and net-pen salmon aquaculture: turning conceptual antagonism toward a common purpose. Fisheries 13(4):9-13.

Stickney, R.R. 1994. Principles of Aquaculture. New York, Chichester, Brisbane, Toronto, Singapore: John Wiley & Sons Inc. 502 pp.

Thompson, A. 1990. The danger of exotic species. World Aquaculture 21(3):25-32.

Turgeon, D.D. (chair) et al. 1988. Common and Scientific Names of Aquatic Invertebrates from the United States and Canada: Mollusks. American Fisheries Society. Special Publication 16.

U.S. Congress, 1972. Federal Food, Drug and Cosmetic Act as amended, August 1972. U.S. Government Printing Office, Washington, D.C.

Wildsmith, B.H. 1982. Aquaculture: the legal framework. Toronto, Canada: Emond-Montgomery Ltd. 313 pp.

Williams, A.B. (chair) et al. 1989. Common and Scientific Names of Aquatic Invertebrates from the United States and Canada: Decapod Crustaceans. American Fisheries Society. Special Publication 17.

Williams, E., F.S. Craig III and J.W. Avault, Jr. 1975. Some legal aspects of catfish and crawfish farming in Louisiana. A case study. LSU Agricultural Center, Louisiana Agricultural Experiment Station. Bulletin No. 689.

Williams, R.R. and D.V. Lightner. 1988. Regulatory status of therapeutics for penaeid shrimp culture in the United States. Journal of the World Aquaculure Society 19(4): 188-196.

CHAPTER 5
SITE SELECTION AND CULTURE SYSTEMS

Selection of a suitable site for your aquaculture operation is of paramount importance. You must consider a number of factors, such as legal restrictions, socio-cultural conditions, economic climate, logistical matters, and processing and marketing capabilities. There are factors that directly affect the culture species, such as biological requirements, climate and weather, pollution and contamination, and land and water needs.

You may grow a culture species under a variety of culture systems. Trout adapt well to raceway culture, salmon to floating net-pens, carp to ponds, and mollusks such as oysters to bottom culture. The culture system you choose must be compatible with the species cultured and with the water supply and other natural resources available.

In this chapter, we discuss factors affecting site selection of the aquaculture operation, and we describe various systems for farming culture species, listing pros and cons. Because ponds are in widespread use, pond construction is discussed in some detail.

WHERE TO LOCATE THE CULTURE FACILITY

The selection of a site for aquaculture depends on: (1) species chosen for culture, (2) legal and socio-cultural aspects, (3) infrastructure requirements, (4) biophysical requirements, and (5) culture system employed. In some instances, a species is chosen for culture before any other consideration. You must choose a location then that meets the needs of the culture species. Some entrepreneurs choose a culture system first, then look for a suitable species to culture. For example, a company may wish to grow fish offshore in submerged net-pens. Regardless of your motives, there is a mingling of requirements that must be considered in choosing the best site.

Webber (1972), Wellborn (1988), Jensen (1990), Lutz (1994), and Avault (1994a) discussed site selection for pond culture. Caine (1987), Ricker et al. (1989), and Pennell (1992) reviewed site selection for net-pen culture of salmon. Cross and Kingzett (1992) outlined criteria for siting molluskan operations. Bean et al. (1988) gave a parish-by-parish assessment in Louisiana for aquaculture potential based on infrastructure and biophysical factors. Avault (1994b, c) discussed various culture systems in use, and listed pros and cons of each system.

LEGAL AND SOCIO-CULTURAL CONSIDERATIONS

Legal and socio-cultural considerations are important, particularly when public waters are leased or used. Refer to Chapter 4 for that section that deals with site selection.

Aquaculturists who own land have relatively few legal and socio-cultural problems compared with those who lease or make use of public waters. You should evaluate fully any public waters considered for aquaculture, even if you can obtain all the necessary permits. Socio-cultural problems often arise when coastal waters are used. In one instance, a private company invested money and 5 years of research to farm shrimp. Young shrimp from public waters were carried with the tides across weirs into private ponds where they were grown to market size. The project was ultimately abandoned to keep the good will of commercial shrimpers who fished public waters. Shrimpers felt that shrimp farms robbed them of young shrimp, resulting in poor catches. In another instance, a commercial shrimp farming company blocked off a coastal bay with a net. Though the waters were legally leased for shrimp farming, hostility arose with the local citizens, and navigation had to be permitted in the area.

In coastal areas, the degree of social problems may depend on the culture system employed. For years certain coastal states have leased water bottoms for oyster culture. The oysters are out of sight and bring little public notice. Bring the oysters to the surface as with raft culture, and suddenly people take note; sometimes they become angry because their recreation is hindered or the beauty of the area is perceived to be spoiled.

Fish farmers have shown interest in cage culture in heated effluents from plants and factories. Public waters have been involved. The warm water extends the growing season through the winter. It cost $1,000 in 1974 just to apply for a permit from the Environmental Protection Agency (EPA). There were 58 pages of proposed EPA regulations. Merely trying to apply would discourage all but the most determined. Although this is a legal concern, the socio-cultural attitude helped to precipitate regulations. An aquaculturist may look upon heated effluents as thermal enrichment, but an environmentalist may see the same thing as thermal pollution.

The Latin America region is especially well suited for aquaculture because of the warm climate and other favorable conditions. The region between the Tropics of Cancer and Capricorn is especially noteworthy. It has year-round favorable water temperatures, relatively low pollution, and high quality waters. Webber (1972, 1973, 1975) and others pointed out that the socio-cultural atmosphere must be carefully studied. Some countries offer inducements such as tax abatement and freedom from import duties to attract aquaculture ventures. On the other hand, the possibility of excessive taxation, expropriation, or arbitrary confiscation, though remote, must be considered. Social unrest and inordinate inflationary pressures may also jeopardize the incipient aquaculture operation.

These risks may sometimes be reduced. For example, a United States corporate entity may be formed and thus be eligible to enter into an agreement with the Overseas Private Investment Corporation (OPIC), formerly a division of the U.S. Agency for International Development (USAID), to secure its investment. OPIC has provided political risk insurance covering war, expropriation, and inconvertibility of currency. OPIC, by providing guarantees for both political and commercial risks, encouraged U.S. banks and institutional lenders to make loans to aquaculture companies at normal commercial terms and interest rates. Another possibility has been the formation of a western hemisphere corporation to secure the advantage of a more favorable tax levy from the U.S. Internal Revenue Service if earnings are to be repatriated into a U.S. parent company.

A country that hosts a foreign aquaculture operation will want to know what is in it for them, and rightly so. A major consideration is the foreign exchange, or hard currency, that will be brought into the country. The number of new jobs created is also desirable. Assuming that labor is not a high-priced item, the aquaculture operation might be labor intensive, and mechanization kept to a minimum.

Finally, when locating in another country, consider the necessities of life for the manager, the technicians, and the workers who must live on or near the aquaculture site. Housing, medical, educational, transportation, shopping, and recreational needs should be considered.

INFRASTRUCTURE REQUIREMENTS
Economics

A particular site may appear nearly perfect from a biophysical standpoint but may be uneconomical. Here are a few factors to consider. The cost of land and the restrictions placed on ownership of land must be weighed. Labor costs and construction costs vary from one place to another. Labor may be low-cost, for example in Africa, but importing certain construction materials could offset the gain. Supplies are needed such as fuel, feed, and equipment. If they are not readily available, they could become costly.

The availability of capital is a prerequisite to construction of any facility. A channel catfish (*Ictalurus punctatus*) farmer who lives near Yazoo City, Mississippi, would probably have less trouble borrowing money locally than would an American shrimp farmer in Indonesia. Having a partner from

Indonesia would make it easier to borrow money in that country. In short, an entrepreneur should consider any and all factors related to economics.

Transportation, Communication, and Power

Supplies must be shipped in to the aquaculture operation, and products must be shipped out. You should consider the road system for trucking, length of haul, railroad service, shipping ports, cargo handling, and airports. Communication systems are vital for any aquaculture operation. Reliable telephone and FAX capabilities are necessary. Dependable electrical power is required. Certain processing operations, such as freezing and cooling, should have a standby generator that runs on gasoline or diesel fuel.

Processing and Marketing

The proximity of aquaculture production to the domestic or foreign market should be given much thought. Ideally the aquaculture operation should be as close as possible to processing and the market to keep transportation costs low. In Central America, high-value species such as shrimp could be shipped to such nearby countries as the United States where a favorable price could be obtained. If so, the product must be of high quality to pass inspection by the Food and Drug Administration. In some instances, the production site (country) is a long distance from the market targeted, but production costs are so low that shipping costs are offset. An example is the farming of shrimp in China and transportation to the United States.

BIOPHYSICAL REQUIREMENTS
Biological Requirements

In Chapter 3 a biological synopsis of various culture species was presented. In selecting a site for the aquaculture operation, you must know the biological requirements of a culture species for reproduction and for grow-out from fry or larvae to market size. For example, water temperature and salinity play a major role in site selection for culture of marine shrimp. Typically shrimp spawn offshore in water that is approximately 28° to 30°C (82° to 86°F) at a salinity of 36 ppt. Pelagic eggs hatch at sea, and early larval stages develop in sea water; postlarvae, which drift into estuaries, grow best in brackish water less than one-half sea strength. In grow-out, species such as *Penaeus monodon* grow best at a salinity of 15 to 25 ppt. The range of temperature that supports normal growth of this species is between 28° to 33°C (82° to 91°F). Growth all but ceases at water temperatures below 24°C (75°F). All too often shrimp farms are located without considering monthly fluctuations of water temperature and salinity. High salinities are a problem in certain countries, such as Indonesia that has a pronounced dry season. Salinities in this country may exceed 45 ppt in ponds because of evaporation. In the Gambia (western

Africa), it may become too cold for optimum growth of shrimp (*P. monodon*) several months each year.

Climate and Physical Conditions of Water

Typhoons-- Ponds and other culture facilities located in coastal areas are particularly affected by climate and physical water conditions. The China coastline along the South China Sea, Japan, and parts of the Philippines have a history of typhoons. On the other hand, Indonesia is less affected by such storms.

Strong Waves-- For net-pen operations, you should consider the wind, waves, tidal currents, and water depth (Caine 1987; Ricker et al. 1989). Long fetches and exposure to prevailing winds can cause problems. Fetches of 4 to 15 km (2.5 to 9.3 miles) may produce waves 1 m (3.3 ft) high (Caine 1987). Strong waves can cause anchoring problems, damage net-pens, and bruise fish against nets. Fish may go off feed following rough seas.

Strong waves may produce a phenomenon known as a seiche. A seiche is a standing wall of surface water blown up by the wind. If the water column is stratified, and there are distinct thermoclines or haloclines, a site within a seiche may have sudden changes in temperature and salinity.

Currents-- Coastal currents are caused by tides, winds, and freshwater runoff. Tides have a persistent effect on current speeds. Currents, by exchanging water through net-pens, provide oxygen, and they flush away feces and waste feed. A flow of at least 10 cm/second (4 in/second) is best throughout most of the tidal cycle (Caine 1987). Pennell (1992) recommended a current flow of 30 to 50 cm/second (12 to 20 in/second). You should measure current speed at the depth where fish live. Excessive current flows stress fish and the anchoring system.

Water Depth-- The water should be deep enough to separate fish from wastes that may accumulate on the bottom. Sufficient depth also allows time for heavier materials to move horizontally with the currents and away from net-pens. In a shallow site, even with moderately fast currents, large pellets will accumulate on the bottom in the vicinity of the pens. Water depth, however, should not be excessive if pens are anchored to the bottom. Caine (1987) recommended a depth of about 50 m (164 ft).

Rainfall-- Rainfall can affect shore-based ponds. Heavy rains may dilute the salinity below that desired for culture. Prolonged drought and evaporation will result in an increase in salinity to abnormally high levels. In Indonesia, for example, the dry season usually lasts about 6 months. During this period salinities may reach 45 ppt and higher. Shrimp do not grow well at this high salinity. Fresh water should be available to dilute high-saline water. You can obtain general information on climate and weather from the State Department of Conservation or the Federal Meteorological Office. Data should be reviewed for 10 years to establish trends.

Finally, the threat of flood waters must be considered. Does the land that you wish to use for aquaculture have a history of flooding? In 1972-73 a number of catfish farms in the Mississippi Delta area went under water from heavy rains.

Pollution and Contamination

In coastal waters an aquaculture production facility runs the risk of pollution. Pollution may come from industrial, agricultural, and residential sources. In one instance a local county government, with approval of the state health department, erected a sewage treatment plant near oyster beds. The plant was needed for the good of the people, yet it destroyed an oyster farm. Bear in mind that aquaculture enterprises in the United States generally have low priority compared with navigation, recreation, oil exploration, and other uses. Thoroughly check all anticipated construction and exploration by industry and by local, state, and federal governments in the area under consideration. You should have a thorough knowledge of zoning regulations for the aquaculture site under consideration. Even then construction of a permanent aquaculture facility may be risky. As populations increase, a greater demand is placed on coastal lands, and there is always public pressure to rezone areas for needed public projects.

Contamination of inland ponds may sometimes occur, even on lands owned by the fish farmer. Major problems occur when ponds are located near row crops such as cotton. Pesticides may kill a culture species or make it unfit to eat because of harmful residues in the flesh. Ponds should not be constructed on land formerly used to grow cotton where DDT and other persistent pesticides have a history unless the soil has been analyzed and is no longer contaminated.

Predators and Pests

Those aquaculture operations sited in public waters may have more problems with predators and pests than those sited inland. Bottom culture of mollusks, for example, will have problems with fouling barnacles and various predators. Salmon grown in net-pens could be affected by harmful plankton. *Chaetoceros convolutus* and *C. concavicornus* are diatoms that cause physical gill damage. *Heterosigma akashiwo* is a flagellate that produces a toxin that kills fish (Pennell 1992). Sea lions and seal rookeries could pose problems if the aquaculture operation is sited nearby. Net-pens all have some fouling, but some areas have less than others. For example, the Tofino area on the west coast of Vancouver Island has light fouling. Net changes are needed less than every 6 to 8 weeks in summer Net-pen operations in the Strait of Georgia, by contrast, have heavy fouling problems. Nets must be changed as often as every 3 weeks in summer (Pennell 1992).

Land and Water Needs

Ponds must be located where a plentiful supply of good quality water is available (Chapter 6). Sometimes it may be possible to manipulate water quality. For example, on Negros and Panay in the Philippines water from freshwater wells allows a blending with saline water to obtain the desired salinity to culture *Penaeus monodon.* Farmers culturing *Macrobrachium rosenbergii* often seek locations that provide sources of both fresh and brackish water. Brackish water is used for larvae culture and fresh water for grow-out.

Inland fish farmers, such as channel catfish farmers, must locate where land has: (1) a suitable price, (2) a topography suitable for constructing ponds economically, (3) a subsoil that contains a sufficient amount of clay to hold water, and (4) protection from potential flood waters. The U.S. Soil Conservation Service can advise a fish farmer on all of these matters. Certain universities, state departments of agriculture, and state departments of conservation also may assist. Relatively flat land is preferred by most fish farmers because there is more control over construction. Ponds can be built to any size and shape. On land that is rolling, construction is influenced by the lay of the land. However, less levee construction is required on land that is gently rolling. Here advantage is taken of natural hollows.

Land unsuited for agricultural crops is often used to advantage for fish farming. It may not cost as much as improved land. Boggy land, land that is subject to brackish water, land that is acid or alkaline, and salt flats behind mangrove forests have all been used to raise crops of fish. Certain wetlands are critical as nursery areas for wild finfish, crustaceans, and mollusks, and should not be destroyed in the development of an aquaculture facility.

A pond is nothing more than an earthen container that holds water. A good subsoil that contains a minimum of 30% clay is best for constructing levees and for keeping seepage to a minimum. Clay soil swells when wet, thereby giving a good seal. Core samples should be taken with a soil auger to the depth at which the pond is to be built to determine if suitable clay is present.

CLASSIFICATION OF CULTURE SYSTEMS

Water is required to grow all aquatic animals regardless of the species cultured, yet there are a variety of culture systems available for aquaculture.

Below is an arbitrary classification of various culture systems, followed by a critique of each regarding: (1) legal-socio-cultural problems, (2) construction of the facility, (3) maintenance, (4) water quantity and quality, (5) feeds and feeding, (6) parasites and diseases, (7) overall control of the environment, (8) harvesting, (9) marketing, and (10) general remarks.

Pond Culture Systems

A pond is an earthen, or sometimes concrete, impoundment that holds water. Water is normally added only to fill the pond or to replace water lost by seepage and evaporation. Sometimes water may be flushed through the pond but usually does not exceed one complete change in 24 hours. Ponds in coastal areas may be flushed by the tides. Ponds may be arbitrarily classified by construction methods, by location, and by use.

Critique-- Ponds have few legal problems except for coastal ponds; land designated "wetlands" cannot be used for pond construction; EPA regulations regarding effluents must be followed. A large area of land for construction is often needed; initial cost can be expensive; construction costs may be high. Maintenance is needed for mowing levees and periodic repair of levees (every 3 to 5 years); maintenance of farm equipment, harvesting gear, and storage facilities are required. A relatively large quantity of water is needed at one time to fill ponds; a costly water well may be required; good quality water is necessary; main problems during grow-out are low dissolved oxygen and high ammonia levels. In some instances supplemental feeds can be used that are not as costly as complete feeds; culture species may obtain some natural food from ponds; crawfish can forage on rice plants and on natural vegetation; herbivorous fish can feed on aquatic plants. Compared with intensive systems, culture species are less apt to have parasite and disease problems, unless high stocking rates are used. It is more costly, however, to treat culture species in a pond because a larger quantity of chemicals is required. There is little or no control over the environment; there is some control over oxygen content in water with supplemental aeration; control over salinity in coastal ponds can be had with site selection. Labor needs for harvesting are high, with much weight to handle at once; it is more difficult to stagger crops compared with intensive culture systems. Often there is a large volume to market at once. Culture species can be alternated with agricultural crops; nutrient-rich water can be used to irrigate agricultural crops. Worldwide, ponds account for the bulk of aquaculture production.

Watershed Ponds-- These ponds, sometimes referred to as hill ponds or ravine ponds, are constructed in hilly or rolling land by building a dam across the narrow neck(s) of the existing topography (Figure 5.1). This is an economical method for building a pond because use is made of a natural hollow. Water used to fill the pond is surface runoff from rainfall; you do not have much control over the water supply. However, money is saved since no well is required. Stocking of ponds and harvesting, if ponds are drained, must be scheduled to take advantage of the rainy season. Ponds are usually drained by gravity. Because the pond bottoms may be uneven, harvest by seining may be difficult. Watershed ponds serve well for cage culture or sportfishing because it is normally not necessary to drain for harvesting.

Figure 5.1 Watershed pond.

Figure 5.2 Excavated pond. Photo courtesy of W. Guthrie Perry, Jr.

Excavated Ponds-- They are dug below ground level solely by excavation, and normally no levees are constructed (Figure 5.2). Generally, excavated ponds are not dug with aquaculture as the primary purpose. Draglines usually dig the ponds, and the soil is used for highway construction and other purposes. Excavated ponds are sometimes called borrow-pit ponds because soil is borrowed for construction elsewhere. Many such borrow-pit ponds have resulted from interstate highway construction. These ponds also may result from strip mining operations. Such ponds sometimes have very acid soils and may require lime. Excavated ponds are usually filled by rainfall and must be drained by pumping. Little or no money is invested, and the ponds show potential for cage culture and for sportfishing operations.

Embankment Ponds-- These ponds, sometimes called levee ponds, are constructed by both excavation and levee construction. The excavated soil is used to form pond banks (Figure 5.3). Such ponds typically are built on relatively flat land. Water usually is supplied from wells or by pumping from a nearby stream; draining is by gravity. Most fish farmers prefer levee ponds because although the initial cost is high, better control over filling and draining is possible. The size, shape, and depth of ponds also can be controlled during construction.

Figure 5.3 Embankment pond.

Marsh Ponds-- They are built in coastal areas where soils may range from clay to those with a high organic content (Figure 5.4). Draglines on mats or pontoons are usually needed to dig these ponds (Figure 5.5). Levees are built above ground level with soil, and material is taken from outside or inside the pond. Levees are built in stages, and the first lift of the dragline may be only 0.6 to 0.9 m (2 to 3 ft). This soil is allowed to settle for a month or so, and then the next layer is added. Shrinkage of levees may be as high as 60%. A berm large enough to offset the weight of the levee is necessary to prevent the foundation from slipping (Figure 5.6). A berm is the ridge between the base of the levee and inside borrow ditch. It should measure from one to three times the width of the levee base. Water for marsh ponds may range from fresh to sea salinity. Ponds are usually filled and drained by pumping; some marsh ponds have weirs (low-level dams) that allow sea water to move in and out with the tides.

Figure 5.4 W. Guthrie Perry, Jr. of the Louisiana Department of Wildlife and Fisheries seining a marsh pond at Rockefeller Wildlife Refuge.

Figure 5.5 Dragline used to dig marsh ponds.

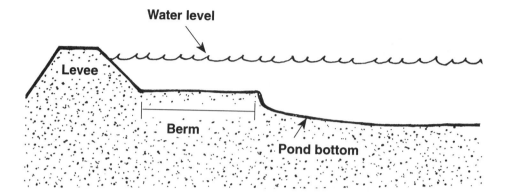

Figure 5.6 Pond showing berm.

Beach Ponds-- Beach ponds are constructed on shore in sandy areas where seepage may be a major problem. In one levee design tested in Louisiana, single-layered, overlapping corrugated sheets were placed just inside two parallel lines of posts. Opposite pairs of posts were secured with galvanized steel cables and eye bolts. The space between the sheets was filled with fine sand (Figure 5.7). Beach ponds made of concrete or with plastic-like liners avoid seepage problems. Taiwan and other island nations often use such ponds (Figure 5.8). Water for beach ponds is brackish or saline and is usually pumped. Some beach ponds have a weir structure and are flushed by the tides.

Figure 5.7 Experimental beach ponds used in Louisiana.

Figure 5.8 Commercial beach ponds used in Taiwan.

Intertidal Ponds-- These ponds are found just off shore. Ancient Hawaiian fish ponds are an example. A cove or bay may be blocked off with a levee or net. Sometimes the levee is a wall of rocks or coral. The levee confines the species being cultured and keeps predators and wild fish out, but it allows water interchange so that tides influence the water depth in the pond. Further off shore, in the deeper sublittoral zone, ponds are difficult to construct.

Ponds are often classified by use. An operation for channel catfish will be used to illustrate. Holding ponds are used to hold fish temporarily for market or to hold fish that will be restocked into other ponds. Brood ponds are used to maintain brood stock or adult fish after the spawning season. Spawning ponds are stocked with brood fish to obtain eggs or young. Rearing ponds are stocked with fry to rear fingerlings. Grow-out ponds are stocked with fingerlings that will be grown out to eating size. Fee-fishing ponds, fish-out ponds, or pay-lakes are stocked with fish, and the public pays for the privilege of fishing.

Ponds may have a special designation, depending on the species cultured and the geographical location. Crawfish (*Procambarus clarkii*) ponds in Louisiana are an example. They are known locally as open, wooded, or rice-field ponds. Open ponds contain only aquatic vegetation, wooded ponds contain a various number of trees, and rice-field ponds grow rice first and crawfish afterward.

188

Raceway Culture Systems

Raceways are typically long, narrow, rectangular trenches in which water is flushed through continuously. The sides and bottom of the raceway may be earthen (Figure 5.9) or concrete (Figure 5.10).

Figure 5.9 Earthen raceways for channel catfish. Photo courtesy of University of Georgia.

Figure 5.10 Concrete raceways being built. Leo Ray (no hat) and co-worker of Fish Breeders of Idaho are pouring concrete into forms of plywood. Raceways in background.

Raceways are various sizes. A common size used for trout is 24 m (80 ft) long and 2.4 m (8 ft) wide, with an average depth of 76 cm (2.5 ft) (Figure 5.11).

Figure 5.11 Typical raceway used for trout culture in Idaho.

Another size used for both trout and channel catfish is 30 m (100 ft) long and 3 m (10 ft) wide, with a depth of 76 to 122 cm (2.5 to 4.0 ft). If the topography of the land has enough slope, a series of raceways is constructed end to end, one flowing into the other. Each unit or raceway is sometimes called a cell. (Figures 5.12, 5.13). Such raceways are usually shorter and wider. The length may be approximately 7.5 to 9 m (25 to 30 ft), and the width is about 3 to 6 m (10 to 20 ft). Water exits one cell and drops 0.3 to 1 m (1 to 3 ft) into the next cell; oxygen is added by water splashing on a perforated surface.

Raceways may be of various sizes, shapes, and materials. Raceways may be circular and made of plastic, fiberglass, or metal. Rectangular tanks made of aluminum and other materials also are used as raceways. Unlike ponds, raceways have a continuous flushing of water. In ponds, bacteria and other microorganisms break down organic matter, resulting from fish feces and waste feed, into harmless compounds. In raceways, these wastes are allowed to accumulate in a settling basin at the drain end where they can be siphoned or pumped out.

Figure 5.12 Raceways with cells for growing channel catfish, Fish Breeders of Idaho.

Figure 5.13 Raceways with cells for growing trout in North Carolina.

Raceways may operate as an open system or as a closed system. In an open system, water enters through the supply line, exits at the drain and is not re-used. Most trout farms have operated in this manner. In a closed system, water is captured as it exits, and may be filtered and pumped back through the system. Make-up water may be added occasionally to replace that lost by evaporation. Sometimes the water is collected in a reservoir where bacteria and other pond organisms "digest" waste products of the culture species. Fish in the reservoir, often various carps and tilapia that feed low on the food chain, help to lower the organic load. The water in the reservoir is pumped into another reservoir above the raceways; from here it flows through the raceways by gravity.

Critique-- EPA regulations evaluate effluents if the system is not closed loop. Far less land is required than that for pond construction; the topography of the land should be gently sloping; construction can be costly if concrete raceways are used. Maintenance involves periodic cleaning of raceways. There must be a good supply of quality water; gravity flow water is ideal; if not gravity flow, there must be a constant power source for pumping; it may be costly; a stand-by power source is needed if electricity is used; low dissolved oxygen, high ammonia levels, and solids from feces and uneaten feed constitute the main problems in water management. Fish are easy to feed and observe; a relatively low labor cost is involved; a complete and costly diet is necessary. Densely stocked culture species are subject to more parasite and disease problems, but it is easy and relatively inexpensive to treat them since small quantities of chemicals are needed when compared with pond treatment. There is some control over the environment by adjusting the flow rate of water, using aeration devices, injecting oxygen, and manipulating stocking rates. Harvesting is relatively easy; labor needs are fewer than those for pond harvesting. Crops can be staggered to provide a product on a regular basis; year-round production may not be possible unless the water temperature can be controlled. Essentials are suitable topography, abundant supply of good quality water, and reliable power source if the water supply is not gravity flow or if the system is closed loop; power requirements may be uneconomical for grow-out.

Tank culture

Tank culture is a term some like to use in place of raceway culture when metal, plastic, or fiberglass tanks are used (Figure 5.14). The tanks are normally above ground, though they may be placed below in the ground or elevated on racks (Figure 5.15). Some tanks may consist of frames with liners.

Critique-- EPA regulations for effluents apply; there is usually some discharge from closed loop systems. A small land area is required to build a facility. Maintenance involves cleaning and scrubbing of tanks. Good quality water must be available; the quantity needed is low if the water is re-used; a constant power source is needed, and a back-up power source; low dissolved oxygen and ammonia buildup are the main problems. A complete feed is needed; Diseases can be considerable, especially with bacteria; culture species in tanks are easy to treat at low cost; if biofiltration is part of the system, certain chemicals cannot be used that kill filter bacteria. There is some control over the environment depending on the particular operation -- temperature, flow rate of water, water hardness, pH, etc. Harvesting can be year-round; it requires little labor; the culture species are harvested clean; you have great control over the time of harvest; you can market year-round if water temperature is controlled. Tank systems are often not economical unless high-value species are cultured.

Figure 5.14 Rectangular aluminum tanks and round fiberglass tanks used in fish culture. Photo courtesy of Fish and Wildlife Service, Stuttgart, Arkansas.

Figure 5.15 Elevated tanks. Water is flushed through tanks and is filtered through rock-filled pit. Photo courtesy of Aquasystems Inc. Warsaw, Illinois.

Cage Culture

Cage culture involves growing a culture species in floating cages or baskets (Figures 5.16, 5.17). Cages may be of various sizes, shapes, and materials. One m^3 (1.3 yd^3) is a common volume, and a mesh size of 2.5 by 3.8 cm (1 by 1.5 in) is preferred. Smaller mesh sizes result in poor water circulation, and fouling with algae is a problem. A size that has been used for channel catfish is 1.2 m (4 ft) x 1.2m x 2.4 m (8 ft).

Figure 5.16 R.D. Guerrero III and R.O. Smitherman examine cage, Philippines.

Figure 5.17 Cage culture of tilapia in the Philippines.

Details of cage construction are discussed by Beveridge (1987). In $1m^3$ cages, fish are stocked at rates as high as $500/m^3$ $(654/yd^3)$. Fish held in cages may be cultured in large reservoirs, rivers, and other water bodies that cannot be drained. Offshore waters also show potential for cage culture. Cage culture in heated effluents of power plants has generated interest, but has not been of major importance. The Japanese have developed submerged cage culture. Cages are submerged to a certain depth to obtain consistent water quality and to minimize turbulence caused by storms. In Southeast Asia, fish are held for spawning, rearing, and even grow-out in hapas (Figure 5.18).

Figure 5.18 Hapas used in the Philippines.

Critique-- There could be legal and socio-cultural problems if public waters are used. There is little or no cost for land if existing reservoirs are available; payment necessary for lease of water rights may be monetary or it may require the release of fish; the main cost is cage construction initially. Maintenance involves cage repair and cleaning of fouling organisms off the mesh of cages; cages need replacing periodically. There is virtually no control over water management in certain reservoirs, but in smaller impoundments there can be; low dissolved oxygen can be a major problem; in rivers near the ocean, tidal flushing can help to maintain water quality. Costly floating feed of highest quality is necessary; feeding is often by boat; you can observe a culture species feeding. Parasites and diseases can be a problem; you can detect the problem quickly; treatment requires time and labor, but otherwise it is not costly. There is virtually no control over the environment except through choice of site location. Harvesting is relatively easy and can be done in small batches; the culture species is caught clean. The market can be furnished with a predetermined weight on a regular basis; water temperature affects growing season. It takes little money to get started.

Pen Culture

Pen culture, or net-pen culture, is a term preferred by trout and salmon farmers instead of cage culture (Figures 5.19 and 5.20). Pens vary in size, but a 6 x 12 m (20 x 40 ft) is typical.

Figure 5.19 Net-pen used in salmon culture, Puget Sound, Washington.

Figure 5.20 A series of floating net-pens used in salmon culture in Puget Sound. Photo at Pacific Ocean Farms, Port Blakely, Washington.

Though pens are usually floated in the water, they also may be secured to the bottom. Pens may be constructed of bamboo poles stuck in the bottom (Figure 5.21). In Manila Bay in the Philippines, such pen culture has been used for milkfish (*Chanos chanos*) and tilapia. Water in the bay receives nutrients from domestic sewage. Fish subsist on natural organisms.

Figure 5.21 Bamboo poles stuck in the bottom to form pen, Leguna de Bay, Manila.

Critique-- There are legal and socio-cultural problems if public waters are leased; pollution from fish wastes can be a major problem. Only a small area is needed for net-pens; construction of net-pens, walkways, and baffles to prevent wave damage constitute the major expense. Repair of nets and cleaning of fouling organisms are necessary; they may take considerable labor. There is little or no control over water quality except choice of site location. A costly high-quality feed is needed; little labor is required to feed fish. Parasites and diseases may pose a problem because of close confinement. There is little or no control over the environment. Harvesting is relatively easy; fish are clean at harvest; dates of harvest can be staggered. A year-round supply is usually not possible unless the water temperature is favorable; if salmon are cultured, it may be best to harvest when wild salmon are least abundant for market.

Silo Culture

Silo culture involves the culture of fish in vertical units. An early experimental unit, used at the Benner Spring Fish Research Station, was a cylindrical tank 5 m (16.5 ft) high and 2.3 m (7.5 ft) in diameter, with two 15-cm (6-in) drains at the base (Figure 5.22). Capacity was about 20,628 liters (5,450 gal). Water was pumped through the system at 1,703 liters (450 gal) per minute, and high density stocking was possible. One commercial operation used 75,700-liter (20,000-gal) steel silos that were 5.3 m (17.5 ft) across and 4 m (13 ft) deep. Other vertical units in which fish have been cultured include jars and 208-liter (55-gal) drums. Silos have an advantage where land availability is a constraint, and some are portable. Even so, this culture system has not caught on in commercial production.

Figure 5.22 Silo culture operation. Photo courtesy of Marine Protein Corporation, Rebersburg, Pennsylvania.

Critique-- EPA regulations affect any discharge of effluents. Only a small area of land is needed; the main expense is construction of silos. The upkeep of silos is relatively low. The quantity of water needed is relatively low if the system is closed loop; the quality must be very high, and there must be a constant reliable power source; a back-up power source is needed; low dissolved oxygen content and high ammonia levels are the main problems. Costly high-quality feeds are required; there is little wasted feed because feeding can be monitored closely. Fish crowding increases the chances of parasites and diseases, especially if the water quality is not maintained; fish are easy and inexpensive to treat. Excellent control of the environment is possible; oxygen content can be maintained by injection of liquid oxygen and with aeration; water temperature can be maintained with heaters, and ammonia can be reduced to less harmful compounds by use of filters. Harvesting is relatively easy; fish are clean; you can harvest in batches and stagger dates of harvest. The market can be supplied with the quantity needed on a year-round basis with planning. The facility is sometimes portable; most silo systems are not profitable unless a high-value culture species is grown.

Sea Ranching

Sea ranching or ocean ranching applies to "homing" species such as salmon. Adult fish are stripped of eggs and sperm. Resulting fertilized eggs are hatched, the larvae fed, and the young eventually released into a stream that reaches the sea. After a period of years, the surviving fish return to the same stream where they were released. They are captured and slaughtered for market or used for brood stock. There is interest in applying this culture system to other fish species. Channel catfish can be fed in cages and eventually released to open water. The fish, being programmed, return to the cages for feed where they can be trapped.

In Japan, species other than salmonids have been reared in floating net-pens as juveniles. Just prior to feeding, a device inside each pen emits a sound and vibration. The fish become programmed to this and associate it with feed. After 16 weeks they are released into ocean waters. They can be called in with sound for feeding, and can be captured by netting. Up to 20% recovery is possible.

Critique-- There are legal problems though some states allow salmon ranching. Construction of a hatchery is necessary for spawning and rearing of fry; nursery tanks and possibly net-pens are needed for the nursery phase. Maintenance is required for the hatchery, but not for grow-out. There is virtually no control over water quality except initial site selection. Fry and fingerlings are fed before release; high quality feed is needed but it is relatively low cost because only small quantities are needed. Fingerlings can receive prophylactic treatment before release, but after release there is no control over parasites and disease. There is no control over the environment once fish are released. Harvesting and labor needs are sporadic. There is little control on supplying the market demand because you must wait for the fish to return from the sea. The survival of fish is very low, but the money invested is relatively low.

Bottom Culture

Bottom culture refers to culture of oysters and other mollusks that are grown on water bottoms. This is one of the oldest and most widespread culture systems in the world. Oyster spat (young), attached to substrate (cultch), are seeded in preferred waters. In Louisiana and elsewhere, the state leases water bottoms to oyster growers. Markers are used to set boundaries, but public navigation is not restricted. Once seeded, the oysters are on their own, because little management is used in this extensive type of aquaculture. The next step is the harvest.

Critique-- Most farmers usually lease water bottoms from the government. No construction is involved; a boat and equipment may be needed to disperse molluskan seed and to harvest the crop. Maintenance is required for the boat and harvesting gear. There is no control over the water quality except through site location. Mollusks use natural foods, mainly plankton. There is virtually no control over parasites, diseases or predators; a crop can be harvested, however, before certain predators become too abundant during certain seasons of the year. There is no control over the environment. Harvesting is sporadic and seasonal. Marketing is seasonal, but the product can be supplied almost year-round. Main labor needs are for seeding spat oysters or other mollusks and for harvesting; poaching is sometimes a problem.

Off-bottom Culture

Off-bottom culture of oysters and other mollusks entails such techniques as culturing on floating rafts (raft culture), strings (string culture), and sticks (stick culture). Off-bottom culture is a more intensive type of aquaculture. More labor, care, and expense are involved, but yield per unit area is greater. Major problems with off-bottom culture in the United States are interference with navigation and recreation, fouling, and high-cost labor. With certain types of off-bottom culture, mollusks can be towed to selected waters for desired salinities; predators and competitors also can be avoided.

Critique-- Legal problems can be expected with public and governmental agencies in many countries. Materials are needed to construct rafts and other culture units; boats are often needed. Maintenance of rafts and other off-bottom structures is required. Water quality depends on site selection. Mollusks use natural foods, mainly plankton. There is little control over the environment, with some exceptions. Rafts can be towed to selected growing waters or to waters low in salinity to avoid predators. Also, mollusks can be raised at a desired water depth where food is abundant and predators less abundant. Harvesting can be staggered, but it is mostly seasonal. Mollusks grown off-bottom must compete in price with mollusks raised on the bottom. Off-bottom culture can be labor intensive.

CONSTRUCTION OF LEVEE PONDS

Levee ponds are the mainstay of aquaculture in the United States and many countries, so some detail will be given to their construction (Lawrence 1949; United Nations Development Program 1984). Marsh ponds are discussed by Perry (1972), and Milne (1972) devotes much of his book to the engineering aspects of ponds and facilities in coastal waters.

Clearing Pond Area

Before construction begins, the entire pond area must be cleared of all trees, brush, and weeds, usually with a bulldozer. Tree roots must be completely removed. Any woody material left behind in the dam area will eventually rot and may result in a leak. Grass sod must be also scraped away and piled to the side. It can be used later to cap levees after they have been built.

Staking the Levees

Once the area has been cleared, the outline of the levee foundation is marked with stakes (Lawrence 1949). The layout should show the proposed top width of the levee when it is finished and the area the levee foundation will cover (Figure 5.23). Two rows of top-width stakes mark the top of the levee. If the top width of the levee is to be 3.7 m (12 ft), the stakes are set in parallel rows 3.7 m apart, and they extend in a line for the length of the proposed levee. Reference stakes are set at both ends of the top-width stakes. The reference stakes are outside the construction area. They serve as reference points when the top-width stakes are run over or covered during construction. Toe stakes mark the base of the levee. These stakes run parallel to and outside of the top-width stakes. The distance between top-width stakes and toe stakes depends on the slope of the levee and the height of the levee including the freeboard.

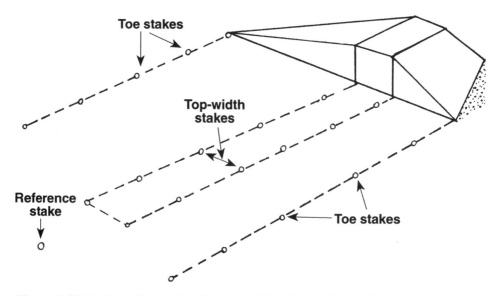

Figure 5.23 Portion of levee showing top-width stakes and toe stakes.

The sides of an earthen levee must have a certain minimum slope to provide stability. The slope may be 2:1, 3:1 or greater. If a levee has a 2:1 slope, then for a dam height (H) the toe stakes are set twice the distance (2H) from the top-width stakes (Figure 5.24). If, for example, the levee height is 1.8 m (6 ft), the toe stakes on each side of the top-width stakes will extend out 2H or 3.6 m (12 ft).

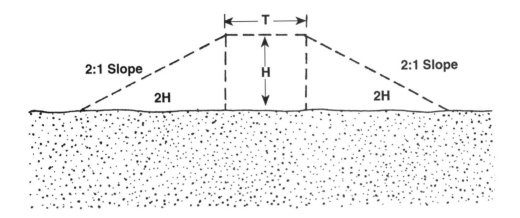

Figure 5.24 Levee showing 2:1 slope. T = top width. H = height.

The slope of the levee depends on type of soil, size of pond, and the amount of wind and wave action. Generally, soil with a heavy clay content holds better, and a steeper slope can be maintained. Soil with silt or sand does not compact as well, and a more gradual slope is needed. Small ponds of only 2 ha (5 ac) or less need only a 2:1 slope, but larger ponds should have a 3:1 or greater slope. If the pond is subject to heavy wind and wave action, slopes of 4:1 may be needed. Many fish farmers prefer at least a 3:1 slope for both stability and ease of maintenance when mowing grass. Some fish farmers may compromise, a 3:1 slope on the inside levee, where erosion is most likely to occur, and a 2:1 slope on the outside.

All earthen dams must have some extra height, known as freeboard, above the water level. Freeboard prevents water from waves and floods from flowing over the levee. Water leaving or entering a pond over a levee may result in loss of the culture species and may encourage erosion. The freeboard required affects the height of the dam and consequently the dimensions of the dam base. Ponds of 1.2 ha (3 ac) or less need about 60 cm (2 ft) of free-board. A 90-cm (3-ft) freeboard is recommended for levees that impound larger areas and where wind and wave action are great. In countries with a monsoon season, freeboard may be even higher. Some aquaculturists are experimenting with a freeboard of only 15 cm (6 in) for levees that have minimal traffic. On windy days, waves break over the top of the levee rather than directly into the levee. This reduces levee erosion. Moreover, the cost of pond construction can be reduced.

Staking Levees on a Slope

Sometimes the slope of the ground varies greatly from the inside levee to the outside levee. If the elevation between toe stakes is greater than 60 cm, it is necessary to establish the distance of the toe stakes on each side of the levee separately if a 2:1 slope is desired. Similar adjustments must be made for a 3:1 slope if the elevation between toe stakes is 90 cm or greater. The toe stakes are first set at a distance of 2H from the top-width stakes to determine points A and B (Figure 5.25). However, the slope on the side from point A to the top of the levee is greater than 2:1 because the ground slopes downhill. To correct for this, the height (h) between point A and the top of the levee is determined, and 2h is measured out from the top width to establish the corrected toe stake location at point A^1.

The slope on the side from point B to the top of the levee is less than 2:1. This is because the ground level slopes uphill from this point to the center of the levee base. The height (h^1) between point B and the top of the levee is determined, and $2h^1$ is measured out from the top width to give the corrected toe stake location at point B^1.

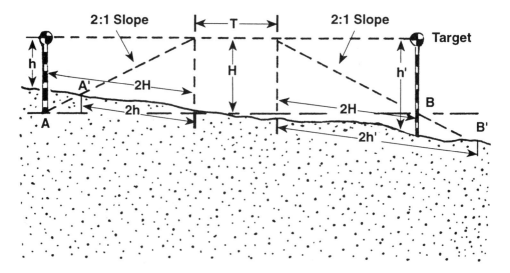

Figure 5.25 A method for setting toe stakes on a site having a greater slope than 2 feet between upstream and downstream toes. After Lawrence 1949.

Core Trench

When all staking has been completed, the core trench is dug. Impervious clay must extend the full length of the levee and must be well bound with the subsoil to prevent a leaky dam (Figure 5.26). The core trench is dug about 3 m (10 ft) wide or the width of most bulldozer blades. It must run the full length of the levee and be deep enough to reach good clay subsoil. When the core trench is complete, it is filled with clay excavated from outside the proposed pond. In some areas sufficient clay is available throughout the soil profile, and it is not necessary to dig a core trench. In this case only top soil is removed before construction of the dam begins.

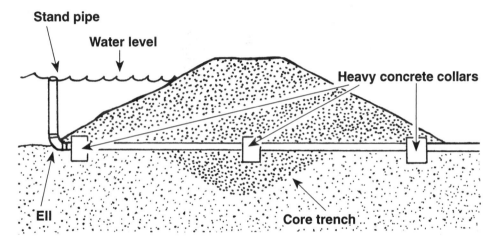

Figure 5.26 Cross section of levee showing core trench, drain pipe, stand pipe, and concrete collars that serve as anti-seep collars.

Installing the Drain

All ponds should have a drain pipe so that all water may be completely drained from the pond. The drain pipe should be installed at the lowest point in the pond, and should have a fall of about 1 cm/1 m (1 ft/ 100 ft), or 1%. A check should be made before the pond is filled with water to be sure that there are no low spots from which water will not drain. The drain pipe is laid in a ditch cut through the dam foundation (Figure 5.27). A backhoe may be used to dig the ditch, and the drain pipe is installed and covered with soil. A bulldozer can now run over the buried pipe with no damage.

Various types of pipe have been used, including PVC, galvanized iron, and transite that is an asbestos-cement pipe. Transite pipe containing asbestos is no longer in use. PVC pipe is often preferred because it is easy to handle, has a long life, and is less costly.

Figure 5.27 Drain pipe of PVC being laid in ditch cut through levee.

Once the pipe has been laid, concrete collars should be poured at the joints, or anti-seep collars put around the pipe to obtain water tightness (Figure 5.26). Following this, clay should be well packed around the pipe to prevent water from seeping along the pipe surface and to prevent small animals such as crawfish from digging along the pipe. The concrete collars or anti-seep collars also help in this task.

Various types of drain structures can be installed. Perhaps the most common is the stand pipe or turndown pipe (Figure 5.28). This device acts as an overflow and as a drain pipe, and it allows desired water levels simply by adjusting the pipe. Threaded galvanized iron or PVC pipe is commonly used, and the pipe is joined by an elbow connection. To drain a pond, the stand pipe is pushed over. A screen on the end of the stand pipe prevents fish loss. Sometimes a sleeve, with a larger diameter than the stand pipe, is placed over the stand pipe (Figure 2.28). The sleeve remains about 30 cm (1 ft) or more off the bottom. When excess water leaves the pond, as during a rain, the water is pulled off the bottom. Bottom water is of poorer quality than surface water. Some people prefer to place the stand pipe on the outside of the pond. The water level can be manipulated easily by lowering or raising the stand pipe without getting into the pond. Moreover, if water is let out, it comes off the bottom. A danger of the outside stand pipe is that it can be knocked over, so precautions should be taken.

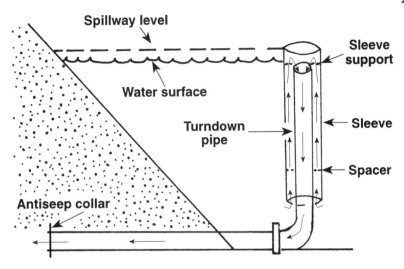

Figure 5.28 Turndown stand pipe with sleeve. Figure courtesy of USDA Soil Conservation Service.

The diameter of the pipe depends on pond size and amount of water to be drained. For ponds 1.2 ha (3 ac) or less, a 15- to 20-cm (6- to 8-in) pipe is sufficient. A 0.4-ha (1-ac) pond that is 1.5 m (5 ft) deep with a 15-cm diameter pipe, takes about 2.5 days to drain. Ponds between 6 to 8 ha (15 to 20 ac) require 20- to 30-cm (8- to 12-in) pipe.

Various other types of drains have been used, including those with shear-gate valves and gate valves. These are most often used for watershed ponds. Monks, or drain structures with dam boards, also are used (Figure 5.29).

Figure 5.29 Drain structure with dam boards.

The water level is manipulated by removing or adding boards to the structure. Most monks have two sets of boards, one set in front of the other. By leaving out the bottom board on the set of boards nearest to the pond, excess water during flushing or rainfall is removed from the bottom. This drainage system is common on shrimp farms. One of the most expensive drain systems is the concrete kettle and catch basin system.

Harvest Pit

Some ponds are constructed with a harvest pit that covers 5% to 10% of the pond bottom. It is located in the drain area and is 60 cm (2 ft) or deeper than the rest of the pond bottom. Here the culture species gathers for harvest as the pond is being drained. The remainder of the pond bottom should have a slope or drop of 6 cm (0.2 ft) for each 30 m (100 ft). A greater slope may result in erosion of the bottom, and a lesser slope will retard proper drainage. Generally, the culture species is harvested with seines or nets when the pond is partly drained regardless of the drain system used. Up to 80% of the crop may be harvested before a pond is completely drained. Some farmers, however, allow shrimp or fish to go through the drain pipe, and they are caught outside the levee in a box.

Completing the Levees

Once the drain line has been installed, construction of the levees can continue (Figure 5.30). Filling the above-ground portion of the levees is the most expensive operation in building a pond. Good quality clay should be applied in layers and compacted before the next layer is added. There will be a 5% to 10% settling of levees when the pond is complete, and this should be taken into account when calculating total dam height.

Figure 5.30 Bulldozer constructing levee.

Various methods are available to obtain the desired levee slope. The triangle method is a method that works for small ponds (Figure 5.31). If a 2:1 slope is desired, the triangle will have a 0.6 m (2 ft) side and a 1.2 m (4 ft) side. A third piece of wood completes the triangle. A small spirit level is attached parallel to the 1.2 m side. A common method is to reset toe stakes at 30 cm (1 ft) vertical heights as construction of levees progresses.

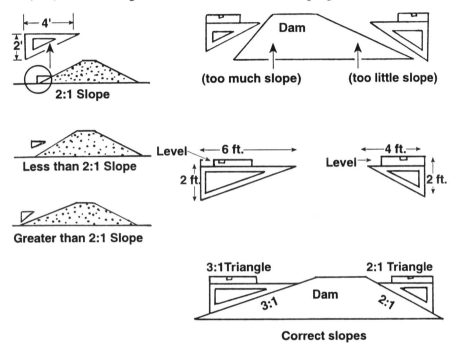

Figure 5.31 Home-built triangle to get 2:1 slope. After Lawrence 1949.

Protecting the Pond Levees

Pond levees must be protected from erosion. This is done with sodding, riprap, booms, berms, cross levees, fencing, and shoreline vegetation.

The higher the clay content in levees, the less the erosion. Nevertheless, all ponds have some erosion. After pond construction, levees should be seeded with grass. If it is fall, rye grass or other cool-season grass gives a quick cover and will last until summer. In southern states, bermuda underseeded with centipede is a good combination to plant in spring when rye grass begins to die out. Bermuda, like rye grass, gives a quick cover. Centipede grass will eventually take over and crowd out the bermuda grass. In northern states and elsewhere, various clovers and bluegrass have been used. The Soil Conservation Service or the Cooperative Extension Service can be consulted for the best grass to plant.

Riprap is any material that helps break up wave action onto the levees (Figure 5.32). Pieces of concrete and large rocks are often used. They are placed at the water's edge where wave action is the greatest. Booms are made of old poles or logs, lashed together and placed at the water's edge. Berms, like those used in marsh pond construction, are sometimes used in inland ponds. A berm 2.4 to 3 m (8 to 10 ft) in width will help provide adequate protection from wave action. Cross levees extend partway out into the pond (Figure 5.33). They are finger-like projections from the main levee that help break up waves. Cross levees are helpful in large ponds with long distances (fetch) exposed to winds. Cross levees work well with pay-lakes where harvesting is done by fishers, but they may interfere with seine harvesting.

Figure 5.32 Pond with riprap consisting of broken concrete.

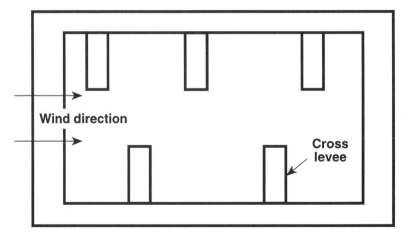

Figure 5.33 Top view of sportfishing pond with cross levees.

Fencing is practiced in areas where cattle drink from ponds. The ponds should be fenced off so that cattle may use only one small area.

Certain species of marginal vegetation, such as spike rush (*Eleocharis obtusa*), are sometimes planted or encouraged to grow at the water's edge to combat erosion (Figure 5.34). If semi-aquatic plants are used, be sure that they do not invade the pond and become a problem. Dense vegetation may encourage snakes and other predators and pests, too.

Figure 5.34 Spike rush growing along pond edge to prevent erosion.

Other Considerations

Levee ponds with sufficient freeboard are usually safe from flood waters. Stand pipes serve as trickle tubes to remove excess water. Watershed ponds that use surface run-off water require a spillway (Figure 5.35). A diversion ditch may be needed to handle excess water.

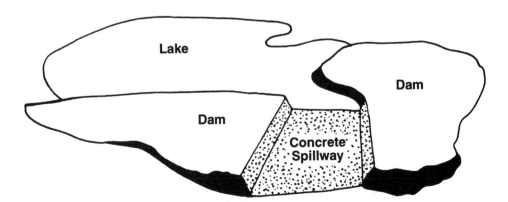

Figure 5.35 Spillway to handle excess water.

The spillway should allow excess water to leave the pond in thin sheets. A culture species may leave the pond if the depth of the outflow is greater than 7.6 cm (3 in). To determine the size of the spillway required, the watershed draining into the pond should be estimated. This figure, in hectares, is divided by 2.65 (2 if in acres) to give a rough estimate of the spillway width. An extra 3 m (10 ft) should be added as a safety margin.

For example, assume that a watershed has 16 ha (40 ac). Dividing by 2.65 (by 2 for acres) gives 6 m (20 ft) as the width of spillway needed. Add 3 m as a safety margin, and you have a spillway 9 m (30 ft) wide. All spillways, regardless of width, should have a minimum drop of 0.9 m (3 ft) on the outside to prevent entry of wild fish. Rocks or a concrete slab in the spillway prevent erosion. Sodded spillways may be adequate if surplus water is not excessive. Diversion ditches divert excess water around the pond. Muddy water also may be shunted around a pond. A pipe from ditch to pond should be installed so that water can either enter the pond or be shunted around the pond.

A final consideration is the need to deepen the pond edge by 45 to 76 cm (18 to 30 in) (Figure 5.36). This helps to keep unwanted aquatic weeds from getting a foothold at the water's edge. An exception to the rule is when muskrats (*Ondatra zibethica*) are a serious problem. They dig holes in the levee and may cause leaks and cave-ins. If the levee has a gradual slope at the water's edge, muskrats are less apt to burrow than if the levee is steeper.

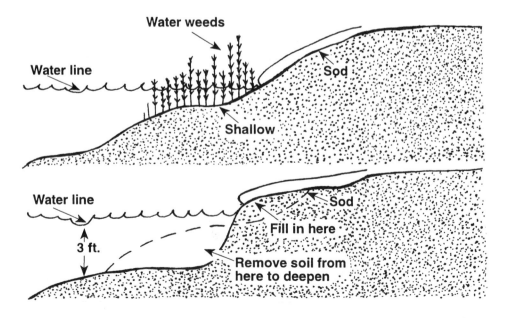

Figure 5.36 Pond edges should be deepened to keep aquatic weeds from growing.

THE POND LAYOUT

In the previous discussion a few basics were covered for pond construction. However, before the first pond is constructed, you must decide the pond layout. What size ponds should be constructed? What is the best depth and shape? How should they be arranged? Finally, who will construct the ponds and what will it cost?

Size of Ponds

The size of the ponds depends on general topography, experience of the fish farmer, culture species grown, water management, harvesting, marketing, and economics. The physical characteristics of the land will dictate to a degree the size of ponds that can be constructed. Generally, a beginning farmer should start with small ponds of 0.4 to 2 ha (1 to 5 ac), depending on whether culture is extensive, semi-intensive, or intensive. A master plan allows for larger ponds once experience is gained. Experienced channel catfish farmers use ponds of various sizes, depending on the particular operation. On the basis of trial and error, grow-out ponds may be 2 to 4 ha (5 to 10 ac) or 4 to 8 ha (10 to 20 ac). Brood ponds and rearing ponds are smaller, usually ranging from 1.2 to 2 ha (3 to 5 ac). Farmers in the Philippines prefer 0.5 ha (1.2 ac) ponds for intensive culture of shrimp. In Taiwan and Japan, ponds are often much smaller than this.

There are advantages and disadvantages of both large and small ponds regarding water management. Large ponds, without mechanical aeration, are less apt to have oxygen depletion than are small ponds because of better wind circulation. If the wind is strong, erosion of pond levees can become a problem. If disease occurs, it would be better to lose fish in a small pond for economic reasons.

Harvesting and marketing must be considered in determining pond size. Do you have the necessary gear to harvest fish properly and do you have a market for all the fish you harvest at one time? For example, assume that a 4-ha pond (10-ac) pond is stocked with 10,000 finfish per ha (4,000/ac). This is a total of 40,000 fish. If they are grown to 0.5 kg (1.1 lb) each, you have 20,000 kg (44,100 lb) of fish to harvest and market, assuming no mortality. If all you have is one 15-m (50-ft) long seine and a number 3 washtub, you have an impossible job ahead of you. Can you sell all of these fish at once? If fish are partially harvested by topping off, many of these problems are alleviated.

Finally, economics play a major role in deciding what size pond to construct. Larger ponds are cheaper to build than smaller ponds because less soil is moved for each hectare of pond constructed. The cost of pond construction is based largely on the volume of soil needed for the levees. For a 2:1 slope the formula, using English measurements, is L(2H + T)H ÷ 27 =

cubic yards per linear foot of levee where H = height of levee in feet, T = top width of levee in feet, and L = linear feet of levee. For a 3:1 slope, the formula is L(3H + T)H ÷ 27.

Problem and Solution. Assume a pond with a 2:1 slope, levee height of 8 ft, and a top width of 12 ft. Calculate cubic yards of soil needed per linear foot of levee.

From the above formula, L(2H + T)H ÷ 27, we derive: 1(2 x 8 + 12)8 ÷ 27 and this equals (16 + 12)8 ÷ 27 that equals 28 x 8 ÷ 27, giving 8.3 yd^3 of soil per linear foot of levee. Also assume that the pond is rectangular and is 100 ft wide and 400 ft long. The total length of levees is 1,000 linear ft, two sides 100 ft wide and two sides 400 ft long. Therefore, 1,000 x 8.3 = 8,300 yd^3 of soil.

Problem and Solution. Using metric measurements, calculate the volume of soil in a pond levee with a 2:1 slope, top width of 3.5 m and a height of 2.5 m.

In this example, we will calculate cubic meters of soil in two steps. First, the rectangular portion of the levee shows 2.5 x 3.5 x 1 = 8.75 m^3 of soil per linear meter of levee (Figure 5.24). Next, the pond levee has two triangular portions of equal dimensions. Combined, soil contained here is 2.5 x 5 x 1 = 12.5 m^3. The total volume of soil per linear meter of levee is then 8.75 + 12.5 = 21.25 m^3. If the inside slope is 3:1 and the outside slope is 2:1, the volume of soil must be calculated separately for each triangular portion of the levee. This two-step method can be used to calculate the volume of soil in a levee when English measurements are used; divide by 27 and the answer is in cubic yards.

Problem and Solution. Is it less costly to build ten 1-ac ponds or one 10-ac pond based on the volume of soil required? Assume that all ponds are square and have levees with a 2:1 slope, top width of 10 ft and a height of 8 ft, and that the ten 1-ac ponds do not connect with one another.

For a 1-ac pond each of the four sides will be 209 ft (there are 43,560 ft^2 in an acre). Therefore L(2H + T)H ÷ 27 gives 4 x 209(16 + 10)8 ÷ 27 = 6,430 yd^3 of soil required for one 1-ac pond. Ten 1-ac ponds would require 10 x 6,4300 = 64,300 yd^3 of soil. For a 10-ac pond each side is 660 ft. Therefore L(2H + T)H ÷ 27 gives 4 x 660 (16 + 10)8 ÷ 27 = 20,337 yd^3 of soil. Thus one 10-ac pond requiring 20,337 yd^3 of soil would be more than three times cheaper to construct than ten 1-ac ponds requiring 64,300 yd^3 of soil. Further, more land is required for the ten 1-ac ponds, costing more.

Depth and Shape of Ponds

The depth of ponds depends on species cultured, feed delivery system, water management system, and on geographic location. Shrimp ponds in the Philippines and Indonesia, where formulated feeds are used, are close to 122 cm (4 ft) in depth. Ponds for channel catfish and most other warmwater culture species should average 122 cm in depth. Where extensive culture is practiced, shrimp ponds may average 45 to 60 cm (18 to 24 in). Crawfish ponds in Louisiana average 46 to 61 cm (18 to 24 in) in depth. Rice is often planted as a forage crop for the crawfish (Figure 5.37). In Asia milkfish (*Chanos chanos*) ponds are only about 46 cm (18 in) deep. This is because the soil of the pond bottom is fertilized to produce algae and other organisms as food for the fish. It is therefore necessary for sunlight to reach the pond bottom. Milkfish ponds in Taiwan, where ponds are fertilized to produce plankton and fish are fed, may be 122 cm deep.

Figure 5.37 Shallow crawfish pond in Louisiana with rice forage.

Deeper ponds are more expensive to construct, and water near the bottom often becomes depleted of oxygen during summer because of stratification. A water circulation system that moves water throughout the water column can sometimes eliminate this problem. In northern states ponds must be deeper, 1.8 to 2.4 m (6 to 8 ft). This is to safeguard against winter kill caused by low dissolved oxygen. When ice forms on the surface followed by snow, sunlight is blocked out. This reduces sunlight, photosynthesis, and oxygen production. In summer, trout may seek deeper water because it is cooler.

Pond shape is dictated by harvesting techniques, water management, and economics. Ponds constructed long and rectangular facilitate ease of harvest. Some fish farmers like a pond that is one and a half to two times as long as it is wide. This accommodates their harvesting gear. Channel catfish farmers, for example, pull a seine through the pond with two tractors, one going down each levee. Consider also the distance necessary to move soil during construction; the further it takes to move soil, the more it costs.

Some ponds are round. They are more difficult to construct and require more land, but they may be easier for maintaining good water quality. Square or rectangular ponds may have low dissolved oxygen in the corners because of poor water circulation. Round ponds, usually 1 ha or less (2.5 ac), are most often used in high-intensive culture, such as shrimp culture. Paddlewheel aerators, positioned at the outer perimeter of the pond, circulate the water throughout the pond. Feces and other wastes are moved by mechanical circulation to the center. A stand pipe with an outer sleeve removes the wastes. Wyban and Sweeney (1991) described a round pond used for commercial shrimp culture. In grow-out, it can produce 4,000 kg (8,820 lb) per crop (Figure 5.38). A center drain removes sludge. A skimmer box removes windblown debris and foam generated from paddlewheel aeration.

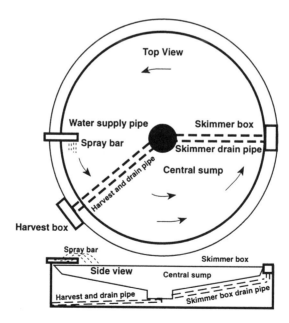

Figure 5.38 Round pond design by the Oceanic Institute, Makapuu Point, Honolulu, Hawaii. After Wyban and Sweeney 1991; modified by Rosenberry, World Shrimp Farming 1992 Volume 17 Number 3.

Small nursery ponds made of concrete are often square. Aeration may be from rows of submerged air stones. The drain is located in the center (Figure 5.39). Some ponds may have a trench down the center where wastes that collect are removed by manual pumping (Figure 5.40). Although a rectangular or round pond may have advantages, a square pond is cheaper to construct based on earth-moving requirements. However, other factors already discussed must be considered.

Figure 5.39 Small concrete nursery ponds used in Taiwan for shrimp.

Figure 5.40 Concrete pond with trenches to collect sludge for manual removal.

Problem and Solution. How many linear feet of levee are there to construct in a square 1-ac pond versus a rectangular 1-ac pond?

A square 1-ac pond will have all four sides 209 ft long. This gives 835 total linear ft. A rectangular pond might have two sides 100 ft long and two sides 436 ft long, giving a total of 1,071 linear ft.

Arrangement of Ponds

The numbers of ponds, size of ponds, and their arrangement depend on land available for construction, capital required, and other factors already discussed. In Jamaica, a typical tilapia operation devotes 10% of pond space to spawning activities, 30% to fingerling production, and 60% to grow-out. An operation for channel catfish might have four square or nearly square ponds where levees are shared, thus lowering construction cost (Figure 5.41). A well is in the center; less pipe is required for the drain and supply lines. Another possible arrangement uses rectangular ponds (Figure 5.42). Here again common levees are shared. Regardless of the size or shape, ponds should have the same depth and width, so that the same harvesting gear may be used for all. Notice that ponds shown in Figure 5.42 for grow-out of channel catfish use most of the area and that a much smaller area is required for a rearing pond, holding pond, and a spawning pond. Storage area would include buildings to store feed, chemicals, seines, nets, and farm equipment. A pole shed with a tin roof is commonly used to house tanks needed to hold and sort fish before stocking or shipment (Figure 5.43). A fish farmer should think about future needs. Let's look at a hypothetical master plan.

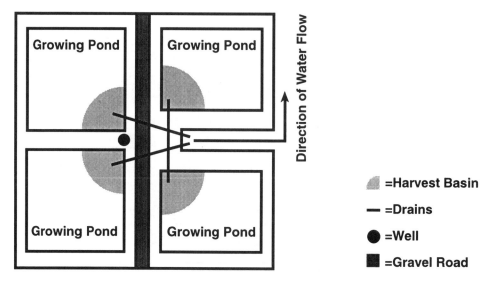

Figure 5.41 Possible arrangement for grow-out ponds. After Lee 1971.

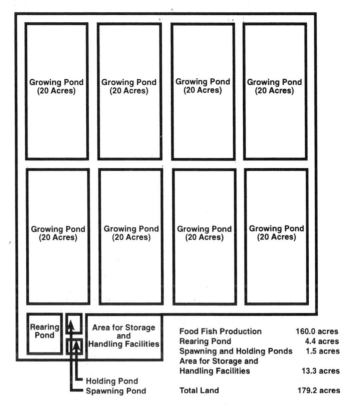

Figure 5.42 Arrangement of ponds for producing food fish and fingerlings. Note that a portion of each pond is occupied by the levee; therefore, the area of water in each pond is somewhat less than 20 acres. After Lee 1973.

Figure 5.43 Pole shed with concrete tanks. Water is flushed through tanks with pumps, and electric agitators aerate water.

Problem and Solution. A channel catfish farmer wishes to build sixteen 4-ha (10-ac) ponds to grow out channel catfish. The farmer also wants to spawn fish and rear fingerlings to stock grow-out ponds. How many and what size brood ponds and rearing ponds are needed?

Assume that grow-out ponds are stocked at a rate of 12,500 fingerlings per ha (5,000/ac), then 64 ha x 12,500 (160 ac x 5,000) = approximately 800,000 fingerlings needed. Assume that each pair of brood catfish produces 10,000 young, then 80 pair of brood catfish are needed. Half will be males and half will be females. If each fish averages 1.8 kg (4 lb), then we would require 288 kg (635 lb) of brood fish. A 1-ha (2.5 ac) pond would suffice as a brood pond. However, as a safety margin against oxygen depletion, a larger pond double in size might be advisable. Some farmers separate brood stock by sex into separate ponds until the spawning season begins. One or two spawning ponds, about the same size as brood ponds, would be required. The rearing pond would be somewhat larger. If fry are stocked into a rearing pond at a rate of 60,000/ha (24,000/ac) to grow to fingerling size, then a 13.3-ha (33-ac) rearing pond would be needed. It would be best, however, to have three 4.5-ha (11-ac) ponds or possibly five 2.6-ha (6.6-ac) ponds so that a smaller number of fingerlings would be handled at any one time. Also, it is a good idea to spread out fingerlings in several ponds. This will avoid a total loss caused by disease or low dissolved oxygen. The pond sizes used in this example are odd sizes to fit the particular problem.

Contracting Construction of Ponds

Some fish farmers may own or have access to a bulldozer and other equipment. If not, how is work contracted? Once the pond layout is determined, bids may be obtained from various construction companies. Bids may be based on the total job, often called a turn-key operation, on the volume of soil to move, or on the hours required. Turn-key operations require that the contractor build the entire pond system. The contractor is furnished with the plans, and buys and installs pipe and other materials in addition to building the levees. This is the most expensive way to build ponds. Even experienced construction companies must pad the bid to take into account unforeseen problems such as increased cost of pipe and inclement weather. Cost of construction can be lowered if the fish farmer contributes some work such as staking off levees.

The charge for levee construction can be based on volume of soil to move. The bid will reflect the distance the earth must be moved and how busy the potential contractor is at the time. An almost exact cost can be determined before work begins. Clearing of trees and brush from the land may be bid separately. The fish farmer stakes off the levees, lays pipe, and does other necessary work.

The hours of work required also may be a basis for bidding. If the fish farmer overestimates the total hours needed, there is usually no penalty. The contractor charges only for those hours worked and not for the estimated hours. The fish farmer must decide what kind of equipment is needed, and how many hours the construction will take. Normally, a bulldozer with operator rents by the hour. The more hours requested, the lower the rate may be. Bulldozers, depending on the size and other factors, may rent for $50 an hour to more than $100 an hour. Some bulldozers can be leased, and the fish farmer furnishes the operator. A fish farmer should consult with the Soil Conservation Service, Cooperative Extension Service, or other appropriate agency.

STUDY QUESTIONS

1. List and briefly discuss factors that must be taken into consideration when choosing a site for aquaculture.

2. List and briefly define the culture systems used in aquaculture. Give an example of a culture species commonly grown in each system.

3. Assume a pond with a 3:1 slope, levee height of 8 ft, and a top width of 15 ft. Calculate cubic yards of soil needed per linear foot of levee.

4. Using metric measurements, calculate the volume of soil per linear meter in a pond levee with a 3:1 slope, top width of 3.5 m, and a height of 2.5 m.

5. Illustrate with examples ways in which to lower the cost of building ponds, relative to earth moving. Show math.

6. Besides the cost of construction, what are the best size, shape, depth, and arrangement for ponds? Qualify your answer.

7. A pond is 20 acres (ac) in size. How many hectares (ha) are these?

8. A pond has one levee that is 38 meters long. How many feet are these?

9. A pond has two sides that are 300 ft long and two sides that are 400 ft long. How many surface acres are these? Convert this answer to hectares.

REFERENCES

Allen, J.S. and A.C. Lopinot (no date). Small lakes and ponds: their construction and care. Illinois Department of Conservation, Division of Fisheries. Fishery Bulletin No. 3. 23 pp.

Anonymous. 1969. Standards for fish hatchery development. U.S. Department of Interior, Fish and Wildlife Service, Bureau of Sport Fisheries and Wildlife, August 1969. 13 pp.

Anonymous. 1971. Ponds for water supply and recreation. U.S. Department of Agriculture, Soil Conservation Service. Agriculture Handbook No. 387. 55 pp.

Anonymous. (no date). Aquaculture facilities, ponds, pens, tanks, cages. Kevgor Aquasystems, P. O. Box 488512, 595 Burrard St., Vancouver, B.C. V7X1A8 Canada.

Armstrong, J., H. Bissell, R. Davenport, J. Goodman, M. Hershman, J. Sorensen, L. Sloan and D. Wormhoudt. 1974. Coastal Zone Management: The Process of

Program Development. Coastal Zone Management Institute, P.O. Box 221, Sandwich, MA 02563. 177 pp.

Avault, J.W., Jr. 1974. The EPA's proposed regulations affect cage culture in heated effluents. Commercial Fish Farmer & Aquaculture News 1(1):14-15.

Avault, J.W., Jr. 1994a. Where to locate your aquaculture operation. Aquaculture Magazine 20(1):76-80.

Avault, J.W., Jr. 1994b. Culture systems for growing aquatic species: Part I. Aquaculture Magazine 20(5):59-64.

Avault, J.W., Jr. 1994c. Culture systems for growing aquatic species: Part II. Aquaculture Magazine 20(6):75-80.

Bean, R.A., T. Baum, M. Lamon, J.W. Avault, Jr., M.W. Moody, L. de la Bretonne and G.L. Jensen. 1988. Louisiana aquaculture potential: a parish-by-parish assessment. Louisiana State University Agricultural Center. 323 pp.

Beveridge, M. 1987. Cage Aquaculture. Surrey, England: Fishing News (Books) Ltd. 352 pp.

Brett, J.R. 1974. Marine fish aquaculture in Canada. In Aquaculture in Canada: the practice and the promise. Fisheries Research Board of Canada. Bulletin 188:55-84.

Buss, K., D.R. Graff and E.R. Miller. 1970. Trout culture in vertical units. Progressive Fish-Culturist 32(4):187-191.

Caine, G.D. 1987. Biophysical criteria for siting salmon farms in British Columbia. Aquaculture Association of B.C. Suite 52, Comp. 103, 5331 Hammond Bay Road Nanaimo, B.C., V9S 5N7. 49 pp.

Chesness, J.L., J.L. Stephens and T.K. Hill. 1972. Gravity flow aerators for raceway fish culture systems. University of Georgia, Georgia Agricultural Experiment Station. Research Report 137. 21 pp.

Cross, S.F. and B.C. Kingzett. 1992. Biophysical criteria for shellfish culture in British Columbia, a site capability evaluation system. Aquametrix Research Ltd., 204-2527 Beacon Avenue, Sidney B.C. V8L IYI. 40 pp.

Down, R. 1973. Culture and politics of off-bottom oyster farming in Cape May County, New Jersey. Proceedings of the World Mariculture Society 4:369-387.

Eipper, A.W. 1960. Managing farm ponds for trout production. New York State College of Agriculture. Cornell Extension Bulletin 1036. 31 pp.

Fournier, F. 1975. Institutional constraints to the development of aquaculture. Marine Fisheries Review 37(1):31-32.

Gates, J.M., G.C. Matthiessen and C.A. Griscom. 1974. Aquaculture in New England. University of Rhode Island. Marine Technical Report Series No. 18. 77 pp. (see especially pages 56-68 on land site availability).

Grizzell, R.A. 1967. Pond construction and economic considerations in catfish farming. Proceedings Southeastern Association of Game and Fish Commissioners 21:459-472.

Hall, M.D. 1972. Confinement catfish culture. Proceedings Catfish Production and Management Conference, University of Illinois 1972:26-30.

Hill, T.K., J.L. Chesness and E.E. Brown. 1973. A two-crop fish production system. Transactions American Society of Agricultural Engineers 16(5):930-933.

Hill, T.K., J.L. Chesness and E.E. Brown. 1973. Growing channel catfish, *Ictalurus punctatus* (Rafinesque), in raceways. Proceedings Southeastern Association of Game and Fish Commissioners 27:488-499.

Jensen, J.W. 1990. Watershed fish production ponds, site selection and construction. Southern Regional Aquaculture Center Publication 2394.

Kato, J. 1975. Guide to design and construction of coastal aquaculture ponds. Japan International Cooperative Agency. 76 pp.

Kelly, J.R. 1973. An improved cage design for use in culturing channel catfish. Progressive Fish-Culturist 35(3):167-169.

Landy, B.A. 1975. Constraints on aquaculture projects. Marine Fisheries Review 37(1): 33-35.

Lawrence, J.M. 1949. Construction of farm fish ponds. Alabama Agricultural Experiment Station, Auburn, Alabama. Circular No. 95. 55 pp.

Lee, J.S. 1971. Catfish Farming. Mississippi State University Curriculum Coordinating Unit for Vocational-Technical Education. 103 pp.

Lee, J.S. 1973. Commercial Catfish Farming. Illinois: The Interstate Printers & Publishers Inc. 263 pp.

Leitritz, E. 1972. Trout and salmon culture. California Department of Fish and Game. Fish Bulletin No. 107. 169 pp.

Lutz, C.G. 1994. Site selection for Louisiana finfish production. LSU Agricultural Center, Louisiana Cooperative Extension Service. Publication 2543.

Milne, P.H. 1972. Fish and Shellfish Farming in Coastal Waters. London: Fishing News (Books) Ltd. Press. 208 pp.

Moss, D. D. 1974. Design and plan for an aquaculture research center in Columbia. Aid for International Development, Auburn University Report. Mimeographed 43 pp.

New, M. 1975. The selection of sites for aquaculture. Proceedings of the World Mariculture Society 6:379-388.

Nyegaard, C. 1973. Coho salmon farming in Puget Sound. Washington State University, College of Agriculture, Washington Cooperative Extension Service. Extension Bulletin 647. 14 pp.

Pennell, W. 1992. Site selection handbook. Province of British Columbia Ministry of Agriculture, Fisheries & Food Aquaculture and Commercial Fisheries Branch. 15 pp.

Perry, W.G., Jr. 1972. Marsh pond construction. Proceedings of the World Mariculture Society 3:149-165.

Ricker, K.E., J.W. McDonald and B. de Lange Boom. 1989. Biophysical suitability of the western Johnstone Strait, Queen Charlotte Strait and west coast Vancouver Island regions for salmonid farming in net cages. Province of British Columbia, Ministry of Agriculture and Fisheries, Aquaculture and Commercial Fisheries Branch. 126 pp.

Roe, A. and E. Segal. 1974. Engineering and economic design considerations for aquaculture facilities. Proceedings of the World Mariculture Society 5:371-378.

Swingle, W.E. 1971. A marine cage design. Progressive Fish-Culturist 33(2):102.

United Nations Development Program. 1984. Inland Aquaculture Engineering. Food and Agriculture Organization of the United Nations. 591 pp.

U.S. Department of Interior. 1970. National Estuary Study. Volume 5, Appendix F.

Webber, H.H. 1972. The design of an aquaculture enterprise. Proceedings Gulf and Caribbean Fisheries Institute 24:117-125.

Webber, H.H. 1973. Risks to the aquaculture enterprise. Proceedings of the World Mariculture Society 4:19-33.

Webber, H.H. 1975. Crustacean aquaculture in Middle America. Marine Fisheries Review 37 (1):24-30.

Weeks, J.P. and C.B. Ogburn. 1975. Catfish production guide. Auburn University, Alabama Cooperative Extension Service. Circular E-18. 51 pp.

Wellborn, T.L. 1990. Site selection of levee-type fish production ponds. Southern Regional Aquaculture Center, Publication 2409.

Wyban, J.A. and J.N. Sweeney. 1991. Intensive Shrimp Production Technology. The Oceanic Institute Shrimp Manual. The Oceanic Institute, Makapuu Point, Honolulu, Hawaii. 158 pp.

CHAPTER 6
WATER REQUIREMENTS

A sufficient supply of good quality water is essential in aquaculture. In this chapter, we discuss various sources of water and determine the quantity and quality of water required. The quantity of water required depends on the species cultured, density or stocking rate, culture system employed, rate of water exchange, and size of operation. The quality of source water will be considered from two standpoints. First, we consider basic parameters, such as water temperature, salinity, dissolved oxygen, free carbon dioxide, total alkalinity, and total hardness, and how these parameters relate to reproduction, growth, and general well-being of culture species. Second, we consider various pollutants and toxins that may be found in source water and how they may affect culture species.

SOURCES OF WATER

Sources of water for aquaculture include: (1) rainfall and surface runoff, (2) streams and rivers, (3) lakes and reservoirs, (4) brackish water, (5) saline water, (6) well or ground water, (7) springs, and (8) municipal water.

Rainfall and Surface Runoff

Rainwater and surface runoff are the chief sources of water to fill watershed ponds and excavated ponds. The amount of runoff entering a pond depends on the size and nature of the watershed and the volume of rainfall. A watershed can be described by the phrase "water runs downhill." Watersheds are separated by divides that are usually ridge tops. The type of soil and vegetative cover, and the degree of soil saturation, affect the amount of runoff. Runoff is greatest from clay soils, least for sandy soils, and intermediate for loamy soils. Runoff from grasslands is twice as much as from forests. Fish ponds should not be constructed in poorly vegetated or row-cropped watersheds because runoff will be laden with silt. Agricultural land also may be a source of pesticide contamination.

Streams and Rivers

A portion of a stream or river may be diverted to fill ponds (Figures 6.1, 6.2). In some instances, a pump is used to transfer water directly from a stream into ponds. This is common practice of crawfish (*Procambarus* spp.)

farmers in Louisiana. A stream, or a portion of it, may be diverted through raceways. The water may or may not be reused. In the Snake River valley of Idaho, an underground or "lost" river emerges from a bluff and flows by gravity through trout raceways (Figure 6.3). Streams and rivers are used for cage culture and net-pen culture.

Figure 6.1 Water control structure in Jamaica diverting water of Black River to ponds.

Figure 6.2 A portion of Black River being diverted to tilapia ponds.

Figure 6.3 A portion of a lost river in Idaho emerging from bluff supplies raceways. Note netting to prevent bird predation.

If stream or river water is used, legality and the possibility of pollution should be considered. You should check pollution from upstream agricultural, industrial, and municipal sources. The U.S. Environmental Protection Agency has regulations for effluents from culture facilities. Other requisites for stream and river water are: (1) adequate flow, (2) absence of excessive flooding, (3) a well-vegetated watershed, (4) relatively clear water that carries little silt, and (5) ability to screen out or remove wild fish.

Lakes and Reservoirs
Water may be pumped from lakes or reservoirs to fill ponds. If so, water should be filtered to keep out wild fish. Cage culture and net-pen culture are practiced in certain areas, but legal-socio-cultural issues must be considered in public waters. Culture systems such as raceways and tanks may rely on lake water as a source (Figure 6.4). Water flows by gravity from a reservoir lake through the culture facility. The system may be recirculating. If so, effluent is collected below in a second reservoir. The water quality is improved through biological and chemical processes in the lake. Water is pumped back to the first reservoir for re-use. Reservoir lakes should have several days of extra water supply for the culture facility in case the pump breaks down. The extra days allow a cushion of time for repair or replacement.

Figure 6.4 Reservoir in North Carolina being used as water source for raceways. Photo at Jennings-Sunburst Trout Farm, located in Sunburst, North Carolina.

Brackish Water

Estuaries represent a meeting place of fresh water, as runoff from land, and the sea; water quality is subject to particularly drastic changes. The salinity of estuarine water depends on rainfall, the amount of runoff from the land, and evaporation. During periods of high rainfall, rivers and streams emptying into estuaries may reduce salinity to near fresh water, less than 0.5 ppt. During periods of drought and high evaporation the salinity may reach or exceed that of the sea, approximately 36 ppt.

If estuaries are considered as a water source, you should study the water quality for a period of several years. Often such information is available from governmental agencies. In addition to water quality, pollution and legal aspects must be considered.

Brackish water is used to fill ponds constructed in the coastal zone. Ponds with weir structures are flushed with the tides. Shrimps, certain species of finfish, and mollusks are cultured in brackish water. Mollusks, being sessile, do not require ponds and may be cultured in open waters, either on the water bottom or off-bottom as in raft culture. Protected ocean bays can be used for net-pen culture.

Saline Water

Saline water, or seawater, provides a source of water for sea ranching and for submerged net-pen culture. The water quality of seawater is relatively constant, compared with estuarine water. Perhaps a major concern is for occasional oil spills. In off-shore waters an occasional violent storm may pose a problem for net-pen culture; that is why pens should be submerged.

Well Water

Well water, or ground water, is often used to fill channel catfish (*Ictalurus punctatus*) ponds (Figure 6.5). It is a reliable source and is usually located on the fish farmer's property. Wells also may furnish water for tank culture, silo culture, and for hatchery systems; they can be a source for mariculture. The cost of a well is determined by the diameter of the pipe or casing and depth of well.

Figure 6.5 Drilling rig bringing in water well at Ben Hur Farm, LSU Agricultural Center.

A pump is needed to bring the water up and out of the ground. Pumps require fuel such as natural gas, propane, gasoline, and diesel fuel (Figure 6.6). The best power source depends on site location, dependability, and cost. In developed countries, electricity is often preferred by aquaculturists because it is dependable; yet in developing countries diesel-powered pumps are frequently preferred. If electricity is used, it is necessary to have a standby generator on hand. The generator should be powered with fuel to safeguard against power outages caused by storms.

In some instances, the water table is near the surface, and water may flow on its own accord. Certain aquifers are recharged with river water. The Ben Hur Farm aquaculture facility of the LSU Agricultural Center is located near the Mississippi River. During spring rains when the river rises, the water well at Ben Hur has an artesian flow of water.

Figure 6.6 Diesel power unit for water well at Ben Hur Farm.

Well water is usually not be suitable for aquaculture as it comes out of the ground, but this can be rectified. Some common problems may involve low or high water temperatures, low level of dissolved oxygen, high free carbon dioxide content, high hydrogen sulfide content, and high ferrous iron content. If the water temperature is too low, a warming reservoir can be used. Well water is pumped (or allowed to flow if the well is artesian) into a reservoir where it is allowed to warm. Once the desired temperature is reached, water is moved to culture ponds. If the water temperature is too high, the same technique may be used. Atmospheric temperature helps stabilize water temperature.

Aeration of well water will help solve problems of low dissolved oxygen, high free carbon dioxide, and high hydrogen sulfide or iron content. Aeration of well water may be accomplished a number of ways. Here are a few examples: (1) splash incoming water over a series of screens to expose it to the atmosphere (Figure 6.7) or put a specialized valve on the water supply pipe to break water flow into small droplets (Figure 6.8), (2) pump water first into a reservoir for aging before filling culture ponds, (3) use mechanical aerators, (4) allow water to flow over a well-sodded levee before entering pond, and (5) allow water to flow down an open ditch before entering culture ponds.

Figure 6. 7 Well water being aerated through a series of screens before entering ponds.

Figure 6.8 Special valve on end of pipe to break water up into a froth. Note angle of pipe to augment breaking up of water column.

Springs

Springs furnish a good source of water for raceways and ponds. There are two types of springs. In one type, water comes out of the ground in a very small area to produce a rather heavy, constant flow. The other type usually covers a large area; water seeps out of the ground. Strip mine pits are sometimes filled from such seepage. Since springs are supplied from ground water, problems are similar to those for well water. Again, corrective measures listed above may be employed when applicable.

Municipal Water

Municipal or treated domestic water is sometimes used when only a small quantity of water is needed. An example might be a tank-culture system that is recirculating. In some instances only a part of the aquaculture operation uses municipal water -- a hatchery, holding tanks, or tanks for the culture of live shrimp food, to name a few. Chlorine must be removed or the culture species will die. Aeration of water for a day or so will usually remove chlorine. Chlorine, being a gas, will dissipate. Make-up water can be aerated in a reserve tank before it is added to the system. If only a small amount of water is involved, sodium thiosulfate can be added to water to neutralize chlorine. A large volume of water may be expensive to treat.

QUANTITY OF WATER NEEDED

The quantity of water required depends on: (1) the species cultured, (2) density or stocking rate of the culture species, (3) culture system employed, (4) rate of water exchange (evaporation, seepage, and waste), and (5) size of the operation.

Some culture species require very high-quality water, whereas other species do not. Rainbow trout (*Oncorhynchus mykiss*), for example, require a higher oxygen content than do tilapia. To maintain a high level of oxygen, a greater volume of water may be required if other options, such as mechanical aeration, are not available.

The density, or stocking rate, of a culture species also determines the quantity of water needed. For example, assume that channel catfish fingerlings are stocked into a grow-out pond at a rate of 5,000/ha (2,000/ac). Generally the pond is filled once, and water is added later only to replace that lost from evaporation and seepage. Bacteria and other microorganisms are able to decompose fish wastes into harmless byproducts. If, however, channel catfish are stocked at a rate of 20,000/ha (8,000/ac), it may be necessary to flush extra water through the pond from time to time to maintain good water quality. Accumulated waste products from fish cause deterioration of water quality. At the higher stocking rate, pond microorganisms are not able to decompose or assimilate wastes as quickly as they accumulate. Flushing helps to remove wastes mechanically.

Regardless of the species cultured or the stocking density, a sufficient quantity of water must be available to maintain high-quality water. The rest of our discussion will focus on the quantity of water required for different culture systems of various sizes.

Pond Culture

The volume of water required to fill a pond is usually expressed in cubic meters or in acre feet. To determine cubic meters of water required to fill a pond, multiply average length of the pond (m) x average width (m) x average depth (m). The average depth of the pond can be estimated if it is not known by taking depth soundings at intervals. Most ponds have some slope to the inside levee, so this must be considered when determining the average depth of the pond. If you wish to convert cubic meters to liters, multiply by 1,000 (one cubic meter = 1,000 liters). If you wish to convert liters to gallons, divide by 3.785 (1 gal = 3.785 liters).

One acre foot is the amount of water required to cover 1 acre 1 foot deep. If, for example, a 5-ac pond has an average depth of 5 ft, the pond contains 25 ac ft (5 x 5) of water. The surface acreage can be determined if it is not known. Use the following formula: average length of pond (ft) x average width (ft) ÷ 43,560 = surface acres (43,560 ft^2 = 1 acre).

Problem and Solution. A pond is 1,000 ft long, 871 ft wide and has an average depth of 4 ft. Calculate the acre feet of water needed to fill the pond. Surface area equals 1,000 x 871 ÷ 43,560 = 20, and acre feet equals 20 x 4 = 80.

If well water is used to fill ponds, the capacity of the well is usually expressed in gallons per minute (gpm). This can be converted to acre feet because 1 ac ft of water contains approximately 326,000 gal. This information is needed when determining the size of water well required. For example, a well producing 1,000 gpm produces 4.4 ac ft of water in 24 hours. A 1,000 gpm well is considered adequate for a 40-ac fish farm. If the 40 ac of ponds average 4 ft deep, then 160 ac ft (40 x 4) of water are needed to fill all ponds. The well should take a little over 36 days (160 ÷ 4.4 ac ft in 24 hours) to produce 160 ac ft of water.

Normally, not all ponds are filled simultaneously; instead they are usually filled one or a few at a time. Regardless, no pond should require more than 2 weeks to fill. Prolonged shallow water invites invasion of obnoxious aquatic weeds. Ponds of most aquaculture operations need filling only once per year. Some grow-out ponds for channel catfish may go 5 years or more before being drained. Fish are harvested by seining with the pond full of water. Small holding ponds and spawning ponds may sometimes need refilling more than once per year.

Once ponds are filled, water is needed to replace that lost from seepage and evaporation. Water also may be required to flush ponds to improve water quality. Seepage can be minimized by building ponds in an area containing sufficient clay. Bentonite or plastic-like sealers reduce seepage in porous soils, but they are an added expense. Evaporation may be almost negligible in moist, cool climates, but may be quite high in hot climates. Evaporation loss may reach 2.5 cm (1 in) per day in dry tropical areas. Boyd (1982, 1985, 1986, 1987) and Yoo and Boyd (1994) expressed the water budget for a typical levee pond as P + WR = (S + E) ΔV where:

P = Precipitation
WR = Water required from well
S = Seepage
E = Evaporation
ΔV = Change in storage

In research ponds at the Ben Hur Farm of the LSU Agricultural Center, the annual loss of water to evaporation may reach 122 cm (48 in). This is offset by an annual rainfall of 152 cm (60 in). The critical need for water is in summer when evaporation, coupled with seepage, is highest. Fish farmers using ground water should have virtually no trouble getting this extra water when it is needed. Those depending on surface runoff, however, must wait as patiently as possible until it rains.

Problem and Solution. Assume that a fish farm contains 20 ponds with a total of 400 surface acres. The average depth of all ponds is 4 ft, and ponds are filled once during the year. Annual evaporation and seepage losses total 36 in., and annual rainfall is 24 in. Determine: (1) total acre feet of water needed to fill all ponds, (2) size and number of wells in gallons per minute required, and (3) quantity of water needed to replace that lost by evaporation and seepage.

(1) The acre feet of water needed to fill all ponds is: 400 surface ac x 4 ft = 1,600.
(2) As stated earlier, a 1,000 gpm well is adequate for a 40-ac fish farm. For a 400-ac fish farm, 10 wells producing 1,000 gpm are required. When fish farms exceed 40 ac, wells larger than 1,000 gpm are often required. The number of wells needed and their capacity should be carefully evaluated. Factors to consider include feasibility and cost of sinking various sized wells, layout of the particular fish farm, and schedule of harvesting and filling ponds.
(3) The acre feet of water needed to replace that lost by evaporation and seepage is: 36 in. loss - 24 in. gain = 12 in. or 1 ft of water to replace. For 400 ac of ponds this becomes 400 ac ft (400 x 1) of water.

Raceway Culture

The quantity of water required for raceway culture is usually expressed in terms of flow rate. In Idaho, trout farmers use cubic feet per second (cfs). In

North Carolina and certain other locations, flow rate is expressed in gallons per minute (gpm). One cfs equals approximately 450 gpm. Those raceway operations using metric terms express flow rate as cubic meters per second or liters per second. Trout farmers know that a certain flow-rate capacity produces a certain weight of fish. For example, Idaho trout farmers can produce up to 15,000 lb of trout for each cfs. The system is open, and water is not recirculated. With added aeration and oxygen injection, this weight is increased.

The quantity of water needed to supply raceways also depends on whether the system is open or recirculating. Figures 6.9 and 6.10 depict a recirculating system used for grow-out. Gravity-flow water leaves an uphill reservoir and flows through a series of raceways (Figure 6.9). From there it empties into a concrete ditch that empties into an earthen pond. Water is then pumped uphill to the reservoir (Figure 6.10).

Hill et al. (1973) described a recirculating raceway system used in Georgia. The system consists of eight connecting raceways. Each raceway is 30 m (100 ft) long, 3 m (10 ft) wide at the bottom, and has a side slope of 2:1 and an average depth of 91 cm (3 ft). Each raceway holds 144 m^3 (5,083 ft^3) of water. Therefore, eight raceways contain 1,152 m^3 (40,666 ft^3) of water. Cubic feet can be converted into gallons with the following formula: cubic feet to gallons = number of cubic feet x 7.481. Therefore, 40,666 ft^3 = 304,222 gal (40,666 x 7.481). Expressed still another way, the volume of water in all eight raceways combined is only 1,152 m^3 or less than 1 ac ft of water.

The water supply for this particular raceway system comes from a 2-ha (5-ac) lake containing 25,893 m^3 (21 ac ft) of water. A 2,271-liters/minute (600-gpm) well provides extra water when needed. Water is pumped from the 2-ha lake at a rate of 2,006 liters/minute (530 gpm) to the first raceway. From there on, the water flows by gravity to each succeeding raceway, and the water eventually returns to the 2-ha lake.

Problem and Solution. Assume that this system (Hill et al. 1973) is open (water is not reused) and that each raceway is separate and receives 2,006 liters/minute. What volume of water would be needed in a 24-hour period?

Since there are eight raceways, 16,048 liters/minute (8 x 2,006) or 4,240 gpm (8 x 530) are needed. For one hour, a total of 962,880 liters (60 x 16,048) or 254,400 gal (60 x 4,240) would be needed, and for 24 hours 23 million liters (6.1 million gal) are needed. This is a lot of water, and the pumping expense could be high. That is why most raceway systems use gravity-flow water from a natural river, stream, or spring.

234

Figure 6.9 Raceways being fed water from a gravity-flow reservoir uphill. Photo at Farmer's catfish operation in Arkansas.

Figure 6.10 Water pumped uphill to reservoir. Photo at Farmer's catfish operation.

Tank and Silo Culture

The quantity of water needed for tank and silo culture is relatively low if a recirculating system is used. Hall (1972) described a "fish barn" facility consisting of 2.83 m³ (100 ft³) capacity tanks receiving one water exchange every 8 hours. Each tank has its own separate inlet and outlet. Once water leaves the outlet, it is filtered through a gravel pit, returned to a reservoir pond, and ultimately re-used. From this, you can calculate the quantity of water needed based on the number of tanks. The volume of water needed for one tank each day (three 8-hour periods) would be 8.5 m³ (300 ft³). If the facility included 100 tanks, then 850 m³ (30,000 ft³) of water would be needed each day. Up to 10% to 15% of this volume may be required daily for make-up water because of evaporation and other losses. Allen (1972) described another tank facility consisting of 1,590-liter (420-gal) fiberglass tanks. This system, also recirculating, used flow rates varying from 12.5 to 47 liters/minute (3.3 to 12.5 gpm) for each tank.

In silo culture, the Pennsylvania Fish Commission has used silos that are 2.3 m (7.5 ft) in diameter and 5 m (16.5 ft) tall. A flow rate of 1,136 liters/minute (300 gpm) has been used. (Personal communication, C.H. Sanderson, Pennsylvania Fish Commission 1974.)

Cage and Net-pen Culture

The quantity of water required for cage or net-pen culture depends on several factors: stocking density of the culture species, water quality, and whether or not the species is cultured in an enclosed reservoir or an open-water system such as a river or ocean bay. Schwedler et al. (1989) found that when channel catfish were grown to 454 to 681 g (1 to 1.5 lb), fish reared in open ponds outperformed those reared in cages for feed conversion and growth. Fish in open ponds had access to natural food organisms. Davis et al. (1991) compared production of pan-sized channel catfish (227 g, 0.5 lb) in ponds and in cages held in ponds. They concluded that neither density nor production system affected production. Pan-sized catfish could be cultured well above 12,500 fish per hectare (5,000/ac).

Fish held in cages or net-pens cannot tolerate low levels of dissolved oxygen as well as the same species that is loose in a pond. For example, channel catfish loose in a pond show stress and may begin dying when the dissolved oxygen drops to approximately 1 ppm. In cages, fish will show signs of stress when the oxygen level reaches 2 ppm. As the oxygen level in a pond drops, fish swim to the surface to gulp oxygen. Fish in cages are crowded, and only the most robust can fight their way to the surface.

Cages or net-pens may be placed in reservoirs that contain native species. If so, these native species compete with the culture species for dissolved oxygen, and their waste products added to those of culture species help deteriorate water quality. Consequently, stocking rates of culture species should be reduced.

Cages or net-pens are often placed in streams or ocean bays. Very high stocking rates are possible. This is because of the flushing action from river and tidal currents. They maintain proper dissolved oxygen levels and remove wastes.

Sea Ranching

The quantity of water needed in sea ranching is normally low. A small volume of water is required for the hatchery, and the open sea furnishes space and water for growth of fish. Need for hatchery water is usually sporadic, occurring principally during the spawning season. There is an intermediate stage when young salmon are grown in net-pens before release. The weight handled, compared to grow-out in net-pen culture, is relatively low; so the quantity of water required is low.

Bottom Culture

The quantity of water needed for bottom culture of mollusks usually depends on the area of water bottoms leased from the state or government. A lessee may sometimes have several leases, but the total amount usually cannot exceed a certain hectarage, such as a 40-ha (100-ac) limit. Though mollusks are grown on a relatively small area, food (plankton) is carried in with the tides.

Off-bottom Culture

Tides carry in food and help to flush out waste products. Tremendous weight of mollusks can be produced with off-bottom culture in a relatively small area. For example, 300,000 kg/ha (267,900 lb/ac) of mussels (*Mytilus edulis*) have been grown in Galician bays of Spain. Yields of this magnitude, however, depend on a much larger volume of water than the area containing the rafts of mussels. Like bottom culture, water rights are generally leased from the government.

Open Sea Mariculture

Like off-bottom culture, there is potential to culture a tremendous weight of fish in a small area. Submerged pen culture is gaining interest. Again, though a species may be cultured in a relatively small area, the contiguous open sea dilutes wastes, and currents remove them.

QUALITY OF WATER NEEDED

All culture species and their various life stages have particular requirements for good quality water. The quality of certain sources of water, such as ground water from springs and wells, is relatively constant. Other water sources, such as estuarine waters, are subject to radical changes. Carefully check the history of these sources of water, rather than make a one-time evaluation of quality.

In this section, we look at the quality of source water from two standpoints. First, we consider basic parameters, such as water temperature, salinity, dissolved oxygen, free carbon dioxide, total alkalinity, and total hardness, and how these parameters relate to growth, reproduction, and general well-being of culture species. Second, we consider various pollutants and toxins that may be found in source water and how they affect culture species. For a more comprehensive treatment of water quality needs, refer to Water Quality Criteria of the National Academy of Science (1972). Many recommendations in this section regarding water quality are taken from this source. Other references are EPA (1976) and the critique of the EPA report by the American Fisheries Society (Thurston et al. 1979). Yoo and Boyd (1994) reviewed water supply for pond aquaculture.

Temperature

Perhaps no other factor, with the exception of salinity and dissolved oxygen, has such a profound effect on culture species as does water temperature. Fishery biologists long ago recognized this and lumped fishes into one of three categories for temperate climates: warmwater species, those that thrive above 21°C (70°F), and coldwater species, those that thrive below 21°C. Coolwater species prefer mid-range temperatures. Tropical and sub-tropical species do not grow well when water temperatures drop below approximately 26° to 28°C (79° to 82°F). The rainbow trout thrives at water temperatures between 7° and 15°C (45° and 59°F) (Table 6.1). At these temperatures, the channel catfish merely exists, growing very little if any. On the other hand, the channel catfish thrives in water at 28° to 32°C (82° to 90°F). At these temperatures, rainbow trout perish.

Table 6.1 Effect of water temperature on selected culture species; figures rounded off to the nearest whole number.

Channel catfish minimum spawning temperature, 21°C (70°); optimum hatching 27°C (81°F); best growth 28° to 32°C (82° to 90°F); feeding activity very low at 13°C (55°F) and below (West 1966; Avault 1971).

Bigmouth buffalo (*Ictiobus cyprinellus*) optimum spawning, 17°C (63°F); spawning range, 14° to 27°C (57° to 80°F); hatch of normal larvae, range 14° to 17°C (Eddy and Surber 1947).

Smallmouth buffalo (*I. bubalus*) optimum spawning temperature, 17°C (63°F); spawning range, 14° to 24°C (57° to 75°F); hatch of normal larvae, range 14° to 21°C (57° to 70° F) (Walker and Frank 1952).

Common carp (*Cyprinus carpio*) upper lethal temperature for juveniles when acclimated at 20°C (68°F) was 31° to 34°C (88° to 93°F) (24-hour TL50); upper lethal temperature for juveniles when acclimated at 26°C (79°F) was 36°C (97°F) (24-hour TL50) (Black 1953); optimum spawning, 20°C (68°F); spawning range, 16° to 26°C (61° to 79°F); hatch of normal larvae, range 17° to 22°C (63° to 72°F) (Swee and McCrimmon 1966; Carlander 1969).

Rainbow trout prefers temperatures between 7° and 13°C (45° to 55°F), a desirable range for rearing; a maximum summer temperature of 16° to 18°C (60° to 65°F) is satisfactory; winter temperatures below 5°C (40°F), no growth; temperatures above 21°C (70°F) tolerated for short periods (Davis 1961). In Idaho, trout growth is maximized at 14° to 15°C (58° to 59°F).

Brown trout (*Salmo trutta*) grows and functions better at temperatures slightly above those for rainbow trout, whereas brook trout (*Salvelinus fontinalis*) functions better at temperatures below rainbow trout (Davis 1961).

Atlantic salmon (*Salmo salar*) optimum growth for juveniles, 16° to 18°C (61° to 64°F); preferred range for adults, 14° to 16°C (57° to 61°F) (Ferguson 1958); spawning range, 4° to 6°C (39° to 43°F); hatch of normal fry 0.5° to 7°C (33° to 45°F) (DeCola 1970).

Pacific salmon, upper lethal temperatures -- coho salmon (*Oncorhynchus kisutch*), 25°C (77°F); chinook salmon (*O. tshawytscha*), 25°C; sockeye (*O. nerka*), 24°C (75°F); pink (*O. gorbuscha*), 24°C; and chum (*O. keta*), 24°C. Lower lethal temperatures with prior acclimation to 23°C (73°F) -- coho, 6°C (43°F); chinook, 7°C (45°F); sockeye, 7°C; chum, 7°C. Preferred range for most species was 12° to 14°C (54° to 57°F) (Brett 1952). Optimum temperature for growth -- chinook, 14°C; coho, 16°C (61°F) (Pennell 1992).

Pompano (*Trachinotus carolinus*) stop feeding and go into shock at water temperatures below 12°C (54°F) and die at 10°C (50°F); feeding reduced at 17°C (63°F); best growth at 25°C (77°F); can tolerate up to 33°C (91°F) (Moe et al. 1968; Finucane 1970).

Tilapia (*Oreochromis* spp. and *Tilapia* spp.) are tropical fish that die when water temperatures become too low. In laboratory studies, *O. mossambicus* began dying at 12°C, *O. aurea* at 7°C, and their hybrids between these temperatures (Avault and Shell 1968).

Milkfish (*Chanos chanos*) reached maturation and reproduced at water temperatures ranging from 25° to 30°C (77° to 86°F) (Lee 1985). During transport, oxygen consumption of milkfish fry increased five times when temperature is elevated from 20° to 32°C (68° to 90°F) (Villaluz 1986).

Freshwater prawn (*Macrobrachium rosenbergii*) larvae had maximum survival at 28° to 30°C (82° to 86°F) (Sick and Beaty 1974); maximum growth of larvae at 30°C; larvae die below 13°C (55°F) (Fujimura 1966).

Brown shrimp (*Penaeus aztecus aztecus*) growth of postlarvae in laboratory is nil at 11°C (52°F) (Zein-Eldin and Aldrich 1965); rate of growth increases with temperatures up to 32°C (90°F); survival greatly reduced at 33°C; death at 35°C (95°F); no appreciable growth below 20°C (68°F); production best between 22° and 30°C (72° to 86°F) (Zein-Eldin and Griffith 1966).

Pink shrimp (*Penaeus duorarum*) juveniles and adults tolerate temperatures between 11° and 40°C (52° and 104°F); individuals may die when exposed to a low of 10°C (50°F) for 6 to 10 hours; pink shrimp seldom seen in natural waters at 36°C (97°F); in ponds, feeding activity low if temperature drops below 18°C (64°F) (Tabb and Yang 1972).

American lobster (*Homarus americanus*) optimum growth for larval lobsters from stage 1 to 4 is 20° to 23°C (68° to 73°F) (Hughes and Mathiessen 1962); optimum temperature for culture is 24°C (75°F) (Ford et al. 1975).

American oysters (*Crassostrea virginica*) live in waters with a minimum temperature of 1°C (34°F) during winter in northern states to a maximum of 36°C (97°F) in the Gulf of Mexico; on flats exposed to sun the temperature of oysters has reached 46° to 49°C (115° to 120°F); maximum rate of ciliary activity (feeding) is 25° to 26°C (77° to 79°F); above 32°C (90°F) ciliary movement rapidly declines; successful mass spawning and setting at 20°C (68°F) and above; inhibition of growth and feeding below 8°C (46°F) (Galtsoff 1964).

Blue mussel (*Mytilus edulis*) growth and filtration decrease when water temperature reaches 20°C (68°F) (Lutz and Darling 1980).

Water temperature directly affects growth, reproduction, larval development, and general well-being of culture species. As an example, we will look at the channel catfish in detail. In southern states, channel catfish normally do not spawn until the water temperature reaches a minimum of 21°C (70°F). If fish spawn at 21°C and the water temperature suddenly drops, perhaps because of a cold front, adult catfish abandon the eggs, which often are destroyed by fungus. If eggs are removed from the pond and hatched artificially, some danger of loss is removed, particularly if water temperature is controlled. A water well with a constant temperature or a water heater is good insurance against an unexpected cold front. To avoid losses caused by a drop in water temperature, a catfish farmer can delay stocking brooders until the water temperature reaches 24°C (75°F). Delayed stocking is especially wise for a fish farmer who allows brood fish to hatch eggs in the pond.

Hatching is also governed by water temperature. At an average water temperature of 28°C (82°F), eggs hatch in 5 days; at 27°C (81°F), 6 days; and at 26°C (79°F), 7 days (Avault unpublished data). It appears that a 1°C change in water temperature affects the date of hatching by approximately 1 day. The optimum temperature for incubation of eggs is approximately 27°C. While water temperature can become too low, it also can become too high for hatching of eggs. Toward the end of the hatching season, crooked-tailed and other kinds of malformed catfish may occur. When this happens, the young fish develop too quickly and oxygen becomes deficient, especially to body extremities.

Water temperature affects growth and feeding activity of channel catfish. Generally, the best growth and feed conversion efficiency occurs at approximately 28° to 32°C (82° to 90°F). Below and above this temperature range growth and feed efficiency decrease. When the water temperature drops to 13° to 16°C (55° to 61°F), channel catfish feed very little. Any day that the water temperature is 18°C (65°F) or above is considered a growing day. Experienced catfish farmers know how many growing days are needed to produce marketable catfish when they start with fingerlings of a particular size.

Most catfish farms are located in the southern part of the United States that has a relatively long growing season. Because the channel catfish is cold blooded, it cannot regulate its body temperature. As water temperatures get lower, the fish itself becomes cold and lethargic. Metabolism of a fish is directly affected by water temperature. All body processes, including digestion, slow down in cold weather. At extremes in water temperatures, both high and low, fish are stressed and become more susceptible to disease.

Problem and Solution. Assume that two channel catfish farms each have 40 ha in production. One farm is located south of the other and has 1 more month of growing season, based on water temperature. Both farms stock fingerlings in March at a rate of 12,500/ha. Fish are fed at a rate of 3% body weight per day. Later, as winter approaches, fish in northern ponds cease to grow when they reach a weight of 0.5 kg. Fish in southern ponds continue to grow for 1 more month. How much extra growth did the southern farm obtain during the 1-month period, and what did this mean in added income?

The total weight of fish, beginning with the start of the 1-month period, is 250,000 kg (12,500 x 40 x 0.5 kg). If fed at 3% of body weight during this 1-month period, then 225,000 kg of feed were used by fish (250,000 x .03 x 30 days). Assume the conversion of feed to fish flesh was 1.75. If so, the fish added an additional 128,571 kg in growth. If fish sold for $1.75 per kg, then this added production amounted to a gross of $226,800. In this example, we simplified the calculations. We assumed no mortality and no fish growth in the northern ponds. Nevertheless, the longer growing season translates into added income.

Hauling procedures for fish are affected by water temperature. It is much easier and safer to transport fish during cool months than during hot months. In cool water, fish are less active and are much easier to handle. When hauling fish during the summer, it often helps to add ice to the hauling tank to lower water temperatures. Ice should be made from water without chlorine. If the ambient water temperature is 30°C (86°F), it could be lowered to 25°C (77°F) with addition of ice.

Other culture species are affected by water temperature (Table 6.1). For example, Pacific salmon (*Oncorhynchus* spp.) under certain conditions may die when the water temperature drops below 7°C (45°F); they prefer water temperatures between 12° and 14°C (54° and 57°F). Pompano die when the water temperature drops below 10°C (50°F) and grow best at temperatures above 25°C (77°F). Brown shrimp have no appreciable growth below 20°C (68°F); best growth is at temperatures between 22° and 30°C (72° and 86°F). *P. monodon* may die when the water temperature is below 13°C (55°F) or above 33°C (91°F). The range of temperatures that supports good growth for this species is between 28°C and 33°C (82° and 91°F). *P. vannamei* is typically stocked into ponds after water temperature is consistently above 20°C (68°F). Growth rates are not acceptable in most cases until pond temperatures are above 23°C (73°F). *P. japonicus, P. chinensis*, and *P. penicillatus* are all considered coolwater species. These shrimp are able to survive or grow in water as cold as 15°C (59°F) (Main and Fulks 1990).

In certain shrimp farming regions, strategies were developed that took temperature into account. For example, in Taiwan where *P. monodon* has been cultured, two crops per year had been possible. Sometimes a third crop could be grown in the South but not in the North. *P. penicillatus*, more tolerant to cool water than *P. monodon*, was considered in northern Taiwan for culture as a third crop.

In cool Canadian waters it may take up to 8 years to grow the American lobster to a market size of 0.5 kg (1.1 lb). By controlling water temperature at 20°C (68°F), this time can be reduced to 2 years. *Macrobrachium rosenbergii* has maximum growth at 30°C (86°F) and dies below 13°C (55°F).

242

The American oyster has mass spawning and setting of spat at 20°C and above.

Recommendations: (1) You must determine the effect of water temperature on each life stage of the culture species. (2) It is necessary to determine lower and upper lethal water temperatures, tolerance ranges, and optimum ranges of water temperature.

Salinity

Salinity is a measure of the total concentration of dissolved solids in seawater. The open ocean has a salinity of approximately 35 ppt. This salinity worldwide varies less than 10%. Not only is the total salt content of seawater relatively constant, but the ratios of the major constituents are as well (Table 6.2).

Table 6.2 Major constituents of seawater.

Constituent	g/kg of water at 35 ppt salinity
Chloride	19.353
Sodium	10.760
Sulfate	2.712
Magnesium	1.294
Calcium	0.413
Potassium	0.387
Bicarbonate	0.142
Bromide	0.067
Strontium	0.008

The principal negatively charged ions (anions) are chloride, sulfate, bicarbonate, and bromide. The principal positively charged ions (cations) are sodium, magnesium, calcium, potassium, and strontium. These nine ions comprise more than 99% of the total dissolved constituents of seawater.

Aquatic species may be classified as either freshwater, brackishwater, or saltwater. Some species require both fresh water and saline (or brackish) water at some time in their life cycle, and euryhaline species such as tilapia are equally at home in fresh or brackish water. Therefore in selecting source water for a particular species, the requirements of all life stages must be considered (Table 6.3). It may be necessary to have access to both fresh and saline water, depending on the species cultured.

Table 6.3 Effect of salinity on selected culture species.

Channel catfish eggs tolerated up to 16 ppt; at hatching tolerance dropped to 8 ppt; following yolk absorption, tolerance increased to 9 to 10 ppt (Allen and Avault 1969); fish successfully cultured in brackishwater ponds with salinities from 2 to 9 ppt (Perry and Avault 1969, 1973).

White catfish (*Ictalurus catus*) and blue catfish (*I. furcatus*) both have a slightly higher salinity tolerance than channel catfish (Allen and Avault 1971).

Buffalo fish (*Ictiobus* spp.) salinity tolerance is very similar to that of channel catfish (Hollander and Avault 1975).

T. zilli and *O. mossambicus* are among the most salinity tolerant of tilapia and can be acclimated up to 35 ppt salinity. *O. aurea* and *O. niloticus* are less salinity tolerant. Red tilapia can be cultured in salinities up to 17.5 ppt (Stickney 1986).

Salmonid alevins can live for at least 10 weeks at 25 ppt salinity; at 30 ppt, Atlantic salmon is more tolerant than brown and sea trout (*S. trutta fario*); at 40 ppt salmon live for 18 days, brown trout for 11 days, and sea trout for 9 days; at 50 ppt alevins of the three live about a week (Bishai 1961). Optimum salinity for salmon after smoltification, about 28 to 30 ppt (Caine 1987). Salinity fluctuations of 4 to 5 ppt in a week can be dangerous; avoid sites with unstable salinity regimes (Pennell 1992).

Pompano withstood sudden change in salinity from 29 to 9 ppt (Moe et al. 1968); can be maintained in salinities as low as 1.3 ppt (Allen and Avault 1970).

Red swamp crawfish (*Procambarus clarkii*) newly hatched young die at salinities above 15 ppt; intermediate-sized crawfish die at 30 ppt, and adults tolerated salinities of 30 ppt for one week (Loyacano 1967); in pond studies crawfish grow and reproduce in salinities of 6 ppt and below (Perry 1971).

Macrobrachium rosenbergii larval stages are relatively euryhaline (Fujimura 1966); best survival for larval stages 1 and 2 was 10 ppt; stages 3 to 5, 14 ppt; stage 6, 10 to 12 ppt; stages 7 and 8, 10 ppt (Sick and Beaty 1974); after metamorphosis, postlarvae usually remain in brackish water for 1 or 2 weeks before migrating to fresh water (Ling 1969).

Brown shrimp young have a wide salinity tolerance from 2 to 35 ppt; evidence that juvenile shrimp grow best in ponds of 15 to 25 ppt (Broom 1970); in lab, maximum growth of postlarvae is between salinities of 8.5 and 17 ppt (Bidwell 1975).

Pink shrimp, regardless of size, can tolerate a wide range of salinities, less than 1 ppt (Gunter and Hall 1965) to a maximum of 60 ppt (Simmons 1957); optimum salinities may be relatively high as compared with those of white or brown shrimp; juvenile shrimp prefer salinities of 20 ppt or more (Hildebrand 1955).

White shrimp (*P. setiferus*) have similar tolerances to pink and brown shrimp (Broom 1970). There were no differences in spawning success of *P. setiferus* at salinities of 20, 25, or 30 ppt (Ogle 1992). In the laboratory, 8-day and 22-day-old postlarvae *P. vannamei*, held in 32 ppt salinity, were transferred directly to lower salinities. Survival of 8-day-old postlarvae after 24-hour exposure to salinities of 32, 16, 8, 4, and 2 ppt was 97%, 93%, 20%, 8%, and 2% . Survival of 22-day-old postlarvae after 24-hour exposure to the same salinities was 99%, 98%, 84%, 63%, and 40% (numbers rounded off). Another study investigated the effect of salinity upon growth of 22-day-old postlarvae that had been acclimated to salinities of 16, 8, 4, and 2 ppt. The study ran for 30 days at water temperatures of 16°C (61°F) and 28 to 30°C (82 to 86°F). Shrimp were fed daily with a commercial diet. Growth was best at highest temperatures and salinities of 8 and 14 ppt. (Ogle et al. 1992).

Blue crab (*Callinectes sapidus*) optimum salinities for survival and growth of pelagic larvae, 15 to 45 ppt; adults can tolerate salinities ranging from 0.7 to 88 ppt; crabs can adapt quickly to salinity changes (Costelow 1967).

American oyster favorable range of salinity is 5 to 30 ppt; growth and gonadal development inhibited outside this range; sudden change in salinity, during hot weather, could result in mortality -- from 10 to 12 ppt transfer to 32 to 33 ppt resulted in death in one instance (Galtsoff 1964).

Species that spend most of their lives in fresh water but go to sea to spawn are known as catadromous. A common catadromous fish in the United States is the American eel (*Anguilla rostrata*). Species that spawn in fresh water, but spend most of their lives in the sea, are known as anadromous. Salmon spend most of their lives in the sea but enter fresh water to spawn. Some freshwater fishes, such as the rainbow trout, have anadromous races that commonly go to sea but return to fresh water to spawn. *M. rosenbergii* larvae develop in brackish water, but postlarvae ultimately migrate to fresh water.

Penaeid shrimp, such as *P. aztecus,* spawn offshore in salinities at or near sea strength. The shrimp larvae drift inshore where they grow in lower salinity water. Juveniles and adults ultimately migrate back offshore. Salinity is of paramount importance when selecting a site for shrimp culture. Shrimp hatcheries require water at 28 to 36 ppt for both reproduction and larval rearing. Ideally, the hatchery should be next to the ocean or should have access to seawater from a well. If the hatchery is in an estuary, salinity may fluctuate too much, and there is a danger of pumping silt-laden water. Grow-out facilities, however, should be located where less saline water is available. In nature, shrimp normally grow in 36 ppt salinity when offshore. Aquaculturists, however, have learned that many species obtain maximum growth at lower salinities. Chien (1992) summarized the salinity requirements of *P. monodon*: ideal salinity is 10 ppt for early postlarvae, 15 to 20 ppt for late postlarvae, and 15 to 25 ppt for juveniles. Salinities of 15 to 25 ppt are ideal for grow-out.

High or low salinity is a problem in some shrimp-producing countries. This is caused in part by poor site selection initially and in part by fluctuations in rainfall. During the wet season, which may last for 6 months in some countries, salinities may be lowered to near fresh in extreme instances. On the other hand the dry season, coupled with a high evaporation rate, may result in salinities approaching or exceeding 40 ppt. To salvage a poor site selection, some shrimp farmers look for a shrimp species that grows at elevated salinities during the dry season when salinities exceed 36 ppt. In Japan, *P. japonicus* is grown in ponds that are flushed daily with the tides, indicating that this species should tolerate and grow at relatively high salinities. Wyban and Sweeney (1991) reported that *P. vannamei* gave good growth at salinities of 33 ppt. *P. stylirostris* is somewhat more tolerant to salinity than *P. vannamei*. *P. merguiensis* and *P. chinensis* (*orientalis*) are relatively tolerant of high salinities and can be cultured in salinities approaching 40 ppt. *P. semisulcatus* is a candidate species for culture in countries bordering the Arabian Gulf. It can withstand extremely high salinities (Farmer 1981). Salinities in the Gulf generally range from 38 to 42 ppt.

Species that occur naturally in estuaries are tolerant to wide ranges in salinity, the American oyster being an example. This species can grow in salinities ranging from 5 to 30 ppt. The deadliest enemies of oysters are various gastropods inhabiting coastal waters. The most widely distributed species is the common oyster drill (*Urosalpinx cinerea*). Fortunately, brackish water effectively bars drills from waters below 12 to 17 ppt at summer temperatures. In site selection, this fact should be given serious consideration.

Certain freshwater species not normally found in brackish water have been successfully cultured in brackishwater ponds. Examples are the channel catfish (Perry and Avault 1969) and various species of buffalofish (*Ictiobus* spp.) (Hollander and Avault 1975). Parasites, diseases, and off-flavor were of no consequence when these fish were grown in brackish water.

Recommendations: (1) A careful study must be made to determine the effect of salinity on each life stage of the species to be cultured. (2) It is also necessary to determine lower and upper lethal salinities, tolerance range, and optimum range of salinity for reproduction and growth. (3) Ideally source water in estuaries should not vary more than 10% in salinity. This condition, however, is seldom met.

Dissolved Oxygen

Temperature, salinity, and elevation all affect the amount of DO (dissolved oxygen) that water is capable of holding at saturation. When these three factors increase, oxygen at saturation decreases (Table 6.4).

Table 6.4 Oxygen saturation in ppm for fresh and salt water at various temperatures (and elevations for fresh water).

Temperature °C (°F)	Fresh water			Salt water[a]
	sea level	305 m, 1,000 ft elevation	1,524 m, 5,000 ft elevation	sea level
5 (41)	12.8	12.3	11.0	10.0
10 (50)	11.3	10.9	9.4	9.0
15 (59)	10.1	9.7	8.4	8.1
20 (68)	9.1	8.9	7.6	7.4
25 (77)	8.3	8.1	6.9	6.7
30 (86)	7.6	----	----	6.1

[a] Specific gravity of salt water is 1.025

This is unfortunate because culture species become more active as water temperature rises, and they therefore require more oxygen. Moreover, minimum tolerable DO levels often increase with a rise in water temperature. Burdick et al. (1954), for example, reported a 40% to 50% increase in minimum tolerable DO for three species of trout when the water temperature rose from 12° to 20°C (54° to 68°F). Moss and Scott (1961) found that minimum DO levels tolerated by channel catfish increased when temperature rose from 25° to 35°C (77° to 95°F).

Certain sources of water, especially springs and well water, are chronically low in dissolved oxygen. This, however, should not preclude their use. Oxygen content can be increased by aeration and other methods mentioned earlier; further detail is given in the next chapter. Other sources of water such as streams and lakes may not contain a sufficient concentration of DO. Again, this is usually of no consequence if this water is used to supply ponds, raceways, or tanks where it can be aerated. Nevertheless, aeration may be an added expense. If the culture system involves large bodies of water -- such as culture in coastal waters, open-sea mariculture, or cage culture in lakes or streams -- then DO should be carefully monitored during site selection. It may not be possible to aerate such large bodies of water. It is highly doubtful, however, that oxygen depletion would become a problem involving the ocean proper, barring some catastrophe.

The DO concentration required by each species depends on its life stages and on such activities as reproduction, growth, and general metabolism (Table 6.5).

Table 6.5 Effect of dissolved oxygen on selected culture species.

Channel catfish juveniles died at 1.0 to 1.1 ppm DO at a water temperature of 25° to 35°C (77° to 95°F) (Moss and Scott 1961). Catfish reduce feed intake following episodes of DO below 1 or 2 ppm (Tucker et al. 1979).

Rainbow trout had 50% of 6-month-old fish die at 1.3 to 1.6 ppm DO at water temperatures of 13° to 20°C (55° to 68°F) (Alabaster et al. 1957); yearlings first began to die at 1.3 to 2.5 ppm DO at a water temperature of 11° to 22°C (52° to 72°F) (Burdick et al. 1954).

Salmonids in general: below 3 ppm DO is incipient lethal level; lowest safe level is 5 to 7 ppm; optimum level is 9 ppm and above (various authors).

Coho salmon juveniles were held in 20°C (68°F) fresh water and subjected to various concentrations of dissolved oxygen; growth and food consumption declined when oxygen was lowered from 8.3 to 6 ppm, and declined more sharply with further reduction of oxygen; food conversion was slightly depressed at 4 ppm; fish began dying at 2.1 to 2.3 ppm (Herrmann et al. 1962); yearlings died, 50% loss, at a dissolved oxygen concentration of 1.2 to 1.6 ppm when temperature was 14°C (57°F) (Townsend and Earnest 1940).

Sockeye salmon had most adults die at 2.3 to 2.7 ppm DO at 21° to 23°C (70° to 73°F). Most adult chinook salmon died at 2.3 to 2.7 ppm DO at a water temperature of 21°C (Chapman 1940).

Red swamp crawfish juveniles 9 to 12 mm in length (0.4 to 0.5 in) had an LC50 between 0.75 and 1.10 ppm DO; the LC50 for 31 to 35 mm (1.2 to 1.4 in) juveniles was 0.49 ppm DO (Melancon and Avault 1976); crawfish in burrows tolerated oxygen concentrations as low as 0.2 to 1.4 ppm with no mortality; burrow water served as a humidity source to keep gills wet (Jaspers and Avault 1969); crawfish die in traps if oxygen is 1 ppm or less particularly if water temperature is above 22°C (72°F) (Avault et al. 1974).

Brown shrimp juveniles die at low DO levels of 0.7 ppm while subadults began dying at 1.6 ppm. DO should never drop below 5 ppm in ponds (Bidwell 1975).

The lethal DO concentration for *P. japonicus* is between 0.7 and 1.4 ppm; *P. japonicus* appears to tolerate lower DO levels than *P. monodon* (Egusa 1961). Juvenile *P.*

vannamei and *P. monodon* survived over a 16-day period when DO was held at 1.17 and 1.21 ppm (Seidman and Lawrence 1985).

Hardshell clam (*Mercenaria mercenaria*) eggs developed at oxygen levels down to 0.5 ppm but had 100% mortality at 0.2 ppm; larval growth was normal at oxygen levels at or above 4.2 ppm but was curtailed at 2.4 ppm or below (Morrison 1971).

Boyd (1990) reviewed oxygen requirements of various culture species. Chien (1992) reviewed oxygen requirements of penaeid shrimp. DO requirements of finfish, particularly salmonids, are well documented by Doudoroff and Shumway (1970). Generally, a deficiency of DO can result in reduced fecundity of fish or prevent their spawning. However, there is little or no evidence that the adverse effect on egg production occurs at DO levels higher than those needed for successful hatching of eggs. Various culture species will, of course, respond differently. The development and growth of salmonid embryos, for example, are retarded; their size at hatching is reduced, and hatching is usually delayed by any reduction of DO from the air-saturation level. The sensitivity of embryos to low DO increases with age and is greatest just before hatching. On the other hand, embryos of some culture species can develop at DO levels of less than 2 ppm and hatch successfully into viable larvae.

Growth of larval salmonids is reduced only slightly at DO levels as low as 3 ppm, according to Doudoroff and Shumway (1970). Juvenile salmonids, however, may experience reduced growth at DO levels considerably less than saturation. For general metabolic activities, critical or limiting DO levels may be near saturation levels at moderately high temperatures.

Recommendations: (1) For warmwater species, general recommendations are that DO should be above 5 ppm. Under extreme conditions, however, the DO may range between 3 and 4 ppm for short periods during any 24-hour period, provided that the water quality is favorable in all other respects. In stratified lakes, the DO requirements may not apply to deep waters. (2) For coldwater species, it is necessary that the DO be at or near saturation. This is especially important during spawning when DO must not drop below 7 ppm. For good growth and general well-being of trout and salmon, DO should not be below 6 ppm. DO should never drop below 4 ppm at any time under any conditions. (3) Surface dissolved oxygen concentrations in coastal waters and estuaries should not drop below 4 to 5 ppm. For optimum conditions a minimum of 5 ppm dissolved oxygen is required.

Free Carbon Dioxide

Free carbon dioxide (CO_2), which is a gas like oxygen, is normally not a limiting factor in source water. Excess free CO_2 may be present in ground water, but it can be removed with vigorous aeration.

Culture species react differently to various levels of free CO_2 in the water, and this depends on DO levels and water temperature. Basically, CO_2 resulting from respiration of culture species leaves the organism by diffusion. A high concentration of CO_2 in the water makes it more difficult for CO_2 to diffuse out of the species. Thus, it begins to accumulate internally. Phytoplankton, bacteria, and other pond organisms also contribute to CO_2 production during respiration, more so than the culture species. As CO_2 accumulates, the blood pH is lowered, and this may have detrimental effects. The greater the concentration of carbon dioxide in the blood, the less readily will the animal's hemoglobin combine with oxygen. Thus the presence of much CO_2 in the blood raises the minimum tolerable oxygen concentration. The problem compounds as water temperature rises.

Fish can tolerate higher concentrations of free CO_2 than was formerly believed. Concentrations necessary to impair the ability of fish to extract DO from the water generally have been above levels likely to be found even in polluted waters. McNeil (1956) found virtually no effect of free CO_2 levels as high as 40 ppm on minimum levels of DO tolerated by coho salmon at a water temperature of 21°C (70°F). In one of his experiments, the initial DO level was 5.8 ppm or more, and temperature was 20°C (68°F). With these conditions the minimum tolerable DO level was not evident until a concentration of 70 ppm free CO_2 was reached. Alabaster et al. (1957) reported an approximately linear relation between concentrations of free CO_2 and low levels of DO lethal to rainbow trout. The minimum tolerable level of DO increased two-fold when CO_2 increased from 0 to 40 ppm. It increased up to three-fold with an increase to 60 ppm CO_2. Most fish species can adjust to gradually increased CO_2 levels if the increase occurs over approximately 10 days.

Recommendations: Concentrations of free CO_2 above 20 ppm rarely occur in ponds, but they may in intensive culture systems. Fish acclimate to carbon dioxide levels as high as 60 ppm with little effect. However, fish are able to respond to slight gradients and many avoid free carbon dioxide levels as low as 1 to 6 ppm. If carbon dioxide is present in the water source, vigorous aeration will alleviate the problem.

Alkalinity, pH, and Dissolved Solids and Hardness

Alkalinity-- Alkalinity is defined as the sum of exchangeable bases reacting to neutralize acid when an acid is added to water. Alkalinity is due primarily to bicarbonates (HCO_3^-), carbonates (CO_3^{--}), hydroxides (OH^-), or a certain mixture of these. In some instances, particularly in seawater, anions of various weak acids, particularly carbonic acid, boric acid, phosphoric acid, and silicic acid, contribute to titratable alkalinity. In this case, the weak acids are not necessarily charge balanced by hydrogen ions, but instead by some of the major cations present in water (sodium, magnesium, calcium, and potassium ions).

Alkalinity plays two important roles in water. Bicarbonates, and carbonates to a lesser degree, are a storehouse of carbon needed in photosynthesis. They also constitute the major buffering system to reduce fluctuations in pH. Boyd and Walley (1975) considered the following ranges for total alkalinity in fresh water: low, less than 20 ppm; intermediate, 20 to 40 ppm; and high, above 40 ppm. They studied surface waters of Alabama and Mississippi. In certain areas where the watershed was fertile, values above 100 ppm were not unusual, and occasional samples were above 300 ppm total alkalinity.

pH-- The pH is an index of hydrogen ion activity. There is a relationship between acidity, alkalinity, and pH. Water with a pH of 4.5 or lower has no measurable alkalinity, and water with a pH of 8.3 or higher has no measurable acidity. In between pH 4.5 and 8.3, water may have both acidity and alkalinity at the same time. In natural water, where pH may often be in the vicinity of 8.3, little or no CO_2 is present.

The pH has an effect on both water quality and on aquatic biota. The availability of some nutrients and toxicity of certain substances vary with the hydrogen ion concentration. Phosphorous is unavailable at both low and high pH. Some trace metals become more soluble at low pH. At higher pH values, iron tends to become unavailable to plants. The toxicity of ammonia to fish increases with an increase in pH. These are only a few examples. We will look at more later.

The effect of pH on freshwater fish is well summarized by Swingle (1961). The desirable pH range is 6.5 to 9.0. Low production occurs at pH levels above 9.5 and at pH levels below 6.0. The acid death point is pH 4. The alkaline death point is pH 11. Boyd (1989) suggested similar ranges for culture species in brackish water. He further noted that brackish waters are well buffered against pH change, and that pH seldom falls below 6.5 or rises above 9.

Dissolved Solids and Hardness-- Total dissolved solids is a term that describes dissolved materials in fresh water. The most common constituents of total dissolved solids in natural water include carbonates, sulfates, chlorides, phosphates, and nitrates. These anions occur in combination with such cations as calcium, sodium, potassium, magnesium, and iron. Hart et al.

(1945) gave figures on total dissolved solids for inland waters of the United States: 5% have a dissolved solids concentration under 72 ppm, about 50% under 169 ppm, and 95% under 400 ppm.

The quantity and quality of dissolved solids play a role in determining the variety and abundance of plants and animals in water. They serve as nutrients in productivity, affect osmotic stress, buffer chemical changes, and may be toxic under some conditions. The role of nutrients in productivity is covered in Chapter 8. Regarding osmotic stress, dissolved solids normally do not reach levels that are harmful to fish. The toxicity level may range as high as 5,000 to 10,000 ppm for dissolved solids, depending on species and prior acclimation. Several dissolved materials are toxic at relatively low concentrations.

Hardness is a component of total dissolved solids and is due chiefly to the cations of calcium (Ca^{++}) and magnesium (Mg^{++}). Other ions such as strontium, barium, manganese, iron, copper, zinc, and lead add to hardness, but since they are usually in trace amounts their role is minimal. While calcium and magnesium contribute to hardness and productivity, other elements, if in sufficient concentrations, are toxic and may reduce productivity.

Hardness may be expressed as: (1) temporary hardness, often referred to as carbonate hardness, (2) permanent or non-carbonate hardness, and (3) total hardness, temporary and permanent hardness combined. If total hardness is equal to or less than the total alkalinity, it means that calcium and magnesium are associated with carbonates and bicarbonates and therefore all hardness is temporary or carbonate hardness. If total hardness exceeds total alkalinity, it means that part of the calcium and magnesium is combined with negative ions (sulfates and chlorides) other than carbonates or bicarbonates.

Because total hardness is a property not attributable to a single constituent, some standard way must be used for expressing the concentration. This is done by reporting total hardness in terms of an equivalent concentration of calcium carbonate. This can be done by titration of the water sample with a standard solution. If, for example, 4 ml of a 0.01 mole standard solution of EDTA, a chelating agent, is used to reach the end point during titration of a 50-ml water sample, then: 20 x 4 = 80 ppm total hardness expressed as $CaCO_3$ (Swingle 1969).

Water is often referred to as hard or soft. Durfor and Becker (1964) used the following classification for hardness range (ppm of $CaCO_3$): 0 to 60, soft; 61 to 120, moderately hard; 121 to 180, hard; >180, very hard.

For years biologists have used total water hardness of fresh water as an index of potential productivity of aquatic species. More emphasis, however, is now placed on specific ions. Greene (1969) correlated different levels of Ca^{++} and Mg^{++} ions to fish production. On the basis of production of fathead minnows (*Pimephales promelas*) in experimental pools, he concluded that magnesium hardness had no measurable effect on fish production. An increase in hardness from addition of $CaSO_4$ did increase production. Boyd and Walley (1975) found that the average Ca^{++} and Mg^{++} ratios in Alabama and Mississippi surface waters ranged from 2 to 6 ppm Ca^{++} for every 1 ppm Mg^{++}. de la Bretonne et al. (1969) studied the effect of total water hardness on crawfish (*Procambarus clarkii*) production. The total hardness was adjusted with calcium chloride to levels of 9 (control), 50, 100, 150, and 200 ppm in experimental pools. They concluded that as total water hardness increased so did crawfish production up to a hardness level through 100 ppm. Above 100 ppm production did not increase significantly.

Recommendations: (1) The total alkalinity in fresh water should not be below 20 to 25 ppm at any time. The total alkalinity should not drop more than 25% below the initial level. (2) For optimum production in fresh water, bicarbonate alkalinity should be 100 ppm or above. (3) Ideally, pH should range from 6.5 to 8.5 in fresh water and in saline water. (4) Total dissolved solids should be in sufficient concentrations to provide for good production of culture species. The ranges given by Hart et al. (1945) can be used as a general guide. (5) Source water should contain a minimum of 20 ppm total hardness for good production. (6) Optimum production probably occurs at total hardness levels at or above 100 ppm. (7) Determinations should be made also on specific ions, such as Ca^{++} and Mg^{++}, in determining water quality.

Chlorine

Chlorine, a gas, is widely used for disinfecting potable water supplies. It also is used to treat sewage effluents, and it is used in power plants, textile and paper mills, and certain other industries. Potable water (or municipal water) is sometimes used in small-scale culture operations. The concentration of chlorine present may be toxic or have sub-lethal effects to culture species.

Stream water that receives effluents containing chlorine or hypochlorites is generally not suitable for culture operations. The toxicity of chlorine to aquatic life depends on the concentration of residual chlorine remaining and the relative amount of free chlorine.

Free chlorine is toxic in itself to aquatic organisms. Combinations of chlorine with ammonia, cyanide, and organic compounds, such as phenols and amines, may be even more toxic. They also may impart off-flavors to seafood. Chlorine at 0.05 ppm was the critical level for young Pacific salmon exposed for 23 days (Holland et al. 1960). The lethal threshold for chinook salmon and coho salmon over 72 hours was less than 0.1 ppm chlorine.

Oysters are sensitive to chlorine concentrations of 0.01 to 0.05 ppm. At 1 ppm oysters cannot pump effectively (Galtsoff 1964).

Recommendations: (1) Municipal water used in culture should be aged in an open container for at least 1 day and aerated to expel chlorine. (2) Chlorine in municipal water also can be removed with an activated charcoal filter (Spotte 1970) or by addition of sodium thiosulphate. (3) In streams, total residual chlorine should not exceed 0.05 ppm for up to 30 minutes in any 24-hour period. (4) For longer periods, residual chlorine should not exceed 0.003 ppm. (5) Free residual chlorine in seawater should not exceed 0.01 ppm.

Ammonia

Ammonia may be discharged into streams from a variety of industrial processes and cleaning operations. Ammonia also results from decomposition of organic matter. Ammonia gas is soluble in water. Although ammonia is acutely toxic to aquatic life, its degree of toxicity varies according to its chemical state. This depends on pH and water temperature (Table 6.6).

Table 6.6 Percentage un-ionized ammonia in aqueous solution at different pH values and temperatures. Source: Boyd 1990.

pH	Temperature (^{o}C)								
	16	18	20	22	24	26	28	30	32
7.0	0.30	0.34	0.40	0.46	0.52	0.60	0.70	0.81	0.95
7.2	0.47	0.54	0.63	0.72	0.82	0.95	01.10	1.27	1.50
7.4	0.74	0.86	0.99	1.14	1.30	1.50	1.73	2.00	2.36
7.6	1.17	1.35	1.56	1.79	2.05	2.35	2.72	3.13	3.69
7.8	1.84	2.12	2.45	2.80	3.21	3.68	4.24	4.88	5.72
8.0	2.88	3.32	3.83	4.37	4.99	5.71	6.55	7.52	8.77
8.2	4.49	5.16	5.94	6.76	7.68	8.75	10.00	11.41	13.22
8.4	6.93	7.94	9.09	10.30	11.65	13.20	14.98	16.96	19.46
8.6	10.56	12.03	13.68	15.40	17.28	19.42	21.83	24.45	27.68
8.8	15.76	17.82	20.08	22.38	24.88	27.64	30.68	33.90	37.76
9.0	22.87	25.57	28.47	31.37	34.42	37.71	41.23	44.84	49.02
9.2	31.97	35.25	38.69	42.01	45.41	48.96	52.65	56.30	60.38
9.4	42.68	46.32	50.00	53.45	56.86	60.33	63.79	67.12	70.72
9.6	54.14	57.77	61.31	64.54	67.63	70.67	73.63	76.39	79.29
9.8	65.17	68.43	71.53	74.25	76.81	79.25	81.57	83.68	85.85
10.0	74.78	77.46	79.92	82.05	84.00	85.82	87.52	89.05	90.58
10.2	82.45	84.48	86.32	87.87	89.27	90.56	91.75	92.80	93.84

It is un-ionized ammonia (NH_3) that is toxic to culture species. Ammonium (NH_4^+) is generally unable to cross tissue barriers. As the pH of water increases, NH_3 increases and NH_4^+ decreases. For example, Chen and Chin (1989) reported that 0.07 ppm ammonia-N was twice as toxic to postlarvae of *P. monodon* at pH 9.1 as at pH 8.3.

Ammonia is reported in various ways. It is important to distinguish between values that refer to un-ionized ammonia only, ionized ammonia only, and values that include both un-ionized and ionized forms. When the word ammonia alone is used in the literature, it includes both un-ionized and ionized forms. Ammonia-N and TAN include un-ionized plus ionized ammonia as nitrogen. TAN stands for total ammonia nitrogen. Ammonia is the un-ionized form (NH_3), whereas ammonium is the ionized form (NH_4^+). NH_3-N stands for un-ionized ammonia as nitrogen, and NH_4^+-N stands for ammonium as nitrogen.

Various workers have studied ammonia toxicity to culture species. The European Inland Fisheries Advisory Commission (1973) reported that short-term exposure of freshwater fish to ammonia as NH_3 was toxic at concentrations between 0.7 and 2.4 ppm. Ball (1967) and Colt and Tchobanoglous (1976) reported that the 96-hour LC50 value of ammonia to fish ranged from 0.5 to 3.8 ppm. (See Box 6.1 for discussion of bioassay tests.)

Box 6.1 Bioassays.

Bioassays are conducted to determine the effect of a given condition (e.g., low DO), pollutant, toxin, or substance on aquatic species. From an aquaculture standpoint, water quality requirements are based on results of bioassay tests. The bioassays are conducted under controlled laboratory conditions according to Standard Methods for the Examination of Water and Wastewater (American Public Health Association 1989).

There are two types of bioassays in use: (1) the static bioassay in which the test animals are held in tanks or containers with the pollutant or toxin, and (2) the continuous flow or flow-through bioassay in which the test solution is renewed continually. Temperature, dissolved oxygen, pH, total alkalinity, and other water quality parameters are carefully monitored in both static and flow-through systems; they may affect toxicity results. Test animals are first acclimated to laboratory conditions for at least 2 weeks. Usually only one species is tested at a time. Test animals are stocked into containers with various concentrations of the pollutant, toxin, or condition present. The bioassay is typically conducted over a 96-hour (4-day) period, during which dead animals are recorded at 1, 2, 4, 8, 16, 24, 48, 72, and 96 hours.

Harmful effects may be described by one or more of the following terms: (1) acute -- involves a stimulus severe enough to bring about a response speedily, usually within 4 days for fish. (2) subacute -- involves a stimulus less severe than an acute stimulus, producing a response in a longer time; the condition may become chronic. (3) chronic --

involves a lingering or continuous stimulus; often signifying periods of about 10% or more of the life span. (4) lethal -- causes death. (5) sublethal -- insufficient to cause death, and (6) cumulative -- brought about, or increased in strength, by successive additions.

Toxicity results are usually reported as the median tolerance limit (TLm or TL50) or median lethal concentration (LC50). In any case, the symbol signifies the concentration that kills 50% of test animals within a specified time span, usually 96 hours. Occasionally an LD50 is given. This refers to a test animal that was given a dose, orally or injected, of a particular material. EC50 has been used to denote the condition or toxicant concentration affecting a specific response such as growth rate for a given time. The LC50 is a convenient reference point for expressing acute lethal toxicity of a given toxicant to the average test animals. It also makes it convenient to compare results from one study with another. The fish farmer, however, is more interested in the threshold concentration when culture species first begin to die. Therefore, it would be beneficial to use a 96-hour LC01. A "safe level" has been calculated based on the incipient LC50 value with an application factor of 0.1 (Sprague 1971). For example, if the incipient 96-hour LC50 value of a certain substance to a juvenile shrimp is 20 ppm, then the safe level is 2.0 ppm.

Recommendations: (1) Concentrations of materials that are nonpersistent or have noncumulative effects should not exceed 0.1 of the 96-hour LC50 at any time or place. The 24-hour average of the concentration of these materials should not exceed 0.05 of the LC50 after mixing. (2) For toxicants that are persistent or cumulative, the concentrations should not exceed 0.05 of the 96-hour LC50 at any time or place, nor should the 24-hour average concentration exceed 0.01 of the 96-hour LC50. (3) When two or more toxic materials are present at the same time, it is assumed that their individual toxicants are additive.

Ruffier et al. (1981) reported that the 96-hour LC50 value of ammonia was 1.5 to 3.1 ppm for channel catfish and 0.32 ppm for rainbow trout. Chen et al. (1989) reported that the safe level for *P. japonicus* PL-10 or younger was 0.78 ppm ammonia-N and 0.05 ppm NH_3-N. Beyond PL-10 the safe level increased to 2.83 ppm ammonia-N and 0.18 ppm for NH_3-N. Their study was conducted at a salinity of 33 ppt, pH of 8.1, and water temperature of 30°C (86°F). Johnson and Finley (1980), Alabaster and Lloyd (1982), and Boyd (1990) reviewed ammonia toxicity, primarily for freshwater fish and invertebrates. Delistraty et al. (1977), Jayasankar and Muthu (1983), Wickens (1985), and Chen et al. (1989) reported on ammonia toxicity to marine crustaceans. Chien (1992) reviewed ammonia toxicity to marine shrimp. Hui et al. (in press) reported on toxicity of ammonia and nitrite to freshwater crawfish.

Recommendations: (1) Though ammonia-N toxicity varies with culture species, their various life stages, and environmental conditions, ammonia-N in source water should be below 0.2 ppm. (2) Source water should not contain a concentration of un-ionized ammonia greater than 0.02 ppm at any time.

Total Dissolved Gases

The atmosphere contains a mixture of gases, with N_2 (78% by volume) and O_2 (21% by volume) predominating. Trace amounts of the gases Ar, CO_2, Ne, and He also are present. Each gas exerts a measurable pressure, and the sum of these pressures constitutes atmospheric or barometric pressure. The pressure of an individual gas in air is called a partial pressure. Gases dissolve in water, and the pressure of an individual gas is called tension.

Under normal conditions, the total gas pressure in air is in equilibrium with that in water. There are times, however, when the total gas pressure in water exceeds that in the atmosphere. The water is then said to be supersaturated with gas. When this happens, culture species may develop gas bubble disease (GBD). Gas bubbles form on the external surfaces and later under the skin and eventually in the blood. When bubbles get under the eyes, the condition is often referred to as popeye (exopthalmia). There are several ways to cause GBD from supersaturation. Ground water may sometimes be supersaturated with nitrogen. Spring water and well water are not in contact with the atmosphere, so equilibrium cannot be reached. Excessive growth of phytoplankton may result in supersaturation of oxygen during daylight. Other factors affecting supersaturation include barometric pressure, hydrostatic pressure, and relative humidity (Water Quality Criteria 1972). GBD has occurred from using heated effluents of power stations. Demont and Miller (1971) and Malous et al. (1972) reported GBD among fish and mollusks living in heated effluents of steam-generating stations.

Recommendations: (1) Data available for salmonid fish suggest that culture species are protected only when total dissolved gas pressure in water is no greater than 110% of the existing atmospheric pressure. (2) When ground water is used to supply culture facilities, it should be vigorously aerated. (3) If water is heated or salinity increased significantly for culture systems, total gas pressure should be carefully monitored.

Suspended and Settleable Solids

Suspended and settleable solids include inorganic and organic materials. Inorganic components include sand, silt, and clay that originate from erosion, agricultural runoff, placer mining, strip mining, gravel operations, dusts from coal washeries, and building projects. The organic fraction includes greases, oils, tars, animal and vegetable fats, paper mill wastes, sawdust, various materials from city sewers, bacteria, plankton, and other microscopic materials.

Suspended solids are fine particles held in suspension for long periods, depending on the intensity of water turbulence. Fine silt particles, when dispersed into fresh waters, remain almost continuously suspended, and suspension of clay mineral particles may be maintained even by thermally induced motions in water. Moreover, clay particles may have similar electrostatic charges. When one particle comes in contact with another both are repelled, and the particles remain in suspension. The term turbidity is often used when speaking of suspended solids.

Suspended solids affect light penetration, temperature, toxins, and aquatic life. Suspended particles inhibit penetration of sunlight. Surface waters warm more rapidly than do bottom waters, and this could delay spawning by as much as 1 month. Suspended mineral particles, electrostatically charged, may absorb pesticides and heavy metals, and remove them from solution; this could render them non-toxic. Suspended solids affect culture species by inhibiting growth of phytoplankton and other aquatic food organisms. Very turbid or muddy water also can stress culture species by clogging their gills, preventing successful development of eggs and larvae, and inhibiting growth.

Settleable solids consist of materials that settle out readily in still water. They may cover the bottom of a stream or lake with a blanket of material that smothers bottom food organisms or fish eggs. Such deposits may deplete bottom oxygen supplies and generate hydrogen sulfide, carbon dioxide, methane, or other noxious gases.

Recommendations: (1) Aquatic communities should be protected if the following maximum concentrations of suspended solids exist: high level of protection, 25 ppm; moderate protection, 80 ppm; low level of protection, 400 ppm; very low level of protection, more than 400 ppm. (2) For effective photosynthetic production of oxygen, at least 10% of incident light should reach the bottom. (3) Since even minor deposits of settleable solids may affect aquatic life, source water should be relatively low in such materials.

Tainting Substances

Source water should not impart an off-flavor to the flesh of culture species. These off-flavors, sometimes described as earthy, musty, or muddy, may be caused by chemical compounds or by certain organisms. A number of chemical compounds may cause off-flavor. Effluents from oil refineries may give culture species an oily taste. Pulp mill effluents can give them a bad taste, and phenolic compounds are often associated with tainting problems. Effluents from various other industrial plants also should be suspect.

Oils and oil products may have an adverse effect on culture species. Pollution may be in the form of floating oils, emulsified oils, or solution of the water soluble fraction of these oils. Floating oil may adhere to the gills of culture species, interfering with respiration. It also may be toxic to the culture species. Such oils may be detrimental to plants, and they may contain tainting substances. Sedimented oil may interfere with bottom food organisms.

Oil pollution poses a threat to brackish and saline waters. Accidental oil spills constitute about 10% of oil entering marine waters. The other 90% originates from normal operations of oil-carrying tankers, other ships, offshore production, refinery operations, and the disposal of oil-waste materials. Toxicities of oil and oil products vary greatly. Mills and Culley (1971) determined acute toxicity of four oils and two oil-spill removers on *Penaeus setiferus* and *P. aztecus*. The ranges of 48-hour LC50 values for the four oils with shrimp ranged from 1 to 40 ppt. Oil-spill removers were more toxic to shrimp than the four crude oils. The Ameroid and Corexit removers had 40-hour LC50 values of 2.5 and 5,000 ppm respectively.

Off-flavors produced by pond organisms have been attributed to various species of actinomycetes bacteria, such as *Streptomyces tendae*, and to blue-green algae such as *Oscillatoria tenuis*, *Symploca muscorum*, and *Anabaena* sp. The metabolites geosmin (1, 10-trans-dimethyl-trans-9-decalol) and MIB (2-methylisoborneol) have been isolated and labeled the culprits in producing the musty or off-flavor (Johnson and Kuan 1987; Dionigi et al. 1990; Dionigi et al. 1991; Dionigi et al. 1992; Lorio et al. 1992). Culture species get the off-flavor by ingesting small amounts of the algae and probably by absorption across the gill membrane.

Lovell and Sackey (1973) conducted controlled experiments where channel catfish were stocked into stainless steel tanks containing either the blue-green algae *S. muscorum* or *O. tenuis*. Tanks with catfish but no algae were maintained as controls. Within 1 day, fish from *S. muscorum* tanks developed a distinct off-flavor that became stronger at 2 days and reached maximum intensity at 10 days. The blue-green alga *O. tenuis* also affected fish flavor but not as severely as *S. muscorum*. Fish held in water with *S. muscorum* for 14 days were transferred to fresh, flowing water. After 3 days at 20°C (68°F), the flavor of fish improved significantly; at 10 days the taste of these fish was not significantly different from that of fish in control tanks.

Off-flavor in fish is a serious problem. At any given time, 50% to 80% of channel catfish in commercial ponds may have off-flavor. Blue-green algae and actinomycetes bacteria are often associated with "old" ponds where fish have been cultured for years, and the nutrient loading is high. The ponds are typically very rich in nutrients and organic matter, contain an abundance of fish wastes, and have a relatively high pH. Such ponds may have a predominance of blue-green algae over the more desirable green algae.

Some blue-green algae are scum-forming and give the appearance of green paint floating on the surface. Green algae produce a uniform color throughout the water.

Recommendations: (1) No oil should be visible on the water surface. (2) Emulsified oils should not exceed 0.05 of the 96-hour LC50. (3) The concentration of hexane extractable substances (exclusive of elemental sulfur) in air-dried sediments should not increase above 1,000 mg/kg on a dry weight basis. (4) Source water containing tainting substances should be avoided. (5) If you want to buy an established fish farm, determine if off-flavor has been a problem. To determine off-flavor, take fish from suspected waters, fillet them, wrap in aluminum foil with no seasoning added, and cook at 191°C (375°F) for 15 to 30 minutes. Fish from "clear" water should be treated likewise. A panel of judges should then compare the smell and taste of both. Ratings range from 0 to 7 as follows: 0, excellent; 1, very good; 2, good; 3, fair; 4, just acceptable; 5, not quite acceptable; 6, very poor and inedible; 7, extremely poor, repulsive. (6) If fish are not present in the water suspected, place fish in floating cages for a period of not less than 48 hours. The flesh can then be tested for tainting substances as already described. (7) Since off-flavor problems may be seasonal, a sample of fish should be tested periodically, especially prior to harvest for processing. (8) Purging, as described by Lovell and Sackey (1973), may be a partial solution.

Hydrogen Sulfide

Sulfides are constituents of industrial wastes, such as those from tanneries, paper mills, chemical plants, and gas works. Hydrogen sulfide also is produced by anaerobic decomposition of sewage and other organic matter. Hydrogen sulfide, a poisonous gas, is present in coastal areas where peat and rotting marsh vegetation abound. Soluble sulfides in water react with hydrogen ions to form HS^- or H_2S, the proportion depending on pH (Table 6.7).

The toxicity of sulfides is primarily from H_2S rather than the sulfide ion. Upon solution, hydrogen sulfide dissociates as follows: $H_2S \rightarrow HS^- + H^+$ and $HS^- \rightarrow S^{--} + H^+$. At pH 9, most of the sulfide is in the form of HS^-; and at a pH of 6 most is present as H_2S. Consequently as the pH decreases, toxicity of hydrogen sulfide increases.

Table 6.7 Influence of pH on un-ionized hydrogen sulfide.

pH	Conversion factor	Total hydrogen sulfide (ppm)	Un-ionized hydrogen sulfide
6.0	0.83	6.82	5.66
6.5	0.61	6.82	4.16
7.0	0.33	6.82	2.25
7.2	0.24	6.82	1.64
7.5	0.14	6.82	0.96
7.7	0.091	6.82	0.62
8.0	0.048	6.82	0.33

Source: Bonn and Follis 1967.

Recommendations: (1) To protect culture species within acceptable limits of pH and temperature, the concentration of total sulfides should not exceed 0.002 ppm. (2) To increase pH and favor the less toxic ionized hydrogen sulfide, agricultural limestone can be added to water. If free carbon dioxide is present, vigorous aeration will help to remove it, thus increasing the pH.

Metals

Metals are present in water in trace amounts. Their toxicity to aquatic life has been reviewed by Doudoroff and Katz (1953), McKee and Wolf (1963), and Eisler (1973). For a general description of metals in water the reader is referred to Hem (1970). The United States Fish and Wildlife Service, Patuxent Wildlife Research Center at Laurel, Maryland, has published a series on the hazards of metals and toxins to fish, wildlife, and invertebrates.

Lethal toxicity of metals depends not only on their concentration in water but also on water quality. Spotte (1970) listed seven factors that affect toxicity of metals: pH, dissolved oxygen, temperature, volume of the solution relative to fish size, frequency with which the solution is renewed, synergism with other substances in solution, and the level of organics.

Metals may enter water by erosion of rocks and sediments, from various industrial plants and mining operations, and as residues from certain pesticides. Metals also may enter culture water when metal tanks, pipes, fittings, and the like are used in construction. Galvanized iron, aluminum, copper, and brass have been used. Of these, aluminum is the least toxic to culture species. The others are highly toxic in small amounts.

Following are brief descriptions of the toxicity of aluminum, cadmium, chromium, copper, iron, lead, mercury, nickel, and zinc.

Aluminum-- Aluminum is the third most abundant element in the earth's outer crust, yet it rarely occurs in natural water in concentrations greater than a few tenths of a ppm. The suspended precipitate of ionized aluminum is toxic. In most natural fresh waters, the ionized or potentially ionizable aluminum is in the form of anionic or neutral precipitates. Anything greater than 0.1 ppm is deleterious to growth and survival of culture species. Concentrations of aluminum exceeding 1.5 ppm present a hazard to marine life, and 0.2 ppm or less presents minimal risk.

Cadmium-- Cadmium is a dangerous cumulative metal. Poisoning is chronic because there is almost no excretion of this metal by culture species. Levels of cadmium should not exceed 0.03 ppm in water having a total hardness above 100 ppm as $CaCO_3$. They should not exceed 0.004 ppm in waters with a hardness below 100 ppm. For crustaceans and the eggs and larvae of salmon, levels of cadmium should not exceed 0.003 ppm in hard water or 0.0004 ppm in soft water at any time or place. In saline waters, cadmium concentrations equal to or exceeding 0.01 ppm may be hazardous to marine life.

Chromium-- Chromium has caused a cumulative toxicity to rainbow trout and chinook salmon. For culture species, total chromium in water should not exceed 0.05 ppm. Notice here the use of the term "total" chromium since there is more than one form of chromium. There are different chemical forms of each metal in water; some are toxic to aquatic life, others are not. This depends on water quality as already outlined. A form of metal may be in an ionized or un-ionized state; metals also may form hydroxides or basic carbonates. Some forms of a given metal are relatively non-toxic but they can be potentially toxic. Since the form of a metal may change while the metal *per se* does not, the total concentration of each metal must be determined.

Copper-- Copper is a particularly toxic metal, especially in water with low alkalinity. Mollusks and algae are very sensitive to copper. Certain compounds, such as copper sulfate, are used to control some types of obnoxious algae. In Water Quality Criteria (1972), research is summarized: Acceptable reproduction of brook trout occurred in soft water (45 ppm as $CaCO_3$) when copper was present between 0.010 ppm and 0.018 ppm. Atlantic salmon avoid a concentration of 0.004 ppm copper. Copper is toxic to oysters in concentrations varying from 0.1 ppm to 3 ppm. Oysters and certain marine organisms accumulate and concentrate copper. Copper is more toxic when present with zinc, cadmium, mercury, and pentachloro-phenate. This additive toxicity is called synergism.

Thus far in our discussion of toxic effects of metals we have concerned ourselves only with various culture species. It may be of equal merit to determine toxic effects on lower forms of plants and animals that occur naturally in water. For example, plants and animals constituting the food chain in ponds have a real bearing on production of the species cultured and on their general well-being. Phytoplankton is sensitive to cupric ion and is easily killed by it. If this happens, not only is the food chain affected, but oxygen depletion may occur. The oxygen-producing phytoplankton no longer adds oxygen to the system; instead it uses oxygen in the decay process. Therefore, when determining 96-hour LC50 values, it would be wise to test the most sensitive species present as well as the culture species. The zooplankter *Daphnia magna* is often chosen as a test animal.

Iron-- Iron is found in ground water in the reduced state as ferrous (Fe^{++}) iron. This form of iron is soluble, and in the presence of oxygen it is oxidized to the ferric (Fe^{+++}) species, which is very insoluble. Oxidized iron often forms hydroxides, or it may exist as some form of organic complex. When in the ferric state, a rust-colored precipitate is often prevalent. Iron, particularly when occurring as a precipitate, can be most detrimental to culture species. Gills are clogged, thus interfering with respiration. Moreover, gill filaments are often inflamed, and capillaries are congested. Ferric precipitates are also detrimental in hatcheries where eggs or larvae are present. Iron may completely foul filter beds and pipes in tank culture systems.

There are several ways to remove iron from water. Iron can be removed by a combination of automatic chlorination and fine filtration. Chlorine chemically oxidizes iron (forming a precipitate), kills iron bacteria, and eliminates disease bacteria. A fine filter then removes the precipitate. Spotte (1970) discussed removal of iron in tank-culture systems. On a larger scale involving ponds, water containing iron can be pumped into a settling reservoir before it is supplied to culture ponds. The tolerance limit of iron is 0.3 ppm soluble iron in fresh and saline waters.

Lead-- As early as 1968 approximately 163,265 mt (180,000 tons) of lead were put into the atmosphere from combustion of leaded gasoline (Council of Environmental Quality 1971). Concern over this air pollution resulted in usage of non-leaded gasoline in automobiles. The rate of lead entering our oceans from air pollution in 1972 was approximately 10 times the rate introduced by natural weathering.

In fresh water, lead has a low solubility of 0.5 ppm in soft water, and only 0.003 ppm in hard water. The toxicity of lead is greatest in soft water. The concentration of lead in fresh water should not be higher than 0.03 ppm at any time or place for protection of aquatic life. In saline water, concentrations of lead should not exceed 0.02 of the 96-hour LC50. Further, it is suggested that concentrations of lead equal to or exceeding 0.05 ppm are hazardous to marine life. Levels less than 0.01 ppm pose a minimal risk.

Mercury-- Mercury enters the water from leaching of geological formations. Increasing amounts of mercury are being added to the environment from manufacturing processes or through disposal of industrial and consumer products. Mercury released by weathering processes is approximately 230 mt (254 tons) per year worldwide. The amount released by burning of coal has been 2,721 mt (3,000 tons) per year. In urban areas from 181 to 227 kg (400 to 500 lb) of mercury are discharged to receiving waters each year per 1 million people.

World attention was focused on mercury poisoning when people began dying from eating contaminated fish and shellfish. This occurred during the middle and late 1950s in Minamata, Japan. Following this, other countries became aware of mercury poisoning. In the United States, mercury was found in swordfish (*Xiphias gladius*), and European countries took note of the problem. In Germany, the Federal Ministry of Health established a tolerance limit of 1 ppm for mercury residues in fish and 0.7 ppm for crustaceans and mollusks. Sweden and Finland adopted Germany's tolerance limits. In the United States, the Food and Drug Administration established a tolerance limit of 0.5 ppm for total mercury residues.

Mercury is a cumulative metal. Culture species can build residues of this metal through biological magnification. In this process, mercury contained in organisms eaten by fish increases at each trophic level of the food chain. The magnitude of bioaccumulation of mercury is determined by the type of culture species, its exposure, feeding habits, metabolic rate, age and size, quality of water, and the degree of mercury pollution in water.

Rucker and Amend (1969) reported that rainbow trout contained mercury levels of 4 and 17.3 µg/g in muscle and kidney tissue after being exposed to 60 µg/liter ·of ethylmercury 1 hour a day for 10 days. Freshwater phytoplankton, macrophytes, and fish are capable of biologically magnifying mercury from water 1,000 times according to Chapman et al. (1968). Some freshwater invertebrates also have a 10,000 magnification (Hannerz 1968).

Recommendations from Water Quality Criteria (1972) are: (1) The concentration of total mercury (inorganic and organic forms) should not exceed a total body burden of 0.5 µg/g wet weight in any aquatic organism. (2) Total mercury in fresh water should not exceed 0.05 µg/liter. (3) Total mercury in saline water should not exceed 0.1 µg/liter.

Nickel-- This metal is toxic to aquatic life in low concentrations. Concentrations of nickel at or below 100 μg/liter should not be harmful to marine or freshwater aquatic organisms.

Zinc-- The total alkalinity of water greatly affects toxicity of this metal as does the DO level. In low alkaline water and with reduced DO, zinc is especially toxic. Because zinc is toxic to aquatic life, galvanized tanks and pipes should be avoided in culture or hatchery operations. Some aquaculturists have solved the problem by painting galvanized tanks with an epoxy paint or with a tar-like material used to protect nets and seines. The safe level of zinc in water recommended by the EPA is 100 μg/liter.

Pesticides

Pesticides are chemicals, natural or synthetic, used to destroy, prevent, or control pests. The most common pesticides are insecticides, herbicides, and fungicides. In the United States, more than 1,000 active pesticidal chemicals have been formulated into more than 60,000 preparations. Pesticide usage had been increasing at an annual rate of 15%. However, there is a push for "sustainable agriculture" in United States, which calls for use of fewer pesticides. Great alarm has been expressed over the widespread use of pesticides. In the President's Science Advisory Committee report on the use of pesticides (1963), one of the recommendations was that various concerned agencies monitor pesticide residues in air, water, soil, wildlife, fish, and people. The Bureau of Sport Fisheries and Wildlife later conducted a nationwide survey (Johnson et al. 1967). Johnson and Finley (1980) reported on the toxicity of more than 400 chemicals, including insecticides, herbicides, and industrial chemicals, to fish and aquatic invertebrates.

Sources of Pesticide Contamination-- Major sources of pesticides in water are runoff from treated lands, industrial discharges, and domestic sewage. Significant contamination also may occur in fallout from atmospheric drift and in precipitation (Tarrant and Tatton 1968).

When choosing a site for the aquaculture operation and for a water source, consider possible contamination from pesticides. In estuarine waters, it is probably wise during site selection to analyze native aquatic species for pesticide residues. Estuaries that receive large volumes of water from streams should be suspected of pesticide contamination, because agricultural lands may drain into the streams. Inland source water that receives runoff from agricultural lands should generally be avoided.

During 1974, a rash of fish kills in commercial ponds was reported in agricultural areas of Arkansas, Louisiana, and Mississippi, and elsewhere in the South. In northeast Louisiana, for example, the first fish kill of the year from insecticide poisoning was reported 26 July 1974 (Walker 1975). By 20 September 1974, 26 similar reports were received from catfish and shiner (*Notemigonus crysoleucas*) producers, affecting 212 ha (530 ac). The total area of catfish ponds affected in Mississippi during 1974 was double the area of Louisiana. Arkansas was the second most affected state. Walker (1975) analyzed 22 whole samples of fish to determine the extent of pesticide residues (Table 6.8). Residues of both toxaphene and endrin (two organochlorides used on cotton) were especially noteworthy. When DDT was banned by the EPA in 1972, some farmers (particularly cotton farmers) substituted endrin, an organochloride. Toxaphene had also been commonly used by cotton farmers. Today, organochloride insecticides are banned in the United States.

Table 6.8 Analysis of 22 whole-body samples of catfish and shiners in Northeast Louisiana 1974 for pesticide residues.

Pesticide	FDA allowable levels in fish (ppm)	Maximum concentration (ppm)	Occurrence out of 22 samples
Methyl parathion	----	0.063	9
DDT metabolites	5.0	0.241	17
Dieldrin	0.3	0.01	8
Endrin	0.3	0.566	22
Toxaphene	5.0	6.475	13

Source: Walker 1975.

Pesticides are applied for control of a particular pest (target species), but non-target species may be affected. Harmful effects of pesticides on aquatic species and on the environment include: (1) acute toxicity where non-target species are killed, (2) chronic toxicity where growth, reproduction, and general well-being of aquatic species are adversely affected, (3) residues and accumulation of pesticides in the flesh, and (4) odors or bad taste imparted to flesh of culture species.

Acute Toxicity-- Pesticides are toxic to culture species in varying concentrations (Table 6.9). Great differences in susceptibility to different compounds exist between species. For example, Pickering et al. (1962) reported that 96-hour LC50 values for various fish species exposed to organophosphates ranged from 5 to 610,000 µg/liter.

Table 6.9 Acute toxicity of selected pesticides to selected culture species.

Pesticide	Organism	Acute toxicity LC50 Concentration	Hours	Reference
		Organochloride Insecticides		
Aldrin	*Procambarus clarkii*	38.0 ppb	120	Hendrick & Everett 1965
	Salmo gairdneri	17.7 µg/l	96	Katz 1961
	Oncorhynchus kisutch	45.9 µg/l	96	Katz 1961
Endrin	*P. clarkii*	0.3 ppm	72	Muncy & Oliver 1963
	S. gairdneri	0.6 µg/l	96	Katz 1961
	O. kitsutch	0.5 µg/l	96	Katz 1961
	Crassostrea virginica (eggs)	790.0 ppb	48	Davis & Hidu 1969
DDT	*P. clarkii*	0.6 ppm	72	Muncy & Oliver 1963
	S. gairdneri	7.0 µg/l	96	Macek & McAllister 1970
	Ictalurus punctatus	16.0 µg/l	96	Macek & McAllister 1970
	Penaeus duorarum	0.12 µg/l	28	Nimmo et al. unpublished
	Callinectes sapidus	19.0 ppb	96	Mahood et al. 1970
		Organophosphate Insecticides		
Malathion	*P. acutus*	50,000 ppb	96	Carter & Graves 1973
	S. gairdneri	70 µg/l	96	Macek & McAllister 1970
	O. kisutch	101 µg/l	96	Macek & McAllister 1970
	I. punctatus	8,970 µg/l	96	" " "
	C. virginica (eggs)	9,070 ppb	48	Davis & Hidu 1969
	(larvae)	2,660 ppb	14 (days)	" " "
Methyl-parathion	*P. acutus*	3 ppb	96	Carter & Graves 1973
	Mugil cephalus	5,200 ppb	96	Eisler 1969
	S. gairdneri	2,750 µg/l	96	Macek & McAllister 1970
	O. kitsutch	5,300 µg/l	96	" " "
	I. puntatus	5, 710 µg/l	96	" " "
Carbaryl[R] Sevin	*P. acutus*	500 ppb	96	Carter & Graves 1973
	S. gairdneri	4,340 µg/l	96	Macek & McAllister 1970
	O. kisutch	764 µg/l	96	" " "
	I. punctatus	15,800 µg/l	96	" " "
	C. virginica (eggs)	3,000 ppb	48	Davis & Hidu 1969
	(larvae)	3,000 ppb	14 (days)	" " "
		Herbicides		
Diquat	*S. gairdneri*	11,200 µg/l	48	Gilderhus 1967
	O. tshawytscha	28,500 µg/l	48	Bond et al. 1960
	Pimphales promelas	5,600 µg/l	96	Mount & Stephan 1967
Molinate	*Orconectes nais*	5,600 µg/l	48	Sanders 1970

Toth et al. (1988) compiled the 96-hour LC50 of 105 pesticides to six aquaculture species including channel catfish and red swamp crawfish. Carter and Graves (1973) exposed white river crawfish (*Procambarus zonangulus*), channel catfish, and bullfrog tadpoles (*Rana catesbeiana*) to six organophosphate, four carbamate, and four organochloride insecticides. With few exceptions crawfish were the most sensitive to insecticides, and bullfrog tadpoles were the least sensitive. For example, they found that methyl parathion, an extensively used organophosphate, is 2,133 times more toxic to crawfish than to bullfrog tadpoles. They concluded that higher animals (from a phylogenetic standpoint) are less affected by insecticides than are lower forms. Crawfish, which belong to the same phylum as insects, are more sensitive to insecticides than are bullfrog tadpoles. Higher animals possess much better systems for detoxifying insecticides. It follows then, that plankton, benthos, insects, and lower forms of life are slower to recover from pesticide poisoning than are fish.

Toxicity of pesticides may be modified by differences in formulation, environmental conditions, and size, age, and physiological condition of the culture species. Though the 96-hour LC50 has helped standardize methods for determining acute toxicity, many researchers conduct tests under varying conditions and water quality. EPA guidelines suggested that reconstituted water be used and that salts and other constituents be added to standardize dilution water (Stephan 1975).

Chronic Toxicity-- Most information on the effects of pesticides to aquatic life is limited to acute toxicity. The few chronic tests conducted indicate that toxic effects occur at much lower concentrations. Mehrle and Mayer (1975) reported chronic effects of toxaphene. Low concentrations caused stunted growth in the three species of fish they studied. Skeletal fragility (broken back syndrome) was also common. No doubt the latter was caused by elimination of vitamin C from their diet; vitamin C is used for detoxification of toxaphene. Reduced fecundity is also a chronic effect of pesticides.

Residues and Accumulation-- Some pesticides, particularly the organochloride compounds, are extremely stable. They degrade slowly or form persistent degradation products. Aquatic animals may accumulate these compounds directly by absorption from water and by eating contaminated food organisms. As residues are passed on through the food chain through each trophic level, they increase in concentration; the concentration may be many thousand times greater in organisms at the end of the food chain. In Louisiana, crawfish and rice are alternated in the same fields. Residues of aldrin and dieldrin were determined for crawfish (*Procambarus clarkii*) cultured in rice fields, where these two chemicals were used at the time (Hendrick et al. 1966). In this study, crawfish flesh contained residues of both chemicals in excess of FDA tolerance limits. Because of the persistence and residues of certain pesticides, the FDA has established tolerance limits for residues in fish. Residues in aquatic species and in our environment are closely monitored and reported in the quarterly Pesticide Monitoring Journal.

Pesticides may impart odors or a bad taste to the flesh of culture species. Taste tests already described should be conducted if this problem is suspected.

Recommendations: (1) Source water that is suspect of pesticide contamination should not be used for aquaculture. (2) As a safeguard, aquatic species native to the area should be examined for pesticide residues, if surface or estuarine waters are used as a source of water supply. (3) All agricultural and industrial activities, and their anticipated development, must be considered when selecting a source of water.

Other Pollutants and Toxins

Polychlorinated biphenyls (PCBs)-- PCBs are a group of chlorinated hydrocarbons developed for commercial use as electrical transformer insulation fluids, extreme pressure oils and greases, hydraulic fluids, fire retardants, and plasticizers. PCBs are extremely stable and inert compounds. As a result they have accumulated in native fish species. PCBs have widespread distribution. They have been found in fish and wildlife in many parts of the world. Biphenyls may have 1 to 10 attached chlorine atoms, making possible more than 200 compounds. The FDA and U.S. Department of Agriculture set allowable concentrations of PCBs at 2 ppm as residues in the flesh of fish (Anonymous 1989). Concentrations of PCBs as low as 0.01 μg/liter in water can lead to accumulation in aquatic animals. PCB concentration should not exceed 0.002 μg/liter in water at any time or place. Residues in body tissues of any aquatic organism should not exceed 0.5 μg/g.

Detergents-- Phosphates have been included in household detergents to improve their effectiveness. Phosphates usually do not have direct, serious effects on aquatic life, but they may result in obnoxious algal blooms, that may deplete oxygen.

Cyanides-- Cyanides may be present in industrial wastes derived from gas works, coke ovens, scrubbing of gases in steel plants, metal plating operations, and chemical industries. Toxicity of cyanides is affected by pH, temperature, and dissolved oxygen. Free cyanide (CN^- and HCN) occurs mostly as molecular hydrogen cyanide, the more toxic form. Free cyanide of 0.05 to 0.01 ppm as CN^- has been fatal to fish. No concentration of cyanides should ever exceed 0.005 ppm in fresh water. Concentrations of cyanide equal to or exceeding 0.01 ppm constitute a hazard to marine life; levels less than 0.005 ppm present minimal risk.

PUMPING WATER

Once a sufficient supply of good quality water is found, pumps are sometimes required to fill the pond or culture unit. Certain culture systems may not require that water be pumped, for example watershed ponds, gravity-flow raceways, cage and net-pen culture in rivers and lakes, ocean ranching, and bottom culture of oysters. Pumps are sometimes required to drain excavated ponds and certain other culture systems that cannot be drained by gravity.

A pump and power unit must be carefully chosen that fits the particular need of the aquaculture operation. Most crawfish farmers pump water from a stream next to ponds. A portable surface source pump or stationary surface source pump is commonly used (Baker 1983). A different type of pump is required by catfish farmers who use ground well water. The power source, too, must be carefully chosen. Pumps with motors exceeding 7.5 hp usually require 3-phase electricity over single phase. Certain culture operations may be best suited for diesel-powered motors. Wheaton (1977) reviewed the various types of pumps and power sources used in aquaculture. Salassi and Musick (1983) provided an economic analysis of pumping systems. Selection of the proper pump was discussed by Harrison and Choate (1968), Keese (1979), Baker (1987), and Yoo and Boyd (1994).

STUDY QUESTIONS

1. List eight sources of water used in aquaculture. Give an example of a culture system and culture species for each. List advantages and disadvantages for use of each water source. Can disadvantages be overcome?

2. List five factors that determine the quantity of water required to grow a culture species.

3. A pond is 2,000 ft long, 1,500 ft wide, and averages 4 ft deep. Calculate the surface acres and acre feet of water.

4. A pond is 1,000 ft long, 400 ft wide, and 4 ft deep. How many hours will it take to fill this pond with a well producing 500 gpm?

5. Assume that a fish farm contains 10 ponds totaling 150 surface acres. The average depth is 4 ft. Annual evaporation and seepage losses total 36 in., and annual rainfall is 28 in. Calculate: (a) total acre feet of water needed to fill all ponds, (b) size and number of wells in gpm required, and (c) quantity of water needed to replace that lost by evaporation and seepage.

6. A pond is 500 m long, 200 m wide, and 1 m deep. What is the volume of water for this pond?

7. What is the best range of water temperature for growing channel catfish, rainbow trout, the freshwater prawn *Macrobrachium rosenbergii*, and the shrimp *P. monodon?*

8. What is an anadromous species and a catadromous species?   Illustrate with an example of each.

9. How do temperature, salinity, and elevation affect the amount of dissolved oxygen in water?

10. What are the important roles of total alkalinity in water?

11. What is the range of total hardness (ppm) for fresh water that is conducive to good fish production?

12. Discuss three water quality parameters that are affected by the pH of water.

13. Regarding heavy metals, what do synergism and biomagnification mean? Illustrate with examples.

14. What are sources of pesticide contamination?

15. A raceway system contains 450 m³ of water. How many liters is this? Convert this answer to gallons.

16. A raceway has a flow of 450 gpm. What is this in cubic feet per second, and in liters per minute?

17. A pond is 40 acres in size. How many hectares is this?

REFERENCES

Alabaster, J.S. and R. Lloyd. 1982. Ammonia. pp. 85-102. In Water Quality Criteria for Freshwater Fish. FAO, Butterworths.

Alabaster, J.S., D.W.M. Herbert and J. Hemens. 1957. The survival of rainbow trout (*Salmo gairdneri* Richardson) and perch (*Perca flavescens* L.) at various concentrations of oxygen and carbon dioxide. Animal Behavior 9(3-4):187-192.

Allen, K.O. 1972. Factors affecting growth and survival of catfish reared in tanks. Presented 4th Annual Convention Catfish Management Workshop, Catfish Farmers of America. Mimeograph 6 pp.

Allen, K.O. and J.W. Avault, Jr. 1969. Effects of salinity level on growth and survival of channel catfish, *Ictalurus punctatus*. Proceedings Southeastern Association of Game and Fish Commissioners 21:319-331.

Allen, K.O. and J.W. Avault, Jr. 1970. Effects of salinity and water quality on survival and growth of juvenile pompano, *Trachinotus carolinus*. pp. 147-155. In Louisiana State University Coastal Studies Bulletin No. 5.

Allen, K.O. and J.W. Avault, Jr. 1971. Notes on the relative salinity tolerance of white and blue catfish. Progressive Fish-Culturist 33(3):135-137.

American Public Health Association. 1989. Standard Methods for Examination of Water and Wastewater. 17 edition. American Public Health Association, Washington, D.C. 1,469 pp.

Anonymous. 1989. What are PCBs. Sport Fishing Institute Bulletin No. 405.

Avault, J.W., Jr. 1971. Twenty key questions on oxygen depletion, your fish and you. Fish Farming Industries 2(2):14-19.

Avault, J.W., Jr. and E.W. Shell. 1968. Preliminary studies with hybrid tilapia, *Tilapia aurea* x *T. mossambica*. Proceedings of the World Symposium on Warm-Water Pond Fish Culture. FAO Fisheries Report No. 44, 4:237-242.

Avault, J.W., Jr., L.W. de la Bretonne and J.V. Huner. 1974. Two major problems in culturing crayfish: oxygen depletion and overcrowding. In International Symposium on Freshwater Crayfish, Baton Rouge, Louisiana 2:139-144.

Baker, F.E. 1983. Pumping systems-economics. Crawfish Tales 2(4):24-30.

Baker, F.E. 1987. Selecting a pumping plant for aquaculture. Louisiana Cooperative Extension Service Bulletin. 21 pp.

Ball, I.R. 1967. The relative susceptibility of some species of freshwater fish to poisons-I ammonia. Water Research 1:767-775.

Bidwell, J.P. 1975. Brown shrimp culture at the Gulf Coast Research Laboratory. Seascope 5(3/4):1 and 6.

Bishai, H.M. 1961. The effect of salinity on the survival and distribution of larval and young fish. Journal du Conseil 26:166-179.

Black, E.C. 1953. Upper lethal temperatures of some British Columbia freshwater fishes. Journal Fisheries Research Board of Canada 10:196-210.

Bond, C.E., R.H. Lewis and J.L. Fryer. 1960. Toxicity of various herbicidal materials to fish. pp. 96-101. In 2nd Seminar on Biological Problems in Water Pollution. R.A. Taft Sanitary Engineering Center Technical Report W60-3.

Bonn, E.W. and B.J. Follis. 1967. Effects of hydrogen sulfide on channel catfish, *Ictalurus punctatus*. Transactions American Fisheries Society 96(1):31 -36.

Boyd, C.E. 1982. Hydrology of small experimental fish ponds at Auburn, Alabama. Transactions American Fisheries Society 111:638-644.

Boyd, C.E. 1985. Pond evaporation. Transactions American Fisheries Society 114:299-303.

Boyd, C.E. 1986. Influence of evaporation excess on water requirements for fish farming. In Proceedings on Climate and Water Management -- A Critical Era and Conference on the Human Consequences of 1985's Climate. American Meteorological Society, Boston, Massachusetts.

Boyd, C.E. 1987. Water conservation measures in fish farming. In 5th Conference on Applied Climatology. American Meteorological Society, Boston, Massachusetts.

Boyd, C.E. 1989. Water quality management and aeration in shrimp farming. Fisheries and Allied Aquacultures, Auburn University, Alabama Agricultural Experiment Station. Departmental Series No. 2l. 83 pp.

Boyd, C.E. 1990. Water Quality in Ponds for Aquaculture. Auburn University, Alabama Agricultural Experiment Station. 482 pp.

Boyd, C.E. and W. Walley. 1975. Total alkalinity and hardness of surface waters in Alabama and Mississippi. Auburn University, Alabama Agricultural Experiment Station. Bulletin 465. 16 pp.

Brett, J.R. 1952. Temperature tolerance in young Pacific salmon genus *Oncorhynchus*. Journal Fisheries Research Board of Canada 9(6):265-323.

Broom, J.G. 1970. Shrimp culture. Proceedings of the World Mariculture Society 1:62-68.

Burdick, G.E., M. Lipschuetz, H.J. Dean and E.J. Harris. 1954. Lethal oxygen concentrations for trout and smallmouth bass. New York Fish and Game Journal 1(1): 84-97.

Caine, G.D. 1987. Biophysical criteria for siting salmon farms in British Columbia. Aquaculture Association of B.C. Suite 52, Comp. 103, 5331 Hammond Bay Road, Nanaimo, B.C. V9S 5N7.

Carlander, K. 1969. Handbook of Freshwater Fishery Biology. Iowa: Iowa State University Press. Volume 1. 105 pp.

Carter, F.L. and J.B. Graves. 1973. Measuring effects of insecticides on aquatic animals. Louisiana Agriculture 16(2):14-15.

Chapman, W. 1940. Effects of decreasing oxygen supply on sockeye and chinook salmon. Transactions American Fisheries Society 69:197-204.

Chapman, W., H.L. Fisher and M.W. Pratt. 1968. Concentration factors of chemical elements in edible aquatic organisms. UCRL-50564 Lawrence Radiation Laboratory, University of California; Livermore, California. 50 pp.

Chen, J.C. and T.S. Chin. 1989. Effect of ammonia at different pH levels on *Penaeus monodon* postlarvae. Asian Fisheries Science 2(1989):233-238.

Chen, J.C., C.C. Tu and W.S. Yang. 1989. Acute toxicity of ammonia to larval *Penaeus japonicus*. Journal of Fisheries Society of Taiwan 16(4):261-270.

Chien, Y.H. 1992. Water quality requirements and management for marine shrimp culture. pp. 144-156. In Proceedings of the Special Session on Shrimp Farming. Baton Rouge, Louisiana: World Aquaculture Society. 301 pp.

Chin, T.S. and J.C. Chen. 1987. Acute toxicity of ammonia to larvae of the tiger prawn, *Penaeus monodon*. Aquaculture 66: 247-253.

Colt, J. and G. Tchobanoglous. 1976. Evaluation of the short-term toxicity of nitrogenous compounds to channel catfish, *Ictalurus punctatus*. Aquaculture 8:209-224.

Costelow, J.D., Jr. 1967. The effect of salinity and temperature on survival and metamorphosis of megalops of the blue crab, *Callinectes sapidus* Rathburn. Duke University Marine Laboratory, Durham, North Carolina. Contribution No. 305, Series A.

Council on Environmental Quality. 1971. Environmental quality, the second annual report. U.S. Government Printing Office, Washington, D.C.

Davis, H.C. and H. Hidu. 1969. Effects of pesticides on embryonic development of clams and oysters and on survival and growth of the larvae. Fisheries Bulletin 67(2): 383-404.

Davis, H.S. 1961. Culture and Diseases of Game Fishes. Berkley and Los Angeles, California: University of California Press. 332 pp.

Davis, S.A., T.E. Schwedler, J.R. Tomasso and J.A. Collier. 1991. Production characteristics of pan-size channel catfish in cages and open ponds. Journal of the World Aquaculture Society 22(3):183-186.

DeCola, J.N. 1970. Water quality requirements for Atlantic salmon. U.S.D.I. Federal Water Quality Administration Report CWT 10-16.

de la Bretonne, L.W., Jr., J.W. Avault, Jr. and R.O. Smitherman. 1969. Effects of soil and water hardness on survival and growth of the red swamp crawfish, *Procambarus clarkii*, in plastic pools. Proceedings Southeastern Association of Game and Fish Commissioners 23:626-633.

Delistraty, D.A., J.M. Carlberg, J.C. Van Olst and R.F. Ford. 1977. Ammonia toxicity in cultured larvae of the American lobster (*Homarus americanus*). Proceedings of the World Mariculture Society 8:647-672.

DeMont, D.J. and R.W. Miller. 1971. First reported incidence of gas-bubble disease in the heated effluent of a steam generating station. Proceedings Southeastern Association of Game and Fish Commissioners 25:392-399.

Dionigi, C.P., D.A. Greene, D.F. Mille and P.B. Johnsen. 1990. Mixed function oxidase inhibitors affect production of the off-flavor microbial metabolite geosmin. Pesticide Biochemistry and Physiology 38(1990):76-80.

Dionigi, C.P., D.F. Mille and P.B. Johnsen. 1991. Effects of farnesol and the off-flavor derivative geosmin on *Streptomyces tendae*. Applied and Environmental Microbiology 57(12):3,429-3,432.

Dionigi, C.P., D.F. Mille, A.M. Spanier and P.B. Johnsen 1992. Spore and geosmin production by *Streptomyces tendae* on several media. Journal of Agricultural and Food Chemistry 40(1):122-125.

Doudoroff, P. and M. Katz. 1953. Critical review of literature on the toxicity of industrial wastes and their components to fish. II. The metals as salts. Sewage Industrial Wastes 25(7):802-839.

Doudoroff, P. and D.L. Shumway. 1970. Dissolved oxygen requirements of freshwater fishes. FAO Fisheries Technical Paper No. 86 FIRI/T86 Water Pollution. 291 pp.

Durfor, C.N. and E. Becker. 1964. Public water supplies of the 100 largest cities in the United States, 1962. U.S. Geological Survey Water-Supply Paper 1812. 364 pp.

Eddy, S. and T. Surber. 1947. Northern fishes. Minnesota: University of Minnesota Press.

Egusa, S. 1961. Studies on the respiration of the "kuruma" shrimp *Penaeus japonicus* Bute II. preliminary experiments on its oxygen consumption. Bulletin Japanese Society of Scientific Fisheries 27:650-659.

Eisler, R. 1969. Acute toxicities of insecticides to marine decapod crustaceans. Crustaceana 16(3):302-310.

Eisler, R. 1973. Annotated bibliography on biological effects of metals in aquatic environments. No. 1-567, EPA-R3-73-007, Program Element 1B1022. Superintendent of Documents, U.S. Government Printing Office, Washington, D.C. (567 abstracts from 1897 to 1972 with indices by metal and taxa).

EPA. 1976. Quality Criteria for Water. U.S. Environmental Protection Agency, Washington, D.C. 256 pp.

European Inland Fisheries Advisory Committee (1973). Water Quality Criteria for European Freshwater Fish. Report on Ammonia and Inland Fisheries. Water Research 7:1,011-1,022.

Farmer, A.S.D. 1981. Prospects for penaeid shrimp culture in arid lands. pp. 860-897. In Advances in Food Producing Systems for Arid and Semi-arid Lands. Academic Press Inc.

Ferguson, R.G. 1958. The preferred temperature of fish and their midsummer distribution in temperate lakes and streams. Journal Fisheries Research Board of Canada 15:607-624.

Finucane, J.H. 1970. Pompano mariculture in Florida. Marine Technology Society 1970:135-143.

Ford, R.F., J.C. Van Olst, J.M. Carlberg, W.R. Dorband and R.L. Johnson. 1975. Beneficial use of thermal effluent in lobster culture. Proceedings of the World Mariculture Society 6:509-519.

Fujimura, T. 1966. Notes on the development of a practical mass culturing technique of the giant prawn *Macrobrachium rosenbergii*. Indo-Pacific Fisheries Council, FAO Regional Office for Asia and the Far East, Bangkok, Thailand, 12th Session.

Galtsoff, P.S. 1964. The American oyster, *Crassostrea virginica*. Fishery Bulletin of the Fish and Wildlife Service Volume 64. Superintendent of Documents, U.S. Government Printing Office, Washington, D.C. 480 pp.

Gilderhus, P.A. 1967. Effects of diquat on bluegills and their food organisms. Progressive Fish-Culturist 29(2):67-74.

Greene, G.N. 1969. Effects of water hardness on fish production in plastic pools. Proceedings Southeastern Association of Game and Fish Commissioners 23:455-461.

Gunter, G. and G.E. Hall. 1965. A biological investigation of the Caloosahatchee estuary of Florida. Gulf Research Report 2(1): 71 pp.

Hall, M.D. 1972. Confinement catfish culture. pp. 26-30. In Catfish Production and Management Conference, University of Illinois at Urbana, Champaign.

Hannerz, L. 1968. Experimental investigations on the accumulation of mercury in water organisms. Report of the Institute of Freshwater Research, Drottingholm No. 48:120-176.

Harrison, D.S. and R.E. Choate. 1968. Selection of pumps and power units for irrigation systems in Florida. University of Florida, Florida Agricultural Extension Service. Circular 330.

Hart, W.B., P. Doudoroff and J. Greenback. 1945. The evaluation of the toxicity of industrial wastes, chemicals and other substances to freshwater fishes. Waste Control Laboratory, the Atlantic Refining Company of Philadelphia.

Hem, J.D. 1970. Study and interpretation of the chemical characteristics of water. 2nd edition. Geological Survey Water-Supply Paper 1473. United States Government Printing Office, Washington, D.C.. 363 pp.

Hendrick, R.D. and T. R. Everett. 1965. Toxicity to the Louisiana red crawfish on some pesticides used in rice culture. Journal of Economic Entomology 58(5):958-961.

Hendrick, R.D., T.R. Everett and H.R. Caffey. 1966. Effects of some insecticides on the survival, reproduction, and growth of the Louisiana red crawfish. Journal of Economic Entomology 59(1):188-192.

Herrmann, R.B., C.E. Warren and P. Doudoroff. 1962. Influence of oxygen concentration on the growth of juvenile coho salmon. Transactions American Fisheries Society 91(2):155-167.

Hildebrand, H.H. 1955. A study of the fauna of the pond shrimp (*Penaeus duorarum* Burkenroad) grounds in the Gulf of Campeche. Institute of Marine Science University of Texas 4(1):169-232.

Hill, T.K., J.L. Chesness and E.E. Brown. 1973. A two-crop fish production system. Transactions American Society of Agricultural Engineers 16: 930-933.

Holland, G.A., J.E. Lasater, E.D. Neumann and W.E. Eldridge. 1960. Toxic effects of organic and inorganic pollutants on young salmon and trout. Washington Department Fisheries. Research Bulletin No. 5 264 pp.

Hollander, E.E. and J.W. Avault, Jr. 1975. Effects of salinity on survival of buffalo fish eggs through yearlings. Progressive Fish-Culturist 37(1):47-51.

Hughes, J.T. and G.C. Mathiessen. 1962. Observations of the biology of the American lobster. Limnology and Oceanography 7(3):414-421.

Hui, J., J.W.Avault, Jr. and P. Medley. in press. Toxicity of ammonia and nitrite to juvenile red claw crayfish, *Cherax quadricarinatus*. In 10th International Symposium on Freshwater Crayfish, Adelaide, Australia.

Jaspers, E. and J.W. Avault, Jr. 1969. Environmental conditions in burrows and ponds of the red swamp crawfish *Procambarus clarkii*. Proceedings Southeastern Association of Game and Fish Commissioners 23:592-605.

Jayasankar, P. and M.S. Muthu. 1983. Toxicity of ammonia to the larvae of *Penaeus indicus*. Indian Journal Fisheries 30(1):1-12.

Johnsen, P.B. and J.C.W. Kuan. 1987. Simplified method to quantify geosmin and 2-methylisoborneol concentrations in water and microbiological cultures. Journal of Chromatography 409(1987):337-342.

Johnson, R.E., T.C. Carver and E.H. Dustman. 1967. Indicator species near the top of the food chain chosen for pesticide base levels in fish and wildlife. Pesticides Monitoring Journal 1(1):7-13.

Johnson, W.W. and M.T. Finley. 1980. Handbook of Acute Toxicity of Chemicals to Fish and Aquatic Invertebrates. U.S. Department of Interior, Fish and Wildlife Service. Resource Publication No. 137. 98 pp.

Katz, M. 1961. Acute toxicity of some organic insecticides to three species of salmonids and to the threespine stickleback. Transactions American Fisheries Society 90(3):264-268.

Keese, C.W. 1979. Evaluating irrigation pumping plant performances. Texas A & M, Texas Agricultural Extension Service. Energy Information Leaflet 1718.

Lee, C.S. 1985. Environmental factors in the reproduction of milkfish. pp. 99-114. In Reproduction and Culture of Milkfish. Oceanic Institute Makapuu Point and Tungkang Marine Laboratory, Tungkang Pingtung. 226 pp.

Ling, S.W. 1969. The general biology and development of *Macrobrachium rosenbergii* (de Man). Fisheries Report FAO 3(57):607-619.

Lorio, W.J., P.W. Perschbacher and P.B. Johnson. 1992. Relationship between water quality, phytoplankton community and off-flavors in channel catfish (*Ictalurus punctatus*) production ponds. Aquaculture 106(1992):285-292.

Lovell, R.T. and L.A. Sackey. 1973. Absorption by channel catfish of earthy-musty flavor compounds synthesized by cultures of blue-green algae. Transactions American Fisheries Society 102(4):774-777.

Loyacano, H.A. 1967. Acute and chronic effects of salinity on two populations of red swamp crawfish, *Procambarus clarkii*. M.S. Thesis, Louisiana State University. 30 pp.

Lutz, R.A. and I.C. Darling (editors). 1980. Mussel Culture and Harvest: a North American Perspective. Amsterdam-Oxford-New York: Elsevier Science Publishing Company Inc. 350 pp.

Macek, K.J. and W.A. McAllister. 1970. Insecticide susceptibility of some common fish family representatives. Transactions American Fisheries Society 99(1):20-27.

Mahood, R.K., M.D. McKenzic, D.P. Middaugh, S.J. Bollar, J.R. Davis and D. Spitsbergen. 1970. A report on the cooperative blue crab study, South Atlantic states. U.S. Department of Interior, Bureau of Commercial Fisheries. 32 pp.

Main, K.L. and W. Fulks (editors). 1990. The culture of cold-tolerant shrimp: Proceedings of an Asian-U.S. Workshop on Shrimp Culture. Oceanic Institute Makapuu Point, Hawaii. 215 pp.

Malous, R., R. Keck, D. Maurer and C. Episano. 1972. Occurrence of gas bubble disease in three species of bivalve mollusks. Journal Fisheries Research Board of Canada 29:588-589.

McKee, J.E. and H.W. Wolf (editors). 1963. Water quality criteria. 2nd edition. California State Water Resources Control Board. Publication 3-A (Reprint December, 1971). 548 pp.

McNeil, W.J. 1956. The influence of carbon dioxide and pH on the dissolved oxygen requirements of some fresh-water fish. M.S. Thesis, Oregon State College, Carvallis, Oregon. 82 pp.

Mehrle, P.M. and F.L. Mayer. 1975. Toxaphene effects. Sport Fishing Institute 268:3.

Melancon, E.J. and J.W. Avault, Jr. 1976. Oxygen tolerance of juvenile red swamp crawfish, *Procambarus clarkii* (Girard). In International Symposium on Freshwater Crayfish, Kuopio, Finland 3:371-380.

Mills, E.R. and D.D. Culley, Jr. 1971. Toxicity of various offshore crude oils and dispersants to marine and estuarine shrimp. Proceedings Southeastern Association of Game and Fish Commissioners 25:642-650.

Moe, M.A., Jr., R.H. Lewis and R.M. Ingle. 1968. Pompano mariculture: preliminary data and basic considerations. Florida Board of Conservation Marine Laboratory Maritime Base, Bayboro Harbor, St. Petersburg, Florida. Technical Series No. 55. 65 pp.

Morrison, G. 1971. Dissolved oxygen requirements for embryonic and larval development of the hardshell clam, *Mercenaria mercenaria*. Journal Fisheries Research Board of Canada 28(3):379-381.

Moss, D.D. and D.C. Scott. 1961. Dissolved oxygen requirements of three species of fish. Transactions American Fisheries Society 90(4):377-393.

Mount, D.I. and C.E. Stephen. 1967. A method of establishing acceptable toxicant limits for fish -- melathion and the butoxyethanol ester of 2,4-D. Transactions American Fisheries Society 96(2):185-193.

Muncy, R.J. and A.D. Oliver. 1963. Toxicity of ten insecticides to the red swamp crawfish, *Procambarus clarkii* (Girard). Transactions American Fisheries Society 92(4):428-431.

Nimmo, D.R., R.R. Blackman, A.J. Wilson, Jr. and J. Forester. Toxicity and distribution of Arolor[R] 1254 in pink shrimp (*Penaeus duorarum*). Gulf Breeze Laboratory, Environmental Protection Agency, Gulf Breeze, Florida. Unpublished data.

Ogle, J.T. 1992. The effect of salinity on spawning frequency of *Penaeus setiferus* in aquaria. Gulf Research Reports 8(4):427-429.

Ogle, J.T., K. Beaugez and J.M. Lotz. 1992. Effects of salinity on survival and growth of postlarval *Penaeus vannamei*. Gulf Research Reports 8(4):415-421.

Pennell, W. 1992. Site selection handbook. Province of British Columbia, Ministry of Agriculture, Fisheries and Food Aquaculture and Commercial Fisheries Branch. 15 pp.

Perry, W.G., Jr. 1971. Salt tolerance and factors affecting crawfish production in coastal marshes. Annual Meeting Louisiana Crawfish Farmers Association, September 14, 1971. University of Southwestern Louisiana, Lafayette, Louisiana. Mimeograph 6 pp.

Perry, W.G., Jr. and J.W. Avault, Jr. 1969. Culture of blue, channel and white catfish in brackishwater ponds. Proceedings Southeastern Association of Game and Fish Commissioners 23:592-605.

Perry, W.G., Jr. and J.W. Avault, Jr. 1973. Influence of floating and sinking feeds and fingerling size on channel catfish production. Proceedings Southeastern Association of Game and Fish Commissioners 27:500-511.

Pickering, Q.H., C. Henderson and A.E. Lemke. 1962. The toxicity of organic phosphorus insecticides to different species of warmwater fishes. Transactions American Fisheries Society 91(2):175-184.

Pote, J.W., C.L. Wax and C.S. Tucker. 1988. Water in catfish production: sources, uses, and conservation. Mississippi State University, Mississippi Agricultural and Forestry Experiment Station. Special Bulletin 88-3.

President's Science Advisory Committee. 1963. Use of pesticides. The White House, Washington, D.C. 25 pp.

Privette, C.V. (no date). Selecting a pumping plant for most efficient use. Clemson, University, South Carolina Agricultural Extension Service Bulletin.

Rucker, R.R. and D.F. Amend. 1969. Absorption and retention of organic mercurials by rainbow trout and chinook and sockeye salmon. Progressive Fish-Culturist 31:197-201.

Ruffier, P.H., W.C. Boyle and J. Kleinschmidt. 1981. Short-term acute bioassays to evaluate ammonia toxicity and effluent standards. Journal of Water Pollution Control Federation 53:367-377.

Salassi, M.E. and J.A. Musick. 1983. An economic analysis of rice irrigation pumping systems in Louisiana. Department of Agricultural Economics. LSU Agricultural Center, Louisiana Agricultural Experiment Station. D.A.E. Research Report No. 617.

Sanders, H.O. 1970. Toxicities of some herbicides to six species of freshwater crustaceans. Journal of Water Pollution Control Federation. 42 (8, part 1):1544-1559.

Schwedler, T.E., J.R. Tomasso and J.A. Collier. 1989. Production characteristics and size variability of channel catfish reared in cages and open ponds. Journal of the World Aquaculture Society 20(3):158-161.

Seidman, E.R. and A.L. Lawrence. 1985. Growth, feed digestibility, and approximate body composition of juvenile *Penaeus vannamei* and *Penaeus monodon* grown at different dissolved oxygen levels. Journal of the World Mariculture Society 16:333-346.

Sick, L. and H. Beaty. 1974. Culture techniques and nutrition studies for larval stages of the giant prawn, *Macrobrachium rosenbergii*. Georgia Marine Science Center, University System of Georgia, Skidaway Island, Georgia. Technical Report Series No. 74-5. 30 pp.

Simmons, E.G. 1957. An ecology survey of the upper Laguna Madre of Texas. Institute of Marine Science University of Texas 4(2):156-200.

Smith, C.E., R.G. Piper and H.R. Tisher. 1981. The use of clinoptilolite and ion exchange as a method of ammonia removal in fish cultural systems. U.S. Department of Interior, Fish and Wildlife Service Developments in Fish Culture. Bozeman Information Leaflet Number 20. 17 pp.

Spotte, S. 1970. Fish and Invertebrate Culture Water Management in Closed Systems. New York, London, Sydney, Toronto: Wiley-Interscience, A Division of John Wiley & Sons Inc. 145 pp.

Sprague, J.B. 1971. Measurement of pollutant toxicity to fish III. Sublethal effects and "safe" concentrations. Water Research 5:245-266.

Stephan, C.E. (project officer). 1975. Methods for acute toxicity tests with fish, microinvertebrates and amphibians. The Committee on Methods for Toxicity Tests with Aquatic Organisms. National Environmental Research Center, Office of Research and Development, U.S. Environmental Protection Agency. EPA-660/3-75-009. 62 pp.

Stickney, R.P. 1986. Tilapia tolerance of saline waters: a review. Progressive Fish-Culturist 48(3):161-167.

Swee, U.B. and H.R. McCrimmon. 1966. Reproductive biology of the carp, *Cyprinus carpio* L., in Lake St. Lawrence Ontario. Transactions American Fisheries Society 95:372-380.

Swingle, H.S. 1961. Relationship of pH of pond waters to their suitability for fish culture. Proceedings Pacific Congress 9(1957), Volume 10.

Swingle, H.S. 1969. Methods of analysis for waters, organic matter, and pond bottom soils used in fisheries research. Auburn University, Alabama Agricultural Experiment Station. 119 pp.

Tabb, D.C. and W.T. Yang. 1972. A manual for culture of pink shrimp *Penaeus duorarum*, from eggs to postlarvae suitable for stocking. University of Miami. Sea Grant Special Bulletin No. 7. 59 pp.

Tarrant, K.R. and J. Tatton. 1968. Organochlorine pesticides in rainwater in the British Isles. Nature 219:725-727.

Thurston, R.V., R.C. Russo, C.M. Fetterolf, Jr., T.A. Edsall and Y.M. Barber. 1979. A Review of the EPA Red Book: Quality Criteria for Water. Water Quality Section

of the American Fisheries Society 5410 Grosvenor Lane Bethesda, Maryland 20014.
313 pp.

Toth, S.J., G.L. Jensen and M.L. Grodner. 1988. Acute toxicity of agricultural chemicals to commercially important aquatic organisms. LSU Agricultural Center, Louisiana Cooperative Extension Service. Publication 2343.

Townsend, L.D. and D. Earnest. 1940. The effects of low oxygen and other extreme conditions on salmonid fish. pp. 345-351. In Proceedings of the 6th Pacific Scientific Congress 1939.

Tucker, C.S., C.E. Boyd and E.W. McCoy. 1979. Effects of feeding rate on water quality, production of channel catfish, and economic returns. Transactions American Fisheries Society 108:389-396.

Villaluz, A.C. 1986. Fry and fingerling collection and handling. pp. 153-180. In Aquaculture of Milkfish (*Chanos chanos*) State of the Art. The Oceanic Institute Makapuu Point Waimanalo, Hawaii. 284 pp.

Walker, B.T. 1975. Pesticides and aquaculture. Presented Annual Convention Catfish Farmers of America. Memphis, Tennessee. Mimeograph 9 pp.

Walker, M.C. and P.T. Frank. 1952. The propagation of buffalo. Progressive Fish-Culturist 14:129-130.

Water Quality Criteria. 1972. A Report of the Committee on Water Quality Criteria, Environment Studies Board, National Academy of Science, National Academy of Engineering, Superintendent of Documents, U.S. Government Printing Office. 594 pp.

West, B.W. 1966. Growth, food conversion, food consumption, and survival at various temperatures of the channel catfish, *Ictalurus punctatus* (Rafinesque). M.S. Thesis, University of Arkansas.

Wheaton, F. 1977. Aquaculture Engineering. New York-Chichester-Brisbane-Toronto: John Wiley & Sons Inc. 708 pp.

Wickens, J.F. 1985. Ammonia production oxidation during culture of marine prawns and lobsters in laboratory recirculated system. Aquaculture Engineering 4:155-174.

Wyban, J.A. and J.N. Sweeney. 1991. The Oceanic Institute Shrimp Manual. Intensive shrimp production technology. The Oceanic Institute Makapuu Point, Hawaii. 158 pp.

Yoo, K.H. and C.E. Boyd. 1994. Hydrology and Water Supply for Pond Aquaculture. New York-London: Chapman & Hall, an Avi Book. 483 pp.

Zein-Eldin, Z.P. and D.V. Aldrich. 1965. Growth and survival of postlarval *Penaeus aztecus* under controlled conditions of temperature and salinity. Biological Bulletin Marine Biological Laboratory, Woods Hole 129(1):199-216.

Zein-Eldin, Z.P. and G.W. Griffith. 1966. The effect of temperature upon the growth of laboratory-held postlarval *Penaeus aztecus*. Biological Bulletin Marine Biology Laboratory, Woods Hole 131(1):186-196.

CHAPTER 7
WATER MANAGEMENT

In Chapter 6 we discussed the quality of the water source required for various culture species. This quality seldom remains constant. It may change seasonally and from activities of the culture species. In this chapter, we discuss management of water quality. Before the water can be intelligently managed, knowledge is required of natural phenomena affecting changes in water quality. In addition to naturally occurring seasonal changes, the culture species have a deleterious effect on water quality. Their waste products and the culture species themselves consume oxygen in all types of culture systems. Ammonia, nitrite, hydrogen sulphide, and other harmful substances may accumulate.

NATURAL PHENOMENA AFFECTING WATER QUALITY
Oxygen

Sources-- Natural means by which oxygen is added to water are:

(1) Oxygen diffuses directly from the atmosphere to the water. The air contains approximately 21% oxygen. The partial pressure or tension of oxygen in the air drives oxygen into the water until the partial pressure of oxygen in water is equal to that in air. When this occurs, movement of oxygen molecules from air to water ceases. This oxygen is normally confined only to that thin film of water directly exposed to the air. That is why, when oxygen is virtually depleted in a pond, fish are often seen gulping at the surface.

Water circulation from the wind, or from other means, exposes more surface water to the atmosphere. This allows more oxygen to diffuse into the water. The mixing of water from circulation also allows deeper penetration of dissolved oxygen below the surface film. Wind circulation is an important consideration in pond design. Large ponds typically have better wind circulation than small ponds. The long axis of ponds should be parallel to the prevailing wind. Excessive wind circulation, however, may result in erosion of levees. Ponds with excessive freeboard, especially small ponds, often have poor wind circulation as do ponds surrounded by trees.

(2) Photosynthesis by green plants is the major source of oxygen. Plants containing chlorophyll in the presence of light use CO_2 to produce carbohydrate and oxygen: $6CO_2 + 6H_2O \rightarrow C_6H_{12}O_6 + 6O_2$. The carbohydrate is stored by plants, and the oxygen is dissolved in water and becomes available for aquatic life. Unlike oxygen derived from the atmosphere, oxygen derived from

photosynthesis is more widely distributed in the water column and normally occurs wherever green plants are found. A shortage of CO_2, lack of sufficient light, and a lack of nutrients all limit photosynthesis.

Reduction of Dissolved Oxygen-- Oxygen is reduced in natural water by:
(1) Cessation of wind circulation reduces exposure of water to the atmosphere, so less oxygen is absorbed into water.
(2) An inhibition or cessation of photosynthesis may dramatically reduce dissolved oxygen in water.
(3) During respiration of pond organisms, oxygen is used. Every living plant and animal requires oxygen to live and "breathe." Aerobic bacteria, phytoplankton, zooplankton, and other microorganisms consume large quantities of oxygen.
(4) Aerobic decomposition of organic matter uses oxygen in the process.
(5) Oxidation-reduction reactions are chemical reactions that are continuous in natural waters. Many of these reactions use oxygen. An example is ferrous iron + oxygen → ferric iron. In the absence of oxygen, ferric iron is reduced to ferrous iron.
(6) An increase in water temperature reduces the ability of water to hold dissolved oxygen. As water becomes warmer, it holds less oxygen at saturation.
(7) An increase in salinity likewise reduces the ability of water to hold dissolved oxygen. As salinity increases, water holds less oxygen at saturation.
(8) A decrease in barometric pressure lowers the ability of water to hold dissolved oxygen.
(9) The addition of water low in dissolved oxygen, such as ground water, lowers dissolved oxygen content in water.

Oxygen Debt-- The oxygen debt or deficit is the difference between the dissolved oxygen (DO) concentration at saturation and the measured DO concentration or: $OD = C_s - C_m$ where OD = oxygen debt in ppm, C_s = DO at saturation, and C_m = measured DO. The OD value is positive when the DO concentration in water is below saturation and negative when the DO concentration in water is greater than saturation. Oxygen moves from air to water and vice versa, depending on a positive or negative oxygen debt.

When DO is deficient, an oxygen debt occurs. Normally, aerobic bacteria in the presence of oxygen decompose organic matter. This organic matter consists of dead plants and animals and their byproducts, as well as wastes from culture species. Phytoplankton and zooplankton are constantly dying and multiplying at the same time. Dead plankton and other organic matter rain down from surface water to lower depths. Oxygen is used in the decay process, and may become deficient in deeper waters. When this occurs, anaerobic bacteria continue the decay process. In the absence of oxygen, nitrogenous wastes are reduced to ammonia. Other reduction processes also occur. Sulfates are reduced to sulfides; ferric iron is reduced to ferrous iron. Certain end products, such as ammonia and hydrogen sulphide, can be toxic to culture species. As these various processes continue further, the oxygen debt builds up. If oxygen is increased in waters, the debt must be paid back before any appreciable concentration of DO can be measured. Chemically reduced forms are now oxidized. Ammonia is now oxidized to nitrite and eventually to nitrate, which is an oxygen-consuming reaction. Sulfides are oxidized to sulfates, and ferrous iron is oxidized to ferric iron.

Oxygen Demand-- The demand for oxygen in water is usually expressed in terms of biochemical oxygen demand (BOD) and chemical oxygen demand (COD). The BOD is the amount of dissolved oxygen necessary to oxidize the readily decomposable organic matter. To measure the BOD of water, a full bottle of sample water is sealed and held in the dark at 20°C (68°F) for 5 days. The measured loss of DO in milligrams per liter is the BOD. The standard BOD is of little use in evaluating oxygen dynamics within a pond, but it is useful in assessing the pollution potential of effluents (Boyd 1990). The COD is used in aquaculture primarily as an index of organic matter concentrations. It is a measure of the amount of oxygen needed to degrade the organic matter. The COD is expressed in milligrams of oxygen per liter.

Free Carbon Dioxide
Sources-- Natural sources of free carbon dioxide are:
(1) Well water and spring water are typically high in free carbon dioxide, and may be a major source of carbonates and bicarbonates.
(2) Free carbon dioxide is produced during respiration of aquatic organisms. It is a byproduct of organic matter decomposition.
(3) Compared with oxygen, only a minute amount of free carbon dioxide is present in the atmosphere.

Reduction of Free Carbon Dioxide-- Free carbon dioxide is reduced in culture waters by several means:
(1) Photosynthesis is a chemical reaction that reduces the carbon dioxide concentration in water.
(2) Agitation of water, such as from strong wind circulation, is a physical process that may move carbon dioxide from water to the atmosphere.
(3) A minor mechanism is the addition of calcium hydroxide which combines with free carbon dioxide as follows: $CO_2 + Ca(OH)_2 \rightarrow CaCO_3 + H_2O$ and $CaCO_3 + CO_2 + H_2O \rightarrow Ca(HCO_3)_2$.

Oxygen-Carbon Dioxide Fluctuation

Oxygen and carbon dioxide are interrelated. During the day, carbon dioxide is used in photosynthesis and oxygen is produced. As the day progresses, free carbon dioxide may be depleted as dissolved oxygen increases (Figure 7.1). This depletion is especially pronounced in waters with low alkalinity (< 20 ppm). The amount of oxygen produced by phytoplankton during the day is roughly equivalent to the amount of oxygen consumed by the phytoplankton bloom at night.

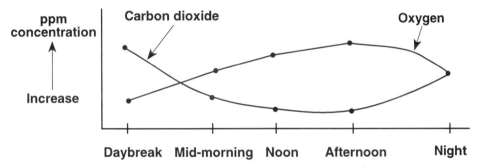

Figure 7.1 Schematic daily pulse of oxygen-carbon dioxide.

Romaire (1985) noted that the denser the phytoplankton bloom, the more pronounced the fluctuation. Pond waters with a light bloom have flatter oxygen-carbon dioxide curves, as shown in Figure 7.1. Since free carbon dioxide is a mild acid, its removal causes a shift in pH toward the alkaline side. The oxygen content is highest during mid-afternoon. When sunlight decreases significantly, photosynthesis all but ceases. At night no oxygen is produced. Because respiration continues, DO decreases and free carbon dioxide increases. Free carbon dioxide is highest at daybreak. Similarly, DO is lowest at daybreak. During daylight hours, respiration requires oxygen just as it does at night; however, more oxygen is produced than is needed, and some of this surplus is carried over into the night. Some oxygen may be lost during the day by diffusion from water to the atmosphere .

The Carbonate Buffer System

Alkalinity and carbon dioxide are often considered together as the carbonate buffer system. Carbon dioxide, unlike most other dissolved gases in water, reacts with water to form a weak acid, carbonic acid. This in turn dissociates into bicarbonate that, in turn, may dissociate to carbonate, depending on the pH. They may react with cations, particularly with calcium cations, to form solid carbonates. Although carbon dioxide is highly soluble in water, it is only a minor constituent of the atmosphere. Less than 1% of the carbon dioxide dissolved in water forms carbonic acid, and this acid strongly dissociates (Boyd 1990). Various reactions illustrate the dynamics of the system:

(1) CO_2 (gas) $\rightarrow CO_2$ (aq)
(2) CO_2 (aq) $+ H_2O \rightarrow H_2CO_3$
(3) $H_2CO_3 \rightarrow H^+ + HCO_3^-$
(4) $HCO_3^- \rightarrow H^+ + CO_3^{--}$
(5) $2HCO_3^- + Ca^{++} \rightarrow Ca(HCO_3)_2$
(6) $CO_3^{--} + Ca^{++} \rightarrow CaCO_3$ and
(7) $CaCO_3 + CO_2 + H_2O \rightarrow Ca(HCO_3)_2$

Most of the HCO_3^- is produced from the reaction shown in (7) and in similar reactions not shown. The above reactions are dynamic, and at any one time various mixtures of anions may contribute to alkalinity. Carbonates may be present with bicarbonates or hydroxides, but because hydroxides react with bicarbonates to form carbonates, bicarbonates are not found when hydroxides are present. Free carbon dioxide reacts with carbonates and hydroxides to form bicarbonates; therefore, when free carbon dioxide is present neither carbonates nor hydroxides will be found in measurable amounts. Hydroxides are normally present only in highly alkaline waters.

The occurrences of H_2CO_3, CO_2, HCO_3^-, CO_3^{--} and OH^- are given below for various approximate pH ranges:

pH 4 to 8.3	H_2CO_3 and CO_2
pH 4 to 10.5	HCO_3^-
pH 8.3 to 14.0	CO_3^{--}
pH 10.5 +	OH^-

Separation of the various forms of alkalinity is based on the assumption that the end point of phenolphthalein (approximate pH of 8.3) gives a satisfactory division between carbonates and bicarbonates. In more alkaline water, from pH 8.3 to 10.5, there may be a mixture of HCO_3^- and CO_3^{--}, but the bicarbonate decreases sharply as the pH value approaches 10.4. At relatively high pH values, insignificant amounts of bicarbonate are present.

In waters that are exposed to air and that are more acid than pH 5.5, acidity is assumed to be caused by stronger acids than CO_2. However, water from deep wells may contain up to 200 ppm of free carbon dioxide, with corresponding lower pH. Upon exposure to air, free carbon dioxide is lost until equilibrium is reached with CO_2 in the atmosphere.

Alkalinity is sometimes expressed as phenolphthalein alkalinity, methyl orange alkalinity, and total alkalinity. A water sample containing the indicator phenolphthalein is titrated with HCl or another strong acid. The hydrogen ions from the acid balance the anions, and at a pH of 8.3 the water sample turns a faint pink. The amount of acid required to lower the pH to 8.3 is a measure of alkalinity caused by CO_3^{--} and OH^-, and is known as the phenolphthalein alkalinity. If the pH is less than 10.5, then phenolphthalein alkalinity is caused entirely by CO_3^{--}. Titration continues, with the indicator methyl orange added, until the water sample turns orange at a pH of about 4.5. In more alkaline waters it is yellow, and in more acid waters it is red. This is the amount of HCO_3^- present and is known as methyl orange alkalinity. Total alkalinity is phenolphthalein alkalinity and methyl orange alkalinity combined. In waters suitable for culture species the majority of alkalinity is methyl orange or bicarbonate alkalinity. Often methyl orange alkalinity is the only alkalinity test run.

Of what value is alkalinity to the aquaculturist who wants to maintain good water quality? Alkalinity is important for two reasons, photosynthesis and buffering capacity. Both are indirectly related. A pH buffer is anything that prevents a rapid change in pH. Bicarbonates and carbonates act as buffers. During photosynthesis, free carbon dioxide is used as a source of carbon. As CO_2 is removed, the pH becomes more alkaline because of shifts in the carbonate equilibrium. Once CO_2 becomes depleted, HCO_3^- dissociates to supply CO_2 for photosynthesis. This tends to prevent a further increase in pH. If HCO_3^- is also depleted, CO_3^{--} then hydrolyzes to produce more HCO_3^- that further hydrolyzes to produce CO_2 and H_2O. Photosynthesis is curtailed because only certain blue-green phytoplankton can function well at higher alkalinities. At night, as photosynthesis ceases but respiration continues, CO_2 is produced; it combines with H^+ to shift back to HCO_3^-. This removal of H^+ prevents a rapid drop in pH. This simple equation shows this back and forth buffering action: $CO_2 + H_2O \leftrightarrow H_2CO_3 \leftrightarrow H^+ + HCO_3^- \leftrightarrow H^+ + CO_3^{--}$.

Overturn and Stratification

Overturn and stratification are normally occurring phenomena in ponds and lakes in temperate regions. The following is a generalization of these occurrences, and for further detail limnology texts such as Reid (1961), Ruttner (1971), or Wetzel (1983) should be consulted.

During the spring, winds may mix the water so that temperature is uniform from the surface to the bottom. This is the time of spring overturn. Oxygen is usually the same from the surface to the bottom. As spring progresses, the air temperature increases as does the surface water temperature. Any stratification of water temperature that arises is destroyed by mixing with the onset of even a relatively weak wind. However, as the weather warms rapidly the wind can no longer completely mix surface waters with deeper waters. This is because warm surface waters are less dense than colder, deeper waters. Little by little, as summer progresses, stratification occurs. Warmer upper water and cooler bottom water are produced. Limnologists call the upper portion the epilimnion and the bottom portion the hypolimnion. In between these two layers is the thermocline (Figure 7.2). By definition, the thermocline is the zone where the water temperature decreases by 1°C for each 1 m (3.3 ft) in depth. Surface waters become the productive area and contain sufficient oxygen for aquatic life. Aerobic conditions prevail, and free carbon dioxide is at a low concentration. Deep or bottom waters are typically low in oxygen, accumulate free carbon dioxide, and may be anaerobic.

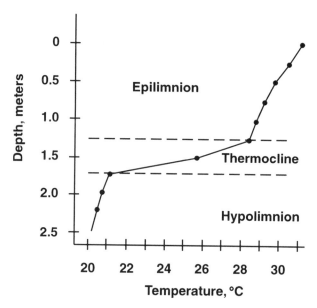

Figure 7.2 Thermal stratification in ponds.

Fall brings on a cooling of surface water that becomes denser and sinks. Gradually, as cooling and mixing continue, the thermocline is whittled away. Eventually the water temperature is the same from the surface to the bottom. Oxygen too is the same from the surface to the bottom; conditions are similar to spring overturn. In some temperate regions, fall overturn eventually results in the water being 4°C (39°F) from top to bottom. Water is densest at this temperature. As winter approaches, the water cools at the surface below 4° to 0°C (39° to

32°F). Since the difference in water density between 0°C and 4°C is slight, only a minimum stratification occurs -- a shallow surface layer exists at 0°C, and the rest of the water column is at 4°C. Besides seasonal spring and fall overturns, overturns also may occur during a prolonged cool spell in summer, during intense wind, and after heavy rains.

WATER MANAGEMENT IN PONDS
Factors Leading to Oxygen Depletion

Oxygen depletion is the single biggest problem in water quality management. In ponds, culture species are often stocked at high density and fed heavily. This greatly increases the BOD and increases the risk of oxygen depletion. Oxygen depletion may result from several possibilities.

Cloudy or Rainy Weather-- Several days of cloudy or rainy weather may lead to a phytoplankton die-off. Photosynthesis is curtailed because of low light intensity. The phytoplankton now becomes a major consumer rather than a producer of oxygen. This problem is compounded in a pond that has a vigorously growing phytoplankton bloom.

Exhaustion of Nutrients -- Nutrients, particularly phosphate in fresh water and nitrogen in saline water, may become exhausted, especially in surface waters. Photosynthesis is limited . This may be caused in part by a vigorously growing bloom that uses up the nutrients. In low alkalinity ponds (< 20 ppm), the lack of CO_2 may become a limiting factor for photosynthetic activity.

Overstocking-- Ponds may be overstocked with a culture species. Waste products from the culture species and uneaten feed contribute to the BOD. These wastes accumulate faster than they can be "digested" by pond organisms. The "correct" stocking rate varies greatly, depending on the species cultured, stocking density, aeration system, and other factors. One guide to achieving the best overall stocking density is the measured oxygen content in water. Follow guidelines outlined in Chapter 6.

Blue-green Phytoplankton Scums-- Blue-green algae, such as *Anacystis*, *Anabaena*, and *Nostoc*, may form dense scums on the surface of the water. This limits photosynthesis to only the top few centimeters. Consequently, oxygen levels may be very high in surface waters but lacking in deeper waters. Sunlight is blocked from reaching these depths. At first it may seem desirable to have supersaturation of DO in surface waters, but this is not the case. The problem is not the DO, but the dense plankton bloom. The BOD is very high in such situations, and during the night the oxygen may become depleted. Moreover, a very strong wind or hard, cold rain may result in a turnover. When this occurs, the top layer of water containing oxygen is suddenly diluted with bottom water void of oxygen; oxygen depletion may result. The term "summer kill" is sometimes used to denote such a turnover.

Boyd et al. (1975) described oxygen depletion involving blue-green phytoplankton but with a different set of conditions. Conditions included bright days, low carbon dioxide concentrations, and high pH. The bloom may suddenly die, depleting oxygen. In this instance, depletion of the nutrient phosphorus or a shortage of carbon dioxide or bicarbonate may have contributed to the die-off of blue-green algae.

Hot Weather-- Very hot, muggy days with no breeze provide a condition for oxygen depletion. Very warm water, above 32°C (90°F), holds little oxygen at saturation. With no breeze, little or no oxygen is added through circulation. Culture species and decay processes are most active in warm water.

High Salinity Water-- In brackish or saltwater ponds, high evaporation may occur, raising the salinity. If high saline water results, coupled with high water temperature, the water will contain very little DO at saturation. This problem is particularly prevalent in certain shrimp-growing countries where low-salinity water is not available to dilute high-salinity water.

Die-off of Aquatic Weeds-- A die-off of aquatic weeds may, through oxidation, cause oxygen depletion. If a pond is heavily infested with weeds, only small plots should be sprayed with herbicide at a time.

Ice Cover-- Ponds may ice over in northern states. A snow cover over the ice blocks out light, halting photosynthesis. With no oxygen produced, a winter kill of fish may occur.

Nutrient Accumulation and Oxygen Depletion

There are several levels of management for culture species in ponds. Boyd (1990) listed them as: (1) stocking only; (2) stocking and fertilizing with chemical fertilizers, manures, or both; (3) stocking, fertilizing, and supplemental feeding; (4) stocking and feeding; (5) stocking and feeding, with aeration, water exchange, or both during crisis when DO becomes low; (6) stocking and feeding with aeration, water exchange, or both on a more or less continuous basis.

To increase production, it is necessary to increase the food supply for culture species. This is accomplished by increasing nutrients (fertilizers) in pond waters, which increases production of natural food organisms. Feeds also can be used. Regardless of the means for increasing production, there will be an increase in the concentration of nitrogen, phosphorous, and organic matter. Oxygen demand and concentrations of toxic metabolites, such as ammonia and carbon dioxide, will increase. As the level of nutrients increases, there is a corresponding increase in production and an increase in water pollution.

Oxygen depletion occurs most often in semi-intensive and intensive culture systems where high rates of feeding are practiced. Boyd (1985, 1990) noted that the difference of inputs (fertilizers and feed) and outputs (fish production) is often termed the surplus. He reviewed the fate of nutrients and organic matter introduced into pond waters. In ponds with channel catfish (*Ictalurus punctatus*) only 26% of the nitrogen and 30% of the phosphorus from feed were assimilated by fish. Most phosphorus not harvested in fish was adsorbed by pond muds. The remainder of the nitrogen and organic matter apparently was lost from ponds, for no accumulation was detected in muds. Denitrification and ammonia volatilization apparently removed large amounts of nitrogen. Organic matter was decomposed by pond microorganisms. In intensive culture of *Penaeus monodon*, only 20% of the nitrogen from feed was used by shrimp (Chen and Liu 1988). Avnimelech and Lacher (1979) reported that in intensive pond culture of carp only 11% of the nitrogen and 32% of the phosphorous from feed was used by fish.

As nutrients accumulate, they are used by phytoplankton, may be adsorbed on pond muds, or remain in organic matter or sludge. Some excess nutrients can be removed by culture species that feed on plankton and on other pond organisms. In Israel it is common practice to stock "sanitary species" with the major species being cultured. Sanitary species feed at various trophic levels. The fish include the silver carp (*Hypophthalmichthys molitrix*), which feeds on phytoplankton; bighead carp (*Aristichthys nobilis*), which feeds on zooplankton; and grass carp (*Ctenopharyngodon idella*), which feeds on higher plants. Various species of tilapia, other carps, and mullet (*Mugil* spp.) are also commonly used. Mollusks, which are filter feeders, remove plankton and particulate matter, but their use in removing excess nutrients has been less well explored when compared with finfish.

Sludge, consisting of uneaten feed and fecal wastes, may accumulate in large quantities in intensive culture systems. It is a common problem in intensive shrimp farming. It can be handled by one of several methods. In water exchange, water near the pond bottom, where sludge is concentrated, is drained to a settling reservoir. New water is added to the pond. Ponds can be designed to collect sludge that, in turn, can be removed with pumps (See Figure 5.40 in Chapter 5.), even while the pond is still full of water and shrimp are growing. In Taiwan, it is common practice to remove sludge from a pond following harvest of shrimp (Figure 7.3). The sludge is removed with a strong hose and push broom. In some instances, a layer of sand is laid down after removing sludge. In Southeast Asian countries and parts of Europe, it is common practice to follow fish production with the planting of a land crop; this helps remove excess nutrients and sludge. Sundstrom et al. (1988) collected sediments from the bottom of a pond that had been in fish production for years. They found that the pond mud contained relatively high levels of calcium and magnesium. Phosphorus, potassium, copper, zinc, and manganese levels in pond muds were comparable to levels in field soil. In greenhouse studies, bell peppers grew well in pond sediments.

Figure 7.3 Husband and wife team in Taiwan clean sludge from bottom of shrimp pond after shrimp harvest.

Phytoplankton, Turbidity, and Water Color

As nutrients accumulate in pond waters, dense blooms of phytoplankton usually occur along with a change in turbidity and water color. Aquaculturists, particularly shrimp farmers, have developed water management practices based on the density of plankton blooms, turbidity, and color of water.

The density of a phytoplankton bloom can be measured by counting the number of cells per milliliter, by measuring the chlorophyll a concentration, and by a Secchi disc reading. As the nutrients increase, the number of phytoplankton cells per ml increases. There is also a corresponding change in the type of phytoplankton species represented, and there is usually a reduced diversity of species. Boyd (1990) reported that in six fertilized ponds, total phytoplankton counts ranged from 1,000 to 21,000 per ml; chlorophyll a ranged from 13 to 55 µg/liter. One also would expect high values for both readings in ponds where the culture species is fed. Boyd (1990) noted that results were so variable that it was difficult to use them to manage pond water.

The turbidity of water is relatively easy to measure with a Secchi disc, and results are used in water management. Turbidity is caused by suspended matter, primarily plankton and suspended soil particles, in water that interferes with passage of light through water. If Secchi disc visibility is caused by plankton, it can be used as a management tool (Figure 7.4). To obtain the Secchi disc reading, lower the disc into the water until it just disappears. Record the depth. Lower the disc a little more, and then raise until it just reappears. Record the depth. The average of these two depths is the Secchi disc visibility. Chien (1992) reported that a desirable Secchi disc reading in *P. monodon* ponds is 30 to 40 cm (12 to 16 in) in summer and 20 to 30 cm (8 to 12 in) in winter. Boyd (1990) evaluated Secchi disc visibilities for fish and shrimp ponds as follows:

Secchi disc visibility	Comments
less than 20 cm	Pond too turbid. If pond is turbid with phytoplankton, there will be problems with low DO concentrations. When turbidity is from suspended soil particles, productivity will be low.
20 to 30 cm	Turbidity becoming excessive.
30 to 45 cm	If turbidity is from phytoplankton, pond is in good condition.
45 to 60 cm	Phytoplankton becoming scarce.
more than 60 cm	Water is too clear. Inadequate productivity and danger of aquatic weed problems.

The color of pond water varies. A change in color or intensity indicates a change in phytoplankton flora and density. A pond with a predominance of green phytoplankton will usually have a green color; blue-green phytoplankton often impart a bright blue-green color, and there are a host of other colors. Suspended soil particles produce muddy water. Humic substances (e. g. leaves from an oak tree or pine tree) impart a tea or cola color. An experienced pond manager can sometimes read these signs and take appropriate action, such as water exchange and emergency aeration. For example, the author, working on National Fish Hatcheries, used color of pond water as an indication of the well-being of a phytoplankton bloom. Freshwater ponds were fertilized to produce fingerlings of several sportfish. Pond water with a healthy phytoplankton bloom was green, whereas a dying bloom began to take on a brownish color. A faint odor could sometimes be noted by smelling a handful of water. These indications, however, were always verified with water analysis.

Figure 7.4 John Hargreaves formerly of the LSU Agricultural Center with Secchi disc used to measure turbidity of water.

Avoiding and Combating Oxygen Depletion

In countries with temperate climates, most problems occur in summer. In tropical and sub-tropical countries, they occur year-round. In brackishwater ponds, the problem is compounded. By knowing what to look for and what to do -- before culture species begin dying -- losses can be avoided. Chemical methods, such as the Winkler method or its modification, are easy to use to monitor DO levels. A number of kits are available for commercial fish farmers (Figure 7.5). Polarographic methods also are available for certain water quality parameters such as DO and water temperature (Figure 7.6).

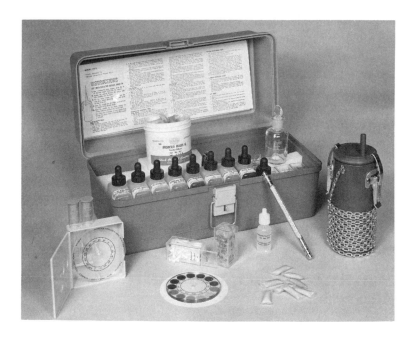

Figure 7.5 A commercial water analysis kit used by fish farmers. Photo courtesy of Hach Chemical Company.

Figure 7.6 John Hargreaves using polarographic method to measure dissolved oxygen and temperature.

Check Pond Water Daily-- Dissolved oxygen should be checked in ponds at daybreak. Most farmers monitor DO throughout the night until daybreak during summer. The oxygen content should be measured in surface waters, at mid depth, and near the bottom to obtain an oxygen profile. Boyd et al. (1978) developed methods for predicting early morning DO in ponds. They determined the water temperature and the density of the phytoplankton communities based on Secchi disc visibility. Oxygen consumption by plankton is usually the major demand on DO at night in fish ponds. From data, a computer simulation model was developed for nighttime decline in dissolved oxygen. Boyd et al. (1978) noted that there is an easier method to predict DO values. DO is measured an hour or two after dusk and again after 2 to 3 hours. The two DO concentrations can be plotted versus time, and a straight line drawn through the two points to predict DO at daybreak (Figure 7.7).

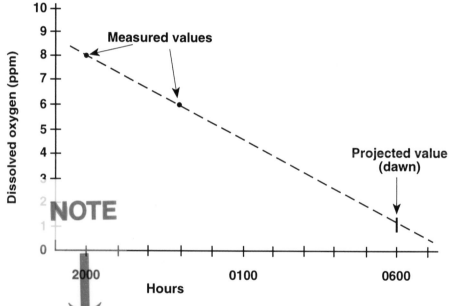

Figure 7.7 Estimating dissolved oxygen at daybreak.

Check Phytoplankton Blooms-- As mentioned earlier, a healthy bloom in ponds is indicated by a particular color. In freshwater ponds, this color is often green, whereas a change from green to brown indicates a dying bloom. A sour odor is sometimes associated with this condition. Birds may congregate around a pond that is "going bad." They catch fish as they pipe to the surface. If a nutrient shortage is suspected, the pond could be fertilized with a phosphate fertilizer, preferably liquid. Fertilizer containing nitrogen must not be used. It narrows the carbon:nitrogen ratio. This speeds bacterial decomposition of organic matter and removal of oxygen.

Blue-green blooms have been treated in freshwater ponds by floating a bag containing 0.8 kg/ha (0.75 lb/ac) of copper sulphate in surface waters. Burlap bags containing copper sulphate have been towed behind a boat, and the chemical has been sprayed into pond waters. This should not be attempted in low-alkaline waters. In waters below 20 ppm total alkalinity, copper sulphate is highly toxic. Kleinholz (1990) reported that copper sulphate is often used in channel catfish ponds to kill blue-green algae, with the hope of reducing the likelihood of off-flavor. The rate of copper sulphate to use is often calculated as follows: copper sulphate (ppm) = total alkalinity (ppm) ÷ 100. Jackson (1974) reported that application rates have varied from 0.025 to 2 ppm. Simazine and Solricin 135 also have been used to control phytoplankton blooms.

Boyd (1990), however, reported that use of chemicals to control blooms gave questionable results. He noted that both copper sulphate and simazine are very effective algaecides, but low DO concentrations following treatment limit use of these chemicals in catfish ponds. Moreover, unless the condition that led to dense blooms, in this case excess nutrients, is corrected, these blooms will reoccur. Boyd (1990) further reported that production of catfish in ponds treated with simazine was significantly less than production in non-treated ponds. Treatment of scum-forming blue-green algae with localized applications does have some merit. In this situation, blue-green scums may be windrowed to one end of the pond, allowing spot treatment.

Adjust Feeding Rates-- In static ponds with no mechanical aeration, feeding rates should be lowered during very hot summer days or during several consecutive days of cloudy, rainy weather. If, for example, 27 kg (60 lb) of feed are used in a particular pond, then it may be wise to cut this amount by half. This is only a temporary situation, and a full ration can be used again when the weather improves.

It is wise to determine whether or not the culture species is eating all the feed. If floating feed is used, this is easy to determine. If sinking feed is used, the feeding area can be seined along the bottom an hour or two after feeding to determine if feed remains. This is labor intensive, and few farmers do this. Many shrimp farmers use a lift-net to determine if feed has been eaten. Feed is placed on the net, and the net is raised 2 to 4 hours after feeding (Figure 7.8).

Water Exchange-- There are other methods for avoiding or combating oxygen depletion, most notably water exchange and aeration. New water can be added to the pond and aerated as it enters. "Dead water" low in DO should be removed from near the pond bottom. Note, however, that bottom waters may contain solid wastes that could pollute receiving waters. Therefore the depth at which water is removed should be determined with care. Certain brackishwater ponds may be flushed with the tides.

Figure 7.8 Lift net used by shrimp farmers to see if feed has been eaten.

Water exchange also is beneficial because it flushes excess nutrients from ponds, and it removes toxic metabolic wastes such as ammonia. Water exchange may dilute water in shrimp ponds so that salinity does not become excessively high, and it may help to regulate water temperature.

Boyd (1990) suggested that water should first be drawn off near the bottom. The amount removed should be equal to the amount of new water added. Water pumped into ponds should be applied at the surface and enter at the end of the pond opposite the drain. If the water is drawn off and pumped in at the same time, discharge water will contain a mixture of new and old water.

Chien (1992) reviewed water exchange strategies for shrimp ponds. In Taiwan, shrimp ponds with a low stocking rate or low shrimp biomass have daily water exchange rates of 1% to 5%, mainly to compensate for water evaporation and seepage. In semi-intensive and intensive shrimp ponds, daily water exchange rates are 10% or greater. Chien (1992) suggested that new water be added and old water be removed at the same time. Paddlewheel aeration should mix both waters. His rationale is that lowering the water level first may result in an elevated water temperature. This reduces the capacity of the water to hold oxygen. In instances where scums, shrimp feces, or dead floating plankton appear on the surface, this surface water is discharged. If low salinity is a problem, surface waters may be discharged after rainfall. Fresh water is not as dense as saline water and may remain on the surface for a while.

Mechanical Aeration-- Water can be aerated with various mechanical devices. The goal is to expose as much water to the air as possible and at the same time increase water circulation. By increasing the surface area of water, diffusion of oxygen from the atmosphere to pond water is enhanced. Some aerators send water into the air. The droplets absorb atmospheric oxygen and fall back into the pond. Others aerate by circulating surface waters, and still others inject air into the water. The depth of water circulation depends on the type of aerator used, and in some cases, such as with paddlewheels, the depth setting.

Common types of aerators include vertical pumps or bubblers (Figure 7.9), pump sprayers or bank washers (Figure 7.10), paddlewheel aerators or splashers (Figures 7.11a, b), propeller-aspirator-pumps or injectors (Figure 7.12), and diffusers (Figure 7.13). The aerators listed above are normally in a fixed location and powered with electricity. Generally, the paddlewheel is the most efficient aerator for transferring oxygen to water. Boyd and Ahmad (1987) evaluated various aerators, including tractor-powered aerators and electric aerators. Boyd and Watten (1989) reviewed aeration systems in aquaculture. Boyd (1989) reviewed aeration in shrimp farming.

Figure 7.9 Vertical pump aerator (bubbler).

298

Figure 7.10 Pump sprayer aerator (bank washer).

Figure 7.11a Paddlewheel aerator.

Figure 7.11b Paddlewheel aerators in operation.

Figure 7.12 Propeller aspirator (injector aerator).

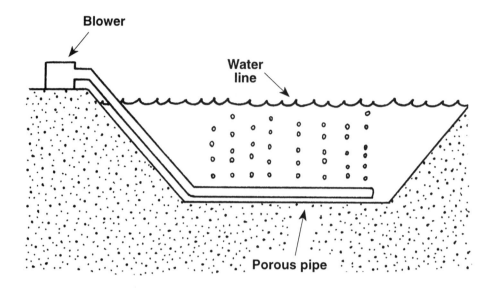

Figure 7.13 Diffuser aeration consisting of plastic hoses and air stones powered with an electric motor.

Aeration devices may be run routinely during nighttime to early morning, the critical period for low dissolved oxygen. Some diffusers, placed near the pond bottom, may start during daylight hours. The strategy here is that as oxygen is produced in surface layers, the air bubbles from aeration help mix it throughout the pond. Plemmons and Avault (1980) ran vertical-pump aerators 24 hours a day and produced up to 14 mt/ha (6.25 tons/ac) of channel catfish. No doubt some DO may have been lost at the surface during peak photosynthesis, when waters were supersaturated with DO, but oxygen was maintained throughout the water column. Oxygenated water at the pond bottom is particularly important in shrimp farming. Shrimp spend much time on the bottom, particularly since sinking feed is used.

The number of aerators to use is a consideration. Chien (1992) reported that shrimp ponds in Taiwan are equipped with six to eight paddlewheel aerators (horsepower not stated) per hectare (2 to 3 per acre). The number of paddlewheel aerators used and the amount of time each unit is run depend on shrimp biomass in the pond and water quality. In a 3- to 4-month grow-out, farmers seldom aerate during the first month, except during a cloudy day or when otherwise needed. From the third month on, the aerators run continuously. In a typical 1-ha intensive pond, aeration is started with two units shortly after postlarvae are stocked. During the last part of the culture period at least four aerators, and up to eight, operate nearly continuously. The aerators are normally 1-hp each. In some instances 2-hp aerators are used. This is the largest size that should be used in ponds 1 to 1.5 meters (3.3 to 5 ft) deep. If aerators are larger, they tend to scour the bottom and put soil sediments into the water column.

The placement of aerators in a pond depends on the number used, configuration of the pond, and other factors. The best area to place a single paddlewheel aerator is at the middle of a long side. This aerator near shore propels water across to the short side (Figure 7.14). The worst arrangement is to place the aerator in one corner of the pond to direct flow diagonally across the pond. Boyd (1989) discussed various placements with diagrams. Generally, aerators should be placed to maximize circulation throughout the pond and to avoid leaving any dead areas. The configuration with baffle levees in Figure 7.14 was developed for use in crawfish ponds. Crawfish ponds are typically planted with forage such as rice. The vegetation restricts normal water circulation. The baffle levees funnel the water current with more force throughout the pond. Since crawfish are harvested by trapping and not seining, the baffle levees do not interfere.

In some shrimp ponds, aerators are placed all along the periphery of the levee. All aerators flow water in the same direction so that one aerator complements the other. This placement results in a circular motion of water current that, in turn, causes sediments to settle out in the center of the pond. They can be removed through a center drain or by pumping. Regardless, place aerators so that sediments do not pile up in one part of the pond unless they are removed.

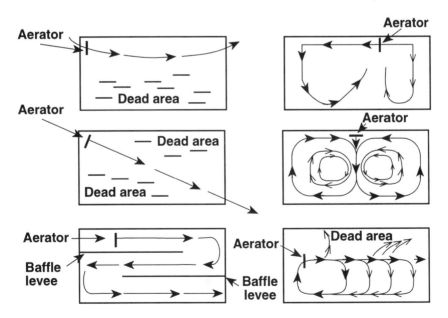

Figure 7.14 Placement of aerators influences degree of circulation. After Boyd 1989.

Emergency Aeration-- If oxygen depletion occurs, finfish can be seen gulping at the surface. Shrimp, crawfish, prawns, and other culture species may appear at the surface and lie on their sides. Quick action is needed to aerate water. Tractor-powered aerators are mobile and normally used for emergencies (Figures 7.15a, b). When using emergency aeration, the immediate goal is to save the culture species and not necessarily to increase oxygen at all depths. Therefore when water is removed from the pond and sprayed into the air or at an angle onto the surface, it should not be drawn off near the bottom (Figure 7.16). Rather the intake should be placed 30 to 60 cm (1 to 2 ft) below the surface.

Figure 7.15a Tractor-powered emergency aerator.

Figure 7.15b Tractor-powered emergency aerator in operation.

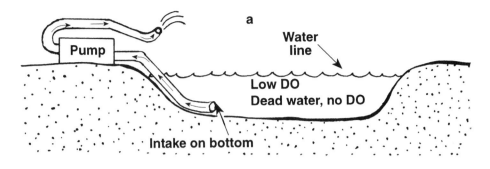

a

Water line

Pump

Low DO
Dead water, no DO

Intake on bottom

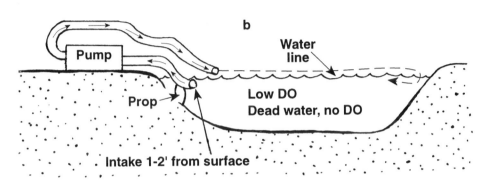

b

Water line

Pump

Prop

Low DO
Dead water, no DO

Intake 1-2' from surface

Figure 7.16 Depth at which to draw water. (a) Water drawn off near the bottom is low in DO and compounds the problem. (b) Water drawn off near the surface is correct way.

Figure 7.17 Windmill aerator prevents snow-covered ice from cutting off sunlight for photosynthesis. Photo courtesy of USDA-SCS. Clifford Cox, photographer.

Other Methods-- Another emergency measure is the use of potassium permanganate. It has been applied at a rate of up to 6 ppm to alleviate oxygen depletion, but Tucker and Boyd (1977) questioned its effectiveness. Some fish farmers report that running around in the pond with several motor boats will help increase the DO. A boat crisscrossing a 0.4-ha (1-ac) pond for 4 hours agitated the water enough to raise the DO from 0.3 to 2 ppm (Swingle 1968). In waters that freeze, any means should be used to prevent a permanent ice cover. In Figure 7.17 an aerator operated by a windmill circulates water and prevents ice formation.

Off-flavor

Causes-- Off-flavor of fish flesh, as discussed in Chapter 6, is usually associated with the presence of actinomycetes bacteria and certain blue-green algae. Channel catfish and other culture species get off-flavor by ingesting small amounts of the algae, but mostly by absorption across gill membranes. Blue-green algae, and probably actinomycetes bacteria, are often associated with "old" ponds where the culture species has been grown for years or with ponds where the culture species is stocked at high density and fed heavily. Such ponds are enriched from feeding.

In a "new" pond, green algae grow and use free CO_2 (carbon dioxide) during photosynthesis. As the pond becomes enriched, the algae grow rapidly and soon deplete available CO_2. Since CO_2 is a mild acid, its removal tends to shift the pH upward, the degree depending on the buffering capacity of pond water. Green algae now shift to HCO_3^- (bicarbonate) as a source of carbon for photosynthesis, and it too can become depleted. Now, the only source of usable carbon left is from CO_3^{--} (carbonate). Green algae cannot use CO_3^{--} but certain blue-greens can, so they expand in numbers and may dominate green algae. Light intensity becomes a limiting factor as blooms become denser (Tucker 1994). Gas-vacuolate blue-greens rise to the top and form a skim on the surface where light intensity is the greatest. Other conditions favoring blue-greens include: high surface water temperatures (>20°C, 68°F), long periods of high light, increased water retention time (decreased flushing), and water column stratification (Paerl 1994).

Prevention and Control-- Reducing blue-greens and off-flavor include several possibilities (Avault 1982; Boyd 1994).
(1) Keep the stocking rate of the culture species relatively low to lessen the organic load and nutrient input. This recommendation, however, is often difficult to follow if you maximize production and profit.
(2) Lower the pH, increase concentrations of combined inorganic nitrogen, increase concentrations of carbon dioxide, or increase turbidity of water with suspended clay particles (Boyd 1994). Treatment of ponds with aluminum

sulfate (alum) or calcium sulfate (gypsum) can lower phosphorous concentrations and reduce algae abundance.

(3) Flush water through ponds to dilute organic wastes.

(4) Aerate water to speed up oxidation of organic matter and break up stratification of the water column.

(5) Increase the buffering capacity of pond water with addition of lime.

(6) Speed up decomposition of organic matter on pond bottoms by drying and lightly disking. Remove sediment from pond bottoms.

(7) Treat plankton blooms with biweekly applications of copper sulfate. The efficacy of this practice, however, is suspect. Spot treating blue-greens that have windrowed to one end of the pond may help to curtail such blooms.

(8) Practice polyculture with species to reduce the organic load and blue-green abundance. Canfield and Shireman (1994) reported that bighead carp ate large algae and reduced the ratio of blue-green to green algae. They suggested that stocking bighead carp may be a practical method for shifting the algae community structure from a few large taxa to many small taxa.

(9) Alternate fish with plant crops to remove excess nutrients.

(10) Grow culture species in brackish water. Channel catfish grown in brackish water with salinities ranging from 1.5 to 8 ppt were free of off-flavor (Avault 1982).

(11) In shrimp farming, fertilization that favors diatom production and reduction of benthic algae may lower the incidence of off-flavor.

Purging-- We know a lot about off-flavor: what causes it and possible methods for its control. It is doubtful, however, that fish farmers will adjust culture methods to prevent the occurrence of off-flavor. They stock at relatively high rates and practice heavy feeding. With channel catfish, ponds are seldom drained, and topping-off for harvesting is the norm. Catfish farmers feel that to make a profit they must push production to the limit. Many farmers who have fish with off-flavor simply wait until the fish come back "on-flavor."

A possible solution is to purge fish that have off-flavor. Depuration (purging) of oysters and other mollusks is common practice. Purging of fish with off-flavor works. Fish are held in tanks with clean, flowing water for about 7 days, depending on intensity of off-flavor and water temperature. Heikes (1993) developed a procedure for in-pond purging. A floating bag or containment unit constructed of vinyl-liner material is pulled around a live-car containing channel catfish. The whole unit is towed to the water inlet of the pond. Water from a well is flushed through the containment bag to replace pond water. In one study, 2,268 kg (5,000 lb) of catfish were purged of off-flavor within 48 hours.

The advantage of this system is that fish can be purged in the production pond and do not have to be handled twice, that is, removed from the pond and placed into onshore purging tanks. Moreover, the vinyl liner is portable and can be moved from pond to pond.

Testing for Off-flavor-- It is standard practice to taste-test channel catfish before harvesting and processing. A dressed whole catfish is cooked inside a paper bag in a microwave oven until done. No salt or spices are used. A panel of experts smells and tastes the fish. If any off-flavor is noted, the fish are not harvested for processing. Van der Ploeg and Johnson (1994) suggested the following terminology for off-flavor description:

Category	Description
Acceptable	nut-like, chicken, corn, butter
Vegetable	celery, mushroom, onion
Decay	egg/sulfury, sewage, rotten, decaying vegetation, moldy
Earthy/musty	earthy/geosmin and musty/MIB
Woody/pine	woody/pine
Lipid oxidation	cardboard, fish-oil, paint
Chemical	

Their **flavor rating quality** is as follows:
0. Acceptable to the consumer. No off-flavor detected by tasting sample.
1. Off-flavor at threshold level detected by tasting
2. Distinct off-flavor detected by tasting
3. Off-flavor detected in odor of cooked sample
4. Off-flavor detected in odor of raw sample

Other Management Problems in Ponds

Ammonia, nitrite, hydrogen sulfide, high or low temperature and salinity, high concentrations of carbon dioxide, and soft or acid conditions may become problems. Carbon dioxide levels may be reduced by aeration and by stimulation of the phytoplankton bloom. Soft or acid water can be corrected by adding lime, and high alkaline water can be fertilized with acid-forming fertilizers (Chapter 8).

Ammonia-- Boyd (1990) noted that low dissolved oxygen is the first problem to develop as aquaculture is intensified. It is not common to have problems with ammonia except in aerated ponds that allow higher stocking densities and higher feeding rates. Once aeration is applied, feeding rates can be increased and ammonia then becomes the next limiting factor. Ammonia is produced during the breakdown of proteins. Culture species digest the protein in feed and excrete ammonia.

Total ammonia nitrogen (TAN) entering a pond varies with the amount of feed used and the percentage of protein in the diet. Li and Lovell (1992) fed channel catfish five diets containing 24%, 28%, 32%, 36%, and 40% protein in intensively stocked ponds over a 141-day growing season. Mean harvest of fish was 7,559 kg/ha (6,750 lb/ac). They found that TAN and NO_2^- in pond water increased linearly as dietary protein increased and was correlated with total protein fed. However, NH_3 was not influenced by different levels of dietary protein.

Ammonia also enters pond water from bacterial decomposition of organic matter such as fecal solids and uneaten feed. TAN is composed of toxic un-ionized ammonia (NH_3) and non-toxic ionized ammonium (NH_4^+). Depending on pH, a proportion of TAN exists as toxic un-ionized ammonia. This proportion increases as pH and water temperature increase. Toxic un-ionized ammonia as low as 0.6 ppm is capable of killing certain culture species. Concentrations as low as 0.06 ppm, if prolonged, may reduce growth and reduce ability to use oxygen.

There are measures to alleviate high ammonia concentrations: (1) Feeding rates can be lowered to reduce the organic load. Moreover, a high-quality feed that does not contain more protein than required should be used. (2) New water containing no ammonia can be added to ponds. (3) Superphosphate can be added to stimulate phytoplankton growth that, in turn, uses nitrogenous compounds. (4) The pH can be lowered to favor the ionized form of ammonia, although this may not always be practical. (5) Dry pond bottoms can be disked and treated with calcium oxide to hasten ammonia loss.

Nitrites-- Sometimes nitrites accumulate from oxidation of ammonia faster than they can be converted to nitrates, and they also may accumulate from incomplete denitrification. The bacterium that converts ammonia to nitrite prefers high temperatures but will function at low temperatures (15° to 20°C or 59° to 68°F). However, the bacterium that converts nitrite to nitrate functions poorly at temperatures below 15°C. That is why in temperate countries nitrite buildup usually occurs in spring and fall. Nitrite in the blood of fish interferes with the blood's ability to transport oxygen to the cells in the body. In finfish, nitrite combines with the blood hemoglobin to form methemoglobin. This results in brownish-colored blood, hence the term brown-blood disease.

The 96-hour LC50 values of nitrite to freshwater fish range from 0.66 to 200 ppm, and for freshwater crustaceans it ranges from 8.5 to 15.5 ppm (Colt and Armstrong 1979). This wide range in values, especially for finfish, is affected by the chloride content of the test water. Unless this concentration is known, bioassay values may be difficult to interpret. Toxicity increases with decreasing DO and pH.

In shrimp the respiratory pigment is hemocyanin, which can still bind oxygen in the presence of oxidizing agents such as nitrite (Needham 1961). Chien (1992) reviewed nitrite toxicity to *Penaeus monodon* and other shrimp species. Generally, the safe concentration ranged from 1.3 to 10.6 ppm nitrite. As shrimp increased in size, their tolerance to nitrite increased. Wickins (1976) reported that the 48-hour LC50 for seven penaeid species averaged 170 ppm nitrite.

The concentration of chlorides present in water affects nitrite toxicity. Chloride, like nitrite, moves into the blood of fish through the gills, and it counteracts nitrite. TAN, nitrites, and chlorides should be determined weekly. A minimum of 3 ppm chloride for each 1 ppm nitrite should be present in water (Schwedler et al. 1985). In later research, Tucker et al. (1989) suggested a ratio of 6:1. A simple method to increase chlorides in water is to add salt. The amount of salt required to provide 1 ppm chloride per acre foot of water is 4.5 lb. The following formula, using English units, may be used to calculate the amount of salt (NaCl) to add for a 6:1 ratio (Jensen and Avery 1990):

(1) (6 x N) - Cl = ppm Cl needed ; where N = nitrites and Cl = chlorides present in pond water, then
(2) Acre feet x ppm Cl needed x 4.5 = pounds of salt required.

Problem and Solution. Assume that a water sample is taken in a pond with 80 ac ft of water. The chloride content is 15 ppm, and nitrite is 8 ppm. How much salt should be added to obtain the minimum 6:1 ratio?

First, the chloride required is calculated: (6 x 8) - 15 = 33 ppm Cl needed, and 80 x 33 x 4.5 = 11,880 lb of salt needed.

Hydrogen Sulfide-- Hydrogen sulfide may accumulate in anaerobic areas of a pond. It is usually more of a problem in brackishwater ponds than in freshwater ponds because of the abundance of sulfate in brackishwater ponds. It can be avoided by keeping water well oxygenated at all depths. Once present, hydrogen sulfide can be removed by water exchange and by adding potassium permanganate (Boyd 1990). Raising the pH by liming will favor the less toxic form of hydrogen sulfide.

Temperature and Salinity-- High or low temperature and salinity are major problems in certain shrimp-growing areas. The best way to avoid these problems is through a thorough study during site selection. Except for this, one can culture those species that best fit the environmental conditions that are prevalent at the time. This may mean switching species during the dry period or during the cool period (Refer to Chapter 6).

Environmental and Conservation Considerations

Environmental-- Wastes from the culture species along with uneaten feed may cause a pollution problem when ponds are drained. Normally feces and uneaten feed are diluted and gradually mineralized to nutrients that are cycled back into phytoplankton. However, organic wastes may accumulate faster than they can be used by microorganisms if the culture species is stocked at high densities or fed heavily.

Pruder (1992) and Boyd and Musig (1992) addressed the problem of pollution from discharge of effluents. Pruder noted that pond effluent discharged into receiving waters is often re-used by neighboring shrimp farms. Boyd and Musig summarized it well: The first evidence of overfeeding is low concentrations of DO. Aeration augments the DO supply and permits greater addition of feed. The next sign of overfeeding comes when ammonia levels become too high. (This author had been on the downwind side of a recently drained pond of shrimp, *Penaeus monodon,* in the Philippines. The ammonia smell was so strong that our group had to move.) Water exchange rates can be elevated to partially remove ammonia, and allow a further increase in feeding rates. With continuous aeration and a high rate of water exchange, a further increase in stocking and feeding rates results in deterioration of pond bottoms and effluents.

Boyd and Musig (1992) listed ways to improve the quality of effluents and reduce their volume as follows: (1) use quality feed, (2) limit the quantity of feed used, (3) use feeding practices that reduce the quantity of unconsumed feed, (4) employ efficient aeration techniques, (5) exchange no more water than necessary, (6) do not dispose of sediment from pond bottoms into effluent canals, and (7) dry pond bottoms between crops.

A major pollutant in pond effluents is settleable solids. The EPA recommended the following methods for curtailing this pollution (Barker et al. 1974):

(1) Where topography and economics permit, effluents from fish ponds at harvest should be released into holding ponds for settling and biodegradation.
(2) When draining ponds to mid-depth, water should be removed at mid-depth and not near the bottom.
(3) Water should not be removed during seining; the fish stir up mud and solids.
(4) Land deposition of effluents and land filtration of effluents should be considered. Effluents from fish ponds are high in nutrients.
(5) Biological filters and polyculture should be used when applicable (Chapter 14).

Conservation-- Water is one of our most precious natural resources. Earlier we discussed water exchange as one management technique to improve water quality. Although water exchange often improves water quality, this use must be balanced with conservation of water. In Taiwan, the lavish use of fresh water to dilute salinity in shrimp ponds resulted in land subsidence in some instances. Then there is the danger of saltwater intrusion into freshwater aquifers. In some regions of the South, the water table has dropped significantly because of the large amount of water withdrawn for catfish farming.

There are ways to conserve and use water wisely. Following are a few examples:

(1) Reduce loss of water from seepage by constructing ponds on soils with a high clay content.

(2) Store rainfall whenever possible. In Louisiana, crawfish (*Procambarus clarkii* and *P. zonangulus*) ponds are usually filled from about mid September to mid October. Often only 15 cm (6 in) of water are pumped into ponds initially, enough to flush crawfish out of burrows. Rains in November and beyond help to add "free" water to bring water depth to 46 cm (18 in). Traditionally, crawfish farmers relied mainly on water exchange to flush ponds, particularly when rice forage was decomposing. Now, some farmers are using paddlewheel aeration to maintain oxygen levels in ponds. Fish farmers who use watershed ponds long ago learned how to "harvest" rainfall and use it wisely. In some instances, where a series of ponds is located together, the bottom pond is harvested (drained) first. Then the pond above it is drained into the first pond, and so on.

(3) Do not drain ponds to harvest. When a culture species is "batch" harvested, a pond is usually drained partly, seined, then drained completely. Now some pond culture regimes employ "cull" harvesting. This involves pulling a seine through the pond to remove marketable animals. A mesh size is used that allows small, sub-market animals to escape. A like number of larvae or fingerlings is restocked as are removed.

(4) In a system of levee ponds, one pond can be pumped (drained) into an adjacent empty pond. Some water can be transferred with siphon hoses. This not only conserves water, but also allows pond bottoms to dry out and to restore aerobic conditions.

(5) Practice wise use of make-up water. Many ponds lose water to evaporation or seepage. In some instances, make-up water is added to bring the water level up to the top of the stand pipe or drain structure. If it rains after that, water overflows the pond through the drain structure. Pote et al. (1988) suggested a "6/3" management scheme. Make-up water is not added until the pond is 6 inches below the top of the drain pipe. Instead of adding 6 inches of water, however, only 3 inches (8 cm) are added. Thus the pond is still 3 inches low. This allows for additional water if it rains.

(6) Farm shrimp species that grow well in high-salinity waters. In Chapter 6 we discussed salinity requirements of penaeid shrimp. To review, many shrimp farmers try to maintain a salinity of 15 to 25 ppt, for this is the optimum salinity for growth of many species. The sea is about 35 ppt. Thus fresh water is pumped into ponds after partial filling with seawater. During the dry season, in

some countries, addition of fresh water is required because of evaporation and concomitant salinity increase. Certain species grow well in high-salinity waters, thus negating the need for fresh water to dilute ocean water. In arid lands (Middle East), *Penaeus semisulcatus* is able to withstand extremely high salinities. It does not require a brackishwater phase in its life cycle (Farmer 1981).

WATER MANAGEMENT IN RACEWAYS

Water management in raceways is determined by the species cultured, its size, stocking rate, water temperature, rate of water flow, oxygen content of water, and general ambient water quality. The actual flow rate of water required has been determined from various charts using the above parameters. Meade (1974) gave an example, quoting the "Morris C. Croker Fish Energy Charts." A flow rate of 45 liters/minute (12 gpm) is needed to maintain 45 kg (100 lb) of 15-cm (6-in) chinook salmon (*Oncorhynchus tshawytscha*) held at 14°C (57°F). We will assume that the source of water is of good quality. To generalize, low dissolved oxygen, buildup of nitrogenous wastes, accumulation of settleable solids, and discharge of effluents are major management considerations.

Dissolved Oxygen

Elevated water temperatures increase activity of culture species and increase oxygen consumption. Brockway (1950) found that an increase in water temperature from 8° to 16°C (46° to 61°F) may result in a tenfold increase in the rate of excretion by trout, thus increasing the BOD.

Feeding may immediately increase the amount of oxygen used by a species. In one study, 1,500 brook trout (*Salvelinus fontinalis*) averaging 13 g (0.5 oz) were fed 300 g (11 oz) of food (Davis 1961). Following this, 70% of the total amount of DO present was used. Many trout farmers use demand feeders that avoid sudden DO stress. When trout are hand fed, a good deal more oxygen should be present in water during and immediately after feeding than is needed under ordinary circumstances. This phenomenon should also be carefully noted for pond culture.

Various aerators are used in raceways to increase DO in water (Figure 7.18). Chesness et al. (1972) described the efficiency of a splash board (Figure 7.19) and riser pipe aerator (Figure 7.20). Both are gravity flow operated. Injection of pure oxygen into the water has allowed production to double or even triple for the same flow rate of water. Visscher and Dwyer (1990) reviewed oxygen supplementation.

Figure 7.18 An electric aerator used in Idaho trout raceway. Photo courtesy of USDA. SCS, Clifford Cox, photographer.

Figure 7.19 Splash board in raceways. Notice ribbed and porous surface. Photo courtesy of University of Georgia, College of Agriculture. D. V. Cleveland, photographer.

Figure 7.20 Riser pipe aerator. Photo courtesy of University of Georgia, College of Agriculture. D.V. Cleveland, photographer.

Ammonia

In an open raceway system, ammonia is flushed out with the effluents, and oxidation of ammonia to nitrate is negligible. In a recirculating system involving an earthen reservoir, conditions are essentially the same as those for a pond. The difference depends on the time water remains in the reservoir before re-use. The quantity of ammonia produced in a raceway depends on the amount of feed used and on the protein content, as it does for ponds.

Brockway (1950) discussed ammonia reduction in raceways based on the depth of water and water exchange rate. He gave an example of raceways 4.6 m by 46 m (15 ft by 150 ft) with a water depth of 61 cm (24 in) and a change of 0.9% of the total water volume every hour. The ammonia content was 0.8 ppm when fish were stocked at a rate of 16 kg/m^3 (1 lb/ft^3) of water. When the water was lowered to a depth of 30 cm (12 in) and the rate of change thereby increased to 1.8% per hour, the ammonia concentration was reduced to 0.3 ppm.

Settleable Solids

Settleable solids accumulate if the flow rate of water is slow enough to allow solids to settle out. Water can be changed more quickly in a relatively small-volume raceway, and the change is more uniform. In wide and deep raceways, even with a comparatively large water supply, much of the water is changed slowly. There is a tendency for water to flow at the surface, with poor circulation near the sides, bottom, and corners. Because of their weight, waste products tend to accumulate at the bottom.

Even with attention given to water flow and circulation, settleable solids will accumulate. They can be removed near the drain end of the raceway with some type of suction device that avoids stirring up materials or injuring fish. Such devices, which operate on the principle of a vacuum cleaner, are easy to use in shallow trout raceways. Baffles can be placed at intervals across and near the bottom of the raceways. This accelerates water flow below the baffles, resulting in a scouring of the bottom. Settling ponds also may be used to collect fecal solids and uneaten feed.

Earthen raceways, such as those described by Hill et al. (1973), are relatively large and more difficult to clean. Their raceway system consisted of a series of connecting raceways, one flowing into the next. Water quality is poorest in the last raceway. The use of culture species as biological filters such as crawfish, bigmouth buffalo (*Ictiobus cyprinellus*), and certain species of tilapia shows promise. These species feed on waste materials and waste feed. They are used in the last raceway to improve water quality before the water is reused.

Figure 7.21 Leo Ray, Fish Breeders of Idaho, grows channel catfish and blue catfish in a series of raceways; the last raceway contains tilapia.

Leo Ray of Fish Breeders of Idaho (Figure 7.21) grows channel catfish in a series of connecting raceways. The last raceway contains tilapia, that ingest wastes and uneaten feed from catfish above. Water from the last raceway enters a biodegradation pond.

Effluents

The Environmental Protection Agency (1974) recommended that with an instantaneous grab sample, settleable solids in effluents should not exceed net values of 0.2 ppm and 3.3 ppm in flow-through culture systems and pond culture systems, respectively. This recommendation was given with the objective of preventing pollution in native streams. However, many receiving streams exceed this criterion before addition of aquaculture effluents. This early EPA recommendation is under constant scrutiny and subject to change. Some states have added their own regulations in addition to those of the EPA. In Louisiana, the Department of Environmental Quality (1992) stated that Best Management Practices (BMPs) should be designed to prevent or reduce pollution of the waters in the state. Effluent regulations and guidelines for aquaculture were reviewed by Orellana (1992).

Barker et al. (1974) described a semi-closed-loop system (recirculating) that used reservoirs to furnish water to raceways and separate oxidation ponds to mineralize raceway effluents. The system is not completely closed since periodically a portion of the wastewater is released to an adjoining stream and replenished with fresh water from upstream. Stechey (1991) designed a settling basin with four zones to handle solids (Figure 7.22). See also Chen et al. (1994).

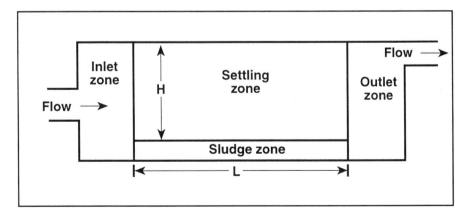

Figure 7.22 Four principal zones of a rectangular continuous-flow settling basin. After Stechey 1991, courtesy of Northern Aquaculture.

The inlet zone distributes influent across the full width and depth of the basin to reduce the velocity of water flow. The settling zone is the quiet, flowing part of the basin where solids settle out. In the settling zone, particles are affected by two main forces. Gravity results in particles dropping out, and at the same time the flow of water tends to push particles forward through the basin. The sludge zone is where solids accumulate on the basin floor. The outlet zone is where water is gently skimmed from the basin. Stechey (1991) also described an in-raceway settling area (Figure 7.23). Solids are settled out at the downstream end of the raceway. In this instance, the inlet (for solids) consists of a screen to keep fish from entering the settling zone.

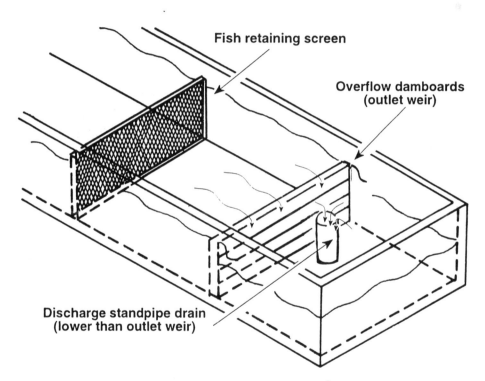

Figure 7.23 In-raceway settling area; typically about 1.5 ft^2 of surface area should be provided for each gpm of water. After Stechey 1991, courtesy Northern Aquaculture.

WATER MANAGEMENT IN SILOS

Low dissolved oxygen, ammonia buildup, declining pH, and buildup of solids are all water management considerations associated with silos. The Pennsylvania Fish Commission gave a detailed coverage of these problems (Annual Report 1975). Silos used in the research were 5 m (16.5 ft) high, 2.3 m (7.5 ft) in diameter, and held 21 m^3 (5,453 gal or 729 ft^3) of water. Silos were stocked with 22,000, 7.6-cm (3-in) rainbow trout (*Oncorhynchus mykiss*). A water flow of

1,136 liters/minute (300 gpm) was used, and pure oxygen was injected into each silo. Water temperature ranged from 10° to 11°C (50° to 52°F). During the study, DO could be maintained with this flow and with injection of pure oxygen. However, as fish grew and the fish load increased, dissolved oxygen declined. The pH values in three of the silos started at 8.18, 8.17, and 8.14 and fell to 7.72, 7.44, and 7.35 at the end of the project. Ammonia levels in the above three silos were 0.98 ppm, 1.35 ppm, and 1.97 ppm, respectively.

A decrease in ammonia levels and a subsequent increase in DO was realized whenever: (1) a partial fish kill in a silo reduced the total fish load, (2) a partial harvest of fish was made, or (3) feeding rates were lowered. The flow rate of 1,136 liters/minute was fast enough to remove most organic waste materials; screens were cleaned daily. Production of trout was 160 kg/m^3 (10 lb/ft^3) of water with a flow rate of 1,136 liters/minute, and with injection of pure oxygen.

Meade (1974) discussed water management in closed-loop culture with salmonids. His facility consisted of four silos, with two tanks measuring 152 cm (60 in) in diameter and 305 cm (120 in) in height, and the other two, 152 cm in diameter and 366 cm (144 in) in height. Thus, two separate culture units were provided, each consisting of two tanks and associated biological filters, pumps, refrigeration, and heaters. Water was continuously recirculated and maintained at 14°C (57°F) with a refrigeration unit in summer and with direct steam injection heaters during winter.

Flow rates were based on two requirements: minimal vertical velocity to remove particulate material, and the minimal flow necessary to remove dissolved metabolic wastes. A high-volume flow of 727 liters/minute (192 gpm) was sufficient for the vertical velocity to flush a silo. Since the system was capable of 1,500 liters/minute (396 gpm), two silos could be flushed at once. Silos were kept free of particulate matter by flushing for 15 minutes every 2 hours. The minimum flow rate needed to support 100 kg (220 lb) of 15-cm (6-in) chinook salmon at 14°C was 38 liters/minute (10 gpm), or 33% of that recommended for a flow-through system.

At a maximum stocking density, a silo 152 cm in diameter and 336 cm high supported 400 kg (882 lb) of chinook salmon averaging 15 cm in length. The flow rate needed was 62 liters/minute (16 gpm). Dissolved oxygen was maintained at 6 ppm or higher with liquid oxygen. Incoming water was discharged directly above the diffuser plate where gaseous oxygen entered. To remove particulates, culture water passed over a stainless steel screen and later passed through a clarifier tank. Ammonia and nitrite were removed primarily with biological filtration.

WATER MANAGEMENT IN CAGES AND NET-PENS

In static ponds, essentially the same conditions prevail for cage culture as when fish are stocked free into ponds. Oxygen depletion, however, is more critical, and fish in cages may succumb at DO levels that are not detrimental to fish free in a pond. For example, channel catfish in cages may begin dying when DO drops to 2 ppm, although this level ordinarily is not lethal in an open pond. At Clemson University, South Carolina, a miniature paddlewheel is mounted on each cage. Wings on the outside funnel water current directly through the cage (T. E. Schwedler 1988, personal communication).

An especially important consideration in cage and net-pen culture is good water circulation (Schmittou 1969). When arranging cages or net-pens, take advantage of the prevailing wind and water flow to maximize circulation. This will help keep DO levels up and will aid in removing wastes. In some cases, it may be feasible to tow cages or net-pens periodically from one area to another for better circulation.

Most salmon are cultured in floating net-pens within public waters. The accumulation of uneaten feed and feces below net-pens may pose environmental problems. These problems are minimized by following guidelines that take into account the size of the operation, depth of water beneath net-pens, and mean current velocity as measured mid-way between the bottom of the net-pens and the sea floor (Weston 1986). For example, a salmon farm producing more than 45,351 kg (100,000 lb) per year should locate in water with a minimum depth of 18.3 m (60 ft) if the current is only 10 cm/second (0.2 knots). (See also Chapter 5.)

Fouling of cages and net-pens is a serious problem because this retards water circulation. Beveridge (1987) listed three management options:
(1) The problem is accepted, and management procedures are developed accordingly. This option involves periodic changing and drying out of netting material to remove algae and other fouling organisms.
(2) To reduce the problem, chemical or biological agents may be used, and high-pressure spraying has also been effective. The netting material can be dipped in a solution of an antifouling agent. Most antifouling agents contain a biocide that slowly leaches so that the net surface is permanently surrounded by a thin layer of toxic material. This prevents the susceptible juvenile planktonic stages of fouling organisms from getting attached to the netting. The ideal compound should release the toxin at a controlled rate over an extended period.

In some instances a herbivorous species, such as one of the tilapias, can be stocked into cages along with the culture species. The tilapia gleans algae off the mesh. Yellowtail (*Seriola quinqueradiata*) cages in Japan generally do not have a major fouling problem because the fish, during normal movement, constantly brush against the netting.
(3) A fouling-resistant netting or a rotating design net-pen can be used. Using as large a mesh size as possible will reduce fouling problems. A mesh size of 2 by 4 cm (0.75 to 1.5 in) is desirable for finfish, but fingerlings of sufficient size must be used. Net-pens can be rotated to expose the fouling organisms to sunlight and

UV light. However, prolonged exposure to UV light may result in accelerated degradation of the nets. Milne (1972) and Beveridge (1987) discussed materials used for cages and floating net-pens to avoid fouling problems.

Cage culture in heated effluents poses a few additional management problems; one is gas bubble disease. Other problems relate primarily to a thorough investigation of the site before culture begins to ensure that effluents are not harmful to culture species nor to the environment.

WATER MANAGEMENT IN RECIRCULATING SYSTEMS

Recirculating or closed-loop systems may involve tanks, certain raceways, silos, and all systems where water is re-used. Make-up water is added to replace that lost by evaporation and during backflushing to purge solid wastes. Spotte (1979) and Lucchetti and Gray (1988) covered the topic of recirculating systems well and should be consulted for greater detail. Lai and Klontz (1980) evaluated environmental and nutritional factors influencing the performance of biofilters. Hargreaves (1992) discussed management strategies for culture of tilapia in recirculating systems. Major water management considerations involve: total ammonia nitrogen (TAN), nitrite, biochemical oxygen demand (BOD), total suspended solids (TSS), water temperature, and carbon dioxide.

Biological Filtration

The process used to treat water in recirculating systems is called "fixed-film" filtration. Bacteria remain fixed to the surface of the biofilter medium in a thin film. Here they draw dissolved wastes, oxygen, and other required nutrients from the passing water. Coffin et al. (1992) described and rated six fixed-film biofiltration processes, namely the trickling filter, rotating biological filter, (Figure 7.24), fluidized bed, upflow sand, rapid sand, and bead filter (Figure 7.25a, b). Of these, the bead filter was the most efficient.

Biological filtration was defined by Spotte (1979) as the mineralization, nitrification, and denitrification of organic nitrogenous compounds by bacteria suspended in water and attached to substrate in the filter bed. Heterotrophic and autotrophic bacteria are the major bacteria groups present. Heterotrophic species use organic compounds excreted by culture species as energy sources and convert them into simple compounds, principally ammonia. This process is called mineralization.

Figure 7.24 Biological rotating filter.

Figure 7.25a Steve Abernathy, who cultures tilapia in a recirculating system at Robert, Louisiana (near New Orleans), with bead filter.

Figure 7.25b Beads used in filter to provide surface area for bacteria.

Once organics are mineralized, biological filtration moves to the second step, which is nitrification. Nitrification is the biological oxidation of ammonia to nitrite and of nitrite to nitrate by autotrophic bacteria (Spotte 1970) (Figure 7.26). These bacteria require an oxygen-rich environment and inorganic carbon in the form of bicarbonate as their source of carbon. *Nitrosomonas* sp. and *Nitrobacter* sp. are the principal nitrifying bacteria in culture systems. *Nitrosomonas* oxidizes ammonia into nitrite. *Nitrobacter* oxidizes nitrite into nitrate.

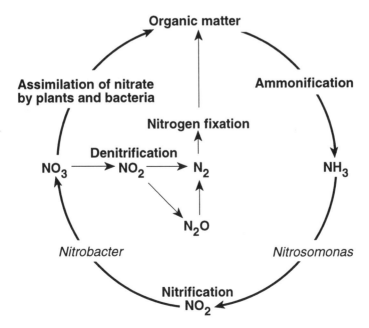

Figure 7.26 The nitrogen cycle. Reprinted by permission of John Wiley & Sons.

Denitrification is the third and last stage in biological filtration. In this process nitrite or nitrate is converted by facultative anaerobic bacteria to either nitrous oxide or free nitrogen. This last phase is seldom employed because only a few culture species are sensitive to NO_3^-.

The Filter Bed-- A sufficient surface area is important for bacterial attachment. Surface area may be provided by shell or gravel, koch rings, beads, by detritus particles, and by other materials that offer substrate. Bacteria also are found, to a lesser degree, suspended in water. Surface area is important for establishment of a bacterial population. Small gravel, for example, offers more surface area per unit volume than does larger gravel. However, circulation of water through filter beds is impaired if gravel is too small. Gravel measuring 2 to 5 mm (0.8 to 2 in) is about the correct size, and an angular gravel is preferred to smooth round gravel.

The Bacteria-- A commercially prepared concentration of bacteria can be used to seed the system. Zobell and Michener (1938) found that most marine bacteria also can be grown in fresh water if the water is freshened gradually -- in increments of 5%. Nitrifiers are among the bacteria that are unable to make sudden changes. In a marine system, nitrification progresses best when salinity is at normal sea strength and diminishes as fresh water is added. Sudden changes in salinity should be avoided because bacterial metabolism is temporarily suppressed, and ammonia accumulates. In brackishwater systems, make-up water should be prepared in a separate container first, then added to the culture system.

The rate at which nitrifying bacteria assimilate and process waste is controlled by a number of factors (Coffin et al. 1992; Drennan and Malone 1992).

(1) Temperature affects the well-being of nitrifiers. In marine systems, optimum temperatures are 30° to 35°C (86° to 95°F) and in fresh water 30°C. Heating and cooling units should be of sufficient capacity to maintain water temperature within 2°C of optimum. Generally, it is more efficient to heat the water in the tank than the building. Tanks, as well as the building in which they are housed, should be well insulated to reduce heat loss and conserve energy.

(2) The optimum pH range for nitrification is between 7.5 and 8.0. Above a pH of 8 ammonia toxicity increases to the culture species. A pH below 7 inhibits nitrification. The pH in the water tends to become more acidic over time. This is because carbon dioxide accumulates from respiration of culture species and from the activity of bacteria. Recirculating systems, therefore, should have a degassing column to remove excess carbon dioxide (Drennan and Malone 1992).

(3) Dissolved oxygen concentrations below 3 ppm inhibit nitrification. Aeration can be achieved with low-pressure, regenerative blowers and air stone diffusers.

The goal should be to maintain DO levels at 6 ppm. If additional aeration becomes necessary, injection of pure oxygen is the next step.
(4) Alkalinity should be maintained at concentrations above 100 ppm (as $CaCO_3$).

Oxygenation-- Spotte (1970) compared the filter bed to a huge respiring organism. When it operates properly, much oxygen is consumed. If the oxygen consumed during filtration (OCF) is high, nitrifiers are at work. Hirayama (1965) filtered sea water from a culture system through a column of sand in an old filter bed. The DO was 6.5 ppm before entering the column and 5.3 ppm after passing through sand. Meanwhile, ammonia dropped 58% and nitrite 61%. Both aerobic and anaerobic bacteria are found in filter beds. Aerobes are more desirable, and efforts should be made to keep the system well oxygenated. When anaerobes function, many of their metabolites are toxic.

An airlift pump is one of the best ways to circulate water. An airlift is essentially a vertical piece of pipe that extends both below the filter bed and above the water level (Figure 7.27). Air enters the bottom of the pipe and mixes with water. This mixture rises, and at the same time water near and outside the inlet is pulled in. At the top of the pipe, the air-water mixture is spilled out. The volume of air necessary to operate an airlift increases with decreasing percentage of submergence. Spotte (1970) calculated the percentage of submergence. In Figure 7.28 the distance between the air inlet and discharge point (A to C) equals 91 cm (3 ft) and the total lift (A to B) equals 30 cm (1 ft). Therefore: 91-30 ÷ 91 = 67% submergence.

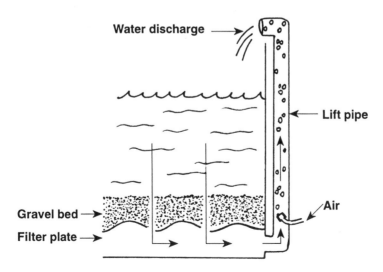

Figure 7.27 Water circulation through a subgravel filter by an airlift. Reprinted by permission of John Wiley & Sons.

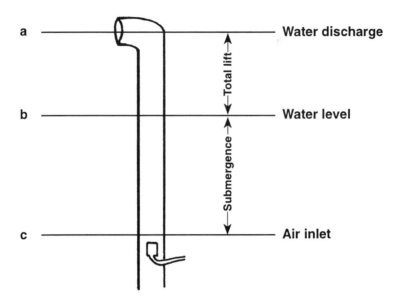

Figure 7.28 Operating principles of an airlift. Reprinted by permission of John Wiley & Sons.

For greatest efficiency, an airlift should have a smooth effluent rather than a gurgling sound. A gurgling sound indicates that either the air volume is too great for the diameter of the pipe and much of the air escapes directly through the water and into the atmosphere, or the pipe is not submerged enough. Spotte (1970, 1979) goes into detail on variations of this basic concept.

Conditioning the System-- A conditioned system is one in which the filter bacteria and nitrogenous wastes are in equilibrium, that is, wastes are converted to the end products. Before culture species can be grown in a recirculating system involving tanks or other small units, the system must be conditioned. Systems can be conditioned by several methods: (1) overcompensating the system with "conditioning" species, (2) gradual conditioning of the system, and (3) elevating water temperature.

Overcompensating involves the stocking of a conditioning species in excess. This method uses species that are tolerant to ammonia and other metabolites. In marine systems, marine turtles and diamondback terrapins are tolerant to ammonia and other metabolites. In freshwater systems, various turtles are again suitable, along with certain fish species such as carp, eels, and catfishes.

The second method is used to condition a system if hardy species are not available. Culture species are added to the system gradually, and at no time is ammonia allowed to exceed 0.2 ppm. In a conditioned system, ammonia is less than 0.1 ppm.

The third method uses either the first or second method, plus a temporary elevation of the water temperature to speed the process of conditioning. The time to condition a system varies, and 2 to 4 weeks or longer is usually the minimum time for optimum conditioning. In the beginning, ammonia levels may be high. This is because heterotrophic bacteria predominate over autotrophic bacteria.

In a new system there also is a time lag between the drop in ammonia and oxidation of nitrite. Consequently, nitrite may temporarily accumulate. If culture species are introduced too soon, nitrite poisoning could occur. Konikoff (1975) found that the 24-hour TLm value for 40-g (1.4-oz) channel catfish exposed to nitrite at 21°C (70°F) was 34 ppm. The 48-, 72-, and 96-hour TLm values were 29, 27, and 25 ppm, respectively. Nitrite-poisoned catfish died with the mouth open and the gill covers closed. The pectoral and dorsal spines were locked erect, but the body was relaxed. The blood of nitrite-poisoned catfish was a distinctive dark chocolate brown; the color persisted several hours after death.

Removal of Solids

Up to now we have discussed the breakdown of wastes chemically by nitrifying bacteria to less harmful byproducts. Solids can be removed physically to lessen the biological oxygen demand. Two methods have been used: foam fractionation and sludge removal.

Foam Fractionation-- Foam fractionation removes fine suspended solids (< 30 μm in size) and dissolved organic matter (proteins). It is accomplished by bubbling air through water to produce a foam that traps the solids and organics. The foam is easily removed and discarded from the system. This technique is sometimes called protein skimming because organic substances are removed from solution. Several airstripping devices are available for use in small systems. Spotte (1970) described a device using the direct-current method (Figure 7.29). Air from a compressor is injected through a diffuser (2). As it rises in the column (1), it mixes with the water. Oxygen in the air then oxidizes and coagulates part of the dissolved organic matter. The separation chamber includes a dry upper portion (3). The coagulated material builds up as a frothy scum on the surface of the water in this chamber. When it has accumulated in sufficient quantity, it is forced through a connecting tube into another completely dry container (5). This container is periodically removed and cleaned. Excess water is returned to the system from the bottom of the separation chamber through a return line (4).

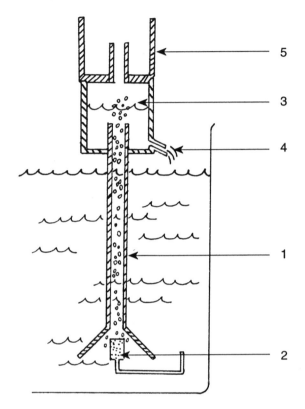

Figure 7.29 Direct current airstripping device. Reprinted by permission of John Wiley & Sons.

Sludge Removal-- Coffin et al. (1992) described rapid solids removal for a bead filter. The bead filter uses low density polyethylene beads as filter medium in a pressurized upflow biofilter. The beads float naturally to the top half of the container. The sequence of events includes filtration, backwashing, settling, and sludge removal (Figure 7.30). Solids accumulate and adhere to the beads during filtration. The beads are mixed mechanically to break solids loose. Mechanical mixing is stopped, and the solids and excess bacteria settle to the bottom of the cone-shaped biofilter where they are drawn off. Beads float back to the top of the container.

Other Considerations

Ozone-- Ozone has been used to reduce the number of microorganisms and to lower the dissolved organic level in circulation water. An ozonator and an airstripper may be used together.

Ultraviolet Irradiation-- Burrows and Combs (1968) substantially reduced the incidence of disease in cultured salmon after irradiation of water with UV.

Use of Chemicals for Disease Control-- Certain chemicals sometimes used to combat disease of culture species should be avoided. Formalin, copper sulfate, or other copper compounds, and certain bactericides have adverse effects on filter bacteria. If fish are diseased, remove them from the system and treat elsewhere.

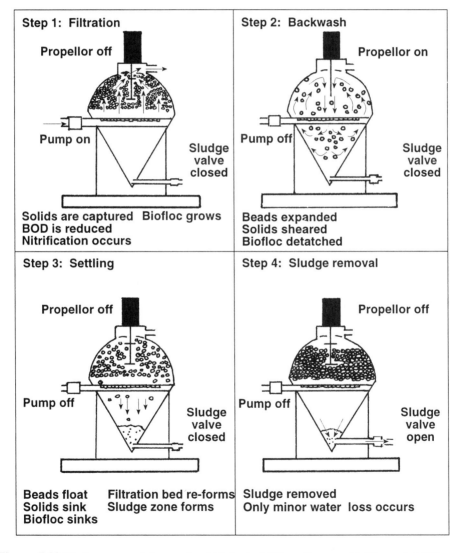

Figure 7.30 Sludge removal from a bead biological filter. Source: Coffin et al. 1992.

WATER MANAGEMENT IN OPEN WATERS
Bottom Culture
Water management with bottom culture of mollusks such as oysters depends on proper site selection (Chapter 5). Being sessile for the most part, mollusks must simply endure any adverse conditions such as drastic salinity changes, siltation, pollution, and drastic changes in temperature, If an oil spill occurs in the area, sweepers can be used.

Off-bottom Culture
With off-bottom culture, mollusks can sometimes be towed to selected areas to obtain more favorable water quality. Such movements might be to lower salinity, to avoid certain predators, or to plankton-rich water for more favorable growth. Mollusks may also be moved vertically in the water column. Finally, protective barriers discussed by Milne (1972) may help to avoid damage caused by storms.

Open Sea Mariculture
Oddly enough, water management is possible in open-sea mariculture by artificial upwelling of nutrients. This in turn increases the food supply, principally plankton, for filter feeders. This is discussed in Chapter 8.

WATER ANALYSIS
Hanfman (1988) compiled a list of publications on water management in aquaculture. Golterman's publication (1969) and the handbook by Swingle (1969) have been used for their methodology on water analysis. A complete source of information on water analysis is the Standard Methods for the Analysis of Water and Wastewater of the American Public Health Association et al. (1989). The manual by Boyd and Tucker (1992) was developed with aquaculture in mind. For analysis of saline water, Strickland and Parsons (1965) is generally accepted as an excellent reference.

In Chapter 6, we discussed various water quality parameters, toxins, pollutants, and pesticides to consider for analysis when selecting a water source. In most instances, these need be checked only once, unless an event occurs that requires another analysis. This might be aerial application of pesticides over or near an aquaculture facility, or the dumping of toxic wastes into a stream that supplies an aquaculture operation.

When fish are stocked into ponds or other culture systems, the water quality changes because of respiration and the pollution from feces and other waste products. Certain water quality parameters, therefore, need to be monitored routinely.

Griffin and Mitchell (1988) suggested water quality parameters to monitor for finfish in freshwater ponds. They placed them in two groups: (1) stable and relatively constant and (2) unstable and fluctuating. The relatively stable water quality parameters include total alkalinity, total hardness, and chloride. Parameters that fluctuate include dissolved oxygen, carbon dioxide, ammonia, nitrite, hydrogen sulfide, pH, and temperature. While other parameters can cause water quality problems, most problems will be caused by those mentioned. The stable water quality parameters need to be tested only before stocking of culture species and then spot checked once or twice a year. The only way that an appreciable change in the level of these stable parameters can occur is if there is a sudden change in water volume, such as from rainfall or dilution of water from other means. Under normal pond conditions, total alkalinity, total hardness, and chlorides will increase slightly during the growing season.

The unstable water quality parameters need to be checked more often. Check oxygen at least once a day, particularly during hot weather and when a large biomass of a culture species is present and being fed heavily. Oxygen is typically lowest at daybreak, and it should be checked then. Many fish farmers check oxygen several times throughout the day, especially before dusk, to determine the trend in oxygen production and loss. If you use an oxygen meter, take the temperature at the same time. Griffin and Mitchell (1988) suggested that the pH should be measured every day or so, after checking oxygen and temperature. They reasoned that the presence and toxicity of ammonia, carbon dioxide, and hydrogen sulfide are related to pH of water. Factors such as temperature also affect toxicity, but pH is the major factor. In Chapter 6 we discussed the relative toxicity of unstable parameters, such as hydrogen sulphide and ammonia, and gave charts to show the effect of pH.

The suggestions above will serve as a guide, but each culture system must have a water testing regime suited to its particular needs. For example, recirculating systems and shrimp ponds along a coastline may be subject to drastic changes of water quality suddenly. Heavy rainfall or evaporation during the dry season will change salinity in shrimp ponds. Chien (1992) reviewed water management in shrimp ponds. Among others, he listed temperature, salinity, pH, dissolved oxygen, ammonia, nitrite, and hydrogen sulphide as parameters to monitor routinely. Hirono (1992) discussed water management practices of shrimp farmers around the world.

STUDY QUESTIONS

1. How is oxygen added to pond water naturally?
2. How is dissolved oxygen reduced in pond waters?
3. How does an oxygen debt occur in pond waters?
4. What is the daily oxygen-carbon dioxide fluctuation? Illustrate with a diagram.
5. How does the carbonate buffer system work?
6. What is overturn and stratification in pond waters?

7. What are factors leading to oxygen depletion in pond waters?

8. How can we avoid problems with oxygen depletion?

9. What conditions in ponds contribute to off-flavor?

10. What are some measures that can be used to prevent obnoxious blue-green phytoplankton blooms?

11. What can be done to lower the concentration of un-ionized ammonia?

12. What causes a buildup of nitrites in pond water?

13. Assume a pond with 10 ac ft of water contains 18 ppm chloride and 6 ppm nitrite. How much salt should be added to obtain a 6:1 ratio of chloride to nitrite?

14. How can we improve the quality of effluents and reduce their volume?

15. How can we conserve and use water wisely?

16. What are the main water quality problems in raceway culture and how can they be solved?

17. What can we do to manage water quality in net-pen culture?

18. How is water quality managed for recirculating systems?

19. Can we manage water quality in bottom and off-bottom culture?

20. What water quality parameters would you measure daily in channel catfish ponds, and what parameters would you measure several times a year?

21. What water quality parameters would you check in shrimp ponds? How often?

REFERENCES

American Public Health Association, American Water Works Association, and Water Pollution Control Federation. 1989. Standard Methods for the Examination of Water and Wastewater. 17th edition. APHA, Washington, D.C. 1,467 pp.

Annual Report. 1975. Rearing trout in silos. Pennsylvania Fish Commission. 53 pp.

Avault, J.W., Jr. 1982. Avoiding diseases by growing catfish in brackish water. Aquaculture Magazine 8(3):49-50.

Avnimelech, Y. and M. Lacher. 1979. A tentative nutrient budget for intensive fish ponds. Bamidgeh 31:3-8.

Avnimelech, Y., B. Weber, B. Hepher, A. Milstein and M. Zorn. 1986. Studies in circulated fish ponds: organic matter recycling and nitrogen transformations. Aquaculture and Fish Management 17:231-242.

Barker, J.C., J.L. Chesness and R.E. Smith. 1974. Pollution aspects of catfish production -- review and projections. Environmental Protection Technology Series EPA 660/2-74-064. Superintendent of Documents, U.S. Government Printing Office. 121 pp.

Beveridge, M. 1987. Cage Aquaculture. Surrey, England: Fishing News (Books) Ltd. 352 pp.

Black, C.A., D.D. Evans, J.L. White, L.E. Ensminger and F.E. Clark. (editors). 1965. Methods of soil analysis, chemical and microbiological properties. pp. 771-1572. In Agronomy No. 9, Part 2. New York: Academic Press Inc.

Boyd, C.E. 1985. Chemical budgets for channel catfish ponds. Transactions American Fisheries Society 114:291-298.

Boyd, C.E. 1989. Water quality management and aeration in shrimp farming. Auburn University, Alabama Agricultural Experiment Station. Departmental Series No. 2. 83 pp.

Boyd, C.E. 1990. Water Quality in Ponds for Aquaculture. Auburn University, Alabama Agricultural Experiment Station. 482 pp.

Boyd, C.E. 1994. Opportunities for management of phytoplankton in aquaculture waters. p. 69. In Book of Abstracts of the World Aquaculture Society.

Boyd, C.E., E.E. Prather and R.W. Parks. 1975. Sudden mortality of a massive phytoplankton bloom. Weed Science 23:61-67.

Boyd, C.E., R.P. Romaire and E. Johnson. 1978. Predicting early morning dissolved oxygen concentrations in channel catfish ponds. Transactions American Fisheries Society 107(3):484-492.

Boyd, C.E. and T. Ahmad. 1987. Evaluation of aerators for channel catfish farming. Auburn University, Alabama Agricultural Experiment Station. Bulletin 584. 52 pp.

Boyd, C.E. and B.J. Watten. 1989. Aeration systems in aquaculture. Aquatic Sciences 1(3):425 -472.

Boyd, C.E. and Y. Musig. 1992. Shrimp pond effluents: observations of the nature of the problem on commercial farms. pp. 195-197. In Proceedings of the Special Session on Shrimp Farming. Baton Rouge, Louisiana: World Aquaculture Society. 301 pp.

Boyd, C.E. and C.S. Tucker. 1992. Water analysis and pond soil analysis for aquaculture. Auburn University, Alabama Agricultual Experiment Station. 183 pp.

Brockway, D.R. 1950. Metabolic products and their effects. Progressive Fish-Culturist 12:127-129.

Burrows, R.E. and B.D. Combs. 1968. Controlled environments for salmon propagation. Progressive Fish-Culturist 30:123-136.

Canfield, D.E., Jr. and J.V. Shireman. 1994. Factors influencing the abundance of blue-green algae in southern waters. p. 65. In Book of Abstracts of the World Aquaculture Society.

Chen, J.C. and P.C. Liu. 1988. Feeding and nitrogen loading in an intensive prawn culture pond. Paper presented in Prawn Feed and Nutrient Symposium, National Taiwan Ocean University, Keelung, Taiwan. (in Chinese with English abstract.)

Chen, S., D. Stechey and R.F. Malone. 1994. Suspended solids control in recirculating aquaculture systems. pp. 61-100. In Aquaculture Reuse Systems: Engineering Design and Management. Amsterdam-New York-Oxford-Shannon-Tokyo: Elsevier Science Publishing Company Inc. 333 p.

Chesness, J.L., J.L. Stephens and T.K. Hill. 1972. Gravity flow aerators for raceway fish culture systems. University of Georgia, Georgia Agricultural Experiment Station. Research Report 137. 21 pp.

Chesness, J.L., W.H. Poole and T.K. Hill. 1975. Settling basin design for raceway fish production systems. Transactions American Society of Agricultural Engineers 18(1): 159-162.

Chien, Y.H. 1992. Water quality requirements and management for marine shrimp culture. pp. 144-156. In Proceedings of the Special Session on Shrimp Farming. Baton Rouge, Louisiana: World Aquaculture Society. 301 pp.

Coffin, D.E., B. Chitta and R.F. Malone. 1992. Biofiltration for recirculating finfish culture systems. pp. 80 to 85. In Proceedings of the Louisiana Aquaculture Conference. Baton Rouge, Louisiana: LSU Agricultural Center. 94 pp.

Colt, J. and D. Armstrong. 1979. Nitrogen toxicity to fish, crustaceans, and mollusks. University of California, Davis, Department of Civil Engineering. 30 pp.

Davis, H.S. 1961. Culture and Diseases of Game Fishes. Berkeley and Los Angeles, California: University of California Press. 332 pp.

Department of Environmental Quality. 1992. Environmental Regulatory Code IX Water Quality Regulations. Baton Rouge, Louisiana. 414 pp.

Drennan, D.G. and R.F. Malone. 1992. Design of recirculating systems for intensive tilapia culture. pp. 86-94. In Proceedings of the Louisiana Aquaculture Conference. Baton Rouge, Louisiana: LSU Agricultural Center. 94 pp.

English, W.R. and T.E. Schwedler. 1994. Management of toxic algal blooms in catfish ponds. p. 70. In Book of Abstracts of the World Aquaculture Society.

Environmental Protection Agency. 1974. Development document for proposed effluent limitations guidelines and standards of performance for the fish hatcheries and farms. Point Source Category, U.S. Environmental Protection Agency, Office of Air and Water Programs Effluents Guidelines Division, Washington, D.C. 20460.

Farmer, A.S.P. 1981. Prospects for penaeid shrimp culture in arid lands. pp. 859-897. In Advances in Food Producing Systems for Arid and Semi-arid Lands. San Diego, California: Academic Press Inc.

Golterman, H.L. 1969. Methods for Chemical Analysis of Fresh Waters IBP Handbook No. 8. Oxford and Edinburgh: International Biological Programme by Blackwell Scientific Publications. 166 pp.

Griffin, B.R. and A.J. Mitchell. 1988. Water quality testing, what to test for and when. Aquaculture Magazine 14(3):63-64.

Hanfman, D.T. 1988. Water quality management in aquaculture 1979-1987. Quick Bibliography Series. U.S. Department of Agriculture, National Agricultural Library NAL-Bibliography. QB 88-48.

Hargreaves, J.A. 1992. Culture of tilapia in closed systems. pp. 75-79. In Proceedings of the Louisiana Aquaculture Conference. Baton Rouge, Louisiana: LSU Agricultural Center. 94 pp.

Heikes, D. 1993. In-pond purging for catfish with off-flavor. Aquaculture Magazine 19(4):28-33.

Hill, T.K., J.L. Chesness and E.E. Brown. 1973. A two-crop fish production system. Transactions American Society of Agricultural Engineers 16:930-933.

Hirayama, K. 1965. Studies on water control by filtration through sand bed in a marine aquarium with closed circulating system. I. Oxygen consumption during filtration as an index in evaluating the degree of purification of breeding water. Bulletin Japanese Society of Scientific Fisheries 31:977-982.

Hirono, Y. 1992. Current practices of water quality management in shrimp farming and their limitations. pp. 157-165. In Proceedings of the Special Session on Shrimp Farming. Baton Rouge, Louisiana: World Aquaculture Society. 301 pp.

Izaguirre, G. 1994. The use of copper sulfate to combat algae producing off-flavor in drinking water reservoirs. p. 72. In Book of Abstracts of the World Aquaculture Society.

Jackson, G.A. 1974. A review of the literature on the use of copper sulphate in fisheries. U.S. Fish and Wildlife Service. Report No. FWS-LR-74-06. 88 pp.

Jensen, G. and J. Avery. 1990. Nitrite management in commercial ponds. Aquaculture Information Series. Louisiana Cooperative Extension Service Publication 2386.

Johnson, P.W. and J. Sieburth. 1974. Ammonia removal by selective ion exchange. Aquaculture 4:61 68.

Kleinholz, C. 1990. Water quality management for fish farmers. Langston University, Langston, Oklahoma. Extension Facts. 8 pp.

Konikoff, M. 1975. Toxicity of nitrite to channel catfish. Progressive Fish-Culturist 37(2):96-98.

Lai, K.V. and G.W. Klontz. 1980. Evaluation of environmental and nutritional factors influencing the performance of biofilters in fish rearing systems. Fishery Resources College of Forestry, Wildlife, and Range Sciences, University of Idaho, Moscow, Idaho. 139 pp.

Li, M. and R.T. Lovell. 1992. Effect of dietary protein concentration on nitrogenous waste in intensively fed catfish ponds. Journal of the World Aquaculture Society 23(2):122-127.

Lucchetti, G.L. and G.A. Gray. 1988. Water reuse systems: a review of principal components. Progressive Fish-Culturists 50(1):1-6.

Manual of Methods for Chemical Analysis of Water and Wastes. 1974. Ohio: U.S. Environmental Protection Agency, Environmental Monitoring and Support Laboratory. Cincinnati, Ohio. 298 pp.

Meade, T.L. 1974. The technology of closed system culture of salmonids. Animal Science/NOAA Sea Grant University of Rhode Island. Marine Technical Report 30. 30 pp.

Milne, P.H. 1972. Fish and Shellfish Farming in Coastal Waters. London: Fishing News (Books) Ltd. 208 pp.

Needham, A.E. 1961. The problem of methemocyanin. Nature (London) 189:308-309.

Orellana, F.X. 1992. Characterization of Effluents from Commercial Crawfish Ponds in South Louisiana. M.S. Thesis, Louisiana State University. 98 pp.

Paerl, H.W. 1994. Ecology of freshwater bloom-forming blue-green algae. p. 64. In Book of Abstracts of the World Aquaculture Society.

Plemmons, B. and J.W. Avault, Jr. 1980. Six tons of catfish per acre with constant aeration. Louisiana Agriculture 23(4):6, 7&9.

Pote, J.W., C.L. Wax and C.S. Tucker. 1988. Water in catfish production: sources, uses, conservation. Mississippi Agricultural and Forestry Experiment Station. Special Bulletin No. 88-3.

Pruder, G.D. 1992. Marine shrimp pond effluent: characterization and environmental impact. pp. 187-190. In Proceedings Special Session on Shrimp Farming. Baton Rouge, Louisiana: World Aquaculture Society. 301 pp.

Reid, G.K. 1961. Ecology of Inland Waters and Estuaries. New York: Chapman & Hall, Ltd. London, Reinhold Publishing Corporation. 375 pp.

Romaire, R.P. 1985. Water quality. pp. 415-455. In Crustacean and Mollusk Aquaculture in the United States. Westport, Connecticut: Avi Publishing Company Inc. 476 pp.

Ruttner, F. 1971. Fundamentals of Limnology. 3rd edition. 1971. Canada: University of Toronto Press. 295 pp.

Schmittou, H.R. 1969. The culture of channel catfish, *Ictalurus punctatus* (Rafinesque), in cages suspended in ponds. Proceedings Southeastern Conference of Game and Fish Commissioners 23:226-244.

Schwedler, T.E., C.S. Tucker and M.H. Beleau. 1985. Non-infectious diseases. pp. 497-541. In Channel Catfish Culture. Developments in Aquaculture and Fisheries Science. Volume 15, New York: Elsevier Science Publishing Company Inc. 657 pp.

Sousa, R.J., T.L Meade and R.E. Wolke. 1974. Reduction of ammonia by salinity and pH manipulation. Proceedings of the World Mariculture Society 5:343-354.

Spotte, S. 1970. Fish and Invertebrate Culture, Water Management in Closed Systems. New York-London-Sydney-Toronto: Wiley-Interscience, A Division of John Wiley & Sons Inc. 145 pp.

Spotte, S. 1979. Fish and Invertebrate Culture, Water Management in Closed Systems. 2nd edition. New York-London-Sydney-Toronto: Wiley-Interscience, A Division of John Wiley & Sons Inc. 179 pp.

Stechey, D. 1991. Build your own settling pond. Northern Aquaculture 7(5):22-25 & 28.

Strickland, J.D. and T.R. Parsons. 1965. A manual of sea water analysis. 2nd edition. Fisheries Research Board of Canada. Bulletin No. 125. 203 pp.

Sundstrom, F.J., J.E. Sedberry, Jr. and J.W. Avault, Jr. 1988. Feasibility of catfish pond sediment as a growing medium. Communications in Soil Science and Plant Analysis 19(1):117-126.

Swingle, H.S. 1961. Relationship of pH of pond waters to their suitability for fish culture. Proceedings Pacific Congress 9(1957), Volume 10.

Swingle, H.S. 1968. Fish kills caused by phytoplankton blooms and their prevention. Proceedings of the World Symposium on Warm-Water Pond Fish Culture. FAO Fisheries Report No. 44, 5:407-411.

Swingle, H.S. 1969. Methods of Analysis for Water, Organic Matter, and Pond Bottom Soils Used in Fisheries Research. Auburn University, International Center for Aquaculture. 119 pp.

Tucker, C.S. 1994. Rationale for management of phytoplankton communities in fish ponds. p. 63. In Book of Abstracts of the World Aquaculture Society.

Tucker, C.S. and C.E. Boyd. 1977. Relationship between potassium permanganate treatment and water quality. Transactions American Fisheries Society 106:481-488.

Tucker, C.S., R. Francis-Floyd and M.H. Beleau. 1989. Nitrite induced anemia in channel catfish, *Ictalurus punctatus* Rafinesque. Bulletin of Environmental Contamination and Toxicology 43: 295 -301.

Van der Ploeg, M. 1994. Etiology of microbial off-flavors in aquaculture. p. 71. In Book of Abstracts of the World Aquaculture Society.

Van der Ploeg, M. and P.B. Johnson. 1994. Testing flavor quality of aquaculture products. p. 76. In Book of Abstracts of the World Aquaculture Society.

Visscher, L. and W.P. Dwyer (compilers). 1990. Oxygen supplementation, a new technology in fish culture. U.S. Department of Interior, Fish and Wildlife Service Region 6. Information Bulletin # 2.

Weston, D.P. 1986. Recommended interim guidelines for the management of salmon net-pen culture in Puget Sound. Science Applications International Corporation, 13400-B Northup Way, Suite 38 Bellevue, WA 98005.

Wetzel, R.G. 1983. 2nd edition. Limnology. CBS College Publishing, Saunders College Publishing, Holt, Rinehart and Winston, The Dryden Press. 767 pp.

Wickens, J.F. 1976. The tolerance of warm-water prawns to recirculating water. Aquaculture 9:19-37.

Zobell, C.E. and H.D. Michener. 1938. A paradox in the adaptation of marine bacteria to hypertonic solutions. Science 87:328-329.

CHAPTER 8
FERTILIZATION, LIMING, AND POND MUDS

Fertilization was first attempted centuries ago in Chinese carp ponds with manures and other organic materials to achieve the same purpose as in fields -- increased crop production. In this chapter, we discuss benefits of fertilization and liming, and the function of pond muds. Fertilization is accomplished by addition of nutrients to ponds or by liberation of nutrients. Adding lime to ponds helps to neutralize acid soils, and other benefits may be derived. Pond muds serve as a storehouse for nutrients; they house benthic organisms, and they affect availability of nutrients to water.

WHY FERTILIZE PONDS
There are many benefits to fertilization of pond waters:
(1) Fertilization increases production of culture species by increasing biomass of phytoplankton and subsequent links in the food chain.
(2) Increased production of pond organisms through fertilization reduces the cost of supplemental feed.
(3) A growing phytoplankton bloom helps to remove nitrogenous wastes such as ammonia, other toxic substances, and will tie up heavy metals.
(4) A healthy phytoplankton bloom helps to enrich pond waters with dissolved oxygen.
(5) A phytoplankton bloom produces turbidity that helps reduce bird predation of culture species.
(6) Fertilization helps to control submerged aquatic weeds by encouraging growth of a phytoplankton bloom, that shades out rooted vegetation.
(7) Fertilization may indirectly control mosquitoes by controlling weeds.
(8) Fertilization may help to clear muddy water.

Fertilization is recognized throughout the world as a means to increase fish production. Early research in Europe was summarized by Demoll (1925), Schäperclaus (1933), and Nees (1949). Mortimer and Hickling (1954) published a classic review of fertilizer use in fish ponds. Hepher (1962a) summarized 10 years of research with fertilization in Israel. In the United States, Swingle and Smith (1939) and Swingle (1947) pioneered use of fertilizers in fish ponds. Boyd (1989) discussed fertilization of shrimp ponds, and he (1990) gave a thorough review on the benefits of fertilization for increasing fish yields.

Fertilization and Food Webs

The natural fertility of water in ponds depends on two factors -- the surrounding soil and the water source. In watershed ponds, the fertility of surrounding soil determines whether or not pond water is fertile. Boyd (1976a) noted that unfertilized ponds in well-managed pastures had greater plankton production than unfertilized ponds in woods. Levee ponds, with no watershed, depend on bottom muds for fertility. Marsh ponds, near the mouth of the Mississippi River for example, may be very fertile because of the rich alluvial soil. Intertidal ponds depend on fertility from ocean waters, and water fertility in all types of ponds is affected by the source of water used.

Swingle and Smith (1939) of Auburn University began research with pond fertilization in 1934. They found that in Alabama, and elsewhere in the southeastern United States, production of fish was increased by 100% to 400% with fertilizers. They correlated a direct relationship between production of phytoplankton and fish production. As phytoplankton increased from fertilization, so did fish production.

Within a food chain there exists different nutritional or trophic levels. These trophic levels are classified according to function (producers, consumers, and decomposers) and not by species.

Producers consist of autotrophic organisms that convert simple inorganic compounds into organic compounds. They produce their own food and do not depend on other organisms for food. There are two types of autotrophic organisms, phototrophic and chemotrophic. Phototrophic organisms, such as phytoplankton, other green plants, and some bacteria, use light as a source of energy during photosynthesis. Chemotrophic organisms derive their energy from oxidation of certain inorganic substances. Examples of chemotrophic forms are sulphur, iron, and nitrifying bacteria.

Consumers consist of heterotrophic organisms that are incapable of synthesizing matter from the sun's energy and require organic compounds that are already formed. They depend on producers for food either directly or indirectly. Within the heterotrophic group, three categories are noted:
(1) Holozoic organisms ingest solid food and digest it internally. They may be herbivores that feed on green plants, or they may be carnivores that eat herbivores or other carnivores.
(2) Saprophytic organisms lack a digestive cavity and absorb organic food from the environment.
(3) Parasitic organisms live in or on other living organisms and obtain food from the host.

Mixotrophic organisms are capable of both autotrophic and heterotrophic modes of nutrition. *Euglena* sp., for example, can manufacture its own food by photosynthesis, yet it also can live saprophytically.

338

Decomposers are heterotrophic bacteria and fungi that break down organic matter to the elemental state, thereby returning nutrients and their own cells into the cycle for use by producers.

Phytoplankton is the first link in the photosynthetic or grazing food chain. Phytoplankton organisms are fed on by zooplankton that are fed on by various invertebrates; and culture species in turn feed on the invertebrates. This is a simple food chain. Fertilization, by enriching pond waters, encourages growth of phytoplankton "blooms," which through the food chain results in increased fish crops. The transfer of food energy from the first link (phytoplankton) to the last (culture species) results in a loss of energy as heat; 80% to 90% is lost at each transfer or link. The number of links in a food chain is usually limited to four or five.

The Eltonian pyramid of numbers illustrates changes in biomass (Figure 8.1) and loss of energy. The shorter the food chain -- or the closer the culture species is to the first link -- the greater the available energy. Put another way, the longer the food chain from phytoplankton to culture species, the lower the production. Greater production can obtained from culture of aquatic animals low on the food chain, such as filter feeding mussels or oysters.

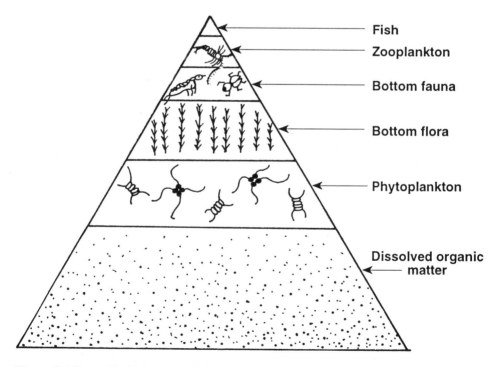

Figure 8.1 Pyramid of biomass and dissolved organic matter demonstrating energy leaks with each succeeding link. Modified after Juday 1942.

There are two basic types of food chains:

(1) The grazing food chain begins with green plants, then grazing herbivores (example: zooplankton feeding on phytoplankton), and ultimately to carnivores (animal eaters).

(2) The detrital food chain begins with decaying organic matter, then microorganisms, and then to detrital feeding organisms (detritivores) and their predators.

Ponds used in aquaculture may have the grazing food chain and/or the detrital food chain. Ponds receiving inorganic fertilizer typically have a grazing food chain. In some ponds, where organic fertilizers are used, zooplankton becomes the first link in the food chain. This produces a detrital food chain.

Crustaceans benefit from a detrital-based food chain. In natural estuaries, the detrital-based food chain is important for growth and development of larval shrimp. Moreover, certain weired marsh ponds used in shrimp farming may have a predominately detrital-based food chain. The extensive type of crawfish farming practiced in Louisiana relies on both detrital-based and grazing food chains. Crawfish feed on decaying organic matter that is coated with associated microorganisms. They also feed directly on green rooted vegetation that, in this case, serves as the first link in the grazing food chain.

In Figure 8.2, two simple food chains are noted, both beginning with phytoplankton. The first goes from phytoplankton → zooplankton → predaceous diptera larvae → bluegill (*Lepomis macrochirus*) → largemouth bass (*Micropterus salmoides*) → people. The other food chain, involving common carp (*Cyprinus carpio*), has a similar pattern. These food chains become food webs when side paths are taken. For example, fry or young of all three fish species may feed on zooplankton. The backswimmer (*Notonecta* spp.), a predaceous insect, may feed on fish fry. In ponds crowded with bluegill, the bluegill may eat largemouth bass eggs. All aquatic life ultimately dies, is decomposed, and nutrients are released to begin the cycle again. Aquatic species also release nutrients directly into the water without first dying and decomposing. In ponds heavily stocked with fish, wastes from the fish themselves add considerable nutrients to water.

Fertilization and Weed Control

Ponds choked with rooted weeds are difficult to manage (Chapter 12). Smith and Swingle (1941, 1942) described a method for controlling weeds with fertilizers. They applied fertilizer in late winter and early spring to weed-infested ponds. Filamentous alga was produced that wrapped up and smothered weeds. The filamentous alga in turn died and was replaced with phytoplankton when the water warmed in the spring.

340

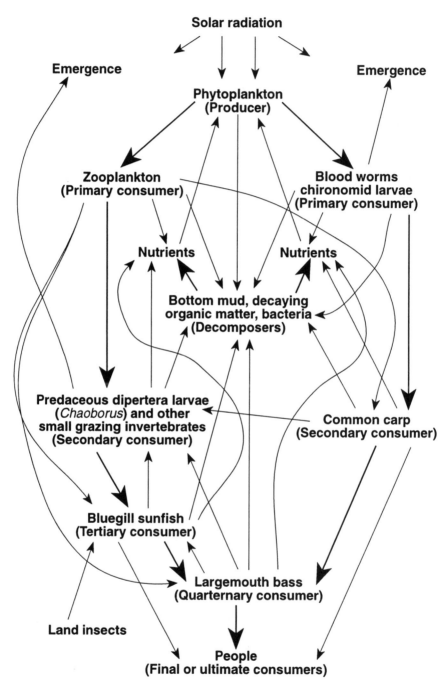

Figure 8.2 An example of a simple food web in a pond containing three species of finfish and people.

Ponds with clear water and no rooted weeds may be fertilized to prevent invasion of weeds. In the southeastern United States, ponds may be fertilized around the first week in February or when water temperatures reach 18°C (64° F). The phytoplankton produced acts as a shield by reducing light reaching the pond bottom. This prevents the start of rooted weeds. Boyd (1975) found that when Secchi disk visibilities averaged 1.7 m (5.7 ft) in ponds, weeds were a problem, but when they averaged 0.4 m (1.3 ft), ponds were essentially weed free. The control of aquatic weeds through fertilization also aids in better water circulation by wind. Such floating plants as the duckweeds (*Lemna* spp. and *Spirodela* spp.) and bladderwort (*Utricularia* sp.) are discouraged by good wind circulation.

Fertilization to Control Mosquitoes

Swingle et al. (1963) suggested pond fertilization to control the mosquito (*Anopheles quadrimaculatus*), the intermediate host of the malarial parasite. The immature form of this mosquito lived among aquatic weeds in pond waters of the southeastern United States, and in the early 1930s malaria was a minor problem. County health officers tried several methods to control the anopheline mosquito. The mosquitofish (*Gambusia affinis*) was relied on for biological control. In addition, water was drawn down to strand weeds, or weekly spraying with oil was practiced. The mosquitofish was ineffective when aquatic vegetation reached or pierced the water surface. Likewise, other methods to control mosquitoes were ineffectual as long as weeds were present. When aquatic weeds were controlled through fertilization, the number of hiding places for mosquitoes was reduced, and other methods for mosquito control became more effective.

Fertilization to Clear Muddy Water

Swingle and Smith (1947) used two to three applications of barnyard manure at 2,241 kg/ha (1 ton/ac) per application at 3-week intervals. This usually cleared muddy waters. The release of CO_2 from decay of organic matter caused the precipitation of suspended soil colloids. Use of 84 kg/ha (75 lb/ac) of cottonseed meal and 28 kg/ha (25 lb/ac) of superphosphate at 2- to 3-week intervals also aided in clearing muddy water. However, all procedures to clear muddy waters are ineffectual unless the source of muddy water is stopped. Moreover, adding large quantities of organic matter could present problems with low dissolved oxygen, so be careful.

WHEN NOT TO FERTILIZE PONDS

There are several instances when fertilization of ponds is not feasible.

(1) Ponds with excess outflow of water lose nutrients before they can be used. The detention time of water in ponds should exceed 7 days for optimum use of nutrients. Schroeder (1975a) reported that the rate of phytoplankton and zooplankton grow-in following fertilization was 2 to 3 days and 5 to 7 days,

respectively. Methods for increasing detention time of water in watershed ponds include diversion of excess water away from ponds and enlargement of ponds.

Intentional water exchange flushes nutrients and plankton from ponds and counteracts fertilization. Water exchange should be limited, when ponds are fertilized and first stocked with shrimp or other culture species.

(2) Ponds with acid soil bottoms may not respond to fertilization. In this case, corrective liming should be practiced before fertilization.

(3) Ponds with a very fertile watershed may not require fertilization. Watershed ponds, for example, located near a pasture may receive ample nutrients from runoff. As another example, brackishwater ponds at Rockefeller Wildlife Refuge, located in southwest Louisiana, are fertile and require no added nutrients. These ponds maintain rich plankton blooms year-round.

(4) Ponds used to culture coldwater species such as rainbow trout (*Oncorhynchus mykiss*) should probably not be fertilized, except in certain instances to control weeds. Dense phytoplankton blooms caused by fertilization will result in stratification of dissolved oxygen so that it is found only in surface waters. Moreover, winter kill caused by oxygen depletion could become a problem because of the decomposition of organic matter, in this case phytoplankton. Winter kill may occur when ice covers the surface, followed by snow that excludes light penetration from pond waters. Eipper (1964) wrote that few trout farmers in New York fertilized ponds. In Pennsylvania, trout ponds are normally not fertilized, but when they are, a single application of 10-10-10 at 336 kg/ha (300 lb/ac) has been used.

(5) Ponds can be too fertile, whether from fertilization or from natural means. In this case, a Secchi disk disappears only a few centimeters below the water surface. Like coldwater ponds, warmwater ponds with dense plankton blooms will also stratify. As a pond becomes richer in nutrients, photosynthetic activity often increases until the dense layer of phytoplankton in the upper layer of water shades the deeper water, and total oxygen production may actually decline (Hepher 1962b). Free carbon dioxide may be completely depleted. Photosynthesis virtually ceases, as does oxygen production. The pH climbs toward the alkaline side, and this may stress fish. The increase in pH, coupled with high fertility in pond water, favors the growth of obnoxious scums of blue-green phytoplankton and filamentous algae such as *Pithophora* sp. Dense blue-green plankton blooms are often associated with off-flavor in culture species.

(6) In ponds where both fertilzation and feeding are practiced, water gradually accumulates nutrients. Fertilization, therefore, becomes less important as feeding rates increase, and eventually can be discontinued.

(7) Fertilization should cease when the cost is greater than the economic gain, in this instance increased crop production. Fish production may increase significantly with the first application of fertilizer. Additional applications

further increase production but in smaller increments. At some point, it costs more to fertilize than you earn from the fish crop.

TYPES OF FERTILIZERS
There are two types of fertilizers, organic and inorganic or chemical.

Organic Fertilizers
Mortimer and Hickling (1954) classified organic fertilizers as follows:
(1) those containing little or no carbohydrates -- such as dried blood, urine, guano, offal, and liquid manure,
(2) those containing considerable carbohydrates with nitrogenous matter -- such as manure, brewery refuse, and sewage, and
(3) those containing mainly carbohydrates -- such as plant material, cellulose waste, and wood shavings.
Table 8.1 lists various organic fertilizers and shows percentages of major nutrients.

Table 8.1 Various organic fertilizers showing percentages of water and major nutrients.

Farm Animals

Manures	Water	N	Average Percentages P_2O_5	K_2O
Horse	48	0.49	0.26	0.48
Cow	75	0.43	0.29	0.44
Pig	74	0.84	0.39	0.32
Sheep	60	0.77	0.39	0.59
Poultry	57	1.31	0.40	0.54

Plant Materials

Hays	N	P_2O_5	K_2O
Alfalfa	2.3	0.5	2.6
Bermuda	1.1	0.4	1.8
Cattail	0.93		
Clover	2.0	0.4	1.7
Corn fodder	1.1	0.3	1.0

Table 8.1 continued.

Hays	N	P_2O_5	K_2O
Cotton bolls (dry)	1.3	2.0	4.0
Johnson grass	1.0	0.6	1.5
Kudzu	2.5	0.5	1.0
Lespedeza sericea	2.1	0.5	1.2
Peanut (without nuts)	1.6	0.3	1.5
Rice straw	0.6	0.2	1.5
Marsh or swamp hay	1.2		
Native grasses, western	1.3		
Seaweed, dry	0.8-1.8		
Wire grass	0.9		

Organic Meals			
	N	P_2O_5	K_2O
Cottonseed meal	6.0	2.5	1.5
Corn meal	1.3	0.3	2.6
Soybean meal	7.1	1.4	2.0
Peanut meal	6.9	1.2	1.5
Linseed meal	5.1	2.0	1.8
Fish meal	10.0	6.0	0.5
Crab meal	5.0	3.7	0.5
Shark meal	12.6	4.6	
Shrimp meal	7.5		
Whale meal	12.6	1.4	

Forest Products			
	N	P_2O_5	K_2O
Oak leaves	0.8	0.3	0.1
Pine needles	0.5	0.12	0.03
Sawdust, pine	0.2	0.12	0.5
Sawdust, hardwood	0.5	0.3	0.7

Source: H.S. Swingle 1961. Management of impounded waters. Unpublished lecture notes.

Table 8.2 shows average production of manure per year for common farm animals. As you can see, the type of organic material affects the nutrient content. There also can be great variation within the same type of manure or other organic fertilizer. This depends on the type of livestock, feed eaten by livestock, age of manure, and exposure of manure to the weather (Boyd 1990). For a comparison with data from Swingle (1961), shown in Tables 8.1 and 8.2, refer to Morrison's data (1961).

Table 8.2 Average production of manure per year for common farm animals.

Animal	Kilograms (pounds) manure per year per 454 kg (1,000 lb) live weight	
Horse	10,884	(24,000 lb)
Cow	13,605	(30,000 lb)
Pig	16,780	(37,000 lb)
Sheep	8,616	(19,000 lb)
Poultry	3,900	(8,600 lb)

Source: H.S. Swingle. 1961. Management of impounded waters. Unpublished lecture notes.

Advantages-- There are advantages and disadvantages for use of organic fertilizers. Some advantages are:

(1) Organic fertilizers have a shorter production cycle than inorganic fertilizers. Zooplankton, such as *Daphnia* spp. and other microorganisms, may feed directly on organic matter, thus shortening the food chain. In this case, the phytoplankton link in the food chain is temporarily bypassed. Some aquatic plants, such as duckweed, can directly assimilate the complex dissolved organic matter contained in manure. Thus, yields of duckweed in manured ponds are much higher than yields in ponds receiving inorganic fertilization alone.

(2) They decompose to liberate free carbon dioxide. Free carbon dioxide may be used directly during photosynthesis or it may combine to form bicarbonates and carbonates, both storehouses for carbon.

(3) They help to clear muddy water. Positively charged cations produced from decomposition of organic matter combine with negatively charged clay particles; flocculation occurs and muddy water settles out. Clear water is sometimes an advantage. For example, this author, working at the National Fish Hatchery in Frankfort, Kentucky, assisted in fertilizing largemouth bass spawning ponds with cottonseed cake. In this instance, zooplankton density was increased for fry without phytoplankton. Following spawning, schools of bass fry could be

spotted easily and netted out. Ponds eventually became clogged with dense growths of filamentous algae.

(4) They also serve as supplemental feed. In some cases organic manures may be eaten directly by aquatic species (Collis and Smitherman 1978). In the Indo-Pacific Region it is common to see hog pens, poultry pens, and even latrines built next to or over fish ponds. Tilapia, various carps, and other species may feed directly on the droppings. It is therefore sometimes difficult to distinguish between the use of organic manure as food or fertilizer.

(5) They may help to condition pond muds. In newly constructed ponds, adding organic fertilizers helps to form the desirable pond muds. This is beneficial for the growth of benthos (bottom organisms). Further, the formation of bottom muds helps to prevent seepage by sealing the pond bottom.

Disadvantages-- Some disadvantages of organic fertilizers are:

(1) The Food and Drug Administration in the United States has classified farmyard manures as filth. However, the FDA has allowed individual states to set their own standards. It is uncertain whether aquatic species grown in ponds with farmyard manure would be accepted by the U.S. consumer as human food. In China and certain other countries, however, manure is an integral part of pond culture.

(2) Organic fertilizers are generally more expensive than inorganic fertilizers.

(3) More labor is required to apply organic than inorganic fertilizers. Only a few sacks of inorganic fertilizer will provide the same amount of chemical nutrients as will many kilograms of organic fertilizer. Organic fertilizer may be high in moisture and carbon content, and this adds to the weight that must be handled.

(4) Organic manures are prone to promote growth of undesirable filamentous algae. This is partly because waters fertilized with organic materials tend to be clear (Swingle 1947).

(5) They may "smother" the pond bottom. The use of green manure with hard plants, such as mangrove leaves as used in Indonesia, may cause the formation of cellulose-mud that smothers the pond bottom. The harder parts of plants, put in as green manure, should be removed once the softer parts have decomposed.

(6) Manures may cause oxygen depletion. Organic fertilizers use oxygen as they decompose. Schroeder (1974) developed a method for quantitatively predicting oxygen depletion. It was based on the biochemical oxygen demand (BOD), the percentage of dry organic manure used, and the temperature of pond water. Collis and Smitherman (1978) noted that use of cow manure could not exceed 80 kg/ha dry matter per day (71 lb/ac per day). This rate could be increased up to 200 kg/ha per day (179 lb/ac per day) with aeration. Boyd (1990) noted that applications of more than 50 kg/ha per day (45 lb/ha per day) should be made with caution.

(7) They may increase the potential for disease. Where *Salmonella* is a problem, poultry manure should not be used. Mortimer and Hickling (1954) quoted Sklower (1950) that poultry manure is liable to cause mold infections in fish. Gill rot also has been associated with organic manures. Contrary to this, G.L. Schroeder (personal communication Israel, 1979) found that the parasite, *Lernaea* sp., survived in non-manured ponds but not in manured ponds. He postulated that the higher biological activity in manured ponds affected the life cycle.

Inorganic Fertilizers

Inorganic or chemical fertilizer is usually preferred over organic fertilizer when it is available. It has none of the disadvantages of organic fertilizer. It is usually less costly and easier to apply because of less bulk to handle. Sources of inorganic fertilizers are listed in Table 8.3. Inorganic fertilizer is termed complete when it contains the three basic nutrients of nitrogen, phosphorous, and potassium and incomplete when one or more of these nutrients are missing.

Chemical compounds used to fertilize pond waters are the same as those used for agricultural crops. Swingle and Smith (1939) found that in freshwater phytoplankton efficiently used inorganic fertilizers in vitro with N-P ratios (nitrogen to phosphate) of 2:1. Since in natural waters soluble phosphate is rapidly bound by adsorption or precipitation, the amount of phosphate was doubled for use in pond water, giving a 4:4.6 N-P ratio. Very small amounts of potassium appeared necessary in vitro, and since the fertilizer was to be widely used throughout the southeastern United States, a small amount was included. The result was approximately an 8-8-2 N - P_2O_5 - K_2O fertilizer mixture. The nutrient content of fertilizers has traditionally been expressed as percentages of equivalent N, P_2O_5 and K_2O (See Boyd 1982 for detailed discussion.). Eight pounds (3.6 kg) of N or P_2O_5 are enough to supply 1 ppm in about 3 ac ft (3,700 m^3) of water; similarly 2 lb (0.9 kg) of K_2O would supply about 0.25 ppm.

THE NUTRIENTS

Nitrogen

Nitrogen is a basic component of protein and is found in all living cells. It may exist as elemental nitrogen (N_2), nitrite (NO_2^-), nitrate (NO_3^-), ammonia (NH_3), or ammonium (NH_4^+). The form(s) of nitrogen present in water and pond muds depends on several factors, so when nitrogen is measured, a total determination is needed.

Table 8.3 Principal source of inorganic fertilizers showing percentages of major nutrients

	Percentage		
	N	P_2O_5	K_2O

Nitrogen

	N	P_2O_5	K_2O
Sodium nitrate	16		
Calcium nitrate	15		
Potassium nitrate	13	0	24
Ammonium nitrate	35		
Ammonium sulfate	20		
Ammoniated superphosphate	3	16	
Ammophos	11	48	
Calcium cyanamide	22		
Urea	45		
Uramon	40		
Calurea	34		

Phosphate

	N	P_2O_5	K_2O
Superphosphate	0	18-20	
Triple superphosphate	0	48-54	
Rock phosphate	0	25	
Bonemeal	1	20	
Basic slag	0	8	
Ammophos	11	48	

Potash

	N	P_2O_5	K_2O
Potassium chloride - (Muriate of potash)	0	0	48-50
Potassium sulfate	0	0	48
Manure salts	0	0	20
Kainit	0	0	12

Source: H.S. Swingle 1961. Management of impounded waters.
Unpublished lecture notes.

Sources-- Several sources of nitrogen are available for ponds:

(1) Fixation of atmospheric nitrogen by certain bacteria, molds, and algae may add substantial amounts of nitrogen to pond waters. The bacterium *Azobacter* sp. and the blue-green algae *Nostoc* sp. and *Anabaena* sp. fix nitrogen. Mortimer and Hickling (1954) cited one example where about 202 kg of nitrogen were fixed per ha (180 lb/ac) in 60 days. Fixation does not occur if other forms of nitrogen are already present. A neutral or slightly alkaline pH and the presence of ample phosphates are favorable for nitrogen fixation. For this reason, adding phosphate fertilizer often enhances nitrogen fixation.

(2) Release of nitrogen held on soil or organic matter particles may be a second but minor source. All forms of nitrogen are highly soluble in water and are not readily adsorbed on mud or organic matter particles. For this reason, there is less storage of nitrogen as there is with phosphate or potassium. Ammonium (NH_4^+) is adsorbed by the ferric-hydroxide, organic matter complex, or by clay particles that have unsatisfied negative charges.

(3) A third source of nitrogen is liberation from the decay of organic matter. As a pond ages, it accumulates organic matter in the bottom muds. If rooted aquatics are killed, organic matter becomes available for decay and liberation of nutrients including nitrogen.

Snow (1954) termed the process of killing aquatic vegetation and the resultant decay "vegetation conversion." He killed rooted aquatic vegetation with herbicides. The liberated nutrients increased phytoplankton growth and consequently fish production. European and Asiatic workers grow terrestrial cover crops on drained pond bottoms. When ponds are flooded, the organic matter decays and nutrients are liberated. This "green manuring" is sometimes practiced in the United States with grasses and other crops.

Stanley (1974) liberated nutrients by using grass carp (*Ctenopharnygodon idella*). He found that when the fish were fed *Elodea* sp. in tanks, ammonium and orthophosphate increased about 5-fold as a result of excretion by grass carp.

(4) Rainfall may contribute from 6 to 12 kg/ha (5 to 10 lb/ac) of nitrogen per year.

(5) Substantial amounts of nitrogen are added to ponds whenever aquatic species are fed. The pond receives organic matter from fish feces and from uneaten feed.

(6) Nitrogen can be increased in pond water by adding inorganic and organic fertilizers.

Loss of Nitrogen-- Nitrogen may be lost from ponds in several ways:

(1) Volatilization is a process where pond nitrogen is lost to the atmosphere as a gas. To avoid loss, it is desirable to have nitrogen in the form of ammonium and adsorbed on pond muds. This form is less likely to volatilize. This benefit, however, should be balanced by the fact that un-ionized ammonia is highly toxic

to culture species. To lessen the loss of nitrogen fertilizer to the atmosphere, some workers suggest addition of small frequent doses. Others suggest two portions during the winter when denitrification is at a minimum.

(2) Nitrogen may be lost from ponds through erosion. This probably occurs when ponds are drained.

(3) Leaching can occur, particularly if ponds are left dry for long periods and rain occurs.

(4) Nitrogen is removed with the fish crop. For example, a 100 kg (220 lb) crop of bluegill removes about 3.6 kg (8 lb) of nitrogen (Hickling 1962).

Should you use nitrogen fertilizer in the fertilizer mixture? Mortimer and Hickling (1954) reviewed use of nitrogenous fertilizer. They concluded that adding nitrogen to pond water did little to increase production. In newly constructed ponds, however, nitrogen should probably be included in fertilization. Once pond muds and organic matter accumulate, it is doubtful that addition of nitrogen will significantly increase fish production. Swingle et al. (1963) found that omission of both nitrogen and potassium from 15-year-old freshwater ponds previously fertilized with a complete N-P-K fertilizer had no significant effect on fish production.

In some instances, however, omitting nitrogen resulted in delayed development of phytoplankton, and rooted aquatic weeds posed a problem. Where aquatic weeds are a problem, nitrogen probably should be included. Once a phytoplankton bloom is obtained, nitrogen may be omitted. Leaving out nitrogen can reduce the cost of fertilization by as much as two-thirds. Boyd (1990) noted that nitrogen fertilizers are expensive because natural gas is used as the energy source in industrial fixation of atmospheric nitrogen.

Boyd (1990) reported that nitrogen is more important as a limiting factor in brackishwater ponds than in freshwater ponds. He suggested that a fertilization program for brackishwater ponds should use more nitrogen and less phosphorous than that recommended for freshwater ponds. A 20:1 ratio of N:P should be used when growth of diatom communities is desired.

Phosphorus

Phosphorus is the single most essential element in pond fertilization for freshwater ponds, and there is virtually universal agreement that using phosphate fertilizer will significantly increase fish production. Phosphorus is usually the first limiting factor in production of phytoplankton. There are numerous citations of increased fish production with phosphate fertilizer. Hickling (1962), for example, increased fish production 300%, from 208 kg/ha (186 lb/ac) to 770 kg/ha (688 lb/ac), by adding 22 kg of P_2O_5 per ha (20 lb/ac). Phosphorus is absorbed by plants mainly as orthophosphate ($H_2PO_4^-$). It may be found in soils and water, but usually at levels below 1 ppm. Fish farmers generally must rely on phosphate fertilizers to supply this element.

Availability-- The availability of phosphate to phytoplankton is affected by several factors, including the amount of clay and organic matter on the bottom. When phosphate fertilizer such as superphosphate is added to water, phytoplankton may remove appreciable amounts. However, most of the phosphorus eventually moves to the bottom mud. Here, it may exist as inorganic or organic phosphorus. If the inorganic form is insoluble, the phosphorus is made unavailable to phytoplankton until a chemical reaction renders it soluble. The solubilities of calcium phosphate compounds decrease with increasing pH. Phosphate tends to precipitate as insoluble aluminum phosphate compounds with decreasing pH. Thus, the maximum solubility of phosphates in mud or soil occurs somewhere between a soil pH of 5.5 and 6 (Boyd 1979a).

Phosphorus also may become adsorbed on clay or on organic matter particles. This is why, in some instances, adding phosphate fertilizer gives no appreciable increase in fish production -- most of the phosphorus is "tied up" with the bottom muds and organic matter. Some researchers feel that bottom muds must be saturated with phosphate before this fertilizer becomes effective. This also helps to explain the "residual effect," when two and three years after phosphate fertilization good fish crops are produced.

Lime may be added to ponds to modify soil pH. In addition to affecting soil pH, liming indirectly supplies OH^- ions to acid soils. The OH^- ions replace, and consequently release, phosphate ions that are bound on clay, organic matter particles, or on iron and aluminum complexes. If pond soils are too alkaline, and this is usually not the case, acid-forming fertilizers may be used.

Loss of Phosphorous-- Phosphorous may be permanently lost from ponds at draining and crop removal. Hickling (1962) quoted Fish (1960) that a crop of tilapia weighing 136 kg (300 lb) would remove about 4.5 kg (10 lb) of phosphate from the pond. The pond originally received 13.6 kg (30 lb) of P_2O_5. Hickling assumed that if 4.5 kg were removed with the crop, some 9 kg (20 lb) were still unaccounted for. An estimated 0.9 kg (2 lb) were lost at draining, meaning that 8.2 kg (18 lb) remained adsorbed to pond muds. Much of this phosphate is released when the pond is refilled for the next fish crop, thus giving the residual effect.

Potassium

Potassium, often called muriate of potash or simply potash, is the third major element in fertilizers. The potassium ion (K^+) is the form used by plants. Though potassium is one of the essential nutrients, its importance for increased fish production is doubtful. Mortimer and Hickling (1954) stated that tilapia contained only 0.32% potash and that the potash content was the same in fish grown in acid, unfertilized, and unlimed ponds as those grown in ponds with potash fertilizer. Hickling (1962) reported that including potassium in the fertilizer mixture did not increase fish production when used with low levels of phosphorus. However, when substantial amounts of phosphorus were used, addition of potassium resulted in increased fish production. In one instance, at a high dosage of 45 kg/ha (40 lb/ac) of P_2O_5, addition of 17 kg/ha (15 lb/ac) of potash increased fish production by 18%.

Potassium, which is quite soluble, is found in some ground water in appreciable amounts. It is also readily adsorbed by clay and organic matter particles as an exchangeable ion. When supplemental feed is used, potash is sure to increase from the breakdown of fish feces and uneaten feed. Swingle et al. (1963) included potash in their fertilizer mixture but pointed out that, after a few years, pond muds and organic matter have accumulated potash and that it could be excluded from the fertilizer mixture.

PREPARATION OF FERTILIZER FORMULATIONS

Inorganic fertilizers may be applied as a mixture of N-P-K or applied individually. When 100 lb of an 8-8-2 fertilizer are applied, 8 lb of both nitrogen and phosphorus as P_2O_5 are added as are 2 lb of potassium as K_2O. (For conversion to metric units, 2.205 lb = 1 kg, and 1 hectare = approximately 2.5 acres.) All three elements come together in the same bag. However, the bag will contain more than just 18 lb (8 + 8 + 2 = 18) of desired nutrients. Fertilizers contain impurities that are not needed. Sodium nitrate ($NaNO_3$), a source of nitrogen, contains only 16% nitrogen. So to obtain 8 lb of nitrogen, use 50 lb of $NaNO_3$, (8 ÷ 16% = 50 lb needed).

Other impurities are also present in a fertilizer mixture. Once all three nutrients with impurities are added to the bag to obtain an 8-8-2 mixture, commercial dealers add enough inert material, such as agricultural limestone or brick dust, until a total of 50 or 100 lb is reached. This allows for a uniform size bag. Therefore, for a pond to receive 8 lb of nitrogen, 8 lb of phosphorus, and 2 lb of potassium per acre, you fertilize at a rate of 100 lb of 8-8-2 per ac. The fertilizer mixture contains 18 lb of needed elements, impurities from the fertilizer sources, and enough filler to bring the total to 100 lb.

Problem and Solution. Determine the percentage of each element in a particular fertilizer source.

First, determine the atomic weight of each element present in a given fertilizer source. Use a chart found in most chemistry texts. Then calculate the percentage of the element present.

For NaNO$_3$

Element	Atomic weight
Na	23
N	14
O	+ 16 x 3
	85 and 14 ÷ 85 x 100 = 16%N.

The percentage of N, P$_2$0$_5$, or K$_2$O can be calculated in a like manner with other fertilizer sources.

Problem and Solution. Make a fertilizer mixture containing 8 lb of N, 8 lb of P$_2$0$_5$ and 2 lb of K$_2$O. Further, assume that the mixture will be made with ammonium nitrate, 33.5% N; superphosphate, 20% P$_2$0$_5$; and muriate of potash, 50% K$_2$O. Finally, how many pounds of filler will be needed to make up a 100 lb bag?

Element needed	Amount of fertilizer required
N	8 ÷ 33.5% = 24 lb
P$_2$0$_5$	8 ÷ 20% = 40 lb
K$_2$O	2 ÷ 50% = 4 lb

The bag of 8-8-2 will then contain:

Ammonium nitrate	24 lb
Superphosphate	40 lb
Muriate of potash	4 lb
Filler	32 lb
Total	100 lb

If this is a commercial formulation, the bag will contain 32 lb of filler. If, however, you make an 8-8-2 mixture, omit the filler since it is not needed.

Suppose a pond has a good phytoplankton bloom, and it is maintained with superphosphate only. In this case, add only 40 lb of superphosphate per acre for each application. This is equivalent to fertilizing at a rate of 100 lb of 0-8-0 per ac. Note here that ponds are fertilized on the basis of surface area and not on the basis of water volume.

Problem and Solution. Fertilize a 10-ac pond at a rate of 100 lb of 8-8-0, using ammonium nitrate and superphosphate as sources of fertilizers. Ammonium nitrate comes in 100 lb bags and superphosphate in 80 lb bags. Assume that three applications are made. Following this, continue phosphate fertilization only, at a rate of 100 lb of 0-8-0 per ac, for three more applications.
Determine:
(1) How many bags (round off to nearest half bag) of each fertilizer are needed for the first application?
(2) How many bags of each fertilizer are needed for all three applications?

(3) How many bags of superphosphate are needed for three additional applications when ammonium nitrate is omitted?

The solution is:

(1) From the previous problem, 24 lb of ammonium nitrate are needed to obtain 100 lb of 8-0-0. Since 10 ac are to be fertilized, it will take 240 (10 ac x 24) lb of ammonium nitrate, and hence two and a half bags (240 ÷ 100 = approximately 2.5). Similarly, 40 lb of superphosphate are needed for 100 lb of 0-8-0. Therefore 400 lb (10 ac x 40) of superphosphate per application are needed, and hence five bags (400 ÷ 80 = 5). Notice in this problem filler is not calculated. That is necessary only with commercial fertilizer mixtures. Even so, express the rate as 100 lb of 8-0-0 or 0-8-0.

(2) With a total of three applications, needed are: 7.5 bags of ammonium nitrate (3 x 2.5) and 15 bags of superphosphate (3 x 5).

(3) Three additional applications of 100 lb of 0-8-0 per ac require 15 more bags (3 x 5) of superphosphate.

APPLICATION OF FERTILIZER

Fertilizer applications should be tailored for each specific aquaculture operation. In the United States, we usually do not rely on fertilization to increase fish crops as much as they do in Europe and the Indo-Pacific Region. We rely mostly on feeding in monoculture (culture of a single species). Many of our culture systems, such as net-pen, raceway, and off-bottom culture, do not call for fertilizers. The early work of Swingle and Smith (various papers) dealt largely with largemouth bass and bluegill, both sportfish. With this species combination, fish are normally not fed formulated feeds, but instead rely on natural organisms produced through fertilization. There are, of course, other instances where fertilization may be important, such as in weed control.

Fertilization requirements of traditional agricultural crops usually involve a soil analysis before planting. In some instances, a sample of foliage from the crop being grown can be analyzed to determine nutrient(s) required with additional applications of fertilizer.

Determination of fertilization requirements of pond water is far less exact. Nutrient content of pond water and pond mud could be analyzed. The abundance of phytoplankton and benthos can be determined quantitatively. However, these analyses take time, and results may vary greatly and be difficult to evaluate. Most pond managers measure the density of the plankton bloom as an index for the need to fertilize pond waters. A plankton bloom dense enough to restrict view of a Secchi disk at between 30 to 46 cm (12 to 18 in) is desirable for weed control and good fish production. Fertilize ponds frequently enough to maintain this bloom. The frequency will vary from pond to pond.

Formerly it was thought that fertilizer should be broadcasted over the pond surface from a boat. Also, fertilizer has been poured in a line along the water's edge, but this much trouble is not necessary. Probably the easiest and best way is to put fertilizer on an underwater platform (Figure 8.3) (Lawrence 1954). The platform should lie about 30 cm (1 ft) below the water surface. One platform will serve about 4 to 6 ha (10 to 15 ac) of water.

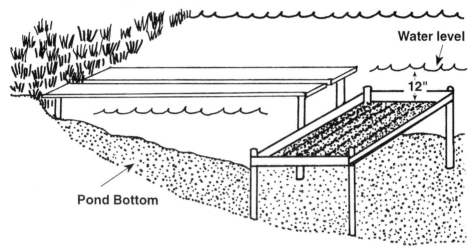

Figure 8.3 Fertilizer platform.

Advantages of using fertilizer platforms are:
(1) It takes less time and labor to fertilize ponds.
(2) Nutrients go into solution in top waters where photosynthetic activity is greatest.
(3) Nutrients are less apt to be tied up with pond muds.
(4) Nutrients go into solution over a longer period.

Some workers place fertilizer in porous bags. The bags are suspended in water so that nutrients are released as fertilizer dissolves. Like fertilizer platforms, bags allow nutrients to enter the water column.

Liquid, inorganic fertilizer is even more efficient to use than granular, inorganic fertilizer. It is easier to apply, and less is required, so it is cheaper. Monthly application rates of a 10-34-0 fertilizer range from 5 to 19 liters/ha (0.5 to 2 gal/ac) (Boyd 1984). An 11-37-0 formulation was also used effectively. Murad and Boyd (1987) got good results when using phosphoric acid (0-54-0) alone at an application rate of 17 kg/ha (15 lb/ac), lowering still the cost of fertilization.

Liquid fertilizer should be diluted with water and splashed on the water surface. Do not pour liquid fertilizer directly into pond water. The fertilizer is heavier than water and will settle to the bottom.

SELECTED FERTILIZATION PROGRAMS

Fertilization plays an integral role for increasing fish production in various countries, particularly where commercial feed is seldom used. Here are selected examples.

Sportfishing Ponds

Boyd and Snow (1975) outlined a procedure they recommended for sportfishing ponds in Alabama and the southeastern United States.

(1) In mid-February or early March, apply 40 lb/ac of 20-20-5 fertilizer. Follow with two more applications at 2-week intervals.

(2) Make three more applications of 40 lb/ac of 20-20-5 at 3-week intervals.

(3) Continue applications monthly or whenever the water begins to clear -- when a Secchi disk or shiny object is visible in 46 cm (18 in) of water.

(4) Discontinue fertilization by the last week in October. Dobbins and Boyd (1976) and Lichtkoppler and Boyd (1977) further refined this procedure.

Channel Catfish in Ponds

Boyd and Snow (1975) suggested that in channel catfish (*Ictalurus punctatus*) ponds in which fish are fed, applications of fertilizer should begin in the spring after filling the pond. Fertilization is suspended when feeding rates reach 11 kg/ha (10 lb/ac) per day, or when turbidity caused by plankton restricts underwater visibility to 46 cm (18 in). Only two or three applications are needed. In old ponds, where several crops of catfish have been raised, fertility may be sufficient so that no fertilization is required. Fertilization may play a more important role in rearing ponds containing catfish fry. Fry benefit directly from the zooplankton as food. Sometimes catfish are stocked into ponds at low rates and no feed is given. In this case, fertilize ponds for the duration.

Trout and Salmon in Ponds

Trout and salmon are usually cultured in raceways or ponds where fertilization is not practiced. Mortimer and Hickling (1954) quoted Wiesner (1936), stating that in Europe trout grow well in fertilized carp ponds. They also quoted Scheuring (1939), who stated that rainbow trout flourished in ponds receiving diluted clarified sewage at Munich. However, rainbow trout are liable to fungus diseases.

Milkfish Ponds

Milkfish have been cultured extensively in Java, Taiwan, and the Philippines. Their production relies on fertilizers. Various methods have been used. In the Philippines they are known as the lab-lab, lumut, and the plankton method. Detailed accounts of milkfish culture, where fertilization is discussed, were given by Hora and Pillay (1962), Hickling (1962), Tang and Chen (1967), and Tang (1976).

Lab-lab Method-- Lab-lab is a complex of blue-green algae, diatoms, and other associated organisms cultured on the pond bottom (Figure 8.4). In most ponds, bottom soils function mainly as a storehouse for nutrients, but in milkfish ponds they are a "bed" for establishment of the algal pasture or lab-lab. This algal pasture is grazed by milkfish, and rather intricate methods involving fertilization promote its growth. Methods to grow lab-lab and culture milkfish vary from country to country, but certain things are common, and a generalized account follows.

Figure 8.4 Shallow milkfish pond in the Philippines showing lab-lab.

Ideal conditions call for clear water with a salinity of 10 to 40 ppt (25 ppt and above is optimum) and water temperatures above 23° to 25°C (73° to 77°F). The pond bottom should be relatively hard, fertile, and high in clay and organic matter content. The elevation of the pond bottom should be a minimum of 0.2 m (8 in) above mean sea level. Ponds below this level are hard to manage because of seepage and difficulty in drying pond bottoms. Pond soils are prepared before stocking milkfish. They may be lightly cultivated, dried out until they crack, and then filled with the tide to a depth of 3 to 5 cm (1 to 2 in) to cover the entire bottom. In some instances this alternate drying and filling may be repeated several times. The productivity of soils is increased by accumulation of nutrients and by decomposition of organic matter. Tobacco dust or tea seed cake is often added to water to control predatory fish.

In the Philippines, fertilization involves both organic, usually chicken manure, and inorganic fertilizer. About one-half of the fertilizer is applied to the drained pond bottom before water is let in. The other half is applied after milkfish are stocked. After a growth of lab-lab is obtained, the water depth is gradually raised to 15 to 45 cm (6 to 18 in), and care is taken not to agitate the water and break the lab-lab mats loose from the bottom.

In Taiwan, four applications of fertilizer may be made. From December to March, ponds remain dry since it is too cold to culture milkfish. Fertilizers such as rice bran, groundnut, and night-soil are applied at this time. Inorganic fertilizers are sometimes used early in the season. From March to June, during the rainy season, a second application of fertilizer is made, along with tea seed cake. A third application is made from June to September, and a fourth after September. The ultimate water depth is maintained at 25 to 35 cm (10 to 14 in). Tang and Chen (1967) estimated that the average yield of lab-lab is 25,000 kg/ha (22,325 lb/ac), and that this can maintain an average milkfish production of 2,000 kg/ha (1,786 lb/ac).

In Indonesia green manure, such as mangrove leaves, is piled in heaps around ponds. In the brackishwater ponds of Java, 1,680 kg/ha (1,500 lb/ac) of mangrove leaves are used, with two or three applications per year. The green manure is stacked in heaps rather than broadcast on the bottom. Mud may top the piles to prevent the heaps from drifting. As it rots, nutrients are liberated. Much of the pond fertility is also derived from source water. This is accomplished by alternately filling and drying ponds, thus accumulating nutrients.

Lumut Method-- Lumut consists primarily of filamentous algae and associated organisms (Figure 8.5). It is less desirable than lab-lab and is usually cultivated when ponds have a lower elevation than mean sea level and are difficult to dry. Pond bottoms are typically soft, and seepage is prevalent. The salinity range favorable for lumut is 25 ppt and below. The water level should range from 20 to 60 cm (8 to 24 in). To prepare the pasture bed, the pond is drained and exposed to the sun for several days. This hastens decomposition of organic matter and thus enrichment of the pond bottom. Fertilization is at a rate of approximately 40-50-0 (N - P_2O_5 - K_2O) plus 1,000 kg/ha (893 lb/ac) of organic manure. Lumut responds better to inorganic fertilizers than to organic fertilizers. Tang (1976) estimated natural production of lumut from 3,000 to 5,000 kg/ha/year (2,679 to 4,465 lb/ac/year). From this amount of food, about 120 to 200 kg/ha (107 to 179 lb/ac) of milkfish can be expected.

Figure 8.5 Pond in the Philippines with lumut. Note sticks in the pond to keep lumut from blowing to one side of the pond.

Plankton Method-- Conditions favorable for the plankton method include a fertile, soft bottom, salinity of 25 ppt and below, and a water level of 70 to 100 cm (28 to 39 in). Ponds are thoroughly dried, and chicken manure is applied to the bottom at a rate of 2,000 kg/ha (1,786 lb/ac). Following this, water is let in until the depth of 70 to 100 cm is reached. Inorganic fertilizer is applied at a rate of 25 kg/ha (22 lb/ac) of 16-20-0 at 2-week intervals, until a total of 75 kg/ha (67 lb/ac) has been applied. In old ponds, phosphate fertilizer alone may be all that is used, and in some instances organic manures are not used at all.

Animal Husbandry Combined with Fish Culture

Animal husbandry and fish culture are often combined in Europe, the Indo-Pacific Region, and elsewhere. The manure from animals may be added to ponds by hand or added directly by the animals themselves. In the latter case, droppings from the ducks and geese may enter the water directly. Manure from chickens and hogs can be washed into ponds. In this situation, feed pens are built over or next to ponds. Examples of animal husbandry/fish culture follow.

Fish-Cum-Duck Culture-- Adding ducks to ponds allows the space above the water column to be used. Woynarovich (1979) reviewed the practice of growing ducks and fish together. He calculated that one duck produces 6 kg (13

lb) of droppings during a 30- to 40- day period. At least 500 ducks can be kept on 1 ha of pond (200/ac) for 1 year, which corresponds to 36 mt/ha (16 tons/ac) of duck manure. Further he estimated that each 100 kg (220 lb) of duck manure, distributed continuously in pond water, may result in an increase of 4 to 6 kg (9 to 13 lb) of fish flesh. The droppings increase fish production by several means: (1) Certain species of fish, such as tilapia, may feed directly on the droppings.
(2) Some of the manure is mineralized, thus releasing nutrients that enhance phytoplankton growth.
(3) The non-mineralized fraction of the manure is fed on directly by zoo-plankton. *Daphnia* sp., for example, grazes on suspended particles of manure and associated bacteria.

Use of animal manure is an age-old practice, as pointed out earlier. Though techniques vary, manure usually is spread on the pond bottom at 1 to 2 mt/ha (893 to 1,786 lb/ac). Manure also can be placed in several heaps in the pond. Several applications may be made during one growing season. Either way, the manure decomposes and consumes oxygen; methane, hydrogen sulfide, and ammonia often develop.

The addition of soft, fresh droppings by ducks lessens these problems. As the droppings continuously enter the pond in small quantities, they are readily digested by the pond system and do not accumulate. This concept -- continuous addition of soft, fresh manure over the whole pond surface -- is known as the carbon-manuring technique. Ducks then become carbon-manuring machines. Very large quantities, 30 to 60 mt/ha/100 days (13 to 26 tons/ac/100 days), of manure can be added safely with ducks.

Fish-cum-duck culture is widespread in certain countries, and in Taiwan up to 3,500 kg of fish/ha (3,125 lb/ac) have been produced. For duck meat, fish-cum-duck culture is most beneficial. A fish pond provides a healthy environment, and ducks are usually free of parasites and diseases. The natural pond foods of ducks are rich in protein, and feeds need contain only 13% to 14% digestible protein as opposed to 16% to 18% for pen-reared ducks. Ducks reared on ponds might produce 200 to 300 g (6 to 11 oz) of digestible protein per duck.

Use of Swine Manure-- A hog produces 1.6 to 1.8 mt (1.7 to 2 tons) of manure, including urine, per year. Generally, the fresh manure of 15 to 25 pigs can be used per ha (6 to 10/ac). In some instances, manure is washed directly into ponds daily (Figure 8.6) or shunted through a silo to produce biogas for household uses (Figure 8.7). If dry, manure is softened in water and may be dispensed from a boat.

Buck et al. (1979), working in Illinois, stocked three Chinese carps, common carp, largemouth bass, a hybrid buffalo (*Ictiobus*), and channel catfish into each of two ponds. A two-section swine house was constructed on a levee between the two ponds. One section contained five growing pigs (39 pigs/ha or 16/ac), and the other eight pigs (66 pigs/ha or 27/ac). Two consecutive lots of pigs were fattened during the study. Over a fish-growing period of 170 days, the net increments in fish biomass were 2,971 kg/ha (2,653 lb/ac) in the pond receiving waste from five pigs and 3,834 kg/ha (3,424 lb/ac) in the pond receiving waste from eight pigs.

Figure 8.6 Hog pen built over pond in the Philippines. Poultry wastes also are used.

Figure 8.7 Hog wastes here are first shunted through a silo where methane is produced. Effluent from this enters ponds, Philippines.

Use of Cow Manure-- In Israel, cow manure has been used in polyculture ponds. Schroeder and Hepher (1979) reported on use of fluid cow manure. Their ponds, 400 m² (478 yd²), were stocked with common carp, silver carp (*Hypophthalmichthys molitrix*), and tilapia in a ratio of approximately 3:1:2. Cow manure containing 12% dry matter was applied 6 days a week at a daily rate of 200 liters/ha (21 gal/ac) when fish biomass was less than 500 kg/ha (446 lb/ac). Ammonium sulfate and superphosphate were applied every 2 weeks at 600 kg/ha (536 lb/ac). When chicken manure was available, 200 liters/ha were applied once every 2 weeks. When fish biomass exceeded 1 mt/ha (893 lb/ac), the rate of manuring was raised to 500 liters/ha/day (53 gal/ac/day) and to 700 liters/ha/day (75 gal/ac/day) when the biomass reached 3 mt of fish per ha (1.3 tons/ac). The rate of chemical fertilization remained constant at all times. Daily growth of fish ranged from 20 to 40 kg/ha (18 to 36 lb/ac).

Schroeder (1976 personal communication, Dor Hof Hacarmel, Israel) gave this general rule for use of cow manure in Israeli ponds containing common carp, silver carp, and tilapia. When a pond contains less than 2 mt/ha (0.9 tons/ac) standing crop of fish, use 25 liters (7 gal) of manure (12% dry matter) daily for each 100 kg (220 lb) of fish. When a pond contains more than 2 mt/ha, use 35 to 50 liters (9 to 13 gal) daily for each 100 kg of fish. Generally, a conversion of dry cow manure to fish averages 3 or 4 to 1. Production may reach 4,000 kg/ha/year (3,5721 lb/ac/year) without additional feeds. Intensive manuring in conventionally fed fish ponds doubled yields of fish with half the usual feed requirements.

Use of Human Sewage

In Israel, sewage from a town of 5,000 fed directly into a 4-ha (10-ac) pond yielded 2,800 kg of fish/ha (2,500 lb/ac) in 6 months with no supplemental feeding. Sewage from a 500-person kibbutz fed into a 3-ha (7.4-ac) pond, where supplemental feed was used, yielded 8,600 kg of fish/ha (7,680 lb/ac) in 8 months as compared with 4,700 kg/ha (4,197 lb/ac) in adjacent ponds not receiving sewage. Fish grown in sewage are held for several weeks in freshwater ponds before marketing to flush out any residual objectionable odors and pathogens. Allen et al. (1976) pointed out inherent problems with use of sewage in culture ponds. They grew salmonids in brackishwater ponds receiving waste water after it was clarified and aerated. The bacterium *Vibrio anguillarum* became a problem, but was controlled when fish were treated with 4.5 mg of Terramycin® per 45 kg (100 lb) of fish/day for 15 days.

The gastro-intestinal tracts of fish were examined, and almost one half of the microorganisms recovered were members of the Enterobacteriaecae -- indicating a contamination of public health significance. However, after depuration none of the fish contained pathogenic organisms. The total coliform and fecal strepto-cocci in waste water initially gave high counts, but the counts dropped within a few days after depuration. If culture species grown in ponds receiving sewage are declared safe to eat, it is doubtful whether they will be accepted as human food in the United States. One possible solution is to grow fish such as tilapia in waste water, purge them of pathogens, and then reduce them to fish meal for use in animal feeds.

Another possibility is to grow aquatic plants in waste-water lagoons; the plants remove excess minerals and dissolved organic nutrients and are in turn used in animal feeds. In Israel at Dor, the yield of duckweed in cow-manured ponds was many times greater than in adjacent ponds receiving inorganic fertilization. It appears that the dissolved organic complex molecules in manure are important. Culley and Epps (1973) reported that various species of duckweed grown in lagoons receiving livestock wastes were high in protein, grew rapidly, and removed large quantities of nitrogen, phosphorus, and potassium from waste water. Using duckweed in poultry diets has shown promise. The main deterrent is the high water content of the plant, which must be handled.

Crustaceans in Ponds

Less attention has been given to use of fertilizers for pond culture of shrimp and freshwater prawns. Various organic feeds add to the fertility of the water as well as provide feed. Nutrients may be added to tanks for growing single-species algae, that are used to feed larval stages of crustaceans.

Ling (1969) recommended that in Malaysia 200 kg/ha (179 lb/ac) of cow dung and 10 kg/ha (9 lb/ac) of lime be added monthly to ponds containing *Macrobrachium rosenbergii*. In India, four species of penaeid shrimp are grown in rice fields following harvest (George et al. 1968). Rice is harvested in September or October, then fields are allowed to flood with the tides, bringing in young shrimp. No fertilizer is added, but no doubt residual fertilizer from the rice is beneficial. In the Philippines, shrimp and milkfish (*Chanos chanos*) are sometimes cultured together. Ponds are fertilized with milkfish in mind.

Boyd (1990) reviewed various fertilization regimes for brackish water with shrimp primarily in mind. He gave this general recommendation: If water exchange rates are 5% to 10% per day, fertilize two or three times per week. Fertilize ponds once or twice a week when first stocked, and limit water exchange. If feed is not applied to ponds and waters are infertile, continue heavy fertilization until harvest. If feed is used, it will ultimately provide the nitrogen and phosphorous required by phytoplankton. Boyd (1989) also noted that water low in silica (< 1 ppm) could be fertilized with silicate at 30 kg/ha (27 lb/ac). This enhances production of diatoms, an important food for shrimp.

Villalon (1991) described a step-by-step fertilization procedure for semi-intensive culture of shrimp in Latin America (Ecuador). His criterion for dosage was to ensure that pond water contains 1.3 ppm nitrogen and 0.15 ppm phosphorous. Inorganic fertilizers consisting of urea and triple superphosphate were commonly used. Wyban and Sweeney (1991), working in Hawaii, did not mention fertilization in their round ponds stocked at super high densities of 75 shrimp per m^2 (750,000/ha or 300,000/ac).

Fertilization in crawfish ponds has met with limited success. Clark et al. (1974) found that fertilization with 8-8-8 in experimental pools gave approximately the same production, 694 kg/ha (620 lb/ac), as that from use of natural aquatic plants: 778 kg/ha (693 lb/ac) with smartweed (*Polygonum* sp.), and 675 kg/ha (603 lb/ac) with alligator weed (*Alternanthera philoxeroides*). Crawfish farmers in Louisiana, where the red swamp (*Procambarus clarkii*) and white river crawfish (*P. zonangulus*) are grown, rely on natural aquatic plants or rice forage to feed crawfish. Romaire (1976) reported that growth of crawfish in ponds receiving inorganic fertilization was poor, only 192 kg/ha (171 lb/ac). In ponds receiving rice hay and bahiagrass hay, production was 736 and 732 kg/ha (657 and 654 lb/ac), respectively. No doubt the hays served as both fertilizer and feed. Forney (1968) recommended use of fertilizers to grow bait crawfish (*Orconectes immunis*) in New York ponds. He used 6-12-6 and 0-12-0 fertilizers to maintain a plankton bloom. The complete fertilizer was applied at 3-week intervals during spring and summer at a rate of 224 kg/ha (200 lb/ac), or he used 1.7 to 2.7 m^3/ha (20 to 30 bu/ac) of manure at 3-week intervals. Further, he reported that he produced 381 kg/ha (340 lb/ac) of crawfish when 3.4 mt/ha (1.5 tons/ac) of hay were applied in combination with 448 kg/ha (400 lb/ac) of superphosphate.

Mollusks

It is generally not feasible to fertilize waters where mollusks such as oysters are grown. Most are open water, and it is too expensive to fertilize. In ponds, however, it may be beneficial. Being filter feeders low on the food chain, mollusks directly benefit from increased plankton. Of particular interest is the potential of liberating nutrients from the ocean depths through artificial upwelling. These nutrients, upon reaching the surface, increase phytoplankton production manyfold and hence increase production of mollusks.

The classic example of natural upwelling occurs off the coast of Peru, where up to 10 million mt (11 million tons) of principally anchovies (*Anchoa* spp.) had at one time been harvested each year. The upwelling is brought about by offshore winds. When the winds blow the surface water away from the coast, the only waters available to replenish those waters are from deep below. These waters are nutrient rich because of dead plankton and other organisms that constantly rain down from surface waters. All oceans show low nutrient values in offshore surface waters. The nutrients increase with increasing depth and reach a maximum concentration at approximately 700 to 1,000 m (2,296 to 3,280 ft).

There are methods for artificially bringing nutrient-rich waters to the surface. Stommel et al. (1955) described a "salt fountain" in which deep water is slowly pumped toward the surface through a pipe. Since salinity is lower in deep water, and thus less dense, water has a tendency to rise. Moreover, as the water rises slowly toward the surface, its temperature tends to equilibrate with that outside the pipe. In an open-ocean environment, holding upwelled water at or near the surface is a real problem and can be attempted in one of several ways: use of floating enclosures and heating, or dilution with fresh water to lower its density.

Roels (1975) suggested that upwelled water that had been mechanically pumped could be used to flow through on-shore tanks where mollusks are cultured. He described a research facility at St. Croix, Virgin Islands, where deep water was continuously pumped into 45,420-liter (12,000-gal) pools containing planktonic diatoms. Eight species of shellfish have been cultured successfully in the diatom-rich pools. He found that the nutrient maximum (basically nitrate, phosphate, and silicate) in the St. Croix area occurred between 762 and 914 m (2,500 and 3,000 ft). An added advantage of the deep water is that no predators, parasites, or pollutants are normally present. Roels estimated that commercial production of mollusks for food requires about 94,625 liters (25,000 gal) of deep water per minute. He further suggested various geographic locations where artificial upwelling operations might succeed.

LIMING PONDS
Why Lime Ponds
Ponds may be limed to obtain one or more of the following benefits:
(1) Total hardness and total alkalinity are increased, and the pH buffer system is enhanced.
(2) Liming neutralizes acid soil conditions, thus increasing the pH and availability of phosphorous (Boyd and Scarsbrook 1974).
(3) Liming adds calcium, a plant nutrient. If dolomitic limestone is used, magnesium, also a plant nutrient, is added.
(4) Addition of calcium is directly beneficial to crustaceans.
(5) Liming may serve as a disinfectant or sterilant.
(6) Decomposition of organic matter in pond muds is speeded up.
(7) Lime helps to flocculate (settle out) clay particles in muddy water.

Total Hardness, Total Alkalinity, and the Buffer System-- The importance of total hardness, total alkalinity, and the buffer system was discussed in Chapter 6. To review, waters with a total alkalinity or total hardness of less than 10 ppm rarely produce good crops of fish. At 20 ppm, production of phytoplankton may be adequate, and at 50 ppm and above, phytoplankton growth and resulting fish production is best. Liming is generally recommended when total hardness is less than 20 ppm (as $CaCO_3$).

Arce and Boyd (1975) found that liming increased both total hardness and total alkalinity. Before liming, total hardness in 10 study ponds ranged from 5 to 14 ppm, and total alkalinity varied from 11 to 18 ppm. Several months after ponds were limed, the average total hardness and total alkalinity reached 38 ppm and 42 ppm, respectively. When $CaCO_3$ is added to pond waters, the calcium contributes to increased hardness, and the carbonate contributes to increased alkalinity. By increasing the alkalinity, the availability of carbon dioxide for photosynthesis was increased. Increased alkalinity also improves the buffering system against sudden changes in pH.

Liming Neutralizes Acid Soils-- Addition of lime to acid pond soils increases the pH, allowing better release of nutrients, particularly phosphorus. This in turn enhances plankton growth and the production of organisms in the food chain. Bowling (1962) found that liming increased production of benthic organisms. The lime reacts with bottom muds and neutralizes acidity by exchanging basic for acidic ions on cation exchange sites. In instances where fertilization has proved unsuccessful, acid soil conditions should be suspect. Addition of lime, with no fertilization, may increase production simply by allowing release of nutrients locked up with pond muds.

Lime Adds Nutrients-- Calcium, as a nutrient, is required only in minute amounts to grow good fish crops. Hickling (1962) reported that reasonable crops of fish can be grown in ponds where lime is barely detectable. Nevertheless, some calcium must be present for plant growth.

Importance of Calcium to Crustaceans-- The element calcium is most important for growth and well-being of crustaceans; it is necessary for new shell formation following molting. Smitherman et al. (1967) found that growth and survival of crawfish (*Procambarus clarkii*) in experimental pools were low when total water hardness was less than 20 ppm. Crawfish shells remained soft. Even when crawfish were fed a pelleted feed, growth and survival were poor if hardness was low. de la Bretonne et al. (1969) stocked crawfish in pools containing different hardness levels. Growth and survival of crawfish increased up to a total hardness level of 100 to 150 ppm. Above this level, no added benefits were noted.

Quicklime as a Disinfectant or Sterilant-- Quicklime, by its caustic, toxic action, helps control fish and crustacean parasites and diseases. Liming pond bottoms with calcium oxide or calcium hydroxide kills bottom-dwelling, free-swimming stages, resistant stages, eggs, and intermediate stages of parasitic forms living in intermediate hosts such as snails (Figure 8.8).

Figure 8.8 Bottom of shrimp pond in Indonesia was disked after draining. Lime will be applied next.

Snow and Jones (1961) described the effects of liming ponds with calcium hydroxide. They limed ponds at rates of 415 to 747 kg/ha (370 to 667 lb/ac), 1,568 to 2,118 kg/ha (1,400 to 1,900 lb/ac), or 2,912 kg/ha (2,600 lb/ac). All ponds were filled with water at time of application. A noticeable reduction in insect forms was achieved at the low liming rates, and an almost complete kill at the medium and high rates. At the highest lime dosage, water pH reached 11 to 12. Return of animal life was rapid; insects recovered within 3 weeks. A marked reduction of rooted vegetation occurred at medium and high rates of lime application. Death of plants occurred in ponds given the higher rate, but phytoplankton developed within 14 days after lime treatment. They concluded that a rate of 1,120 to 2,800 kg/ha (1,000 to 2,500 lb/ac) is sufficient for most conditions, and that normally a limed pond can be safely stocked with fish 10 days after application.

In China, quicklime and tea cake are routinely used as a disinfectant and sterilant. If the pond is dry, 364 kg/ha (325 lb/ac) of quicklime is applied; double the amount is used if the pond contains water. Schäperclaus (1933) recommended that a rate of 995 to 1,492 kg/ha (889 to 1,332 lb/ac) of calcium oxide be applied.

Decomposition in Muds-- When lime is added to an acid pond bottom, soil pH increases; this augments a release of nutrients from pond muds that, in turn, enhances the decomposition of organic matter. Organic matter is less apt to accumulate.

Flocculation Properties-- Both calcium and magnesium ions are positively charged. When they come in contact with negatively charged clay particles in muddy water, the clay is flocculated and settles to the bottom.

Amount of Lime to Use

The amount of lime required for pond soils depends on the pH of soils. This is the same criterion used for liming cropland. Schäperclaus (1933) gave liming rates for ponds based on pond soil pH and soil texture (Table 8.4). Further, liming is indicated if either the total hardness or total alkalinity of pond waters is below 20 ppm. Boyd (1974, and 1979b) gave a step-by-step procedure for determining liming rates in ponds.

Table 8.4 Lime requirements of bottom muds based on pH and texture of mud.

Mud pH	Lime requirement (kg/ha as $CaCO_3$)		
	Heavy loams or clays	Sandy loam	Sand
< 4.0	14,320	7,160	4,475
4.0 - 4.5	10,740	5,370	4,475
4.6 - 5.0	8,950	4,475	3,580
5.1 - 5.5	5,370	3,580	1,790
5.6 - 6.0	3,580	1,790	895
6.1 - 6.5	1,790	1,790	0
> 6.5	0	0	0

Source: Schäperclaus (1933).

Sources of Lime

There are several sources of lime: calcium carbonate, $CaCO_3$; calcium oxide or quicklime, CaO; and calcium hydroxide or hydrated lime, $Ca(OH)_2$ (Table 8.5). Other sources include basic slag, calcium cyanamide, calcium sulphate, and calcium nitrate. Calcium carbonate, also known as ground limestone, contains up to 40% calcium. It is relatively insoluble and slow to act. Because of this, it is safe to apply to ponds containing fish. This form of lime is readily available and economical in cost. Calcium oxide, which contains about 71% calcium, is soluble and caustic.

Take great care when applying calcium oxide. This form is used to disinfect pond bottoms, and it may be used in ponds with a very low soil pH, in the range of 3.5 to 5. Calcium oxide may be applied to ponds to partially satisfy lime requirements quickly. Calcium carbonate may be applied next to bring the soil pH up to the desired range of 6.5 to 7. Calcium hydroxide, which contains approximately 54% calcium, is relatively soluble. It therefore acts quickly to increase soil pH. It may be toxic to plant and animal life, and it is irritating to the skin. Calcium hydroxide is usually preferred over quicklime whenever a quick-acting lime is needed.

Table 8.5 Principal forms of lime.

	Approximate pounds[a] required to equal 1 ton[b] $CaCO_3$
Calcium carbonate limestone ($CaCO_3$)	2,200
Dolomitic limestone ($CaCO_3 + MgCO_3$)	2,000
Basic slag	3,000
Burned lime (CaO)	1,200
Hydrated lime (Ca (OH)2)	1,500

[a] 2.205 lb = 1 kg
[b] 1 ton = 0.9074 mt
Source: H.S. Swingle 1961. Management of Impounded Waters, Lecture Notes.

Application of Lime

Lime can be applied to either dry pond bottoms or to ponds full of water, whichever is the easiest. If quick-acting lime is used, it may be necessary to wait 2 to 3 weeks before adding fish. This will allow water pH to stabilize. Best results are obtained by spreading lime over the entire bottom or surface. In some instances where ponds are very large, lime may be applied in 500 kg (1,102 lb) piles along shallow water edges. Normally, lime is applied only every 2 or 3 years, though this could vary greatly. The best time of year to apply lime is during late fall or early winter, or before fertilizers are applied in the spring. Lime and phosphate fertilizer should not be applied at the same time. The calcium will precipitate the phosphorus. Lime is lost in ponds from outflow, seepage, and leaching. Do not lime ponds when water retention time is less than 3 weeks.

The benefits of lime can be checked 3 to 4 weeks after application by determining the increase in total alkalinity and total hardness. Both should be above 20 ppm (Boyd 1990). If not enough lime was added, make another application and check alkalinity and hardness again in 3 to 4 weeks.

Adverse Effects of Excessive Liming

Avoid overliming. Excessive liming may result in a loss of valuable adsorptive properties of pond mud and in reduced availability of nutrients. For example, excessive amounts of lime may cause phosphorus to become tied up as insoluble apatite, thus making phosphorus unavailable for phytoplankton growth. That is why ponds should not be limed and fertilized at the same time. Another danger of overliming is the very rapid change of water pH that may occur, particularly if quick-acting forms of lime are used. The water pH could rise to more than 10. To avoid sudden, drastic rises in pH when these forms of lime are used, it is wise to apply lime in small annual doses. Using relatively slow-acting, relatively insoluble calcium carbonate as the lime source will greatly lessen sudden pH changes.

FUNCTION OF POND MUDS

When a newly constructed pond is filled with water, the pond bottom is mostly mineral soil. However, as the pond ages, true pond mud begins to form. Plants and animals die, sink to the bottom, and are decomposed by micro-organisms. Much of the broken-down organic matter exists as humus. Fish feces and uneaten feed also contribute to the accumulation of organic matter on pond bottoms. If manures are used, they too contribute to the accumulation. A complex of clay soil particles, humus, and microorganisms forms true pond mud.

Pond mud has several functions:

(1) It helps seal pond bottoms against seepage.

(2) It aids in the mineralization of organic matter.

(3) It provides a storehouse for nutrients, and it releases nutrients to the overlying water.

(4) It provides food and shelter to bottom-dwelling organisms.

Mineralization

The breakdown of organic matter by bacteria and other microorganisms produces humus, and nutrients are released. This release of nutrients is called mineralization. Nutrients may be released into the surrounding water where they are recycled through the food web, or they may be adsorbed on the mineral fraction of pond mud.

The rate at which mineralization takes place depends on a number of factors, according to Boyd (1992):

(1) Composition of organic matter and nutrients available. Generally, materials with a high fiber content, such as the stems and roots of plants, decompose slowly. On the other hand, organic matter from uneaten feed and

fecal waste of culture species decompose more quickly. This is caused in part by the higher nitrogen content of the materials relative to the carbon content. A low carbon:nitrogen ratio favors rapid decomposition. Microorganisms use nitrogen and oxygen in decomposition. Thus as the carbon:nitrogen ratio is lowered, particularly below 17:1, decomposition of organic matter is enhanced. In situations where there is a high C:N ratio, say 100 and above, the addition of urea or other nitrogen-containing fertilizer will lower the C:N ratio and speed up decomposition of organic matter. If, however, there is a great abundance of organic matter, it is wiser to remove some of the material to prevent oxygen depletion.

(2) Temperature. Most microorganisms function best at temperatures of 25° to 35°C (77° to 95°F).

(3) pH. Boyd (1992) reported that the best pH for decomposition of soil organic matter in brackishwater ponds is between 7.5 and 8.5. For freshwater ponds, a pH of 7 is about ideal.

(4) Moisture and time. When ponds are drained, pond muds are exposed to the air, and decomposition of organic matter is enhanced. If, however, pond muds are excessively dried out, decomposition will decline. A rain adds moisture to organic matter and decomposition will begin anew. The optimum moisture content for decomposition of organic matter is about 20%, but this will vary among soils of different ponds (Boyd 1992).

(5) Oxygen supply. When a pond is first flooded, air is driven out of the soil. Aerobic microorganisms become active and oxidize organic matter. Once the oxygen is used up in the mineralization process, and this time may be only a day or so, anaerobic bacteria continue the decomposition. Now decomposition greatly slows down, and compounds formed are in the reduced state. Sulfates are reduced to sulfides. Nitrogenous compounds are reduced to ammonia or nitrogen gas. Iron is present in the soluble ferrous state. Some of the organic matter may be reduced to methane. If oxygen returns to the surface skin of the pond mud, the ferrous iron becomes ferric, sulfides are oxidized to sulfates, and ammonia is oxidized to nitrite and then to nitrate. If, however, ponds are exceptionally deep or stratified, there is a risk of a permanent deoxygenated layer. The lack of oxygen and the presence of certain compounds in the reduced state, hydrogen sulfide for example, are detrimental to most aquatic life. This deep deoxygenated water is then considered "dead," and this is one reason why ponds ordinarily should not be too deep.

Storage and Release of Nutrients

The surface skin of pond mud, which is only a few millimeters thick, is a chemical laboratory. This surface is strongly adsorptive of both positive and negative ions because of the formation of a colloidal ferric hydroxide-humus complex and exchange sites on expanding lattice clays. Positive charges are carried on the ferric hydroxide portion and negative charges on the humus portion. Therefore, positively charged ions, such as NH_4^+ and K^+, are attracted to and held (adsorbed) by the humus portion. Similarly, negatively charged ions such as SO_4^{-2} and phosphate, including ($H_2PO_4^-$, HPO_4^{-2}, or PO_4^{-3}) are adsorbed by the ferrous hydroxide portion. When oxygen is shut off from the pond mud-water interface, an interesting phenomenon takes place. Both positive ions and negative ions are given off to the water in considerable quantities.

The pH of the pond mud also has an effect on the storage and release of ions (nutrients). Colloidal ferric hydroxide is amphoteric. Its charge changes gradually from positive to negative as the pH of the surrounding medium is increased from pH 7 to 10. At and above the iso-electric point, where the charge is zero, there are no forces to hold the negatively charged humus counterpart, or any other negatively charged ion, such as phosphate. This is why when pond muds are very acid, liming liberates nutrients.

Food and Shelter

As the nutrient-rich pond mud accumulates, benthic organisms multiply. These fish-food organisms are relished by bottom feeding species such as common carp. The carp ingests the pond mud, sifts out food organisms, and spits out the rest. Evidence of this can be noted after draining carp ponds. The bottom of ponds is often dotted with pock marks where the carp have been feeding. In the Indo-Pacific Region and elsewhere, a mixture of species is often stocked into ponds to use natural fish-food organisms fully.

In the United States, however, most of our culture systems are monoculture -- the culture of single species. The catfish farmer, for example, stocks at high rates, 25,000/ha (10,000/ac), feeds heavily, and harvests. The fish feed almost entirely on the commercial feed. Benthic food organisms, for the most part, go unused. Further, nutrients accumulate in pond muds because they are not removed through the food web. Consequently, the excess nutrients cause problems with low dissolved oxygen and obnoxious algae scums.

The pond mud shelters and hides aquatic species, which is especially important for species that molt. Both freshwater crawfish and shrimp (*Penaeus* spp.), for example, often burrow into the pond mud during molting for protection.

MANAGEMENT OF POND MUDS
The Dry Period

When a pond is drained, you may notice an obnoxious odor caused by the end-products of anaerobic decomposition. Methane, ammonia, and hydrogen sulfide are often smelled. When pond muds are in an anaerobic condition (in a reduced state), soil may be dark black because certain reduced compounds are a deep black. When ponds are in an aerobic condition, (oxidized state), soil may be brown or its natural color.

It is beneficial to dry out a pond bottom after draining to restore aerobic conditions (Figure 8.9). In Europe, the fish crop is often harvested in the fall, and the ponds are left to dry over the winter. Fish grow little or none during winter, so no production is lost. In Germany, fish ponds might grow crops of fish for three successive years and then land crops for three years. In China, there is a frequent alternation of rice crops with fish crops. The periodical drying out of brackishwater ponds in Indonesia, Taiwan, and the Philippines is common practice. If acid soil conditions prevail, however, it may be best to keep ponds full with water to prevent oxidation and promotion of acid sulphate conditions. The advantages of a dry period have been well documented (Hoffman 1934; Lin 1949; Schuster 1949; Wunder 1949; Mortimer and Hickling 1954; and Hickling 1962).

Figure 8.9 Pond bottom in Honduras being dried out after harvest by draining.

The drying out of a pond bottom is beneficial for several reasons:
(1) Harmful fish parasites and insects are killed. Beneficial food organisms, such as chironomid larvae, are less affected since they burrow underground.
(2) Maintenance and repairs to levees can be accomplished.
(3) Mineralization can continue at a greater rate because of aerobic conditions. Wunder (1949) stated that production of fish can double following a dry year because fertility is restored.
(4) An oxygen debt in pond muds can be alleviated.

The time that a pond should remain dry may vary. Generally, a pond should remain dry for at least 10 days after draining. Boyd (1992) suggested about a 2-week dry period for shrimp ponds. A longer period may enhance desiccation, which retards decomposition of organic matter. If pond bottoms dry out too much, flushing with water is beneficial. Light plowing of the bottom is sometimes beneficial since this speeds aerobic decomposition, but it also accelerates desiccation. If the pond mud is shallow, avoid deep plowing.

Maintaining Aerobic Conditions

In earlier discussions, we stressed the importance of maintaining aerobic conditions in bottom waters. All too often, water management has meant maintaining sufficient DO levels to prevent oxygen depletion. Less attention has been paid to management of pond bottoms. As stocking density and feed inputs increase, a point is reached when bacteria and other microorganisms can no longer break down organic matter fast enough to prevent its accumulation. Moreover, dissolved oxygen is soon exhausted.

Boyd (1992) felt that feeding rates above 100 to 150 kg/ha per day (89 to 134 lb/ac per day) in shrimp ponds could not be used for long without serious problems with bottom soil deterioration. Stocking rates of *Penaeus monodon* in excess of 20/m^2 (200,00/ha or 80,000/ac) will lead to serious problems. Higher stocking rates with *P. vannamei* are permissible because this shrimp is harvested at a smaller size (20 to 25 g) before the critical feeding rate is reached. *P. monodon* are usually harvested when they reach 30 to 35 g.

Sediments

Water exchange and mechanical aeration have improved water quality in grow-out ponds. Pond managers could maintain good water quality if only they would not overstock culture species and overfeed. Instead, once the water quality is improved through various means, more fish or shrimp are stocked and feed inputs go up. Inevitably, sediments accumulate (Boyd 1995). Boyd (1992) estimated that for an annual production of 3,000 kg/ha (2,679 lb/ac) of shrimp, sediment yield would be 609 mt of dry sediment per ha (269 tons/ac). If this material is deposited uniformly over the pond bottom, it would form a 7.5-cm (3-in) deep layer.

There are a number of ways in which to deal with sediments:

(1) Reduce stocking densities and feed inputs as suggested by Boyd (1992).

(2) Build settling trenches in the pond (Refer to Chapter 5 Figure 5.40.). Sediments drift by gravity into trenches where they are removed by pumping while shrimp are still being grown.

(3) In small concrete-lined ponds, the drain can be placed in the center (Figure 8.10). Aerators positioned along the sides create a circular water motion. Sediments settle out in the center of the pond. The riser pipe can be raised

periodically to remove the sludge. Boyd (1992) felt that in earthen ponds of 0.25 ha (0.6 ac) or larger, it is not practical to produce strong enough water current to move sediment to the center of the pond. If excessive aeration is used, bottom material is eroded where water current is the swiftest and sediment will accumulate in the center of the pond (Figure 8.11). Unless this sediment is removed, anaerobic conditions will develop.

Figure 8.10 Center drain used in Taiwanese concrete pond.

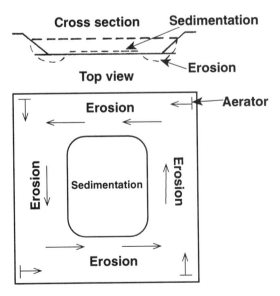

Figure 8.11 Erosion and sedimentation in an intensive shrimp pond caused by water currents from aerators. After Boyd 1992.

(4) Following harvest (pond draining), sediments can be removed. Effluents from ponds can be passed through a sediment basin before they are discharged into coastal waters. Later, fresh sand may be spread in a thin layer over the cleaned pond bottom.

(5) Allow pond bottoms to remain dry following harvest, lightly disk the bottom, and encourage aerobic conditions.

CHRONIC ACID SOILS

In many parts of the world, chronic acid soils are a major problem (Dost and Breemen 1982). Industrialized areas in the United States, Japan, and Europe have problems with acid precipitation. Oden and Anderson (no date) and Oden and Ahl (no date) pointed out that the content of nitrate and sulphur in precipitation has increased 3% to 7% per year, and that in only a few decades, yearly average pH values in Scandinavia have dropped by two units. Annually, more than 91 million mt (100 million tons) of sulphur dioxide have been released by industry into the atmosphere over Europe and North America. As sulphur dioxide enters the atmosphere, it may drift over the Scandinavian countries, be converted to sulfur trioxide, and ultimately converted to sulfuric acid when it rains. Consequently, the pH in lakes in Finland, Sweden, and Norway drops to pH 5 and even lower. Total hardness is usually only 20 to 30 ppm. This widespread chronic low pH problem has been most detrimental to their freshwater crawfish industry. Both Sweden and Finland have liming programs to improve water quality. Limestone is spread over the ice of selected lakes. When the ice melts, the limestone is distributed.

Acid soils may come about by other means. Approximately 20 million ha (50 million ac) exist worldwide. The soils are sulfidic and are generally associated with mangrove, nipa, or "gelam" vegetation. Mangrove vegetation and sulfidic soil occur in the general locations of the tropics -- on the seaward extensions of large deltas, in sluggish estuaries, and along prograding lagoonal coasts. Most of the sulfidic soils are so acidic (pH< 3.5) that it is not possible to grow rice or other crops. Hickling (1962), however, pointed out that acid gelam soils in Malacca and elsewhere can produce good crops of fish.

Acid sulphidic soils may result from the activity of sulphur bacteria. In a typical mangrove swamp, sulphur bacteria use sulfates from seawater to reduce (decompose) organic sediments. Sulphur or sulfides are produced as a byproduct. Even so, the soils do not turn acid as long as they are submerged in water under anaerobic conditions. Once the soils are exposed to air, aerobic conditions prevail and sulfuric acid is produced. This causes a severe drop in pH.

Experimental ponds of the Brackishwater Aquaculture Center (BAC), Leganes, Iloilo, Philippines, demonstrated this problem. Following rain, fish kills often occurred. The banks of the ponds were dried out and highly acidic; the rain washed the acid soil into the ponds. Typical indicators of the acid sulfate soils are the presence of jarosite, $KFe_3 (SO_4)_2 (OH)_6$, which gives dried soils a yellow, mottled appearance. High iron content, especially the precipitates of ferric oxide, completely coated some pond bottoms during flooding.

There are several solutions for overcoming sulphidic soils. Brinkman and Singh (1982) discussed methodology for reclamation of brackishwater ponds with acid sulphate soils.

(1) During site selection for an aquaculture operation, the soil pH readings can be misleading. If the pH is read shortly after the soil is sampled, and if the sample is still wet, the true pH value may not be evident. The BAC recommended the following procedure for determining soil pH: Take a core sample 0 to 100 cm (40 in) deep in the test area. Place the sample in a plastic bag that is allowed to receive air. After one month, take the pH of the core sample at 25 cm (10 in) increments. As a comparison, the pH should be determined in a like manner immediately after the initial sample is taken. Boyd (1992) suggested another method to test for potential acid sulphate soils. Soil is mixed with 30% hydrogen peroxide. After 10 minutes, the pH of the mixture should be 3.5 or less. Universal pH paper with a pH range of 0 to 6 is suitable for field use.

(2) It was recommended that a wooden or bamboo wall be built at the foot of the levee to hold back soil from entering the pond. Vegetation or other cover should be encouraged to grow on levees.

(3) The pond bottoms can be tilled to speed oxidation and hence, production of sulfuric acid. The ponds are then flushed with water and drained. This mechanical process can be repeated several times.

(4) Ultimately liming will be beneficial.

(5) Finally, ponds can be kept full of water at all times to keep the pond mud in a reduced state. This last method has been used in China.

STUDY QUESTIONS
1. List reasons for fertilizing ponds.
2. In a food chain, what are producers, consumers, and decomposers?
3. Describe the two basic food chains.
4. Give an example of a food web in pond waters.
5. List times when you would not fertilize pond waters.
6. List advantages and disadvantages of organic fertilizers.
7. You will fertilize a 17-ac lake at a rate of 100 lb of 8-8-0 per ac with ammonium nitrate and superphosphate. Assume that ammonium nitrate comes in 100-lb bags and superphosphate in 80-lb bags. Two applications will be made. Following this, you will fertilize three more times with phosphate only, at a rate of 100 lb of 0-8-0 per ac. (1) How many bags (round off to the nearest half bag) of each fertilizer are needed for the first application? (2) How many bags of each fertilizer are needed for both applications? (3) How many bags of superphosphate are needed for three additional applications?

8. Describe the lab-lab system for fertilizing milkfish ponds in the Philippines.

9. Discuss, in outline form, fertilization programs related to animal husbandry for fish-cum-duck, swine-fish, and cow-fish.

10. List reasons for liming ponds.

11. What factors determine the amount of lime to use? How often are ponds limed?

12. What are major sources of lime? Describe characteristics of each.

13. List functions of a pond mud.

14. What factors determine the rate of mineralization for organic matter?

15. What steps would you take to manage pond muds?

16. How can you reduce the buildup of sediments in a shrimp pond?

17. What causes acid soils?

18. How would you check for acid soils?

19. How would you correct acid soils?

REFERENCES

Allen, G.H., A. Busch and W. Morton. 1979. Preliminary bacteriological experiences with waste water-fertilized marine fish ponds, Humboldt Bay, California. pp. 492-499. In Advances in Aquaculture. FAO Technical Conference on Aquaculture, Kyoto, Japan. 653 pp.

Arce, R.G. and C.E. Boyd. 1975. Effects of agricultural limestone on water chemistry, phytoplankton productivity, and fish production in soft water ponds. Transactions American Fisheries Society 104(2):308-312.

Avault, J.W., Jr. 1976. Crayfish in Europe -- Some facts and folklore. Presented Annual Meeting Louisiana Crawfish Farmers Association, Nicholls State University, Thibodaux, La. Mimeograph 9 pp.

Baab, J.S., G.L. Hamm, KC. Haines, A. Chu and O.A. Roels. 1973. Shellfish mariculture in an artificial upwelling system. Proceedings National Shellfisheries Association 63:63-67.

Bowling, M.L. 1962. The effects of lime treatment on benthos production in Georgia farm ponds. Proceedings Annual Conference Southeastern Association of Game and Fish Commissioners 16:418-424.

Boyd, C.E. 1974. Lime requirements of Alabama fish ponds. Auburn University, Alabama Agricultural Experiment Station. Bulletin 459. 19 pp.

Boyd, C.E. 1975. Competition for light by aquatic plants in fish ponds. Auburn University, Alabama Agricultural Experiment Station. Circular 215. 19 pp.

Boyd, C.E. 1976a. Water chemistry and plankton in unfertilized ponds in pastures and woods. Transactions American Fisheries Society 105:634-636.

Boyd, C.E. 1976b. Liming farm fish ponds. Auburn University, Alabama Agricultural Experiment Station. Leaflet 91. 6 pp.

Boyd, C.E. 1979a. Water quality in warmwater fish ponds. Auburn University, Alabama Agricultural Experiment Station. 359 pp.

Boyd, C.E. 1979b. Lime requirement and application in fish ponds. pp. 120-122. In Advances in Aquaculture. FAO Technical Conference on Aquaculture, Kyoto, Japan. 653 pp.

Boyd, C.E. 1982. Water Quality Management for Pond Fish Culture. Amsterdam-Oxford-New York: Elsevier Science Publishing Company Inc. 318 pp.

Boyd, C.E. 1984. Fluids beat granular in fish pond trials. Solutions 28 (February):56-62. Fluid Fertilizer Industry, Peoria, Illinois.

Boyd, C.E. 1989. Water quality management and aeration in shrimp farming. Fisheries and Allied Aquacultures, Auburn University, Alabama Agricultural Experiment Station. Department Series No. 2. 83 pp.

Boyd, C.E. 1990. Water Quality in Ponds for Aquaculture. Auburn University, Alabama Agricultural Experiment Station. 482 pp.

Boyd, C.E. 1992. Shrimp pond bottom and soil sediment management. pp. 166-181. In Proceedings of the Special Session on Shrimp Farming. Baton Rouge, Louisiana: The World Aquaculture Society. 301 pp.

Boyd, C.E. 1995. Bottom soils, sediment, and pond aquaculture. New York: Chapman & Hall. 348 pp.

Boyd, C.E. and E. Scarsbrook. 1974. Effects of agricultural limestone on phytoplankton communities of fish ponds. Arch. Hydrobiology 74:336-349.

Boyd, C.E. and J.R. Snow. 1975. Fertilizing farm fish ponds. Auburn University, Alabama Agricultural Experiment Station. Leaflet 88. 6 pp.

Boyd, C.E. and W.D. Hollerman. 1981. Methods of applying liquid fertilizer to fish ponds. Proceedings of Fish and Wildlife Agencies 35:525-530.

Brinkman, R. and V.P. Singh. 1982. Rapid reclamation of brackish water fish ponds in acid sulfate soils. pp 318-330. In Proceedings of the Bangkok Symposium on Acid Sulfate Soils. January 18-24, 1981.

Buck, D.H., R.J. Baur and C.R. Rose. 1979. Experiments in recycling swine manure in fish ponds. pp. 489-492. In Advances in Aquaculture. FAO Conference on Aquaculture, Kyoto, Japan. 653 pp.

Buckman, H.O. and N.C. Brady. 1967. Sixth edition. The Nature and Properties of Soils. New York: MacMillan Company Inc. 567 pp.

Clark, D.F., J.W. Avault, Jr. and S.P. Meyers. 1974. Effects of feeding, fertilization, and vegetation on production of red swamp crawfish, *Procambarus clarkii*. In International Symposium on Freshwater Crayfish, Baton Rouge, Louisiana 2:125-138.

Collis, W.J. and R.O. Smitherman. 1978. Production of tilapia hybrids with cattle manure or a commercial diet. In Symposium on the Culture of Exotic Fishes, Auburn, Alabama. Fish Culture Section, American Fisheries Society 1978:43-54.

Culley, D.D. and E. Epps. 1973. Use of duckweed for waste treatment and animal feed. Journal of Water Pollution Control 45 (2):337-347.

de la Bretonne, L.W., Jr., J.W. Avault, Jr. and R.O. Smitherman. 1969. Effects of soil and water hardness on survival and growth of the red swamp crawfish, *Procambarus clarkii*, in plastic pools. Proceedings Southeastern Association of Game and Fish Commissioners 23:626-633.

Demoll, R. 1925. Teichdungung (Pond manuring). Hanbook d. Binnenfishcherei Mitteleuropas 4:53-160.

Dobbins, D.A. and C.E. Boyd. 1976. Phosphorus and potassium fertilization of sunfish ponds. Transactions American Fisheries Society 105 (4):536-540.

Dost, H. and N. V. Breemen (editors). 1982. Proceedings of the Bangkok Symposium on Acid Sulphate Soils. January 18-24, 1981.

Dugan, G.L., C. Golueke and W.J. Oswald. 1972. Recycling system for poultry wastes. Journal of Water Pollution Control Federation 44(3):432-440.

Eipper, A.W. 1964. Growth, mortality rates, and standing crops of trout in New York farm ponds. Cornell University, New York Agricultural Experiment Station. Memoir 388. 67 pp.

Environmental Protection Agency. 1975. Proceedings of a conference on emerging environmental problems: acid precipitation. EPA-902/9-75-001. 115 pp.

Fish, G.R. 1960. The chemical composition of fish ponds and their resultant crop of *Tilapia* species. Current Affairs Bulletin Indo-Pacific Fisheries Council, Bangkok. No. 28.

Forney, J.L. 1968. Raising bait fish and crawfish in New York ponds. New York State College of Agriculture. Cornell Extension Bulletin 986. 31 pp.

George, M.J ., K.H. Mohammed and N.N. Pillai. 1968. Observations on the paddy-field prawn filtration of Kerala, India. Proceedings World Scientific Conference on the Biology and Culture of Shrimps and Prawns. FAO Fisheries Report 2(57):427-442.

Gooch, B. 1967. Appraisal of North American fish culture fertilization studies. Proceedings of the World Symposium on Warm-Water Pond Fish Culture. FAO Fisheries Report No. 44, 3:13-26.

Grant, C. 1976. Report on a visit as soil consultant to the brackish water aquaculture center at Leganes Iloilo, The Philippines. Unpublished Mimeographed Report. 10 pp.

Hepher, B. 1962a. Ten years research in fish pond fertilization in Israel. Bamidgeh 14(2):29-38.

Hepher, B. 1962b. Primary production in fish ponds and its application to fertilization experiments. Limnology and Oceanography 7(2):131-136.

Hickling, C.F. 1962. Fish Culture. London: Faber and Faber. 295 pp.

Hoffman, W.E. 1934. Preliminary notes on the freshwater fish industry of South China, especially Kwangtung Province. Lingnan University Scientific Bulletin No. 5.

Hora, S.L. and T.V.R. Pillay. 1962. Handbook on fish culture in the Indo-Pacific Region. FAO Fisheries Biological Technical Paper No. 14. 204 pp.

Ingle, R. M., A.R. Ceurvels and R. Leinecker. 1955. Chemical and biological studies of the muds of Mobile Bay. A report to the Division of Seafoods, Alabama Department of Conservation. 14 pp.

Juday, C. 1942. The summer standing crop of plants and animals in four Wisconsin lakes. Transactions Wisconsin Academy of Science 29:1-82.

Lawrence, J.M. 1954. A new method of applying inorganic fertilizer to farm fish ponds. Progressive Fish-Culturist 16:176-178.

Lebeau, F., J.W. Avault, Jr. and S. Bravo. 1976. Evaluation of aquaculture production project in the Philippines, appropriation No. 492-11-180-266. Auburn University, Alabama Agricultural Experiment Station. Mimeograph 30 pp.

Lichtkoppler, F. and C.E. Boyd. 1977. Phosphorus fertilization of sunfish ponds. Transactions American Fisheries Society 106(6):634-636.

Lin, C.K. 1988. Acidification and reclamation of acid sulfate soil fish ponds in Thailand. pp. 71-74. In Proceedings First Asian Fisheries Forum, Manila, Philippines.

Lin, S.Y. 1949. Pond culture of warm-water fishes. UNESCO Conference. Warm Springs.

Ling, S.W. 1969. Methods of rearing and culturing *Macrobrachium rosenbergii* (DeMan). Proceedings World Scientific Conference on the Biology and Culture of Shrimps and Prawns. FAO Fisheries Report 31(57):607-619.

Maciolek, J.A. 1954. Artificial fertilization of lakes and ponds, a review of the literature. U.S. Department of Interior, Fish and Wildlife Service. Special Scientific Report Fisheries No. 113. 41 pp.

Morrison, F.B. 1961. Feeds and Feeding Abridged. Clinton, Iowa: The Morrison Publication Company. 696 pp.

Mortimer, C.H. and C.F. Hickling. 1954. Fertilizers in fish ponds. Colonial Office Fishery Publications: No. 5: 155 pp.

Murad, A. and C.E. Boyd. 1987. Experiments on fertilization of sportfish ponds. Progressive Fish-Culturist 49(2):100-107.

Nees, J.C. 1949. Development and status of pond fertilization in Central Europe. Transactions American Fisheries Society 76:335-358.

Oden, S. and R. Anderson. No date. The long-term changes in the chemistry of soils in Scandinavia due to acid precipitation. (This paper refers to section 5.1 of Sweden's case study for the United Nations Conference on the human environment). 20 pp.

Oden, S. and T. Ahl. No date. The long-term changes in the pH of lakes and rivers in Sweden. (This paper refers to section 5.2 of Sweden's case study for the United Nations conference on the human environment). 13 pp.

Odum, E.P. 1971. 3rd edition. Fundamentals of Ecology. Philadelphia-London-Toronto: W.B. Saunders Company Inc. 574 pp.

Potter, T. and D. Leary. 1976. A proposal to identify the problems caused by acid sulfate soils in brackish water fish ponds and to develop methods for improving them. Unpublished Research Proposal. Brackish Water Aquaculture Center, Leganes Iloilo, Philippines.

Prowse, G.A. 1967. A review of the methods of fertilizing warm-water fish ponds in Asia and the Far East. Proceedings of the World Symposium on Warm-Water Pond Fish Culture. FAO Fisheries Report No. 44, 3:7-12.

Raymond, L.P., P.K. Bienfang and J.A. Hanson. 1974. Nutritional considerations of Open Sea Mariculture. Pennsylvania: Dowden, Hutchinson and Ross Inc. 410 pp.

Roels, O. A. 1975. Artificial upwelling a breakthrough for mariculture. Commercial Fish Farmer and Aquaculture News 1(5):8-12.

Romaire, R.P. 1976. Population dynamics of red swamp crawfish, *Procambarus clarkii* (Girard), in ponds receiving fertilization and two agricultural forages as supplemental feeds. Louisiana State University, M.S. Thesis. 103 pp.

Ryther, J.H. 1975. Preliminary results with a pilot plant waste recycling marine-aquaculture system. Woods Hole Oceanographic Institute, Woods Hole, Mass. Unpublished Manuscript. 50 pp.

Schäperclaus, W. 1933. Textbook of Pondfish Culture. Berlin: Book Publishing House, Paul Parry. Translation FL 311, U.S. Department of Interior, Fish and Wildlife Service.

Scheuring, D.L. 1939. Die reinigung und verwertung der abwaser von Munchen. (Purification and utilization of Munich sewage) Natur u. Volk 69:390-402. (Not seen).

Schroeder, G.L. 1974. Use of fluid cowshed manure in fish ponds. Bamidgeh 26(3):84-96.

Schroeder, G.L. 1975a. Nighttime material balance for oxygen in fish ponds receiving organic wastes. Bamidgeh 27(3): 65-74.

Schroeder, G.L. 1975b. Effect of bromex-50 on plankton populations in fish ponds. Bamidgeh 27(1):3-7.

Schroeder, G.L. and B. Hepher. 1979. Use of agricultural and urban wastes in fish culture, pp. 487-489. In Advances in Aquaculture. FAO Technical Conference on Aquaculture, Kyoto, Japan. 653 pp.

Schuster, W. 1949. Fish culture in brackish water ponds of Java. Indo-Pacific Fishery Publications No.1. FAO.

Shigueno, K. 1975. Shrimp Culture in Japan. Tokyo: Association for International Technical Promotion. 153 pp.

Sklower, A. 1950. Carp breeding in Palestine. Archiv. fur Fischereiwissenschaft, 2nd Jahrg, Hft 3/4 continued in ibid, 3rd Jahrg, Hft 1/2 pp. 90-119.

Smith, E.V. and H.S. Swingle. 1939. The relationship between plankton production and fish production in ponds. Transactions American Fisheries Society 68:309-315.

Smith, E.V. and H.S. Swingle. 1941. The use of fertilizer for controlling the pond weed, *Najas guadalupensis.* Transactions North American Wildlife Conference 6:245-251.

Smith, E.V. and H.S. Swingle. 1942. The use of fertilizer for controlling several submerged aquatic plants in ponds. Transactions American Fisheries Society 71(1941): 94-101.

Smitherman, R.O., J.W. Avault, Jr., L.W. de la Bretonne and H.A. Loyacano. 1967. Effects of supplemental feed and fertilizer on production of red swamp crawfish, *Procambarus clarki*, in pools and ponds. Proceedings Southeastern Association of Game and Fish Commissioners 21:452-458.

Snow, J.R. 1954. Vegetation conversion in pond fish culture. Proceedings Southeastern Association of Game and Fish Commissioners 8:106-110.

Snow, J.R. and R.O. Jones. 1959. Some effects of lime and applications to warmwater hatchery ponds. Proceedings Southeastern Association of Game and Fish Commissioners 13:95-101.

Snow, J.R. and R.O. Jones. 1961. Changes in warmwater ponds after hydrated lime applications. Progressive Fish-Culturist 23(2):51-60.

Spatarv, P. 1976. Natural feed of *Tilapia aurea* Steindachner in polyculture with supplementary feed and intensive manuring. Bamidgeh 28(3):57-63.

Standard, H. 1973. Draft development document for effluent limitations guidelines and standards of performance. U.S. Environmental Protection Agency, Contract Number 68-01-05-95. 275 pp.

Stanley, J. 1974. Nitrogen and phosphorus balance of grass carp, *Ctenopharngodon idella*, fed *Elodea egeria densa*. Transactions American Fisheries Society 103(3):587-592.

Stommel, H., A.B. Aarons and D. Blanchard. 1955. An oceanographic curiosity: the perpetual salt fountain. Deep Sea Research 3:152-153.

Sunderlin, J.B., M. Brenner, M. Castanga, J. Hirota, R.W. Menzel and O.A. Roels. 1975. Comparative growth of hard shell clams (*Mercenaria mercenaria* Linne' and *Mercenaria campechiensis* Gmelin) and their F_1 cross in temperate, subtropical, and tropical natural waters and in a tropical artificial upwelling mariculture system. Proceedings of the World Mariculture Society 6:171-183.

Swingle, H.S. 1947. Experiments on pond fertilization. Auburn University, Alabama Agricultural Experiment Station. Bulletin No. 264. 34 pp.

Swingle, H.S. and E.V. Smith. 1939. Fertilizer for increasing the natural food for fish in ponds. Transactions American Fisheries Society 68:126-135.

Swingle, H.S. and E.V. Smith. 1947. Management of farm fish ponds. Alabama Polytechnic Institute, Alabama Agricultural Experiment Station. Bulletin 254. 32 pp.

Swingle, H. S., B.C. Gooch and H.R. Rabanal. 1963. Phosphate fertilization of ponds. Proceedings Southeastern Association of Game and Fish Commissioners 17:213-218.

Tang, Yun-an. 1976. Handbook in coastal fish farming: a pattern for training in this type of aquaculture for the South China Sea Region. South China Sea Fisheries Development and Coordinating Programme Indo-Pacific Fisheries Council. Unpublished Manuscript. 218 pp.

Tang, Yun-an and S.H. Chen. 1967. A survey of the algal pasture soils of milkfish ponds in Taiwan. Proceedings of the World Symposium on Warm-Water Pond Fish Culture. FAO Fisheries Report No. 44, 3:198-209.

Traux, R.E., D.D. Culley, M. Griffith, W.A. Johnson and J.P. Wood. 1972. Duckweed for chick feed. Louisiana Agriculture 16(1):8-9.

Villalon, J.R. 1991. Practical manual for semi-intensive commercial production of marine shrimp. Texas A & M Sea Grant Program TAMU-SG-91-501. 104 pp.

Wiesner, E.R. 1936. Die Kunstliche dungung in der teichwirtschafe (Artificial manuring in pond fisheries) Fachpr. Tschechoslowakel 262 pp. (Photocopy supplied by I.G. Farben Industrie to I. E. I.) (Not seen).

Wohlfarth, G.W., G. Hulata, I. Karplus and A. Halevy. 1985. Polyculture of the freshwater prawn *Macrobrachium rosenbergii* in intensely manured ponds, and the effect on stocking rates of prawns and fish on their production characteristics. Aquaculture 46:143-156.

Woynarovich, E. 1979. The feasibility of combining animal husbandry with fish farming, with special reference to duck and pig production. pp. 203-208. In Advances in Aquaculture. FAO Technical Conference on Aquaculture, Kyoto, Japan.

Wunder, W. 1949. Fortschrittliche karpfenteichwirtschaft (Progressive pond culture of carp). E. Schweitzerbart'sche Verlagsbuchhandlung, Erwin Nagele, Stuttgart 1949:386 pp.

Wyban, J.A. and J.N. Sweeney. 1991. The Oceanic Institute Shrimp Manual, Intensive Shrimp Production Technology. The Oceanic Institute Makapuu Point, Honolulu, Hawaii. 158 pp.

CHAPTER 9
FEEDS AND NUTRITION

We saw in the last chapter that production of culture species in ponds could be increased by addition of fertilizer. Even so, fertilization produces only a finite number of natural food organisms, and stocking rates of a culture species must be limited to reflect this. By addition of feed, production can be increased many times over that of fertilization.

In this chapter, we discuss types of feeds. These include feeds of plant origin, animal origin, and formulated diets. Requirements of a good feed, such as palatability, feed conversion, pellet stability in water, cost, and quality, are covered. Energy, digestion, and metabolism are discussed as related to species, age, and the environment. Nutrient requirements, feed formulations, and feeding practices are reviewed.

WHY FEED CULTURE SPECIES

There are several reasons for feeding culture species:

(1) A fish crop produced through fertilization, say 500 kg/ha (447 lb/ac) of channel catfish (*Ictalurus punctatus*), generally gives too little income to be worthwhile. With use of feed, this production can be increased up to 10,000 kg/ha (8,930 lb/ac). The cost of feed adds to production costs, but it is worth it. Regardless of this variable cost for feed, fixed costs, such as those for pond construction, remain the same whether 500 kg/ha or 10,000 kg/ha of catfish are produced.

(2) Some ponds may have such poor soils that fish production is very low. In areas where fertilizer is scarce or impractical, supplemental feeding is a necessity.

(3) The stocking rate of a culture species can be increased with use of feed. If the market calls for a 1 kg (2.2 lb) fish, then in fertilized ponds a low stocking rate may be necessary. This will allow each fish enough natural food to reach the desired weight. If, however, a farmer wants to increase yield to produce a more profitable crop, it will be necessary to stock fish at a higher density. There will be better use of natural food in the pond because there are more fish to search for it. However, the weight of each fish may be lower than the desired weight of 1 kg. By using feed, both high total production and desired weight per fish can be obtained.

(4) Some culture systems, such as raceway, cage, net-pen, and tank culture, require formulated feeds, since there are virtually no natural food organisms available.

SOME PROBLEMS WITH OVERFEEDING

Although feeding is beneficial, there are problems with overfeeding. The costs of feed and labor to put it out are not perceived as a problem, because increased profit should offset these costs. A farmer might feel that there is virtually no limit to the number of fish or crustaceans that can be stocked as long as enough feed is used. This is not so. Several factors limit stocking rates of culture species and amount of feed used. Most important of these are problems with low dissolved oxygen, increased levels of ammonia and other nitrogenous substances, parasites and disease, obnoxious blue-green phytoplankton blooms with associated off-flavor, economics, and increased pollution in effluents.

Low dissolved oxygen and ammonia accumulation in ponds and other culture systems may result if the culture species is overfed. In ponds with no flowing water or aeration, channel catfish may be stocked at rates up to 7,500/ha (3,000/ac) and fed up to a rate of approximately 67 kg/ha/day (60 lb/ac/day). If either rate is exceeded, problems may occur that are associated with decomposition of fish feces and uneaten feed. Moreover, excess nutrients produced from mineralization encourage dense phytoplankton blooms along with an increase in the BOD.

The rainbow trout (*Oncorhynchus mykiss*) has a higher oxygen demand than channel catfish and is even more sensitive to poor water quality. Tilapia, on the other hand, are more tolerant of poor water quality and may be stocked at rates of 12,500 to 20,000/ha (5,000 to 8,000/ac) and fed at correspondingly higher rates. Stocking and feeding rates for all species can be increased if water is flushed through the culture facility or aeration is provided.

Parasites and diseases are especially prevalent when culture species are overfed while grown under crowded conditions. This is because culture species become stressed from low dissolved oxygen or other factors leading to poor water quality. Obnoxious blue-green phytoplankton blooms may develop in ponds that have excess organic matter, and the musty or off-flavor of fish flesh may occur. Further, some blue-greens have a tendency to form thin scums on the water surface. This may block out sunlight to deeper water, limiting photosynthesis and oxygen production.

Overfeeding results in poor conversion of feed into flesh. A culture species can use only so much feed efficiently. Excess is wasted, thus making it a costly practice. Excess feed and fish wastes, in the form of settleable solids, can become a major pollutant in pond effluents.

GENERAL TYPES OF FEED

A vast array of feedstuffs and feeds is used in aquaculture. Some aquaculture operations use various agricultural byproducts on hand, and formulated diets are less important. Such feedstuffs frequently serve a dual role as both feed and fertilizer. Other operations rely on formulated feeds. These diets may be supplemental, providing most of the nutrients and vitamins, or complete, providing all of the required nutrients and vitamins. Hickling (1962), Huet (1970), and Hepher (1988) discussed various feedstuffs and feeds used in aquaculture. Below is an arbitrary classification with selected examples.

Feeds of Plant Origin

Phytoplankton-- Encouragement of phytoplankton blooms in ponds with fertilizer is termed fertilization (Chapter 8). However, specialized techniques are used to produce phytoplankton, called "green water," in tanks (Treece and Wohlschlag 1990; Liao et al. 1991). Sterilized water is added to a small flask or other container, and nutrients are added. A pure culture of the desired alga species is inoculated into the container (Figure 9.1). Fluorescent lighting is used to warm water and to initiate photosynthesis. As the alga increases in density, it is divided into ever larger containers and ultimately into tanks (Figure 9.2). Phytoplankton, such as *Skeletonema* sp., is fed to early larval stages of penaeid shrimp. Larvae of oysters and other mollusks also are fed phytoplankton in hatcheries. In some instances, phytoplankton and larval shrimp are cultured together in the same tank. In other instances, alga is cultured separately and introduced into tanks containing larvae.

Figure 9.1 Alga being started in small containers.

Figure 9.2 As alga increases, it is transferred ultimately to large tanks like these.

Yeast-- Yeast, a unicellular fungus, has occasionally been used to feed early larval stages of shrimp. As the non-feeding shrimp nauplii metamorphose into the early zoea stage, they can ingest food particles 3 to 5 microns in size. Yeast is in this size range. Yeast is more likely used as feed for rotifers.

Forages-- Forages as used here refer to grasses, hays, aquatic plants, and vegetation in general. Hickling (1962) fed cut napier grass that he had grown on land to grass carp (*Ctenopharyngodon idella*). He estimated that in 2 months 150 fish consumed 8,620 kg (19,007 lb). Since the fish gained a total of 177 kg (390 lb), the crude conversion rate was about 48 to 1. Grass carp, *Tilapia melanopleura*, and *T. zilli*, all herbivorous fish, feed on various aquatic plants as well as on tender leaves of cassava, sweet potatoes, banana leaves, and other land plants. Vegetation may be cut and placed in heaps in ponds, or aquatic plants may be grown in ponds and the fish stocked later.

Crawfish, particularly *Procambarus clarkii*, feed on vegetation. Avault and Brunson (1990) reviewed use of forages for feeding crawfish (*P. clarkii*). *P. clarkii* has been fed rice hay, bahiagrass hay, sweet potato leaves and trimmings, sugarcane bagasse, and other forages (Figure 9.3). In one study, more than 3,000 kg/ha (2,679 lb/ac) of crawfish were grown on rice hay following harvest of grain (Day and Avault 1984). The stubble was left in the field. Crawfish fed on the decaying stubble that was coated with microorganisms associated with decay. Generally, crawfish grow well on an array of materials once the carbon:nitrogen ratio (C:N) of a material drops to 17:1 or lower over time. Certain materials such as sugarcane bagasse have such a high initial C:N ratio, well over 100, that they are generally not suitable as forage unless fertilizer high in nitrogen is also added.

Figure 9.3 Rice has reached senescence and grain will be harvested. As straw decomposes, bacteria and other microorganisms serve as food for crawfish.

Root crops-- Potatoes and manioc are used as feed. Potatoes have been fed to carp (*Cyprinus carpio*) and to signal crawfish (*Pacifastacus leniusculus*). Manioc flour is used to feed tilapia in the Congo. The tubers and leaves of gabi are used to feed tilapia in the Philippines (Figure 9.4).

Grains, Seeds, Seedcakes-- These include such feedstuffs as corn and corn meal, lupine, cottonseed meal, soybeans, soybean meal, broken rice, and rice bran. They are fed whole, ground into a meal, or made into cakes. Some are unsuitable for human consumption because of spoilage or weevil damage. Cereals (rye, barley, oats, and wheat) provide excellent food for carp, other cyprinids, and fish that eat grain. Pulse foods (lupine, soybeans, peas, and beans) are commonly used to feed carp and other cyprinids. Lupine is an excellent carp feed and is easy to prepare by grinding. Drawbacks are that it is expensive and does not always store well under wet conditions. Soybean meal or cake is a popular feed for a variety of species, because of its impressive amino acid profile. Corn, or maize, is often used to fatten carp. It is relatively inexpensive and easy to grind into meal. Huet (1970) pointed out that it produces flesh that does not keep long. For this reason, its use should be stopped several weeks before harvest. In parts of Austria and elsewhere in Europe, a mixture of ground wheat, corn, and soybean is used to fatten carp. Rice bran and corn meal are used in Southeast Asia for feeding tilapia and carp (Figure 9.5).

Fruits-- *Colossoma macropomum* and certain other species in this genus feed on fruits, nuts, seeds, and leaves.

Figure 9.4 Gabi growing on levee of rice field in the Philippines.

Figure 9.5 Tilapia being fed corn meal in the Philippines. Note feeding ring to keep corn meal from drifting.

Feeds of Animal Origin

Manures-- Various animal manures are considered organic fertilizers, but some fish consume them directly. Manures, such as dried poultry wastes (DPW), have been fed to a number of terrestrial animals including ruminants and swine.

Stickney et al. (1977) fed *Oreochromis aureus* with a commercial trout diet or with the same trout diet supplemented with 10%, 20%, or 30% DPW. The DPW was not incorporated into the trout diet but fed in addition. Fish initially grew best on the trout diet only, but growth was not significantly different from the three test diets after 10 weeks. However, increased DPW supplementation resulted in decreased growth. Feed conversions were 1.02, 1.06, 1.25, and 1.40 for trout diet, and trout diet plus 10%, 20%, and 30% DPW, respectively.

Collis and Smitherman (1978) fed all-male hybrids (female *O. niloticus* x male *O. hornorum*) cattle manure in ponds. In other ponds, fish were fed a commercial channel catfish diet containing 36% crude protein. Over 103 days, 28,385 kg/ha (25,344 lb/ac) of fresh manure were added to the first set of ponds, resulting in an average fish production of 16 kg/ha/day (14 lb/ac/day). Addition of 3,521 kg (7,764 lb) of the commercial diet gave an average fish production of 26 kg/ha/day (23 lb/ac/day). Net yields of fish were 1,646 kg/ha (1,470 lb/ac) and 2,063 kg/ha (1,842 lb/ac) for manure and the catfish diet, respectively. Feed conversion ratios, based on dry matter inputs/gain and crude protein inputs/gain, were 3.3 and 0.62 for the manure treatment, and 1.3 and 0.48 for the commercial diet. Throughout the study, hybrid tilapia fed vigorously on manure, and stomachs of 96% sampled contained manure. Dissolved oxygen was consistently lower in ponds receiving manure, but it did not become critical until manure inputs reached 95 kg/ha/day (85 lb/ac/day) dry matter. At this point, DO fell below 0.5 ppm in some ponds.

In some countries, animal pens have been constructed over or near ponds. In the Philippines, manure from 40 to 60 hogs per ha (16 to 24/ac) or from 1,000 to 1,500 ducks per ha (400 to 600/ac) serves as feed or fertilizer for tilapia in ponds.

Zooplankton-- Cladocera or water fleas such as *Daphnia magna* have been cultured as live food. Pennak (1953) discussed the general life history of cladocera. Ponds or outdoor tanks are fertilized with organic materials such as manure or cottonseed cake. *D. magna* can be caught with a plankton net and fed to fry. This practice is seldom used today since dried formulated feeds are available. However, if fry are reluctant to accept dried feed, *D. magna* will often get them started. Rotifers are cultured in the laboratory as food for larval forms of various culture species, such as red drum (*Sciaenops ocellatus*) (Wohlschlag and Arnold 1990; Liao et al. 1991).

Scientists in Poland used electric illumination at night to attract zooplankton to coregonid fish fry (*Coregonus lavaretus and C. peled*). The fish were reared in cages held in lakes. Mesh sizes of cages ranged from 0.3 to 0.8 mm. A mesh size of 1.0 mm allowed fry to escape (Szczerbowski and Mamcarz 1984; Mamcarz and Nowak 1987).

Artemia-- *Artemia*, called brine shrimp, is the mainstay for production of freshwater prawn and marine shrimp larvae. *Artemia* and its culture were reviewed by Sorgeloos et al. (1987), Decleir et al. (1987), Treece and Wohlschlag (1990), and by Browne et al. (1991). *Artemia* eggs (cysts) are first collected in nature, although they have been produced under controlled conditions. In the Great Salt Lake and elsewhere, *Artemia* usually form cysts when adverse conditions prevail, such as the onset of severe cold weather. Spotter planes have been used to locate the cysts that may windrow near shore. Floating lines are used to concentrate cysts. They are then collected, placed in burlap sacks, and temporarily stored in a warehouse (Figure 9.6). Next, they are separated from sand, other foreign material, and placed into sealed cans until use. The collection and sale of *Artemia* is big business, and a number of companies market worldwide.

Figure 9.6 Mark Lamon of Ocean Star International Inc. secures a sack containing *Artemia* cysts, sand, and other debris. The Great Salt Lake is in the background.

The decapsulation of cysts improves the hatchability of *Artemia* into nauplii (Browne et al. 1991). The hard shell (chorion) that encysts the dormant *Artemia* embyro is removed by chemical methods. The procedure requires hydration of the cysts, removal of the chorion with a hypochlorite solution, and washing and deactivation of the hypochlorite. Decapsulation results in a naked, viable embryo. The decapsulated cysts can then be hatched into nauplii or they can be fed directly.

Crow (1987) described a method for producing *Artemia* nauplii to feed larval crustaceans. He used 57-liter (15-gal) cylindrical, polyethylene tanks with conical bottoms. Salinity in hatching tanks was 12 ppt, and temperature was 27° to 28°C (81° to 82°F). Water was aerated continuously, and 100 g (3.5 oz) of eggs were incubated in each tank. One gram of brine shrimp eggs contains 300,000 to 500,000 cysts. Most cysts hatched in 24 hours. Crow (1987) concluded from his study that prawn larvae should be stocked at approximately 200/liter (757/gal) and fed brine shrimp at 10 nauplii per ml. Commercial hatching tanks for *Artemia* are shown in Figure 9.7, and feeding of *Artemia* to marine shrimp larvae is shown in Figure 9.8.

Figure 9.7 Tanks with tapered bottoms used to hatch *Artemia* at farm in Indonesia.

Insects-- Lights have been placed over ponds to attract insects. Spoiled meat suspended over ponds attracts flies that lay eggs; resulting maggots fall into the water (Figure 9.9). In Brazil, maggots have been used to feed frogs. The practice of feeding silk worm pupae to common carp is ancient in China.

Figure 9.8 Nelson Bayron feeds *Artemia* to mysis stage of *Penaeus monodon*, Tungkang Marine Laboratory Taiwan. Note black overhang to reduce light.

Figure 9.9 Maggots produced from rotten meat.

Forage Fish-- Fathead minnows (*Pimephales promelas*) have been stocked at rates varying from 2,500/ha (1,000/ac) into grow-out ponds containing channel catfish or blue catfish (*Ictalurus furcatus*). This practice may be followed when large catfish, up to a kilogram or more, are grown, or when brood stock are grown or maintained. The minnows are stocked beginning February 15 in the southeastern United States (Prather et al. 1954). They begin spawning when the water temperature reaches 16°C (61°F). The eggs are laid on the undersides of rocks or boards. A stocking rate of 2,500/ha should yield 168,000 young. Generally, channel catfish do not feed well on the minnows until the catfish have reached approximately 0.5 kg (1.1 lb) in size. The practice of stocking minnows as forage (food) is especially desirable when catfish are overwintered in ponds.

Goldfish (*Carassius auratus*) have been stocked into ponds as forage for brood largemouth bass (*Micropterus salmoides*), and they have been grown as "feeder fish" for carnivorous ornamental fish.

Meat, Fish, and Their Byproducts-- Before dry diets, liver, spleen, and other slaughterhouse products were used in salmonid culture. Spleen has been used exclusively for trout fry up to 4 to 6 weeks of age. Liver is also a good starter feed. Both it and spleen are usually fed in a pulp or blended form.

Early farmers of channel catfish blended liver, froze it, and used it as needed for young fry. Liver and spleen are of less importance now than formerly because of their high cost, poor availability, and need for cold storage. Prawn larvae and juveniles have been fed ground testes of fish (Figure 9.10).

Figure 9.10 Testes of fish ground up for feeding larval prawns in Hawaii.

In grow-out systems, fresh meat, mainly from horses and cattle, has been used by inland salmonid farms. Trout took it readily but several drawbacks were noted. It easily caused inflammation of the intestines, and it produced a poor quality trout flesh. Moreover, fish fed meat produced abundant excrement with much sinew. This polluted the water.

Denmark's salmonid culture was founded on the availability of marine fish as feed. Most Danish trout farms are on the peninsula of Jutland, and are close to a port where fish are landed daily. Fish used as trout feed had no commercial value as human food.

In southern Spain, chicken entrails have been fed to eels (*Anguilla* spp.). Channel catfish farmers have fed brood catfish with various species of cut fish. Usually the fish were frozen and thawed when needed. A hatchet was used to chop fish into chunks. In Japan, culture of yellowtail (*Seriola quinqueradiata*) depends on trash fish, such as mackerel (*Scomber japonicus*), as feed. The fresh meat of clams and mussels is used as feed for shrimp in China and elsewhere. The anchovy (*Anchoa* spp.), menhaden (*Brevoortia* sp.), and Atlantic croaker (*Micropogonias undalatus*) have been made into fish meals. Such meals are usually incorporated into formulated diets, but they have been fed as is to culture species.

Formulated Diets

Formulated diets consist of a mixture of ingredients rather than just a single ingredient or feedstuff. The diets may be supplemental or complete.

Supplemental Diets-- Supplemental diets in combination with natural pond organisms serve as food for culture species. Supplemental diets usually contain a variety of nutrients but may be low in vitamins and minerals. Protein levels also may be relatively low compared with complete diets. Natural food in a pond supports a finite standing crop of the culture species. When the standing crop is low, the amount of natural food exceeds the requirements for maintenance and growth. As the standing crop increases, because of increased growth or increased stocking density, natural food organisms become overtaxed. They alone are insufficient for maintenance and growth. If pond waters are fertilized, the biomass of both natural food organisms and the culture species will increase. Ultimately, however, a point is reached when available natural food is sufficient only for maintenance. There is no gain or loss in weight of the culture species. This point is termed "carrying capacity" of the pond. Hepher (1988) also used the term "critical standing crop" (CSC). To increase the standing crop above the CSC, the culture species can be fed a supplemental diet of adequate nutrition.

Natural food contains 50% to 60% protein on a dry matter basis (Hepher 1988). This is above the protein requirement for most culture species. When a culture species lives exclusively on natural food, the excess protein is used for energy. Therefore when the CSC is reached, it is energy that is in short supply, not protein. This is why supplemental diets should be relatively high in feedstuffs that provide energy. Moreover, such feedstuffs usually cost less than those that provide protein, particularly those from animal sources.

Hepher (1988) noted, however, that as the standing crop of a culture species continues to increase, the proportion of protein in the supplemental diet should increase relative to that of energy. He illustrated this principle by describing the "dilution" of a complete diet with a diet rich in carbohydrates, as practiced on some farms in Israel. Dilution of feed is done with sorghum and a 25% protein pelleted feed in a stepwise fashion as follows:

Standing Crop of Fish	Feeding Strategy
Up to 700 kg/ha (625 lb/ac)	Sorghum only
700 to 1,200 kg/ha (625 to 1,071 lb/ac)	75% sorghum + 25% pellets
1,200 to 1,500 kg/ha (1,071 to 1,339 lb/ac)	50% sorghum + 50% pellets
1,500 to 1,800 kg/ha (1,339 to 1,607 lb/ac)	25% sorghum + 75% pellets
Over 1,800 kg/ha (1,067 lb/ac)	Pellets only

Thus each diet covers the nutritional requirements up to a given critical standing crop, at which point it is substituted with a diet of a higher nutritional value. Notice in this feeding regime that a single feedstuff, sorghum, supplements the formulated diet. Another option is to adjust the nutrient level in a formulated supplemental feed. For example, the protein/energy ratio can be adjusted up or down, depending on the stocking density and standing crop. Such diets were employed by the channel catfish farming industry in the United States when the industry was just beginning. Stocking rates then were relatively low 2,500 to 3,750/ha (1,000 to 1,500/ac), and fish were expected to derive some protein and vitamins from natural pond organisms.

Complete Diets-- Complete diets contain all the essential nutrients in amounts necessary for normal growth. A vitamin premix is added to provide all necessary vitamins and in the quantity required. Additionally, complete diets are highly digestible. This reduces unnecessary waste. These diets are used in intensive culture systems, such as raceways, recirculating systems, and floating net-pens, where natural food is of no consequence. They also may be used in ponds when the culture species is stocked at very high rates. For example, a formulated supplemental diet may be adequate for channel catfish stocked at a rate of 3,707/ha (1,500/ac). At rates above this, a nutritional deficiency may occur, such as a lack of vitamin C.

Form of Diets-- Most formulated diets are in powder, meal, crumble, or pelleted form (Figure 9.11), but there are many variations. Powder or meal forms normally are used for fry or larvae; crumbles are used for juveniles, and pelleted diets are used as the culture species increases in size. Pelleted diets are various sizes to correspond to the culture species' size. Two types of pellets are used, the compressed or sinking pellet and the extruded or floating pellet.

Figure 9.11 A pelleted diet used to feed alligators in Louisiana.

Figure 9. 12 Dough ball, containing primarily fish meal, fed to eels in Japan.

Formulated diets may take other forms. In Japan, fish meal and other ingredients are mixed with water daily to form a dough ball. This is fed to eels (Figure 9.12). Some milkfish farmers in Taiwan use this form of feed for brood stock. Culley et al. (1977) developed a feed for bullfrog tadpoles (*Rana catesbeiana*) that is a firm, putty-like paste that adheres to a piece of screen. Microencapsulation of crustacean diets has promise. The capsules are various sizes, corresponding to the larval stage being cultured.

REQUIREMENTS OF A GOOD FEED

Feeds, whether they are formulated or agricultural byproducts, must be available in the quantities required when needed. The cost must be economical. There are also other considerations.

Feed Conversion

A feedstuff or formulated diet should give a good conversion into flesh. The feed conversion ratio (FCR) is calculated by the kilograms of feed to produce 1 kg of growth. If, for example, a 0.5 kg fish is fed 1 kg of feed and grows to 1 kg, the FCR is 2 (1 kg feed ÷ 0.5 kg weight gain = 2). The lower the number of the FCR the more efficient the culture species is in converting feed to flesh. It is important to understand factors affecting feed conversion ratios since feed cost is likely to be the largest, single variable cost. It is 50% of the total in many instances. Feed conversion is affected by type of feed, type and size of species, culture system, water quality, and other factors.

Type of Feed-- Huet (1970) gave examples of feed conversion ratios for various feedstuffs: lupine fed to carp, 4; soya to carp, 4; maize for carp and cyprinids, 5; cereals to carp and cyprinids, 4 to 6; leaves of water and land plants to herbivorous tilapias, 15 to 20; raw, fresh fish to trout, 6 to 8; fish meal to various species, 1.5 to 3; shrimps to salmonids, 4 to 6; fresh meat to salmonids, 5 to 8; and spleen to young salmonids, 3. Note that fish and meat give relatively high feed conversion ratios because of their high moisture content. For this reason, some like to qualify the conversion ratio as on a wet weight basis or as on a dry weight basis (Parker 1987). The latter uses the total weight of the feed minus the weight of water present. The same can be said of plants, especially aquatic plants.

The form of the feedstuff affects the FCR. For example, Walker et al. (1966-67) fed crawfish (*Procambarus clarkii*) waste shells in two forms to channel catfish. One form was fed fresh ground; the other was dried and then compressed into a pellet. The first form dissipated rapidly upon contact with water, and catfish derived little value. The pelleted form held together much better, and the FCR was lower.

The digestibility of formulated diets affects feed conversion ratios. Finfish and crustaceans digest certain ingredients better than others. Generally, a good, dry, complete, formulated feed has a conversion rate of 1 to 2.5 for most species of finfish and 1.5 for penaeid shrimp.

Type of Species and Size-- Fish convert feed more efficiently than do cattle, swine, or chickens. Only chickens, with a feed conversion ratio close to 2, approach fish. Fish have good feed conversion ratios because:
(1) They are able to convert a variety of feedstuffs and feed into flesh.
(2) Water helps to support the weight of the culture species, so less energy is required.
(3) Being cold blooded, culture species do not expend energy to maintain body temperature.
(4) They can excrete nitrogen in the form of ammonia; this saves energy.

Feed conversion ratios have been established for some species cultured under commercial conditions. Channel catfish fed formulated diets in ponds have feed conversion ratios ranging from 1.5 to 2.0. Ratios vary little if catfish are cultured intensively and fed a complete diet. Salmonids in intensive culture and carp in ponds have feed conversion ratios of about 2 when fed formulated diets. Tilapia may have ratios as low as 1 in ponds and not much above this in other culture systems. Eels (*Anguilla* spp.) have feed conversion ratios of 1.4 and 7.1 for formulated diets and raw fish, respectively. Feed conversion ratios of crustaceans in ponds have varied greatly; when clam meat was fed to shrimp, feed conversion ratios varied from a low of 5.7 to a high of 19.7 (Shigueno 1975). *Penaeus monodon* cultured intensively with a complete diet has an FCR of about 1.5 when fed a pelleted ration. *M. rosenbergii* fed a pelleted diet in tanks had an FCR as low as 1.3 after 1 month (Willis et al. 1976).

As a culture species increases in size, the FCR becomes less efficient because more feed is used to maintain body mass. From the standpoint of feed cost, it is best to produce the lowest, acceptable market weight of a culture species. For example, you may get an FCR of 1.5 growing a channel catfish to 0.5 kg (1.1 lb), but you might get an FCR of 2 or more growing the same fish to 1 kg (2.2 lb). The extra feed required to get the added growth may be uneconomical. Willis et al. (1976) found that feed conversion ratios increased significantly as *M. rosenbergii* increased in size, and Shigueno (1975) reported the same for shrimp.

Culture Systems-- Basically two methods are used for reporting feed conversion ratios. In ponds, the culture species may derive some of its food from natural organisms, so the FCR reflects a combination of both the feed added and natural food. Such a conversion is not a true conversion of feed alone and has been designated by the capital letter "S" (Swingle 1958). The S is affected by stocking rate and fertility of the water, as well as quantity and quality of feed added. However, many ponds are stocked at such high rates per hectare that pond organisms form an insignificant part of a culture species diet -- for example, channel catfish at 30,000/ha (12,000/ac) and *P. monodon* at 250,000/ha (100,000/ac). A true conversion, capital letter "C," is designated for intensive culture systems such as raceways. They have virtually no natural organisms available. Most workers simply refer to the feed conversion ratio as FCR and describe the conditions for its calculation.

Water Quality and Other Factors-- Overfeeding leads to poor feed conversion. A culture species can use efficiently only a certain amount of feed. Excess feed, above their need, is poorly converted to flesh. The rest is voided as waste. Sometimes the proper amount of feed is used, but the culture species may not be feeding well on a particular day. That day's feed may serve only to pollute the water. This is why most fish farmers prefer to use extruded (floating) diets. They can see the fish feed. Shrimp farmers using sinking diets place some feed on an underwater lift net. Two hours later the net is raised to determine if shrimp are feeding well (Figure 9.13).

Stress caused by parasites, diseases, and disturbances may result in a culture species feeding poorly. In one study, snakes and an alligator (*Alligator mississipiensis*) stressed caged channel catfish, resulting in poor growth and feed conversion (Green et al. 1978).

Figure 9.13 Lift net being raised in shrimp pond 2 hours after feeding to see if feed has been eaten.

Pellet Stability in Water

Formulated diets used for growing finfish should remain intact in water for at least 15 to 20 minutes. Finfish are usually quick to come to feed. Crustacean diets must remain intact for approximately 4 hours because crustaceans are slower to come to feed. Moreover, they munch feed rather than gulp it like finfish. This results in flaking off of particles.

Size

The feed must be small enough for the culture species to swallow. When culturing live food for shrimp and prawns, this is a major concern. Most early larval stages of shrimp require very small food particles. With finfish, most commercial diets are in a variety of pellet sizes corresponding to the size of fish being grown.

Attractants

Odoriferous attractants, such as squid oil, fish solubles, viscera, and extracts of tubiflex worms, are sometimes added to crustacean diets, as are flavorings such as cheese, butter, bacon, and poultry. An attractant should not only draw crustaceans to the feed, but also keep them there until they have eaten. A crustacean attractant should be durable for about 4 hours in water. Diets for salmonids and most finfish normally do not contain special attractants. The fish meal and other basic ingredients present serve as attractants. The National Research Council (1993) reviewed the subject.

Palatability and Physical Structure

The palatability and physical structure of a feed are especially important in crustacean diets, and they are summarized by New (1976). He pointed out that shrimp have a definite preference for certain diets. The Oregon moist pellet was developed for trout with palatability in mind. Physical variations of feed include flakes, jells, pastes, and pellets of various shapes and forms. Moisture content and particle size of ingredients affect physical structure and palatability.

Pigment Additives

Pink-fleshed trout and salmon have high market appeal because that is the color of these fish in nature. It is what the consumer is accustomed to eating. Carotenoids may be transferred from feed to the flesh of trout and salmon. Carotenoid-containing ingredients include shrimp meal, lobster meal, and crawfish meal. Color is one of the major factors that determines the price of live kuruma shrimp (*Penaeus japonicus*). Astaxanthin from crawfish wastes is one of the most effective pigments for this (Chien and Jeng 1992). A white-fleshed product is desired with channel catfish and certain other culture species, and no coloration additives are required.

Cost and Quality

The purchase of feed, particularly for use in semi-intensive and intensive culture systems, is usually the largest, single variable cost. A good quality feed must be economical, but this does not imply that the lowest cost feed is always the best buy.

Several factors must be considered when shopping for the best quality feed at the best price. Buy a feed with a minimum of fines. Fines is a term used to describe the dust that flakes off of pellets. Fines, if fed along with the pellets, merely fertilize or pollute the water. Some aquaculture operations are able to collect fines from the bottom of bulk-feed storage silos (Figure 9.14). The fines are in turn used to feed fry or larvae. Floating feeds usually have fewer fines than sinking feeds.

Figure 9.14 Bulk feed storage in silos for trout adapted to collect fines. Photo at Rangen Trout Farm in Buhl, Idaho.

The digestibility of feed must be high. Not all culture species are able to digest the same ingredients with equal efficiency, as we will discuss later. Undigested ingredients simply pass through the gut of the culture species into the water.

Do not pay for protein that is not needed. Some people judge the quality of feed by the percentage of protein present. They may feel that the higher the protein content, the better the feed. Each culture species and its life stages has a particular requirement for protein. Young animals typically require a higher percentage of protein than do large animals of the same species. There are, of course, differences between species. For example, the eel being carnivorous requires a higher protein feed than does the common carp, an omnivorous feeder. Protein, particularly from animal sources, is a high-cost feedstuff when compared with most other ingredients. Fish wastes produced from excess protein in the diet have a deleterious effect on the water quality. The greater the protein content the greater the amount of ammonia produced.

Feed should be bought fresh and should not have been stored by the feed manufacturer for more than a month. If the feed is in bags, check the lot number to determine when the feed was made. If there are signs of grain weevils or other insects, the feed should be rejected. In the final analysis, a prerequisite of a good feed is the feed conversion ratio or, better yet, the cost of feed to produce a kg of weight gain.

ENERGY, DIGESTION, AND METABOLISM

Culture species require energy for maintenance and growth; some energy is lost or wasted in the process. The nutritional value of a diet is determined by the ability of the culture species to digest the food. Digestion depends on the physical and chemical properties of the food and on the digestive system of the culture species. Metabolism is the biological process of using energy obtained from oxidation of food. The metabolic rate is affected by biological factors: type of species, size, age, and physiological condition; and by environmental factors, water temperature and feed quality. Hepher (1988), Lovell (1989), and Steffens (1989) reviewed digestion and metabolism.

Energy

Energy Definitions-- Classically, energy is defined as the capacity to do work and is required for all life processes of an animal. Food energy is defined in terms of calories. A gram calorie (gcal) is defined as the amount of energy required to raise 1 g of water 1°C (precisely from 14.5° to 15.5° C or 58° to 60° F). The calorie here is referred to as a small calorie and was so designated by being spelled with a lower case c. A kilocalorie (kcal) is equivalent to 1,000 calories and has been referred to as a large Calorie and was so designated by being spelled with a capital C.

Two kinds of energy result from catabolism (destructive metabolism), free energy (ΔF) and heat energy (ΔH). Free energy is used for work, whereas heat energy is used only for body temperature control. The latter is not important to fish. Energy for maintenance is used by a culture species just to maintain normal body functions with no increase in weight. Once the maintenance requirement has been met, additional food left over goes toward growth. The remaining energy is wasted by fish through feces, urine, and gill excretions. Total energy requirement equals that used for maintenance and for growth in addition to that which is wasted.

Energy has been expressed as gross energy, digestible energy, and metabolizable energy. Gross energy (GE) is expressed as kilocalories per kilogram of feed or kcal/kg. The GE value of a feed has no relationship to the feed's digestible, metabolizable, or net energy values. Digestible energy (DE) is that energy absorbed from diet. It is measured by calculating energy difference between dietary intake and fecal energy. Metabolizable energy (ME) is used by the culture species for accomplishing work, growth, fattening, and reproduction. It represents DE less energy lost from the body through gill excretions and urinary wastes. ME is seldom used for reporting in aquaculture because it is difficult to obtain from experimental tests.

Factors Affecting Energy Requirements-- Energy requirements differ for each culture species and are affected by such factors as type of species, age, size, and activity; by environmental factors such as water temperature; and by feed type. The carp, a sluggish fish, has a lower energy requirement than trout. The pompano (*Trachinotus carolinus*) is a highly active species, and you would expect it to have a high energy requirement. Feeding habits of a species have a bearing on energy requirements. Carnivorous species generally have a high metabolic rate, herbivorous species a low rate, and omnivorous species an intermediate rate. Carnivorous species derive much of their food energy from protein. Breakdown of protein for energy is inefficient, relative to breakdown of lipids, because deamination of protein requires extra energy.

Age and size of a culture species usually affect energy requirement. Smaller, younger fish have a higher energy requirement than do larger, older fish because normally they are more active.

An increase in activity also increases energy requirements. Such activity could be brought about by spawning, feeding, or swimming against a current.

Water temperature affects energy requirements. The body temperature of cold-blooded aquatic species fluctuates with the surrounding water temperature. Schäperclaus (1933) reported that a 10 degree increase in water temperature nearly doubles metabolic rate of fish. Fish consume more oxygen at a higher temperature. This increased oxygen intake increases metabolic rate and therefore energy requirements. Low dissolved oxygen in water increases the respiratory rate and hence energy requirements. However, if the DO is critically low, the respiratory rate will ultimately decline, and death will occur.

The amount of protein in the diet affects energy requirements. A diet containing a high percentage of protein, when protein is used as an energy source, increases the species' metabolic rate. On the other hand, a diet with a low level of protein may result in poor growth. The amount of DE in a diet influences the amount of food a fish consumes. A culture species eats to satisfy its energy requirement. If a diet contains a high level of lipids or carbohydrates and a low level of protein, a culture species could eat enough to appease its appetite without meeting protein requirements for rapid growth. Furthermore, a high level of DE, relative to protein, could result in deposition of fat. There is an optimum ratio of energy-to-protein for diets. The optimum DE/P ratio for channel catfish fingerlings and production diets is 8 to 9 kcal/g of protein (Stickney and Lovell 1977). This range approximates DE/P requirements for carp and warmwater fishes in general.

Sources of Energy-- Energy (calories) comes from the three basic food groups, protein, lipids, and carbohydrates. The average gross calorie value of these food groups is 5.65 kcal/g of protein, 9.45 kcal/g of lipid, and 4.0 kcal/g of carbohydrate. These are total calories and not all are available to the body. Based on digestibility (and correcting protein for the calories present as nitrogen and unavailable for energy), these figures drop to 4 kcal/g of protein, 9 kcal/g of lipid, and 4 kcal/g of carbohydrate.

These last three values have been used over the years to approximate average digestible calories available for all animals. These values will of course vary from species to species. With some species digestible calories can be calculated more closely. Phillips and Brockway (1959) calculated the caloric value of trout diets while taking into account the digestibility of the three food groups. They quoted other authors in establishing values for digestibility of energy for the three food groups as follows: protein, 90% digested; lipid, 85% digested; and carbohydrate as starch, 40% digested.

To determine available calories in trout diets, we find for protein, 5.65 (total kcal/g of protein) - 1.3 (kcal as nitrogen and unavailable for energy) x 0.90 (percentage protein digested) = 3.9 kcal available to trout/g of food protein. For lipid, 9.45 (total kcal/g of fat) x 0.85 (percentage of lipid digested) = 8.0 kcal available to trout/g of food fat. For carbohydrates, 4.00 (total kcal/g of carbohydrate) x 0.40 (percentage carbohydrate digested as starch) = 1.6 kcal available to trout/g of food carbohydrate as starch. The figure of 1.6 kcal is much less than the figure of 4 kcal used as a standard for most species.

Lovell (1989) noted that although warmwater herbivores and omnivores digest and metabolize carbohydrates relatively well, salmonids use some sources of carbohydrates poorly. If glucose is the source of carbohydrate (99% absorbed), the caloric value per gram of carbohydrate would be 4.00 x 0.99 = 3.96 kcal/g of glucose. If sucrose is the source of carbohydrate (78% absorbed), the caloric value per gram of carbohydrate would be 4.00 x 0.78 = 3.12 kcal/g of sucrose.

Digestible energy values have been established for channel catfish (National Research Council 1977) as follows: 3.5 kcal/g of protein, 8.1 kcal/g of lipid, and 2.5 kcal/g of crude carbohydrate.

Caloric Needs of Culture Species-- Caloric needs of culture species have been expressed as: (1) a function of species, body surface area, and water temperature, (2) the kcal required to produce 1 kg of fish, and (3) the kcal required per gram of food.

The caloric requirement of carp for maintenance and growth has been set at 25 gcal/sq dec/hour at 15°C (59°F) (National Research Council 1977). Body surface, expressed in terms of square decimeters (0.1 of a meter squared), can be estimated by the equation: body surface = body weight in grams$^{0.67}$ ÷ 10. A 100-g carp, then, has a surface area of $100^{0.67}$ ÷ 10 = 2.154 sq dec. The total caloric need per square decimeter per day is 25 gcal/hour x 24 = 600 gcal/day or 0.6 kcal/day. The daily caloric need for a 100-g growing carp is 2.154 sq dec x 0.6 kcal/day = 1.29 kcal or 1,292 kcal/100 kg of fish/day.

Dietary efficiency for other species can be calculated in a similar manner. Schäperclaus (1933) gave the caloric needs of a rainbow trout as 60 gcal/hour/sq dec. This active species, then, has more than double the energy requirement of carp. And 60 gcal/hour x 24 = 1,440 gcal/day/sq dec or 1.44 kcal/day/sq dec. If we assume the trout also weighs 100 g, then 2.154 sq dec x 1.44 (kcal required/sq dec/day by rainbow trout) = 3.1 kcal required by the rainbow trout per day. In both examples, using carp and rainbow trout, body surface is calculated the same way. It is a function of weight. The shape of the fish, however, affects the area of body surface relative to body weight. Simply put, a compressed fish will have more body surface than will a cylindrical fish when both species weigh the same. The calculated caloric requirement, then, is approximate.

A second way to express caloric needs is as the kcal required to produce 1 kg of flesh; figures have been established for various species. Trout require about 3,960 kcal to produce 1 kg of flesh; channel catfish require 3,740 kcal, and chinook salmon (*Oncorhynchus tshawytscha*) 4,070 kcal.

Finally, a third way is to estimate the kcal that should be present in each kilogram of feed. Generally, if a diet gives a feed-to-fish growth conversion of 1.7 or less, then the diet should be adequate in energy. The rationale is that energy for maintenance will be supplied before energy is supplied for growth. Therefore, if trout require 3,960 kcal to produce 1 kg of fish flesh, the feed should contain 2,329 (3,960 ÷ 1.7) kcal per kg of feed, catfish 2,200, and chinook salmon 2,394. This assumes that each species has a 1.7 feed conversion.

Digestion

Digestion involves conversion of foods into simpler compounds that can be absorbed from the digestive tract. This is accomplished through the action of various enzymes that are secreted into the digestive tract. The nutritional value of any feed is based on its DE. When formulating feeds, the DE rather than the GE must be taken into account. Aquaculturists, when buying feed, should also take note of the specific ingredients listed. Just checking the crude protein content is not enough. In years past, feed manufacturers paid attention to the percentage of protein, carbohydrates, and fat present in their diets, and ingredients were substituted depending on availability. Less attention was paid to the digestibility of ingredients.

Fish meal and soybean meal, both sources of protein, are readily digested by channel catfish (Table 9.1) and by most species, but certain grains are not. Fats and oils are readily digested (90% to 98%) by non-herbivorous fishes (salmon, trout, catfish); fibrous feeds have very low digestibility. Soluble sugar (glucose) is readily digested by trout, channel catfish, carp, and eel, but dextrin (partially hydrolyzed starch) and starch are not highly digestible. Digestibility of raw corn starch for channel catfish and trout is low, 60% and 30%, respectively. Cooking by extrusion of feeds improves digestibility of corn starch for most fishes. When trout are fed high levels of starch, liver damage may result. Catfish farmers have complained that high levels of raw corn in feeds "soured" or polluted the water.

Other factors, such as physical properties of feed, type of species, kind and quality of digestive enzymes in the gastrointestinal tract, and water temperature, also affect digestibility. Finely ground ingredients in a diet are more readily digestible than those more coarsely ground. Finely ground ingredients offer more surface area for contact with digestive enzymes.

Some fishes have an acidic stomach; others like the carp lack the acidic phase of digestion because they have no true stomach. Carp can digest proteins of plants as well as monogastric mammals but not as well as ruminants. The grass carp has pharyngeal teeth and the mullet (*Mugil cephalus*) a gizzard, both for grinding food. Length of the digestive tract varies from 1/2 to 2/3 the body length for carnivorous species. It is five to six times the body length for herbivorous species.

The rate of digestion varies with the water temperature, although digestibility of protein remains relatively constant. Generally, digestion slows as the water temperature decreases. Feeds of animal origin are digested more quickly than those of plant origin. Digestion is faster for panfishes (Centrarchidae) than for larger game fishes. Panfishes digest about 50% of the stomach volume in 5 hours at water temperatures between 18°C (64°F) and 24°C (75°F), 75% in 12 hours, and 100% in 21 hours. Northern pike (*Esox lucius*), found in cooler waters, requires about 20 hours for a 50% reduction of stomach contents and 50 hours for 100%. The grass carp passes food through the digestive tract in less than 8 hours at 30°C (86°F). About 50% passes out as feces.

Table 9.1 Average percentage apparent digestibility of protein in feedstuffs for channel catfish.

Feedstuffs	Percentage digestibility	Source of data [a]
Animal products		
Fish meal (Anchovy)	90	A.U.
Fish meal (Anchovy)	85	F.F.E.S.
Fish meal (Menhaden)	87	A.U.
Fish meal (Menhaden)	74	F.F.E.S.
Meat and bone meal	75	A.U.
Feather meal	74	A.U.
Feather meal	63	F.F.E.S.
Oilseed meals		
Soybean meal (49% protein)	84	A.U.
Soybean meal (49% protein)	72	F.F.E.S.
Soybean meal (44% protein)	77	A.U.
Cottonseed meal (41% protein)	81	A.U.
Cottonseed meal (41% protein)	76	F.F.E.S.
Corn gluten meal (60% protein)	80	F.F.E.S
Grains and grain byproducts		
Ground corn, raw	60	A.U.
Ground corn, extrusion cooked	66	A.U.
Ground wheat	84	A.U.
Wheat bran	82	A.U.
Wheat shorts	72	A.U.
Rice bran	71	A.U.
Distillers' dried solubles	67	F.F.E.S
Fibrous feeds		
Alfalfa meal	13	A.U.
Alfalfa meal	12	F.F.E.S

[a] F.F.E.S. is Fish Farming Experimental Station, U.S. Department of Interior, and A.U. is Auburn University
Source: Stickney and Lovell 1977.

Metabolism

Metabolism is defined as the biological processes of using absorbed nutrients for growth and other synthesis and for energy expenditure (Lovell 1989). Metabolism involves the chemical breakdown of food; proteins are broken down into amino acids, lipids into fatty acids, and carbohydrates into glucose. These energy-rich compounds are subsequently used by the animal for all vital functions. Amino acids, fatty acids, and glucose are absorbed into the bloodstream and distributed to various tissues. These compounds are then metabolized within the cells of each tissue.

In most animals, glucose is the major source of energy. It is oxidized to CO_2, H_2O, and energy. Glucose can be stored as glycogen in the liver and muscle. Fatty acids similarly are broken down into CO_2, H_2O, and energy. On a weight basis, lipids produce about twice the energy as carbohydrates. Excess fatty acids are stored in the animal as fat.

The major function of protein is to serve as a source of amino acids for synthesis of body protein. This process requires a considerable amount of energy, which is usually supplied by the breakdown of glucose and fatty acids. If inadequate amounts of glucose or fatty acids are present, then the organism will break down amino acids to produce energy.

Reactions involving the decomposition and liberation of energy (destructive metabolism) are described by the term catabolism; those of a synthetic nature (constructive metabolism) are referred to as anabolism. The metabolic rate of any animal is measured by heat produced or oxygen consumed per unit body weight per unit time. The metabolic rate is affected by the same factors as those affecting energy requirements previously discussed.

The basal metabolic rate (BMR) is the oxygen consumed while the animal is at rest. The BMR is difficult to determine since the resting state of fishes is difficult to describe, and water conditions such as temperature must be defined. Therefore, the term Standard Metabolic Rate (SMR) is used for fishes and a Standard Environmental Temperature (SET) should be established for each species. SET for catfish has been given at 30°C (86°F). SET for carp has been suggested at 25°C (77°F), and European eels at 22°C (72°F). The maximum metabolic rate (MMR) depicts an organism that is momentarily highly active, for example during feeding.

NUTRIENT REQUIREMENTS

Nutrients used by culture species come from protein, carbohydrates, lipids, vitamins, and minerals. Significant knowledge is available to formulate nutritional diets for salmonids, channel catfish, carp, eel, and penaeid shrimp. Knowledge is also available for tilapia, yellowtail, red sea bream (*Pagrus major*), milkfish (*Chanos chanos*), ayu (*Plecoglossus altivelis*), and various Chinese carps. The feeding and nutrition of fish were reviewed by Halver (1972, 1989), Pearson (1972), Price et al. (1976), Hepher (1988), Lovell (1989), and Steffens (1989). The National Research Council compiled knowledge on the nutrient requirements of trout, salmon, and catfish (1973), warmwater fishes (1977), coldwater fishes (1981), warmwater fishes and shellfishes (1983), and fish (1993). New (1976, 1987) reviewed dietary needs for shrimps and prawns, and

Sick and Millikin (1983) did likewise for prawns. Stickney and Lovell (1977) and Robinson (1991) reviewed nutrition and feeds for channel catfish. The annual proceedings (journal) of the World Mariculture (Aquaculture) Society (Avault 1970-1985) included nutritional papers on various culture species. Tacon (1992) compiled an annotated list of FAO field documents on food and feeding of fish and shrimp.

Protein

Protein is the major organic material in fish tissue, making up about 65% to 75% of the total on a dry-weight basis. Animals consume protein to obtain amino acids. Once consumed, protein is digested or hydrolyzed to release free amino acids that are absorbed from the intestinal tract and distributed by the blood to various tissues. Amino acids are used to repair or replace worn tissue or to build new tissue. Inadequate consumption of protein results in cessation of growth and a loss in weight. If excess protein is consumed, it will be metabolized to produce energy.

Amino acids, the building blocks of protein, can be placed into one of two groups, nonessential (dispensable) and essential (indispensable). Nonessential amino acids can be readily synthesized by the animal to promote growth. Essential amino acids cannot be synthesized and must be present in the diet. Most animals, including fish, require the same 10 essential amino acids namely arginine, histidine, isoleucine, leucine, lysine, methionine, phenylalanine, threonine, tryptophan, and valine. The National Research Council (1993) gave amino acid requirements for a number of finfish species.

The protein requirement of a culture species is directly influenced by the amino acid composition of the diet. The diet then should consist of a well-balanced mixture of essential amino acids. The most economical source of amino acids is from natural proteins found in feedstuffs such as fish meal and soybean meal. The proper amount of protein (amino acids) in the diet will vary from species to species. Moreover, a number of factors affect protein requirements including: (1) type of species, age, and size. (2) water quality, (3) natural food present in pond waters, (4) daily feed allowance, (5) non-protein energy, and (6) quality of protein.

Type of Species, Age, and Size-- Feeding habits of a species in nature give some indication of protein requirements. Highly carnivorous species, such as eels, require high amounts of protein. Usui (1974) stated that about 30% of the eel farmers in Japan feed raw fish. Formulated feed is made chiefly from fish meal with added carbohydrate. At some farms in southern Spain, eels are fed exclusively on chicken entrails.

Generally, the protein requirements of culture species decrease with increasing size and age. Practical diets for trout usually contain 40% to 55% protein with starter diets and 30% to 40% with production diets. Protein requirements of salmon are similar. Practical diets for channel catfish contain 35% to 40% to grow fry to fingerlings, 25% to 36% for growing fingerlings to sub adults, and 28% to 32% for adults and brood fish (National Research Council 1977) (Table 9.2). Lovell (1989) noted, however, that in most catfish ponds several sizes of fish are grown simultaneously. Therefore, a 32% protein feed that is amino acid-balanced is most commonly used.

It is difficult to generalize on protein requirements of penaeid shrimp; culture techniques, species differences, and other factors must be considered. Moreover, shrimp "munch" on feed, which results in the leaching of nutrients into water. This makes it more difficult to assess protein requirement.

Table 9.2 Recommended protein levels in percentage of practical fish diets (as-fed basis).

Species	Fry to fingerlings	Fingerlings to sub adults	Adults and brood fish
Channel Catfish	35 - 40	25 - 36	28 - 32
Eel	50 - 56	45 - 50	- a
Carp	43 - 47	37 - 42	28 - 32
Ayu fish	44 - 51	45 - 48	-
Red sea bream	45 - 54	43 - 48	-

[a] Blank spaces mean data were lacking on quantitative requirements.
Source: National Research Council 1977.

Deshimaru and Shigeno (1972) obtained excellent growth of *Penaeus japonicus* with protein levels as high as 60%. Forster (1975) pointed out that lower levels of protein have generally been adequate for other penaeid shrimp. He suggested that *P. japonicus* requires a high level of protein because it is predominately carnivorous, compared with *P. setiferus*, *P. aztecus*, and other detritus-feeding shrimp. In another study, *P. japonicus* grew well on a diet with 35% crude protein, but the shrimp had unlimited access to algae, zooplankton, and detritus (Balazs et al. 1973). Colvin and Brand (1977) reported that the protein requirement for early postlarval (7 to 15 mg) *P. californiensis* and *P. stylirostris* was 44%. When these two species reach 0.5 g in size, the protein requirement drops to 30% to 35% of the diet, and below 30% when shrimp reach the juvenile stages. Zein-Eldin and Corliss (1979) reported that *P. aztecus* cultured in aquaria grew best with a diet containing 52% protein. Tacon (1987) summarized protein requirements for various marine shrimp (Table 9.3).

Table 9.3 Dietary protein requirements (in % of dry diet)
for different *Penaeus* species.

P. setiferus	28 - 32
P. vannamei	30 - 35
P. stylirostris	30 - 44
P. indicus	30 - 43
P. monodon	34 - 55
P. aztecus	40 - 51
P. merguiensis	42 - 55
P. japonicus	52 - 57

Source: Tacon 1987, Food and Agriculture Organization.

Protein requirements of *Macrobrachium* sp. have been reported. Smith et al. (1976) reported excellent growth of *M. rosenbergii* in ponds fed a diet containing 20% crude protein. They obtained 1,660 kg/ha (1,482 lb/ac) when large juveniles were stocked and reared for 146 days. Willis et al. (1976) found that trout chow (40% protein) produced excellent growth and survival of *M. rosenbergii* cultured in tanks. New (1990) noted that the prawn *M. rosenbergii* is omnivorous and that prawn feeds are cheaper than feeds for marine shrimp because less protein is required. He summarized the work of others regarding protein requirements as follows: in Hawaii, 24% to 39% (Corbin et al. 1983); in Thailand, 22% to 30% (ASEAN/ UNDP/FAO 1988); in Taiwan, 28% to 36% (Hsieh et al. 1989); and in French Guinea, 25% to 30% (IFREMER 1989). New (1990) stressed the importance of natural food in ponds for supplying a portion of the protein requirement.

Water Quality-- Both water temperature and salinity affect protein requirement. Lovell (1975) pointed out that both coldwater and warmwater finfish respond to higher protein levels at higher water temperatures because of increased metabolism. At temperatures below 24°C (75°F), channel catfish grew no better in ponds on 35% than on 25% protein feeds. However, when water temperatures exceeded 24°C, the fish gained more on 30% and 35% protein feed. Catfish grown in northern ponds have lower protein requirements than those grown in southern ponds. Wilson (1989) quoting others reported that chinook salmon required feed with 40% protein at 8°C (46°F) and 55% protein at 15°C (59°F), and that striped bass (*Morone saxatilis*) required 47% protein at 20°C (68°F) and 55% protein at 24°C (75°F).

Halver (1972) stated that as salinity increases, protein requirements for salmonids increase. In one study, rainbow trout required a 40% protein diet at 10 ppt salinity, but this increased to 45% at 20 ppt salinity. The same phenomenon was observed with coho salmon (*Oncorhynchus kisutch*).

Natural Food Present-- Species cultured in ponds usually derive some protein from natural organisms. Production of channel catfish in fertilized ponds with no feed given may range from 150 to 300 kg/ha (134 to 268 lb/ac), depending on fertility of water. At relatively low stocking levels of channel catfish, such as 3,700/ha (1,500/ac), fish derive a portion of their protein requirement from natural organisms, with the rest coming from a supplemental diet. If the stocking rate is increased to near 10,000/ha (4,000/ac), then fish are almost completely dependent on protein provided in formulated diets.

It is difficult to adjust the protein level in a diet to correspond to the natural food present and to the stocking density of the culture species. Hepher (1988) discussed in detail ways in which to estimate the contribution that natural food plays in the diet of a culture species, but he noted the difficulty in making this assessment. For example, we can determine the biomass of various food organisms present in pond waters, but we do not know what portion of this is available for a particular culture species. He also noted that the biomass of pond organisms is dynamic and constantly changing. Hepher's feeding regime involving dilution of a complete ration, discussed earlier, is based primarily on biomass of the culture species in Israeli waters.

Daily Feed Allowance-- When finfish are fed all that they can eat, relatively low levels of protein are necessary. For example, when channel catfish are fed as much as they will eat in ponds, 25% to 30% protein is adequate for fish larger than 115 g (0.25 lb). But when feeding is restricted to 25 to 30 kg/ha (22 to 27 lb/ac) daily, the fish grow better with higher protein levels.

Non Protein Energy-- As pointed out before, there is a certain optimum DE/P ratio. If a feed is overbalanced with protein, some protein may be used for energy. This is wasteful since protein is much more expensive than lipids or carbohydrates. The latter two food groups should provide energy requirements to spare protein.

Quality of Protein-- Aquaculturists are apt to check the protein level of a feed, but equally important is the quality of protein. Table 9.1 demonstrated the digestibility of certain protein sources. Fish meals are an excellent source of animal protein, and soybean meal provides a good source of protein derived from plants. A complete protein must contain all of the 10 essential amino acids and in the right amounts.

Requirements of essential amino acids are given for selected culture species in Table 9.4. Culture species also require other amino acids, but they are not considered essential since they can be manufactured by the culture species.

Table 9.4 Indispensable amino acid requirements expressed as a percent of dietary protein.

Amino Acid	Japanese eel	Common carp	Channel catfish	Chinook salmon
Arginine	4.5	4.2	4.3	6.0
Histidine	2.1	2.1	1.5	1.8
Isoleucine	4.0	2.3	2.6	2.2
Leucine	5.3	3.4	3.5	3.9
Lysine	5.3	5.7	5.0	5.0
Methionine	5.0	3.1	2.3	4.0
Phenylalanine	5.8	6.5	5.0	5.1
Threonine	4.0	3.9	2.0	2.2
Tryptophan	1.1	0.8	0.5	0.5
Valine	4.0	3.6	3.0	3.2

Source: National Research Council 1977 and 1983.

In commercial diets of channel catfish, soybean meal is usually a major protein source. Soybeans are deficient in methionine, and this amino acid is usually the first limiting amino acid in catfish feeds. Lysine may be a limiting factor if the feed contains a high level of corn or other grain proteins and a low level of soybean meal. A deficiency of methionine or lysine in most animal feed, such as poultry, is corrected by adding synthetic free amino acids to the diet. However, free methionine and lysine are poorly used by catfish and can be quite expensive. Thus the amino acid balance must be obtained by using proper combinations of feedstuffs. Fish meal generally provides the demand for indispensable amino acids, but it is costly.

Certain amino acids may spare others. Cystine may spare methionine. Channel catfish have a methionine requirement of 2.3% of total protein in the absence of cystine, but up to half of the methionine required can be replaced by cystine. This sparing action is also noted with salmonids.

Toxic effects from gross imbalance of some indispensable amino acids may occur. An inhibition of growth may occur in salmonids, either when isoleucine is threefold in excess of leucine or when threefold leucine is fed with isoleucine held at the requirement.

Carbohydrates

Carbohydrates are the least expensive form of dietary energy, but their use by culture species varies (Hepher 1988; Halver 1989; National Research Council 1993). In nature, many culture species such as the eel and trout live near the apex of the food pyramid. As carnivores, these species have a metabolism to deal with high levels of protein. Conversely, the ability to metabolize diets with carbohydrates is often poor. Omnivorous and herbivorous culture species are able to use carbohydrates more efficiently. Even though carbohydrates are the cheapest source of energy in diets, less is known about their role in nutrition. No specific carbohydrate requirement has been established for fish.

Plants are the major sources of carbohydrates in fish feeds. Carbohydrates occur in three basic forms: sugars, starches, and fiber. Sugars are highly soluble mono- and disaccharides such as glucose and sucrose; they are usually found in relatively low levels in feedstuffs. Starches are somewhat soluble, and are components in corn gluten meal, soybean meal, and wheat. Fiber, principally cellulose, is the insoluble, structural component of plant cell walls found in high concentrations in such feedstuffs as alfalfa meal.

The interest in carbohydrates for use in formulated diets is because of the "protein sparing effect." In one study with fingerling channel catfish, approximately 0.23 g of carbohydrate per 100 g of diet spared 0.05 g of protein, based on diets containing 9.3% to 18.6% dextrin (Stickney and Lovell 1977). In another study, diets containing 2.5% to 10% dextrin progressively increased growth, but diets containing 15% to 20% dextrin reduced growth.

Salmonids use carbohydrates less efficiently than channel catfish. Digestible carbohydrate should not exceed 12% in diets. Higher levels may result in liver abnormalities, poor growth, and even death. Carbohydrates are absorbed as simple sugars, but they differ in digestibility. Channel catfish use polysaccharides, such as dextrin, for growth better than disaccharides or simple sugars. Yet red sea bream grow better on diets containing glucose than on diets containing dextrin.

Besides being a source of energy and sparing protein, carbohydrates have other functions. They may serve as precursors for various metabolic intermediates, such as non-essential amino acids needed for growth. Starches also aid in the pelleting qualities of diets by binding ingredients.

Lipids

Lipids serve as a major source of energy in diets, and they spare protein. They are especially important as an energy source for coldwater and marine culture species. These species have limited ability to use carbohydrate for energy. Essential fatty-acid requirements have been demonstrated for several species of fish such as rainbow trout. Although linolenic acid is important for growth, more polyunsaturated and longer-chain fatty acids (C22 or C24 omega-3 series) are required for maximum growth.

Oils, hard fats, such as beef tallow, and soft fats have been used in diets. Digestibilities will vary, depending on the type of lipid, and will vary from culture species to culture species. Commercial trout diets usually contain 12% to 16% lipid for starter diets and 6% to 8% lipid for production diets. Most commercial diets for channel catfish contain less than 8% lipid. Diets with 12% lipid have been used efficiently by channel catfish reared at 28°C (82°F), whereas 5% lipid was sufficient at 23°C (73°F). Commercial diets for carp may contain 10% to 15% lipid at warm temperatures, whereas lower lipid levels are used at temperatures below 20°C (68°F). Eel diets may contain up to 10% lipid. Commercial diets for ayu usually contain 5% or less lipid.

Several problems are noted with improper use of lipid in diets. Rancid lipid can be toxic to fish. This develops during feed storage, since feed with a high lipid content spoils much sooner than feed with a low lipid content. Addition of antioxidants and stabilizers, such as vitamin C, to feed and proper storage help avoid this. Lipid levels of 10% to 12% hamper feed pelleting; thus feed manufacturers are reluctant to use high levels of fat in diet formulations. If higher levels of lipid are desirable for certain culture species, oils may be added to the feed surface after pelleting. Too much lipid in the diet may result in excessive fat deposits laid down in the viscera. This is wasted when culture species are dressed out. Moreover, excess lipid may result in unhealthy, fatty livers.

The flavor of a culture species may be affected by the type of lipid used in feed formulations. Culture species reared on safflower oil or corn oil may taste better than those fed beef tallow or fish oil. Those reared on fish oil may develop an objectionable fishy flavor. Sargent et al. (1989) suggested that we now have the capability to "tailor" (within limits) the total lipid content of a given culture species by the kind and amount of lipid ingredients added to feed. Emphasis should be placed on producing farmed fish with optimal *n*-3 PUFA levels to provide a product with a natural taste and good nutritional quality.

Vitamins

Vitamins are organic substances that are essential in minute amounts for animal nutrition. They act in regulation of metabolic processes but do not provide energy or serve as building blocks for tissue growth. Vitamins are present in natural foodstuffs, or they are sometimes produced within the body.

The existence of vitamins was virtually unknown until around the start of the 20th century. The existence of a vitamin-like factor was first noted in the Orient. People who ate unpolished rice seemed to be free of beri beri; those who ate polished rice contracted beri beri more frequently. It was reasoned that some nutritive factor in rice polishings prevented this disease. It was later learned that this factor was water soluble and was an amine (nitrogen-containing). Since the factor was essential for life and contained nitrogen, it was named a vitamine.

Later, in the United States, it was discovered that some factor in the butterfat of milk prevented night blindness in calves. However, the factor was fat soluble instead of water soluble and did not contain nitrogen. From this, it was concluded that there were two factors, both of which were essential for life, but since only one contained nitrogen, the term was changed to vitamin. Also, the anti-night blindness factor was called vitamin A and the anti-beri beri factor vitamin B. A third factor in fresh fruits and vegetables was discovered that prevented scurvy. It was designated vitamin C. Later, it was found that vitamin B consisted of two different factors, both water soluble. The two factors were distinguished by calling one vitamin B_1 and the other vitamin B_2. Eventually other B vitamins were discovered, the last being vitamin B_{12}.

A total of 16 different vitamins function in animal nutrition. In addition to those already mentioned, there are vitamins D, E, and K. All B vitamins and vitamin C are soluble in water. Vitamins A, D, E, and K are soluble in fats. Initially, vitamin nutrition depended on use of feedstuffs containing necessary vitamins, but today laboratory synthesis of vitamins is common.

Function of Vitamins-- The function of vitamins in finfish diets is documented by Halver (1972, 1989) and by the National Research Council (1993). New (1976, 1987) reviewed information on shrimp and prawns. The need for vitamins in diets was first noted around 1935, and in 1940, vitamin deficiency of thiamin in trout diets was recognized. Yeast was added to the diet to correct the deficiency.

Before about 1960 channel catfish were expected to secure vitamins from natural organisms in the pond. Catfish were stocked at low densities, 3,700/ha (1,500/ac). However, as management techniques improved, catfish were stocked at ever increasing rates of 5,000/ha (2,000/ac) and even above 20,000/ha (8,000/ac). Moreover, new culture techniques, such as cage culture and raceway culture, were introduced which crowded fish even more. Now, channel catfish became more dependent on formulated diets to supply needed vitamins.

Vitamin C deficiency was noted when crowded catfish were fed a supplemental diet. The diseased fish usually showed crooked backs, irregular swimming, tetany when handled, poor growth, and even mortality. Vitamin C, or ascorbic acid, is necessary for the formation of collagen and normal cartilage as well as bone. The function of vitamins, along with deficiency symptoms and sources, is summarized in Tables 9.5 and 9.6. Note that certain vitamins may be destroyed during feed preparation or lost during storage. For this reason, a modest excess of vitamins is added to the diet. Some vitamins, like ascorbic acid, are partially damaged by extrusion of diets. To overcome this, ascorbic acid can be added to the feed after extrusion.

Table 9.5 Vitamin function and deficiency/symptoms for aquatic species.

Vitamin	Function	Water-Soluble Vitamins Deficiency / Symptom
Thiamin (B$_1$)	Essential for good appetite, normal digestion, growth and fertility; involved in carbohydrate metabolism of salmon; important in diet of plant-eating fish.	Poor appetite, muscle atrophy, convulsions, instability and loss of equilibrium, edema, poor growth, congestion of fins and skin, fading of body color, lethargy.
Riboflavin (B$_2$)	In several enzyme systems related to energy and protein metabolism; involved in retinal pigment during light adaptation.	Corneal vascularization, cloudy lens, photophobia, incoordination, abnormal pigmentation of iris, striated constrictions of abdominal wall, dark coloration, poor appetite, anemia, poor growth, hemorrhage in skin and fins.
Pyridoxine (B$_6$)	Involved in protein and essential fatty acid metabolism; important in diets of carnivorous species.	Nervous disorders, epileptiform fits, hyper-irritability, ataxia, anemia, loss of appetite, edema of peritoneal cavity, odorless serous fluid, rapid onset of rigor mortis, rapid breathing, flexing of opercles, iridescent blue coloration, exophthalmos.
Pantothenic Acid	Is a part of acetyl coenzyme A in various metabolic reactions; essential for development of central nervous system; a key vitamin for normal physiology of growing fish.	Clubbed gills, necrosis, scarring and cellular atrophy of gills, gill exudate, prostration, loss of appetite, lethargy, poor growth, hemorrhage in skin, skin lesions and dermatitis.
Niacin	In enzyme systems related to glycolysis and tissue respiration.	Tetany induced by stress, lethargy, reduced coordination, and photophobia, loss of appetite, poor food conversion, fish may turn dark.
Biotin	Required in carboxylation and decarboxylation; involved in general lipid synthesis.	Loss of appetite, lesions in colon, altered coloration, muscle atrophy, spastic convulsions, fragmentation of erythrocytes, skin lesions, poor growth.
Folic Acid	Required for normal blood cell formation and is involved as a coenzyme in one-carbon transfer mechanisms. Has a role in blood glucose regulation and improves cell membrane function and hatchability of eggs.	Lethargy, fragility of caudal fin, dark coloration, macrocytic anemia, poor growth.

Table 9.5 Continued

Vitamin	Function	Deficiency / Symptom
Vitamin B$_{12}$	A coenzyme in several biochemical reactions.	Poor appetite, low hemoglobin, fragmentation of erythrocytes, macrocytic anemia, reduced growth.
Inositol	myo-Inositol is a structural component of living tissue; role in lipid metabolism. Is an emergency carbohydrate source in muscle.	Poor growth, distended stomach, fin erosion, sometimes anemia.
Choline	A lipotrophic and antihemorrhagic factor preventing development of fatty livers. Involved in synthesis of phospholipids and in fat transport; essential for growth and good food conversion.	Hemorrhagic areas in the kidneys and enlarged livers, reduced weight gain.
p-Aminobenzoic Acid	A growth-promoting vitamin in microorganisms. No positive function or deficiency signs noted in most fish, a folic acid precursor in trout.	None noted.
Ascorbic Acid(Vitamin C)	Necessary for formulation of collagen and normal cartilage, tooth, and bone formation; wound healing A coenzyme with folic acid.	Scoliosis, lordosis, impaired formation of collagen, abnormal cartilage, eye lesions, hemorrhagic skin, liver, kidney, intestine, and muscle, reduced growth, broken-back syndrome, tetany when handled.

Fat - Soluble Vitamins

Vitamin	Function	Deficiency / Symptom
Vitamin A	Promotes growth, essential for health of epithelial cells; aids in resistance to infection, possibly a visual function for deep-dwelling shrimp.	Poor growth. Ascites, edema, exophthalmia, hemorrhagic kidneys.
Vitamin D	Essential for maintaining homeostasis of calcium and inorganic phosphate.	No significant change in growth or mortality.
Vitamin E	Acts as an antitoxidant and as a metabolic regulation.	Muscular distrophy, reduced growth, pericardial edema.
Vitamin K	Essential for prothrombin formation and blood clotting; involved in synthesis of RNA.	Anemia, prolonged coagulation time.

Data summarized from Halver 1972 with permission from Academic Press; National Research Council 1977, 1983, 1993; and Stickney and Lovell 1977.

Table 9.6 Sources and general comments for vitamins.

Vitamin	Sources	General Comments
Thiamin (B$_1$)	Soybeans, cereal bran, dried yeast, fresh organ meats, fresh glandular tissue.	Thiamin is lost when prepared under alkaline conditions or in the presence of sulfide. Can be lost by holding wet diet ingredients too long in storage; good stability in dry pellet diets.
Riboflavin (B$_2$)	In plants and in animal glandular tissues, fresh meats, cereal, grains, and oil-seed proteins.	Requires protection from intense light.
Pyridoxine (B$_6$)	Cereal grains and byproducts, yeast, and fresh organ meats.	Must be protected from air and sunlight to avoid loss in feeds.
Pantothenic Acid	Cereal bran, yeast, organ tissues, fish flesh.	Is stable only when diet kept cool and dry. Excessive heat during diet preparation should be avoided. Certain cereal brans may have pantothenic acid with low digestibility.
Niacin	Rich sources are yeast, legumes, and organ meats. Is found in most animal and plant tissues.	Very stable. Niacin added to diet as supplement relatively unchanged in formulation of diets.
Biotin	Fish meal, peanut meal, soybean meal, whey, yeast, distiller's byproducts.	The diet should be protected from strong oxidizing agents. Raw egg white binds biotin, making it unavailable. Biotin is one of the most expensive vitamins to add to fish diets.
Folic Acid	Yeast, fish tissues, and glandular tissues (liver and kidney).	Activity lost during extended storage and when exposed to sunlight.
Vitamin B$_{12}$	Meats and other animal byproducts; fish meal.	Easily destroyed by heating; storage conditions should be cold and of short duration.
Inositol	Present in large amounts in most fish feed ingredients.	Sometimes referred to as muscle sugar. Very stable, normal diet preparation and storage adequate for protection.
Choline	Wheat germ, soybean, and other vegetable meals; heart, liver, and other organ meats.	Choline hydrochloride, a common supplementary form used in fish diets, reacts with tocopherol and vitamin K preparations. Thus choline should be added in a water carrier and the fat-soluble vitamins in an oil carrier to prevent reaction.

Table 9.6 Continued

Vitamin	Sources	General Comments
p-Aminobenzoic Acid	Not well known.	Apparently not a limiting factor in feeds.
Ascorbic Acid (Vitamin C)	Beef liver and kidney, fresh fish tissues, citrus fruits, fresh insects.	Should add synthetic supplement when intensive type of culture is employed and when stocking rates of channel catfish exceed 5,000/ha.
Vitamin A	Fish oils, fish meals, and other fisheries products that contain fish oil residues.	Hypervitaminosis A may occur if tuna, shark, or ling viscera are used in preparation of moist diets. Synthetic vitamin A is readily available.
Vitamin D	Fresh liver oil.	Hypervitaminosis D has been reported with trout resulting in impaired growth, lethargy, and dark coloration. Excess vitamin D may also result in fragile bones and poor growth. Care should be taken with diets when using fish viscera containing large amounts of vitamin D.
Vitamin E	Wheat germ oil, soybean oil, corn oil.	Hypervitaminosis E results in poor growth, toxic liver reaction, death.
Vitamin K	Alfalfa leaves, soybeans, animal livers.	Diet should be kept dry with a minimum exposure to air oxidation, and fed as soon as possible after manufacture.

Data summarized from Halver 1972 with permission from Academic Press; National Research Council 1977, 1983, 1993; and Stickney and Lovell 1977.

422

Vitamin Requirements-- The vitamin requirements of culture species depend on the type of species, size, age, environmental stresses, water temperature, nutrient interrelationships, and culture system. Vitamin requirements are usually expressed as a function of the diet formulation. The recommended allowances for warmwater species -- based on experiments primarily with channel catfish, carp, and eel -- are given in Table 9.7. Vitamin requirements for salmonids have been summarized in Table 9.8. Vitamin premixes for shrimp (Table 9.9) are based on research, mostly qualitative.

Table 9.7 Recommended allowance for vitamins in supplemental and complete diets for warmwater fish.

	Amount (per kg) in dry diet [a]	
Vitamin	Supplemental	Complete
Vitamin A activity	2,000 IU	5,500 IU
Vitamin D activity	200 IU	1,000 IU
Vitamin E	11 IU	50 IU
Vitamin K	5 mg	10 mg
Choline	440 mg	550 mg
Niacin	17 - 28 mg b	100 mg
Riboflavin	2 - 7 mg b	20 mg
Pyridoxine	11 mg	20 mg
Thiamin	0	20 mg
D - Calcium pantothenate	7 - 11 mg b	50 mg
Biotin	0	0.1 mg
Folacin	0	5 mg
Vitamin B_{12}	2 - 10 ug	20 mg
Ascorbic acid	0 - 100 mg b	30 - 100 mg
Inositol	0	100 mg

a These amounts do not allow for processing or storage losses. Other amounts may be more appropriate for various species and under various environmental conditions.
b Highest amounts probably appropriate when "standing crop" of fish exceeds 500 kg/ha (447 lb/ac) of water surface.
Source: National Research Council 1977.

Table 9.8 Vitamin requirements for growth of selected salmonids [a].

Vitamin (mg/kg dry diet)	Rainbow trout	Brook trout	Brown trout	Chinook salmon	Coho salmon
Thiamine	10 - 12	10 - 12	10 - 12	10 - 15	10 - 15
Riboflavin	20 - 30	20 - 30	20 - 30	20 - 25	20 - 25
Pyridoxine	10 - 15	10 - 15	10 - 15	15 - 20	15 - 20
Pantothenate	40 - 50	40 - 50	40 - 50	40 - 50	40 - 50
Niacin	120 - 150	120 - 150	120 - 150	150 - 200	150 - 200
Folacin	6 - 10	6 - 10	6 - 10	6 - 10	6 - 10
Cyanocobalamin	R[b]	R	R	0.015 - 0.02	0.015 - 0.02
myo-Inositol	200 - 300	R	R	300 - 400	300 - 400
Choline	R	R	R	600 - 800	600 - 800
Biotin	1 - 1.2	1 - 1.2	1.5 - 2	1 - 1.5	1 - 1.5
Ascorbate	100 - 150	R	R	100 - 150	50 - 80
Vitamin A	2000 - 2500	R	R	R	R
Vitamin E [c]	R	R	R	40 - 50	R
Vitamin K	R	R	R	R	R

[a] Fish fed at reference temperature with diets at about protein requirements
[b] R = required
[c] Requirement directly affected by amount and type of unsaturated fat fed
Source: Halver 1972, with permission from Academic Press.

Minerals

Minerals, which are inorganic elements, are required for various metabolic processes. Culture species also use minerals to maintain osmotic balance between fluids in their body and water. Finfish and crustaceans require relatively large quantities of calcium and phosphorus compared with other minerals. Carp, rainbow trout, and crustaceans usually absorb enough calcium from the water to meet their requirements, if sufficient phosphorus is available in the diet.

The channel catfish benefits only slightly if calcium is added to the diet, but the eel requires a dietary source of calcium. The freshwater crawfish (*Procambarus clarkii*) grows best if total water hardness is around 100 ppm. Calcium is required for new shell formation.

Levels of dissolved phosphate are very low in natural waters compared with calcium. Deformed backs (lordosis) and heads have been associated with phosphorus deficiency in carp. Phosphorus, though found in fish meal and other animal sources, is not readily available, and for that reason it is often added to the diet.

Table 9.9 Composition of some shrimp vitamin prefixes (mg/kg dry diet)

	Premix number (a)				
	1	2	3 (b)	4 (b)	5
Vitamin A (IU/kg)	-	40,000	6,614	-	8,818
β - Carotene	48	-	-	33	-
Vitamin D (IU/kg)	24,000	2,500	1,323	20,000	2,205
Vitamin E (IU/kg)	110	275	295.4	362	8
Vitamin K (menadione)	20	25	3.54	33	1
Vitamin C	20,000	4,512	530	8,220	-
Thiamine hydrochloride	20	50	4.44	50	2
Vitamin B_2	40	400	31.5	164	4
Niacin	200	750	109.5	658	33
Calcium pantothenate	300	500	101.7	247	8
Pyridoxine hydrochloride	60	100	10.35	50	-
Folic Acid	4	30	4.2	12	0
Vitamin B_{12}	0.4	0.1	0.04	0.3	0
Biotin	2	10	0.35	5	-
Choline chloride	3,000	2,500	4,002	6,577	440
Inositol	2,000	2,000	552	3,288	-
Para-aminobenzoic acid	50	400	-	329	100

(a) 1. Kanazawa et al. (1970); 2. Deshimaru and Shigueno (1972); 3. Forster and Beard (1973); 4. Deshimaru and Kuroki (1974a); 5. Balazs et al. (1974b). All authors cited in New 1976.

(b) Other strengths of vitamin premixes were also used in these papers. Source: New 1976 with permission from Elsevier Science.

Below are various sources and availability of phosphorus (Lovell 1978):

Source	Availability of phosphorus (%)
dicalcium phosphate	80
fish meal, meat, and bone meal	50
soybean meal	40
grains	33

Minimum requirements of available phosphorus in diets of eel, channel catfish, carp, and red sea bream are 0.3%, 0.45% to 0.8%, 0.6% to 0.75%, and 0.65% respectively.

Dietary requirements for other minerals were reviewed by Hepher (1988) and the National Research Council (1993). Natural feedstuffs are usually adequate in S, K, Mg, Na, and Cl. However, feed low in animal products, such as fish meal, may be deficient in trace minerals. When less than 15% of the diet is composed of animal products, a trace mineral supplement is necessary to provide sufficient Mn, Cu, Zn, Fe, I, and Co.

Nonnutrients

Nonnutrients may include antinutrients present in feedstuffs, fiber, food contaminants, and food additives.

Antinutrients-- Various substances that occur naturally in plant materials or raw fish from which feedstuffs are derived may adversely affect culture species (National Research Council 1993).

Raw soybeans contain crystalline globular proteins that act as trypsin inhibitors. These proteins can be inactivated by heat processing. Hemagglutinating agents and phytic acid in soybeans also have been identified as antinutrients. Hemagglutinatins are inactivated by pepsin in the stomach. Phytates form protein-phytic acid complexes that may reduce bioavailability of protein and certain minerals. Mineral supplementation is suggested when diets contain high levels of soybean meal relative to fish meal.

Cottonseed meal use is limited in diets because of its gossypol content. Excessive amounts in feed can depress growth and cause damage to organ tissues. Cottonseed meal also is a primary source of cyclopropenoic fatty acids (CFAs). CFAs are carcinogens when fed in combination with aflatoxins for rainbow trout.

Rapeseed and other oilseed crops contain glucosinolates. The compounds upon enzymatic hydrolysis release substances that inhibit uptake of iodine by the thyroid. Iodine supplementation in the diet corrects the problem.

Raw fish may contain the thiamin-destroying enzyme thiaminase. Species that contain thiaminase and those that do not were listed by the National Research

Council (1983). Feeding fresh fish and feeding a separate diet containing thiamin avoids the problem. Heating raw fish reduces thiaminase activity.

Fiber-- Fiber is the nonnutritive portion of feed ingredients that is classified as crude fiber in proximate analysis (Hardy 1989). It is indigestible by salmonids and other carnivorous species, but channel catfish have intestinal microflora capable of digesting a portion of dietary fiber. Some herbivorous species, such as the grass carp, are able to derive nutrients from fiber (Stickney 1975). Fiber may facilitate binding of semipurified diets and may extend a diet to provide equitable distribution of nutrients to fish. Generally, however, fiber is not included in diets; instead it is avoided. In diets of culture species that do not have the ability to digest fiber, levels of fiber above 3% to 5% should not be used (National Research Council 1983). Since fiber is not digested, it passes out in fecal wastes and becomes a pollutant in water.

Feed Contaminants-- Feed contaminants may include such items as soil, weed seeds, pesticide residues, and pathogenic organisms. The latter include *Salmonella* sp., a bacterium found in fish meal. Diets containing more than 12% moisture can support bacterial, mold, and yeast growth unless they are stored frozen (Hardy 1989). Mold growth is visible in 3 days when semimoist feeds are held at room temperature (22°C, 72°F), whereas it may not be visible for 10 to 20 days if feeds are refrigerated at 1° to 3°C (34° to 37°F) (Hardy 1989). He listed more than 20 compounds used in the feed industry to inhibit fungal or microbial growth.

Drugs and Antibiotics-- Drugs are added to feed to treat, cure, mitigate, or prevent disease (Hardy 1989). A number of drugs are effective against fish diseases, but in the United States the only ones approved for use with fish feeds include sulfamethazine, furox, and terramycin® (Hardy 1989). Romet-30® is a more recent addition. In Europe, oxalinic acid is used in feeds as an antimicrobial drug. Medicated feeds have specific labeling requirements, including a withdrawal period before fish can be marketed for human food.

Hormones-- Hormones have been used to promote growth and to produce monosex fish. Growth promoters, such as diethylstilbestrol, have been used in meat-producing animals such as cattle. However, use of steroids in domestic animal feeds is no longer permitted in many parts of the world because of concern for residues in the flesh. Previously growth promoters usually were not included in production diets of fish. Sometimes addition of hormones to fry diets for a short time pose no threat to humans who eventually consume the fish (Hardy 1989).

The use of hormones to produce all-male red tilapia is standard practice in Jamaica. Methyl- or ethynyl-testosterone is added to fry diets to produce all male fish. Hanley (1992) described the standard procedure: Brood tilapia are stocked into ponds with no special care. Resulting fry, usually 5 days old, are seined and put into tanks. Fry are fed diets containing 30 to 70 mg of methyltestosterone per kilogram of feed for about 28 days (Figure 9.15). A variation of this procedure is to feed fry medicated feed while they are held in floating pens or hapas.

Figure 9.15 Red tilapia fry receive hormone in feed that produces all males.

Carotenoid Supplements-- Fish culturists have used ingredients, such as crawfish meal and shrimp meal, in feed to improve the color or quality of the product. The meal is derived from processing wastes. More than 300 pigments are found in various plants and animals, with xanthophylls and carotenoids being the most important classes (Hardy 1989). Xanthophylls are found in plants and carotenoid pigments in crustacea and fish. The pigment astaxanthin, derived from crawfish waste, has been incorporated into feeds for salmon, red sea bream, and shrimp. The finfish develop a beautiful, enhanced red or pink flesh. Shrimp appear to benefit in other ways from astaxanthin, including increased growth and survival and overall good coloration (Chien and Jeng 1992). Astaxanthin has been synthesized, but this form is not used widely because it is not a natural substance.

Pellet Binders-- A number of materials are used as binders in feed. Some binders are byproducts of cereal grains or other plants, and they may provide nutrients. Examples are high-gluten wheat flour and potato starch. Other common binders that do not provide nutrients include bentonite, lignin sulfonate, and hemicellulose extract. Bentonite is a naturally occurring mineral; it is available as either sodium bentonite or calcium bentonite. Sodium bentonite swells in water; calcium bentonite does not. When added to feed at 2%, bentonite acts as a binding agent. It also acts as a lubricant that increases pellet mill production rates and pellet die life (Hardy 1989). Lignin sulfonate is a product of the wood-pulping industry. It aids in pellet binding, reduces fines, and allows addition of more steam during the manufacture of compressed pellets. It may consist of up to 4% of the feed. Hemicellulose extract is a product made by spray-drying the concentrated, soluble byproduct of pressed wood manufacture. It is less commonly used than lignin sulfonate.

Flavorings and Attractants-- Cobb (1971) suggested that diets might be formulated for use shortly before culture species are harvested. He mentioned adding vegetable oil to the diet to improve the texture and quality of lipids, and adding flavor agents. The goal is to produce a more palatable product. Attractants are sometimes added to diets to attract the culture species. Generally, fish meal and other ingredients provide enough attractants for use in channel catfish and most other finfish diets. Salmonids, however, are more sensitive than some finfish. Soybean meal may result in reduced feed intake. Adding a "fishy" component to mask the soybean taste may be required (Hardy 1989). Adding attractants to shrimp feeds is more commonplace. Squid oil and the extract of crustaceans, such as crawfish meal, shrimp meal, and krill meal, have all been used.

Water-- The water content of feeds ranges from 6% to 10% for dry compressed or extruded pellets and 65% to 70% for some wet pellets (Hardy 1989). Some species, such as salmon fry and largemouth bass, accept moist feeds more readily than dry feed. Chinook salmon reared in marine net-pens grow more rapidly when fed diets containing 15% to 30% water than when fed dry diets (Hardy 1989).

NUTRITIONAL DISEASES

Snieszko (1972) defined nutritional diseases as those that can be attributed to deficiency, excess, or improper balance of components present in food. Culture species from the wild or those stocked at relatively low rates in ponds seldom show signs of nutritional diseases. This is because natural food organisms usually provide essential growth factors such as vitamins and minerals. The culture species' growth is limited to the amount of energy and protein in natural foods. With increased stocking rates of culture species in ponds and more use of intensive culture systems, nutritional diseases are becoming more noticeable. Most early research on nutritional diseases dealt with salmonids in the United States and with cyprinids in Europe. Roberts and Bullock (1989) and Schäperclaus et al. (1991) reviewed nutritional diseases of fish. Nutritional diseases of channel catfish were summarized by Lovell (1979).

Protein

The protein requirement of a culture species is influenced not only by the protein quality and the energy content of the feed, but also by environment and other factors already discussed. Overall protein deficiency and lack of an indispensable amino acid result in reduced growth. The skin of the culture species may darken. Other clinical signs, depending on which amino acid is deficient, include loss of weight, dorsal fin erosion, spinal abnormalities, and cataracts. It is unusual, however, to come across acute single amino acid deficiencies, and it is difficult to access under culture situations. Deficiencies may be a result of improper formulation or from using ingredients with intrinsic specific amino acid deficiencies or in imbalanced proportions. They may also result from improper processing of the diet because of excessive heat or chemical treatment during preparation. Prather and Lovell (1973) reported that too high a level of protein or too high a ratio of protein to energy in the diet can depress the growth rate of channel catfish. This is because protein is broken down and used for energy.

Carbohydrates

Most culture species do not use high levels of carbohydrate well for energy because of poor digestibility. Excess starch may suppress digestion of protein, fat, and gross dietary energy. Enlarged livers may occur in trout and catfish fed with high carbohydrate diets. Sekoke disease may occur in carp fed diets high in starch. The symptoms are like those of diabetes in mammals.

Lipids

Nutritional diseases in the past often involved feeding of trout with warm-blooded animals from which the fat was not removed. Feeding with marine trash fish that contained rancid oil also posed a problem. Auto oxidation of unsaturated fatty acids destroys vitamin E and leads to morbid changes, especially to the liver. Addition of vitamin E to the diet acts as an antioxidant. In nature, salmonids do not contain reserve lipid and therefore are not able to use excess lipid in their diet.

In silk-producing countries like China, spent silk worm pupae have been fed to carp and to other fish. Often the dried pupae contained rancid fat. This has resulted in weight loss and leads to death. Fish fed largely with fresh pupae frequently developed fatty livers unless they were fed with defatted pupae. Excess lipid in the diet also may result in clogged tubes through which eggs pass and in deposition of fat in the body cavity. The latter reduces the dressing percentage during processing. Excess lipid results in reduced appetite; fish tend to stay separate from other fish and often float near shore. To avoid disease, culture species should receive a well-balanced diet free from excessive lipid, hard animal fat, and rancid oils.

A deficiency of omega-3 fatty acids in trout diets may cause discoloration, hypersensitivity to shock, and large livers. The nutritional need for omega-3 fatty acids was not demonstrated for channel catfish (Stickney and Andrews 1972), although Lovell (1979) reported that channel catfish fed a lipid-free diet gained markedly less weight than those receiving soybean oil. Schäperclaus et al. (1991) noted that warmwater fish, such as carp, can live for a long time without essential fatty acids (EFA) with no visible signs of impairment. Nevertheless, best growth is achieved when the feed contains linolenic acid or fatty acids of the linolenic acid series.

Vitamins

Vitamins, like minerals, are known as micronutrients because they are required in relatively small quantities. In commercial aquaculture, diets are usually not deficient in one specific micronutrient. Additionally, it is often difficult to diagnose a problem for lack of one specific vitamin. However, research under controlled conditions has been conducted using diets deficient in one specific component. This allows identification of vitamin requirements and the diseases resulting therein with a deficiency.

Nutritional diseases of fish caused by vitamin deficiencies were summarized by Snieszko (1972), Roberts and Bullock (1989), Schäperclaus et al. (1991), and the National Research Council (1993). Lovell (1979) reviewed vitamin deficiencies of channel catfish. Deficiency symptoms for fish are summarized in Table 9.5.

Vitamin deficiency symptoms have been demonstrated in channel catfish for 14 vitamins. Some symptoms have been subtle, others more dramatic such as the broken back syndrome (Figure 9.16). This disease is a result of vitamin C deficiency that impairs collagen formation. Collagen is needed for good bone formation. At stocking rates up to approximately 3,400 fish/ha (1,360/ac), the disease does not occur when a supplemental diet lacking ascorbic acid is used. At stocking rates above this, or in intensive culture systems, fish often develop deformed or separated spinal columns. When a complete diet including ascorbic acid is used, the problem disappears.

Nutritional gill disease of salmonids is caused by a deficiency of pantothenic acid. When affected, fish experience respiratory difficulties and loss of appetite. They tend to congregate near water inflow and remain almost motionless. Gill filaments thicken, become club-like, and may grow together at the tips. The disease can be prevented by feeding a diet containing sufficient pantothenic acid. Information on shrimp diseases related to vitamin deficiency or excess was reviewed by (New 1976). Excess vitamin C may inhibit shrimp growth, and excesses of some vitamins may be toxic.

Figure 9.16 Top two fish are normal channel catfish, showing top view and side view. Bottom two fish show broken back syndrome, one fish with vertical curvature (lordosis) and the second with lateral curvature (scoliosis). Photo courtesy of R.T. Lovell Auburn University.

Minerals

Generally, all necessary minerals are available in most diets for culture species. When a mineral deficiency arises, it is usually because of reduced bioavailability of the mineral rather than a deficiency (Roberts and Bullock 1989). This may come about by a dietary imbalance or with the mineral in an unsuitable form. It also may be related to interaction with other dietary ingredients such as vitamins and fibers. In the carp and other cyprinid fish, the stomach lacks acid secretion. This prevents absorption of organically bound minerals, especially phosphorus. Lack of phosphorus in diets of certain species may result in reduced growth and increased mortality. Certain fish meals used in practical diets contain high levels of calcium. This greatly reduces the availability of certain trace minerals. That is why such diets should be supplemented with minerals.

Thyroid tumors have occurred in salmonids because of iodine deficiency. Goiter is especially prevalent with hatchery reared fish when diets are mainly of mammalian origin. Use of iodized salt in feed is effective for prevention of goiter. Fish meals contain iodine, so modern diets with fish meal normally are not iodine deficient.

Other mineral micronutrients affecting growth of fish include iron, copper, manganese, and zinc. Generally, an excess of certain minerals in the water, such as iron and zinc, may result in disease and possibly death. Deficiencies of manganese and zinc have been noted (Roberts and Bullock 1989). A lack of manganese may result in poor growth and development of cataracts. Manganese supplementation may be necessary when fish meals make up the bulk of the diet. Zinc deficiencies may result when the diet contains zinc-binding agents such as phytic acids and calcium. Poor growth, skin and fin lesions, and development of cataracts may occur.

FEED FORMULATIONS

Agricultural byproducts and wastes are usually fed as is. Formulated feeds are processed diets consisting of selected feedstuffs, such as soybean meal and fish meal, that provide nutrients in the quantity and quality required. Formulated feeds have a definite shape, size, and moisture content. When formulating a feed for a culture species, consider the availability and cost of ingredients to provide a least-cost diet, type and size of species being cultured, pelleting requirements, and storage.

Least-cost Diets

A major goal in formulating diets is to provide quality feed at the lowest possible cost. If we know the nutritional requirements of a culture species, the nutrient content and digestibility of feedstuffs, and the availability and cost of feedstuffs, a least-cost diet can be formulated. Certain ingredients with a similar nutrient composition can be substituted for one another, depending on availability and cost.

Substituting ingredients to achieve a least-cost diet, however, must be done with care. For example, in 1993 in southern states, the cost of cottonseed meal was relatively low compared with soybean meal, and some channel catfish farmers felt that it would be a good substitute. Soybean meal has one of the best amino acid profiles of all protein-rich plant feedstuffs for meeting the essential amino acid requirements of channel catfish. Cottonseed meal, on the other hand, has a low availability of the essential amino acid lysine. Supplementation with synthetic lysine may be necessary. Another shortcoming of cottonseed meal is its content of free gossypol, which is moderately toxic to certain animals. Regarding digestibility, soybean meal and cottonseed meal are similar (Table 9.1).

It is important to know not only the ingredients needed, but also the quantity required. For example, in 1975 in the United States, the vitamin biotin cost about $13 a kg for a 0.1% concentrate. If the formulated diet contains 0.1% of biotin, the cost of biotin per metric ton of feed is $13.00. Therefore, it is of economical importance to determine the biotin requirement since its cost is high. Fish meal in 1975 cost about $275 per ton. If a diet contains 20% fish meal, then this ingredient costs $55 for every ton of diet formulated. For a 1% drop in fish meal, the feed processor could save $2.50 per ton of feed. Ingredients in a least-cost diet may vary from year to year to reflect the cost of individual ingredients. Nevertheless, the nutritional quality remains the same.

Type and Size of Species

As discussed earlier, each species has particular nutritional requirements. Sometimes a "new" species is brought under culture whose nutrient requirements are not well known. In this instance the requirements for a related species, whose nutrient requirements are known, can be discretely substituted. Generally, most variation among culture species is between warmwater and coldwater species; fresh, brackish, and saltwater species; and between finfishes and crustaceans. Knowing the feeding habits of a species in nature is also of value. This can be ascertained by stomach analysis and by examination of type and length of gut, presence or absence of teeth in the mouth, and other morphological characteristics. The size of a culture species also affects the formulation of feeds; younger stages usually require a higher level of protein.

Pelleting Requirements

Pelleting is affected by several factors, including fat content, moisture, and humidity. The fat level should be no lower than 2% or 3% to lubricate the holes in the die and to reduce dustiness, and no higher than 8% to 10% to avoid excessive die lubrication resulting in poor compaction of the feed mixture (Hardy 1989).

Feed Packaging and Storage

Feed should be packaged in multi-wall bags or have plastic liners to retard moisture uptake and to help protect flavor, aroma, and color (Figure 9.17). Many farmers buy feed in bulk (loose) to reduce cost. Bulk feed is usually stored in silos (Figure 9.14). Either way, bag or bulk, feed should be stored in a cool, dry, dark area. Generally, dry feeds should be used in 90 days and moist feeds in 60 days. For maximum storage life, dry feeds should be kept where temperatures do not exceed 20° to 22°C (68° to 72°F), and relative humidity should remain below 75%. Semimoist feeds that require frozen storage should be kept at -20°C and thawed just before use (Hardy 1989).

Factors influencing deterioration of feed are moisture, temperature, light, and oxygen. Feed of relatively high moisture content deteriorates quickest. Molds are a major problem. Propionic acid has been added to the diet to inhibit molds. High temperatures speed the deterioration process, especially for certain vitamins such as vitamin C. Oxidation of fats during storage destroys essential fatty acids and produces rancidity.

Figure 9.17 Shrimp feed in bags, Indonesia.

FORMS OF FEEDS

Various forms of experimental diets are available, but most commercial diets can be classified as either paste, flake, meal, or pellet. Feed processing is well summarized by Gaudet (1970), Hardy (1989), Lovell (1989), and the National Research Council (1993).

Paste

Pastes or cakes are used primarily in eel culture. The ingredients are stored in powdered form and do not require cold storage. To make a batch of feed, mix the ingredients with water and 5% to 10% vitamin oil to make a paste. The percentage of vitamin oil added is varied according to water temperature. Below

18°C (64°F) about 5% by weight is added; above 18°C about 10% is added (Usui 1974). The paste, which looks like a dough ball, is made chiefly of fish meal with added carbohydrate; it is about 52% protein, 24% carbohydrate, 4% fat, 10% water, and 10% ash. This paste is placed on a mesh tray partly submerged in water. Eels go through the mesh or climb over the top to reach the food.

Flake

The flaking process involves finely ground ingredients blended with water to form a slurry, which is passed between heated rollers. The thin sheets of the diet produced are crumbled into flakes. The flakes maintain their integrity in water and float or sink slowly. Boonyaratpalin and Lovell (1977) discussed processing of flake rations. They noted that chitin from shrimp shells is important for imparting physical properties to the flakes. They further noted that vitamin C is lost, and that astaxanthin should be added. Flake diets are used for crustacean larvae and for ornamental fish; they are very palatable.

Meal

Starter feeds for trout and channel catfish fry and for other larval species must be small. Such feeds, called meal, are usually made by first pelleting or extruding the feed mixture then crushing it to the desired size. Feeds with small particles are referred to as crumbles. Even though the feeds are fed as small particles, prior pelleting helps to minimize separation of formula ingredients when the feed is placed in water. Topical application of fat to the small particles reduces leaching of micronutrients.

Pellets

Most grow-out feeds for finfish and crustaceans are in pellet form. Pellets may be hard and dry, cooked and extruded, or soft and moist. Pelleting involves the use of moisture, heat, or pressure to agglomerate ingredients. Steam or hot water is usually added during pelleting. This gelatinizes starch present that aids in binding the pellet together. Usually enough steam is added to increase moisture content to 16% and temperature to 85°C (187°F) before passing ingredients through the pellet die (Figure 9.18). Pellets are discharged onto a screen belt or dryer and air-cooled within 10 minutes to slightly above ambient temperature and dried to below 13% moisture. Additives may be used to help bind the pellet, but high-quality feeds can be made without binding if good pelleting procedures are used. Some processors, however, like to use binders since this allows greater flexibility in choosing ingredients. Hard, dry pellets usually sink in water, disintegrate fairly rapidly, and cost less than extruded pellets.

Extruded pellets (Figure 9.19) are produced with high levels of moisture, heat, and pressure. Usually the ingredients are conditioned with steam or water, and

436

they may be cooked before extrusion. The mash or mixture, which contains about 25% water, is compacted and heated to 135° to 175°C (275° to 347°F) under high pressure. As the mixture is squeezed through die holes, part of the water in the super-heated dough immediately vaporizes and causes expansion. Heat-sensitive vitamins are added topically after extrusion and drying. Extruded feeds are usually made in pellet form, but shrimp feeds may be in a spaghetti form or other configuration.

Figure 9.18 Pellet die with compressed feed being pressed out.

Figure 9.19 Extruded feed pellets.

Extruded feeds have advantages and disadvantages. Stability in water is excellent, and few fines are produced. The feed floats, which allows a farmer to see fish feeding. Regarding disadvantages, it costs 8% to 15% more to process than non-extruded pellets, and second, it is expanded so much that a fish may fill its stomach without consuming enough nutrients for maximum growth. All things considered, most farmers prefer extruded feeds for surface-feeding culture species.

Moist, soft diets are sometimes preferred for fish that strike their food, such as trout and salmon. Pellets are produced by using a high-compression hard pellet mill and adding fat, lecithin, or water up to a total of 18% to 20% moisture. Normally, the moisture of feeds stored at ambient temperature must be below 13% to avoid microbiological growths. Pellets with higher moisture than this must be kept frozen until used.

Most moist, soft diets are made by the "Oregon moist pellet" process. This diet is made with about 30% to 40% fish and fish viscera that is pasteurized (cooked) to kill disease organisms. The cooked fish is added to a dry meal of ingredients, mixed to a doughy consistency, and forced through holes in a plate similar to that used for making macaroni. The diet is cut off to appropriate lengths and stored frozen. The Abernathy pellet, developed for salmon, is a simpler version of the Oregon moist pellet. The diet consists of dry ingredients with approximately 30% water added.

SOME PRACTICAL FEED FORMULATIONS

A number of commercial companies manufacture feeds, but in many cases specific ingredients are not listed. However, practical feeds used on a commercial scale have been formulated by various research groups. Following are selected examples of practical feed formulations.

Channel Catfish

Four feed formulations have been used for channel catfish (Table 9.10.). Note that only soybean meal and vitamin premix are common to all diets. Fish meal, found in three diets, and soybean meal are both high quality animal and plant protein sources, respectively. The Stuttgart formula is the only diet containing rice bran and rice mill dust. Stuttgart, Arkansas, is in the heart of a rice-growing area, and rice byproducts are readily available at a reasonable cost, allowing for manufacture of a least-cost diet. By the same token, the Kansas State formula is high in wheat byproducts. This formula is relatively low in protein, approximately 25%, compared with the other three formulas which range from 32% to 36% protein. The lower formula is appropriate for a cooler climate.

Table 9.10 Channel catfish ration formulations that have been used at the Fish Farming Experimental Station (Stuttgart, Arkansas), the Skidaway Institute of Oceanography and Coastal Plain Station (Savannah, Georgia), the Department of Fisheries and Allied Aquacultures (Auburn University), and the Department of Biology and Department of Grain Science (Kansas State University)

Ingredient	Percent of diet			
	Stuttgart	Skidaway	Auburn #4	Kansas State
Menhaden fish meal	12.00 (a)	10.00	10.00	
Meat and bone meal				15.22
Soybean meal 44% protein	20.00	35.00	51.20	25.84
Soybean meal 49% protein				
Yellow corn		28.95	22.70	5.00
Distiller's dried grains with solubles				
Dried distiller's solubles	8.00		7.50	
Rice bran	25.00			
Rice mill dust	10.00 (b)			
Wheat			5.00	23.03
Wheat middlings				19.25
Ground sorghum				1.13
Corn gluten meal		20.00		
Cottonseed meal	10.00			
Blood meal	5.00 (c)			3.06
Feather meal	5.00			
Dehydrated alfalfa	3.50			
Animal tallow		2.50	2.00	1.45
Dicalcium phosphate		3.00	1.00	4.16
Limestone				0.47
Mineralized, iodized salt	1.00	0.25		0.39
Vitamin premix	0.50	0.25	0.50	1.00
Trace Mineral Premix		0.05	0.08	

(a) Herring fish meal (70 percent) may be substituted at 10.0% of the diet and distiller's dried solubles adjusted to 10.0% of the diet.

(b) Wheat shorts, wheat middlings, cereal grains, vegetable or fish body oil, and a pellet binder may be used for rice by-products.

(c) Blood meal and feather meal may be used interchangeably.

Source: Stickney and Lovell 1977.

Table 9.11 Typical formula and specifications for trout pellets (a)

Ingredients	Percentage by weight
West Coast Canadian or Alaskan herring meal, maximum fat 10.5%, minimum protein 70% immediate past season	49.8
(a) Lecithin (blended with fish meal)	0.2
Corn gluten meal, 41% protein, 1% fat, 6% fiber. (Blend of 60% prime and 25% feed grade can be substituted)	5.0
Toasted, defatted soy flour, maximum fat 0.5%, minimum protein 50%	5.0
Steam dried brewer's yeast, minimum protein 40%, minimum fat 0.7%, maximum fiber 3.0%	4.0
A and D feeding oil, nonsynthetic, stabilized	6.0
Condensed fish solubles, dried on wheat middlings (equivalent to 100% condensed fish solubles)	5.0
Soluble dried blood flour	2.0
Kelp meal	2.0
Wheat standard middlings	7.0
Dried skim milk	5.0
Unextracted liver meal	5.0
Vitamin premix	4.0

(a) National Fish Hatchery diet specifications for 1970-71. Courtesy of Bureau Sport Fisheries and Wildlife, U.S. Department of Interior

Source: Halver 1972 with permission from Academic Press.

Salmonids

A typical formula for trout pellets and for salmon moist pellets is presented in Table 9.11 and Table 9.12, respectively. Common to both formulations is the high percentage of fish or meat products necessary for diets of carnivorous species, concomitant with a relatively high protein content.

Table 9.12 Typical formula and specifications for moist salmon pellets[a].

Ingredient	Percentage by weight
Herring meal	27
Wheat middlings	11.3
Dried skim milk	4
Wheat germ meal	5
Corn distiller's solubles	5
Brewer's yeast	3
Tuna viscera	20
Turbot	10
Beef liver	10
Crab solubles	2
Vitamin and antioxidant mix	1
Cod liver oil	1
Choline chloride	0.7
	100

[a] Frozen pellets specified by Willard National Fish Hatchery, Cook, Washington. (D. Cairns, Personal communication 1965).
Source: Halver 1972 with permission from Academic Press.

Carp and Eel

Carp diets (Table 9.13) are relatively high in plant products as compared with eel diets, which are high in percentage of fish meal (Table 9.14). Carp are omnivorous but eels are highly carnivorous.

Table 9.13 Forty percent protein carp grower diet (Saku).

Ingredient	International feed no.	Amount in diet (%)
Fish meal mech. extd., 65% protein [a]	5-01-982	46
Wheat middlings, It. 9.5% fiber	4-05-205	28
Rice, bran, w. germ, meal solv. extd.	4-03-930	7
Wheat, bran	4-05-190	5
Soybean, seeds, meal solv. extd., 44% protein (a)	5-20-637	5
Yeast, torula, dehy.	7-05-534	4
Corn, gluten, meal	5-02-900	1.5
Vitamin premix	--	0.5
Mineral premix	--	0.5
Sodium chloride	--	0.5
Potassium phosphate	--	

[a] 6.25 x percent nitrogen
Vitamin premix: vitamins added to cellulose powder to make 0.5% of diet (mg/kg).
Source: National Research Council 1977.

Table 9.14 Forty-six percent protein eel grower diet.

Ingredients of air-dry feed mixture	International feed no.	Diet Number		
		1 (%)	2 (%)	3 (%)
Fish meal mech. extd., 65% protein [a]	5-01-982	69	67	62
Potato, starch, boiled, dehy.	4-03-783	20	24	22
Soybean, seeds, meal solv. extd.	5-04-604	--	--	5
Yeast, brewers, or	7-05-527	3	3	4
yeast, torula	7-05-534	--	--	--
Liver, meal, or	5-00-389	2	1	2
milk, skim, dehy.	5-01-175	--	--	--
Vitamin premix	--	1	2	2
Mineral premix	--	2	2	2
Others	--	3	1	1

[a] 6.25 x percent nitrogen
[b] Attractants and binders: cellulose, carboxymethyl, corn gluten meal, blood meal.
Source: National Research Council 1977.

Crustaceans

Table 9.15 depicts a generic diet used on a commercial scale for shrimp and prawns. The diet is an extruded spaghetti-type and holds up well in water.

Table 9.15 Example of a 38%-39% protein shrimp feed.

Material	Percent
Fish meal with fish solubles [a] (61% crude protein)	24.5
Crawfish or shrimp head meal [a] (40% crude protein)	10.0
Soybean meal (45% crude protein)	36.6
Rice bran or wheat middlings (13-16% crude protein)	20.0
Corn or potato starch	2.9
Fish oil (menhaden, cod, herring)	2.0
Binder [b]	3.0
Mineral mix [c]	0.5
Vitamin mix [c]	0.5

[a] Cholesterol (0.5%) should be added if animal protein supplies less than half of total crude protein. [b]Alginates with Na-hexametaphosphate; hemicelluloses or ligno-sulfonates; plastic polymers. [c] Commercial premix for catfish feed.
Source: National Research Council 1983.

FEEDING PRACTICES
When to Begin

Fry and larvae of finfish and crustaceans usually have a period, just after hatching, when they live off their yolk. The first larval stage of shrimp does not feed until it changes into the second stage. This is when live food should be available. Fry of finfish also live off their yolk. The length of time varies with the species and water temperature. Channel catfish fry after hatching remain in the yolk or sac-fry stage for about 3 days, trout and salmon much longer. Regardless, it is of utmost importance to begin feeding immediately after the sac fry become swim-up fry. This stage is noted when fry no longer ball up in one corner of the trough near the bottom but instead swim up to the top and disperse. They are looking for food.

Frequency of Feeding

The frequency of feeding depends on the species, size, culture system, stocking rate, and water temperature. Fry of many finfish are initially fed six to eight times a day. They are fed all they will consume in about 10 minutes. The number of feedings per day may be reduced as the fish grow. The rule for trout is to feed six times daily when there are 1,750 fish to a kg (794/lb), four times per day at 900 per kg (408/lb), and three times at 100 per kg (45/lb). Most species in grow-out systems are fed once or twice per day 7 days per week. Stomachless fish, such as carp and tilapia, cannot consume large quantities of feed at any one time, and it may be best to feed them two or more times a day in grow-out. Most catfish farmers feed once a day, but feeding twice daily may produce 20% more gain than once daily feeding. However, the cost of labor and other economics must be considered. Species confined in tanks, cages, and raceways should probably be fed twice per day, since they do not have access to natural food. Fish stocked in ponds at very high rates have less natural food available than fish stocked at lower rates, and twice daily feeding should be beneficial.

Shrimp and prawn larvae may have live *Artemia* present in nursery tanks at all times. Once the postlarval stage is reached, formulated diets usually substitute for the live food. In intensive grow-out of shrimp, four to six feedings a day are not uncommon.

The temperature of the water reflects the frequency of feeding. Trout grow at temperatures ranging from 5°C to 20°C (41° to 68°F). Below and above these temperatures, growth all but ceases. Some trout farms stop all feeding at 4°C (39°C). Above 20°C, low dissolved oxygen may become a problem, and feeding is often curtailed. Channel catfish feeding is sometimes stopped when the water temperature drops below 10°C to 12°C (50° to 54°F). When this happens, fish usually lose weight through the winter. One guide for winter feeding of catfish in ponds is to feed between 0.75% and 1% of their estimated body weight when the water temperature at 1 m (3.3 ft) depth is 13°C (55°F) or above.

Amount

The amount of feed to use varies with species, size, culture system, water temperature, type of food, and other factors. Generally, the culture species are fed a certain percentage of their body weight daily. Shrimp, trout, salmon, and catfish in grow-out ponds might be fed 3% of body weight per day with a dry pelleted feed. If, for example, a pond contains 1,000 kg of fish and you want to feed at 3%, then 30 kg (0.3 x 1,000) of feed are required per day.

When fry or very small fingerlings are first stocked into grow-out ponds, they are often fed all that they will eat in about 10 minutes. To calculate feed required at a percentage of body weight would not be practical, since only a small handful might be required per hectare. It would be better to feed lightly around the pond edge to be sure that all the fry received some feed. Once fish begin feeding well and they increase in size, the feed required can be calculated on a percentage of body weight. If fish are fed twice a day, then they receive a half ration at each feeding. Since fish continue to grow, the amount of feed required increases over time. The amount of feed should be increased weekly or every 2 weeks to accommodate increased growth. This can be done by sampling the fish to estimate growth.

Problem and Solution. Assume that a raceway contains 5,000 trout that have been fed daily at 3% of body weight for a 2-week period. How would you determine the new amount of feed?

Sample the fish and determine their weight. Assume that you weigh a sample of 500 fish and that they weigh a total of 100 kg. Then 5,000 fish weigh a total of 1,000 kg, and the daily feeding rate of 3% now calls for 30 kg of feed.

Some fish farmers do not sample fish. They simply feed all the fish will eat in about 10 minutes. There are advantages and disadvantages to this. First, labor is saved and fish are not disturbed during handling. It is not unusual for fish to go off feed for several days after handling. A disadvantage is that fish may be overfed, even though all the feed is cleaned up. Fish can use efficiently only so much feed. Excess, even though eaten, is converted poorly to flesh. A compromise is to estimate growth without handling fish in order to adjust feeding. Because feed is ordinarily the single, largest variable cost, feeding management can be crucial to profit or loss of a culture species.

Problem and Solution. Assume that the last time you checked your fish you estimated a standing crop of 1,000 kg of fish. Since then you have fed fish at a rate of 3% daily for 2 weeks. How many kilograms of feed should be used daily beginning in the third week?

Assume the fish cultured are channel catfish with a feed conversion of 1.75. Then 1,000 kg (fish standing crop 2 weeks ago) x 0.03 = 30 kg per day or 30 x 14 = 420 kg of feed used over a 2-week period. Fish gained a total of 240 kg (420 ÷ 1.75). The standing crop in the pond is now 1,240 kg (1,000 + 240), and the amount to feed daily is 37.2 kg (1,240 kg x 3%).

This figure, 37.2 kg, is approximate because it assumes no mortality and does not take into account that fish grow daily. Nevertheless, it does approximate feed required for practical purposes. Previously, we have discussed the amount of feed required daily. We can also calculate estimated feed required for the whole growing season. This will assist with cash flow projections for the year or for the growing season. Computer programs have been developed to calculate daily growth of culture species; this allows for pinpoint calculations of feed required by weight each day.

Problem and Solution. Assume that you stock a total of 10,000 salmon in a culture system and that you plan to grow them to 1 kg each. Further assume a feed conversion of 2. How much feed is required?

Assume the salmon fingerlings weighed 250 kg at stocking. Therefore, 9,750 kg of fish flesh will be grown (10,000 - 250). At a feed conversion of 2, a total of 19,500 kg of feed will be required (9,750 x 2) to grow each fish to 1 kg.

The amount of feed given to fish is affected by other factors. Fish on a maintenance diet receive less feed than those being grown out for market. Brood fish or fish in a pay-lake may be fed just enough to maintain body weight with no growth. In such situations, fish would be fed 0.5% to 0.75% of body weight daily with a dry pelleted feed. Occasionally, fish will feed very lethargically or stop feeding altogether. In this case, the amount fed should be decreased or even stopped until the cause is determined.

Some possible reasons for poor feeding might include poor water quality such as high ammonia content or low DO, reduced or elevated water temperatures, poor feed quality, or a parasite and disease problem. When a floating feed is used, fish can be observed during feeding. When a sinking feed is used, some pellets can be placed on an underwater feeding tray or net to determine if feed has been eaten. If a culture species is to be harvested and transported, stop all feeding several days ahead of harvest. This allows it time to clean out its system and to "harden." When certain species grow fast, such as grass carp, the flesh becomes soft and they are easily injured by handling. When feeding is stopped for several days, the fish harden and can be handled more easily.

Feeding Charts

Frequency of feeding and amount fed, as seen earlier, are affected by species, size, culture system, and water temperature. Many aquaculture farms use feeding charts to establish feeding programs to accommodate these variables. The feeding chart for channel catfish (Table 9.16) is typical for the southeastern United States. Fingerlings are stocked April 15 when water is cool (20°C or 68°F), so the feeding rate is relatively low (2%). As time passes, the fish become larger and the water temperature rises -- and so does the feeding rate. By July 15 the water temperature reaches 29°C (84°F), and the fish average 0.16 kg (0.35 lb). Even though water temperature is still climbing, the feeding rate is lowered slightly to 2.8%. This reflects two factors. First, as water temperature rises, so does the chance of having low DO problems, and care must be taken not to overfeed. Second, as fish increase in size, the feeding rate is lowered because larger fish require less feed than smaller fish when related as a percentage of body weight fed.

Table 9.16 Suggested maximum feeding rate and feeding frequencies for fry or small fingerlings and for food-sized channel catfish at different water temperatures [a]

Water Feeding Temperature °C	Fry or Fingerlings		Food-Size Fish	
	Feeding Frequency	Feeding Rate % (Daily)	Feeding Frequency	Feeding Rate % (Daily)
31° and above (87° F and above)	2 times/day	2	1 time/day	1
27° - 30° (80° - 86°F)	4 times/day	6	2 times/day	3
20° - 26° (68° - 79°F)	2 times/day	3	1 time/day	2
14° - 19° (58° - 67°F)	1 time/day	2	1 time/day	2
10°- 14° (50°- 57° F)	alternate days	2	alternate days	1
9° and below	3rd to 4th day	1	3rd to 4th day	1/2

[a] Conversions of °F to °C rounded off to nearest whole number
Source: Robinson and Lovell 1984.

The chart shows frequency of feeding. If fish are fed twice daily, half a ration is fed at each feeding. If aeration is available or fresh water for flushing the pond, the feeding rate could be increased. Determine ultimate feed conversion ratios to be sure that the extra feed is used efficiently. Note in the chart that the feeding program reflects a particular type of feed. In this case the feed contains 36% protein and 2.88 kcal of digestible energy. Each fish farm should establish a feeding chart to reflect the feed used and the particular conditions of the farm. A basic feed chart for channel catfish can therefore be modified, usually by trial and error and the experience of the fish farmer. A typical feeding chart for rainbow trout (Table 9.17) demonstrates that as the water temperature rises, the feeding rate increases, never decreases, and as the size of fish increase, the feeding rate decreases.

Table 9.17 Feed chart for trout based on feeding a percentage of bodyweight daily (a)

Number fish Per kg	Water temperature °C						
	4 - 7° (40 - 45°F)	- 9° (- 48°F)	- 10° (- 51°F)	- 12° (- 54°F)	- 14° (- 57°F)	- 16° (- 60°F)	- 17° (- 63°F)
2645	4.1	4.5	4.8	5.1	5.9	6.5	6.9
1322	4.0	4.2	4.7	5.0	5.8	6.0	6.3
661	3.9	4.1	4.6	4.9	5.4	5.7	5.9
441	3.6	4.0	4.5	4.8	5.0	5.1	5.3
220	3.2	3.8	4.2	4.5	4.6	4.7	5.0
176	3.0	3.4	3.9	4.2	4.4	4.6	4.7
132	2.9	3.2	3.7	3.8	3.9	4.0	4.3
88	2.7	2.9	3.3	3.4	3.5	3.6	3.9
66	2.0	2.5	3.0	3.1	3.2	3.4	3.7
44	1.9	2.2	2.6	2.8	2.9	3.0	3.3
33	1.7	2.0	2.4	2.5	2.6	2.7	3.0
26	1.6	1.9	2.1	2.3	2.4	2.5	2.8
20	1.5	1.8	2.0	2.2	2.3	2.4	2.7
15	1.4	1.7	1.8	2.1	2.2	2.3	2.6
13	1.3	1.6	1.7	2.0	2.0	2.2	2.5
11	1.2	1.5	1.6	1.8	1.9	2.0	2.3
9	1.1	1.4	1.5	1.7	1.8	1.9	2.2
7	1.0	1.3	1.4	1.6	1.7	1.8	2.0
4	0.9	1.2	1.3	1.5	1.6	1.7	1.8
2	0.9	1.0	1.2	1.3	1.4	1.5	1.6

(a) Conversion of °F to °C rounded off to the nearest whole number
Source: Data courtesy of Rangen Inc. Buhl, Idaho; Data modified to metric system.

Time of Day

Low DO depresses feeding activity of fish, so feeding should be done as the DO in a pond is on the increase. Moreover, between 1 to 8 hours after feeding in ponds, fish need more oxygen for digestion. Therefore, feeding in ponds should not be done very early in the morning, very late in the afternoon, or at night. Culture species can be fed at almost any time in culture systems where DO is less of a problem. Regardless of the time chosen, stick to a regular schedule. Culture species soon become attuned to feeding at a certain time of day.

There is evidence that the time of day culture species are fed may affect their rate of growth. Meier et al. (1973) found that stimuli of fish (disturbances) caused by daily routine feeding and handling produced marked changes in growth and development. Changes were noted if the disturbances occurred at specific times, such as in the morning. If these disturbances occurred at other times of the day, changes may not have been noted, or detrimental changes such as weight loss occurred. Growth, reproductive condition, and a variety of other physiological changes are regulated in part by interactions of certain daily hormonal rhythms. Disturbances could elicit increased levels of some hormones in the blood, such as prolactin and adrenocortical steroid.

Meier and Horseman (1977), conducted a laboratory experiment with the tilapia *Oreochromis aureus*. They concluded that weight gain over a 25-day period was 80% better in fish exposed daily to a sonic stimulus at dawn than in non-exposed fish. Though the results should be interpreted cautiously, it does imply that the time of day we choose to feed could have a bearing on growth because of hormonal rhythms. Catfish farmers report that when fish are fed in late afternoon fish are often produced with excess fat deposits. Some recommend that channel catfish not be fed after 1 or 2 p.m. (Avault 1985).

Distributing Feed

Feed can be distributed by hand, into feeding rings, with blowers from a tractor, with automatic and demand feeders, and by air.

By Hand-- Sac fry and larvae are often fed by hand initially to be sure that they get off to a good start. Fish farmers with a small pond operation or those with tank culture may continue feeding by hand. This allows them to observe the fish and gauge their well-being. When finfish are given a floating pelleted feed in ponds, feeding initially should be around all four sides of the pond. If a breeze is present, the feed can be distributed along one side. The water current carries the feed across. As fish become accustomed to feeding, they can be fed along one or two sides. Fish soon learn this and the time of day they are to be fed. Shrimp and prawns are usually fed sinking diets, so feed should be distributed widely throughout the pond. Moreover, they are less mobile than finfish.

Carp receiving non-pelleted diets can be fed at certain marked spots in the pond. The spots might be indicated with poles that stick up out of the water. From four to six poles per hectare, well spaced out, are used. A boat is needed to reach spots in large ponds. The spots chosen for distribution should be free of vegetation and have a firm, not mucky, bottom. In India, feedstuffs are placed in porous sacks for major carps (Figure 9.20). Herbivorous fish, such as grass carp, may receive cut vegetation, which is piled in heaps throughout the pond or along edges in very large ponds. Crawfish in Louisiana are sometimes fed forages and agricultural byproducts when natural vegetation is in short supply. The material is also placed in heaps around the pond (Figure 9.21).

Figure 9.20 Porous sacks on poles, Andhra Pradesh, India.

Feeding Rings-- These are sometimes used to prevent feed from being blown all over the pond. When floating vegetation such as duckweed (*Lemna* spp.) is used as feed, floating feeding rings are used. The feeding ring is usually nothing more than a square 1 m by 1 m of bamboo stalks. Feeding rings are also used for rice bran or corn meal (Figure 9.5). Once again, this prevents the feed from being blown over the pond. Moreover, a feeding ring soon becomes established as a feeding station, and fish become accustomed to it. Feeding rings have been used in recirculating systems (Figure 9.22) to prevent feed from being washed through the net dividers.

Figure 9.21 Robert Romaire of the LSU Agricultural Center sets out hay for crawfish.

Figure 9.22 Feeding ring used for tilapia culture in recirculating system. Photo at Steve Abernathy's tilapia farm Robert, Louisiana.

Blowers-- Feed can be blown into ponds with a mechanical blower (Figure 9.23). Feed is placed in a hopper attached to a tractor. Blowers are powered by an auxiliary engine or operated from the power take-off of the tractor. The feed is blown out along the pond edge.

Figure 9.23 Blower disperses feed from hopper into channel catfish pond.

Automatic and Demand Feeders-- Automatic feeders are programmed to deliver a specified amount of feed at pre-determined intervals. The feeder shown in Figure 9.24 has a feed metering device that delivers the pelletized feed through a pair of venturis to entrain the feed in the center of an air stream.

Figure 9.24 Feed is sprayed into pond from a series of automatic feeding devices.

The delivery system uses a pneumatically controlled aluminum pipe that delivers the pellets at the water surface. This particular feeder, which handles both Oregon moist or dry pellets, operates on the available power.

Demand feeders, or self-feeders, permit fish to obtain feed when it is wanted. The fish bump a trigger or tray suspended in the water to release feed. Some feeders release feed only when the weight of it on an underwater pan is reduced. Demand feeders may be stationary at the water's edge or they may be floating. Large ponds may require several feeders. One feeder should handle about 1.5 ha (3.7 ac). Demand feeders are popular in raceway culture of trout (Figure 9.25). Trout have better feed conversion, faster growth, less fish size variation, and fewer problems with low DO. Some feed hoppers are made of see-through materials that permit observation of the feed level at a distance.

Figure 9.25 Demand feeders used in trout raceways.

Air Feeding-- Distributing feed from an airplane is an alternative method for feeding large numbers of animals. It may be used where aerial application is practiced for row crops and airplanes are available. Feed is distributed in a band by the plane flying low over the water.

STUDY QUESTIONS
1. List four reasons for feeding culture species.
2. What are problems with overfeeding?
3. Give examples of feeds that are of plant origin and those that are of animal origin.
4. What is a formulated diet?
5. What is the difference between a supplemental feed and a complete feed? When would you use a supplemental feed and when would you use a complete feed?
6. List and discuss requirements of a good feed.
7. Define, explain, or identify: gross energy, digestible energy, digestible energy/protein ratio.
8. What factors affect energy requirements of culture species?
9. List and discuss factors that affect protein requirements of culture species.
10. What role does carbohydrate play in the diet of culture species?
11. Of what importance is lipid in the diet of culture species?
12. List non-nutrients that may be found in a formulated diet and give their function when applicable.
13. Give examples of nutritional diseases and what causes them.
14. What is a least-cost diet?
15. What forms (shapes) of formulated diets are used in commercial aquaculture? When and with what species would they be used?
16. When should you begin to feed newly hatched fry or larvae of a culture species?
17. What factors affect the frequency of feeding?
18. What factors affect the amount fed each day to a culture species?
19. What are different ways to dispense feed?
20. Assume that you stock 1,000 trout into a raceway. Each trout weighs 0.1 pound at stocking. After stocking, you feed fish until they reach 1 pound each. If it takes 2,000 pounds of feed to grow 1,000 trout to 1 pound each, what is the feed conversion ratio?
21. You wish to estimate feed requirements for the year so you can determine the total cost. You plan to stock channel catfish at 6,000 fingerlings per acre into 100 acres of water. Assume that the fish weigh 0.1 pound at stocking, that you grow fish to an average of 1.5 pounds each, and that the overall feed conversion ratio is 2:1. Assume also that there is no mortality. How many pounds of feed are needed to produce one crop of fish on this farm?
22. What information is needed to develop a feeding chart?

454

REFERENCES

Adelman, I.R. 1978. Influence of temperature on growth promotion and body composition of carp (*Cyprinus carpio*) due to bovine growth hormone. Transactions American Fisheries Society 107(5):747-750.

ASEAN/UNDP/FAO. 1988. Country review paper (Thailand) presented at ASEAN Workshop on Shrimp and Finfish Feed Development, 25-29 October. Johore Bahru, Malaysia. ASEAN/UNDP/FAO Regional Small-scale Coastal Fisheries Development Project, Manila, Philippines, pp. 13-15 (unpublished manuscript).

Avault, J.W., Jr. (editor). 1970-1985. Proceedings (Journal) World Mariculture Society. Louisiana: Louisiana State University Division of Continuing Education.

Avault, J.W., Jr. 1985. Circadian rhythms and fatness in fish. Aquaculture Magazine 11 (5):55-56.

Avault, J.W., Jr. and M. Brunson. 1990. Crawfish forage and feeding systems. Reviews in Aquatic Sciences 3(1):1-10.

Balazs, G.H., E. Ross and C.C. Brooks. 1973. Preliminary studies on the preparation and feeding of crustacean diets. Aquaculture 2:369-377.

Boonyaratpalin, M. and R.T. Lovell. 1977. Diet preparation for aquarium fishes. Aquaculture 12:53-62.

Browne, R.A., P. Sorgeloos and C.N.A. Trotman. 1991. *Artemia* Biology. Boca Raton-Ann Arbor-Boston: CRC Press. 374 pp.

Chien, Y.H. and S.C. Jeng. 1992. Pigmentation of kuruma prawn, *Penaeus japonicus* Bate, by various pigment sources and levels and feeding regimes. Aquaculture 102(1992):333-346.

Cobb, B.F., III. 1971. The use of mariculture to produce a quality food product, a challenge for the future. Proceedings of the World Mariculture Society 2:87-92.

Collis, W.J. and R.O. Smitherman. 1978. Production of tilapia hybrids with cattle manure or a commercial diet. In Symposium on Culture of Exotic Fishes, Auburn, Alabama. Fish Culture Section, American Fisheries Society 1978:43-54.

Colvin, L.B. and C.W. Brand. 1977. The protein requirements of penaeid shrimp at various life-cycle stages in controlled environment systems. Proceedings of the World Mariculture Society 8:821-849.

Corbin, J.S., M.M. Fujimoto and T.Y. Iwai. 1983. Feeding practices and nutritional considerations for *Macrobrachium rosenbergii* culture in Hawaii. pp. 391-412. In CRC Handbook of Mariculture, Volume 1. Crustacean Aquaculture. Boca Raton: CRC Press Inc. 422 pp.

Couch, J.R. 1974. Evaluation of poultry manure as a feed ingredient. World's Poultry Science Journal 30:279.

Crow, C.W. 1987. Effects of brine shrimp (*Artemia salina*) density on development and survival of two densities of larval Malaysian prawns (*Macrobrachium rosenbergii*). M.S. Thesis, Louisiana State University. 34 pp.

Culley, D.D., S.P. Meyers and A.J. Doucette, Jr. 1977. A high density rearing system for larval anurans. Lab Animal, July/August 1977. 5 pp.

Cullison, A. 1975. Feeds and feeding. Reston, Virginia: Reston Publishing Company Inc. 486 pp.

Day, C. and J.W. Avault, Jr. 1984. Crayfish, *Procambarus clarkii*, production in ponds receiving varying amounts of soybean stubble or rice straw as forage. In International Symposium on Freshwater Crayfish, Davis, California. 6:247-265.

Decleir, W., I. Moens, H. Slegers, P. Sorgeloos and E. Jaspers. 1987. *Artemia* Research and its Applications. Wetteren, Belgium: Universa Press. 541 pp.

Deshimaru, O. and K. Shigeno. 1972. Introduction to the artificial diet for the prawn *Penaeus japonicus*. Aquaculture 1:115-133.

Forster, J.R.M. 1975. Studies on the development of compounded diets for prawns. Proceedings International Conference on Aquaculture Nutrition. 1: 229-248.

Gaudet, J.L. (editor). 1970. Report of the 1970 workshop on fish feed technology and nutrition. U.S. Department of Interior, Bureau of Sport Fisheries and Wildlife. Superintendent of Documents, U.S. Government Printing Office. Resource Publication 102. 207 pp.

Green, L.M., J.S. Tuten and J.W. Avault, Jr. 1978. Polyculture of red swamp crawfish (*Procambarus clarkii*) and several North American fish species. In International Symposium on Freshwater Crayfish, Thonon-les Bains, France. 4:287-298.

Halver, J.E. 1970. Nutrition in marine aquaculture. pp. 75-102. In Marine Aquaculture. Corvallis, Oregon: Oregon State University Press.

Halver, J.E. (editor). 1972. Fish Nutrition. New York and London: Academic Press Inc. 713 pp.

Halver, J.E. (editor). 1989. Fish Nutrition. San Diego, California: Academic Press Inc. 798 pp.

Hanley, F. 1992. A guide to the farming of tilapia. Published by Hi-Pro Master Blend Feeds, P.O. Box 24 Old Harbour, St. Catherine, Jamaica. 20 pp.

Hardy, R.W. 1989. Diet preparation. pp. 475-548. In Fish Nutrition. San Diego, California: Academic Press Inc. 798 pp.

Hastings, W.H. 1979. Fish nutrition and fish feed manufacture. pp. 568-574. In Advances in Aquaculture. FAO Technical Conference on Aquaculture, Kyoto, Japan. 653 pp.

Hepher, B. 1988. Nutrition of Pond Fishes. Melbourne, Australia: Cambridge University Press. 388 pp.

Hickling, C.F. 1962. Fish Culture. London: Faber and Faber 24 Russell Square. 295 pp.

Hsieh, C.H., N.H. Chao, L.A. De Oliviera Gomes and I.C. Liao. 1989. Culture practices and status of the giant freshwater prawn, *Macrobrachium rosenbergii*, in Taiwan. Paper presented at the Third Brazilian Shrimp Farming Congress, 15-20 October. Joao Pessoa-PB Brazil, 25 pp. (unpublished manuscript.)

Huet, M. 1970. Textbook of fish culture, breeding and cultivation of fish. Surrey, England: Fishing News (Books) Ltd. 436 pp.

IFREMER. 1989. Freshwater prawn *Macrobrachium rosenbergii* culture in French Overseas Territories: origin, extension and present situation. Poster presentation at Aquaculture '89, 12 February, Los Angeles, California. 17 pp.

Liao, I.C., M.S. Su and H.M. Su. 1991. An overview of live feeds production system design in Taiwan. pp. 135-150. In Proceedings of a U.S.- Asia Workshop. Oceanic Institute, Honolulu, Hawaii.

Lovell, R.T. 1975. How much protein in feeds for channel catfish. Commercial Fish Farmer & Aquaculture News 1(4):40-41.

Lovell, R.T. 1978. Dietary phosphorus requirement of channel catfish (*Ictalurus punctatus*). Transactions American Fisheries Society 107:617-621.

Lovell R.T. 1979. Nutritional disease in channel catfish. pp. 605-609. In Advances in Aquaculture. FAO Technical Conference on Aquaculture, Kyoto, Japan. 653 pp.

Lovell, R.T. 1989. Diet and fish husbandry. pp. 549-604. In Fish Nutrition. San Diego, California: Academic Press Inc. 798 pp.

Mamcarz, A. and M. Nowak. 1987. New version of an illuminated cage for Coregonid rearing. Aquaculture 65:183-188.

Meier, A.H., T.N. Trobec, H.G. Haymaker, R. MacGregor III and A.C. Russo. 1973. Daily variations in the effects of handling of fat storage and testicular weights in several vertebrates. Journal of Experimental Zoology 184:281-288.

Meier, A.H. and N.D. Horseman. 1977. Stimulation and depression of growth, fat storage, and gonad weight by daily stimulus in the teleost fish *Tilapia aurea*. Proceedings of the World Mariculture Society 8:135-143.

National Research Council. 1973. Nutrient requirements of trout, salmon and catfish. National Academy of Sciences. Washington, D.C.: National Academy Press. 57 pp.

National Research Council. 1977. Nutrient requirements of warmwater fishes. National Academy of Sciences. Washington, D.C.: National Academy Press. 78 pp.

National Research Council. 1981 Nutrient requirements of coldwater fishes. No. 16. National Academy of Sciences. Washington, D.C.: National Academy Press. 63 pp.

National Research Council. 1983. Nutrient requirements of warmwater fishes and shellfishes (revised edition). National Academy of Sciences. Washington, D.C.: National Academy Press. 102 pp.

National Research Council. 1993. Nutrient requirements of fish. National Academy of Sciences. Washington, D.C.: National Academy Press. 114 pp.

New, M.B. 1976. A review of dietary studies with shrimp and prawns. Aquaculture 9(1976):101-144.

New, M.B. 1987. Feeds and feeding of fish and shrimp- a manual on the preparation and presentation of compound feeds for shrimp and fish in aquaculture. Aquaculture Development and Coordination Programme, FAO Rome. Report No. ADCP/-REP/87/26. 275 pp.

New , M.B. 1990. Freshwater prawn culture: a review. Aquaculture 88(1990):99-143.

Parker, N.C. 1987. Feed conversion indices: controversy or convention? Progressive Fish-Culturist 49(3):161-166.

Pearson, W.E. The nutrition of fish. 1972. Switzerland: Roche Information Service. 47 pp.

Pennak, R.W. 1953. Fresh-water invertebrates of the United States. New York: The Ronald Press Company. 769 pp.

Phillips, A.M., Jr. and D.R. Brockway. 1959. Dietary calories and the production of trout in raceways. Progressive Fish-Culturist 21:3-16.

Prather, E.E., J.R. Fielding, M.C. Johnson and H.S. Swingle. 1954. Production of bait minnows in the Southeast. Auburn University, Alabama Agricultural Experiment Station. Circular No. 112. 71 pp.

Prather, E.E. and R.T. Lovell. 1973. Response of intensively cultured channel catfish to diets containing various protein-energy rations. Proceedings Southeastern Association of Game and Fish Commissioners 27(24):455-459.

Price, K.W., W.N. Shaw and K.S. Danberg (editors). 1976. Proceedings First International Conference on Aquaculture Nutrition. University of Delaware, College of Marine Studies. 323 pp.

Rivas, R., R. Romaire, J.W. Avault, Jr. and M. Giamalva. 1978. Agricultural forages and by-products as supplemental feed for crawfish. In International Symposium on Freshwater Crayfish, Thonon-les Bains, France. 4:337-342.

Roberts, R.J. and A.M. Bullock. 1989. Nutritional pathology. pp. 423-473. In Fish Nutrition. San Diego, California: Academic Press Inc. 798 pp.

Robinson, E.H. 1991. A practical guide to nutrition, feeds, and feeding of catfish. Mississippi Agricultural & Forestry Experiment Station. MAFES Bulletin 979.

Robinson, E.H. and R.T. Lovell (editors). 1984. Nutrition and feeding of channel catfish (revised). Southern Cooperative Series Bulletin No. 296.

Sargent, J., R.J. Henderson and D.R. Tocher. 1989. The lipids. pp. 153-218. In Fish Nutrition. San Diego, California: Academic Press Inc. 798 pp.

Schäperclaus, W. 1933. Lehrbuch der Teichwirtschaft. U.S. Fish and Wildlife Service. Fishery Leaflet 311.

Schäperclaus, W., (H. Kulow and K. Schreckenbach editors). 1991. Fish Diseases. 5th edition. Volume 2, pp. 1,072-1,092. Translated from German. United States Department of Interior, National Science Foundation, Washington, D.C. 1,398 pp.

Shigueno, K. 1975. Shrimp culture in Japan. Tokyo: Association for International Technical Promotion. 153 pp.

Sick, L.V. and M.R. Millikin. 1983. Dietary and nutrient requirements for culture of the Asian prawn, *Macrobrachium rosenbergii*. pp. 381-389. In CRC Handbook of Mariculture, Volume 1, Crustacean Aquaculture. Boca Raton, Florida: CRC Press Inc. 442 pp.

Smith, T.I., J.P. Sandifer and W.C. Trimble. 1976. Pond culture of the Malaysian prawn *Macrobrachium rosenbergii* (de Man) in South Carolina. Proceedings of the World Mariculture Society 7:625-645.

Snieszko, S.F. 1972. Nutritional fish diseases. pp. 404-434. In Fish Nutrition. New York and London: Academic Press Inc. 713 pp.

Sorgeloos, P., D.A. Bengtson, W. Decleir and E. Jaspers. 1987. Artemia research and applications. Wetteren, Belgium: Universa Press. Volume 1 359 pp. and Volume 2 535 pp.

Steffens, W. 1989. Principles of Fish Nutrition. Chichester, England: Ellis Horwood Limited. 384 pp.

Stickney, R.R. 1975. Cellulase activity in the stomachs of freshwater fishes from Texas. Proceedings Southeastern Association of Game and Fish Commission 29: 282-287.

Stickney, R.R. and J.W. Andrews. 1972. Combined effects of dietary lipids and environmental temperature on growth, metabolism, and body composition of channel catfish. Journal of Nutrition 102:249-258.

Stickney, R.R. and R.T. Lovell. (editors). 1977. Nutrition and feeding of channel catfish. Southern Cooperative Series Bulletin 218. 67 pp.

458

Stickney, R.R., H.B. Simmons and L.O. Rowland. 1977. Growth responses of *Tilapia aurea* to feed supplemented with dried poultry waste. Texas Journal of Science 29 (1 and 2): 93-99.

Suharto, H.H., A. Ismael and A. Poernomo. 1982. Breeding techniques of *Macrobrachium rosenbergii* (de Man) in conical fiber glass tanks. pp. 115-122. In Giant Prawn Farming. Amsterdam, Netherlands: Elsevier Science Publishing Company Inc. 532 pp.

Swingle, H.S. 1958. Experiments on growing fingerling channel catfish to marketable size in ponds. Proceedings Southeastern Association of Game and Fish Commissioners. 12:63-72.

Szczerbowski, J.A. and A. Mamcarz. 1984. Rearing of Coregonid fishes (Coregonidae) in illuminated lake cages. II Environmental conditions during fish rearing. Aquaculture 40:147-161.

Tacon, A.G.J. 1987. The nutrition and feeding of farmed fish and shrimp. A training manual, the essential nutrients. FAO Field Document GCP/RLA/ 075/ITA.

Tacon, A.G.J. 1992. The food and feeding of farmed fish and shrimp, an annotated selection of FAO field documents, 1973-1991. Food and Agriculture Organization of the United Nations. FAO Fisheries Circular No. 849.

Treece, G.D. and N.S. Wohlschlag. 1990. Raising food organisms for intensive larval culture: I Algae. pp. 57-65. In Red Drum Aquaculture, Proceedings of a Symposium on the Culture of Red Drum and Other Warm Water Fishes. Sea Grant College Program, Texas A&M University. 236 pp.

Treece, G.D. and N.S. Wohlschlag. 1990. Raising food organisms for intensive larval culture: III *Artemia*. pp. 71-77. In Red Drum Aquaculture, Proceedings of a Symposium on the Culture of Red Drum and Other Warm Water Fishes. Sea Grant College Program, Texas A& M University. 236 pp.

Usui, A. 1974. Eel Culture. Surrey, England: Fishing News (Books) Ltd. 186 pp.

Walker, W.H., R.O. Smitherman and J.W. Avault, Jr. 1966-67. Crawfish waste -- a potential feed for channel catfish. Louisiana Agriculture 10(2):14-15.

Wilson, R.P. 1989. Amino acids and proteins. pp. 111-151. In Fish Nutrition. San Diego, California: Academic Press Inc. 798 pp.

Willis, S.A., R.W. Hagood and G.T. Eliason. 1976. Effects of four stocking densities and three diets on growth and survival of postlarval *Macrobrachium rosenbergii* and *M. acanthurus*. Proceedings of the World Mariculture Society 7:655-665.

Wohlschlag, N.S. and C.R. Arnold. 1990. Raising food organisms for intensive larval culture: II Rotifers. pp. 66-70. In Red Drum Aquaculture, Proceedings of a Symposium on the Culture of Red Drum and Other Warm Water Fishes. Sea Grant College Program, Texas A&M University. 66-70.

Zein-Eldin, Z.P. and J. Corliss. 1979. The effect of protein levels and sources on growth of *Penaeus aztecus*. pp. 592-596. In Advances in Aquaculture. FAO Technical Conference on Aquaculture, Kyoto, Japan. 653 pp.

CHAPTER 10
MAINTAINING HEALTH OF A CULTURE SPECIES

As culture species become crowded because of higher stocking densities, disease becomes more prevalent. A disease is an abnormal condition of an organism caused by infection, inherent weakness, or environmental stress. It prevents the organism from functioning normally. Death may occur.

Diseases may be classified as infectious, parasitic, or non-infectious. Infectious diseases are caused by microbial organisms -- viruses, bacteria, and fungi. Parasitic diseases are caused by protozoans, helminths (worm-like), crustaceans, and leeches. When disease is caused by an infectious organism, the host is said to be infected -- bacterial infection, viral infection, and fungal infection. When disease is caused by a parasite, the host is said to be infested, for example protozoan infestation. Hereafter, infectious and parasitic diseases will be lumped together and discussed as infectious diseases.

Non-infectious diseases are caused by factors other than living organisms, such as nutritional deficiencies, toxic substances in the water or food, poor water quality, and sundry adverse factors causing stress to culture species. In many instances non-infectious diseases predispose a culture species to invasion by pathogenic organisms. An example is an outbreak of bacterial disease caused by *Aeromonas hydrophila* after channel catfish (*Ictalurus punctatus*) have been exposed to chronically low levels of dissolved oxygen (DO).

In this chapter, we review non-infectious and infectious diseases, discuss life cycles of pathogenic organisms, and suggest methods for their prevention and control.

DISEASE AFFECTS ALL CULTURE SPECIES

Disease may cause serious losses in aquaculture because culture species are often grown under crowded conditions. Water quality deteriorates and disease becomes more prevalent. Klontz (1979) estimated that up to 30 cents of each dollar spent to raise fish goes for some aspect of disease control. Plumb (1979) estimated that 10% of all cultured channel catfish are lost to infectious diseases. The bacterium *Vibrio anguillarum* has caused high mortalities in pen-cultured salmon (*Oncorhynchus* spp.). Glude (1977) noted that oyster beds have been closed at an alarming rate because of deteriorating water quality caused by inadequate treatment of domestic wastes and urban runoff. Lewis et al. (1992) reported that two parasites, *Perkinsus marinus* and *Haplosporidium nelsoni*, caused extensive mortalities of oysters (*Crassostrea virginica*) from 1985 through 1987 in coastal waters of Georgia. A fungal disease caused by *Aphanomyces astaci* has virtually destroyed native crawfish (*Astacus astacus*) in Europe. Aquaculturists must learn to minimize stressful conditions to lessen disease occurrence. If a culture species becomes diseased, methods must be used to correct the problem.

KEY REFERENCES

Diseases of channel catfish have been reviewed (Rogers 1971, McCraren et al. 1975, Plumb 1979); salmonid diseases (Amend 1977, Roberts and Shephard 1986); finfish (Roberts 1989); flatfishes (Liewes 1984); ornamental fish (Axelrod 1989); crustacean diseases (Johnson 1975, 1977); molluscan diseases (Sinderman 1968, 1979; Perkins 1977, Fisher 1988, Elston 1990); and diseases of marine species (Sinderman 1966, 1970, 1977, 1990a, 1990b; Sinderman and Rosenfield 1967). Books or proceedings on diseases of finfish include Schäperclaus (1954), Petrushevskii (1957), Davis (1961), Hoffman (1967), Mawdesley and Lionel (1972), Dill (1973), Duijn (1973), Hoffman and Meyer (1974), and Schäperclaus et al. (1991). A proceedings on diseases of fishes and shellfishes was edited by Snieszko (1970a), and one on diseases of aquatic animals was edited by Amborski et al. (1974a). The National Academy of Sciences (1973) published on aquatic animal health. Roberts (1978) edited a book on fish pathology. The Bureau of Sport Fisheries and Wildlife (1971) prepared a fish disease manual. Sindermann (1977) presented a bibliography of books and other publications on diseases in mariculture, and he listed various universities, agencies, and organizations concerned with diseases of marine animals.

NON-INFECTIOUS DISEASES

Nutritionally Related Diseases

Nutritional diseases are becoming more common because culture species are grown at increasingly higher densities. This places more importance on formulated feed and less dependency on natural food. Chapter 9 presented a cursory review of nutritional diseases.

Besides nutritional and related disorders, Roberts (1978) considered three groups of non-infectious diseases: (1) diseases associated with changes in water quality, (2) diseases resulting from known conditions but whose etiologies are obscure, and (3) diseases resulting from genetic aberrations.

Water Quality Related Diseases

Gas bubble disease (GBD) is caused by supersaturation of water with gas, usually nitrogen or oxygen. Fickeisen and Schneider (1976) reviewed research on GBD up to 1974, and the Transactions of the American Fisheries Society, 109 (6):657-771 (1980), contained a series of papers on GBD. Bouck (1980) defined

GBD as a non-infectious, induced process caused by high uncompensated, total dissolved gas pressure, which produces primary lesions in blood (emboli), tissues (emphysema), and subsequent physiological dysfunctions. Fish develop bubbles under the skin, eyes, gills, and mouth, but gaseous accumulation may also occur in the swim-bladder, visceral peritoneum, liver, and blood vessels. Fish develop a condition similar to diver's bends. A supersaturation of 110% may be detrimental to sac-fry and 115% to adult finfish.

Excess gas may occur during a sudden increase in water temperature. Ordinarily as water temperature increases, excess gas is liberated, but on occasion surplus gas is retained. In ponds, supersaturation of gas may occur from using unaerated ground water. Supersaturation also may occur in late afternoon, especially from dense phytoplankton blooms with little or no water circulation. Agitation and circulation of water aid in release of excess gas. Gas bubble disease has been especially common when fish are cultured in heated effluents of power plants.

Low water temperature has been fatal to tilapia, pompano (*Trachinotus carolinus*), the prawn (*Macrobrachium rosenbergii*), ornamental fish, and to certain other culture species. When culture species are weakened because of low water temperature, they become more sensitive to disease-causing agents. In one cold tolerance test, *Oreochromis mossambicus* began dying at 13°C (55°C), *O. niloticus* at 7°C (45°F), and their hybrids including the reciprocals at 7°C. *O. niloticus*, however, was hardier than the hybrids; some remained alive even after all hybrids had died (Avault and Shell 1968).

Fish farmers sometimes note abnormalities in newly hatched fry when water temperature in hatching troughs is elevated. Embryos develop too quickly and produce crooked tails and humped backs. Drastic changes in water pH coupled with an increase in un-ionized ammonia and water temperature may interact to harm fish, particularly if dissolved oxygen is low. Other water quality related diseases were listed by Wedemeyer (1980) (Table 10.1).

Water-borne irritants such as excess clay turbidity may damage gills, impair respiration, or kill embryos. McNeil and Ahnell (1964) noted that salmonid embryo survival was drastically reduced when fine sediments in spawning gravels exceed 20% by volume of the total substrate. Crouse et al. (1981) noted a significant reduction in coho salmon (*Oncorhynchus kisutch*) production when fine sediments were 26% to 31% by volume of total substrate.

Roberts (1978) described coloration abnormalities of plaice (*Hippoglossoides* sp.) associated with intensive lighting of tanks. Fish became pseudo-albinos. Sunfishes (Centrarchidae) may appear pale and bleached out in very muddy waters. Fish held in shallow pond water with backs exposed may become sunburned. This condition may worsen if bacterial infection follows.

Table 10.1 Stress factors that increase susceptibility to the indicated diseases.

Disease (causative pathogens)	Environmental stress factors predisposing to disease
Furunculosis (*Aeromonas salmonicida*)	Low oxygen (4 ppm); crowding; handling fish in the presence of *A. salmonicida*; handling up to a month prior to an expected epizootic.
Bacterial gill disease of salmonids *Myxobacteria* sp.	Crowding; unfavorable environmental conditions such as chronic low oxygen (4 ppm) and elevated ammonia (1 ppm NH_3-N); particulate matter in water.
Columnaris (*Flexibactor columnaris*)	Crowding or handling during warm (15°C, 59°F) water periods if carrier fish are present in the water supply; temperature increase to about 30°C (86°F) if the pathogen is present, even if not crowded or handled.
Kidney disease (*Corynebacteria* sp.)	Water hardness less than about 100 ppm (as $CaCO_3$); diets containing corn gluten of less than about 30% moisture.
Hemorrhagic septicemia (*Aeromonas* and *Pseudomonas* spp.)	Pre-existing protozoan infections such as *Costia* or *Trichodina*; inadequate cleaning leading to increased bacterial load in water; particulate matter in water; handling; crowding; low oxygen; chronic sublethal exposure to heavy metals, pesticides, or polychlorinated biphenyls (PCBs); for carp, handling after overwintering.
Enteric Redmouth Disease (*Yersinia ruckeri*)	Water temperatures above 13°C (55°F); crowding; handling and grading; high organic content of water.
Vibriosis (*Vibrio anguillarum*)	Handling; dissolved oxygen lower than about 6 ppm, especially at water temperatures of 10° to 15°C (50° to 59°F); brackish water.

Table 10.1 Continued

Disease (causative pathogens)	Environmental stress factors predisposing to disease
Parasite infestations (*Costia, Trichodina, Hexamita*)	Overcrowding of fry and fingerlings; low oxygen; excessive size variation among fish in ponds.
Spring viremia of carp	Handling after overwintering at low of temperatures.
Fin and tail rot	Crowding; improper temperatures; nutritional imbalances; chronic sublethal exposure to PCBs; suspended solids, 200 to 300 ppm chronically.
Coagulated yolk (white spot) disease of eggs and fry	Rough handling; malachite green containing more than 0.08% zinc; gas supersaturation of 103% or more; and mineral deficiency in incubation water.
"Hauling loss" (delayed mortality)	Hauling, stocking, handling, in soft water (less than 100 ppm total hardness); mineral additions not used; CO_2 above 20 ppm.
Blue sac disease of eggs	Crowding; accumulation of nitrogenous metabolic wastes due to inadequate flow patterns.

Source: Wedemeyer Spring 1980.
Authors note: Some chemicals, such as malachite green, can no longer be used.

Some water quality problems can be a direct cause of non-infectious disease. For example, high levels of nitrite cause brown blood disease in channel catfish. Shortages of certain components, such as calcium ions, may bring an onset of a non-infectious disease. Red swamp crawfish (*Procambarus clarkii*) grew poorly when cultured in waters low in calcium ions (total water hardness less than 17 ppm); shells of crawfish were thin, and mortality was high. When cultured in waters with adequate calcium (total hardness $\geq$ 100 ppm), crawfish growth and survival were excellent (de la Bretonne and Avault 1971). In another study, *Oreochromis aureus* that overwintered in water with virtually no hardness began dying, but mortality was stopped when the hardness was increased.

We must again emphasize the importance of knowing the optimum and minimum water quality requirements for each species and its larva or fry as discussed in Chapters 6 and 7.

Diseases of Unknown Etiology

Roberts (1978) discussed two diseases of unknown etiology. The first, proliferative kidney disease, was noted in rainbow trout (*Oncorhynchus mykiss*) in the British Isles and in one case with cultured brown trout (*Salmo trutta*) in Norway. This disease is usually noted in young trout when they are placed in grow-out facilities with certain water supplies. Extremely low water pH seems to be a common feature. Fish affected darken, show slight abdominal swelling, and become very anemic. Diffuse swelling and pallor of the kidney and spleen are noted. An unidentified protozoan kidney parasite was suspect. Another disease that was originally of doubtful origin, ulcerative dermal necrosis (UDN), was first noted in Atlantic salmon (*Salmo salar*) in Britain as early as 1873. It had also been reported for brown trout. This disease appeared to spread from watershed to watershed, and many fish died. Losses are restricted to adults and are greatest in winter when water is frozen. Fish develop gray lesions on the head or adipose fin. Pollution, virus, and external fungi have been suspect causes.

Diseases of Genetic Origin

Diseases of genetic origin might include body malformation including overshot and undershot jaws of fish, anomalous fin development, and fore-shortened opercular growth. Roberts (1978) quoted the work of Svensson in Sweden regarding an apparent genetically controlled condition of Atlantic salmon. A high percentage of fry from specific females, that produce smaller than normal eggs, die between 10 and 20 days after hatching. In other areas, salmonids have developed cystic structures that have no apparent parasitic etiology.

WHAT CAUSES INFECTIOUS DISEASES

Three variables usually occur together for an infectious disease outbreak: (1) the presence of a pathogenic organism, (2) a susceptible culture species as host, and (3) a stressful or predisposing environmental condition (Figure 10.1). You should try to prevent the simultaneous occurrence of all three.

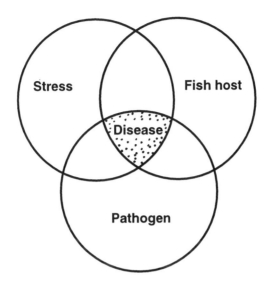

Figure 10.1 Three variables that together may result in a disease.

Pathogen Present

Pathogens attacking a culture species are termed primary pathogens (obligate) or opportunistic pathogens (facultative). Primary pathogens live only as pathogens and require a host for reproduction. Obligate pathogens include all viruses; certain bacteria, such as *Aeromonas salmonicida*; the protozoan parasites *Ichthyophthirius multifiliis* (Ich), *Ichthyobodo,* and *Chilodonella* sp. to name three examples; all tapeworms and spiny-headed worms; and all monogenetic and digenetic trematodes. Primary pathogens must be kept from being introduced into the culture system. Even so, if the culture species is healthy and not stressed, disease may not occur. For example, *Ligictaluridus* sp., a monogenetic trematode, may be found on channel catfish with no apparent harm. If fish are stressed, the parasite may increase in numbers and cause a serious disease. Therapeutic chemicals and drugs are often successful in controlling a disease but they should be used as a last resort.

Opportunistic pathogens are free-living and often ubiquitous in nature. Under certain conditions they parasitize culture species. Examples include the protozoan *Epistylis* sp. and the bacteria *Aeromonas hydrophila* and *Pseudomonas fluorescens*. Certain facultative bacteria are commonly associated with fish. If fish are stressed and become weakened, these bacteria may become pathogenic. The best method to prevent disease caused by facultative pathogens is to avoid stress, since it is virtually impossible to prevent many of the pathogens from existing in most culture facilities. Therapeutic drugs have been used successfully in some instances, but continued use can result in resistant forms of the pathogen.

Susceptible Culture Species as Host

A susceptible culture species that serves as a host is usually one that is weakened because of stress. Further, the type of culture species and its size and age also affect susceptibility. Not all parasites attack all culture species. Most parasites have a specific host or hosts that they parasitize. This is known as host specificity. The protozoan *Ichthyophthirius multifiliis* is not host specific and parasitizes a wide variety of both coldwater and warmwater fishes, including the rainbow trout and the channel catfish. On the other hand, the channel catfish virus has a very narrow host range, limited exclusively to channel catfish. This virus normally kills only fingerlings, though adults may be carriers. Similarly the monodon baculovirus is host specific to *Penaeus monodon*. Generally, the young of most species are more susceptible to parasites than are older individuals.

Stress

Adverse environmental conditions are stressful and can lower the resistance of a culture species to infectious and non-infectious disease. Thus diseases are the result of interactions between the pathogen, the culture species (host), and the environment. The importance of avoiding stress for disease prevention cannot be overemphasized. This subject was reviewed by Wedemeyer (1970), Wedemeyer and Wood (1974), Snieszko (1974), Wedemeyer and Yasutake (1977), Wedemeyer et al. (1977), Meyer (1979), and Adams (1990) .

Stress may be caused by a number of factors. A partial list includes: excessive handling, disturbances, injury during spawning, temperature fluctuations, overcrowding, deteriorating water quality, nutritional deficiency, and toxic substances in feed and water.

When a culture species is handled, it is frequently removed from water; scales and mucus may be knocked off. Such a break in the skin provides a point of entry for pathogens. Handling culture species during summer is more stressful than handling them during winter. Most farmers avoid handling culture species in summer unless they are slaughtered soon after.

Disturbances of all kinds may stress a culture species -- constant bright lights over culture tanks, banging of doors, and loud talking in the hatchery to name a few. In one of our studies, caged channel catfish were greatly stressed in ponds by the presence of an alligator (*Alligator mississipiensis*). Fish refused to eat until the alligator was removed.

Some culture species may become injured during spawning. An anxious male channel catfish may bite the female to coax her into spawning, sometimes resulting in serious injury. Male tilapia, too, often injure females during the spawning.

Overcrowding is a frequent cause of stress. Too many fish stocked into a culture facility frequently results in deteriorating water quality, particularly low

DO and increased ammonia. Deteriorating water quality is probably the factor that stresses culture species the most. In nature, the standing crop of a culture species is limited to the carrying capacity of the water; natural forces such as limited available food and predation hold numbers in check. When culture species are farmed, predators are usually kept out of the system. Since formulated feeds are often used, the density of a culture species greatly exceeds that found in natural waters. The limiting factor now is deteriorating water quality and not food.

Overcrowding also has social implications. Ejike and Schreck (1980) found that parr coho salmon exhibited a pecking order when stocked together and that subdominant individuals became stressed, according to observed behavioral and hormonal patterns. Fish stocked alone showed no signs of stress. Low stocking rates of a culture species do not automatically reduce stress, however. Schmittou (1969) obtained better growth and survival of caged channel catfish when they were stocked at rates of $500/m^3$ ($654/yd^3$) than when stocked at much lower rates. Apparently, fish were so crowded at $500/m^3$ that they could not establish a pecking order. Goyert and Avault (1978) found that when red swamp crawfish were stocked into tanks at low densities of $10/m^2$ ($12/yd^2$), fighting occurred to establish a pecking order, but at high stocking densities of $40/m^2$ ($48/yd^2$), crawfish shifted to a passive behavior.

Nutritional deficiencies and toxic substances in water and feed also stress culture species. Frequently, stress may result from several factors working in a synergistic manner.

HOW INFECTIOUS DISEASES SPREAD

The most common method for spreading disease is when an infected fish comes in contact with an uninfected fish. External parasites are simply passed on to the new host. If the new host has a mechanical injury, such as the loss of scales, this provides a point of entry. At first, the newly infected host may appear normal, and the infection is said to be subclinical or unapparent. Disease can be spread from the urine and feces of an infected culture species. Wild fish and fish eggs may spread disease. Disease may spread from other animals such as turtles, birds, and frogs. Aquatic birds and snails may serve as temporary hosts for parasites affecting culture species.

Amborski et al. (1974b) pointed out that different aquatic animals may harbor the same ubiquitous pathogens. *Aeromonas hydrophila* that may cause red-leg disease in frogs is the same bacterium that affects channel catfish. Some diseases, such as infectious pancreatic necrosis, a viral disease of trout, are passed on from an infected female to young or to eggs. Facultative pathogens may be ever present in water and easily spread.

Nets, fish handling equipment, and boots can spread disease from one culture facility to the next. Parasites such as leeches, fish lice, and monogenetic trematodes have been implicated as vectors of bacterial and fungal diseases. Transfer of infected culture species or contaminated water between ponds, other culture facilities, or between farms spreads diseases.

EFFECTS OF PARASITES ON CULTURE SPECIES
How Parasites Harm Culture Species

Every parasite found in or on a culture species exerts some degree of harm. The extent of harm may be so slight that no external signs are displayed by the host. Even so the parasite involved should not be, although it often is, considered non-pathogenic. However subtle the noxious effect, every parasite is harmful to its host. Aquaculturists often do not view parasites as problems until culture species show signs of stress or begin dying. Less attention has been given to the chronic or long-term effects of parasites when they are present in sublethal numbers. The effect of parasite loads on growth and general well-being of culture species is an important consideration. Any change in the physiological condition of the host or a predisposing environmental condition may result in a supposedly non-pathogenic parasite becoming pathogenic.

Parasites physically harm culture species by: (1) damage of cells, tissues, and organs, (2) mechanical blockage, (3) consumption of the host's blood and food, (4) poisoning caused by toxin production, and (5) infestation of non-specific sites. All of these may reduce the vitality of the host, interfere with normal physiological functions, and result in death.

Damage at the Cell, Tissue, and Organ Level-- At the cell level, viruses attack individual cells that they enter and control. Progeny viruses are released when cells rupture (lysis) or when the virus buds from the cell membrane. Viruses that cause cell lysis are obviously pathogenic. Viruses may cause harm by disrupting cell structure and function. Viral infection usually results in an inflammatory response, necrosis of tissue, or abnormal tissue proliferation. (Necrosis means death of living tissue.) Some protozoa such as *Eimeria* sp. invade cells (Schäperclaus 1991).

Tissues of a culture species may be irritated by parasites. For example, mass infestation of protozoan parasites such as *Ichthyobodo, Trichodina*, and *Chilodonella* on the skin and gills causes copious secretion of mucus. This disturbs the respiratory function of skin and ionic exchanges of blood. Actual tissue damage is more common and can be attributed to many groups of parasites. The young stages of the ciliated protozoan, *Ichthyophthirius*, burrow into the skin of fish, penetrate the subepithelial layer, and cause damage. With mass infestation of *Ichthyophthirius*, upper layers of skin are sloughed off. Parasitic copepods and leeches penetrate the skin with various injurious consequences to fish. At the point of penetration, scales or tissues are destroyed. This often results in open wounds. Fungi, such as *Saprolegnia*, may at first grow on dead tissue of fish resulting from a primary parasite. As the fungus grows, the mycelium penetrates and destroys healthy tissue.

Gill tissues are especially vulnerable to damage from a diversity of ectoparasites. Protozoans, such as Ich, may cause extensive damage to gill filaments. Monogenetic trematodes, such as *Dactylogyrus*, may produce mass epizootics on the gill filaments of host fish and feed on tissue. Gills also can be destroyed by mass infestation with copepods such as *Ergasilus*. Tissues of the alimentary canal and other internal systems can be damaged by the hooks of attaching tapeworms, spiny-headed worms, and digenetic trematodes. Large bleeding ulcers may result. Protozoans, such as some microsporidians and myxosporidians, produce cysts that lodge in the walls of the intestinal tract. Rupturing cysts can damage the mucosa.

Organs are also vulnerable to damage by a diversity of parasites. Larval stages of helminth parasites as well as other parasites may cause extensive damage to organs during their migration through the host's body. The plerocercoid stage of the tapeworm, *Proteocephalus ambloplitis*, infests the gonads of the largemouth bass (*Micropterus salmoides*) and may result in their destruction. Destruction of the eye lens of certain fish species by the larvae *Diplostomum* sp. results in the so-called parasitic cataract. *Myxosoma cerebralis* destroys the cartilage in organs of balance in trout, resulting in impaired coordination. The myxosporidian *Myxobolus* sp. penetrates the heart of common carp (*Cyprinus carpio*). Bauer (1961) reported that yellow-gray cysts were present in the auricle, with one end projecting into the cardiac muscle and the other end into the pericardial cavity. The pericardium was greatly inflamed and thickened and formed numerous adhesions. The cercaria stage of digenetic trematodes may riddle the heart, liver, kidney, and even the brain of a fish host. Cercariae may virtually cover the organs in the metacercariae stage (Avault and Allison 1965).

Mechanical Blockage-- Mechanical blockage may occur in the alimentary canal and other vessels of the host as well as on the gills. Tapeworms and spiny-headed worms may clog the lumen of the gut. Tapeworms may infest the gut of salmon in great numbers causing partial obstruction, and spiny-headed worms may virtually obstruct the gut of fishes in the region of the pyloric caeca. Bauer (1961) noted that the tapeworm *Caryophyllaeus fimbriceps*, when found in the gut of young carp in numbers up to 40, can obstruct the gut of the host. Nematodes are sometimes found in great numbers within the excretory canals of fish. *Camallanus* sp., for example, has been found in mass protruding from the anus of fish.

Mechanical blockage of gills is not uncommon, and a number of ectoparasites are known to virtually cover gill filaments, making respiration difficult. Some organisms, like the stalked protozoan *Epistylis*, are not thought of as parasites in the true sense. *Epistylis* may be found in waters attached to debris, but on occasion it occurs in great numbers on the gills of fish. The protozoans *Scyphidia* and *Trichophyra* also may interfere with respiration.

Consumption of Host's Blood and Food-- Consumption of the host's blood and food may weaken the host. Parasites such as leeches, copepods, monogenetic trematodes, and certain protozoans may cause anemia by feeding on the blood of their hosts. Bauer (1961) noted that one individual species of monogenetic trematode could withdraw about 0.5 cm^3 of blood from a sturgeon (*Acipenser* sp.) in one day. During an epizootic, some sturgeons carrying up to 300 to 400 parasites would have a blood loss of 200 cm^3. Rapid emaciation of fish followed. Tapeworms, nematodes, and spiny-headed worms all feed on the food found in the intestinal tract of the host. When occurring in great numbers, intestinal parasites undoubtedly convert to their use much of the host's food. Among such parasites are the tapeworms *Eubothrium crassum* in salmon, *E. rugosum* in burbot (*Lota lota*), and *Triaenophorus* sp. in pike (*Esox* sp.).

Toxins-- Poisoning caused by toxins results in one of two ways, those caused by the secretions of special poison glands and those caused by the metabolic activity of the parasite. The fish louse, *Argulus*, has mouth armament with a poison gland, the secretion of which may cause severe harm to young carp, eel (*Anguilla*) elvers, and others. Cercariae of digenetic trematodes possess an enzyme in the penetration gland that aids in dissolving tissue. Bacteria, such as *Aeromonas* spp., produce toxins that destroy tissue. Waste products of endoparasites, such as tapeworms, produce toxic effects; and those of certain ectoparasites, such as gill parasites, may produce toxic effects.

Non-specific Sites-- Infestation of parasites to non-specific sites may seriously harm fish. Bauer (1961), quoting the work of others, gave several examples. Great numbers of *Asymphylodora* sp., usually infesting the gut with no measurable harm, were found in the kidneys of the fish *Rutilus rutilus heckeli* in the Sea of Azov. The kidneys were seriously damaged, resulting in impaired water balance and severe abdominal dropsy. In another case, *Eubothrium* sp. penetrated from the gut into the gall bladder of dolly varden trout (*Salvelinus alpinus malma*). The strobila blocked the hepatic duct so that bile could not drain properly. In a third case, mass mortality of *Acerina cernua* was caused by severe infestation with *Diplostomum spathaceum*. The parasite was found not only in the eyes (its normal loci) but also in the brain. Sometimes a parasite or one of its larval stages occurs in a host that is not necessary for the completion of its life cycle. Such a host is called a paratenic host.

Reaction of a Culture Species to Disease

Two major events occur. First, external signs are displayed. The culture species does not appear normal. It may gasp at the surface, respire rapidly, swim lethargically, flash, and rub against the bottom or stop feeding. Certain signs displayed are characteristic of a particular disease. For example, trout with the whirling disease tend to swim around in tight circles.

Second, internal changes are taking place, and a culture species goes through three basic stages. According to Wedemeyer (1980):

(1) Adrenaline and other stress hormones are produced, causing a series of metabolic changes that help culture species resist stress.

(2) Resistance is ultimately reached, and the culture species adjusts -- that is, if the stressor is not too overpowering.

(3) If the disease is too severe or long-lasting, exhaustion occurs. Disease resistance is lost, and death comes.

When culture species are stressed, metabolic changes occur to help the culture species survive. Wedemeyer (1980) listed them as: (1) Blood sugar increases and liver glycogen decreases because of adrenaline production. (2) Blood salt levels decrease. (3) Circulating blood clotting cells increase, and blood clotting time decreases. (4) Inflammation and immune response are suppressed with decreased numbers of circulating white blood cells.

When stress is caused by a parasite, the parasite acts as an antigen, and the host produces antibodies that attack the intruding antigen. A capsule may form around the parasite to wall it off. White blood cells increase in numbers to fight the infection (parasite). Changes may occur in tissues that sometimes give rise to abnormal appearances.

The inflammatory response is the major protective response to tissue damage and is common to all vertebrates. An increased blood supply is sent to the damaged area (hyperemia), and white blood cells flow directly from capillaries into tissues (transudation). The affected part shows reddening, swelling, heat, pain, and may lose function. Inflammation may occur not only in tissues but also in entire physiological systems such as the alimentary canal.

Hypertrophy may occur in poorly specialized tissues, such as epithelium and connective tissues. For example, epithelial hyperplasia may be caused by the reaction of gill epithelium to infestation of various monogenetic trematodes such as *Dactylogyrus*. *Dactylogyrus* also may cause the formation of very long, thin filaments. Eventually the hyperplastic cells are sloughed off, often taking the parasite with them.

Often tissues of a host respond to the presence of a parasite by metaplasia, causing change in function and structure. Such might be a change of cylindrical cells to cuboidal cells. Epithelial tissues of fish contain groups of cells that secrete mucus. Harmful effects on the epithelial tissue result in increased numbers of such cells that are transformed from ordinary epithelial cells.

In some instances, the host may form a sheath-like membrane around the parasites or their larvae. Parasite larvae remaining inside the host for a long time may eventually be killed by calcium deposition (calcification). Sometimes pigment also is deposited which aggregates around the parasite larvae. The pigment is usually a melanin. In some instances, parasites may trigger morbid growth of tissues with formation of tumors. The viral disease caused by *Lymphocytes*, for example, causes hypertrophic growth of fish tissue.

SEASONAL OCCURRENCE OF DISEASES

Disease outbreaks may occur at any time. Yet some diseases seem more prevalent during certain seasons of the year. Four factors relating to seasonality of disease are: (1) physiological condition of the culture species, (2) handling and spawning of the culture species, (3) stress caused by adverse environmental conditions, and (4) the physiological requirements of the disease-causing organism. By understanding these factors you can be better prepared to prevent an occurrence of disease.

Physiological Condition of Culture Species

Each culture species has an optimum water temperature where it functions best. During winter when water temperatures drop in temperate countries, both warmwater and coldwater species become less active. The channel catfish, for example, may virtually cease to feed below 10°C (50°F). Its physiological process slows down; the fish may lose weight, become lethargic, and its ability to produce antibodies lessens. By spring the channel catfish, in its poorest physiological condition, begins to feed more frequently and improves its overall health. Similarly, disease-causing organisms may undergo a winter period of inactivity, and with the onset of spring they too become more active. Only they may recover more rapidly than fish.

Rogers (1969), Meyer (1970), and Plumb (1975) reviewed the seasonal occurrence of finfish diseases and reported that spring is when most diseases are reported. Rogers (1969) noted that cases due to bacteria reached a peak in April and gradually declined throughout the summer, whereas parasitic cases had distinct peaks in March and September. Meyer (1970) noted that the greatest incidence of disease was in April. It had almost 50% more cases than July, the next highest month. Outbreaks occurred regularly from March through July (Table 10.2).

Besides water temperature, other water quality parameters may seasonally lower the physiological condition of culture species. For example, shrimp may be stressed during the dry or rainy seasons if salinity cannot be controlled. Disease may occur. Certain culture species may be stressed during spring or fall when nitrite levels may become elevated.

Table 10.2 Monthly incidence of disease cases(a) July, 1963 - July, 1968.

Cause	Jan	Feb	Mar	Apr	May	June	July	Aug	Sept	Oct	Nov	Dec
Scyphidia	7	4	10	19	11	12	18	0	0	2	5	0
Ichthyophthirius	11	10	9	12	5	3	1	0	1	1	5	0
Chilodonella	4	2	4	4	3	0	2	2	1	0	0	0
Costia	1	3	4	8	2	2	5	2	1	0	2	0
Trichodina	12	2	21	28	27	29	22	3	1	3	6	0
Plistophora ovariae	0	0	9	12	4	2	0	4	3	0	0	0
Henneguya	2	5	8	8	4	4	4	0	1	1	0	0
Trichophyra	4	1	2	8	6	3	5	0	0	0	3	0
Lernaea	0	0	0	5	4	7	7	3	9	2	0	0
Cleidodiscus	7	6	5	13	8	10	16	0	1	0	3	0
Gyrodactylus	4	3	9	16	11	1	1	0	0	0	0	0
Myxobacteria	3	1	3	11	5	8	9	10	5	4	0	1
Pseudomonas sp.	1	0	2	0	2	2	2	3	0	0	2	0
Aeromonas liquefaciens	6	3	5	11	9	13	19	15	7	5	4	2
Oxygen depletions	0	0	0	1	2	13	15	8	3	0	0	0
Totals	63	40	98	166	112	114	127	51	33	18	30	3 = 855
% of Totals	7.4	4.7	11.5	19.4	13.1	13.3	14.8	6.0	3.9	2.1	3.5	0.3 = 100

(a) Data based on golden shiner (*Notemigonus crysoleucas*) and channel catfish (*Ictalurus punctatus*) combined.

Source: Meyer 1970.

Handling and Spawning

A culture species may be handled more at certain times of the year than at others, for example during the spawning season when brood stock are seined and moved. Even without handling, spawning activities stress fish. During spawning, injury may occur to one or both partners. Some brooders discontinue feeding during spawning. Most tilapia, being mouth brooders, cease feeding during egg incubation. Meyer (1970) reported that a peak incidence of protozoan epizootics occurred during and immediately after spawning periods of shiners (*Notemigonus crysoleucas*) and channel catfish. Protozoans were especially prevalent on very young fish.

Stress

The incidence of disease following stress is well documented. A good example is the occurrence of bacterial infections from low DO stress. *Aeromonas hydrophila*, for example, often causes disease 10 to 14 days following low DO. Meyer (1970) documented that epizootics of *A. hydrophila* in channel catfish ponds occurred mostly during summer, coinciding with periods of low DO stress.

Physiological Condition of Parasite

Like culture species, parasites also function best under optimum environmental conditions. Ich is sometimes called a coolwater parasite, and it is most common in spring and fall. When water temperatures exceed 28°C (82°F), this parasite seldom poses a problem. The fungus *Saprolegnia* sp. also favors cooler water. Richards (1978), quoting others, pointed out that saprolegniasis of eels ceased when the water temperature rose above 18°C (64°F). (Note: A word ending in -asis denotes a disease.) On the other hand, fungal infection of white suckers (*Catostomus commersoni*) may take place when temperatures exceed 10°C (50°F). Richards and Roberts (1978) reported that disease outbreaks caused by the bacterium *Cytophaga* (formerly *Flexibacter*) *columnaris* usually occur at temperatures in excess of 18°C (64°F), but highly virulent strains may require a less dramatic temperature rise to produce severe infections. In pond fish culture, the threshold for infection is usually greater than 20°C (68°F).

Water quality also affects the prevalence of certain diseases. Richards and Roberts (1978) noted that *C. columnaris* is more likely to occur in hard water or in water with a high pH and high level of organics.

DIAGNOSING DISEASES

There are five situations in which a culture species should be diagnosed for disease, according to Hoffman and Mitchell (1978):

(1) When there are obvious signs of disease. Fish may be dead and dying, or show external signs of white patches, blotches, swollen bellies, or popped eyes. Fish also may behave abnormally or stop feeding.

(2) When fish appear healthy, but there is reason to suspect the presence of disease agents. This could occur after control measures were used and you want to see if they worked, or if it appears that a chronic disease problem persists.

(3) When shipping live fish to facilities where diseases are known to occur.

(4) When bringing in fish from another farm.

(5) When a pesticide contamination is suspected. As a safeguard in case of legal action, it is necessary to demonstrate that infectious diseases did not kill the fish.

Klontz (1979), McDaniel (1979), and Brown and Gratzek (1980) all gave detailed guidelines for diagnostic methodology. Meyer and Barclay (1990) developed a particularly useful field manual for the investigation of fish kills. The "Bluebook," published by the Fish Health Section of the American Fisheries Society, is widely used by disease diagnosticians (Thoesen 1994).

On-site Inspection

At the site of trouble, observe, record, and collect. Sick and dying culture species may display certain behavior typically seen with certain infectious and non-infectious disease outbreaks. Events 14 days preceding the outbreak of disease should be carefully recorded. Include handling culture species, changes in water temperature, cleaning of culture facilities, and any other germane change or activity. Keep detailed written records, especially if you suspect an outside influence such as nearby crop spraying or dumping of harmful substances into source water. Routine records should show the species affected, size, age, and numbers. Note the type of feed used and date acquired, method of storage, amount fed, method and frequency of feeding, and response to feeding. The estimated standing crop should be calculated.

Detailed written records are important for three reasons. First, you might quickly note that a particular parasite is causing culture species to die, and therefore dispense with further record keeping. If so, the pre-disposing condition (inferior feed, poor water quality, and toxic substances in feed or water, etc.) may not be discovered, and the parasite problem could reoccur. Second, if the crop is insured, a complete written history will be needed of events leading to the fish kill. Finally, if a law suit should ensue, documentation is necessary. In this instance pictures should be taken; the loss should be estimated carefully, and the time when culture species began dying should be noted to the nearest hour.

As records are being made, water and fish samples should be collected. Certain water quality parameters, such as DO, pH, water hardness, and alkalinity, should be measured on site. Others can be measured in the laboratory. Extra samples of water should be frozen and held in case it is necessary to have the water checked for heavy metals and toxins.

Three kinds of fish should be collected: (1) clinically healthy (asymptomatic) fish, (2) clinically sick fish, and (3) recently dead fish (within hours of death). Fish that have been dead for a considerable time may no longer harbor the agent that caused their death. These fish will be examined later for parasites and non-infectious disease symptoms; in addition a sample should be frozen if further analysis is required. McDaniel (1979) suggested a minimum sample size that provides a 95% confidence that an infected specimen will be included in the sample. This assumes a minimum incidence of infection greater than 2% or 5% (Table 10.3).

Table 10.3 The minimum sample size for each lot that provided a 95% confidence that an infected specimen will be included in the fish sampled, assuming a minimum incidence of infection greater than 2% or 5%.

Population or lot size	Incidence 2% size of sample	Incidence 5% size of sample
50	48	34
100	77	44
250	112	52
500	128	55
1,000	138	57
1,500	142	57
2,000	143	58
4,000	146	58
10,000	147	58
100,000 or larger	148	58

Source: McDaniel 1979.

Sending a Culture Species for Examination

Some aquaculture farms are equipped to determine the cause (etiology) of diseases. Certain parasites can be readily identified with a microscope, yet viral and bacterial organisms require isolation and special culture techniques to establish identity. It then becomes necessary to submit culture species to a diagnostician. In 1981, there were approximately 100 laboratories listed in North America where some diagnostic services could be obtained. The Fish Health Section of the American Fisheries Society also has a list of certified diagnosticians.

A culture species may be submitted for examination in one of three ways: live, frozen, or preserved.

(1) Live fish that appear sick but seem healthy enough to survive transit can be transported by automobile. Fish can be placed in a bucket of water with a portable aerator. If the weather is hot, ice in a water-tight bag can be placed inside the bucket. The culture species also may be transported alive in plastic bags. Place five to seven fingerlings, juveniles, or one large animal in about 3 liters (0.8 gal) of water in a plastic bag. Press out the air, and fill the bag to capacity with oxygen. Tie the top securely, and pack the bag in a strong box with a Styrofoam liner. During hot weather place a bag of crushed ice alongside the bag of fish unless the fish are tropical, such as tilapia. The box should be labeled "Biological Specimens -- Perishable." At time of shipment, notify the diagnostic lab when and how the fish will arrive.

(2) Frozen fish also may be sent. If the fish are to be checked for virus, they may be submitted frozen. Some laboratories also accept frozen fish for bacterial examination. If shipped, they should be placed in a thick Styrofoam box and cooled with dry ice. Carbon dioxide from the thawing ice should not reach the fish but should be able to escape from the container. If fish reach their destination in less than 24 hours, wet ice can be used.

(3) Preserved fish are usually not a desired way to ship fish. However, after checking with the laboratory, you may be able to ship preserved fish if certain parasites are suspect -- *Ichthyophthirius multifiliis*, anchor parasites, and leeches. To preserve fish, slit the body cavity and place the fish in a container of 10% formalin for 1 or 2 days. The container can be shipped or you can remove the culture species from the formalin, wrap it in paper or cloth soaked in formalin, place it in a sealed plastic bag, and place this in a box for shipping.

Regardless of the method used, complete data should accompany the specimen including name, address, telephone number, species, water quality data, past history of when the disease outbreak occurred, symptoms while in water, treatment if any, feeding regimes, and any recent stress or handling of fish.

Examination of a Culture Species

Prerequisite for examination of a culture species is knowledge of the anatomy. Also needed are equipment and materials including a microscope, glass slides, cover slips, two dissecting needles, heavy and light scissors, a scalpel with extra blades, and a small bottle with water and eye dropper. If marine species are examined, wet mount preparations of gills or tissues are prepared with 3% salt water. With this equipment and materials, culture species are examined by one of six methods: (1) parasitological, (2) virological, (3) bacteriological, (4) toxicological, (5) hematological, and (6) histopathological.

478

Parasitological-- Parasitological methods involve specimen necropsy both externally and internally. Healthy fish are examined first to establish the normal appearance (Figure 10.2). Next, the external body surfaces and gills of sick fish are examined with the unaided eye to note any abnormalities. Certain large ectoparasites can be seen if present. Many parasites, however, cannot be seen with the unaided eye and require microscopic examination. Start the magnification at 10 x with a dissecting microscope. This magnification allows you to scan a large surface area for parasites that might be overlooked at higher magnification. Monogenea, large protozoans such as Ich, *Epistylis*, *Chilodonella*, and copepod larvae, are seen at 10 x.

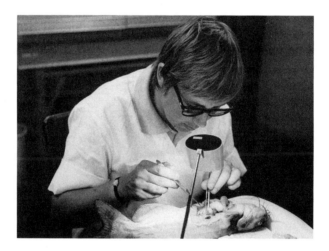

Figure 10.2 Edmonde Jaspers, formerly of the LSU Agricultural Center, examines channel catfish.

After the gills and external surfaces have been examined, wet mounts should be made of gill filaments and of mucus scraped from the body surface. A small portion of gill filaments cut from the outer gill arch is placed in several drops of water between a microscope slide and cover slip. Take mucus samples from the margin of lesions if any are present. Scan samples first at 10 x and then at higher magnification. Certain parasites, such as *Ichthyobodo*, are usually visible only at 500 x.

Begin internal examination by making a ventral midline incision from between the pectoral fins posterior to the anus. If bacterial cultures of the abdominal cavity are to be made, do not incise the anus. Further lateral cuts can be made in the musculature to expose the viscera,. The viscera should be examined for abnormal appearance, color, fluid accumulation, positioning, size changes, or for the presence of cysts, worms, or other parasites. After this examination, the internal organs can be removed, separated, and dissected for further examination. The eyes and brain also can be removed and examined. Make wet mounts of any suspect tissues or cysts.

If parasites are detected during the external or internal necropsy, they must be identified to prescribe the proper control measure. Sometimes a novice may be confused with a larval stage of a parasite that appears wholly unlike the adult. With experience, you should be able to identify many of the commonly occurring parasites -- particularly with the aid of a key, such as Hoffman's (1967) key to the fish parasites of North America or Wellborn and Roger's key to protozoan parasites (1966). A key to major groups of parasites is given in Table 10.4.

Table 10.4 Guide to the general identification of fish parasites [a].

---

1. Organism microscopic 2
    Organism not microscopic, visible to naked eye 4

2. Body one-celled, or part of a group of similar cells . . . . Protozoa
    Body multicellular 3

3. Organism worm-like; equipped with hooks and hooklets at
        posterior end of body; external parasites . . . . Monogenea
    Organism not worm-like; encysted on surface of gills or fins,
        body in form of two hinged halves . . . . Glochidia

4. Organism encysted on external surface of host. 5
    Organism not encysted on external surface of host 8

5. Cyst containing one organism 6
    Cyst containing thousands of organisms (Sporozoa) . . . . Protozoa

6. Body of organism in cyst in form of two hinged halves . . . . .Glochidia
    Body not in form of two hinged halves 7

7. Organism one-celled (*Ichthyophthirius*) . . . . Protozoa
    Organism multicellular . . . . Digenea

8. Body more or less flattened 9
    Body not flat 14

9. Body segmented 10
    Body not segmented 11

480

Table 10.4 continued.

10. Organism with anterior and posterior suckers,
    digestive tract present, external parasites only
    (may occur in mouth) . . . . Hirudinea
    Organism with single anterior holdfast which
    may have several suckers, digestive tract
    absent, intestinal parasites. . . . . Cestoda

11. Organism with mouth and gut cavities, no anus,
    well developed organs of attachment 12
    Organism without mouth or gut cavities;
    poorly developed suckers at anterior end 13

12. Organism equipped with hooks and hooklets
    at posterior holdfast . . . . Monogenea
    Organism lacking posterior hooks, equipped
    with oral and ventral suckers . . . . Digenea

13. Internal organs present, visible with aid
    of reflected light (Caryophyllidea) . . . . Cestoda
    Internal organs absent (larval forms) . . . . Cestoda

14. Body cylindrical 15
    Body not cylindrical 17

15. Body plastic, organism active, movements eel-like . . . . Nematoda
    Body not plastic, form fairly rigid 16

16. Intestinal parasites, organism with numerous
    spines on proboscis at anterior end . . . . .Acanthocephala
    External parasites, organism with antler-like
    protuberances at anterior end (Lernaea). . . . . .Copepoda

17. Body leaf-like; resembling fish scale (*Argulus*) . . . . Copepoda
    Body variable; with obvious appendages for
    attachment to gills of host . . . . Misc. Copepoda

[a] Prepared by F.P. Meyer, former chief of the U.S. Fish Farming
Experimental Station, Stuttgart, Arkansas.
Source: Inman and Hambric 1970.

Knowledge of the life cycle of a parasite and its larval stages is necessary. To verify your diagnosis, parasites can be preserved and sent to a specialist. Protozoans can be killed and preserved in 10% formalin. Monogenetic and digenetic trematodes can be killed in 90°C (194°F) 10% formalin and preserved in 10% formalin. Encysted forms should be freed before killing. Nematodes can be killed in 90°C 70% alcohol. Care should be taken to prevent a fire hazard. The vial of alcohol should be placed in a beaker of water for heating. Acanthocephala should be dropped in 90°C 10% formalin after the proboscis is extended. Parasitic copepods and *Argulus* can be killed and preserved in 70% alcohol. If staining, processing, or mounting is required, refer to Meyer and Olsen (1975).

Virological-- Virological methods involve isolation and identification of the specific virus. Viruses propagate only in living cells. Fish diagnostic laboratories may carry cultures of fish cells that are known to be susceptible to the virus. When a viral problem is suspected, the culture species should be taken to a diagnostic laboratory alive, on ice, or in 50% glycerol depending on the nature of the suspected virus. Brown and Gratzek (1980) described the generalized technique, and McDaniel (1979) outlined in detail the step by step methodology. To generalize, tissues from a culture species suspected of having a viral disease are pulverized, treated with antibiotics, or passed through a bacterial retaining filter. This sample is used to inoculate a layer of fish cells growing in a test tube. Cell cultures are maintained in artificial media and observed with a microscope.

If cell cultures begin dying or show distinct morphological changes, virus is suspect. Presumptive diagnosis of a particular viral disease is made when a cell line develops the particular morphological changes (cytopathic effect, CPE) associated with that virus. Fluorescent antibody staining can detect virus infections. Flourescein tagged (antivirus) antibody combines with the virus, which can be detected with a microscope equipped with a mercury lamp and proper filter. An isolation of virus is confirmed when in later tests the CPE is neutralized by mixing the virus with antiviral antibodies previously made by injecting rabbits. This is known as a virus neutralization test.

Bacteriological-- Bacteriological methods involve culture and staining on nutrient agar. Bacteria can be broken down into two groups depending on reaction to a Gram stain. Gram-negative bacteria appear red or pink. This group of bacteria includes most of the fish pathogens such as *Aeromonas, Pseudomonas, Cytophaga*, and *Vibrio*. Gram-positive bacteria look dark blue under a microscope. *Corynebacterium* is an example. To obtain a sample, cut the culture species open with a sterilized pair of scissors. Take care not to cut open any organs or the alimentary tract. Once laid open, a loop that has been flamed and cooled is used to touch the spleen or kidney. The loop with sample is then used to inoculate a plate containing growth media such as trypticase soy agar or blood agar. The same procedure can be repeated for samples from the liver, kidney, or body tissues. To inoculate a plate, pass the loop lightly over the agar in a zig-zag manner, leaving less and less inoculant as you progress. Incubate plates at 26° to 30°C (79° to 86°F) for 24 to 48 hours for identification and antibiotic sensitivity testing. Tubes (slants) also may be inoculated. Growth patterns of bacterial colonies on both plates and slants are often characteristic of species of bacteria and may aid in identification.

Toxicological-- Toxicological methods, which determine the presence of toxic residues, require expensive equipment and sophisticated techniques such as gas chromatography, atomic absorption spectrometry, and flame photometry. Therefore it is usually necessary to send samples to a toxicology laboratory. Feed and water should be sent frozen in sealed, labeled plastic containers, and fish should be alive or frozen. Since the methodology is time consuming and expensive, the aquaculturist should suggest the possible toxic agent(s) that is suspected.

Hematological-- Hematological methods involve making blood smears for detection of haematozoa or blood examination. For finfish, blood can be obtained from cardiac puncture or caudal puncture. The easiest method, however, is to sever the caudal peduncle of a freshly killed fish. Collect blood in capillary tubes or drop directly onto slides for smears. Smears are air dried, fixed immediately with absolute methyl alcohol, and stained with a blood stain such as Wright-Giemsa. Loeffler's methylene blue is often used for field work. Microscopic examination for the presence of infectious organisms follows.

Histopathological-- Histopathological methods are sometimes used for cases of infectious and non-infectious diseases in which gross findings are not diagnostic. Samples of infected tissue, not to exceed 6 mm (0.25 in) thick, are placed in 10% neutral buffered formalin or Bouin's fixative. Samples can be sliced, a layer at a time, with a micrometer, stained, mounted, and examined under a microscope.

PREVENTION OF DISEASES
There are a number of methods for prevention of disease.

Surveillance of Fish
The health of a culture species should be monitored continually. This is done by noting general behavior and feeding activity, and by occasional examination for infectious and non-infectious disease.

Monitoring Water Quality

Water quality parameters, such as DO, ammonia, and nitrite, should be monitored routinely. Water should be free of toxins.

Use of Disease-free Eggs, Fingerlings, and Larvae

Buy eggs, fingerlings, and larvae from a reputable dealer. Certain states require by law that eggs or young must be certified free of particular diseases. This requires an examination by a qualified pathologist. The culture species need not be certified free from all diseases, and some states have no certification program. Most diagnosticians do not certify fish disease free. They examine fish and report on their finding. A buyer can then accept or reject the fish and ask the dealer about any disease problems.

Viral diseases of salmonids and, more recently, marine shrimps have received much attention as regards certification. Wolf (1988) discussed viral diseases of salmonids having high virulence. If diseases are introduced to a new area or farm, the result can be devastating. Lightner and Redman (1992) noted that transporting penaeid stocks between facilities and between different geographic regions has introduced five of the six known shrimp viruses to regions where they may not have previously existed. Lightner (1983) noted that avoidance of shrimp viral diseases by use of specific pathogen-free (SPF) stocks is emerging in the shrimp farming industry. DeVoe (1992) and Rosenfield and Mann (1992) reviewed the pros and cons of introductions and transfers of culture species, with the aim of achieving a balance between economic development and resource protection.

Some aquaculture farms may have a chronic problem with a particular parasite; others may have an occasional problem. Healthy fish often have low-level populations of parasites, but this should not be cause for rejection. For example, channel catfish may harbor *Trichodina, Chilodonella, Trichophyra,*and *Dactylogyrus*. If such parasites are present, they can be controlled before shipment.

Mitchell and Hoffman (1981) suggested methods to prepare a shipment of channel catfish to states requiring a health permit. Before treatment do not feed fish for 24 hours. Treat fish with formalin in a tank with flowing water. A total water exchange in 30 minutes or less must be possible for fingerling and adult fish, and less than 10 minutes for very small fingerlings, those less than 8 cm (3 in). Fish may be treated with 166 to 200 ppm formalin (37% commercial formaldehyde). In soft, acid waters and in very warm water, not more than 166 ppm should be used. Some farmers use 100 ppm with very small fingerlings and 50 ppm with fry for one-half hour. Fish must be watched constantly during treatment. The more fish being treated, and the greater the parasite load, the greater the chance of stress. Immediately after treatment, fish may gasp at the surface but they usually go down. When they later return to the top a second time and will not scare down when a hand is passed over the top, it is time to flush the tank. Wait at least 48 hours after treatment before fish are shipped.

After treatment and prior to shipment, inspect fish for ectoparasites. Attempts to isolate bacteria and viruses may be futile unless clinical signs are evident. Non-virulent forms of bacteria, such as *Aeromonas hydrophila*, exist in waters and in healthy fish, making isolates from healthy fish questionable. Regarding viruses, the channel catfish virus affects fish less than 13 cm (5 in) long at water temperatures above 21°C (70°F). Unless an active infection is evident, there is no way to detect the virus. During shipment fish may be transported in 10 ppm acriflavine, tris-buffers, or other bactericide to suppress bacterial buildup. Salt can also be added to shipment water to aid fish in osmoregulation and reduce stress.

Control of Wild Fish and Other Animals

Wild fish frequently harbor infectious diseases and must be kept out of culture waters. If they do gain entry, they must be eliminated. As pointed out before, tadpoles, frogs, turtles, and other animals may harbor certain pathogens that infect fish. Certain animals, such as snails and aquatic birds, may serve as temporary hosts for fish parasites. These animals should be controlled if feasible.

Drying Out and Treatment of Pond Bottoms

Pond bottoms can be dried out to help control diseases. They also can be treated with quick lime.

Sanitation

Culture facilities and equipment should be kept clean as a routine practice. Buildup of feces, uneaten feed, dead eggs, and egg shells in culture or hatching units encourage growth of certain disease-causing organisms. Certain fungi, bacteria, and protozoans may first become established on organic matter and later attack young or eggs. Some disease problems can be prevented by disinfecting nets, seines, and other equipment by dipping them in a solution of 10% formalin. Chlorine is also effective at 100 ppm for 1 hour. Nets and seines should be rinsed in water after disinfection.

Clary (1978a) recommended use of settling ponds and sand filters (swimming pool type) to help remove both settleable solids and fish pathogens from trout hatcheries. Two settling ponds in series are constructed at the water source. The ponds, 23 m (75 ft) long, 8 m (26 ft) wide, and 1.5 m (5 ft) deep, remove 90% to 95% of incoming settleable solids. Three aerators, 1,325 liters/min (350 gpm) flow, in each pond help to oxidize organic material, thus reducing toxic un-ionized ammonia. Water also is oxygenated before it enters the hatchery. Water to nursery units is run through two banks of parallel sand filters, thus allowing backflushing without breaking the flow of filtered water. The filters remove all remaining suspended matter that can cause problems with eggs, fry, and fingerlings. If the water supply has a high pathogen load, install an ultraviolet sterilizer. These units kill 95% to 98% of waterborne pathogens (Clary 1978b).

There are three types of ultraviolet energy, long, middle, and short wave. Short waves of about 2537°A (253.7 nanometers) are lethal to microorganisms, but the rays must strike the microorganisms to kill them. Effectiveness also depends on time and intensity. Ultraviolet light from germicidal lamps destroys only microorganisms, with no harm to fish.

Quarantine

When a fish population contacts an infectious disease, isolate it from other fish populations. Mixing diseased fish with healthy fish is a sure way to spread disease. It is also advisable to temporarily quarantine new fish to an operation before mixing them with existing stocks.

Separate Young From Brood Fish

Brood fish may be carriers of a disease organism with no apparent signs. The brood fish may have at one time been survivors of an epizootic, built up an immunity, and retained a few of the pathogens. Their young, however, have not developed immunity and are susceptible. Brood channel catfish, for example, may be carriers of the CCVD with no apparent harm, yet the CCVD is readily passed on to fry and small fingerlings. Certain diseases of trout are readily passed on to eggs and subsequently to young. The best practice is to separate eggs or young from adults as soon as possible.

Destruction of Diseased Culture Species

When certain presently incurable diseases such as CCVD of channel catfish and viral hemorrhagic septicemia (VHS) of trout occur, remove the diseased fish from the culture unit and destroy them.

Change the Environment

To prevent the occurrence of a fish pathogen, you must determine its biological requirements. Ich is known as a "coolwater" protozoan and can be prevented by keeping the water temperature above 28°C (82°F). The CCVD is also temperature dependent, and when the water temperature drops below 18° to 20°C (64° to 68°F), the disease ceases to pose a problem.

Sometimes we can increase the water flow to mechanically flush parasites down the drain. The protozoan Ich has a free swimming stage called a tomite. It can be flushed away from fish that are held in swiftly flowing water.

Some parasites are found on freshwater fishes, others on saltwater species. By culturing a freshwater fish in brackish water and visa versa, it may be possible to control certain parasites. Channel catfish can be cultured in water up to 8 ppt salinity with no noticeable problems from parasites. Allen and Avault (1970) demonstrated in laboratory studies that Ich could be prevented by holding catfish in low salinity water, 1 ppt for up to 1 week.

Immunization

Immunization of fishes was reviewed by Snieszko (1970b), Anderson (1974), Evelyn (1977), Busch (1978a), Amend (1980), and Ellis (1988). Immunology was reviewed in Marine Fisheries Review Vol. 40, No. 3 (1978). Crustacean immunity was reviewed by Söderhäll and Cerenius (1992).

Immunity is a condition of being able to resist a particular disease. This ability may be natural or acquired. Natural immunity means that a species is born with the immunity. For example, the rainbow trout is immune to the CCVD. Acquired immunity can be obtained in one of two ways, passive or active. With passive immunity a species is subjected to prepared antigens (antiserum) that result in the host's producing antibodies.

With active immunity, a species may contact a disease, survive, and later build up an immunity. Some workers have suggested that fish surviving an epizootic of Ich, for example, should be retained as future brood stock in hopes that this immunity will be passed on to progeny. Anderson (1974) quoted Schäperclaus (1954) on acquired immunization with carp. He showed that 1-, 2-, and 3-year-old carp that lived through epizootics of *Aeromonas hydrophila* developed higher and higher degrees of protection against the disease. Schäperclaus suggested that this could immunize carp on a commercial basis. Infected fish could be released into young populations, and those survivors having an acquired immunity would be raised through to market or brood stock size.

Immunization, as now practiced in commercial aquaculture, is a process of exposing an animal to the causative agent of a disease so that the animal is not harmed but instead builds a protective immunity. The vaccine is usually made of killed bacteria so that it is not only immunogenic to the animal but is also safe to handle. A vaccine is prepared from the same serotype variant that is causing the problem. A serotype is a strain of a particular disease organism. A vaccine against a single serotype of an organism (monovalent vaccine) protects against infection by that serotype but may give only partial or no protection against other serotypes of the same organism.

There are several ways to apply a vaccine: injection, oral, spray, and immersion. Injection is effective but can be time consuming and costly. Oral vaccines are administered with the feed. Protection from oral vaccines may be short in duration. Vaccine can be sprayed under pressure through the skin and may show promise for treating large volumes of fish. Immersion seems to be the most practical method. Immersion simply involves dipping batches of the culture species for a short time, perhaps 20 seconds, in a vaccine solution.

The size and age of the culture species and water temperature all influence the effectiveness of immunization. Immunity is related to fish size at vaccination, with larger fish retaining immunity longer. Salmonids must be at least 1 g (0.03 oz) or larger before they respond to vaccination. That is why it is desirable to vaccinate salmonids against enteric redmouth and vibriosis when fish are 4 to 4.5 g (0.14 to 0.16 oz) or larger. Temperature affects the time to acquire immunity and the length of immunity. If fish are immunized in winter, there may be a lag time of 10 to 60 days during which time fish are not protected (Busch 1978a) (Figure 10.3). Channel catfish will not respond to immunization at temperatures less than 14°C (57°F). After immunization, there is a time when fish are protected, the maintenance phase, and when they begin to lose protection, a decline phase. That is why it may be necessary to give a booster immunization; this second vaccination may result in an even higher level of protection.

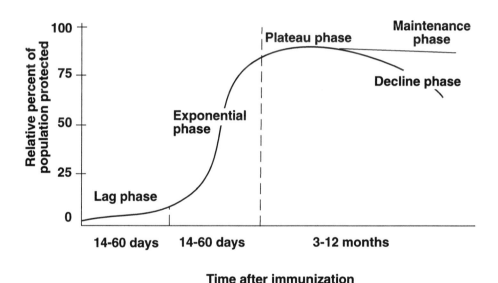

Figure 10.3 The development of relative disease protection in a population of fish after immunization against the same disease. Source: Busch 1978a. Data based on trout.

Biological Controls

Some parasites, particularly certain helminth parasites, spend a part of their life cycle in an intermediate host such as a snail. By controlling these hosts, disease prevention is possible. In one study, the redear sunfish (*Lepomis microlophus*) was used to control snails infested with the white grub (*Posthodiplostomum minimum*) of bluegills (*L. microchirus*) (Avault and Allison 1965). Experimental pools were stocked with infested snails and bluegill, the susceptible host. Half the pools were also stocked with redear; half were not. Redears, by feeding on snails, significantly reduced infestation by *P. minimum* to bluegill. Other helminths may use copepods, insect nymphs, and oligochaetes for intermediate hosts, but biological control is virtually unknown. Probably the most noteworthy example is the stocking of wrasse (*Halichoeres* spp.) into floating net-pens of Atlantic salmon (*Salmo salar*) to control sea lice (*Argulus*).

Use of Resistant Strains and Species

For a parasite to live in or on a host, there must be: (1) suitable conditions for access to the host, involving a dependable means of transmission from one host to another, (2) a portal of entry through skin, gills, and mucus, (3) ability to establish itself in a host when it reaches one, and (4) satisfactory conditions for growth and reproduction after it establishes itself.

The interplay of these factors determines in which host a parasite lives. Every parasite has one or more host species. Others like the channel catfish virus affect only this species of fish and are therefore very host specific. Plumb et al. (1975) fed virus to six strains of channel catfish and noted significant differences in mortality ranging from 10% to 71%. You might then consider farming a strain of channel catfish that is least affected by CCVD if the disease is a serious problem. Another consideration is to grow the blue catfish (*Ictalurus furcatus*).

In one study, bluegill, redear sunfish, and their hybrids were experimentally exposed with cercariae of *Posthodiplostomum minimum* (Avault and Smitherman 1965). Each fish was examined for metacercariae 30 days after fish were exposed to cercariae. Bluegill each averaged 121 parasites, redear sunfish one parasite, and the hybrid was intermediate with 98. This example points out that different species and hybrids may all be infested by a given parasite, but the degree of parasitism may vary greatly.

In some instances, a viral infection has been so devastating that an entire aquaculture industry has been virtually shut down. In Taiwan the monodon baculovirus (MBV) had such an effect beginning in 1988. *Penaeus monodon* was very hard hit by MVB. Some farmers switched to milkfish (*Chanos chanos*) farming; others considered shrimp species that may not be affected by MVB.

Avoidance of Stress

This is one of the most important ways in which to prevent disease. The culture species should be well fed, not overcrowded, and not handled excessively. Good water quality must be maintained. An easy way to avoid stress is to stock the culture species in low numbers and subsequently use a small amount of feed. Water quality should be very good, but production and profit would be low. An aquaculturist must then make a tradeoff by stocking the culture species at relatively high rates to maximize profit, but not high enough to cause chronic stress.

CONTROL OF DISEASES

Non-infectious disease can be controlled by correcting the particular problem -- poor nutrition, toxins in feed or water, and poor water quality. For example, brown-blood disease is caused by poor water quality and was virtually unheard of until farmers began using high stocking densities of channel catfish and high feeding rates. Organic wastes accumulated. Ordinarily, organic wastes are broken down to ammonia to nitrite to nitrate. Un-ionized ammonia (NH_3) is toxic to fish, but ionized ammonium (NH_4^+) is not. Nitrite, an intermediate product of decomposition, is the culprit in brown-blood disease. When the organic load is high, nitrites may accumulate, particularly in cool waters. Nitrite converts the oxygen-carrying part of the blood, hemoglobin, to methemoglobin, thus reducing the ability of the blood to transport oxygen. Fish may become stressed even when 4 to 5 ppm of oxygen are present.

This condition of brown-blood disease can be lessened by: (1) using methods to reduce the organic load, (2) by aeration, or (3) by addition of salt or calcium chloride. (Calculations for determining the amount of salt were given in Chapter 7.) Growing fish in brackishwater ponds appears to offer built-in protection against brown-blood disease.

Controlling infectious disease with therapeutic measures includes injections, feed additives, and use of chemicals for dip, flush, bath, and indefinite treatments. Therapeutic measures should be used only as a last resort, and routine use of chemicals and materials should not be encouraged because disease-causing organisms may develop resistance. Moreover, when treating a culture species, use the maximum recommended dosage rather than a series of sublethal doses.

When chemicals or drugs are used, they must be approved by the U.S. Department of Agriculture, the Food and Drug Administration, and the Environmental Protection Agency. Mention of certain chemicals or drugs in this book does not necessarily mean endorsement, since regulations are constantly changing. When approved chemicals or drugs are used, follow the label directions.

Injection

This method involves injecting individual fish, and it is usually practiced only for expensive brood fish. Terramycin® and chloromycetin have been injected into fish at 33 to 55 mg per kg (15 to 25 mg/lb) of fish to control bacterial infections.

Feed Additives

Oxytetracycline (Terramycin®) and sulfadimethoxine plus ormetoprim (Romet®) are the only drugs registered by the U.S. Food and Drug Administration for use with channel catfish grown for human consumption (Tucker and

Robinson 1990). Both drugs are used to treat bacterial diseases and can be used only in the manufacture of medicated feeds. Drugs should not be added routinely to feed because the bacterial pathogen will build an immunity. Tucker and Robinson (1990) noted that farmers may become frustrated when the medicated feed does not seem to work. They suggested that poor results are caused by: (1) failure of the fish to eat the feed, (2) bacterial resistance to the drug used, or (3) factors other than bacterial infection contributing to the mortality.

Dip Treatment

This technique involves dipping culture species in a medicated solution for a short time. For example, brood fish can be dipped in a 3% salt solution for about 60 seconds. The salt increases the mucus flow of finfish, and the parasites may slough off along with the excess mucus. Salt dips are often used routinely when transferring fish from one culture unit to another. Examples are moving brood stock from a holding pond to a spawning pond and before stocking fingerlings into rearing ponds (Figure 10.4). Acetic acid is also an old standby in dips.

Figure 10.4 Jay Stander of the LSU Agricultural Center prepares a salt dip for fish.

Flush Treatment

This treatment is used for treating culture species in tanks or raceways with flowing water. The chemical drips into the water inlet for a specified period and is gradually flushed throughout the system and out the drain. Half the recommended concentration may be added at the midpoint of the raceway during the initial treatment. It is often difficult to get an exact dosage because water flow rates among culture units vary.

Bath Treatment

Culture species are held in a medicated solution for about 30 minutes or longer. After this they are removed from the solution, or medicated water is replaced with unmedicated water. Such treatment is usually practiced in intensive culture systems such as in tanks. However, polyethylene bags have been placed around cages and floating net-pens for bath treatments of up to 1 hour.

Indefinite Treatment

A chemical is added to water, usually pond water, and left indefinitely. The chemical ultimately breaks down or is otherwise inactivated by natural processes.

CALCULATIONS FOR CHEMICAL TREATMENTS

When chemicals are required, it is necessary to calculate the proper amount to use. This depends on the volume of water to be treated, the concentration of the chemical desired, and its percentage of active ingredient. We usually express the concentration of a chemical to be used in terms of parts per million (ppm). If we add 1 kg of a chemical to a tank containing 1,000,000 kg of water, we have a concentration of 1 part per million. For solutions in fresh water, 1 mg of chemical per 1 liter of water equals 1 ppm. Therefore 1 ppm equals 1 mg/liter. This is because 1 liter of fresh water weighs 1,000,000 milligrams. Salt water is denser (heavier) than fresh water, and 1 ppm and 1 mg/liter are not exactly interchangeable. Jensen (1988), Mitchell and Meyer (1989), Tucker and Robinson (1990), and Creswell (1993) gave common calculations for determination of chemical treatments.

For Ponds

As soon as a pond is filled, calculate the volume of water in cubic meters or acre feet. This information is needed to determine the amount of chemical required for a particular concentration. To calculate acre feet, multiply average water depth by surface acres. Average depth can be determined in feet by sounding along several transects of the pond, adding all measurements together, and dividing by the number of readings. The area of rectangular ponds in surface acres is determined by multiplying the average length (feet) by the average width (feet) and then by dividing that answer by 43,560 (the number of square feet in an acre). An acre foot is a volume of water covering 1 ac to a depth of 1 ft. Since 1 ac ft of water weighs approximately 2,718,144 lb, 2.72 lb of chemical will give 1 ppm in 1 ac ft of water. If the volume of water is calculated in cubic meters, then 1 g/m^3 is equivalent to 1 ppm.

Problems and Solutions. Assume that a pond containing 10 ac ft of water is to be treated with copper sulfate at 0.25 ppm. How much copper sulfate is required? The basic formula is: acre feet x 2.72 x desired concentration, and 10 x 2.72 x 0.25 = 6.8 lb. Assume that we wish to treat this pond with 15 ppm formalin, then: 10 x 2.72 x 15 = 408 lb. Formalin comes in gallons, each gallon weighing about 9 lb. Therefore 408 ÷ 9 = 45 gal.

Assume that a pond is 100 m long, 50 m wide, and 1 m average depth. Calculate the amount of potassium permanganate required for 3 ppm. Cubic meters are 100 x 50 x 1 = 5,000 and 5,000 x 1 (grams per m^3 for 1 ppm) x 3 (3 ppm desired concentration) = 15,000 g required. This weight can be converted to 15 kg (1,000 g = 1 kg) or to 33 lb (454 g = 1 lb).

For Rectangular Tanks

For large tanks we calculate volume in cubic meters, or we can calculate in cubic feet and multiply cubic feet by a factor of 0.0283 (g in 1 ft^3 to give 1 ppm). Assume a tank 20 ft long, 5 ft wide, and 3 ft deep and that we wish to treat with 1 ppm of a given chemical. Then 20 x 5 x 3 = 300 ft^3 of water and 300 x 0.0283 x 1 = 8.5 g. It is probably easier to work with cubic meters, since 1 g in 1m^3 = 1 ppm. In our problem above, 300 ft^3 becomes 8.5 m^3 and 8.5 x 1= 8.5 g to get 1 ppm. (Note: 3.281 ft = 1 m.)

For Round Tanks

If a tank is round and you do not know the volume, first calculate cubic feet by the formula pi x r^2 x d. Assume that a round tank is 5 ft in diameter and 3 ft deep; determine cubic feet as follows: 3.14 (pi) x 2.5 (1/2 the diameter) x 2.5 (1/2 the diameter) x 3 (depth) = 59 ft^3. You may wish to convert to cubic meters because it is easy to remember that 1 g in 1 m^3 = 1 ppm. (Note: 35.3 ft^3 = 1 m^3 = 1,000 liters).

For Tanks With Known Volume

The volume of most tanks is usually known in gallons or liters. If in liters, then 1 mg per liter equals 1 ppm. If in gallons, it is suggested that gallons be converted to liters. (Note: 1 gal = 3.785 liters.)

For Raceways

To calculate the amount of chemical to use, you must know the volume of water and flow rate. Assume that a raceway holds 10,000 gal of water and has a flow rate of 100 gpm. It takes 100 minutes for a complete water change. If the dosage of chemical is added all at once at the water inlet, fish present would receive a relatively strong dose for a few minutes, comparable to a dip treatment. It may be better to drip the chemical into the water inlet for a specified period. Regardless of the method employed, there may be hot spots where the chemical is in a high concentration and other areas within the raceway where the chemical is in a relatively low concentration.

For Feed Additives

This treatment is based on body weight of fish, and standard units of treatment are usually expressed in grams of drug per 100 kg or 100 lb of fish per day. Terramycin® is formulated to deliver dosages of 2.50 to 3.75 g per 100 lb (45 kg) of fish per day. A common feed formulation contains 50 lb (23 kg) of TM-100® per ton of finished feed. TM-100® is a Terramycin® premix containing 100 g of oxytetracycline per pound of premix. The finished feed then contains 2.5 g of oxytetracycline per pound of feed. When fed at 1.0% of body weight per day, the dosage is 2.5 g oxytetracycline per 100 lb of fish per day. The medicated feed is fed for 7 to 10 days. There is a mandatory 21-day withdrawal period before processing. Romet® is formulated to deliver 2.3 g active ingredient per 100 lb of fish per day. Feed fortified with Romet® is fed for 5 consecutive days. Such feed has a low palatability to fish, and extra fish meal is often added to avoid this problem. A 3-day withdrawal period is mandatory before processing.

SOME IMPORTANT CONSIDERATIONS
Be Prepared

When a disease epizootic occurs, immediate action is required. If the problem calls for therapeutic use of chemicals, the chemicals should already be on hand. The amount to use should be pre-calculated, put on charts, and displayed prominently. Once construction of a culture or hatchery facility is completed, the volume of water should be carefully calculated for each pond or unit along with the amount of chemical to give a treatment of 1 ppm and other commonly used concentrations. Equipment required to dispense chemicals should be on hand and be in good working order.

Know Your Chemical

Not all commercial chemicals are chemically pure, and this must be considered when calculating the correct amount to use. If, for example, the recommendation calls for treatment with 1 ppm of a given chemical, and the chemical contains 50% active ingredients, then we must double the amount. Some materials such as commercial formalin, 37% formaldehyde, are not chemically pure but we calculate as if they were.

Solvents, emulsifiers, and other ingredients that make up commercial chemical formulations affect toxicity. For example, Meyer (1967) told of a minnow farmer who controlled *Lernaea cyprinacea* on minnows with a wettable-powder formulation of benzene hexachloride. When an emulsifiable oil formulation containing the same level of active ingredient was used, fish died of acute benzene hexachloride poisoning. The oil carrier made the parasiticide much more available for dissolution.

Chemicals should be bought from reliable dealers to assure purity, and you must be sure that a chemical(s) is approved for use by the Food and Drug Administration and Environmental Protection Agency. Different batches of the same chemical may vary greatly in toxicity to parasites and to fish. Moreover, even though a particular chemical has been used many times, the active ingredient needs to be checked each time. Some manufacturers may change the amount of active ingredient. Each chemical has its peculiarities that affect toxicity. Formalin and copper sulfate if used in combination may be highly toxic to fish. Toxicity of potassium permanganate may be affected by some forms of concrete in tanks.

Chemicals should be stored separately in a cool, dry building. The date that a chemical(s) was received should be noted on the container. In some instances, a chemical may lose its effectiveness from long storage or from improper storage. For example, never allow formalin to freeze; this may change the chemical makeup. Also formalin that has a white cloudiness should not be used, but a rusty color will not matter.

Know Your Water

Water temperature, dissolved oxygen, total water hardness, total alkalinity, pH, iron content, and other water quality characteristics affect toxicity and effectiveness of parasiticides. If pond water is treated, then the intensity of the phytoplankton bloom and organic matter load also must be considered.

Potassium permanganate, formalin, and copper sulfate have all been used as parasiticides. Potassium permanganate is more toxic in water with a high iron content, elevated water temperatures, and a total hardness of less than 40 ppm. Its toxicity decreases as the organic load increases. For years, 3 ppm potassium permanganate was a standard pond treatment for most ectoparasites and certain bacteria such as *C. columnaris*. Boyd (1979), however, pointed out that water contains organic matter and other substances that reduce potassium permanganate's effectiveness. Before this chemical can be effective, the potassium permanganate demand of pond waters must first be satisfied.

To determine this, Boyd (1979) outlined a procedure: Measure 1,000-ml portions of pond water into beakers or Nessler tubes. Add to samples 1, 2, 3, 4, 5, 6, 8 and 10 ppm potassium permanganate and stir. After 15 minutes, determine the lowest concentration of potassium permanganate that has a faint pink color. This concentration may be taken as the potassium permanganate demand of the water sample. Tucker (1989) suggested that the 15-minute $KMnO_4$ demand in ppm be multiplied by 2.5 to obtain an estimate of the required $KMnO_4$ treatment rate. Jee and Plumb (1981) in controlled laboratory studies found that 2 ppm potassium permanganate eliminated *C. columnaris* from water where the only oxidizable substrate was the bacteria, yet in pond water any concentration less than 6 ppm had minimal effect on *C. columnaris*.

During summer, ponds are typically high in organic matter, and stress caused by low DO may bring an onset of disease from *C. columnaris* or other bacteria. If a pond is treated with only 3 ppm, the $KMnO_4$ demand may never be met, much less control the bacterial disease. After determining $KMnO_4$ demand described by Boyd (1979), the proper amount can be added to water. $KMnO_4$ also can be added initially to pond water at 2 ppm. If the purple color turns brown in a few hours, repeat 2 ppm application as many times as necessary to maintain a purple color for 12 hours.

Formalin toxicity is affected by water temperature and pH. Formalin has been recommended up to 250 ppm for 1 hour in tanks and raceways to control most ectoparasites, but this is at water temperatures below 4°C (39°F). At temperatures above 10°C (50°F) the treatment rate must drop to 160 ppm for 1 hour. As pH increases to 9.5, toxicity to rainbow trout and channel catfish increases. Regardless of the rate used, fish must be carefully observed during treatment, and the water must be changed immediately if fish show signs of stress. Formalin has been used for pond treatments at rates ranging from 15 to 30 ppm. Helms (1967) suggested that dissolved oxygen may become depleted as formalin combines with oxygen to form formic acid. Allison (1965) indicated that oxygen depletion is probably the result of decaying plankton killed by formalin, and that the depletion usually occurred 2 to 3 days after treatment.

Copper sulfate is used to control not only fish parasites but also aquatic weeds, particularly certain species of filamentous algae and blue-green phytoplankton. Again, oxygen depletion may occur. Total alkalinity, total hardness, and pH affect toxicity of copper sulfate. Of these, total alkalinity is the major factor modifying toxicity of copper sulfate in water. Tucker and Robinson (1990) used total alkalinity to calculate treatment rates as follows: ppm $CuSO_4 \cdot 5H_2O$ = total alkalinity ÷ 100. In many pond waters, total alkalinity and total water hardness are approximately the same in ppm. Although total alkalinity usually changes slowly in ponds, heavy rainfall can dilute the water and significantly decrease the total alkalinity. Total water hardness has been used to calculate the amount of copper sulfate to use. At a total water hardness of more than 200 ppm, copper sulfate can be applied at levels exceeding 2 ppm but, in waters with only 20 ppm hardness, concentrations as low as 0.02 ppm may kill fish. A guide is:

Total Water Hardness (ppm)	Concentration of Copper Sulfate (ppm)
0 - 49	not safe to use without bioassay
50 - 99	0.5 - 0.75
100 - 149	0.75 - 1.00
150 - 200	1.00 - 2.00

Fish must sometimes be treated in closed, intensive culture systems where biological filtration is used for nitrification. Levine and Meade (1976) reported that certain compounds when used at the recommended dosage had little effect on nitrification whereas other compounds did (Table 10.5).

Table 10.5 Compounds examined and their inhibitory effect on nitrification at recommended treatment levels [a].

Compound	Level	% Inhibition of Nitrification
Chloromycetin [b]	50 ppm	84
Chlorotetracycline [c]	10 ppm	76
Cupric sulfate	5 ppm	0
Formalin [d]	15 ppm	27
Furanace [e]	0.1 ppm	20
Malachite green	0.5 ppm	11
Methylene blue	1.0 ppm	92
Potassium permanganate	1.0 ppm	86
Sodium chloride	5 g/liter	2
Sulfadiazine[b]	25 ppm	74
Sulfanilamide [g]	25 ppm	64
Methanol [b]	25 -27 ppm	0 -43

[a] Adapted from Amlacher (1970) and Snieszko (1975)
[b] Chloromycetin® sodium succinate, Parke-Davis, Detroit, Michigan
[c] Aureomycin, American Cyanamid, Princeton, New Jersey
[d] Commercial Formalin
[e] Furanace®, Abbot Laboratories, North Chicago, Illinois
[f] Sodium Sulfadiazine®, American Cyanamid, Princeton, New Jersey
[g] p=Aminobenzene-Sulfanilamide, Matheson, Coleman and Bell, Norwood, Ohio
[h] Methanol was tested due to its possible use as an exogenous carbon
Source: Levine and Meade 1976.

Know Your Culture Species

The susceptibility of a culture species to chemicals depends on the type of species, age and size, and physiological condition. Generally smaller, younger culture species in poor condition are most susceptible to chemical additives. Recommendations for use of a given chemical at a particular rate cannot be used safely for all species. For example, channel catfish can often withstand up to 250 ppm formalin for 1 hour, but at that rate some rainbow trout strains may perish. Smith and Piper (1972) concluded that death of formalin-treated trout is caused by severe pathology, resulting in their inability to maintain osmotic and acid-base balance. This is further complicated by hypoxia and the inability of fish to maintain normal metabolism. Meyer (1967) noted that malachite green is far less toxic to catfish than it is to sunfishes, and that benzene hexachloride is highly toxic to catfish and sunfishes but only mildly so to certain minnows. (Note: malachite green is no longer approved for use in aquaculture.) Williams and Avault (1976) reported that red swamp crawfish easily withstood various levels of acriflavine, formalin, and potassium permanganate but were highly sensitive to most agricultural insecticides. This appears logical since crawfish and insects are in the same phylum.

Know the Disease

Understanding biological and environmental requirements of disease-causing organisms is prerequisite for their control. For example, bacterial gill disease of trout often emerges when trout are heavily fed and the organic load increases. Discontinue feeding for several days. The disease can be controlled as DO increases and ammonia decreases. Each parasite is sensitive to certain chemicals (killed by chemicals), whereas other chemicals are tolerated. The wrong chemical can be costly and result in loss of the culture species. The protozoan parasite Ich thrives in cool water, the optimum range being 21° to 24°C (70° to 75°F). At these temperatures, the parasite may mature in 3 to 4 days, but at 10°C (50°F) the cycle may require 5 weeks. A standard practice for controlling Ich has been to treat pond waters with an appropriate chemical about every 3 days for a series of 3 to 5 treatments. However, at temperatures below 21°C (70°F), this interval would probably be ineffective. The adult parasite, embedded in the skin of fish, is immune to most chemicals, so the chemical must be applied when the free swimming theront (tomite) stage is present. By understanding the effect of water temperature on the emergence of tomites, you can time the parasiticide application more precisely.

ADMINISTRATION OF CHEMICALS

Chemicals administered to ponds can first be diluted with water and then sprayed from a moving boat or from shoreline with a tractor and pump. Another way is to dribble the diluted chemical over the side of a moving boat into the prop wash or to use a boat bailer. Some chemicals, such as copper sulfate and potassium permanganate, can be put into burlap bags and towed behind a boat. In ponds of 1 ha (2.5 ac) or less the chemical can be broadcasted by hand with a dipper. Many chemicals are caustic, and they may discolor clothing and skin. A mask, goggles, and gloves should be worn.

When treating tanks and other small culture systems, make up a stock solution. This involves mixing a chemical in a given volume of water and then treating from this stock solution. Assume, for example, that you have four culture tanks, each containing 2,000 liters (528 gal) of water and that you wish to add 8 ppm of $KMnO_4$ to each. This gives a total of 8,000 liters (2,113 gal) to treat, and 8,000 x 1 (1 mg/liter = 1 ppm) x 8 = 64,000 mg or 64 g (2.26 oz). Sixty-four grams can be diluted in a known volume of water and then divided equally among the four tanks. Although stock solutions can be kept on hand, some chemicals deteriorate rapidly. It is generally best to prepare fresh solutions as needed.

Registration of Chemicals

Enactment of the Federal Environmental Pesticide Control Act (FEPCA) effective in 1972 required that all chemical uses be approved and registered by the Environmental Protection Agency (EPA) or by the Food and Drug Administration (FDA) (Meyer et al. 1976; Schnick et al. 1979a).

Specific requirements were established for registration of compounds, that generally involved acute and chronic bioassay studies along with residue studies. The compounds fell into several categories of registration including:

(1) Petition for Exemption from Registration: Fishery use does not constitute use of the compound as a pesticide and is therefore exempt from registration requirements.

(2) Generally Regarded as Safe: Fishery use is generally regarded as safe due to a long history of demonstrated safety in a related, nonfishery field.

(3) Not a New Drug: Compound is not a new drug and has been used for a desired purpose for many years.

(4) Petition for Exemption from Tolerance: Registration is required, with possible exemption from tolerance because of the low levels used or because the residual levels present after use are low.

(5) New Animal Drug Application: Any drug or anesthetic used in the production of animals for human food must be registered.

(6) Food Use Registration: Registration is required and maximum residue tolerance must be established which cannot be exceeded; withdrawal times after treatment are often specified.

(7) Nonfood Use Registration: Registration is required but use is limited to nonfood fishes.

Experimental Use Permits are required for field studies in which a pesticide or other experimental compound is used in an area larger than 0.4 ha (1 ac). Since the registration status of a given compound may change, it is important to consult labels on formulations.

Meyer and Schnick (1989) gave a comprehensive review on chemicals for disease control. One of the problems in the aquaculture industry is the lack of registered compounds to prevent and control diseases. The cost to register a new compound requires expensive research. Many private companies are reluctant to conduct this research. The payback is relatively low compared with compounds for traditional agricultural crops. This places much of the burden to register new compounds on various state, federal, and university researchers. Tucker and Robinson (1990) listed only a handful of compounds registered for use by the U.S. Food and Drug Administration. For use as antibiotics, they listed Terramycin® and Romet®. Chemical therapeutants included potassium permanganate, copper sulfate (registered for food-fish use as a herbicide and algaecide), formalin, and salt.

Cost of Treatment

Treating diseased culture species can be costly. In intensive culture systems, a relatively small amount of chemical is required, but for pond treatments the amount escalates. Some chemicals, such as acriflavine, have been used in intensive culture against bacterial infections, but the cost is prohibitive for use in ponds. Sometimes an aquaculturist may have an option of using one of two chemicals for pond treatment. All other factors being equal, cost may be the deciding factor. (Table 10.6).

Table 10.6 Cost of chemical treatments [a].

Treatment	Cost Per Acre Foot
Formalin (15 ppm)	$ 9.00
Potassium Permanganate (2 ppm)	7.50 [b]
Copper Sulfate (1 ppm)	1.62
Salt (25 ppm/1 ppm Nitrite)	3.27
Medicated feed (Terramycin®) at 3% body weight per day	$1.20/100 lb fish

[a] Based on 1980 major farm supply catalog prices
[b] May have to treat with more than 2 ppm depending on permanganate demand of the water.
Source: Compiled by R. Thune, LSU Agricultural Center.

Dorman (1991) suggested that one way in which to save money is to avoid unnecessary chemical treatments. In some instances, ponds are treated prophylactically during fall, winter, and early spring with a parasiticide or medicated feed. Dorman felt that in most cases the treatments were not needed. He presented figures for the cost to use copper sulfate and potassium permanganate to treat pond waters and to use Terramycin® and Romet® as feed additives.

FISH DISEASE INSPECTION AND CERTIFICATION

As aquaculture expands worldwide, there is a massive movement of live fish, eggs, and larvae. This has prompted international, regional, and state concern over the transfer and spread of diseases (DeVoe 1992; Rosenfield and Mann 1992). Some factions wholeheartedly support rigid controls on import/export of live fishery products, whereas some producers fear economic loss because of lengthy regulations and constraints to shipping. Fryer et al. (1979) reviewed certification and inspection.

At the international level, several organizations have studied fish disease problems associated with international transfers of live fish and eggs. In 1968, the European Inland Fisheries Advisory Commission (EIFAC) and the Food and Agriculture Organization (FAO) of the United Nations surveyed laws and regulations regarding international traffic of live fish and eggs and ultimately recommended that a uniform system of health control be established.

General agreement was reached that the following six diseases should be regulated in Europe: viral hemorrhagic septicemia (VHS), infectious pancreatic necrosis (IPN), infectious hematopoietic necrosis (IHN), spring viremia of cyprinids (SVC), whirling disease, and furunculosis. Diagnostic methods were established for these diseases that were acceptable to EIFAC. It was suggested that certification and classifications include: Specific Pathogen Free (SPF), Coded Pathogen Free (CPF), Specific Disease Free (SDF), and Non-controlled. SPF status required a culture species to be free of all species-specific pathogens and to be raised with rigid water quality controls. CPF animals would be free of all diseases listed by international agreement. Rearing establishments could be classified SDF if supplied with water in which some pathogens could exist, but free from certain specified disease agents. For example, furunculosis could be present but not IPN.

In North America, introduction of whirling disease from Europe stimulated amendment of federal law, Title 50, in the United States in 1958. Salmonid eggs must be determined free of VHS and whirling disease. The U.S. Fish and Wildlife Service has a fish health policy that applies to its own fishery facilities. Other than the Title 50 amendment, uniform disease control in the United States has not been successful. Historically, most disease control and certification have dealt with salmonids and other finfish. Crustaceans and mollusks have not received equal attention. However, with the devastation of certain shrimp farming operations by viral diseases beginning around 1988, more attention has been focused on this group of culture species. Canada's Fish Disease Control Policy of 1977, which applies to all of Canada, has well-defined regulations.

At the regional level in the United States, two policies on fish disease regulations are noteworthy. They are the Colorado River Drainage Fish Disease Control Policy implemented in 1973 and the Great Lakes Fishery Commission Fish Disease Control Policy. The first policy, involving seven states, prevented introduction of certain diseases into the Colorado River drainage system by means of inspection. The Great Lakes policy involved states that drained into the Great Lakes. Diseases were categorized as certifiable or as reportable.

At the state level, in a 1978 survey 30 of 45 states responding reported some form of regulation, but a great diversity of regulations existed. Oregon has well-defined guidelines and regulations concerning inspection and certification. Among other things, Oregon classifies diseases as: (1) emergency (whirling disease, VHS), (2) certifiable emergency diseases listed above plus IHN, IPN, Ceratomyxosis caused by *Ceratomyxa shasta*, enteric redmouth, and bacterial kidney disease, and (3) reportable (all diseases listed in 1 and 2) plus *Ichthyophthirius, Ichthyobodo*, the copepods *Lernaea* and *Salmincola*, drug-resistant strains of motile aeromonads, pseudomonads, *Flexibacter, Cytophaga*, Piscine Erythrocytic Necrosis, and *Herpesvirus salmonis*.

BASIC BIOLOGY, PREVENTION, AND CONTROL OF MAJOR DISEASE-CAUSING ORGANISMS

A number of diseases and disease-causing organisms affect culture species. Some may cause catastrophic losses. Examples include viral hemorrhagic septicemia and whirling disease (trout); *Vibrio* (salmon); enteric septicemia of catfish and Ich (channel catfish); *P. monodon* baculovirus (shrimp); and *Perkinsus marinus (Dermocystidium marinum)* (oysters). Others, such as nematodes and most other helminths, are usually not considered as serious. Following is a synopsis of major groups of disease-causing organisms. Examples of selected parasites are given, and methods for prevention and control are discussed.

VIRUSES

Viruses are submicroscopic, obligate parasites that depend on living cells for their reproduction. The largest virus can be seen through the highest power laboratory microscope, but most viruses can be seen only with an electron microscope. All but a few of the largest viruses pass through a porcelain filter whose openings are so tiny that bacteria cannot pass through. The smallest viruses that can pass through the filter are often called filterable viruses.

Viruses consist of a central core of nucleic acid surrounded by a protein coat. The outer protein protective coating for viral nucleic acid is called the capsid. It varies in morphology between groups of viruses. Viruses are grouped according to nucleic acid type (RNA or DNA), size and surface configuration, and resistance to lipid solvents. Differences within main groups are usually detected by small differences in the protein characteristics of the capsid (Brown and Gratzek 1980). Viruses are such incomplete organisms that they must live only as parasites within living cells. A virus attaches to a cell, and the core of the virus penetrates and directs the life processes of the cell, producing many more virus particles. The new virus particles are set free to attack other cells.

Viruses are often host specific. That is, they attack only certain organisms. The channel catfish virus disease (CCVD), for example, affects only channel catfish. In some instances viruses have high specificity for certain tissues and organs. For instance, infectious pancreatic virus of salmonids affects mainly pancreatic tissue.

Channel Catfish Virus Disease (CCVD)

This disease affects channel catfish fingerlings during summer when water temperatures range between 24° and 27°C (75° to 81°F). Losses of fingerlings may exceed 80%. Adults may serve as carriers with no visible sign of having the disease. CCVD is generally confined to southern states but may occur sporadically in other areas where channel catfish are cultured intensively. Clinical signs of the disease include hemorrhaging of fins, distended abdomen, necrosis, and edema in most tissues (Tucker and Robinson 1990; Schäperclaus 1991).

Viral Diseases of Salmonids

Four viral diseases -- infectious pancreatic necrosis (IPN), infectious hematopoietic necrosis (IHN), viral hemorrhagic septicemia (VHS), and the viral disease caused by *Herpesvirus salmonis* -- have been reported. In addition a virus, designated viral erythrocytic necrosis (VEN), has been recognized in chum salmon (*Oncorhynchus keta*) and pink salmon (*O. gorbuscha*). The IPN virus infects fry and fingerlings of several species but rarely infects adults. The disease, first reported in the United States and later in Europe and Japan, causes necrosis of the pancreas and in some cases slight renal or hepatic necrosis. Clinical signs include erratic swimming, mucoid accumulations in the alimentary tract, exopthalmia and darkened color. Shortly before dying, fish lie at the bottom for 1 or 2 hours. Predominant symptoms are similar to VHS and IHN. Therefore a definite diagnosis is possible only through histological and virological investigations.

Survivors of epizootics may become carriers and shed virus with feces and sex products, thus allowing both horizontal and vertical transmission. The virus is easily transmitted by water and probably on the surface of eggs. Brown and Gratzek (1980) noted that the virus has been maintained in the intestines of fish-eating birds for as long as 8 days after experimental exposure. The IPN virus is capable of exceptional resistance against environmental influences. The virus remains infectious when dried in air and stored at 15° to 22°C (59° to 72°F), and it is fully virulent at -20°C and in homogenates even after 8 years (Schäperclaus 1991).

The IHN virus, which has global distribution, affects several salmonids including sockeye (*O. nerka*), chinook salmon (*O. tshawytscha*), and rainbow trout. Infections are most common in western North America in waters below 15°C (59°F). Fish less than 2 months of age are particularly susceptible. Clinical signs of the disease include anemia, distended abdomen, darkening of the skin, hemorrhaging at the base of fins, and popeye. The disease is spread from carrier brood fish. VHS is a highly contagious virus infection. Found in Europe, it infects young trout at temperatures below 8°C (46°F). Clinical signs are similar to those in IPN. *Herpesvirus salmonis* has been reported in Washington state and Japan (McAllister 1978). The virus, which infects rainbow trout, can be transmitted horizontally and vertically. The optimum temperature for virus replication in cell culture is about 10°C (50°F).

Miscellaneous Viral Diseases of Finfish

Lymphocytes is probably the best known virus disease of marine and freshwater fishes, having been reported in 49 species of fishes representing 20 families. The disease, which produces raspberry-like growths on fins, is rarely lethal, but fish may not be salable because of disfigurement. The cauliflower disease of eels was described by Schäperclaus (1991), and Wolf (1988) discussed other fish viral diseases.

Viral Diseases of Shrimp

Sindermann (1990b) noted that the first viral disease reported from marine crustaceans was in the shore crab (*Macropipus depurator*) from the French Coast in 1966. Since that time viral diseases of shrimp have caught the attention of many involved in the shrimp farming industry. Couch (1981), Johnson (1983), Sindermann (1990a, 1990b), Fast and Lester (1992), and Fulks and Main (1992) reviewed knowledge of shrimp viruses.

Six viruses are recognized in penaeid shrimp (Lightner and Redman 1992). The six viruses include: *Baculovirus penaei* (BP), *P. monodon* baculovirus (MBV), baculoviral midgut gland necrosis (BMN), infectious hypodermal and hematopoietic necrosis virus (IHHNV), hepatopancreatic parvo-like virus (HPV), and reo-like virus (REO).

People involved in shrimp farming recognize that introduction of viral-infected larvae to a grow-out facility can be devastating. Much of the effort in virus research, therefore, has concentrated on methods for the identification of viral organisms and their geographical location. Because production of shrimp larvae is a highly complex operation, many shrimp farms opt to buy larvae from shrimp hatcheries that specialize in production of postlarvae. Lightner and Redman (1992) devoted most of their review of shrimp viral diseases on diagnostic procedures. The present diagnostic procedures for penaeid shrimp diseases are based mostly on histology, clinical signs, and histopathology.

Electron microscopy is also important. Quick, reliable methods must be developed for certification and inspection policies.

Viral Diseases of Mollusks

Viral diseases of mollusks were generally unknown until the early 1970s (Sindermann 1990b). Sindermann (1977) reported that most viral diseases in marine and estuarine species are not that well known nor clearly identified as a major problem. A herpes-type virus affects the American oyster (*Crassostrea virginica*). In one instance, oysters transferred to the heated effluent of a power plant (water temperature of 28° to 30°C or 82° to 86°F) from natural waters (water temperature of 12° to 18°C or 54° to 64°F) had higher mortalities and higher virus prevalence (Sindermann 1977). Of the known reported virus infections of oysters, "ovacystis" infection is the most common, but it is probably of no economic importance. It affects the ovarian follicles, but the effect on reproductive performance has not been clearly defined.

Prevention and Control of Viral Diseases

There is no direct treatment for virus infection, but experimental vaccines may be effective in protecting culture species from viral infections. CCVD can be prevented by careful selection of brood stock, by use of 20-cm (8-in) or larger fingerlings, by temperature control, and by avoidance of stress. Plumb et al. (1975) noted that different strains of channel catfish varied in tolerance to CCVD.

Prevention of salmonid viral diseases was reviewed by Amend (1976). Prevention includes separation of eggs and fry from adults, use of eggs and fry certified disease free, isolation of suspected infected fish, and general sanitation. Brown and Gratzek (1980) recommended disinfecting nets, pails, and the like; and dipping eggs in organic iodophors with 100 ppm iodine for 10 minutes. IHN can be prevented by elevating water temperature above 15°C (59°F). IPN has been eliminated at hatcheries by disinfecting with sodium hypochlorite. Batts and Winton (1990) suggested that low levels of bulk-grade iodine could be easily and inexpensively added to hatchery water supplies to help control IHN. Ozone has also been used in salmonid hatcheries.

Chlorine has been used for years as a disinfectant for shrimp facilities (Hnath 1983; LeBlanc and Overstreet 1991a; LeBlanc and Overstreet 1991b). Its effectiveness is reduced in the presence of organic matter such as uneaten feed and waste products. Moreover, chlorine strength is diminished over time.

Calcium hypochlorite (HTH) is a commonly used compound. For control of *Baculovirus penaei* (BP), LeBlanc and Overstreet (1991b) recommended the following:

(1) Tanks and pipes should be disinfected for 1 hour with 200 ppm of HTH, drained, rinsed, and dried for 3 to 4 days.

(2) Walls, floors, and tank exteriors should be washed or sprayed with 1,200 to 1,600 ppm HTH, allowed to remain damp for 30 seconds or more, rinsed, and then dried for 3 to 4 days.

(3) Baths for feet and equipment should contain 1,600 ppm HTH; emersion should last at least 20 seconds.

(4) Earthen ponds should be completely drained and kept dry for 3 weeks.

Other methods are helping to solve the problem of shrimp viruses. Species substitution may be a practical method for avoiding certain viral infections. For example, *P. japonicus* could be substituted in geographical regions where MBV is a problem. The production of specific pathogen free (SPF) shrimp has been accomplished at the Oceanic Institute of Hawaii. Wild brood stock of *P. vannamei* was brought into the hatchery. With rigorous sanitation, shrimp were produced that were free of specific viruses (The Oceanic Institute Newsline March 1990 Volume 3, No. 1).

BACTERIA

Bacteria are minute, one-celled organisms that measure from about 0.4 microns in diameter to 10 microns in length. Some scientists consider bacteria plants; others consider them animals. Still other scientists call bacteria neither and place them in a special group called Protista. Bacteria may have been related to both plants and animals when life began on earth. Bacteria can be found almost everywhere and are probably the most numerous of all organisms. They live in soil, water, air, and in and on living organisms. They live in the presence of oxygen (aerobic bacteria) and in the absence of oxygen (anaerobic bacteria). Some bacteria live in the digestive system of animals and humans and aid in digestion; others fix nitrogen from the air in root nodules of leguminous plants. Bacteria break down organic matter to mineral components and gases and are used to produce buttermilk, cheese, and other products.

Certain bacteria cause diseases in people and animals, and they may be facultative or obligate parasites. Bacteria are often referred to as opportunistic pathogens or secondary invaders. If a culture species is weakened by a predisposing environmental condition, bacteria may become pathogenic. Frequently a break in the skin, a loss of scales or other parts may allow a bacterium a point of entry. Sometimes a protozoan or other parasite causes a point of entry for bacteria.

Nearly all bacteria have a tough protective layer called a cell wall (Figure 10.5). The cell wall keeps large food particles from entering the cell. Other structures typically found in bacteria include a capsule for protection, a cell membrane that separates the cell's cytoplasm from the rest of the cell, and a nuclear body that contains the genetic material.

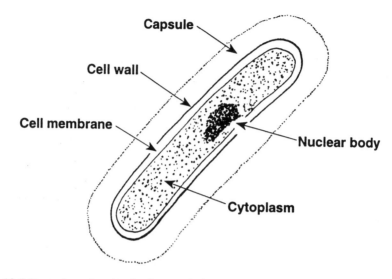

Figure 10.5 Bacterium showing basic morphology.

Bacteria may be divided into four groups based on shape (Figure 10.6). Cocci have a round shape and grow in clusters or chains. Bacilli are shaped like rods. Vibrios are shaped like bent rods, and spirilla have a spiral shape. Bacteria also can be classified as Gram negative or Gram positive, based on the color they turn with a Gram stain. Further classification is based on size, motility, colony characteristics of bacteria, physiological activity, and immunologic reactions.

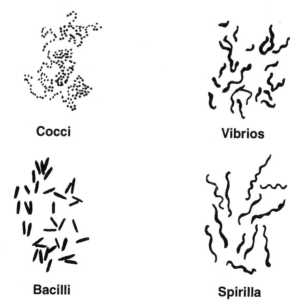

Figure 10.6 Four groups of bacteria based on shape.

Most bacteria reproduce asexually by binary fission. Some bacteria mate and exchange genetic material. Bacteria reproduce at astounding rates, doubling their numbers in less than 20 minutes under ideal conditions. Some bacteria form bacterial spores that are highly resistant to drying, boiling water, and other harsh treatments. Bacteria can be killed by heat, sunlight or ultraviolet light, certain harsh chemicals such as chlorine and alcohol, and with use of antibiotics.

Bacterial Diseases of Finfish

Enteric septicemia of catfish (ESC), caused by the bacterium *Edwardsiella ictaluri*, is the most serious disease problem of commercially raised channel catfish, according to Kaskow (1987). Up to 30% of all diseases reported in the southeastern United Stated in 1986 were diagnosed as ESC. ESC is fairly host specific for channel catfish, although it has been isolated from other catfish species (Tucker and Robinson 1990). The incidence of ESC is highly related to water temperature, the optimum being 22° to 28°C (72° to 82°F). Fish losses to ESC are rare when water temperatures are consistently below 18°C (65°F) or above 29°C (85°F).

Catfish of all sizes are susceptible to ESC, but fingerlings more so (Tucker and Robinson 1990). Catfish may have a hole in the head or bump on top. Fish may practice tail chasing and develop a listless position, with head up and tail down. Scattered hemorrhages may appear on the body as red pimples. Fish, especially fingerlings, may develop ascites. Swollen bellies with bilateral exophthalmia (popeyes) are displayed. Fingerlings with these symptoms look similar to fish with CCVD.

Columnaris disease severely affects catfish, salmonids, and many other culture species. The disease, caused by *Cytophaga columnaris*, is the second most common bacterial disease of farm-raised channel catfish. There is, however, some question about different strains or even species of bacteria being involved. Most epizootics in catfish occur during warm weather; approximately 90% occur between March and October in the southeastern United States. In salmonids, most bacterial diseases are prevalent at water temperatures above 15°C (59°F). Columnaris disease exhibits a variety of clinical signs, depending on the virulence of the strain.

At first, lesions may occur as grayish-white spots. As the lesions enlarge, they become shallow, grayish-white ulcers. Eventually the skin may be destroyed. It looks as if scalding water was poured on fish, exposing underlying musculature. Gill tissue is a common site of damage when highly virulent strains are involved, and may be the only affected area. Lesions on gills show brownish necrotic tissue, starting at the ends and progressing to the base. *C. columnaris*, which is often saprophytic and does not require a host to live, grows best at incubation temperatures of 25° to 30°C (77° to 86°F). Under a microscope, great numbers of the bacteria cells often clump together forming "haystacks." *C. columnaris* infections, which may kill fish 1 to 2 days after onset of disease, are often associated with stress, high water temperatures, crowding, mechanical injury, and poor water quality.

Motile Aeromonad septicemia (MAS) is one of the most common diseases of cultured channel catfish, and all freshwater species of fish are susceptible to it. Synonyms of MAS are hemorrhagic septicemia, infectious dropsy, red sore, and rubella. Diseased fish swim lethargically at the surface and often stop feeding. Fins are usually frayed, hemorrhaging at the base. The abdomen may be swollen; the, liver is pale, the body cavity is filled with fluid, and the eyes bulge. With catfish, MAS usually occurs in the spring and early summer and is frequently associated with environmental stress such as crowded conditions, rough handling, low DO, and rising water temperatures.

The usual causative organisms of MAS are *Aeromonas sobria* and *A. hydrophila* (formerly *A. liquefaciens, A. punctata*). They are facultative bacteria, and ubiquitous in nature where they grow on organic matter. More than one strain occurs, and fish in a given population can develop resistance to one strain but may be susceptible to another. *Aeromonas* has the ability to develop resistance to certain drugs such as Terramycin®. Lewis and Plumb (1979) noted that during the late 1960s and early 1970s, only 10% to 15% of the bacteria from infected catfish were resistant to Terramycin®, but by 1976, 38% were resistant, and it now approaches 50%. This increase was probably caused by the extensive use of Terramycin®. *Pseudomonas fluorescens*, also a facultative bacterium, is often associated with *Aeromonas*. The bacterium *P. fluorescens*, which may produce similar clinical signs in fish, is often identified on culture agar by its greenish-yellow fluorescent pigment and very putrid odor.

Edwardsiellosis of catfish is caused by *Edwardsiella tarda*. The disease is restricted to warmwater fish since salmonids appear immune to it. It has not been observed in farm-raised catfish smaller than 454 g (1 lb), but the bacterium has been isolated from 18 to 23-cm (7 to 9-in) fish held under laboratory stress conditions (Lewis and Plumb 1979). In ponds, the disease is most prevalent during July through October when water temperatures are above 30°C (86°F). Clinical signs of the disease include the presence of gas-filled malodorous lesions in muscle tissue of mature catfish.

During initial stages of the disease, cutaneous lesions 3 to 5 mm (1 to 2 in) in diameter resembling puncture wounds can be seen on the fish. Within 10 to 15 days, the lesions develop into large, gas-filled cavities containing as much as one-third volume of bloody necrotic tissue debris. Death is apparently associated with liver and kidney failure. Aeromonad and pseudomonad bacteria are sometimes secondary invaders, accelerating loss of fish. However, mortality rates seldom exceed 5% in ponds, but may approach 50% if fish are handled. Surviving fish may not be acceptable to processors since ruptured lesions release malodorous gases that may taint the flesh.

Fish pasteurellosis or pseudotuberculosis, caused by the bacterium *Pasteurella piscicida*, has affected a number of cultured finfish throughout the world. It was first reported in white perch (*Morone americanus*) and striped bass (*Morone saxatilis*) during a massive epizootic in Chesapeake Bay (Hawke et al. 1987; Toranzo et al. 1991). It is a serious problem in Japan with cultured yellowtail (*Seriola quinqueradiata*). Robohm (1983) described the organism as a Gram-negative non-motile rod bacterium that grows at 30°C (86°F) but not at 37°C (99°F). Initial signs of the disease in striped bass and yellowtail are loss of locomotion and sinking in the water column. Gill respiration is increased. In yellowtail, numerous white tubercles are found on the spleen, kidney, and liver.

Furunculosi*s*, a bacterial disease caused by *Aeromonas salmonicida*, is a serious problem in freshwater environments. It also has been one of the most common bacterial diseases in cultured salmon in Puget Sound, the other disease being vibriosis. *A. salmonicida* is first contacted during the freshwater culture stages of salmon. At low temperatures, the disease is latent, and host fish act as carriers. When fish are transferred to seawater, the stress of osmotic change weakens them, and disease becomes infectious. Transmission of the disease in seawater is by direct contact and with fish feces.

McCraw (1952) summarized information on furunculosis up to 1952, and Snieszko (1969) condensed further knowledge. McCraw (1952) quoted others, who described *A. salmonicida* (formerly *Bacterium salmonicida*) as causing furunculosis widespread throughout Europe and the United States. Schäperclaus (1991) noted that there are several strains of *A. salmonicida*, with different degrees of virulence. The bacterium grows at temperature ranges between 5° and 30°C (41° to 86°F), with optimum growth at 10° to 22°C (50° to 72°F). The bacterium, an obligate parasite, may affect many freshwater fish species, but it usually is most serious with trout. The disease, especially prevalent during high temperatures of 13° to 16°C (55° to 61°F) and low water level, causes general infection of the kidney, spleen, liver, and muscular tissues. There may be congestion of blood vessels in the abdominal cavity and a discharge of blood and mucus from the vent.

Vibriosis is one of the most common and serious diseases of cultured marine and brackishwater fish. Caused by the bacterium *Vibrio anguillarum*, it is related to the organisms that cause cholera and shellfish food poisoning in humans. Vibriosis may occur at any time; however, it is most common in temperate zones during summer. Epizootics occur most often at water temperatures between 14° to 20°C (57° to 68°F). Clinical signs in cultured salmon include diminished feeding, lethargic movement, hemorrhaging around the base of the pectoral and anal fins, or a bloody discharge from the vent. Internally, pin-point hemorrhaging of the intestinal wall and liver may occur. The spleen is frequently two to three times the normal size.

Enteric Redmouth Disease (ERM) is a bacterial disease reported in rainbow trout during the late 1950s. The disease, first noted in the Hagerman Valley of Idaho, has also been called red mouth disease, red vent disease, and bacterial hemorrhagic septicemia. The bacterium, later identified as *Yersinia ruckeri*, has been placed in the family Enterobacteriaceae.

Busch (1978b) noted that the disease spread by shipment of subclinically infected stocks of fish from an area (Hagerman Valley) where the disease was endemic. ERM caused mortality in both trout and salmon. The rainbow trout appeared to be the most susceptible. The bacterium has not been isolated from warmwater fish (Busch 1978b). Busch also noted that the disease produced most mortalities in the egg through swim-up fry stages. The disease incidence decreases as fish get older. However, while mortalities of marketable fish represent only 14% of total mortalities, they are 76% of the cost in dollars.

Transmission of ERM occurs through the water from feces of infected fish. Survivors of an epizootic are carriers. The clinical pathology of ERM is similar to bacterial hemorrhagic septicemia. Busch (1978b) described ERM as a bacterial hemorrhagic septicemia of salmonid fishes having a very well-defined geographical range and endemic occurrence and capable of causing high mortality.

Bacteria can cause disease of fish eggs. Bacteria belonging to the genera *Flavobacterium* and *Acinetobacter*, both common in the aquatic environment, may cause deterioration of channel catfish and other fish eggs. Schäperclaus (1991) reviewed other bacterial diseases of fish.

Bacterial Diseases of Crustaceans

Three diseases of crustacea have received the most attention, namely: (1) shell disease caused by chitinolytic bacteria, (2) gaffkaemia of lobsters, caused by *Aerococcus viridans* var. *homari*, and (3) vibriosis, caused by several species of *Vibrio* (Sindermann 1990b).

More than 30 species of chitinoclastic bacteria can cause disease in shrimp, prawns, crawfish, and crustaceans. Bacteria associated with the disease include the genera *Vibrio, Pseudomonas*, and *Aeromonas*, but it has not been clearly established which plays the most important role as a disease-causing agent. Amborski et al. (1974b) found that *Pseudomonas* sp. had a role in the shell destruction of crawfish, *Procambarus clarkii*. The disease produced has several names including brown spot disease of shrimp, black spot disease of prawn, and shell disease of crawfish and crustaceans in general.

Chitinoclastic bacteria use the exoskeleton as a source of food. Points of attachment appear as erosive areas. Rough handling of crustaceans may result in breakage of the exoskeleton, thus allowing for colonization of bacteria. Overcrowding of prawns and accumulation of uneaten food encourage the disease. Shrimp infected with the disease show discoloration of body tissues in some instances, but not in others. Blood clotting is slowed or lost, and body parts are occasionally lost. Erosive blackened areas are evident on most crustaceans. Because of periodic molting of the exoskeleton, these bacteria generally do not cause significant mortalities.

Gaffkaemia is a disease of the American lobster (*Homarus americanus*) caused by *Aerococcus viridans* var. *homari*. It is the most virulent systemic bacterial pathogen found in crustaceans. The disease is known as gaffkaemia because an earlier classification placed the bacterium in the genus *Gaffkya*. A pink discoloration of the abdomen may occur, but often no obvious external signs are noted until shortly before death. Infected lobsters become progressively weaker, and mortalities may reach 50%. Deaths escalate when water temperature exceeds 15°C (59°F). Infections in lobsters are almost always fatal, and lobsters typically die in a "spread eagle" position. Sindermann (1990b) reviewed the knowledge of this disease.

Vibriosis, a problem in salmon culture, is also becoming more prevalent in crustacean farming. Several species in the genus *Vibrio* have been identified. Lightner (1983) and Lightner et al. (1984) summarized important aspects of *Vibrio* spp. Infections may be chronic or acute, with mortalities reaching 100%. *Vibrio* is ubiquitous, being found in all major shrimp farming regions. As expected, severe stress caused by poor water quality and other factors usually opens the door for infection with *Vibrio*. *Vibrio* spp. and strains vary greatly in virulence.

Filamentous bacteria of the genus *Leucothrix* and possibly other genera cause filamentous bacterial disease of shrimp and prawns. The bacterium is typically found on gill filaments and body surfaces. If heavy enough infections occur on gills, the host may suffocate. Filamentous bacteria are often a problem in larval rearing tanks.

Bacterial Diseases of Mollusks

Bacillary necrosis, caused by *Vibrio anguillarum* and other marine *Vibrio* spp., is a disease that may produce sudden high mortalities in larvae of the American oyster. Adults are less affected. This may be because the primary defense of mollusks is phagocytosis and encapsulation. Adults are able to handle bacterial pathogens because of their small size. The disease, which may enter through the esophagus, results in lysis and necrosis of tissues. In experimental infection, disease signs are apparent 4 to 5 hours later, and dying may begin in only 8 hours. Death occurs within 18 hours.

A number of mass mortalities of oysters caused by suspect bacteria have been reported in the United States and Japan. A Gram-negative bacterium, probably *Achrombacter*, has caused mass mortalities in Pacific oyster culture in Hiroshima Bay since 1946. Other bacterial diseases, called multiple abscesses and necrotic foci, have been reported.

Prevention and Control of Bacterial Diseases

The best method of prevention is to minimize stress. For example, bacterial gill disease of trout is usually associated with overcrowding, high feeding rates, lowered DO levels, and high levels of un-ionized ammonia. By cessation of feeding for several days, you can correct these conditions and control the disease.

Prophylactic measures are often helpful in preventing disease. After handling channel catfish and other finfish, use a 3% salt treatment for approximately 1 minute or until fish show signs of stress. When transporting culture species, 10 ppm acriflavine for 1 hour has been effective. Furacin is also effective. These treatments help heal injured fins and other body parts. If fish have been stressed because of low DO, medicated feed has been used to prevent a bacterial infection. However, routine use of chemicals and drugs for prophylactic treatments may encourage development of disease-resistant strains.

Valuable brood fish may be injected with drugs such as Terramycin®. Furacin has been used as a bath at 5 ppm active ingredient for 24 hours or 10 ppm for one hour with repeat treatments as required. For channel catfish with ESC, Kaskow (1987) suggested medicated feed with Terramycin® for 10 to 15 days or Romet® for 5 to 7 days or first Romet® for 5 to 7 days followed by Terramycin® for 10 to 15 days. Romet®, though effective, can be unpalatable when incorporated into feed. Addition of extra fish meal to the diet or use of masking attractants helps to increase palatability.

In pond treatments, formalin at 15 to 25 ppm or potassium permanganate at 2 to 3 ppm above the permanganate demand can be used. Formalin can be used as a bath treatment for fish in raceways or tanks by treating with 100 to 250 ppm for up to 1 hour, depending on alkalinity. When treating for bacterial disease, you should determine if the disease-causing bacterium is opportunistic (facultative) or a primary pathogen (obligate). Facultative bacteria are normally found in water and on and in the fish host. Some bacteria are found in the digestive tract and aid in digestion. Controlling facultative bacteria with drugs, then, is not the best solution. Instead, try to eliminate excessive stress.

Immunization of salmonids for ERM and *Vibrio* spp. by immersion has proved successful, and commercial vaccines are available. An injectable vaccine is available for furunculosis, MAS, ESC, and columnaris disease. Keep in mind, however, that a given bacterium may develop different strains, and that a single serotype protects against infection by the same serotype but is less effective or ineffective against related serotypes of the same disease. Ellis (1988) discussed the principles and practices of fish vaccination.

For prevention and control of chitinoclastic bacteria on crustaceans, molted exoskeletons should be removed from the culture system. Be careful to minimize bruising, handling, and overcrowding. Levels of organics in culture systems should be kept as low as possible. Selection of a compromise water temperature must be made for good growth of crustaceans, but note that chitinoclastic bacteria generally show maximum activity at 27° to 30°C (81° to 86°F); selection of a lower temperature may retard bacterial activity.

Perhaps the best method of preventing bacterial disease of mollusks is to choose a grow-out site with good quality water. With intensive culture systems and hatcheries, disinfection offers the best method for controlling bacterial disease. Blogoslawski et al. (1978) investigated several methods of bacterial disinfection. Routine use of hot tap water with a strong detergent solution and a disinfectant for cleaning, such as 5.25% sodium hypochlorite, is recommended for cleaning, even for floors and ceilings. Use of ultraviolet light and ozone gas are two practical methods for prevention of bacterial infections.

PROTOZOANS

Protozoa, a name that means "first animals," are microscopic, unicellular animals. Some are free-living; others are obligate parasites. More than 20,000 different species exist which can be found everywhere in nature. Protozoans live at the protoplasmic level of construction. The protoplasm performs all the life activities without the presence of multicellular structures. The amoeba, simplest of all protozoa, has its protoplasm surrounded by a cell membrane. The protoplasm of the amoeba is differentiated into nucleus and cytoplasm; the nucleus occupies no fixed position. To feed, an amoeba first surrounds a food particle, then engulfs it. A contractile vacuole pumps water out of the cell. Waste products diffuse out across the cell membrane.

Protozoans can be placed under one of four groups based on locomotion (Figure 10.7).

(1) Pseudopodia are temporary projections of cytoplasm that allow amoebas to creep along.

(2) Flagella are whip-like filaments that are lashed about by flagellate protozoans for movement. The flagella may number from one to eight but usually number from one to four.

(3) Cilia are fine hair-like structures that usually surround ciliate protozoans. Locomotion is achieved by rapid beating of cilia, like rowing a boat. Some members of this group possess cilia throughout their life cycle and are true ciliates. Others, like suctorians, have cilia in early stages but are sessile with tentacles as adults.

(4) Spores are produced by sporozoan protozoa. There are no locomotive structures, and movement is achieved passively from host to host, although pseudopodia may be present in early stages. All members of this last group are parasitic.

514

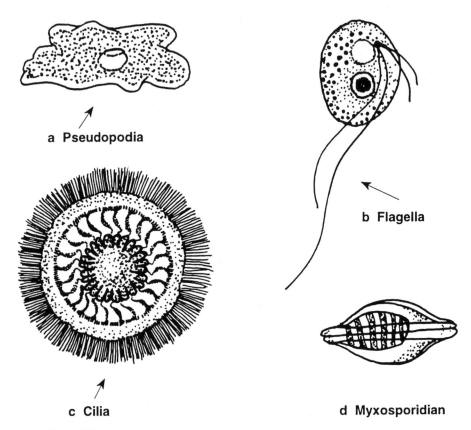

a Pseudopodia

b Flagella

c Cilia

d Myxosporidian

Figure 10.7 Different types of protozoa based on locomotion: (a) an amoeba with pseudopodia, (b) *Ichthyobodo* showing flagella, (c) *Trichodina* with cilia, and (d) a myxosporidian with no visible means of locomotion. Modified from Wellborn and Rogers 1966.

Reproduction in protozoa varies. Some, like the amoeba, divide in two by simple fission. Other protozoans reproduce by budding. A part of the cell swells, and a bud pinches off. Spores are formed by some, and repeated divisions may occur within a single spore.

Nutrition of protozoa is by one of three methods. Holophytic protozoa obtain nutrients by photosynthesis. Holozoic protozoa use plants and animals as food. Saprophytic protozoa absorb organic matter through the cell wall.

Protozoans are responsible for many serious diseases of humans such as malaria and African sleeping sickness. In aquatic species, they can be serious parasites. Like bacteria and viruses, they may cause high mortalities.

Protozoan diseases were reviewed by Hoffman (1967), Hoffman and Meyer (1974), Post (1983), MacMillan (1985), Rogers (1985), Tucker and Robinson (1990), Sindermann (1990a, 1990b), and Schäperclaus (1991).

Protozoan Diseases of Finfish

Ichthyophthirius multifiliis (Ich or white spot disease) is a ciliate characterized by its relatively large size, compared with other protozoans. It has a horseshoe-shaped nucleus (Figure 10.8a). Ich, one of the most devastating parasites affecting channel catfish, may destroy entire populations. It is not host specific and may affect virtually all cultured finfish.

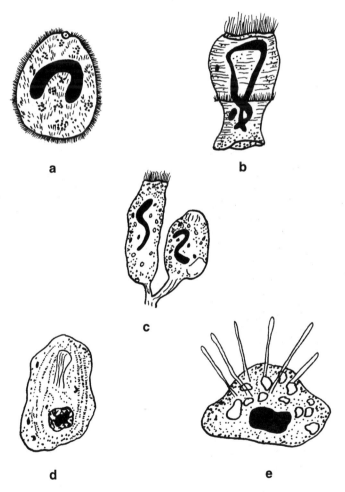

Figure 10.8 Protozoan parasites: (a) *Ichthyophthirius mulitfiliis*, (b) *Ambiphrya*, (c) *Epistylis*, (d) *Chilodonella*, and (e) *Trichophyra.* After Wellborn and Rogers 1966.

The parasite burrows just under the skin of fish, causing white specks that sometimes can be seen with the unaided eye (Figure 10.9). After maturing, the adult parasite, called a trophozoite, leaves the fish and becomes free swimming for up to 6 hours. It eventually attaches to available substrate. A membrane is secreted over the organism, and the cyst undergoes multiple fissions. Up to 1,000 or more young, called tomites, are produced. Development of mature tomites can be completed within 12 hours at 25°C (77°F). When the cyst ruptures, tomites swarm forth seeking a fish host. Once located, tomites penetrate fish by their ciliary action and with the aid of an enzyme. Once having penetrated, the tomites mature into trophozoites and feed on cells and fluids of fish.

Optimal temperature ranges for development to trophozoites ready to emerge from a host are 21° to 24°C (70° to 75°F). Maturation at this temperature occurs in 3 to 4 days. At 16°C (61°F) the entire cycle takes 10 to 14 days. It takes more than 5 weeks at 10°C (50°F). Epizootics usually occur in the spring and fall when optimum water temperatures, 20° to 25°C (68° to 77°F), occur. Temperatures in the southeastern United States are too warm for optimum growth during summer, and the disease seldom occurs at this time.

Figure 10.9 Ich on channel catfish, clearly visible to the naked eye. Photo courtesy of Jill Jenkins-Tiersch of the U.S. Fish and Wildlife Service, Marion, Alabama.

Trichodina spp., a ciliate, occurs on channel catfish and can be found on virtually all freshwater species of cold and warmwater fish (Figure 10.7c). Trichodinids also occur on saltwater fish. The parasite, which may cause extensive mortalities especially of fingerlings, is sometimes associated with poor water quality and accumulation of wastes. Epizootics may occur throughout the year but are more common in spring and fall. The parasite's most prominent feature is its denticulate ring, a sclerotized ring of interlocking denticles forming a circle within the inverted "soup-bowl-shaped" body. The parasite moves rapidly over the surface of gills, fins, and body.

Infested fish show whitish to whitish-gray blotches, and copious amounts of mucus may be noted. Tail fins often become milky and opaque. Fish usually become lethargic and may congregate near incoming water. Heavy infestations of the parasite result in excessive mucus production that impairs respiration. Fish may suffocate, even with sufficient levels of dissolved oxygen in the water. Related genera, *Trichodinella* and *Tripartiella*, also occur on fish.

Ambiphrya (*Scyphidia*) (Figure 10.8b) and *Apiosoma* (*Glossatella*) are very similar parasites, both having an urn-shaped or barrel-shaped body. *Ambiphyra* has a ribbon-shaped nucleus and *Apiosoma* a rounded macronucleus. The organisms are associated with the presence of high amounts of organic matter and are usually found attached to plants, rocks, or other substrate. The parasites, found on all cultured warmwater fish and occasionally on salmonids, are mostly a problem with fry and fingerling fish. Infected fish may not eat and may swim lethargically at the surface. The parasite causes increased sensitivity to low levels of dissolved oxygen because of interference with the gills. Gills become pale and enlarged with pinpoint hemorrhages. Hemorrhaging also may occur on the body.

Epistylis, a stalked protozoan, has a row of cilia at the apical end used for drawing food into the main body (Figure 10.8c). Under microscope the stalks contract periodically, aiding in identification. The parasite is common on rainbow trout in the western United States, may occasionally occur on channel catfish, and will affect other finfish species. In scaled fishes, the parasite causes erosion of skin, scales, and spines resulting in bloody lesions, hence the name "red sore" disease. Infestations on channel catfish involve spines and bones that underlie the skin on the pectoral girdle, head, and the fins. The parasite, associated with high loads of organic matter or pollution, will cause infested fish to flash. Hemorrhaging and excessive localized mucus production are common. Fish eggs are sometimes infested and look "fuzzy."

Chilodonella is found on the gills or skin of freshwater finfish and is distinct with parallel rows of cilia along the body margin. *Chilodonella* is a ciliate with a round to heart-shaped, depressed body (Figure 10.8d). It is a colorless, flattened organism that creeps rapidly about over fins, gills, and body of the host. It is frequently associated with other protozoans previously discussed.

Chilodonella is a coolwater parasite although one species, *C. hexastichus*, causes mortality at water temperatures up to 21°C (70°F).

Ichthyobodo, one of the smallest protozoan parasites, is often overlooked and can be detected only under high magnification (Figure 10.7b). It is teardrop-shaped and appears to be "fluttering" like a tree leaf in a breeze as it attaches to the gills or skin of the fish host. The parasite has one pair of flagella attached to the small rounded blepharoplast, but two smaller flagella appear before division.

Two species of *Ichthyobodo* have been reported, *I. necatrix* and *I. pyriformis*. *I. necatrix* is the most common of the two, and was first described from European fishes. It is widely distributed in the United States. It is common on young trout and salmon, where it is one of the most destructive ectoparasitic protozoans. Fry and fingerling channel catfish are very susceptible to this parasite. *I. necatrix* is flattened with definite dorsal and ventral surfaces. It is oval, with rounded anterior and posterior ends. The ventral surface is concave. *I. necatrix* attaches to the host's body with a flat disc. From the disc small bundles of microtubles extend into the host cell. Portions of the host cell are engulfed by the tubules and are brought into the parasite as food vacuoles. A grayish-white to bluish film, caused by excess mucus production, appears on the skin of the host fish. This is why it is often called the blue-slime disease.

I. pyriformis, which infests both gills and body, is found mainly on trout. It is distinctly pear-shaped and moves with a rapid spiral movement that is different from the darting movements of *I. necatrix*.

Dinoflagellates are identified by a groove around the middle of the cell with a flagellum lying in the groove. *Oodinium* sp., a well-known dinoflagellate, is found on freshwater, brackishwater, and marine fish. The disease caused is often referred to as velvet disease since the parasite may become so abundant on the host that a fine yellowish sheen is seen. The parasite attacks gills and skin and may be found attached to intestinal mucosa. The adult, which is pear-shaped, attaches to fish tissues with root-like appendages. The non-motile adults often have a yellow hue and are frequently found in clusters. When mature, the organism drops off fish, attaches to a hard substrate, and begins to multiply, forming motile dinospores. Once a host is found, flagella disappear and root-like appendages anchor the parasite to the host's tissue where maturation progresses.

Affected fish may scrape themselves or show signs of suffocation. A flashlight used to inspect fish in a darkened room may reflect light back from the *Oodinium* parasites. *Glenodinium*, another dinoflagellate, has been associated with channel catfish mortalities. It is normally a free-living algal cell that may, on occasion, develop a heavy bloom, giving the water a brownish color. Cells of *Glenodinium* may become entrapped in gill lamellae of fish, or they may actively attach, causing a proliferation of gill tissue.

Trichophyra, a suctorian parasite found on the gills of warmwater fish, is distinguished by a round body and suctorial tentacles in the adult stage (Figure

10.8e). It feeds on passing protists as well as epithelial cells. The juvenile stage is ciliated. Under microscope, the parasite looks brownish. It appears as a visible red or orange spot. The parasite may reach large numbers with high organic levels and low temperatures. Gills may swell and become eroded, and anemia may follow. Affected fish become lethargic, may stop feeding, and may gather around inflowing water.

Sporozoan protozoans are responsible for very serious fish diseases. This class of protozoans is known by the morphology of its spores and by the number and location of polar capsules containing coiled filaments. Sporozoan parasites are subdivided into two basic groups, myxosporidians with two or more polar capsules and microsporidians with one polar capsule. Pathologists also recognize two other groups, coccidia and haemosporidea. Schäperclaus (1991), however, pointed out that classification of sporozoa is difficult and that members of sporozoa have a single common feature, the formation of spores. Beyond that, classification is open to conjecture.

Sporozoans are relatively host- and tissue-specific, have complex life cycles, and are untreatable. The life cycle of both myxosporidians and microsporidians begins with the spore. Upon death of the host, the spore drops to the bottom or is accidentally eaten by fish. The polar filament(s) is used to attach to the gut wall. In microsporidia, DNA nuclear material enters host cells through the everted polar filament. The parasite may eventually transfer to the definitive or final loci through infected white blood cells. In myxosporidia, polar filaments are probably used to attach to a cell, after which the sporoplasm of the parasite emerges in amoeboid form and penetrates a cell in the gut wall and perhaps elsewhere. The parasite may eventually work its way to its definitive loci, or it may be carried there by the white blood cells. Once at the loci, sporozoan parasites (now termed trophozoites) divide (shizogony) and fuse (sporogony), forming a mass of spores responsible for disease.

Myxosoma cerebralis, a myxosporidian, causes whirling disease in salmonids, so called because diseased fish swim in circles. The parasite, which enters through any external surface opening, damages the cartilage in the axial skeleton of young fish. This interferes with the function of adjacent neural structures. Coordination is affected when the parasite invades the cartilaginous capsule of the auditory equilibrium organ behind the eye. When fish are disturbed, they whirl frantically as if chasing their tails. The disease was first noted in 1900 after rainbow trout were introduced to Europe. Whirling disease at one time caused catastrophic losses in trout culture in central and north Europe. Today it is not considered as a serious problem because of measures to control it. Schäperclaus (1991) gave a particularly detailed review of this disease. The disease has occurred in certain eastern states and Nevada in the USA.

Henneguya, found on freshwater finfish, is a myxosporidian having two polar capsules and a long tail-like extension of each spore shell. Several apparent site-specific forms of *Henneguya* have been noted on channel catfish, three on the skin and three on gill filaments. On the skin, a papillomatous form creates large lesions on body and fins, and nearly half the body may be affected. The second form creates a pustule or blister. Both forms may disfigure fish, but dressed fish show no signs of the parasite. The third form is of minor importance, occurring as a white cyst on the adipose fin of channel catfish fingerlings. On gills, an interlamellar form may cause extensive damage to channel catfish fingerlings. The second form usually has a few intralamellar cysts per filament, but does not pose a major problem. The third form produces discrete visible cysts on gills. *Henneguya* has also been found in channel catfish viscera.

Protozoan Diseases of Crustaceans

Protozoan parasites and commensals of freshwater crawfish, prawns, and shrimp may be grouped as gregarines, microsporidians, ectocommensals, body invaders, and apostome ciliates (Johnson 1975, 1977).

Gregarine protozoans, such as *Nematopsis* sp., have been observed in the digestive tract of shrimp, usually in the trophozoite or gametocyst form. The life cycle of the parasite involves marine snails or clams. Although the trophozoites attach to the intestinal lining where they absorb food, damage to the host is usually considered minor.

Microsporidian infestation in penaeid shrimp causes a chronic disease referred to as "cotton" or "milk" shrimp. At least four species of microsporidia are parasitic to penaeids. Depending on the species of microsporidian, infestation is throughout the musculature or in particular tissues and organs. Microsporidians are present in affected shrimp in spore form. An envelope encloses spores in some species but not others. *Nosema* is a genus without an enclosing envelope. *Pleistophora* and *Thelohania* are genera with enclosing envelopes.

Shrimp infected with microsporidians are often active and feed normally; however, microsporidians are suspect in preventing egg production of shrimp. Both *Macrobrachium* and crawfish are susceptible hosts to microsporidians, but in the United States the parasite is generally uncommon and not considered a major problem. In Europe, microsporidian infection of crawfish is referred to as the porcelain disease. The microsporidia are present as isolated bundles of spores. In heavily diseased crawfish and prawns the spores are spread throughout the musculature. Spores of *Thelohania* and *Indosporus* are in groups of eight inside a membrane. *Thelohania* spp. spores are egg-shaped, and those of *Indosporus* spp. are egg-shaped with tails. *Pleistophora* spp. and *Nosema* spp. also have egg-shaped spores, but *Pleistophora* spp. are found in groups of 16 or more within a membrane, and *Nosema* spp. are distributed singly. The life cycle of microsporidians in crustaceans is not completely known.

Ectocommensals consist of a myriad of protozoan species that attach to the body surface and gills. Common parasitic genera associated with crawfish and prawns include *Epistylis, Zoothamnium, Lagenophrys, Corthunia*, and *Acineta*. Less common genera are *Vorticella, Vaginicola*, and *Opercularia*. *Acineta* sp. is common in brackish water on prawns. *Corthunia* sp. is found on crawfish and occasionally on prawns in fresh water. *Epistylis, Zoothamnium*, and *Lagenophrys* are found in both fresh and brackish water on crawfish and prawns. *Lagenophrys* is more prevalent on prawns than on crawfish.

Body invaders are those protozoans that may, on occasion, wander about the body. Whether this is an accidental parasitism, and the crustacean serves as a paratenic host, is unclear.

Apostome ciliates are common on crawfish and prawns and have been noted infrequently in the resting stage in shrimp. Apostomes, usually considered commensals, encyst on crustaceans on the exoskeleton. When the crustacean molts, the protozoa hatch and feed on released fluids of the shed exoskeleton. They look like tiny transparent bubbles. After reproduction, the apostomes seek a host. Common apostome genera in North America include *Hyalophysa, Gymnodinioides*, and *Terebrospira*.

Protozoan Diseases of Mollusks

Several protozoan diseases have been identified as serious in North American oyster culture (Sindermann 1990b). A haplosporidian protozoan, *Haplosporidium nelsoni* (called MSX prior to 1966), causes Delaware Bay disease in the American oyster and possibly other oyster species. Affected oysters become emaciated and have weak shell enclosure and shell recession. The disease is highly lethal to oysters, and its prevalence is affected by salinity. During dry years (high salinity) in the mid 1960s, *H. nelsoni* killed oyster beds in Maryland, but during rainy years of 1971 to 1974 the disease was confined to Mobjack Bay and Hampton Roads of lower Chesapeake Bay.

The known, major geographic distribution of the disease includes Delaware Bay and Chesapeake Bay. Infestations occur from mid-May to 1 November. A salinity of 15 ppt or higher is required, and the disease may remain hidden for up to 9 months. June and July infestations become latent in about 5 weeks. Oysters begin dying by 1 August with peak mortalities (50% to 60%) in September.

Haplosporidium costale, also a haplosporidian protozoan, causes seaside disease of oysters. Affected oysters fail to add new "bill" or shell in May, and are in generally poor condition. The disease usually occurs in high salinity water, over 25 ppt, from Long Island Sound to Cape Charles and occasionally near mouths of the Delaware and Chesapeake bays. *H. costale*, which will not tolerate salinities below 25 ppt, may kill 20% to 50% of mature oysters in affected regions. The mortalities are from mid-May to early July. Yearlings tend to escape the disease but 2- to 3-year- olds are severely affected.

Perkinsus marinus ("Dermo") is common in the Gulf of Mexico and lower Chesapeake Bay. This protozoan parasite has been under study for more than 30 years because of its seriousness (Sindermann 1990b). It invades the gut epithelium, possibly through the mantle. The epithelium is destroyed, and the parasite is distributed by the blood to all parts of the body. Normal gonadal development is inhibited, and infected oysters become severely emaciated. Infections rise during warm months and decline during colder months. Infections and resulting mortalities are reduced in salinities below 15 ppt. In European waters, two protozoan parasites, *Marteilia refringens* and *Bonamia ostreae*, have caused serious problems with the oyster *Ostrea edulis*.

As aquaculture of mussels (primarily *Mytilus edulis*), clams (various species), and scallops (several species) increases, protozoan diseases are becoming more noticeable. Haplosporidian protozoans have been reported for moribund mussels in North America, but it is not clear how prevalent they are. In one instance extensive mortality of mussels occurred on Prince Edward Island because of infestation by a haplosporidian protozoan tentatively identified as *Labyrinthomyxa* sp. However significant protozoan infestations of mussels appear to be isolated instances. Sindermann (1990b) reviewed the knowledge of protozoan parasites for mollusks other than oysters.

Prevention and Control of Protozoan Diseases

Treatment of Ich on finfish is very difficult because the trophozoite form of the parasite, found under the skin, is normally not controlled with chemicals. Moreover few chemicals are capable of killing the invasive stages, but tomites and emerged adults are killed easily. Therefore, treatments must be prolonged and multiple and timed to kill the emerging tomite stage.

Tucker and Robinson (1990) discussed two treatment regimens; both are based on treatments that are repeated until the disease is controlled. One regimen consists of treatment with copper sulfate every other day. Five to seven treatments are usually sufficient, but fish should be examined to verify success of treatments. The amount of copper sulfate to use depends on the total alkalinity, total hardness, and pH, already discussed. Generally, copper sulfate should not be used if total alkalinity is less than 50 ppm because it may kill fish. If total alkalinity is above 300 ppm, copper sulfate forms insoluble precipitates, and treatment efficiency is greatly reduced. Copper sulfate may kill a phytoplankton bloom. Therefore great care must be taken to avoid oxygen depletion.

The other treatment regimen involves alternating treatments of potassium permanganate, formalin, and copper sulfate. The treatment rate of potassium permanganate depends on the amount of organic matter in the water. Formalin is used at 15 ppm. Copper sulfate is applied at a rate agreeable to the total alkalinity. The interval of treatment with the three different chemicals varies with the water temperature:

Water Temperature	Treatment Schedule
26°C (80°F)	Every day
21°C (70°F)	Every other day
16°C (60°F)	Every third day
10°C (50°F)	Every fourth day
4°C (40°F)	Once a week

The tomite of Ich can be controlled by elevating the water temperature above 28°C (82°F). This is detrimental to the parasite, and it ceases development. Fish can be held in tanks with swiftly flowing water. Tomites are mechanically flushed down the drain. Channel catfish and other species can be held in 1 ppt salinity for up to 1 week to control Ich (Allen and Avault 1970). Most external protozoan parasites of finfish have been controlled in ponds with 2 to 3 ppm $KMnO_4$ above the permanganate demand, 15 ppm formalin, or copper sulfate at 0.5 to 1 ppm, depending on total alkalinities. In tanks, formalin up to 200 to 250 ppm for 1 hour is effective.

Prevention of all protozoan diseases in ponds can be aided by disking dry pond bottoms and treating them with calcium hypochlorite. In tanks, buildup of feces, uneaten feed, and other organic matter should be avoided since some protozoans, such as *Ambiphrya* and *Epistylis*, may thrive under these conditions.

Whirling disease and other diseases caused by sporozoans can be prevented to a degree. Whirling disease can be prevented by using fish known to be free of the disease. If the water supply is contaminated with *M. cerebralis*, filtration through filters with 10 micron pores removes spores. Sand-gravel filters may be adequate in some instances. Irradiation of filtered water with ultraviolet light (35,000 microwatt seconds/cm^2) kills spores (Hoffman 1976).

Disinfection of a contaminated site is difficult. First, all infested fish must be destroyed by incineration or by deep burial with CaO. Culture facilities should be drained, cleaned, and disinfected with CaO at 380 g/m^2 (1 lb/yd^2) or 3,763 kg/ha (3,360 lb/ac). Calcium cyanamide at 500 g/m^2 (1.3 lb/yd^2) or 4,738 kg/ha (4,231 lb/ac) is also effective, but disinfection procedures may have to be repeated several times (Hoffman 1976). Calcium cyanamide should be flushed out of a pond before fish are stocked.

If a culture facility has a chronic problem of whirling disease, keep young fry and fingerling salmonids in spore-free water in metal or concrete tanks until they are at least 8 to 13 cm (3 to 5 in) long and 8 months old before stocking into grow-out facilities. Schäperclaus (1991) offered eight detailed measures to prevent and control *M. cerebralis*.

The same methods used to prevent and control protozoan diseases of finfish also may apply to crustaceans. Regarding sanitary and other preventive measures, this is generally true. Moreover, chemicals used to treat finfish pathogens are also effective against the same pathogens on crustaceans.

Changing the host species seldom affects the activity of a chemical on pathogens. For example, the protozoan *Zoothamnium* sp. is readily controlled on *Macrobrachium rosenbergii* with 20 ppm formalin.

However, there are profound differences in treatment susceptibility between families, genera, and even host species. A compound readily tolerated by finfish may kill crustaceans. In some instances, crustaceans may be highly tolerant of chemicals. Williams and Avault (1976) reported that red swamp crawfish were highly tolerant to high levels of acriflavine, formalin, and potassium permanganate. Schnick et al. (1979b) compiled a list of chemicals and their acute toxicity to a variety of crustaceans.

In oyster culture, keeping oysters in salinities below 15 ppt will help control *H. nelsoni*, whereas *H. costale* will not tolerate salinities much below 25 ppt. Sindermann (1990b) reviewed other methods for control of protozoan parasites with crustaceans and mollusks.

FUNGI

Fungi (molds) are primitive plants that lack chlorophyll. They are ubiquitous, with more than 1,000,000 species. Fungi are important in yeast fermentation, production of antibodies, in decay of organic matter, and in some instances as fish parasites. Fungi consist of threads called hyphae, which are often branched. Parts of the hyphae grow into the substratum, such as the skin of fish. This part of the fungus, which is like roots, is called mycelium. Both hyphae and mycelium grow until a large cottony tuft is formed. Sporangia usually form at the end of hyphae, and in these up to 800 zoospores are produced. The sporangia eventually rupture and zoospores with two cilia move through the water (Figure 10.10). Each zoospore forms a new hypha.

A second form of reproduction consists of conidia formations that are club-shaped swellings at the end of hyphae. Conidia divide themselves into several parts, which may produce new fungus plants. Both sporangia and conidia formation are asexual, but some fungi have sexual reproduction. This involves antheridium (male gametes) and oogonium (female eggs). The sexual forms are usually required for species identification.

Fungi usually grow on organic matter and absorb nutrients saprophytically. Like bacteria, they are usually secondary invaders. If a fish is injured and a point of entry is provided, fungi can become established on dead cells. Ultimately, live healthy cells and tissues are attacked. Although individual fish may die, fungal disease is usually not catastrophic. It can be, however, when fungi attack eggs in a hatchery. A buildup of organic matter from unclean hatching troughs or water supply or the presence of dead eggs are prerequisite for fungal infections.

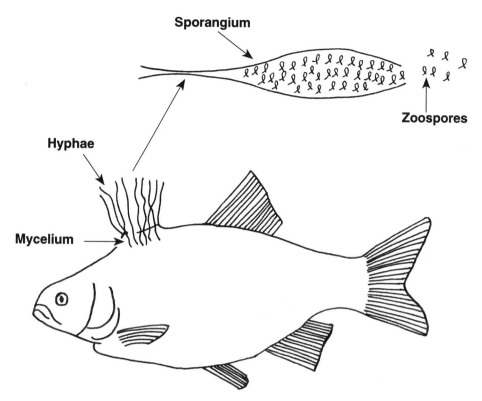

Figure 10.10 Fungi infection of fish showing break in skin for point of entry, mycelium or "roots" of fungus hyphae with sporangia, and enlargement of sporangium with ciliated zoospores.

Fungal Diseases of Finfish

Most fungi that cause disease in fish are members of the family Saprolegniacea. Two common members are in the genus *Saprolegnia* and *Achlya*. Scott and O'Bier (1962) also listed *Aphanomyces, Leptomitus,* and *Pythium* as disease causing.

All finfish species are susceptible to fungal attack. The free-swimming spores usually attach to injured or dead tissues, but some attack apparently healthy animals. Once a colony is established, hyphae invade healthy tissues, producing a cottony growth. *Saprolegnia parasitica*, considered a coolwater organism, has a life cycle of about 24 to 48 hours from zoospore to mycelium to spore. *Saprolegnia* and other water molds may cause catastrophic losses of incubating eggs.

The fungus *Icthyophonus hoferi* is an internal parasite, principally of marine fish. Internal organs may develop nodules. The disease may be passed on to freshwater species through fish feed contaminated with spores from raw fish.

Gill rot, associated with the fungus *Branchimyces*, may be found on a number of culture species where water quality is poor and organic matter high. *Achlya hoferi* is a common fungus that attacks carp in Europe.

Fungal Diseases of Crustaceans

The fungus *Aphanomyces astaci* is notorious in Europe for causing the plague of crawfish. It has virtually devastated native crawfish. Infected crawfish can be identified by their languor. If they are removed from water, their claws hang downward as if paralyzed. There is often a loss of limbs or parts. The fungus attacks the skin and central nervous system. The musculature and connective tissues are seldom attacked. After the crawfish host dies, cottony growths form, especially on the articular membranes and eyes. Unestam (1972, 1973) discussed this fungal disease and others. *Fusarium* and *Ramularia* are other fungi known to invade crawfish.

In penaeid shrimp culture, *Lagenidium* and *Fusarium* have occasionally caused high losses. *Lagenidium* mycelium may appear to replace internal tissues of larval shrimp until shrimp are filled with hyphae. Infected shrimp become immobile and settle to the bottom. Mortalities may reach 100% with larval stages, particularly the protozoea stage. *Fusarium* infection may eventually affect 10% of the body and is generally not a real danger to shrimp in grow-out ponds. However epizootics have occurred with brown shrimp (*P. aztecus*) in tanks with mortality rates up to 90%. Sindermann (1990b) reviewed literature on fungal diseases of marine crustaceans.

Fungal Diseases of Mollusks

Fungi are generally not considered serious pathogens of mollusks. *Perkinsus marinus*, a protozoan parasite already discussed, was first described as a fungus (Mackin et al. 1950). It was called *Dermocystidium marinum* (Dermo) and later *Labyrinthomyxa marina*. Most fungal diseases of mollusks seem to attack external parts, such as shells and the byssus. On occasion fungus may pose a problem in molluskan hatcheries.

Prevention and Control of Fungal Diseases

Sanitation and hygienic cultural practices are essential to control *Saprolegnia*. In channel catfish hatcheries, water temperatures should be maintained at 26° to 27°C (79° to 81°F) and never allowed to drop below 21°C (70°F). Small batches of fish with saprolegniasis can be treated with a 1- to 2- minute dip in a 3% salt solution. Fish in larger culture units can be treated with potassium permanganate or formalin. These treatments kill zoospores but not attached hyphae. Ordinarily fish infected with *Saprolegnia* in ponds are not treated since the disease is seldom catastrophic. Moreover, fungi will simply reinfect fish unless the condition causing stress is corrected. Formalin can also be used as a bath treatment for fish in raceways or tanks by treating with 100 to 250 ppm for up to 1 hour. For egg disinfection, formalin at 100 ppm for 15 minutes is usually effective.

Fungi infections of crustaceans can be prevented and controlled with the same methods as those used for finfish. However, the tolerance levels of crustaceans to a given chemical must first be established. The fungus *Aphanomyces astaci* of European crawfish, principally *Astacus astacus*, has not been controlled. The signal crawfish *Pacifastacus leniusculus* and red swamp crawfish, both resistant to the fungi, have been successfully introduced into European waters.

TAPEWORMS

They are members of an assemblage of worm-like animals called helminths. Besides tapeworms, other helminths include spiny-headed worms, trematodes, nematodes, and leeches. A tapeworm has a head end or scolex and a neck followed by segments or proglottids (Figure 10.11). A major characteristic of tapeworms is the complete lack of a digestive system. These obligate parasites live in the gut or intestine of a host where nutrients are absorbed. The scolex serves primarily as an organ of attachment, and it may have hooks or suckers or sucking grooves (bothria). Just behind the scolex, the neck continually grows and, as it does, forms partitions or proglottids which are collectively called strobila. The proglottids just behind the neck are the youngest and at first are indistinct. As they are pushed back from the scolex, the organs develop. Each proglottid contains both male and female sex organs, and fertilization may occur within a proglottid or between proglottids. Eggs are produced and shed by each proglottid. In some cases, a proglottid may "go to seed" and drop off, shedding hordes of eggs when ruptured. Proglottids full of eggs are said to be gravid.

Tapeworms require several hosts to complete their life cycle. Eggs are shed into the water through the feces of the host. Inside each egg develops a spherical embryo, with three pairs of clawlike hooks, which is known as an oncosphere. In some tapeworms, the embryo is covered by a ciliated embryophore and is called a coracidium. Eggs may be eaten by a crustacean (copepod), or they may hatch and the onchosphere be eaten by a copepod. Coracidia have a brief free-swimming existence in which they roll about, attracting copepods that eat them. Once eaten by a copepod, the onchosphere burrows out of the copepod's gut and into the body cavity (hemocoel) where it develops into the next larval stage, the procercoid. The six hooks are still present. A fish eats the copepod containing the procercoid. The procercoid larvae, when liberated, metamorphose and pass through the wall of the digestive tract as plerocercoid larvae. These larvae migrate into the mesenteries and viscera or musculature of the fish where they usually remain. Because of this migration, tissues and organs may be damaged severely. In some cases the reproductive organs may be so badly damaged that the fish is sterile. When the fish host is eaten by the definitive host, an aquatic bird, mammal, or another fish, the plerocercoid develops into the adult stage in

528

the digestive tract. The adult stage of the parasite, where sexual reproduction occurs, is always found in the definitive host. The copepod and first fish host are called intermediate hosts.

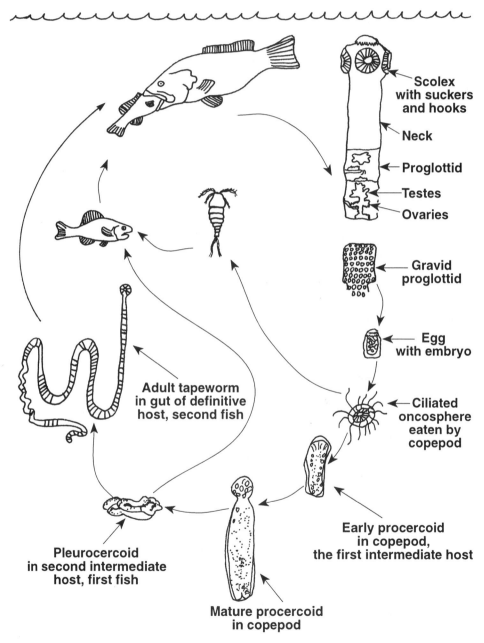

Figure 10.11 Generalized life cycle of tapeworm.

Tapeworms rarely cause losses of fish even though they may become numerous. An exception is the Asian tapeworm lb golden shiner and carp fry. Fish raised for food are usually grown and sold before they have a chance to accumulate the parasite. Exceptions are *Eubothrium* in trout and the Corallobothrids in channel catfish. Brood fish, however, may accumulate the parasite both in the plerocercoid and adult stage. For this reason, old brood stock should be culled.

Tapeworms of Finfish

Corallobothrium spp. are common in channel catfish. The head of *Corallobothrium* lacks hooks but has four suckers and large lappets or folds that surround the suckers. Eggs of *Corallobothrium* are voided with the feces of the host, hatch in water, and are eaten by a small crustacean (copepod). Larvae migrate into fish tissues and develop into plerocercoids. Catfish probably become infested by eating infected copepods, but there is a possibility that there is also a fish intermediate host. The Asian tapeworm, *Bothriocephalus acheilognathi*, is not host specific and attacks several fish species including carp, golden shiner, and grass carp (*Ctenopharyngodon idella*). The parasite accumulates in the anterior part of the fish's intestine that may become obstructed and distended if many worms are present. Mortality of young carp may reach 90%, and small golden shiners are likewise affected.

Tapeworms of Crustaceans and Mollusks

Tapeworms of crustaceans and mollusks are generally not considered serious parasites to culture species. Most of the literature deals with taxonomy and life cycles (Sindermann 1990b).

Prevention and Control of Tapeworms

It is generally not practical to kill the intermediate host, the copepod, except perhaps when Masoten is used to control the Asian tapeworm. Transfer of infested fish to waters where infestation does not occur should be avoided. Bottoms of ponds containing infested fish can be dried, disked, and limed with calcium hydroxide. Di-N-butyl tin oxide has been incorporated into feed to give 250 mg/kg of fish (113 mg/lb of fish) when fish are fed at 3% body weight daily. Yomesan also can be used at 50 mg/kg (23 mg/lb) of fish for 3 days, but it is toxic to fish if used in aquaria or tanks without adequate running water.

SPINY-HEADED WORMS

Like tapeworms, spiny-headed worms are obligate, intestinal parasites that lack a digestive tract. Unlike tapeworms, they have a body that is small and unsegmented, and they have separate sexes. The body is divided into a posterior trunk and an anterior presoma, consisting of a spiny proboscis and an unspined neck (Figure 10.12). The proboscis, and often the neck, is retractile into a proboscis sac or receptacle by being turned inside out. The armature of the proboscis sac varies from a few to many hooks.

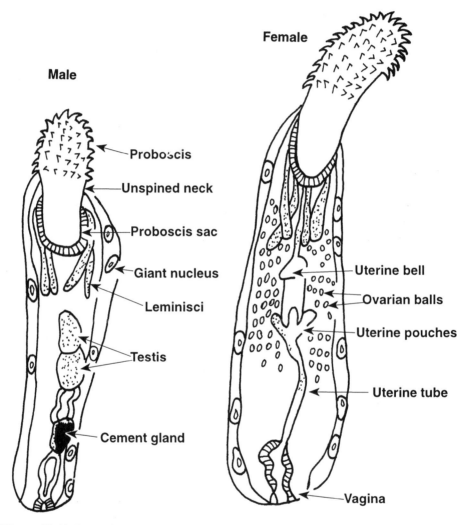

Figure 10.12 Generalized morphology of male and female spiny-headed worm.

The life cycle of spiny-headed worms involves two hosts. Adult worms shed eggs that enter the water through the feces of the definite host. Eggs, which have a well-developed embryo called an acanthor, are eaten by an aquatic crustacean. The acanthor, armed with rostellar hooks and small body spines, hatches and bores into the intestinal wall, eventually reaching the body cavity. The acanthor absorbs embryonic hooks and undergoes a gradual transformation. The proboscis, rudiments of sex organs, and other organs are developed. The fully developed larva is sometimes called an acanthella. The fully developed acanthella encysts to form a cystacanth that is enclosed in a delicate hyaline sheath produced by the larvae. The proboscis is fully formed but inverted, and reproductive organs can be noted. When the definitive host eats the intermediate host, the adult parasite attaches to the wall of the intestinal tract. The parasite can do considerable damage to its host, principally from attachment with its spiny hooks. When the worm moves and reattaches, the old sore may become infected by bacteria. Ordinarily, however, spiny-headed worms are not a serious problem with culture species.

TREMATODES

Trematodes are obligate parasites often referred to as flukes because of their flat, leaf-shaped appearance. There are two principal groups based mainly on their reproductive cycle, monogenetic and digenetic.

Monogenetic Flukes

These are ectoparasites (external) which complete their life cycle on one host. Usually immature worms are morphologically similar to mature forms. Monogenetic refers to direct development of the parasite: adult → egg → immature → adult. Adult parasites are easily identified by the chief organ of attachment, called a haptor, which is at the posterior end (Figure 10.13). There are usually two or four anchors (large hooks) and 12 to 16 hooklets around the margin of the haptor. Haptor morphology, numbers, and arrangement are used to identify different flukes. Individual parasites contain both male and female organs. At the opposite end of the parasite is the prohaptor. It has no hooks but has adhesive capability.

The life cycle is simple. Monogenetic flukes produce few, rather large eggs that often have polar elongations. In some cases, eggs may have hook-like projections. These special structures help attach eggs to the gills or body of the host fish. Some monogenetic flukes such as *Gyrodactylus* give birth to fully developed young. Some monogeneans live on the gills only, others on the body surface.

Two major families of monogenetic trematodes are recognized as fish parasites. Members of the family Gyrodactylidae are typically live bearers. They have a well-developed haptor bearing one pair of large hooks and 16 marginal hooklets. Eyespots are absent. Adults are usually found on the body. Only one genus, *Gyrodactylus*, is represented in North America.

Members of the family Dactylogyridae have a haptor with one or two pairs of anchors and usually 14 marginal hooklets. Eyespots are present. These parasites are found on gills. *Ligictaluridus* spp. (formerly *Cleidodiscus*) are common on the gills of channel catfish (Figure 10.14). Adults of both species are microscopic. The haptor is well developed, bears two pairs of large hooks, and has 16 marginal hooklets. The head end has two pairs of eyespots.

Monogenetic flukes are not serious parasites but on occasion they may kill fish, particularly fingerlings. Monogenetic flukes on the gills may result in suffocation if in great enough numbers. They can be controlled in ponds with formalin at 25 ppm, potassium permanganate at 3 ppm, and Masoten® (Dylox) at 0.25 to 0.5 ppm active ingredient. In tanks, formalin at 166 ppm for 1 hour has been used, but the water must be changed rapidly at termination or at the first sign of stress.

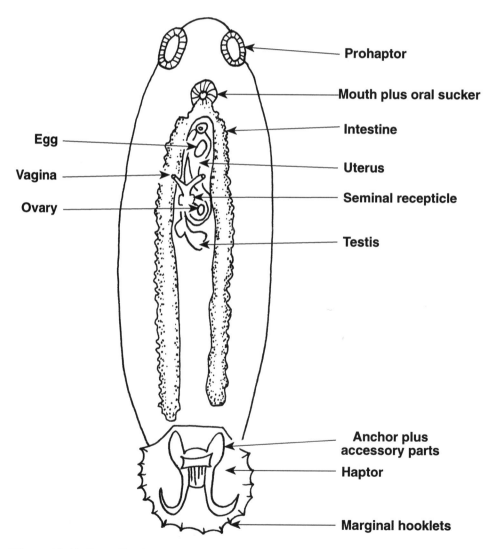

Figure 10.13 Generalized morphology of monogenetic trematode.

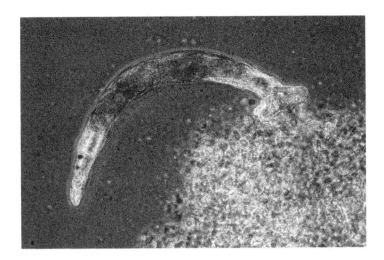

Figure 10.14 Monogenetic trematode taken from channel catfish. Photo courtesy of Jill Jenkins-Tiersch of the U.S. Fish and Wildlife Service, Marion, Alabama.

Digenetic Flukes

These are endoparasites (internal) with a complex life cycle involving two to four hosts. Adult parasites typically have two large suckers, an oral sucker around the mouth and a second sucker called an acetabulum located ventrally in the middle or posterior end of the body. The number and location of suckers may vary, and this is used in part to identify the parasites. All adult fish trematodes contain both male and female organs.

The white grub (*Posthodiplostomum minimum*) will be used to illustrate a generalized life cycle. The adult parasite, found in a heron (Ardeidae), an aquatic wading bird, produces eggs that are passed out into water with the feces of the heron (Figure 10.15). Eggs hatch in about 3 weeks, each producing a ciliated free-swimming miracidium. They penetrate the first intermediate host, a snail (*Physa* spp.), and develop into the second larval stage, the sac-like mother sporocyst. Each mother sporocyst asexually produces several daughter sporocysts, the third larval stage. Some parasite species produce redia instead of daughter sporocysts. The difference is that the redia has a rudimentary mouth, pharynx, and blind gut; daughter sporocysts do not. Daughter sporocysts each produce several hundred cercariae, the fourth larval stage. Cercariae ultimately leave the snail host, and like miracidia they are free swimming. Cercariae have about 24 hours to find a suitable host, such as a bluegill (*Lepomis macrochirus*). Red ear (*L. microlophus*), by feeding on snails, significantly reduce infestation of *P. minimum* metacercariae in bluegill. Red ear are also much less affected by the parasite (Avault and Allison 1965). Generally, digenetic flukes are not a serious threat to culture species.

534

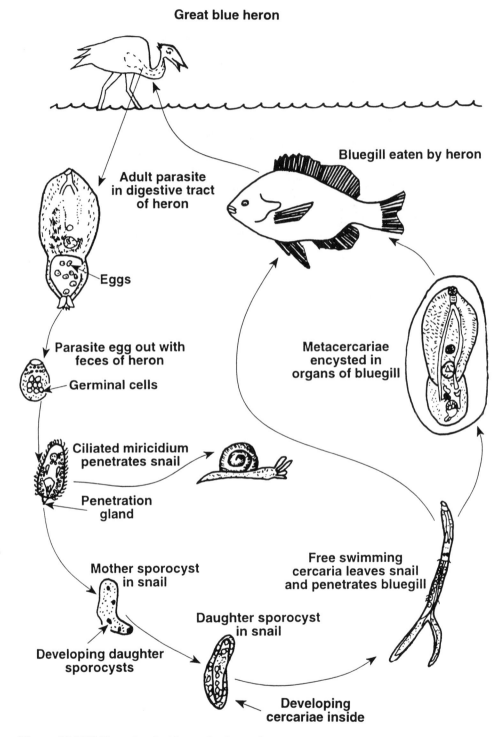

Great blue heron

Bluegill eaten by heron

**Adult parasite
in digestive tract
of heron**

Eggs

**Metacercariae
encysted in
organs of bluegill**

**Parasite egg out with
feces of heron**

Germinal cells

**Ciliated miricidium
penetrates snail**

**Penetration
gland**

**Free swimming
cercaria leaves snail
and penetrates bluegill**

**Mother sporocyst
in snail**

**Daughter sporocyst
in snail**

**Developing daughter
sporocysts**

**Developing
cercariae inside**

Figure 10.15 Life cycle of white grub, digenetic trematode.

NEMATODES

Nematodes, often called roundworms or threadworms, may be free living or parasitic. They are elongated, cylindrical, or spindle-shaped. Nematodes are unsegmented with a smooth glistening outer surface (Davis 1961) (Figure 10.16). Another distinguishing characteristic is the striking radial or biradial arrangement of structures around the mouth. Free-living nematodes are ubiquitous in nature. They are found in sea and fresh water and in the soil. They occur in all types of environments from the polar regions to the tropics, and they are often present in enormous numbers. Parasitic forms attack virtually all groups of plants and animals and may seriously damage food crops. They are also common in aquatic species. Nematodes have separate sexes. Often the male is smaller than the female. Parasitic nematodes are not as specialized for a parasitic existence as are trematodes or tapeworms, and they are generally not too much different structurally from their free-living ancestors. Though they lack a circulatory and excretory system, parasitic nematodes have a complete digestive system.

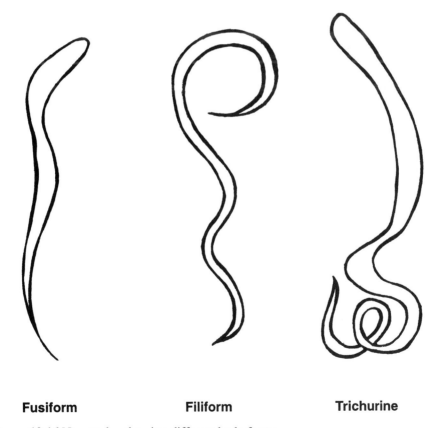

Fusiform   **Filiform**   **Trichurine**

Figure 10.16 Nematodes showing different body forms.

The life cycle of parasitic nematodes is relatively simple. Male and female nematodes mate. The resulting egg cell, after being enclosed in a membrane or shell, segments into 2, 4, 8, 16, etc. cells, until it forms a solid morula. Depending on the type of nematode, various stages of embryo development may occur after formation of the morula stage. Following the morula stage, the embryo undergoes a series of molts. The stage of development at the time eggs are deposited varies greatly, apparently depending on different oxygen requirements for development (Chandler and Read 1961). Embryos may be unsegmented, in early stages of segmentation, or in the tadpole stage. Some are fully developed embryos. Usually no further development occurs until the eggs or embryos have reached a new environment, either outside the body or inside an intermediate host.

Once outside, embryonated eggs may have one of two fates. The simplest is that they are swallowed by a host. The embryos then hatch in the intestine and may develop to maturity there or they may journey through the host's body and back into the intestinal tract. The second possibility is that embryos hatch outside the body where they develop into free-living infective stages. They enter the definitive host by burrowing through the skin. Some parasitic nematodes involve only one host. Others may require an intermediate host, where a larval stage occurs, and a definitive host that usually eats the first host.

Except for *Capillaria* spp. and *Camallanus cotti*, parasitic nematodes are normally not a serious threat in aquaculture although they may make fish flesh wormy and unsuitable for commercial value. Sindermann (1970, 1990a) gave a number of examples of parasitic nematodes in marine fish. Previously, practical aquaculturists have made little or no attempt at controlling parasitic nematodes. Liming of pond bottoms may have some beneficial effect in controlling nematodes.

LEECHES

Leeches are either predaceous or bloodsucking ectoparasites. More than 300 species of marine, freshwater, and terrestrial leeches are known (Barnes 1968). Leeches may range in size from 1 to 20 cm (0.4 to 8 in); most are 2 to 5 cm (0.8 to 2 in) long. The body of a typical leech is often flattened dorsoventrally and is frequently tapered (Figure 10.17). Suckers are found at both ends. The anterior sucker is usually smaller than the posterior sucker and frequently surrounds the mouth. The body of a leech can be divided into five regions. A reduced prostomium and four or five segments form the head region. Dorsally the head bears the eyes and ventrally the anterior sucker. The head is followed by a precliteller region of four segments and a cliteller region of three segments. The middle region, containing 15 segments, comprises the major part of the trunk. The posterior region of a leech is composed of six or seven fused segments, which are modified to form a large sucker.

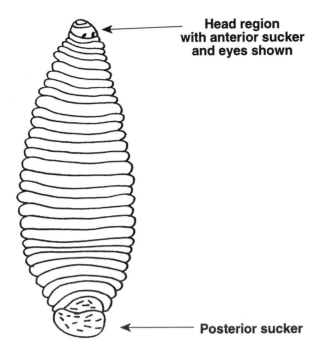

Head region
with anterior sucker
and eyes shown

Posterior sucker

Figure 10.17 Generalized external morphology of a leech.

Parasitic leeches may visit a host intermittently, take a blood meal, and then drop off the host for varying periods. Other leeches may leave the host only to breed. The damage to the host depends on the size of leeches, numbers present, and time leeches spend on the host. Tissue damage caused by leeches paves the way for entrance of other disease-causing organisms.

The life cycle of leeches is simple. Individuals contain both male and female organs. After copulation, eggs are laid in cocoons that are attached to substrate in the water, buried in the mud, or affixed to the host. After hatching, young leeches seek a host for nourishment. Leeches are seldom serious parasites of fish, but they may occasionally produce infestations, particularly on brood fish. Masoten has been used to control carp leeches in Europe. At 5°C (41°F), use 1 ppm; above 5°C, use 2 ppm. Salt baths at 1% to 3% for up to 30 minutes are effective.

CRUSTACEAN PARASITES

Parasitic crustaceans consist of the brachiuran *Argulus* or fish louse and three orders of copepods represented by the genera *Ergasilus, Lernaea*, and *Achtheres* plus *Salmincola*; the latter two genera are from the same order (Bowen and Putz 1966) (Figure 10.18). Collectively, these crustaceans are usually referred to as parasitic copepods. Copepods exist in vast numbers as free-living plankton in

538

both fresh and salt water, where they are an integral part of the food chain. Copepods may serve as intermediate hosts for fish parasites, and copepods themselves may be parasitic. Their main role in causing disease is that they make points of entry for other pathogens.

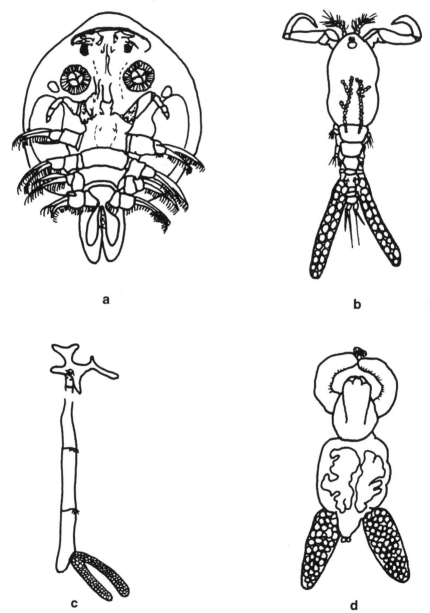

a

b

c

d

Figure 10.18 Crustacean parasites: (a) *Argulus*, (b) *Ergasilus*, (c) *Lernaea*, and (d) *Achthers*. After Hoffman 1967.

Copepods have a life cycle characterized by an increase in complexity through metamorphosis after molting. Successive larval stages increase in size, body segments, and in appendages. With the anchor parasite, *Lernaea,* adults mate and females store eggs in paired sacs attached to the abdomen (Putz and Brown 1968). Eggs hatch into nauplii larvae that are free swimming. The nauplii molt and become metanauplii that, in turn, molt and pass through four successive copepod stages before attaching to a host as adults. The males never become parasitic. Copepod parasites usually attach to the body or fins. Though most copepod parasites seldom cause death in fish, *Lernaea* may cause mass mortalities of fish, particularly carp and carp-like species. This parasite destroys scales and causes hemorrhagic and ulcerated areas, allowing blood loss and entry of secondary infections of other parasites, particularly bacteria, viruses, and fungi.

Masoten, at a rate of 0.25 ppm active ingredient, is effective in controlling most crustacean parasites. Repeat treatments at weekly intervals are necessary. These treatments are effective only at water temperatures of 15° to 27°C (59° to 81°F). Inconsistent results are obtained at high temperatures or high pH. Sindermann (1990a, 1990b) reviewed parasitic crustaceans of marine culture species. He concluded that generally this group of parasites is of academic interest and that seldom does it pose a serious threat.

STUDY QUESTIONS

1. Define, explain, or identify infectious diseases, parasitic diseases, and non-infectious diseases.

2. What three variables must by present at the same time for an infectious disease to occur?

3. Discuss ways in which a culture species can be stressed.

4. What is an obligate parasite, and what is a facultative parasite? Give examples of each.

5. How do infectious diseases spread?

6. How do parasites harm culture species? Give examples.

7. Discuss factors that affect seasonality of diseases.

8. When should a culture species be diagnosed for disease?

9. Why is it important to determine not only the parasite causing the disease but also the conditions leading up to the disease?

10. List and discuss general measures for preventing disease.

11. What is natural immunity, active immunity, and passive immunity?

12. What factors must be considered when passively immunizing a culture species? What are different methods for immunizing culture species?

13. How do you control non-infectious diseases?

14. List general methods for controlling infectious diseases.

15. A rectangular pond is 1,000 ft long, 500 ft wide, and 4 ft average depth. What is the size of this pond in acres? How many acre feet of water does this pond have?

16. Assume that a pond containing 18 ac ft of water is to be treated with copper sulfate at 2 ppm. How much copper sulfate is required?

17. A rectangular pond is 825 m long, 400 m wide, and 1 m average depth. Calculate the amount of copper sulfate needed to treat this pond at 2 ppm.

18. A tank contains 1,500 liters of water. Calculate the amount of potassium permanganate to treat this tank at 3 ppm.

19. A tank contains 1,000 gallons of water. Convert this to liters, then calculate the amount of a chemical needed to treat with 3 ppm.

20. Discuss water quality as it affects toxicity of copper sulfate and potassium permanganate.

21. Discuss the biology of viruses.

22. Give examples of viral diseases of salmonids and marine shrimp.

23. How can you prevent and control viral diseases?

24. Give examples of obligate bacteria.

25. Give examples of facultative bacteria.

26. What can be done to prevent and control diseases caused by facultative bacteria?

27. Classify protozoan parasites according to mode of transportation.

28. How do protozoan parasites reproduce?

29. Give the life cycle of *Ichthyophthirius multifiliis*.

30. How can we control this parasite?

31. How can infestation of protozoan parasites be prevented in general?

32. How do fungi reproduce?

33. How can we prevent fungal diseases from occurring?

34. Define intermediate host, definitive host, loci, and asexual reproduction. Give examples.

35. Describe the life cycle of a typical tapeworm with a drawing. Label the various hosts and the stages of the parasite for each host.

36. How are spiny-headed worms and tapeworms similar? How are they different?

37. Give examples of monogenetic trematodes, listing parasite and host.

38. Describe the life cycle of *Posthodiplostomum minimum* with a drawing. Label the various hosts and the stages of the parasite for each host.

39. Are nematodes, leeches, and crustacean parasites ever harmful to fish?

REFERENCES

Adams, S.M. 1990. Biological Indicators of Stress in Fish. American Fisheries Society Symposium 8. Bethesda, Maryland: American Fisheries Society. 191 pp.

Allen, K.O. and J.W. Avault, Jr. 1970. Effects of brackish water on ichthyophthiriasis of channel catfish. Progressive Fish-Culturist 32(4):227-230.

Allison, R. 1965. The effects of formalin and other parasiticides upon oxygen concentrations in ponds. Proceedings Southeastern Association of Game and Fish Commissioners 16:446-449.

Amborski, R.L., M.A. Hood and R. Miller. (editors). 1974a. Proceedings Gulf Coast Regional Symposium on Diseases of Aquatic Animals. Louisiana State University, Center for Wetland Resources. Publication No. LSU-SG-74-05.

Amborski, G.F., R.L. Amborski and J.C. Glorioso. 1974b. Factors influencing the bacterial diseases of poikilothermic aquatic animals. pp. 19-34. In Proceedings Gulf Coast Regional Symposium on Diseases of Aquatic Animals. Louisiana State University, Center for Wetland Resources. Publication No. LSU-SG-74-05.

Amborski, R.L., G. LoPiccolo, G.F. Amborski and J. Huner. 1974c. A disease affecting the shell and soft tissues of Louisiana crawfish, *Procambarus clarkii*. In International Symposium on Freshwater Crayfish, Baton Rouge, Louisiana 2:299-303.

Amend, D.F. 1976. Prevention and control of viral diseases of salmonids. Journal Fisheries Research Board of Canada 33:1059-1066.

Amend, D.F. (editor). 1977. Proceedings International Symposium on Diseases of Cultured Salmonids. Sponsored by Tavolek Inc., Seattle, Washington. 189 pp.

Amend, D.F. 1980. Development and use of commercial fish vaccines. Salmonid March/April. pp. 8-12.

Amlacher, E. 1970. Textbook of Fish Diseases. Neptune City, New Jersey: T.F.H. Publications Inc. 288 pp.

Anderson, D.P. 1974. Fish Immunology. Neptune City, New Jersey: T.F.H. Publications Inc. 239 pp.

Avault, J.W., Jr. and R. Allison. 1965. Experimental biological control of a trematode parasite of bluegill. Experimental Parasitology 17(3):268-270.

Avault, J.W., Jr. and R.O. Smitherman. 1965. Experimental host specificity of *Pothodisplostomum minimum*. Experimental Parasitology 17(3):268-270.

Avault, J.W., Jr. and E.W. Shell. 1968. Preliminary studies with hybrid tilapia, *Tilapia aurea* x *T. mossambica*. Proceedings of the World Symposium on Warm-Water Pond Fish Culture. FAO Fisheries Report No. 44, 4:237-242.

Axelrod, H.R. 1989. Handbook of Fish Diseases. Translated from German by H.H. Hirschhorn. Neptune City, New Jersey: T.F.H. Publications Inc. 160 pp.

Barnes, R.D. 1968. Invertebrate Zoology. Philadelphia-London-Toronto: W.B. Saunders Company Inc. 743 pp.

Batts, W.N. and J.R. Winton. 1990. Inactivation of infectious hematopoietic necrosis virus by low levels of iodine. U.S. Department of Interior, Fish and Wildlife Service. Information Bulletin No. 90-85,

Bauer, O.N. 1961. Relationships between host fishes and their parasites. pp. 84-103. In Parasitology of Fishes. Translated from Russian to English by Z. Kabata. U.S. Department of Interior. 384 pp.

542

Blogoslawski, W.J., M.E. Stewart and E.W. Rhodes. 1978. Bacterial disinfection in shellfish hatchery disease control. Proceedings of the World Mariculture Society 9: 589-601.

Bouck, G.R. 1980. Etiology of gas bubble disease. Transactions American Fisheries Society 109(6):703-707.

Bowen, J.T. and R.E. Putz. 1966. Parasites of freshwater fish, parasitic copepod *Argulus*. U.S. Department of Interior, Fish and Wildlife Service. Fish Disease Leaflet. 4 pp.

Boyd, C.E. 1979. Water Quality in Warmwater Fish Ponds. Auburn University, Alabama Agricultural Experiment Station. 359 pp.

Brown, E.E. and J.B. Gratzek. 1980. Fish Farming Handbook. Westport, Connecticut: Avi Publishing Company Inc. 391 pp.

Bureau of Sport Fisheries and Wildlife, Region 3. 1971. Fish Disease Manual. U.S. Department of Interior. 183 pp.

Busch, R.A. 1978a. Protective vaccines for mass immunization of trout. Salmonid 1(6):10-14 & 22.

Busch, R.A. 1978b. Enteric red mouth disease (Hagerman strain). Marine Fisheries Review 40(3):42-51.

Chandler, A.C. and C.P. Read. 1961. Introduction to parasitology. New York-London: John Wiley & Sons Inc. 822 pp.

Clary, J. 1978a. Realistic control of fish diseases through hatchery sanitation and water conditioning. Salmonid 1(5):10-11.

Clary, J. 1978b. Ultraviolet sterilization of water for disease control. Salmonid 1(6):17-19.

Couch, J.A. 1974. Free and occluded virus similar to *Baculovirus* in hepatopancreas of pink shrimp. Nature 247(5438):229-231.

Couch, J.A. 1981. Viral diseases of invertebrates other than insects. pp. 127-160. In Pathogenesis of Invertebrate Microbial Diseases. Totowa, New Jersey: Allanheld, Osum.

Creswell, R.L. 1993. Aquaculture Desk Reference. New York: An Avi Book, Chapman & Hall. 206 pp.

Crouse, M.R., C.A. Callahan, K.W. Malueg and S.E. Dominquez. 1981. Effects of fine sediments on growth of juvenile coho salmon in laboratory streams. Transactions American Fisheries Society 110:281-286.

Davis, H.S. 1961. Culture and Diseases of Game Fishes. California: University of California Press. 332 pp.

de la Bretonne, L.W., Jr. and J.W. Avault, Jr. 1971. Liming increases crawfish production. Louisiana Agriculture 15(1):10.

DeVoe, M.R. (editor). 1992. Introductions & Transfers of Marine Species. South Carolina Sea Grant Consortium. 198 pp.

Dill, W.A. (editor). 1973. Symposium on the major communicable fish diseases in Europe and their control. Food and Agriculture Organization. EIFAC/T 17.

Dorman, L.W. 1991. Cost savings possible by watching farm management. pp. 8 & 23. In The Catfish Journal December, 1991,

Duijn, C. V. 1973. Diseases of Fishes. 3rd. edition. Illinois: Charles C. Thomas. 372 pp.

Ejike, C. and C.B. Schreck. 1980. Stress and social hierarchy rank in coho salmon. Transactions American Fisheries Society 109(4):423-426.

Ellis, A.E. (editor). 1988. Fish Vaccination. San Diego, California: Academic Press Inc. 255 pp.

Elston, R.A. 1990. Molluscan Diseases. Washington Sea Grant Program, Seattle and London: University of Washington Press. 73 pp.

Evelyn, T.P.T. 1977. Immunization of salmonids. pp. 161-176. In Proceedings from the International Symposium on Diseases of Cultured Salmonids. Redmond, Washington: Tavolek Inc.,

Fast, A.W. and L.J. Lester (editors). 1992. Marine Shrimp Culture: Principles and Practices. Amsterdam-London-New York-Tokyo: Elsevier Science Publishing Company Inc. 862 pp.

Fickeisen, D.H. and M.J. Schneider. 1976. Gas bubble disease. CONF-741033, Technical Information Center, Energy Research and Development Administration, Oak Ridge, Tennessee, USA.

Fisher, W.S. 1988. Disease Processes in Marine Bivalve Mollusks. Bethesda, Maryland: American Fisheries Society. Special Publication 18. 315 pp.

Fryer, J.L., J.S. Rohovec, E.F. Pulford, R.E. Olson, D.P. Ransom, J.R. Winton, C.N. Lannan, R.P. Hedrick and W.J. Groberg. 1979. Proceedings on Disease, Inspection and Certification of Fish and Fish Eggs. Oregon State University, Sea Grant College Program. Publication No. ORESU-W-79-001.

Fulks, W. and K.L. Main (editors). 1992. Diseases of Cultured Shrimp in Asia and the United States. Proceedings of a Workshop in Honolulu, Hawaii. The Oceanic Institute Makapuu Point P.O. Box 25280 Honolulu, Hawaii. 392 pp.

Glude, J.B. 1977. U.S. shellfish supplies in jeopardy. Commercial Fish Farmer and Aquaculture News 3(6):18 and 20-21.

Golub, E.S. 1977. The cellular basis of the immune response. Sunderland, Massachusetts: Sinauer Associates Inc. 278 pp.

Goyert, J.C. and J.W. Avault, Jr. 1978. Effects of stocking density and substrate on growth and survival of crawfish (*Procambarus clarkii*) grown in a recirculating culture system. Proceedings of the World Mariculture Society 9:731-735.

Halver, J.E. (editor). 1972. Fish nutrition. New York and London: Academic Press Inc. 713 pp.

Hawke, J.P., S.M. Plakas, R.V. Minton, R.M. McPhearson, T.G. Snider and A.M. Guarino. 1987. Fish pasteurellosis of cultured striped bass (*Morone saxatilis*) in coastal Alabama. Aquaculture 65:193-204.

Helms, D.R. 1967. Use of formalin for selective control of tadpoles in the presence of fishes. Progressive Fish-Culturist 29:43-47.

Hnath, J.G. 1983. Hatchery disinfection and disposal of infected stocks. pp. 121-134. In a guide to integrated fish health management in the Great Lakes basin. Great Lakes Fishery Commission, Ann Arbor, Michigan. Special Publication 83-2:

Hoffman, G.L. 1967. Parasites of North American Freshwater Fishes. California: University of California Press. 486 pp.

544

Hoffman, G.L. 1976. Whirling disease of trout. Fish Disease Leaflet 47. 10 pp.

Hoffman, G.L. and F.P. Meyer. 1974. Parasites of Freshwater Fishes. New Jersey: T.F.H. Publications Inc. 224 pp.

Hoffman, G.L. and A.J. Mitchell. 1978. Fish disease diagnosis and control. Commercial Fish Farmer and Aquaculture News 4(4):20-23.

Inman, C.R. and R.N. Hambric. 1970. Diseases and parasites of warm-water fishes. Texas Parks & Wildlife Department Inland Fisheries Function. Technical Series No. 4.

Jee, L.K. and J. A. Plumb. 1981. Effects of organic load on potassium permanganate as a treatment for *Flexibacter columnaris*. Transactions American Fisheries Society 110(1):86-89.

Jensen, G. 1988. Handbook for common calculations in finfish aquaculture. Louisiana: Louisiana State University Agricultural Center. Publication No. 8903. 59 pp.

Johnson, P.T. 1983. Diseases caused by viruses, rickettsiae, bacteria, and fungi. In The Biology of Crustacea. 6:1-78. New York: Academic Press Inc.

Johnson, S.K. 1975. Handbook of shrimp diseases, revised. Texas A & M University. Sea Grant Publication No. TAMU-SG-76-603. 23 pp.

Johnson, S.K. 1977. Crawfish and freshwater shrimp diseases. Texas A & M University, Sea Grant Publication No. TAMU-SG-76-605. 19 pp.

Kaskow, T. 1987. Enteric septicemia of catfish (ESC). California Aquatic Farming (Newsletter), California Aquaculture Association, P.O. Box 1004, Niland, California.

Klontz, G.W. 1979. Fish health management: Volume II concepts and methods of fish disease epidemiology. University of Idaho, Fishery Resources and Office of Continuing Education. 142 pp.

LeBlanc, B.D. and R.M. Overstreet. 1991a. Efficacy of calcium hypochlorite as a disinfectant against the shrimp virus *Baculovirus penaei*. Journal of Applied Animal Health 3:141- 145.

LeBlanc, B.D. and R.M. Overstreet. 1991b. Effect of desiccation, pH, heat, and ultraviolet irradiation on viability of *Baculovirus penaei*. Journal of Invertebrate Pathology 57:277-286.

Levine, G. and T.L. Meade. 1976. The effects of disease treatment on nitrification in closed system aquaculture. Proceedings of the World Mariculture Society 7:483-493.

Lewis, D.H. and J.K. Leong (compilers). 1979. Proceedings 2nd Biennial Crustacean Health Workshop. Texas A & M University, Sea Grant College, TAMU-SG-79-114. 400 pp.

Lewis, D.H. and J.A. Plumb. 1979. Bacterial diseases. pp. 15-24. In Principal Diseases of Farm Raised Catfish. Southern Cooperative Series No. 225.

Lewis, E.J., F.G. Kern, A. Rosenfield, S.A. Stevens, R.L. Walker and P.B. Heffernan. 1992. Lethal parasites in oysters from coastal Georgia with discussion of disease and management implications. Marine Fisheries Review 54(2):1-6.

Liewes, E.W. 1984. Culture, Feeding and Diseases of Commercial Flatfish Species. Netherlands: A.A. Balkema. 104 pp.

Lightner, D.V. 1983. Diseases of cultured penaeid shrimp. pp. 289-320. In CRC Handbook of Mariculture. Crustacean Aquaculture. Boca Raton, Florida: CRC Press. 442 pp.

Lightner, D.V. and R.M. Redman. 1992. Penaeid virus diseases of the shrimp culture industry of the Americas. pp. 569-588. In Marine Shrimp Culture: Principles and Practices, Development in Aquaculture and Fisheries Science. Amsterdam-London-New York-Tokyo: Elsevier Publishing Company Inc. 862 pp.

Lightner, D.V., R.M. Redman, D.A. Danald, R. Williams and L.A. Perez. 1984. Major diseases encountered in controlled environment culture of penaeid shrimp at Puerto Penasco, Sonora, Mexico. pp 25-33. In Proceedings of the 9th and 10th U.S-Japan Meetings on Aquaculture. U.S. Department of Commerce, NOAA. Technical Report NMFS 16.

Mackin, J.G., H.M. Owen and A. Collier. 1950. Preliminary note on the occurrence of a new protistan parasite, *Dermocystidium virginia* (Gamelin). Science 111:328-329.

MacMillan, J.R. 1985. Infectious diseases. pp. 405-496. In Channel Catfish Culture. Amsterdam: Elsevier Publishing Company Inc. 657 pp.

Mawdesley, T. and E. Lionel (editors). 1972. Diseases of Fish. London: Academic Press Inc. 380 pp.

McAllister, P.E. 1978. Viruses and viral diseases of salmonid fishes. Marine Fisheries Review 40(10):21-23.

McCraren, J.P., F.T. Wright and R.M. Jones. 1975. Bibliography of the diseases and parasites of the channel catfish (*Ictalurus punctatus*, Rafinesque). Mimeograph 17 pp.

McCraw, B.M. 1952. Furunculosis of fish. U.S. Fish and Wildlife Service. Special Scientific Report, Fisheries 84.

McDaniel, D. (editor). 1979. Procedures for the Detection and Identification of Certain Fish Pathogens. Fish Health Section of the American Fisheries Society. 118 pp.

McNeil, W.J. and W.H. Ahnell. 1964. Sources of pink salmon spawning relative to size of spawning bed material. U.S. Fish and Wildlife Service. Special Scientific Report, Fisheries 469.

Meyer, F.P. 1967. Chemical control of diseases in warm-water ponds. American Fishes and U.S. Trout News. November-December, 1967.

Meyer, F.P. 1970. Seasonal fluctuations in the incidence of disease on fish farms. pp. 21-29. In a Symposium of Fish and Shellfishes. American Fisheries Society. Special Publication No. 5. 526 pp.

Meyer, F.P. 1979. The role of stress in fish diseases. pp. 7-9. In principal diseases of farm-raised catfish. Southern Cooperative Series No. 225.

Meyer, M.C. and O.W. Olsen. 1975. Essentials of parasitology. Dubuque, Iowa: WM Brown and Company Inc. 303 pp.

Meyer, F.P., R.A. Schnick, K.B. Cumming and B.L. Berger. 1976. Registration status of fishery chemicals, February 1976. Progressive Fish-Culturist 38(1):3-7.

Meyer, F.P. and R.A. Schnick. 1989. A review of chemicals used for the control of fish diseases. Reviews in Aquatic Sciences 1(4):693-710.

Meyer, F.P. and L.A. Barclay (editors). 1990. Field manual for the investigation of fish kills. United States Department of Interior, Fish and Wildlife Service. Resource Publication 177.

Mitchell, A.J. and G.L. Hoffman. 1981. Preparation of live channel catfish to be shipped to certain states requiring a health permit. Mimeograph. 5 pp.

Mitchell, A.J. and F.P. Meyer. 1989. Treatment tips for fish producers. U.S. Department of the Interior, Fish and Wildlife Service. Fish and Wildlife Leaflet 15.

National Research Council. 1973. Aquatic Animal Health. National Academy of Sciences. Wahington, D.C.: National Academy Press. 46 pp.

Perkins, F.O. (editor). 1977. Haplosporidian and haplosporidian-like diseases of shellfish. Marine Fisheries Review 41(1-2):1-80.

Petrushevskii, G.K. (editor). 1957. Parasites and Diseases of Fish. Translated from Russian. Office of Technical Services, U.S. Department of Commerce.

Plumb, J.A. 1975. An 11-year summary of fish disease cases at the Southeastern Cooperative Fish Disease Laboratory. Proceedings Southeastern Association of Game and Fish Commissioners 29:254-260.

Plumb, J.A. (editor). 1979. Principal diseases of farm-raised catfish. Southern Cooperative Series No. 225.

Plumb, J.A., O.L. Green, R.O. Smitherman and G.B. Pardue. 1975. Channel catfish virus experiments with different strains of channel catfish. Transactions American Fisheries Society 104:140-143.

Post, G.W. 1983. Textbook of Fish Health. Neptune City, New Jersey: T.F.H. Publications Inc. 288 pp.

Putz, R.E. and J.T. Brown. 1968. Parasites of freshwater fishes; IV, miscellaneous, the anchor worm (*Lernea cyprinacea*) and related species. U.S. Department of Interior. Fish Disease Leaflet. 4 pp.

Richards, R.H. 1978. The mycology of teleosts. pp. 205-215. In Fish Pathology. London: Bailliere Tindall. 318 pp.

Richards, R.H. and R.J. Roberts. 1978. The bacteriology of teleosts. pp. 183-204. In Fish Pathology. London: Bailliere Tindall. 318 pp.

Roberts, J. (editor). 1978. Fish Pathology. London: Bailliere Tindall. 318 pp.

Roberts, R.J. 1978. Miscellaneous non-infectious diseases. pp. 227-234. In Fish Pathology. London: Bailliere Tindall. 318 pp.

Roberts, R.J. (editor). 1989. Fish Pathology. 2nd edition. London: Bailliere Tindall. 467 pp.

Roberts, R.J. and C.J. Shephard. 1986. 2nd edition. Handbook of Trout and Salmon Diseases. Oxford-London-Edinburgh-Cambridge-Victoria: Fishing News (Books), a Division of Blackwell Science Publications Ltd. 222 pp.

Robohm, R.A. 1983. *Pasteurella piscicida*. pp. 161-175. In Antigens of Fish Pathogens. Collection Foundation Marcel Merieux, Lyon.

Rogers, W.A. 1969. A summary of fish disease cases received over a five-year period at the Southeastern Cooperative Fish Disease Laboratory. Proceedings Southeastern Association of Game and Fish Commissioners 23:353-358.

Rogers, W.A. 1971. Principal diseases of catfish. Fish Farming Industries. Reprinted from January 1971 issue.

Rogers, W.A. 1972. How you can win the fight against fish diseases. Fish Farming Industries 3(4):21-26.

Rogers, W.A. 1985. Protozoan parasites. pp. 28-37. In principal diseases of farm-raised channel catfish. Southern Cooperative Series No. 225.

Rosenfield, A. and R. Mann. (editors). 1992. Dispersal of Living Organisms into Aquatic Ecosystems. University of Maryland. Sea Grant Publication. 471 pp.

Schäperclaus, W. 1954. Fischkrankheiten. Berlin: Academic Verlag. 708 pp.

Schäperclaus, W. (H. Kulow and K. Schreckenbach, editors). 1991. Fish Diseases. 5th edition. Volume 1, pp. 1-594 and Volume 2, pp. 595-1398. Translated from German. United States Department of Interior, National Science Foundation, Washington, D.C.

Schmittou, H.R. 1969. The culture of channel catfish, *Ictalurus punctatus* (Rafinesque), in cages suspended in ponds. Proceedings Southeastern Association of Game and Fish Commissioners 23:226-244.

Schnick, R.A., F.P. Meyer and H.D. Van Meter. 1979a. Announcement of compounds registered for fisheries uses. Progressive Fish-Culturist 41(1):36-37.

Schnick, R.A., F.P. Meyer, L. Marking, T.D. Bills and J.H. Chandler, Jr. 1979b. Candidate chemicals for crustacean culture. Proceedings Second Biennial Crustacean Health Workshop 2:245-294.

Scott, W.W. and A.H. O'Bier. 1962. Aquatic fungi associated with diseased fish and fish eggs. Progressive Fish-Culturist 24(1):3-15.

Sinderman, C.J. 1966. Diseases of marine fishes. Advances in Marine Biology 4:1-89.

Sinderman, C. . 1968. Bibliography of oyster parasites and diseases. U.S. Fish and Wildlife Service. Special Scientific Report - Fisheries 563.

Sinderman, C.J. 1970. Principal Diseases of Marine Fish and Shellfish. New York and London: Academic Press Inc. 369 pp.

Sinderman, C.J. (editor). 1977. Disease Diagnosis and Control in North American Marine Aquaculture. Amsterdam-Oxford-New York: Elsevier Science Publishing Company Inc. 329 pp.

Sinderman, C.J. 1979. Oyster mortalities and their control. pp. 349-360. In Advances in Aquaculture. FAO Technical Conference on Aquaculture, Kyoto, Japan. 653 pp.

Sindermann, C.J. 1990a. Principal Diseases of Marine Fish and Shellfish. 2nd edition. Volume 1, Diseases of Marine Fish. San Diego, California: Academic Press Inc. 521 pp.

Sindermann, C.J. 1990b. Principal Diseases of Marine Fish and Shellfish. 2nd edition. Volume 2, Diseases of Shellfish. San Diego, California: Academic Press Inc. 516 pp.

Sinderman, C.J. and A. Rosenfield. 1967. Principal diseases of commercially important marine bivalve mollusca and crustacea. U.S. Fish and Wildlife Service. Fisheries Bulletin 66:335-385.

Smith, C.E. and R. Piper. 1972. Pathological effects in formalin-treated rainbow trout (*Salmo gairdneri*). Journal Fisheries Research Board of Canada 29(3):328-329.

Snieszko, S.F. 1969. Fish furunculosis. U.S. Fish and Wildlife Service. Fish Disease Leaflet FDL-17. 4 pp.

Snieszko, S.F. (editor). 1970a. A symposium on diseases of fishes and shellfishes. American Fisheries Society. Special Publication No. 5. 526 pp.

Snieszko, S.F. 1970b. Immunization of fishes: a review. Journal of Wildlife Diseases 6:24-30.

Snieszko, S.F. 1974. The effects of environmental stress on outbreaks of infectious diseases of fish. Journal of Fisheries Biology. 1974:197-208.

548

Snieszko, S.F. 1975. Chemicals used most frequently for control of infectious diseases of fishes. Fish Health News, 4, 2.

Söderhäll, K. and L. Cerenius. 1992. Crustacean immunity. pp. 3-23. In Annual Review of Fish Diseases.

Spall, R.D. and R.C. Summerfelt. 1970. Life cycle of the white grub, *Posthodiplostomum minimum* (Maccallum, 1921: Trematoda Diplostomatidae), and observations on host-parasite relationships of the metacercaria in fish. pp. 218-230. In Symposium on Diseases of Fishes and Shellfishes. American Fisheries Society. Special Publication No. 5. 526 pp.

Thoesen, J.C. (editor). 1994. Suggested Procedures for the Detection and Identification of Certain Finfish and Shellfish Pathogens. 4th edition. Fish Health Section, American Fisheries Society.

Toranzo, A.E., S. Barreiro, J.F. Casal, A. Figueras, B. Magarinos and J.L. Barja. 1991. Pasteurellosis in cultured gilthead seabream (*Sparus aurata*): first report in Spain. Aquaculture 99:1-15.

Tucker, C.S. 1989. Methods for estimating potassium permanganate disease treatment rates for channel catfish in ponds. Progressive Fish-Culturist 51(1):24-26.

Tucker, C.S. and E.H. Robinson. 1990. Channel Catfish Farming Handbook. New York: An Avi Book published by Van Nostrand Reinhold. 454 pp.

Unestam, T. 1972. Significance of diseases on freshwater crayfish. In International Symposium on Freshwater Crayfish, Hinterthal, Austria 1:135-150.

Unestam, T. 1973. Fungal diseases of crustacea. Reviews Med. Vet. Mycology 8:1-20.

Wedemeyer, G.A. 1970. The role of stress in the disease resistance of fishes. pp. 30-35. In Symposium on Disease of Fishes and Shellfishes. American Fisheries Society. Special Publication No. 5. 526 pp.

Wedemeyer, G.A. 1980. Environmental stress as a cause of fish disease. Aquamed Spring 1980.

Wedemeyer, G.A. and J.W. Wood. 1974. Stress as a predisposing factor in fish diseases. U.S. Fish and Wildlife Service. Leaflet No. 38. 8 pp.

Wedemeyer, G.A. and W.T. Yasutake. 1977. Clinical methods for the assessment of the effects of environmental stress on fish health. U.S. Fish and Wildlife Service. Technical Paper No. 89. 18 pp.

Wedemeyer, G.A., F.P. Meyer and L.S. Smith. 1977. Environmental stress and fish diseases. Neptune City, New Jersey: T.F.H. Publications Inc. 200 pp.

Williams, J.L. and J.W. Avault, Jr. 1976. Acute toxicity of acriflavine, formalin and potassium permanganate to juvenile red swamp crawfish, *Procambarus clarkii* (Girard). In International Symposium on Freshwater Crayfish, Kuopio, Finland 3:397-404.

Wellborn, T.L. and W.A. Rogers. 1966. A key to common parasitic protozoans of North American fishes. Auburn University, Zoology-Entomology Department, Alabama Agricultural Experiment Station. Fisheries Series No. 4. 17 pp.

Wolf, K. 1988 . Fish Viruses and Fish Viral Diseases. New York: Cornell University Press. 486 pp.

CHAPTER 11
PREDATORS AND PESTS

A number of predators and pests may become a nuisance in aquaculture. Some are a serious threat to the culture species. The backswimmer (*Notonecta* spp.) is an aquatic insect that may virtually eliminate fish fry from a nursery pond. Fish-eating birds may consume significant numbers of fish and crustaceans. The oyster drill (*Thais haemostoma*) is a predacious conch that may cause serious loss of oysters. The muskrat (*Ondatra zibethica*) and nutria (*Myocaster coypus*), both fur animals, may destroy pond levees by their burrowing activities.

In this chapter, we review predators and pests you may come across and suggest methods for prevention and control.

INSECT PREDATORS OF FRY AND LARVAE

Three groups of aquatic, predacious insects are of concern. They include the hemipterans (true bugs), the coleopterans (beetles), and the odonates (dragonflies). The true bugs and beetles must breathe air, whereas the nymph stages of dragonflies are truly aquatic and have gills. The fire ant (*Solenopsis saevissima richteri*) can kill small fish.

True Bugs

Hemipterans are carnivorous and include the water scorpion (*Ranatra* sp.), giant predacious water bugs (*Belostoma* spp. and *Lethocerus* spp.), and the backswimmer. By using piercing beaks, hemipterans inject proteolytic enzymes (digestive juices) that kill and partially digest their prey. Most aquatic hemipterans can carry air below the water surface trapped beneath their wings.

Water scorpions are elongated stick-like bugs, 2.5 to 5 cm (1 to 2 in) in length (Figure 11.1). They have a distinct beak and a "tail" that is used for breathing. They are called scorpions because their forelegs resemble the pedipalps of scorpions. These bugs are poor swimmers and cling to vegetation just below the surface. Eggs, inserted into plant tissue, incubate in 2 to 4 weeks. Nymph development requires more than 5 weeks. Though predacious on fry and larvae, the water scorpion is seldom numerous enough to cause serious losses.

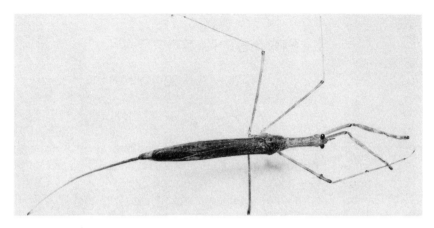

Figure 11.1 Water scorpion. Photos 11.1 to 11.5 courtesy of K. Lyle Center for Wetland Resources, Louisiana State University.

Giant water bugs, about 2.5 to 10 cm (1 to 4 in) long, feed on a number of aquatic organisms (Figure 11.2). Eggs are laid on plant stems, but eggs are often seen on the back of male *Belostoma* sp. and *Abedus* sp. Eggs hatch in 1 to 2 weeks, and 43 to 54 days are required for nymph development. Though highly predacious, the water bug seldom achieves enough numbers to become a serious threat to fry or larvae in ponds.

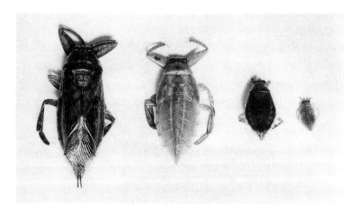

Figure 11.2 Giant water bugs, adult and nymph stages.

The water boatman (Corixidae) are mottled bugs usually less than 1.3 cm (0.5 in) in length. Eggs are deposited by the female on plants, debris, and even on snails over a period of weeks. Eggs hatch in 1 to 2 weeks. More than 5 weeks are required for nymph development. Not considered a serious threat to fry or larvae, water boatmen compete for natural food organisms.

Backswimmers, as the name implies, swim upside down on their backs (Figure 11.3). They are small, usually less than 1.3 cm (0.5 in). They resemble water boatmen, but can be distinguished from them by their method of swimming. Eggs are laid on the surface or inserted into the stems of plants. Approximately 40 days are required for the backswimmer to develop from egg to adult. Backswimmers may reach tremendous numbers and virtually eliminate fry or larvae from a pond.

Figure 11.3 Backswimmer.

Beetles

Coleopterans include a wide diversity of species, but the giant predacious diving beetle (*Cybister* sp.) that reaches 5 to 8 cm (2 to 3 in) in length is the only major species of threat to fry and larvae (Figure 11.4a, b).

Figure 11.4a Diving beetle, adult.   **Figure 11.4b** Diving beetle, larva.

Like all true beetles, they have very hard wing covers, and the head is small. Adults have crushing jaws and tear their prey apart. Larvae look like large worms with grotesque fangs. Their mouthparts are developed for piercing or sucking. Two other groups of beetles, the whirligig beetle (Gyrinidae) and the water scavenger beetle (Hydrophilidae), are often numerous in ponds. They are no threat to fry or larvae of culture species. They feed on detrital material containing small pond organisms.

Dragonflies

Odonates consist of two groups commonly found in ponds, dragonflies and damselflies. Damselflies, which look like miniature dragonflies, are so small that their food usually consists of very small pond organisms such as mosquito larvae. They are no threat to fry or larvae of culture species. Dragonflies that reach 10 cm (4 in) in length are a major predator of fish. However, it is the larvae or naiad stage (Figure 11.5) that is considered the serious predator of fry or larvae. The adult form emerges from water and preys on flying insects.

Figure 11.5 Naiad stage of the dragonfly.

Fire Ants

Fish may gorge on fire ants that have been washed into ponds by rain. Ants sting fish internally, and fish go into a state of tetany. In laboratory studies, Prather (1960) concluded that it was highly unlikely that fire ants are harmful to fish populations when they are eaten by bluegill (*Lepomis macrochirus*) or redear (*L. microlophus*) sunfish. Only small bluegill and redear are killed, and in sportfishing ponds these fish are often overabundant.

Prevention and Control

A number of methods can be used for prevention and control of aquatic insects.

(1) Controlling aquatic weeds robs the insects of habitat and subsequently reduces breeding areas.

(2) Ponds to be stocked with fry or larvae should be filled just before stocking to prevent a buildup of predacious insects.

(3) The time of year when ponds are flooded affects the insect population. In some instances, ponds could be filled when insects are less numerous. For example, Witzig et al. (1981) reported that *Anax junius* and *Belostoma lutarium* could significantly reduce survival of young crawfish (*Procambarus clarkii*). However, this predation could be reduced by filling ponds with water after mid-September in Louisiana.

(4) Predacious insects are more effective in killing fry and larvae than juveniles and fingerlings. Backswimmers, for example, are not effective predators of fingerlings once fingerlings reach 5 cm (2 in) in length. By stocking juveniles and fingerlings whenever possible, you can reduce predation.

(5) Chemicals have been used to control aquatic insects. Several days before stocking, treat pond water with 0.25 ppm methyl parathion, 4 ppm Dylox®, or 0.25 ppm Baytex® (McGinty 1980). He concluded that ponds treated with methyl parathion had more desirable zooplankton for consumption by channel catfish (*Ictalurus punctatus*) fry than ponds treated with Dylox®, and he concluded that methyl parathion was the best pre-stocking treatment for culture of channel catfish fry.

Use insecticides with great caution in crustacean nursery ponds since crustaceans are easily killed by most insecticides. If insecticides are used, test-larvae in cages can be placed later in treated ponds to determine if water is still toxic. Further, insecticides should be applied with care since they kill zooplankton as well as the insects. Check with the Environmental Protection Agency and the Food and Drug Administration to be sure chemicals you use are approved. Regulations are constantly changing.

(6) A 75:25 mixture of diesel fuel and motor oil or cottonseed oil has been sprayed on the water surface to form an oil slick (Figure 11.6). The diesel fuel or diesel fuel-oil mixture clogs breathing tubes when insects come to the surface for air. Spraying should be along the pond edge when there is just enough breeze to carry the oil slick across the pond. Between 9.5 and 28.5 liters/ha (1 and 3 gal/ac) are needed. Dupree and Huner (1984) suggested applying 38 liters/ha (4 gal/ac) of diesel fuel. They bubbled air through the diesel fuel for 24 hours before applying it to ponds. This drives off most of the volatile hydrocarbon compounds that are highly toxic to zooplankton and certain culture species young such as striped bass (*Morone saxatilis*).

Figure 11.6 Jay Stander of the LSU Agricultural Center sprays diesel fuel-oil mixture onto water surface of a nursery pond to kill backswimmers.

Since some air-breathing insects can remain underwater for more than an hour, several applications may be needed. Weekly spraying has been used by some aquaculturists until fry become large enough to escape predation. Spraying is not effective when ponds contain emergent vegetation that prevents complete coverage, when ponds are too large to maintain a slick for up to one hour, when strong wind breaks up the oil slick, or when dragonfly naiads are present.

UNWANTED FISH
Unwanted fish, sometimes referred to as wild or trash fish, compete with culture species for feed, space, and oxygen, and they may introduce parasites. When present in nursery ponds, they may prey on fry or larvae. At harvest, they must be separated from the culture species, costing time and money (Avault 1972).

Prevention and Control
Prevention-- Wild fish may enter ponds in many ways. Observance of the following precautions will help prevent their entry.
(1) To lessen chances of wild fish being introduced, fill ponds just before stocking culture species.

(2) If fingerling fish or larvae are bought from a dealer, they should be inspected. Wild fish are sometimes introduced accidentally by a negligent dealer.

(3) When seining ponds, make sure that wild fish or their eggs are not transferred from one pond to another. After using a seine shake it out, and if possible dry it before use in another pond.

(4) In large ponds with spillways, spillways should have a vertical drop of at least 1 m (3 ft) to prevent wild fish from entering during a flood (Figure 11.7).

Figure 11.7 This spillway with stair steps can produce an aesthetically pleasing waterfall, but it will allow wild fish an opportunity to enter the pond from the outside ditch.

(5) Construct ponds so that flood waters cannot enter over levees or back up through drain pipes.

(6) Use well water to fill ponds if possible. If surface or stream water is used, it should be filtered through Saran screen, 20 meshes/cm (52 meshes/in). Two types of filters are effective.

The sock filter (Figure 11.8) is constructed by sewing two pieces of 1 m width material into a cylinder, with a drawstring closure at the open end to allow for easy cleaning. A sock 3.5 m (12 ft) long can accept a water flow up to 3,785 liters/min (1,000 gal/min). Inspect the sock often enough to remove trash. Dead fish and snakes caught in the sock attract rodents that may chew holes in the sock.

Figure 11.8 Saran screen sock.

The box filter is constructed by securing the Saran screen to the bottom of a wooden box 2.4 m (8 ft) long, 0.9 m (3 ft) wide, and 0.6 m (2 ft) deep. The screen bottom is supported by a wooden grid with 0.3 by 0.6 m (1 to 2 ft) openings to prevent excessive stress and stretching of the material. This type of filter may be mounted in a fixed position between the inlet water line and the water surface, or it may be equipped with a floating device that allows it to follow the changing water level. If the water supply inlet is not an excessive height above the reservoir water level, the floating type is suggested. This allows the sock to remain just below the water surface. The sock has longer life because there is less stress from falling water and because direct sunlight is excluded. If excessive trash is present in the water supply, it is best to pre-filter water through wire-mesh cloth (hardware cloth) with pores larger than Saran screen.

(7) When a pond is draining, wild fish may gather in ditches outside the pond. The water flow attracts them, and they may swim into the pond through the drain pipe. Both ends of the pipe should be screened.

(8) Finally, a drained pond should be left dry long enough for the bottom to crack or until no wet spots remain. Some wild fish, such as bowfin (*Amia calva*), can remain alive as long as pond bottoms are wet and their gills are moist.

Control-- In spite of all precautions, wild fish may enter ponds. Some ponds have a history of contamination with wild fish. Wild fish can be controlled with a predacious fish and with use of chemicals.

In grow-out ponds a predacious fish, too small to eat the culture species, can be stocked to control wild fish and their reproduction. As an example, grow-out ponds can be stocked in March with 13-cm (5-in) or longer channel catfish fingerlings. In May or June, 5-cm (2-in) or longer largemouth bass (*Micropterus salmoides*) are stocked at a rate of 124/ha (50/ac). The bass eat any wild fish reproduction, but they are too small to eat stocked catfish. Fathead minnows (*Pimephales promelas*) may be stocked at 2,500/ha (1,000/ac) to provide extra food for both bass and catfish.

Chervinski (1975) successfully controlled unwanted spawns of *Oreochromis aureus* with the sea basses *Dicentrarchus labrax* and *D. punctatus*. He pointed out that successful control of unwanted fish by predatory fish has two considerations. If too many predators are present in the beginning and there is no increase in number of prey from spawning, predators may starve or die. On the other hand, if the unwanted spawns are too numerous, the predator will not be able to control them, and individuals may become too large to eat. Swingle (1960), Kanyike (1969), and Popper and Lichatowich (1975) also reported on control of tilapia with predacious fish.

Chemicals can be used to control wild fish. Rotenone is a crystalline ketone extracted from roots of certain plant species in the bean (Leguminosae) family. In certain areas it may be called derris or cube. Rotenone is toxic to fish but not very toxic to mammals. Although reports are conflicting, rotenone is more effective at high rather than low water temperatures (> 16°C or 61°F), in acid instead of alkaline waters (pH < 7), and in soft rather than hard water (total hardness < 50 ppm). Rotenone kills fish by blocking electron transport in the respiratory cycle. In advanced stages of rotenone poisoning, circulation in gill filaments is cut off, and the blood stream is not able to supply the body with oxygen. Commercial rotenone can be bought as a liquid or as a powder. Several formulations are available. Note that rotenone is now a restricted use pesticide. Purchasers must have an approved pesticide certification card to buy it.

Most fish species are killed with 1 to 2 ppm of a formulation containing 5% active ingredient (Figure 11.9). However, bullhead catfish (*Ameiurus* spp.), gar (*Lepisosteus* spp.), bowfin, and certain other fish species are much more resistant to rotenone. Other species such as the Atlantic salmon (*Salmo salar*) and gizzard shad (*Dorosoma cepedianum*) are highly sensitive to rotenone. Shad can be selectively killed at concentrations as low as 0.1 ppm with 5% rotenone in ponds containing other fish species. Fish eggs usually are more tolerant to rotenone than are fingerlings.

Probably the best time to use rotenone is after a pond has been drained. After culture species are removed, remaining potholes are treated. However, certain wild fish can survive in a moist pond bottom, and they are easily missed. It may be more effective to add water back to the pond so that the entire pond bottom is covered with a thin sheet of water, then apply rotenone. Rotenone can be applied to ponds full of water but it is more costly. Further, if water is cool (< 16°C) and with a thermocline, rotenone is not as effective.

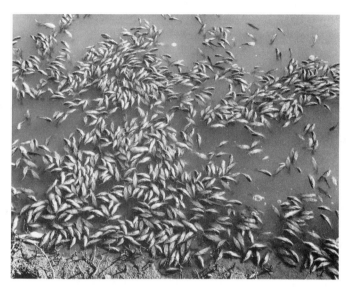

Figure 11.9 Bullhead catfish killed with rotenone. Photo courtesy of U.S. Department of Agriculture, Soil Conservation Service.

Rotenone toxicity may linger in treated water from a day or two up to 1 month in cooler waters. To check toxicity, place a cage containing the culture species in water. If fish are alive 24 hours later, water is assumed non-toxic. Use of $KMnO_4$ to detoxify rotenone is very effective. Double the concentration of rotenone used.

Antimycin, an antifungal antibiotic isolated from the bacteria *Streptomyces* sp., is highly toxic to certain fish species. Green sunfish (*Lepomis cyanellus*) are killed with concentrations as low as 1 ppb. Certain fish species without scales, such as channel catfish, are 20 times more resistant. Because of this, antimycin can be used to eliminate certain wild fish from catfish ponds without harming catfish (Avault and Radonski 1967). Crustaceans are generally tolerant of antimycin. In both fresh and brackishwater ponds, antimycin can be used to eliminate most finfish with no harm to crustaceans. Antimycin, which works well in cool waters, inhibits the electron transport in oxidative phosphorylation systems.

Tea seed cake has been used for decades in Southeast Asia to eliminate finfish from crustacean ponds. The cake is made from wild tea seed after extraction of its oil. Crude saponin, found in the tea seed, will eliminate most finfish. At 1 to 2 ppm, saponin will not harm crustaceans. The toxicant is effective both in fresh and saline water.

In addition to rotenone, antimycin, and tea seed cake, use of ammonium sulfate fertilizer shows promise as a fish toxicant. Ponds drained at harvest are left to dry. Lime is added to dry pond bottoms at 1 mt/ha (1.1 tons/ac). Immediately after liming, ammonium sulfate fertilizer is applied at a rate of 10 g/m^2 (0.3 oz/yd^2) to any wet area. The lime raises the pH, causing ammonia nitrogen to exist as free ammonia (NH_3) which is highly toxic to fish at high concentrations.

PREDATORS AND PESTS OF MOLLUSKS-- OYSTERS, CLAMS, AND MUSSELS

A number of animals are serious predators and pests of mollusks (Flimlin and Beal 1993).

Oyster Drills

The conch or oyster drill may devastate oyster beds (Figure 11.10). The oyster drill is probably the most serious predator of oysters in the Gulf of Mexico. In Louisiana, losses of oyster production statewide may be as high as 50% (Breithaupt and Dugas 1979). In Alabama, May and Bland (1969) observed that during a 9-month period more than 85% of the oysters in a high salinity area were destroyed by oyster drills. On the Atlantic coast, the oyster drills *Urosalpinx cinerea* and *Eupleura caudata* may be serious predators of both oysters and clams. On the Pacific Coast of the United States, the oyster drill *Ocenebra inornata* (formerly known as *Tritonalia japonica*) was accidentally introduced from Japan. It has been responsible for oyster losses up to 90% in some areas (Glude and Chew 1980). Oyster drills are a serious problem in other parts of the world. Matsushima Bay in Japan is plagued with several species of oyster drills. The density of drills is greatest at the mouth of the bay where salinity is highest.

Oyster drills attack mollusks by a combination of drilling and secretion of a paralytic substance. They may drill a hole through the shell, but they usually prefer to bore between valves at the bill. Once the shell has been penetrated, oyster tissues are sucked out by means of a proboscis. Hofstetter (1965) reported that the conch *Thais* sp. can eat almost 100 small oysters per day. Although it will attack larger oysters, oyster spat are the preferred diet. On conch-infested reefs, spat have only a small chance of survival.

Thais lays a large number of eggs in the spring and summer. Eggs are encased in capsules glued to shells, rocks, or pilings. Larval conch escape through the top of capsules and live as planktonic organisms for 30 to 60 days. In this stage they may be dispersed over wide areas, and for this reason the control of the conch is difficult.

Figure 11.10 Oyster drill.

Starfish

Several species of starfish are predators on oysters, clams, and mussels. Along the Atlantic coast of Nova Scotia, *Asterias* spp. have been observed setting on spat collectors shortly after mussels have set. Hurlburt and Hurlburt (1980), who maintained an experimental mussel raft near the mouth of the Damariscotta River in Maine, reported that a settlement of mussels in June was followed by a July/August settlement of starfish. By November, no mussels remained on the collectors. In European and Asian waters, starfish are often common predators of bottom-cultured mussels.

Crabs

Various species of crabs may make serious inroads on cultured mollusks. In the Gulf of Mexico, the blue crab (*Callinectes sapidus*) (Figure 11.11) and the stone crab (*Menippe* sp.) are the chief crab predators. The blue crab chips away part of the oyster's bill and inserts a claw as a wedge, after which the other claw reaches inside the shell and tears off pieces of meat. Along the Atlantic Coast of North America, several crab species, including *Cancer irroratus, Cancer borealis*, and *Carcinus maenas*, may have a serious detrimental impact on bottom-cultured mussels. In the Philippines, juvenile and adult mussels have one main enemy, the crab. *Scylla serrata* is the principal predator although other crab species prey on mussels.

Figure 11.11 Blue crab.

Fish and Ducks

Various fish species, such as the black drum (*Pogonias cromis*), feed on young mollusks. The black drum, with strong pharyngeal teeth, can crush oyster shells. Several species of diving ducks -- such as white-winged scoters (*Melanitta deglandi*), surf scoter (*M. perspicillata*), common scoters (*Oidemia nigra*), and Barrow's golden eye (*Bucephala islandica*) -- may on occasion cause serious losses of seed mussels. Waterstrat et al. (1980) noted that predation by overwintering populations of migratory waterfowl constitutes a major threat to cultured mussels in Washington and British Columbia.

Fouling Organisms and Competitors

There are a number of marine fouling organisms and competitors. They include bryozoans, barnacles, hydroids, algae, slipper shells, and tube-building worms. Bryozoans or moss animals include encrusting (*Membranipora*) or upright and branching (*Bugula*) forms. They look more like plants than animals. Both types may cover the surface of shells and smother the mollusk being cultured. Barnacles (*Balanus*) create a problem by setting on cultch set out for oysters. However, once oyster spat is established, it rapidly outgrows the barnacles. Oysters sometimes compete with themselves. Large oysters may become so covered by spat oysters that it is difficult to separate them.

In Japan, biofouling is a serious problem in off-bottom oyster culture. Fouling organisms restrict water exchange, add weight to culture units, impede growth, and may kill oysters. During one year an outbreak of fanworms (*Hydroides elegans*) occurred in Hiroshima Bay. Nearly, 6,000 oyster rafts were affected and production dropped 60%. Arakawa (1980) listed fanworms, mussels, barnacles, and sea squirts as major fouling organisms, but pointed out that numerous other organisms may act as fouling agents.

Hofstetter (1965) listed several competitors of oysters in the Gulf of Mexico. They included the boring clam (*Diplothyra*), boring sponge (*Cliona*), and the mudworm (*Polydora*). The boring clam is a small, thin-shelled mollusk that bores into the oyster. As it grows, it enlarges its burrow within the shell while maintaining an opening to the outside for breathing and feeding. Oyster shells may become brittle from being riddled with holes. The boring sponge, like the boring clam, penetrates the shell to seek protection. The mudworm enters the oyster while the valves are open and crawls between the mantle and shell, forming a "mud blister." The oyster crab (*Pinnotheres*) also seeks protection within the oyster shell.

Coliform Bacteria

Coliform bacteria has become a major problem in culturing mollusks. In Louisiana waters alone, more than 80,939 ha (200,000 ac) of water bottoms have been closed to oyster culture because of bacterial pollution. All marine fish carry a typical bacterial flora. Public officials are concerned with the total viable bacterial count and indicator organisms as signs of pollution. Mollusks, being filter feeders, concentrate pollutants and may have a higher fecal coliform concentration than surrounding culture waters. To safeguard public health, the National Shellfish Sanitation Program specified that the total aerobic viable count must not exceed $\leq 5 \times 10^5$ cells/ml, and the fecal coliform count must not exceed ≤ 230 cells/100 ml of shucked meats (Slabyj 1980). Shellfish not meeting these standards can be treated in licensed depuration plants. Shellfish exceeding aerobic viable counts of 5×10^5 cells/ml of soft tissue or fecal coliform of 230/100 ml of soft tissue may not be sold as human food.

Red Tide

Dinoflagellates are major components of marine phytoplankton. Many are bioluminescent. When heavy blooms occur, "red tides" are produced. It should be noted, however, that not all red-tide organisms are toxic. Red-tide organisms in the genus *Gymnodinium* and *Gonyaulax* produce toxins that may be taken up by mollusks. When shellfish meats containing toxins are eaten, an intoxicated condition may occur in humans known as paralytic shellfish poisoning. Lips and fingertips tingle, dizziness and respiratory difficulties occur, and equilibrium is affected. The buildup of red-tide blooms may be affected by rainfall, wind, iron content, nutrient levels, water temperature, salinity, and other factors (Dragovich et al. 1963; Sykes 1965; Rounsefell and Nelson 1966; Martin and Chatterjee 1970).

Prevention and Control

Oyster Drills and Starfish-- Chlorinated hydrocarbon pesticides have been used to control oyster drills and certain other predators, but growers are concerned about the uptake of these compounds by the filter-feeding mollusks. Moreover, regulations of the FDA and EPA must be followed. Underwater plows, used before mollusks are seeded, bury oyster drills, starfish, and other predators. Suction devices remove predators and competitors. Oysters can be dipped in a solution of rock salt and then exposed to the air to kill most shellfish predators without harming oysters. Scuba divers can monitor oyster beds. Starfish mops, which are long iron beams with bundles of rope yarn, can be dragged across beds to entangle starfish for removal. Quicklime applied through pumps at 300 kg/ha (268 lb/ac) will control starfish. Periodic freshets from rainfall, which lower the salinity, will help control conchs and certain other predators. If mollusks are cultured off-bottom, it may be feasible to tow culture units to less saline water long enough to control certain predators.

Birds, Crabs, and Fish-- Birds, crabs, and fish can be controlled to a degree. Many aquatic birds that cause harm are migratory and therefore protected by federal and state laws. A permit is required if you wish to kill a limited number of birds. No permit is needed to use scaring devices. Some growers are experimenting with culture of mollusks in baskets that sit on the bottom. One company near Charleston, South Carolina, has placed clams in baskets; the baskets are about 300 cm^2 (10 ft^2) and 30 cm (one ft) deep . Clams filter feed well, but crabs, fish, and most other predators cannot reach the clams.

Fouling Organisms-- Barnacles can foul oysters and other mollusks. When cultch is put out in oyster spawning beds, timing is important. Barnacles may compete with oyster spat if cultch is set out too soon. Once a good oyster set is obtained, barnacles usually cannot compete.

In Arakawa's handbook (1980), methods are discussed for removing fouling organisms. Flaming with a torch is a method of killing organisms attached to the outer surface of oysters. Culture strings are suspended and, after most of the water is gone, a flame is passed over the oysters. Air drying is effective against most fouling organisms. Mussels, for example, die when their internal temperature reaches 38° to 40°C (100° to 104°F), but in Japan oysters do not die until their internal temperatures reach 44° to 48°C (111° to 118°F).

Some growers culture oysters in the intertidal zones with periodic exposure to air. Oyster strings have been submerged in hot water (55° to 60°C or 131° to 140°F) for 10 to 15 seconds, in fresh water up to 50 hours if water is 15° to 20°C (59° to 68°F), or 30 hours at 20° to 25°C (68° to 77°F), or dipped in a brine bath. Fouling organisms have also been removed from oyster strings by scraping and brushing, spraying with jets of water, towing rapidly through water, with electricity, and with chemicals such as chlorine compounds.

Biological methods for controlling fouling organisms show promise. Hidu et al. (1981) found that the rock crab (*Cancer irroratus*), when present in trays of oysters, gleaned fouling organisms from European oysters. Knowledge of the history of fouling organisms allows the oyster growers to modify culture techniques in some instances. Culture strings can be temporarily suspended in deep water to avoid certain fouling organisms that are less apt to go deep. Decoy or throw-away strings are effective. In this case, certain barnacle larvae prefer dark surfaces for settlement. Oysters prefer light. Dark shells can be used to lure barnacle larvae away from light-colored cultch for oysters.

Bacterial Pollution and Red Tides-- To prevent problems with bacterial pollution and red-tide poisoning, avoid waters with such a history. When selecting culture sites, check the history of the waters with available records. In off-bottom culture, it may be possible to tow culture units to unpolluted waters. Rounsefell and Nelson (1966) summarized methods that have been tried for prevention of red-tide organisms. Copper compounds have not been successful. Nutrient levels have been kept low by curbing disposal of nutrient-rich sewage from streams and bays. However, red-tide organisms can thrive in nutrient-poor waters. Perhaps other substances in waste waters are needed by the organisms. Controlling river flows to regulate salinity may hold promise. Aquaculture in bays may add nutrients that encourage competing organisms of dinoflagelates. Addition of underwater barriers and jetties may change water flow and hinder mixing of gulf water and bay water.

A number of other methods for controlling red-tide organisms has been suggested including biological control with bacteria, use of predacious organisms, such as cladocerans, high-frequency waves, changing pH, adsorption of vitamins in waters by dusting waters with charcoal, and use of chemicals such as ammonia, ferric chloride, copper sulfate, and calcium hypochlorite.

SNAILS AS PESTS

Snails may be pests in ponds because they serve as intermediate hosts for certain parasites and because they may compete with the culture species for feed. Drying and disking pond bottoms followed by an application of quicklime will aid in control of snails. Copper sulfate can be applied at 0.1 ppm in soft water or 2 ppm in hard water (Brown and Gratzek 1980). Snail-eating fish, such as the redear (*Lepomis microlophus*) and the black carp (*Mylopharyngodon piceus*), have been effective.

AMPHIBIANS AND REPTILES AS PREDATORS AND PESTS

Frogs, alligators, turtles, and snakes may on occasion become a nuisance. Mature frogs, such as the bullfrog (*Rana catesbeiana*), have a voracious appetite and eat live food such as insects, fish, and crustaceans. Tadpoles compete for space and food, especially in nursery ponds. Alligators (*Alligator mississipiensis*) in several south Louisiana ponds have preyed on catfish (Figure 11.12).

Figure 11.12 Alligator with brood channel catfish. Photo courtesy of W. Guthrie Perry, Jr., Rockefeller Wildlife Refuge, Louisiana Department of Wildlife and Fisheries.

Figure 11.13 Some snakes eat fish and crustaceans.

Turtles (various species) are not thought of as serious predators of fish, but rather they scavenge on dead fish and may eat feed. However, when numerous, they may interfere with normal culture operations. Snakes (various species) may become serious predators of juvenile fish or crustaceans (Figure 11.13).

Prevention and Control

Filling a pond shortly before stocking reduces the problem with predators. Frog meat is a delicacy and can provide food and perhaps added income. Hunting seasons, if in place, should be adhered to. Keeping ponds free of weeds, particularly filamentous algae, reduces habitat for frogs. Removal of floating egg masses from ponds may be an effective way to keep populations under control.

Alligator problems usually involve one animal or relatively few animals. A permit should be obtained before the animals are removed or killed. Usually a State Department of Wildlife and Fisheries, or appropriate federal agency, will remove a nuisance animal.

Turtles are easily removed by trapping (Moss 1953). Wire mesh baskets, with a funnel on one end and baited with dead fish, are effective when placed on or near the pond bottom. Surface traps also work well. A wire basket with the top open is placed partly submerged in water. Turtles walk up on a tiltboard plank and fall into the basket.

Snakes can be best controlled by keeping weeds out of ponds and by keeping levees mowed. Martin (1982) described a method used by one farmer. A mesh screen was used to entrap snakes.

BIRDS AS PREDATORS AND PESTS

Some aquatic birds serve as intermediate or definitive hosts to parasites, but birds are a nuisance because they eat fish or fish feed. The osprey (*Pandion haliaetus carolinensis*) and the eagle (*Haliaetus leucocephalus*) are fish eaters. At the National Fish Hatchery in Frankfort, Kentucky, nearby streams became muddy one year so several ospreys fed on brood fish in clear pond waters. Diving ducks may consume large numbers of fish. Grackles (*Cassidix mexicanus*) catch crawfish and fish in shallow waters and from fish vats. Huner and Abraham (1981) reported that herons (*Nycticorax* spp.), egrets (*Casmerodius albus egretta*), and ibises (*Plegadis* spp.) fed heavily on crawfish. Leo Ray (personal communication 1995) noted that after IHN disease, bird predation was probably the next most serious problem in Idaho trout production. The black-crowned night heron (*Nycticorax nycticorax*) in particular is a serious predator. Ray also noted that ducks have learned to trip demand feeders in trout raceways. They may consume a significant amount of feed during winter.

Beynon et al. (1981) reported that in shrimp ponds, gulls (*Larus* spp.) acted primarily as competitors for feed. Active feeding by gulls was restricted to daylight hours, and feed loss decreased when feed was distributed at or after dusk. They listed a number of bird predators on shrimp including herons, egrets, migratory ducks, and to a lesser extent grebes (*Colymbus* spp.) and shore birds. From their observations, bird predation could reduce shrimp production by 75%.

Martin (1982b) reported several species of birds as serious predators of fish. In one instance, double-crested cormorants (*Phalacrocorax auritus*) (Figure 11.14) were responsible for eating 64% of the fish in a 2.4-ha (6-ac) pond stocked with 14,000 15- to 20-cm (6- to 8-in) channel catfish in a 367-day growing period. A double-crested cormorant can consume 227 to 454 g (0.5 to 1 lb) or more fish per day.

Figure 11.14 Double-crested cormorant.

Littauer (1991a, b), Stickley et al. (1992), Mott et al. (1992), and Mott and Boyd (in press) also reported on predation by the double-crested cormorant. Some Mississippi farmers have lost more than 95% of their catfish fingerlings in unprotected ponds. Most farmers spend an average of 2.6 person-hours per day to harass the birds at an annual cost of $7,400, excluding scaring devices. Cormorants also may spread disease, such as enteric septicemia caused by *Edwardsiella ictaluri*, by transporting infected fish. Birds often move to another location to eat a captured fish due to harassment or need for seclusion. Occasionally these fish are dropped because of attacks from competing birds (Taylor 1992).

The anhinga (*Anhinga anhinga*), with pointed bill and long neck and tail, also may become a predator of fish. Schramm et al. (1987) reported that in Florida, 12 avian species feed entirely on fish and at least 21 additional species include fish in their diets.

Prevention and Control

Control of predatory birds is complicated because of legal restrictions. Most fish-eating birds that frequent aquaculture facilities are legally classified as migratory and are protected by federal and, in most cases, state laws. A copy of the Migratory Bird Conservation Act would be useful to have. Except for threatened or endangered species, such as the bald or golden eagle (*Aquila chrysaëtos canadensis*), no permit is needed to use scare devices and physical barriers against birds. A permit, however, is needed to harass birds with aircraft. In some cases, a permit to kill a limited number of birds may be issued by the U.S. Fish and Wildlife Service.

Littauer (1991a, b), Stickley (1991), and Huner (1993) discussed various methods for prevention and control of avian predators. Huner and Abraham (1981) found that bird predation in crawfish ponds can be prevented by flooding ponds rapidly in the fall and by having vegetation as cover in the pond. Beynon et al. (1981) stated that gull predation on shrimp could be prevented by keeping water in ponds over 1 m deep (3.28 ft) and by reducing water transparency with a phytoplankton bloom. Salmon and Conte (1981) outlined several methods for controlling predatory birds. Physical barriers used to protect fish from birds include raceways completely enclosed with a screen or net (See Figure 6.3). If mesh size is too small, snow may accumulate and collapse the cover. Culture units also can be partially covered with overhead wire, line, net, or screen. Perimeter fencing or nets around ponds and culture facilities provides some protection from wading birds, and it is most effective against herons (Figure 11.15). Note that nets and fencing may kill or injure non-wading birds. Frightening devices have been used for scaring birds (Figure 11.16).

Methods for controlling cormorants include: use of pop-up inflatable scarecrows, stocking larger catfish fingerlings (greater than 20 cm or 8 in) after mid April, stocking shad (*Dorosoma* spp.) in decoy ponds to divert attention of birds, and harassment of bird roosts every evening for a week or until birds disperse. Other methods include gas-operated exploders (Figure 11.17), fireworks, electronic noise makers, bird distress calls, strobe or flashing lights, human effigies, reflective plates or strips, and water spray devices. In many cases, birds learn the pattern for various frightening devices. For example, a gas-operated exploder may go off every 15 minutes. Birds soon adapt to this. If you vary the intervals of the explosion and intensities, birds cannot adapt as easily. A permit to kill birds may be obtained by contacting the U.S. Fish and Wildlife Service, Division of Law Enforcement.

Figure 11.15 Netting to discourage wading birds.

Figure 11.16 Frightening device used in Puerto Rico. Wind blows it about.

Figure 11.17 Gas-operated exploder used to scare birds.

FUR ANIMALS AS PREDATORS AND PESTS

The nutria and muskrat may seriously damage pond levees and buried cables or piping by their burrowing activities, often resulting in pond leakage and damage. In extreme cases levees may cave in, making it hazardous to drive on the levee.

Nutria are primarily nocturnal and feed on 1 to 1.6 kg (2.5 to 3.5 lb) of vegetation a day. Nutria reach sexual maturity between 4 to 8 months, well before they are fully grown. Nutria produce from one to nine young per litter. Their presence is often noted by their tracks, long pellet-shaped droppings with deep groves, and a mound of vegetation piled in a pond. Nutria do not always make burrows if dense vegetation is present or pond levees have a very gentle slope. In the absence of vegetation or if levees have a steep slope, nutria may burrow into levees. Nutria also cause damage by eating crops and pose a problem in rice-growing areas.

Muskrats are active year-round. They frequently move about during daylight. The food of muskrats generally consists of 95% vegetation and 5% animal matter. They may eat a great deal of rice plants if they are readily available. Muskrats are highly prolific. Gestation is only 29 to 30 days, and a female may have up to four litters a year, with one to 11 young per litter. The muskrat lives in self-constructed burrows dug into levees.

The beaver (*Castor canadensis*) and otter (*Lutra canadensis*) may on occasion cause problems. Beavers dam streams, thus choking off the water supply to culture facilities. Otters are very efficient predators on fish and may make serious inroads on them, especially the larger brood fish. Mink (*Mustela vison*) also may kill and eat fish.

Prevention and Control

Miller (1969) and Evans (1970) presented methods for prevention and control of nutria and muskrats. Though it invites aquatic weeds, a gently sloping levee is far less inviting for burrowing than a steep levee. Whenever possible, let harvested ponds dry until it is time for the next fish crop. Open ditches should be kept dry except when ponds are drained. Weeds, brush, and trees should be removed, thus eliminating both feed and cover.

Both nutria and muskrats can be controlled with shooting, trapping, and poisoning. Shooting at night with a shotgun and artificial light can be highly effective in states where this is legal. Nutria can be trapped with a No. 2 double-spring steel trap (jaw spread about 9.5 cm, 3.7 in). No. 3 traps (jaw spread about 18 cm, 7.1 in) will work, but they are cumbersome and cost about twice as much as No. 2 traps. Muskrats are trapped with size 1 or 1.5 (Figure 11.18). Both animals have been trapped with conibear traps that kill the animals instantly and in live traps. Traps are usually placed in runs or in areas of heavy activity. Check trapping regulations.

Figure 11.18 W.C. Guest, formerly of the LSU Agricultural Center, trapping muskrats.

Poisons, such as zinc phosphide, have been used to coat carrots and other baits. Baits are placed on floating platforms or in pathways used by the animals. Meat-eating animals that can vomit -- mink, cats, dogs, eagles, vultures, snakes, and turtles -- are relatively safe when zinc phosphate is used.

Anticoagulant baits are gaining popularity for control of all types of rodents. The bait can be mixed safely with the hands. Its effectiveness depends on repeat feeding by nutrias and muskrats. Two methods have been used to present anticoagulant baits, the lollipop and the floating bait. Both have similar ingredients. The lollipop formula contains 4.5 kg (10 lb) of crushed rolled oats, 2.7 kg (6 lb) of melted paraffin, and 0.5 kg (1 lb) of 0.5% pival anticoagulant concentrate. The mixture of ingredients is heated and poured into paper cups with a 20-cm (8-in) stick. Upon cooling and hardening, the lollipop can be placed near burrowing entrances. The floating bait formula contains a mixture of 6.3 kg (14 lb) crushed rolled oats, 0.5 kg of warm vegetable oil, and 0.5 kg of anticoagulant concentrate. The bait is placed on a floating platform in the water.

Both the otter and mink can be trapped. The fur has been valuable. However, prices for fur have dropped since the mid 1980s because of the anti-fur movement by certain groups.

PESTS WITH FISH FEEDS
Rats and Mice

Rats, mice, weevils, and molds have posed problems in feed storage. Rats and mice eat fish feed and contaminate it with their droppings. Two species of rats that are commonly associated with humans in North America are the Norway rat (*Rattus norvegicus*) and the roof rat (*Rattus rattus*). The house mouse (*Mus musculus*) is also common. Both the Norway rat and roof rat originated in Southeast Asia and are now found in all parts of the world. The roof rat is not as widely distributed in North America as the Norway rat. It is found mostly in warm coastal states. In northern states, the cold climate and the more aggressive Norway rat keep the roof rat in check.

Distinct differences exist between the two species of rats. The Norway rat is an aggressive glutton, will accept a variety of baits, and is easily trapped. The roof rat is a finicky eater, wary, and more difficult to trap. The roof rat's tail is longer than its head and body; it has large conspicuous ears and a pointed muzzle and slim body. The Norway rat's tail will not extend past its nose when stretched over its back; it has inconspicuous ears and a heavier body. The roof rat's droppings are up to 13 mm (one-half inch) long, spindle shaped and curved in contrast to Norway rat droppings that are about the same length but comparatively blunt. Rats have extremely high reproductive rates. They typically breed all year except winter. They may have two to four litters a year with approximately eight per litter.

Rats get into buildings and feed storage bins through open or unscreened doors, windows, ventilators, under shallow foundations of buildings, through cracks in the foundation, through holes around electrical inlets and pipes, and they may be carried in with feed. There are several ways to inspect for rats and mice. Switch on lights in a dark room and look and listen. Check for signs of gnawings, burrows or holes, droppings, tracks in the dust or flour, or smears along walls and pipes. Test baits can be set out.

Insects

Many insects damage grain and feed. Four common species are the granary weevil (*Sitophilus granarius*), the rice or black weevil (*S. oryza*), the lesser grain borer or Australian wheat weevil (*Rhizopertha dominica*), and the Angoumois grain moth (*Sitotroga cerealella*) (Anonymous 1955). Granary weevils cannot fly. Adults live from 7 to 8 months. The females lay from 50 to 250 eggs each. Eggs are placed inside the feed, or kernel. About 4 weeks are required from egg to adult weevil. Both larvae and adults destroy the grain or feed. The rice weevil, a strong flier, has a life cycle similar to that of the granary weevil. It is particularly common in warm countries. The lesser grain borer, a beetle originating in the tropics, has spread to all parts of the world. It spreads by legs and wings. Eggs are placed on the feed, and larvae bore in. The period from egg to adult in summer is about 1 month. Both larvae and adults destroy feed. The Angoumois grain moth, found in all parts of the world, is particularly injurious in the South.

Molds

Molds may attack any organic matter and may spoil fish feed or manufactured crawfish bait. The term mold is applied to certain multicellular, filamentous fungi whose growth on organic matter is readily recognized by its fuzzy or cottony appearance.

Molds are divided into two groups: septate, that is, with cross wall dividing the hypha into cells; and non-septate, with hyphae apparently consisting of cylinders without cross walls. Asexual spores are produced in large numbers and are small, light ,and resistant to drying. They are readily spread through the air. Sexual spores are also produced. All molds have certain requirements for moisture, temperature, oxygen, pH, and food. Moist, humid conditions favor mold. Most molds grow well at ordinary room temperatures. The optimum temperature is from 25° to 30°C (77° to 86°F). Molds require oxygen for growth and can grow over a wide range of hydrogen-ion concentrations, pH 2 to 8.5.

Prevention and Control

Rats and Mice-- There are four essentials for controlling rats and mice.
(1) Eliminate their food source. Keep garbage and refuse in rat-proof silos and buildings.
(2) Remove their shelter. Don't allow litter to accumulate. Keep stored materials off the ground.
(3) Rat proof. Close necessary openings, such as windows, with hardware cloth. Keep doors closed when not in use. Plug all holes and cracks around the building.
(4) Kill rats and mice with traps or poisoned bait (Figure 11.19). To poison rats and mice, anticoagulant poisons, such as pival, fumarin, or warfarin, are mixed with cereals. A continuous supply of fresh bait should be available for at least 10 days. Anticoagulant baits are commercially available. Baits containing the poison diphacinon and chlorophacinone work well. Baits that require bait boxes sometimes do not work well because rats in the field are too wary. For an initial knock-down of a heavy rat population along a levee system, 2% zinc phosphide pellets work well. This is a restricted-use, single dose bait that is used at 6 kg/ha (5 lb/ac).

Insects-- Pest insects can be prevented by buying insect-free feed. Check bags of feed and feed for small holes, sure signs of insect damage. Store feed in metal rat-proof bins and silos. Waste feed should be cleaned up, and empty feed storage facilities should be cleaned and sprayed with an insecticide such as malathion. If feed does get insects, airtight feed bins can be fumigated with compounds such as a mixture of 80% carbon tetrachloride with 20% carbon bisulfide. Be careful when using fumigants, because they are poisonous.

Figure 11.19 Rudy Arce, formerly of the Freshwater Aquaculture Center, Philippines, showing box where rat bait is placed to protect it from rain.

Molds-- Molds can be prevented best by storing feed for only a short time before use and by keeping feed in dry, cool storage. A dehumidifier is effective in closed-storage facilities. Feed with low moisture content is less susceptible to molds. Certain molds are controlled by adding compounds to feed to adjust the pH. Propionate compounds and methyl parabin and propyl parabin have been used to control molds.

CRAWFISH AS PESTS

Burrowing crawfish may damage levees, often resulting in a leaky pond. They can be controlled with poisonous baits, fumigation, and with application of insecticides to water.

For bait, a carrying agent, such as cottonseed meal, is sprayed with an insecticide. The bait is placed near the water's edge on crawfish-infested levees. Crawfish are in the same phylum as insects and are highly susceptible to most insecticides.

Fumigants have been sprayed or poured into crawfish burrows including:
(1) a mixture of 0.5 kg (1 lb) chloride of lime in 11 liters (3 gal) of water.
(2) coal tar creosote dip in a mixture of 1 part to 100 parts water.
(3) 1.9 liters (2 qt) of turpentine and 113 g (0.25 lb) soap powder in 1 liter (1 qt) of water. Use 1 part of this stock solution to 50 parts of water.

(4) 1/2 teaspoon of sodium hydroxide per burrow.

(5) five or 10 drops of carbon bisulphide per burrow. The vaporized carbon bisulphide will quickly kill crawfish, but remember that vapor mixed with air can be highly explosive (Anonymous 1967).

A third way to control crawfish is simply to treat pond waters with an insecticide. It may be more costly to treat this way, but very small amounts are usually required and less labor is needed. Some insecticides like the pyrethroids are highly toxic to crawfish in low concentrations. Jolly and Avault (1978) reported that the 96-hr LC 50 for red swamp crawfish (*Procambarus clarkii*) exposed to Pounce® was 0.39 ppb for newly hatched young and 0.62 ppb for juveniles. Jarboe (1989) reported that permethrin when applied to pond water at very low concentrations (in ppb) reduced populations of red swamp crawfish and white river crawfish (*P. zonangulus*) by 83% and 100%, respectively.

MISCELLANEOUS PESTS

Sandifer et al. (1974) reported that three species of hydrozoans, *Moerisia lyonsi*, *Stylactis arge*, and *Clytia gracilis*, were accidentally introduced into a recirculating system with crab and prawn larvae. The cnidarians competed with larvae for food, and they also preyed directly on decapod larvae. Treatment with 250 ppm formalin for 1 hour was partially successful in controlling the pests. The best method for eradicating the hydrozoans involved sacrificing the infested cultures, scrubbing and flushing tanks and filter beds with hot water, and allowing them to dry for several days. In pen or cage culture, alga slimes often form, restricting water flow. These culture units can be lifted from the water after fish harvest and exposed to sunlight. A simple method to prevent alga buildup is to stock algae-eating fish, such as certain species of tilapia.

STUDY QUESTIONS

1. Describe three groups of insects that are predators of small fish.
2. List and discuss methods for prevention and control of aquatic insects.
3. List and discuss methods for the prevention and control of unwanted fish.
4. What are major predators and pests of oysters?
5. How can we prevent and control them?
6. What can be done to control the double-crested cormorant in channel catfish ponds?
7. How can we prevent and control nutria and muskrats in ponds?
8. What are examples of pests in fish feeds? How can we avoid them?

REFERENCES

Abraham, G.R. 1977. Commensal rodents. Mimeograph 8 pp.

Anonymous. 1955. Stored grain pests. U.S. Department of Agriculture. Farmer's Bulletin No. 1260.

Anonymous. 1959. Anticoagulant rodenticides for control of rats and mice. U.S. Department of Interior, Fish and Wildlife Service. Wildlife Leaflet 402.

Anonymous. 1967. Crayfish control methods. U.S. Department of Interior, Fish and Wildlife Service. Fishery Leaflet 401.

Anonymous. 1974. Rats. U.S. Department of Interior, Fish and Wildlife Service. Circular 22.

Arakawa, K.Y. 1980. Prevention and removal of fouling on cultured oysters: a handbook for growers. (translated by R.B. Gillmor). Marine Sea Technical Report 56.

Arant, F.S., K.L. Hays and D.W. Speake. 1958. Facts about the imported fire ant. Auburn University. Highlights of Agricultural Research 5(4).

Avault, J.W., Jr. 1972. Watch those wild fish; they rob you of profits. Fish Farming Industries 3(3):24-26.

Avault, J.W., Jr. 1981. Prevention of fish diseases: some basics reviewed. Aquaculture Magazine 7(5):40-41.

Avault, J.W., Jr. 1982. Avoiding diseases by growing catfish in brackish water. Aquaculture Magazine 8(3):49-50.

Avault, J.W., Jr. 1988. Birds as predators and pests. Aquaculture Magazine 14(1):64-65.

Avault, J.W., Jr. and G.C. Radonski. 1967. Use of antimycin as a fish toxicant with emphasis on removing trash fish from catfish ponds. Proceedings Southeastern Association of Game and Fish Commissioners 21:472-475.

Barr, J. and J.V. Huner. 1977. Predaceous arthropods: problem in your pond. Farm Pond Harvest 2(3):11-18.

Beynon, J.L., D.L. Hutchins, A.J. Rubino and A.L. Lawrence. 1981. Nocturnal activity of birds on shrimp mariculture ponds. Journal of the World Mariculture Society 12(2):63-70.

Breithaupt, R.L. and R.J. Dugas. 1979. A study of the southern oyster drill (*Thais haemostoma*) distribution and density on the oyster seed grounds. Louisiana Department of Wildlife and Fisheries. Technical Bulletin No. 30.

Brown, E.E. and J.B. Gratzek. 1980. Fish Farming Handbook. Westport, Connecticut: Avi Publishing Company Inc. 391 pp.

Chervinski, J. 1975. Sea basses, *Dicentrarchus labrax* (Linne) and *D. punctatus* (Bloch) (Pisces, Serranidae), a control fish in fresh water. Aquaculture 6(3):249-256.

Dragovish, A., J.H. Finucane and J.A. Kelly, Jr. 1963. Counts of red-tide organisms, *Gymnodinium breve*, and associated oceanographic data from the Florida west coast, 1960-61. Special Scientific Report - Fisheries No. 455.

Dupree, H.K. and J.V. Huner. 1984. Third Report to the Fish Farmer. U.S. Fish and Wildlife Service. 270 pp.

Evans, J. 1970. About nutria and their control. U.S. Government Printing Office. Resource Publication No. 86.

Flimlin, G. and B.F. Beal. 1993. Major predators of cultured shellfish. Northeastern Regional Aquaculture Center University of Massachusetts North Dartmouth. NRAC Bulletin No. 180.

Frazier, W.C. 1958. Food microbiology. New York-Toronto-London: McGraw-Hill Book Company Inc. 472 pp.

Glude, J.B. and K.K. Chew. 1980. Shellfish aquaculture in the Pacific Northwest. Proceedings of the North Pacific Aquaculture Symposium, August 1980, University of Alaska. 25 pp.

Hidu, H., C. Conary and S.R. Chapman. 1981. Suspended culture of oysters: biological fouling control. Aquaculture 22(1981):189-192.

Hofstetter, R.P. 1965. The Texas oyster fishery. Texas Parks and Wildlife Department. Bulletin No. 40.

Huner, J.V. (editor). 1993. Management of fish-eating birds on fish farms: a symposium. National Aquaculture Association and National Audubon Society. 51 pp.

Huner, J.V. and G.R. Abraham. 1981. Observations of wading bird activity and feeding habits in and around crawfish ponds in South Louisiana with management recommendations. Mimeograph 5 pp.

Hurlburt, C.G. and S.W. Hurlburt. 1980. European mussel culture technology and its adaptability to North American waters. pp. 69-98. In Mussel Culture and Harvest: A North American Perspective. Amsterdam-Oxford-New York: Elsevier Science Publishing Company Inc. 350 pp.

Imai, T. (editor). 1977. Aquaculture in shallow seas: progress in shallow sea culture. (translated from Japanese). National Marine Fisheries Service, National Oceanic Atmospheric Administration, U.S. Department of Commerce. 615 pp.

Jarboe, H.H. 1989. Toxicity of permethrin to *Procambarus clarkii* and the effect of permethrin-induced density reduction and supplemental feeding on stunted crawfish populations. Ph.D. Dissertation, Louisiana State University. 111 pp.

Jolly, A.L. and J.W. Avault, Jr. 1978. Acute toxicity of permethrin to several aquatic animals. Transactions American Fisheries Society 107:825-827.

Kanyike, F.S. 1969. Predators of *Tilapia*. FAO Fish Culture Bulletin 1(3):9.

Lawrence, J.J. 1955. Preliminary results on the use of potassium permanganate to counteract the effects of rotenone on fish. Proceedings Southeastern Association of Game and Fish Commissioners 9:87-92.

Lindahl, P.E. and K.E. Obërg. 1961. The effect of rotenone on respiration and its point of attack. Experimental Cell Research 23:228-237.

Littauer, G.A. 1991a. Control of bird predation at aquaculture facilities. Southern Regional Aquaculture Center. Louisiana Cooperative Extension Service Publication 2467. 4 pp.

Littauer, G.A. 1991b. Avian predation. Southern Regional Aquaculture Center. Louisiana Cooperative Extension Service Publication 2466. 4 pp.

Marking, L.L. 1976. Toxicity of rotenone to fish in standardized laboratory tests. In Investigations in Fish Control. U.S. Department of Interior, Fish and Wildlife Service, Washington, D.C. 11 pp.

Martin, M. 1982. Impact of predators on fish farming. Part 1. Aquaculture Magazine 8(2):36-37.

Martin, M. 1982a. Impact of predators on fish farming. Part 2. Aquaculture Magazine 8(3):44-45.

Martin, M. 1982b. Predator article stimulates comments. Aquaculture Magazine 8(4): 46-47.

Martin, D.F. and A.B. Chatterjee. 1970. Some chemical and physical properties of two toxins from the red-tide organism, *Gymnodinium breve*. Fishery Bulletin 68(3):433-443.

May, E.B. and D.G. Bland. 1969. Survival of young oysters in areas of different salinity in Mobile Bay. Proceedings Southeastern Association of Game and Fish Commissioners 23:519-521.

McGinty, A.S. 1980. Survival, growth and variation in growth of channel catfish fry and fingerlings. Ph. D. Dissertation, Auburn University. 63 pp.

Miller, J.E. 1969. Muskrat control. University of Arkansas, Arkansas Agricultural Extension Service. Leaflet 436 .

Miller, J.E. 1971. Beaver-- friend or foe. University of Arkansas, Arkansas Agricultural Extension Service. Circular 539 15 pp.

Moss, D. 1953. Having trouble with turtles. Alabama Department of Conservation 24(6):9.

Moss, D. 1955. The effect of the slider turtle, *Pseudemys scripta scripta* (Schoepff), on the production of fish in farm ponds. Proceedings Southeastern Association of Game and Fish Commissioners 9:97-100.

Mott, D.F., K.J. Andrews and G.A. Littauer. 1992. An evaluation of roost dispersal for reducing cormorant activity on catfish ponds. Proceedings Eastern Wildlife Damage Control Conference 5:205-211.

Mott, D.F. and F.L. Boyd. 1992. Preventing cormorant depredations at aquaculture facilities in the southeastern United States. In Proceedings of the double-crested cormorant: biology, conservation, and management symposium, October 1992, Colonial Waterbird Society Meeting, Oxford Mississippi.

Palmer, C.M. 1959. Algae in water supplies. U.S. Department of Health, Education, Welfare and Public Health Service 88 pp.

Popper, D. and T. Lichatowich. 1975. Preliminary success in predator control of *Tilapia mossambica*. Aquaculture 5(2):213-214.

Prather, E.E. 1960. A note on the results of feeding fire ants to bluegills and red ear sunfish. Proceedings Southeastern Association of Game and Fish Commissioners. 14:124.

Rounsefell, G.A. and W.R. Nelson. 1966. Red-tide research summarized to 1964 including an annotated bibliography. U.S. Fish and Wildlife Service. Special Scientific Report - Fisheries No. 535.

Salmon, T.P. and F.S. Conte. 1981. Control of bird damage at aquaculture facilities. University of California at Davis. Wildlife Management Leaflet No. 475.

Sandifer, P.A., T.I.J. Smith and D.R. Calder. 1974. Hydrozoans as pests in closed-system culture of larval decapod crustaceans. Aquaculture 4:55-59.

Schramm, H.L., Jr., M.W. Collopy and E.A. Okrah. 1987. Potential problems of bird predation for fish culture in Florida. Progressive Fish-Culturist 49(1):44-48.

Slabyj, B.M. 1980. Storage and processing of mussels. pp. 247-262. In Mussel Culture and Harvest: A North American Perspective. Amsterdam-Oxford-New York: Elsevier Science Publishing Company Inc. 350 pp.

Sousa, R.J., F.P. Meyer and R.A. Schnick. (no date). How rotenone is used to help manage our fishery resources more effectively. U.S. Department of Interior, Fish and Wildlife Service, National Fishery Research Center, La Crosse, Wisconsin, 23 pp.

Stickley, A.R., Jr. 1991. Avian predation on southern aquaculture. Southern Regional Aquaculture Center, Louisiana Cooperative Extension Service Publication 2465. 8 pp.

Stickley, A.R., Jr., G.L. Warrick and J.F. Glahn. 1992. Impact of double-crested cormorant depredations on channel catfish farms. Journal of the World Aquaculture Society 23:192-198.

Swingle, H.S. 1960. Comparison evaluation of two *Tilapias* as pond fishes in Alabama. Transactions American Fisheries Society 89(2):142-148.

Sykes, J.E. 1965. Bureau of Commercial Fisheries Symposium on Red Tide. Special Scientific Report - Fisheries No. 521.

Taylor, P.W. 1992. Fish-eating birds as potential vectors of *Edwardsiella ictaluri*. Journal of Aquatic Animal Health 4:240-243.

Terazaki, M., P. Tharnbuppa and Y. Nakayama. 1980. Eradication of predatory fishes in shrimp farms by utilization of Thai Tea Seed. Aquaculture 19(3):235-242.

Van der Ploeg, M. 1991. Testing flavor quality of preharvest channel catfish. Southern Regional Aquaculture Center, SRAC Publication No. 431. 8 pp.

Walker, C.R. 1964. Preliminary observations on the toxicity of antimycin A to fish and other aquatic animals. In Investigations in Fish Control. Bureau of Sport Fisheries and Wildlife Circular 186.

Waterstrat, P., K. Chew, K. Johnson and J.H. Beattie. 1980. Mussel culture: a West Coast perspective. pp. 141-165. In Mussel Culture and Harvest: A North American Perspective. Amsterdam-Oxford-New York: Elsevier Science Publishing Company Inc. 350 pp.

Witzig, J.F. 1980. Spatial and temporal distribution patterns of macroinvertebrate communities in a small crawfish pond. M.S. Thesis. Louisiana State University. 113 pp.

Witzig, J.F., J.W. Avault, Jr. and J.V. Huner. 1981. Predation by *Anax junius* (Odonata: Aeschnidae) naiads on young crawfish. In International Symposium on Freshwater Crayfish, Davis, California 5:269.

CHAPTER 12
AQUATIC PLANTS AND WEEDS

Aquatic plants are an integral part of some culture systems. Green phytoplankton, for example, is the basic link in the grazing food chain and produces oxygen during photosynthesis. It is also important as "green water" in rearing larval shrimp. On the other hand, blue-green phytoplankton may cause pond scums, off-flavor in fish flesh, and deplete oxygen in ponds. Certain rooted plants, like *Najas* spp., may become serious pests and interfere with normal pond operations, yet *Najas* and certain other plant species are relished as food by grass carp (*Ctenopharyngodon idella*).

In this chapter, we classify plants into convenient groups, point out advantages and disadvantages of various plants, and cover the basics of weed control.

CLASSIFICATION OF AQUATIC PLANTS

Although aquatic botanists classify plants according to scientific designations, it is more useful for the aquaculturist to group plants according to the way in which they grow in ponds. Aquatic plants therefore may be classified as algae, floating, submerged or submersed, emersed, and marginal (Figure 12.1). Though most plants can be placed in one category or another, some may fit into more than one. For example, alligatorweed (*Alternanthera philoxeroides*) although a marginal plant also may grow as an emersed plant.

Some useful references on aquatic plant identification and weed control include Palmer (1959), Fassett and Ogden (1960), Eyles and Robertson (1963), Lawrence and Weldon (1965), Winterringer and Lopinot (1966), Hotchkiss (1967), Weldon et al. (1969), Klussman and Lowman (1971), Lewis and Miller (1980), Stucky et al. (1980), Gangstad (1986), Schmidt (1987), Seagrave (1988), Symoens (1988), Langeland (1992), Tiner (1993), and Durborow and Tucker (1994).

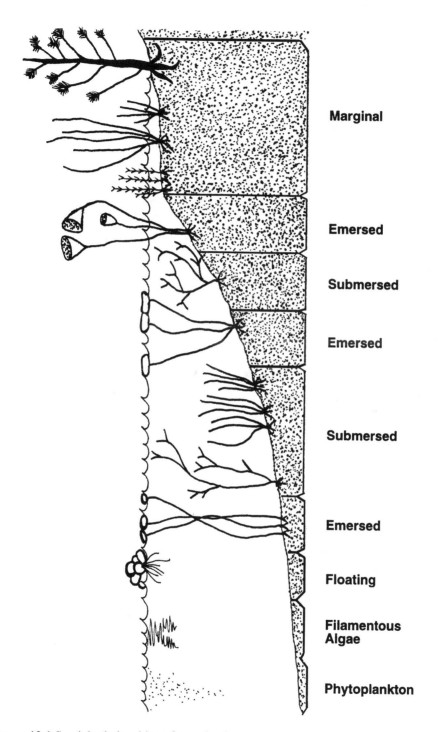

Figure 12.1 Spatial relationships of aquatic plants.

Algae

Algae are subdivided into phytoplankton, filamentous, and stoneworts.

Phytoplankton-- Phytoplankton consists of single-cell plants that float and drift around in the water. Large groups of phytoplankton, known by common names, include the diatoms, desmids, armored flagellates, euglenoids, greens, blue-greens, yellow-greens, browns, golden-browns and reds. The greens and blue-greens are most prevalent in aquaculture operations, except in molluskan culture where diatoms and other marine algae are abundant.

Green algae include such genera as *Chlorella*, *Pediastrum*, *Ankistrodesmus*, and *Scenedesmus*. The most common color, which is grass green to yellow-green, is localized in plastids. Green phytoplankton is typically uniformly dispersed in upper pond waters. The water takes on a green color with no noticeable green streaks.

Blue-green algae include such genera as *Oscillatoria, Anacystis* (formerly *Microcystis*), *Nostoc*, and *Anabaena*. As the name implies, many species of blue-greens have a blue-green color. They are surrounded by a slimy coating, and their internal structure is relatively simple. Heterocysts and gas vacuoles are present. In pond waters, blue-greens often form streaks at the surface, and a good breeze may windrow the algae to one side, giving the appearance of spilt green paint. Water may appear pea-soup green.

Filamentous-- Filamentous algae are typically string-like, forming "pond moss" at the water's surface or bottom. Algae typically begin growth on the bottom. As they grow, oxygen bubbles are trapped in the cottony mass. Eventually the algae float to the surface. Common genera include *Spirogyra, Cladophora, Rhizoclonium, Mougeotia, Zygnema, Hydrodictyon, Oedogonium*, and *Pithophora*. With experience, you can identify some forms in the field. Certain forms of filamentous algae, such as *Spirogyra* and *Hydrodictyon*, occur principally in the winter (Figure 12.2). *Spirogyra* is bright green and, when squeezed by hand, remains slimy. *Hydrodictyon* is lighter green, has a hexagonal net configuration like chicken wire, and becomes dry and cottony when squeezed by hand . As the winter ceases and spring begins, *Spirogyra, Hydrodictyon*, and other winter forms may be replaced by spring forms such as *Oedogonium* and *Rhizoclonium*. These in turn may give way to summer forms such as *Pithophora*. This alga is cottony and may cover a pond's surface in multiple balls rather than in sheets (Figure 12.3).

Genera of filamentous algae are relatively easy to recognize with a microscope and a good key (Palmer 1959). Most species have very characteristic identification features. *Oedogonium* has screw-like threads at the end of cell walls. *Pithophora* has barrel-shaped akinetes present. *Spirogyra* has spiral-shaped structures, like a coiled spring, throughout the strand. It is important to know the type of filamentous alga present in ponds. For example, if *Spirogyra* is present, you could possibly save the cost of chemical treatment by waiting for the water to warm. Moreover, not all forms of filamentous algae can be controlled with the same chemical treatment. Copper sulfate is effective for control of many algae forms except *Pithophora*.

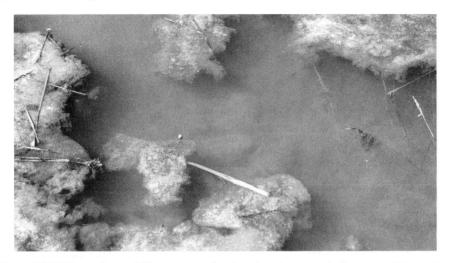

Figure 12.2 Winter form of filamentous alga forming sheets in shallow crawfish pond.

Figure 12.3 *Pithophora*, a filamentous alga, showing characteristic cottony balls.

Stoneworts-- Stoneworts are advanced forms of algae. Though often mistaken for higher vascular plants, stoneworts do not produce flowers or seed. They occur completely submerged in very clear water. Two common forms of stoneworts occur. *Chara*, typically found in hard water, is gray-green and has a rough texture caused by calcium deposits on the plant. A scratchiness is felt when wading bare-legged through *Chara*. This plant is often called musk-grass, because when it is squeezed a musky odor is produced. *Nitella* is similar in appearance to *Chara*. It is dark green, does not have a musky odor, and is more common in soft water.

Floating Plants

Floating plants have true roots, stems, and leaves like all higher plants, but instead of being anchored in the soil like most higher plants, they float about at the surface. Most floating plants have extensive root systems that collect nutrients from the water. Duckweeds (*Lemna* spp. and *Spirodela* spp.) are common floating plants that are often prevalent in ponds protected from wind (Figure 12.4). Watermeal (*Wolffia* spp.) is the smallest of flowering plants. It is no longer than 1.5 mm (1/16 of an inch) in diameter and is bright green. Water pennywort (*Hydrocotyle* spp.) may form floating mats in water though some species grow as marginal plants. The water hyacinth (*Eichornia crassipes*) is variable in size and may range from 8 to 91 cm (3 to 36 in) in height. Flowers, which may be blue, violet, or white, are very showy (Figure 12.5). The plant is a serious pest in the southeastern United States. It may make canals and other waterways virtually impassable. Water lettuce (*Pistia stratioities*) consists of a distinct rosette of light yellow-green leaves. Leaves have distinct veins radiating out. Salvinia (*Salvinia rotundifolia*) has small, bright green leaves arranged along a common stem. The leaf has a distinct midrib and appears folded along its axis. This plant is often found with alligatorweed and water hyacinth.

Figure 12.4 Duckweed, a floating plant, commonly found in wind-protected ponds.

Figure 12.5 Wendell Lorio, formerly of the LSU Agricultural Center, in water choked with the water hyacinth, a floating plant.

Submerged or Submersed Plants

Submerged plants are generally rooted to the pond bottom. If flowers are present, they may extend above the water surface. Submerged plants are typically weak and have little rigidity. Some plant species, such as *Potamogeton americanus*, may have two different leaf types on the same plant. Underwater leaves may be needle-like, whereas surface leaves are broad and flat. Most submerged plants absorb nutrients though both roots and vegetative growth. A number of families are represented.

The water milfoil family contains perennial aquatics that have delicate, feather-like leaves. Members of this family include parrotfeather (*Myriophyllum brasiliense*), broadleaf water milfoil (*M. heterophyllum*), and Eurasian water milfoil (*M. spicatum*).

The hornwort family contains rootless aquatic plants. Leaves are dark green and arranged in whorls. Coontail (*Ceratophyllum demersum*), a common member of the family, can be distinguished from water milfoil by its forking of leaves rather than the feather-like divisions. Spacing between leaf whorls is highly variable, but toward the end of the stem the leaves become very bushy, giving the appearance of a coontail. Fanwort (*Cabomba* spp.) has many thread-like leaves that give the appearance of a fan underwater. The stem may be covered with a gelatinous material.

The pondweed family, the largest family of truly aquatic plants, contains both freshwater and brackishwater species. Leaves are mostly alternate and may be all alike or may be two kinds. Submersed leaves may be thin and linear or all broad;

emersed leaves are broad and more or less elliptical. An example of a freshwater form is *Potamogeton americanus*. Widgeon grass (*Ruppi maritima*) is widespread in salt marshes along the entire coast of the United States. Leaves are thread-like, narrow and extend from an extensive buried root system.

The frogbit family contains plants with slender-stemmed, branching, whorled, thin, linear leaves and plants with long, linear, clustered leaves. The first group contains three species of note: Brazilian elodea (*Egeria densa*), American elodea (*Elodea canadensis*), and hydrilla (*Hydrilla verticillata*). Hydrilla is a serious pest in some states like Florida, Texas, and Louisiana. It may grow in water 12 m (40 ft) deep and form dense mats up to the surface. Hydrilla can be distinguished from the elodeas by hydrilla's cashew-shaped bulbs on the stems. Hydrilla leaves are also finely serrated on margins. Eelgrass (*Vallisneria americana*) is a representative of the second major group in the frogbit family. Roots are buried in mud and leaves are flaccid and ribbon-like (Figure 12.6).

Figure 12.6 Eelgrass, a submerged plant, grows below the water surface. This eelgrass has been uprooted by common carp and is floating on the surface.

The naiad or bushy pondweed family contains aquatic plants with opposite leaves having minute spines on the margin (Figure 12.7). *Najas guadalupenis*, a common species, can be distinguished from *Potamogeton* spp. by having opposite leaves rather than alternate and by its bushy appearance. Like *Potamogeton*, *Najas* can choke a pond with vegetative growth (Figure 12.8).

The bladderwort family contains plants that are submerged or floating and have no roots. The finely divided leaves of *Utricularia* spp. have numerous bladder-like structures that act as traps to capture small invertebrates. Flowers are typically yellow or purple.

The water star grass family, with *Heteranthera dubia* as an example, has long, flexible, grass-like stems and leaves. The small yellow flower is star shaped.

Figure 12.7 *Najas*, a submerged plant showing opposite, flaccid leaves.

Figure 12.8 Fish farmer in pond choked with *Najas*. Photo courtesy of John Wozniak, LSU Agricultural Center.

The buttercup family, with water buttercup *Ranunculus* spp. as an example, contains plants with tufts of thread-like leaves along the stem. *Ranunculus* spp., which resemble *Chara*, have conspicuous yellow or white flowers emerging from the water.

Emersed Plants

Emersed plants are rooted on the bottom but produce most of their leaves and flowers at or above the water surface. Some species possess leaves that are flat and float entirely upon the water surface. Other species have leaves that are saucer-shaped or whose margins are irregular or fluted. A number of families are represented.

The watercress family, represented by *Nasturtium officinale*, is an aquatic herb with creeping stems and rooting at the nodes; leaves are alternate and pinnately compounded.

The figwort family contains creeping fleshy herbs which root at the nodes; leaves are opposite. Stems may be covered with crinkled hairs. Flowers are solitary, pale blue, purple, or white. Water hyssop (*Bacopa caroliniana*) is a representative of this family.

The water lily family contains plants that are rooted and have large floating leaves. Representative species include spatterdock (*Nuphar advena*), fragrant waterlily (*Nymphaea odorata*), white waterlily (*N. tuberosa*), watershield (*Brasenia schreberi*), and American lotus (*Nelumbo lutea*). Spatterdock has yellow solitary flowers. Leaves are shaped like a broad arrowhead. The fragrant waterlily is known for its sweet-scented, white or pink, showy flower. The leaves are split, green on top and often purplish underneath, and lie mostly flat on the water. Flowers of the white waterlily have little or no fragrance. Watershield has elliptical, flat, floating leaves that have a mucilaginous covering on the underside. American lotus has large circular leaves which form a cup or bowl (Figure 12.9). The blooms are large and pale yellow. The seed head is most distinctive and used as decoration.

Figure 12.9 American lotus, an emersed plant.

The water plantain family that contains arrowhead (*Sagittaria* spp.) has lance-shaped leaves that are 4 to 10 cm (1.5 to 4 in) wide (Figure 12.10). The leaves grow to form a rosette from the rhizomes. Tubers are produced at the end of the rhizomes. The white flowers usually arise in whorls of three and may extend 30 cm (12 in) above leaves. Figure 12.11 shows arrowhead in a shallow crawfish pond.

Figure 12.10 Arrowhead, an emersed plant, showing characteristic flower.

Figure 12.11 Arrowhead in shallow crawfish pond.

Marginal Plants

The species comprising this group are most obvious and probably the most widely distributed of rooted aquatics. Many species, such as alligatorweed, are adapted to grow from moist shoreline soils into water up to 0.6 m (2 ft) deep. Others are limited to the shoreline only. Marginal plants consist of divergent families.

The evening primrose family contains the water primrose (*Ludwigia* sp.) (Figure 12.12). It has light green leaves about 8 cm (3 in) long. Flowers are bright yellow, up to 2.5 cm (1 in) in diameter, and have five petals.

Figure 12.12 Water primrose, a typical marginal plant.

The Amaranth family contains the alligatorweed. This plant has opposite, oblong leaves 5 to 13 cm (2 to 5 in) long with a distinct midrib. Flowers are white and clover-like.

The pickerelweed family contains *Pontederia* spp., with thick, creeping rootstock and fibrous roots. Leaves are in a basal cluster, erect, with a fleshy, sheathing petiole, and are heart-shaped to lance-shaped. Flowers are borne on a spike and are violet-blue.

The buckwheat family contains the smartweeds (*Polygonum* spp.) (Figure 12.13). Species in this group have alternate, simple leaves. Jointed stems have swollen nodes surrounded by a thin, clear to brown sheath. Flowers are white or pink.

The cattail family contains large plants that may attain a height of 2 m (6 ft). *Typha* spp. produce distinctive flowers that dry and become coffee brown (Figure 12.14).

Figure 12.13 Smartweed, a common marginal plant, at edge of crawfish pond.

Figure 12.14 Cattail, a marginal plant, showing characteristic coffee brown flower.

The parsley family contains the water pennywort, (*Hydrocotyle* spp). The pennywort, usually found in less than 5 cm (2 in) of water, has round, peltate leaves about 1 to 3 cm (0.5 to 1.2 in) in diameter. Flowers are small, white, and borne on an erect petiole. Dense stands may break loose and float to deeper water.

The arum family, containing golden club (*Oronthium aquaticum*), has stout plants with fleshy clustered leaves. Flowers are borne in clusters at the apex of a stout stalk.

The grass family contains numerous species. Southern water grass (*Hydrochloa caroliniensis*) and knotgrass (*Paspalum distichum*) are representative species. Southern water grass grows from moist shorelines into waters up to 2.5 m (8 ft) deep. The underwater portion of the plant is a mass of leafless stems, whereas the emersed stems have tufts of leaves. Knotgrass grows from the shoreline into waters up to 61 cm (2 ft) deep. It resembles bermuda grass.

The sedge family contains species that resemble grasses or rushes. *Carex* spp. has characteristic 3-sided stems and leaves that are often finely serrated.

The rush family contains about 200 species that appear grass-like. Stems are typically hollow and round, whereas stems of sedges are usually solid and triangular. Soft-stem bulrush (*Scirpus validus*), needle rush (*Eleocharis acicularis*), and spike rush (*E. obtusa*) are common species (See also Figure 5.34). Soft-stem bulrush is recognized by its long, straight, non-branching stems. Stems may be up to 3 m (10 ft) tall and up to 2.5 cm (1 in) in diameter at the base. Stems are spongy and mash easily. Needle rush is fine and grass-like. Dense mats may form, break loose, and drift into deep water. Spike rush is stouter than needle rush and typically grows right at the water's edge.

Woody species, representing a number of families, can be found at the water's edge. The black willow (*Salix nigra*) and buttonbush (*Cephalanthus occidentalis*) are examples.

ADVANTAGES AND DISADVANTAGES OF AQUATIC PLANTS

Often aquatic plants are arbitrarily considered weeds, with little thought given to any beneficial uses. The National Academy of Sciences (1976) explored the conversion of aquatic plants for useful purposes, namely food, fertilizer, paper, fiber, and energy. In this section, we discuss advantages and disadvantages of aquatic plants as they relate to aquaculture. In doing so, it is convenient to lump them into one of two groups -- phytoplankton, and rooted plants plus filamentous algae.

Advantages of Phytoplankton

(1) Phytoplankton has a short life span and can reproduce every few days. Thus, the nutrient flow through the first link in the grazing food chain is continuous.

(2) Phytoplankton is highly nutritious, being higher in protein than most higher plants.

(3) Phytoplankton can produce a large biomass, resulting in greater production with each succeeding link in the food chain.

(4) The small size of phytoplankton makes it an optimum food particle for zooplankton, the second link in the grazing food chain.

(5) Certain fish species, such as silver carp (*Hypophthalmichthys molitrix*), filter phytoplankton directly as food.

(6) Phytoplankton is used to feed larval mollusks and shrimp. Some nurseries isolate a single species of phytoplankton in tanks as food for larvae. Nurseries also use phytoplankton from natural waters that contain a mixture of phyto-plankton species.

(7) Phytoplankton is typically dispersed throughout the pond by wind and waves. This, plus its small size, means that phytoplankton does not interfere with normal pond operations such as stocking, feeding, and harvesting.

(8) Phytoplankton, through photosynthesis, is the main source of oxygen in pond waters.

Disadvantages of Phytoplankton

(1) Blue-green phytoplankton, such as *Nostoc, Anacystis, Anabaena*, and *Nodularia*, may introduce toxic substances into water detrimental to livestock. Lethal substances produced by these algae are retained within the cell and released after death (endotoxin) or secreted from living cells (exotoxin).

(2) Blue-green phytoplankton is frequently associated with the off-flavor or musty taste of fish. Catfish farmers in the United States have identified off-flavor as a major problem. Off-flavor fish cannot be marketed. Instead, they must be held or purged until they come "on-flavor."

(3) Blue-greens may form thin scums on the pond surface, thus blocking out sunlight to deeper waters. The top few centimeters of water may be super-saturated with dissolved oxygen, but deeper waters are virtually devoid of oxygen. A strong wind or cold rain may result in a turnover of water. The thin layer of oxygen is diluted with bottom waters, and oxygen depletion may occur.

(4) A sudden die-off of phytoplankton may result in oxygen depletion. This may occur because of dim sunlight for photosynthesis during cloudy days. It also may occur when certain nutrients, particularly phosphorus in fresh water and nitrogen in brackish water, have become exhausted.

Advantages of Rooted Plants and Filamentous Algae

(1) Rooted plants offer attachment space for natural-food organisms. Collectively these types of organisms are known as periphyton (See also Chapter 14).

(2) Rooted plants and filamentous algae are eaten directly by certain fish species. The grass carp, a voracious plant eater, prefers certain plant species to others. Avault et al. (1968a) listed some plants eaten by grass carp in decreasing order of preference: (a) *Chara* sp., (b) *Najas quadalupensis*, (c) *Potamogeton diversifolius*, (d) *Eleocharis acicularis*, (e) *Ceratophyllum demersum*, (f) *Bacopa*

rotundifolia, (g) *Elodea canadensis*, (h) *Myriophyllum spicatum,* (i) *Vallisneria americana,* (j) *Eichornia crassipes,* (k) *M. brasiliense,* and (l) *Alternanthera philoxeroides*. Both *Tilapia zilli* and *T. melanopleura* feed readily on filamentous algae and soft-stem higher plants. Milkfish (*Chanos chanos*) culture in the Philippines and Indonesia is based on pastures of lab-lab and lamut (See Chapter 8 for further details). The crawfish farming industry in Louisiana is based on development of aquatic pastures (Figure 12.15).

Figure 12.15 Pond in south Louisiana with alligatorweed being used as forage for crawfish.

(3) Rooted plants are able to use nutrients in pond muds that may not be readily available to phytoplankton.

(4) Rooted plants may produce oxygen in relatively deep water. Plants like *Elodea*, that may grow in deep water, produce oxygen in lower water depths.

(5) Certain marginal plants may retard erosion of levees. Pickerelweed and certain spikerushes, such as *Eleocharis obtusa*, have been used, but be careful that the plants do not spread and become a nuisance.

(6) Certain plants, such as the water hyacinth, can remove suspended particles like clay and dissolved impurities (Dinges 1976). Hillman and Culley (1978) used duckweeds to remove excess nutrients from dairy lagoons. Duckweeds, being high in protein, were in turn harvested and incorporated into animal feeds. Skillicorn et al. (1993) reported on use of duckweeds to clean wastewater and as a source of fish and poultry feed.

(7) Rooted plants sometimes become so abundant that their use directly as human food and for other purposes has been investigated. Boyd (1968a, b, 1969) reported on a number of common pond species. In one study involving nutrient analysis of 42 plant species, 18 species had crude protein values (dry weight) of 12% to 18%. Seaweed farming is practiced in certain countries, and suggested reading includes: Rao and Subba (1965), Anonymous (1966), Hunter and Nyegaard (1974), Doty (1977), Abbott et al. (1980), and Abbott (1994).

(8) Rooted plants provide spawning substrate for certain species like common carp (*Cyprinus carpio*). During spawning several males may chase a female carp that spews out eggs as she swims through vegetation. Pursuing males emit sperm. Fertilized eggs are adhesive and stick to vegetation.

(9) Rooted plants and filamentous algae may provide shade for various culture species (Figure 12.16).

(10) Rooted plants provide cover and protection for molting crustaceans.

Figure 12.16 Gabi planted at the water's edge provides shade for fish in a Filipino pond.

Disadvantages of Rooted Plants and Filamentous Algae

(1) Rooted plants have a much longer life cycle than phytoplankton. Thus the rate of nutrient flow is slower.

(2) Rooted plants are relatively large and cannot be used readily by zooplankton unless they become partly decomposed.

(3) Rooted plants and filamentous algae, unlike phytoplankton, are not always uniformly distributed in a pond. The fixed location and large size of rooted plants interfere with fish farming practices, such as feeding and harvesting. Seines may ride over the mass of plants, allowing fish to escape. The weight of plant material caught in the seine may strain equipment or even prevent seining.

(4) Rooted plants and filamentous algae both encourage mosquito production by providing suitable habitat.

(5) Die-offs of rooted plants and filamentous algae may result in rapid decomposition and oxygen depletion.

To sum up the advantages and disadvantages of aquatic plants, it is generally more desirable to develop phytoplankton blooms in ponds than it is to encourage growth of higher plants and filamentous algae. Exceptions were noted above.

PREVENTION AND CONTROL OF AQUATIC WEEDS

A weed is a plant out of place or, simply put, an unwanted plant. Prevention is the easiest and most economical method to avoid aquatic weeds.

Prevention and Control with Habitat

Site Selection-- Proper site selection is the first step in preventing aquatic weeds. Avoid a flowing stream as a water source unless water can be shunted around the pond when desired. Continuous flushing creates clear water and causes low contact times for herbicides and fertilizers.

Pond Construction-- Pond edges should provide a 61- to 91-cm (24- to 36-in) drop-off (See Figure 5.36). Ponds with a very gradual slope from water's edge to pond bank allow aquatic weeds to become established. Once established, some weeds are capable of invading deeper waters. Deepening and dredging shallow pond bottoms with a bulldozer or similar equipment is effective in controlling marginal weeds.

Fertilization-- Pond bottoms can be shaded by maintaining a good phytoplankton bloom through fertilization, thus retarding establishment of weeds. Winter fertilization encourages the growth of winter forms of filamentous algae. The algae wrap up and smother rooted plants, and they later disappear as waters warm in spring (See also Chapter 8). Do not start a fertilization program if weeds are established. Instead, control weeds by other means, such as with chemicals, then begin fertilization.

Plastic Liners and Dyes-- Dark plastic liners have been used to shade out plants. Plastic can be weighted down on pond bottoms with gravel or floated on the water surface. In either case, sunlight is blocked and weeds eventually die. This method can be expensive and may be practical only in small ponds. Dyes also have been used to shade water, but they are expensive and only temporary. Dyes are not effective when there is a large water flow through the pond.

Water Drawdown-- Water drawdown, especially in winter, is an effective way to control weeds. Ponds can be partially or completely drained. Following this, use of chemicals for weed control is most effective. Submerged weeds in particular are killed, but emersed weeds, such as alligatorweed or cattail, may replace submerged weeds.

Physical and Mechanical-- Weeds can be pulled, cut, or raked by hand. This method is usually only temporarily successful. When weedy ponds are to be drained, lanes can be cleared by hand to improve water drainage and to allow the culture species a path to the harvest pit. Mechanical weed cutting has been used. Except for the purpose of harvesting seaweed, it is usually too costly. Weed cutting must be repeated frequently because weeds are not controlled; they are only cut as you would mow a lawn. Mechanical removal of filamentous algae or submersed plants almost always proves futile and may spread the plants.

Wind Circulation-- Certain floating plants, such as duckweed, can be controlled by improving wind action. This may mean removing brush and trees from around the pond.

Biological Controls

Mammals -- Mammals that eat aquatic plants include cattle, hogs, water buffalo (*Bubalis bubalis*), manatee (*Trichechus* spp.), capybara (*Hydrochoerus* spp.), nutria (*Myocaster coypus*), and muskrat (*Ondatra zibethica*) (Figure 12.17).

Figure 12.17 Carabaos in the Philippines feed readily on aquatic plants.

Both cattle and hogs can be turned in to graze on weeds, especially marginal and emersed plants. Their activity may muddy the water, which helps to shade out weeds.

The water buffalo is found throughout the Asian tropics and in more than 30 countries in the Mediterranean basin, South America, and the Caribbean. It feeds readily on aquatic plants and will dive underwater to get them.

The manatee, or sea cow, can reach 3 m (10 ft) in length and weigh up to half a ton. An adult may consume 20 kg (44 lb) of wet vegetation a day. They have potential for control of weeds in water supply canals.

The capybara is a large, brown, tailless, semi-aquatic rodent, which reaches up to 60 kg (132 lb) in South America. The Panamanian capybara reaches half that size. Grasses and aquatic and semi-aquatic plants make up their diet. The capybara is easily tamed and could possibly be bred and domesticated. Such research has been conducted in Venezuela and Columbia. The capybara may become a pest and feed on domestic crops. It should not be introduced into areas where it is not native.

Nutria and muskrats feed readily on aquatic plants. Their fur has value, and their meat is edible. This value, however, is often negated by the damage they do burrowing into levees.

Ducks, Geese, and Swans-- Ducks, geese, and swans forage on vegetation and have been used to control aquatic weeds. In one instance, in Hawaii, 65 Chinese white goslings per ha (26/ac) controlled dense strands of paragrass (*Brachiaria mutica*) and cattail within 2.5 years (National Academy of Sciences 1976). Muscovy ducks at 5 to 8 per ha (2 to 3/ac) have controlled duckweed and some other aquatic plants. Coots (*Fulica americana*) have controlled the water hyacinth. Swans have been used to control aquatic weeds. Ducks and geese provide animal protein, and geese provide fat and goose down. Both ducks and geese may require a diet supplementation since they may not receive enough nutrition from aquatic weeds alone. In tropical countries, shade is necessary. If not handled properly, ducks and geese may become pests in grain crops. Where sanitation is poor, salmonellosis may devastate flocks. This disease can be transmitted in their meat and eggs to humans.

Crawfish-- Crawfish, particularly the red swamp crawfish (*Procambarus clarkii*), can be effective in controlling aquatic weeds. *Orconectes causeyi* and *O. nais* also have been used to control certain plant species. The red swamp crawfish readily feeds on alligatorweed and water primrose. When hungry, it eats water hyacinths. In the southeastern United States, crawfish are seeded into ponds at 28 to 56 kg/ha (25 to 50 lb/ac) during spring or summer. They mate, burrow underground, and emerge in the fall, at which time young are released by the female. Weeds should be controlled by the next spring. Crawfish, such as *P.*

clarkii, P. *zonangulus,* and *Pacifastacus leniusculus,* are relished as food. Other crawfish, such as *Orconectes* spp., are used as fish bait. Crawfish may cause pond leaks by burrowing into levees. When introduced into non-native areas, they may become pests. *P. clarkii,* introduced into California, Japan, and Hawaii, is considered a nuisance by some.

Insects -- The "lily" weevil, an insect, has been used to control the water hyacinth but with little success. The alligatorweed beetle has also given a poor response. Insects are difficult to confine to a given area, and their spread can do irreparable harm. For example, in Louisiana alligatorweed is used as forage in crawfish ponds. This plant is also a mainstay for white-tailed deer (*Odocoileus virginianus*) in marsh lands.

Herbivorous Fish-- A number of fish species has been used successfully to control aquatic weeds. A partial list includes grass carp, common carp, *Oreochromis mossambicus, O. niloticus, Tilapia zilli,* and *T. melanopleura* (Avault et al. 1968a). Ideally a herbivorous fish will meet the following criteria: (1) effectively control weeds, (2) be economical to use, (3) not interfere with other fish species, and (4) add to the fishery.

Grass carp 25 to 41 cm (10 to 16 in) long, when stocked at 50 to 100 per ha (20 to 40/ac), control a wide variety of weeds within a year or two (Avault et al. 1968a). Larger fish can be stocked at 30 per ha (12/ac). Figures 12.18 and 12.19 show before and after pictures when grass carp were stocked into a weed-infested pond. Grass carp are hardy and excellent eating. Their many small bones, however, sometimes make them undesirable for eating.

Figure 12.18 Before: 0.04 ha (0.1 ac) pond 90% covered with *Chara* and *Najas.*

Figure 12.19 One month later after stocking four 41-cm (16-in) long grass carp, weeds were virtually eliminated (Avault 1965).

Although grass carp are highly effective in controlling most weeds, controversy has surrounded this fish in certain states. It is not native to the United States and many other countries. Most fears have to do with its spread to natural waters and its potential harm to native fish species. Avault and Merkowsky (1978) evaluated the hybrid female grass carp x male common carp. The hybrid was not sterile, and it did not effectively control aquatic weeds. The female grass carp crossed with the male bighead carp is a hybrid developed in Hungary that has been used in weed control. Stanley and Sneed (1973) reported on artificial gynogenesis to produce unisex populations of grass carp, and Jensen et al. (1978) reported on feeding of methyltestosterone to grass carp fry to produce unisex fish.

The thrust of these various studies was to produce a fish that was incapable of reproduction but would control weeds. The triploid grass carp, with 72 chromosomes instead of the normal 48, controls weeds without the danger of unwanted reproduction. It is produced by physically shocking fertilized eggs or by emersing them for a prescribed period in either warm or cold water, or by using hydrostatic pressure to stimulate the retention of one set of chromosomes normally lost during cell division (Clugston and Shireman 1987). Treatment does not always produce 100% triploid fish. A number of states allow use of triploid grass carp after verification that the fish are indeed triploid. The number of chromosomes is verified by electronically measuring the volume of the nucleus of a red blood cell after the cell membrane has been chemically removed.

The common carp is effective in controlling filamentous algae, such as *Pithophora* and certain soft plants like *Eleocharis acicularis*, when stocked as 15- to 25-cm (6- to 10-in) fingerlings at 124 per ha (50/ac). Most higher plants, however, are not controlled by carp unless the fish spawn heavily. In this case, carp muddy the water by rooting along the bottom and pulling up plants.

T. melanopleura, when stocked as fingerlings at 2,470 to 4,940 per ha (1,000 to 2,000/ac), controlled a variety of rooted weeds. Best control was obtained in ponds when survival was high and fish spawned. After tilapia reduced weed abundance, fertilization was effective in further control. *T. melanopleura* begins dying when the water temperature drops to 12°C (54°F), and in some countries a stock must be overwintered (Avault et al. 1968b). *O. mossambicus* and *O. niloticus* show little promise for controlling weeds except for filamentous algae.

Chemical Controls

In some instances use of herbicides is the most effective method for controlling aquatic weeds. Aquatic weeds vary in susceptibility to herbicides, and all are not killed by the same herbicide. Because herbicides can be toxic to animals and humans, their use is restricted and only labeled recommendations should be followed. Boyd (1982) summarized herbicides and their concentrations used in weed control, and Table 12.1 condenses select information.

Some Precautions-- Before treating with herbicides, several safety precautions must be followed. First, make sure the herbicide is cleared for use. If it is, follow the label directions carefully. Avoid herbicide contact with the skin, eyes, and clothing, and wear gloves, goggles, and protective clothing. Store all chemicals in a cool, dry area away from food, feed, and seed. Do not permit livestock to graze vegetation around a treated pond until after a heavy rain. Avoid drift during herbicide application. Some herbicides such as 2, 4-D may drift, especially if there is a strong breeze. Sprayers used for herbicides should be thoroughly washed with a detergent and rinsed after each use. For absolute safety, a sprayer used for 2, 4-D should not be used to apply other pesticides. If weed growth is particularly heavy in a pond, it is best to treat 1/3 to 1/2 of the pond and then treat the rest in 2 weeks. Excessive die-off of weeds could result in oxygen depletion.

Methods of Treatment-- Before treatment, identify the weed(s) and choose the proper chemical (Table 12.1). There are several ways to determine the amount of chemical to use.

Table 12.1 Herbicides and their concentrations used to control aquatic weeds.

Type of aquatic weed or aquatic site	Herbicide rate/acre	Time to apply	Remarks
	Floating weeds (unattached, tops above water)		
All weeds (floating mats of alligatorweed, duckweed, fern, water lettuce, water hyacinth)	2,4-D amine 4.0 lb/ac in 100 gal water	On foliage when weeds are actively growing	Spray to uniformly wet foliage. Add 10% fuel oil by volume or 1.0 qt of surfactant to spray mix. Repeat every 4 to 6 weeks. Avoid use in waters for crop irrigation.
Duckweeds, water hyacinth	Diquat at 1.0 gal/ac plus 1.0 pt of surfactant	Same as above	Do not apply to muddy water. Inject into water or apply as surface spray at 150-200 gal water or as aerial spray in 7.5 gal water/ac for duckweed. Add 1 pt surfactant/100 gal water.
Water lettuce	Diquat at 0.5 gal/ac plus 1.0 pt of surfactant	Same as above	Use only aerial spray to control water lettuce or water hyacinth. Wait 10 days after application before using water. Some control of submerged weeds that have not reached the water surface will be obtained by 1.0 gal per surface acre.

Table 12.1 Continued

Type of aquatic weed or aquatic site	Herbicide rate/acre	Time to apply	Remarks
Emersed and marginal weeds (rooted under water, tops above water, or growing on wet soil)			
Broad leaf species (arrowhead, lotus, smartweed, water primrose, white water lily, yellow water lily)	2,4- D low volatile ester (LVE) at 4.0 lb/ac in 100 gal water	On foliage when weeds are actively growing	Spray to uniformly wet foliage. Add 10% fuel oil by volume or 1.0 qt to spray mix. More than one application may be required for some species. Avoid use in waters for crop irrigation.
Grass and grass-like species (perennial grasses and sedges -- cutgrass, knotgrass, reeds, ripgut sedges, cattails, bulrushes, etc.)	Dowpon at 10 to 15 lb/ac in 100 gal water	Apply when grasses are 6" to 8" tall and before heading.	For aerial application apply 10 gal/ac. Add 1.0 qt surfactant per 50 gal of spray. Repeated applications may be needed. Spot treat by mixing 1.0 lb of Dowpon per 10 gal of water. Use on ditch bank and marshes only.
Broadleaf weeds, grasses and weedy species. (cattail, maidencane, smartweed, spatterdock, willow, and others)	Rodeo 1.5 to 7.5 pt/ac broadcast, or 0.75% to 1.5% in spray-to-wet equipment plus 0.5% labeled approved surfactant	To actively growing weeds	See label for proper stage of growth. No restrictions on the use of the water. Do not apply within 0.5 miles upstream of potable water intakes or in tidewater areas.

Table 12.1 Continued

Type of aquatic weed or aquatic site	Herbicide rate/acre	Time to apply	Remarks
Submerged weeds (tops mostly under water, usually rooted or anchored)			
Algae (scums and mosses)	Copper sulfate at 2.0 to 3.0 lb/ac of water	Apply crystals or powder at any state of algae growth by any method to give rapid and uniform distribution. Repeat as necessary to maintain control. Treat only a portion of the pond at once. Apply 3.0 lb/ac ft in ponds with soft water.
Coontail, fanwort, milfoil, pondweeds	Endothall Aquathol liquid at 1.0 to 2.0 gal Aquathol granular at 125 lb to 250 lb/ac (water 4 to 6 ft deep)	Active growth stage	Can be injected into the upper end of the pond or sprayed over surface of pond. Do not use fish for 3 days after treatment. Can be used for other uses within 7 days after treatment. Read the label.
Coontail, naiad, milfoil, fanwort, elodea, pondweeds, hydrilla	Sonar 5P at 10 to 20 lb/surface ac Sonar AS at 1.0 to 2.0 pt/ surface acre	Same as above Same as above	Slow kill. Effective against most rooted plants. If water depth is greater than 6 ft, increase rate by 50%.
Coontail, naiad, milfoil	Diquat at 1.0 to 2.0 gal/surface acre	Same as above	Apply as a direct pour or subsurface injection. Short residual; water may be used for irrigation 11 days after treatment.

Table 12.1 Continued

Type of aquatic weed or aquatic site	Herbicide rate/acre	Time to apply	Remarks
Submerged weeds (tops mostly under water, usually rooted or anchored)			
Chara, coontail, elodea, naiads, milfoil, pondweeds	Dichlobenil 8 lb/ac Casoron G-10 granules at 80 lb/ac	Early in the spring before weeds emerge and when bottoms are exposed	Apply during early spring either to exposed pond bottom or through water. Uniform coverage is essential. Dichlobenil is taken up through the soil, rather than through foliage. Broadcast over surface area. Do not apply to areas where water will be used for irrgation or for livestock or human consumption. Do not fish from treated area for food or feed for 90 days after application.
	Casoron G-10 granules at 100 to 150 lb/ac	Low rate in shallow water, high rate in water up to 6 ft deep	Most effective against pondweeds, water milfoil, coontail, and chara.
	Norosac 10G at 80 to 150 lb/ac	Same as above	Same as above

Source: Modified from Sanders et al. 1994. Louisiana's suggested chemical weed control guide for 1994. Louisiana Cooperative Extension Service 159 pp.

(1) To treat the total water column, first calculate the volume of water (Figure 12.20). The weight of chemical required for treatment can be calculated once the volume of water and the recommended treatment rate in ppm are known (See Chapter 10 for example of calculations). If only one-half of the pond is to be treated, only half as much chemical is used.

(2) When submersed weeds are to be controlled, only the bottom 30 cm (1 ft) needs to be treated (Figure 12.21). A boat carrying application equipment drags a hose or boom just above the pond bottom. The herbicide is dispersed through nozzles, and if it is heavier than water it will sink to the bottom, or additives can be used to get the herbicide to the bottom.

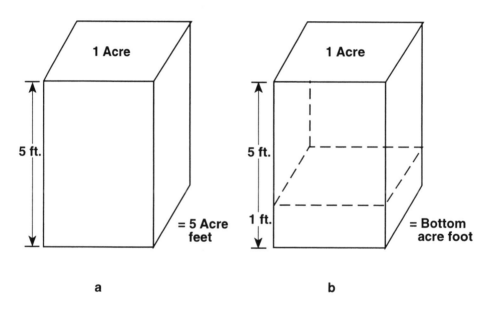

Figure 12.20 Treatment of total water volume   **Figure 12.21**. Treatment of bottom only.

(3) For floating plants like duckweed, one need not treat the whole water column but only the surface (2 or 3 cm). Some chemicals are dripped into the water at the water inlet. Cutrine® plus has been used this way to control algae in flowing water. To determine the amount of chemical required, calculate the flow rate, volume to treat, and concentration of chemical desired.

Herbicides may come in several forms: liquid, granules, and powder being the most common. The form of the herbicide and the particular job for controlling weeds determine the application method.

(1) In flowing waters the drip method works well.

(2) Hand application works well if granules are used. Granules can be broadcast into water by walking along levees or by moving back and forth across

a pond in a boat. If in liquid form, the herbicide, after proper dilution, can be poured over the side of a moving boat into the prop wash. In some instances, when ponds are small, the herbicides can be ladled out in a large dipper and slung out into the water. If fish in the pond are to be harvested, apply the herbicide in select areas only, such as in the harvest basin.

(3) Floating porous sacks have been used with granular or powdered herbicides.

(4) Herbicides in granular or powdered form also can be placed in a burlap bag and pulled about in the pond behind a boat.

(5) Backpack sprayers of 13 liters (3.5 gal) work well in small ponds.

(6) An array of power-operated equipment can be used. Some sprayers are pulled by a tractor and powered by small horsepower centrifugal and siphon pumps. Power sprayers also may be used from boats.

(7) For large areas airplanes and helicopters have been used.

Factors Affecting Weed Control-- Whether herbicide application is successful or not depends on several factors.

(1) The correct herbicide must be used. This can be determined after proper identification of the weed. Do not, for example, expect to get good control of grass-like weeds with 2, 4-D.

(2) For best results, apply chemicals under sunny conditions when the water temperature is 16°C (61°F) or above. Biological and chemical activity is reduced under cold, cloudy conditions.

(3) Best control results when weeds are actively growing and before they go to seed.

(4) The pH, total alkalinity, total water hardness, and other water quality parameters may affect the efficiency of certain herbicides. Copper sulfate, for example, is highly toxic in low alkalinity water (<20 ppm) but is relatively non-toxic in high alkalinity waters.

STUDY QUESTIONS

1. List and define the five groups of aquatic plants based on the way in which they grow in ponds, and give three examples of plant species for each major group.

2. List advantages and disadvantages of phytoplankton in pond water.

3. List advantages and disadvantages of higher plants in pond water.

4. Under the following conditions is phytoplankton or rooted aquatics more desirable: monoculture of channel catfish, monoculture of milkfish, polyculture of grass carp with silver carp and bighead carp, oyster culture, spawning pond for common carp, farming of red swamp crawfish, and a pond with levee erosion?

5. List methods for prevention and control of aquatic weeds, and review each method.

608

6. What factors must be considered when using a chemical to treat weeds in a pond?

REFERENCES

Abbott, I.A. (editor). 1994. Taxonomy of economic seaweeds. California Sea Grant College, Report No. T-CSGCP-031.

Abbott, I.A., M.S. Foster and L.F. Eklund (editors). 1980. Pacific seaweed aquaculture. Proceedings Symposium Sponsored by the Pacific Area Sea Grant Advisory Program and the California Sea Grant College Program. 228 pp.

Anonymous. 1966. Seaweeds are not weeds. U.S. Department of Interior, Fish and Wildlife Service. Circular 130. 6 pp.

Anonymous. 1979. How to identify and control water weeds and algae. Applied Biochemists Inc. 5300 West County Line Rd., Mequon, Wisconsin 53092.

Avault, J.W., Jr. 1965. Preliminary studies with grass carp for aquatic weed control. Progressive Fish-Culturist 27(4):207-209.

Avault, J.W., Jr. and A. Merkowsky. 1978. Evaluation of hybrid (common x grass) carp for weed control. In Symposium on Culture of Exotic Fishes Auburn, Alabama. Fish Culture Section, American Fisheries Society 1978:184-193.

Avault, J.W., Jr., R.O. Smitherman and E.W. Shell. 1968a. Evaluation of eight species of fish for aquatic weed control. Proceedings of the World Symposium on Warm-Water Pond Fish Culture. FAO Fisheries Report No. 44, 5:109-122.

Avault, J.W., Jr., R.O. Smitherman and E.W. Shell. 1968b. Procedures for overwintering tilapia. Proceedings of the World Symposium on Warm-Water Pond Fish Culture. FAO Fisheries Report No. 44, 4:343-345.

Boyd, C.E. 1968a. Fresh-water plants: A potential source of protein. Economic Botany 22(4):359-368.

Boyd, C.E. 1968b. Evaluation of some common aquatic weeds as possible feed stuffs. Hyacinth Control Journal 7:26-27.

Boyd, C.E. 1969. The nutritive value of three species of water weeds. Economic Botany 23(2):123-127.

Boyd, C.E. 1982. Water quality management for pond fish culture. Amsterdam-Oxford-New York: Elsevier Science Publishing Company Inc. 318 pp.

Correll, D.S. and H.B. Correll. 1972. Aquatic and wetland plants of Southeastern United States. Environmental Protection Agency Clean Water - Water Pollution Control Research Series. 16030 DNL 01/72. U.S. Government Printing Office, Washington, D.C. 1777 pp.

Clugston, J.P. and J.V. Shireman. 1987. Triploid grass carp for aquatic weed control. U.S. Department of Interior, Fish and Wildlife Service. Fish and Wildlife Leaflet 8. Washington, D.C.

Doty, M.S. 1977. Seaweed resources and their culture in the South China Sea Region. South China Sea Fisheries Development and Coordinating Programme. SCS/77/WP/60. 12 pp.

Dinges, R. 1976. Water hyacinth culture for wastewater treatment. Texas Department of Health Resources Division of Wastewater Technology and Surveillance, Austin, Texas. 143 pp.

Durborow, R.M. and C.S. Tucker. 1994. Aquatic weed control in catfish ponds. Kentucky State University, Kentucky Cooperative Extension Program, 12 pp.

Eyles, D.E. and J.L. Robertson. 1963. A guide and key to the aquatic plants of the Southeastern United States. U.S. Department of Interior, Fish and Wildlife Service. Bureau of Sport Fisheries and Wildlife Circular 158. 151 pp.

Fassett, N.C. and E.C. Ogden. 1960. A Manual of Aquatic Plants. Madison, Wisconsin: The University of Wisconsin Press. 405 pp.

Gangstad, E.O. 1986. Freshwater Vegetation Management. Fresno, California: Thomas Publications. 380 pp.

Godfrey, R.K. and J.W. Wooten. 1979. Aquatic and Wetland Plants of Southeastern Unites States. Monocotyledons. University of Georgia Press, Athens. 712 pp.

Godfrey, R.K. and J.W. Wooten. 1981. Aquatic and Wetlands Plants of Southeastern United States. Dicotyledons. University of Georgia Press, Athens. 933 pp.

Hillman, W.S. and D.D. Culley. 1978. The uses of duckweed. American Scientist 66(4):442-451.

Hotchkiss, N. 1967. Underwater and floating-leaved plants of the United States and Canada. Bureau of Sport Fisheries and Wildlife. Resource Publication 44. 124 pp.

Hunter, C.J. and C.W. Nyegaard. 1974. Seaweed farming in Puget Sound. Washington State University, Washington Cooperative Extension Service. Extension Bulletin 654. 10 pp.

Jensen, G.L., W.L. Shelton and L.O. Wilken. 1978. Use of methyltestosterone silastic implants to control sex in grass carp. In Symposium on Culture of Exotic Fishes Auburn, Alabama. Fish Culture Section, American Fisheries Society 1978:200-219.

Klussman, W. and F.G. Lowman. 1971. Common aquatic plants. Texas A & M University, Texas Agricultural Extension Service 5M-7-71. 15 pp.

Langeland, K.A. (editor). 1992. Training manual for aquatic herbicide applicators in the southeastern United States. Louisiana State University Agricultural Center, Louisiana Cooperative Extension Service. Publication 2506. 92 pp.

Lawrence, J.M. and L.W. Weldon. 1965. Identification of aquatic plants. Hyacinth Control Journal 4:5-17.

Lewis, G.W. and J.F. Miller. 1980. Identification and control of weeds in southern ponds. Georgia Cooperative Extension Service, University of Georgia, College of Agriculture, Athens. 27 pp.

Lopinot, A.C. 1965. Aquatic weeds. Illinois Department of Conservation Division of Fisheries. Fishery Bulletin No. 4. 52 pp.

Muenscher, W.C. 1944. Aquatic plants of the United States. Ithaca, New York: Comstock Publishing Company Inc. 374 pp.

National Academy of Sciences. 1976. Making aquatic weeds useful: some perspectives for developing countries. National Academy of Sciences, National Research Council, Washington, D.C. 175 pp.

Palmer, C.M. 1959. Algae in water supplies. U.S. Department of Health, Education and Welfare, Public Health Service. Division of Water Pollution Control. 88 pp.

Rao, G. and N. Subba. 1965. Use of seaweeds directly as human food. Indo-Pacific Fisheries Council Regional Studies No. 2. 32 pp.

Sanders, D., E. Puls, Jr., T. Koske, J.M. Cannon and J.E. Boudreaux. (compilers). 1994. Louisiana's chemical weed control guide for 1994. Louisiana Cooperative Extension Service and the Louisiana Agricultural Experiment Station of the LSU Agricultural Center. Publication 1565 159 pp.

Schmidt, J.C. (editor). 1987. How to Identify and Control Aquatic Weeds and Algae. Applied Biochemists Inc. 5300 West County Line Road, Mequon, Wisconsin 53092 USA. 108 pp.

Seagrave, C. 1988. Aquatic Weed Control. Surrey, England: Fishing News (Books) Ltd. 154 pp.

Skillicorn, P., W. Spira and W. Journey. 1993. Duckweed aquaculture. A World Bank Publication. Washington, D.C. 76 pp.

Stanley, J.G. and K.E. Sneed. 1973. Artificial gynogenesis and its application in genetics and selective breeding of fishes. Proceedings Symposium on Early life History of Fish. Oban, Scotland, 1973. International Council for Exploration of the Sea. 21 pp.

Stucky, J.M., T.J. Monaco and A.D. Worsham. 1980. Identifying seedlings and mature weeds common in the United States and Canada. North Carolina Agricultural Research Service and North Carolina Agricultural Extension Service. 197 pp.

Symoens, J.J. (editor). 1988. Handbook of Vegetation Science. Dordrecht, Boston, London: Kluwer Academic Publisher. 385 pp.

Tiner, R.W. 1993. Field Guide to Coastal Wetland Plants of the Southeastern United States. Amherst: University of Massachusetts Press. 328 pp.

Weldon, L.W., R.D. Blackburn and D. S. Harrison. 1969. Common aquatic weeds. U. S. Department of Agriculture. Agriculture Research Service Agricultural Handbook. No. 352. 43 pp.

Winterringer, G.S. and A.C. Lopinot. 1966. Aquatic plants of Illinois. Department of Registration and Education, Illinois State Museum Division and Department of Conservation, Division of Fisheries. Illinois State Museum Popular Sciences Series Vol. 6. 142 pp.

CHAPTER 13
SEED PRODUCTION AND STOCK IMPROVEMENT

Fry or larvae, collectively called seed, are required for grow-out. For some culture species, seed is still caught from the wild. The milkfish (*Chanos chanos*) farming industry has depended mainly on wild-caught fry to stock grow-out ponds. Eel (*Anguilla* spp.) farms in Japan and elsewhere rely on wild-caught elvers, and for years the seed of many riverine species was obtained from natural waters. Some shrimp (*Penaeus* spp.) farms in Central and South America have relied on wild-caught seed from natural waters. With the increased demand for seed at specific seasons, methods have been developed to produce seed of many culture species in captivity.

Seed propagation of culture species has several advantages. In addition to producing sufficient quantities of seed when needed, better quality and higher survival can be obtained. This is because of better fertilization and hatching success, protection against disease, improved water quality, and use of high quality feeds.

Propagation of seed has another important advantage. It allows the aquaculturist to improve the stock. Through selective breeding, production of hybrids, and other breeding techniques, culture species with desirable traits for grow-out can be propagated.

In this chapter, we discuss the quantity of seed required for grow-out, methods of obtaining seed, various spawning types, and factors affecting reproduction. Then seed production is reviewed for finfish, crustaceans, and mollusks. This includes hatchery and nursery techniques, and transportation of eggs and seed. Stock improvement covers those practical techniques that can be used by the farmer, rather than a review of basic genetics. Selective breeding, crossbreeding, hybridization, creation of a synthetic strain, and use of monosex culture species are all techniques that can be incorporated into a commercial aquaculture operation. Finally, the potential of sperm preservation, polyploidy, and transgenic techniques are discussed.

QUANTITY OF SEED REQUIRED

The quantity of seed required for a commercial aquaculture operation depends on the species to be grown, the type of culture system employed, the level of management, the number of crops produced per year, and the size of operation. The age and size of the seed are also important considerations.

Finfish

   Channel Catfish-- Channel catfish (*Ictalurus punctatus*) are typically grown in earthen ponds, although they also are grown in raceways and floating cages. In fertilized ponds, when fish are not fed, stocking rates may range from 750 to 1,250 fingerlings/ha (300 to 500/ac). In ponds, when fish are fed, Thomas et al. (1982) suggested fingerling stocking rates of 1,853 to 2,470/ha (741 to 988/ac) in watershed ponds, 3,705 to 4,940/ha (1,482 to 1,976/ac) in leveed ponds with a low level of management, and 7,410 to 9,880/ha (2,964 to 3,952/ac) with a high level of management. The last involves use of emergency aeration or flushing to improve water quality. Many farmers stock 12,500 to 15,000/ha (5,000 to 6,000/ac) with stationary aeration. In very intensive culture, Plemmons and Avault (1980) stocked up to 31,250/ha (12,500/ac) in ponds with continuous aeration.

   In 30-m long (100-ft) raceways, Hill et al. (1973) stocked 2,000 fingerling catfish into each of eight connecting raceways. The initial raceway received 2,006 liters of water per minute (530 gpm). They concluded that stocking densities could have been higher. In Idaho, warm artesian water on some farms allows raceway culture of channel catfish. Up to 18,141 kg (40,000 lb) have been produced for each 1,700 liters per min (cubic foot per second or 450 gpm) of water flow in concrete raceways. The water was reused in a series of connecting raceways to obtain this high level of production. Fish are grown to roughly 1 kg (2.2 lb) each, and culture is year-round (Avault 1989).

   In cages, stocking rates have ranged from approximately 71 to 530 fish/m^3 (2 to 15/ft^3). Collins (no date) suggested a stocking rate of 282 to 318 fish/m^3 (8 or 9 fish/ft^3). Schmittou (1970) reported that 494 fingerlings/m^3 (14/ft^3) is an optimum stocking rate. At relatively low stocking rates of less than 177 fish/m^3 (5 fish/ft^3), a pecking order developed and fish fought one another.

   The quantity of seed required annually is approximately equal to the initial stocking rate, since one crop can be expected per year. This crop, however, may be partially harvested on a continuous basis (topping off) throughout the year. Thus, after initial stocking, seed is often required year-round to replace harvested fish. If warm artesian water is available, the growing season is 12 months.

   The size of fingerlings used for stocking may vary from 5 to 25 cm (2 to 10 in), depending on culture strategies. Smaller fingerlings cost less but may require two growing seasons to reach market size. In most instances 15- to 20-cm (6- to 8-in) long fingerlings are preferred since this size should reach market size in 180 to 210 growing days.

   Rainbow Trout-- Rainbow trout (*Oncorhynchus mykiss*) are grown in ponds, often for sportfishing, and in floating pens, but mostly they are grown in raceways. In ponds, seed requirements vary. It depends whether fish subsist on natural organisms or whether they receive supplemental feeding. Spring fingerlings 5 to 8 cm (2 to 3 in) long and 2 or 3 months old, or fall fingerlings 13 to 15 cm (5 to 6 in) long and 7 to 8 months old, have been recommended for stocking ponds (Harbell and Carkner 1981). Stocking rates in natural waters may vary from 250 to 1,250 fingerlings/ha (100 to 500/ac). At lower rates growth is faster, and spring stocked trout may be marketable size by late summer or fall. Seed requirements, when fish receive supplemental feed, vary from 2,500 to 5,000/ha (1,000 to 2,000/ac). Seed requirements are discussed by Eipper (1959), Marriage et al. (1971), Landforce (1972), and Harbell and Carkner (1981).

In some countries, such as Finland and Norway, floating pens are used to grow rainbow trout in fresh and brackish waters. In Finland, Huner (1983) stated that pen stocking rates vary from 21 to 42 fingerlings/m^2 (25 to 50/yd^2). Grow-out may last 3 years, so seed requirements are relatively low.

In raceways, seed requirements are based on water flow rates. Assume that 160,091 to 240,136 kg of fish are produced for each cubic meter per second water flow (10,000 to 15,000 lb/ft^3/second). This high production is possible by reuse of water in a series of connecting raceways. Further assume that a 284 to 340 g (10 to 12 oz) fish is marketable. You can then calculate the number of fingerlings required per crop for each unit volume of water flow. Because trout are often grown in constant-temperature water, seed requirements may be year-round. If pure oxygen is injected into raceways, the carrying capacity and seed requirement could double.

Salmon-- The quantity of seed required for the Atlantic salmon (*Salmo salar*) and the Pacific salmon (*Oncorhynchus* spp.) varies with the culture system -- pond culture, ocean ranching, net-pen culture, and raceways. Overall, seed requirements are similar to those of trout, with a few exceptions. First, seed requirements for ocean ranching are virtually unlimited because salmon forage at sea during the grow-out period that may last several years. The limiting factor is the ability of the shore-based hatchery to produce seed. Allee (1982) reported that in 1981 a total of 287 million salmon fingerlings were released by hatcheries from the state of Washington. In 1970, only 127 million had been released. In Oregon, 70 million salmon were released in 1981.

In other culture systems, such as net-pens, seed requirements are influenced by seasonal changes in water temperature and by the size of fish required for market. Without constant water temperatures for most grow-out systems, the length of time to produce a marketable fish is extended. In some instances when a relatively large marketable fish is required, several years may be needed for grow-out.

Bait Minnows-- The fingerling size of bait minnows is generally the market size, so there is usually no grow-out *per se* as with food fishes. After spawning, eggs or fry are transferred to nursery ponds (See also Chapter 3).

Sunfishes-- The largemouth bass (*Micropterus salmoides*) and bluegill (*Lepomis macrochirus*) are popular sportfish used in fee fishing operations. Bluegill fingerlings are stocked into fertilized ponds in the fall in the southeastern United States at a rate of 2,500 to 3,750/ha (1,000 to 1,500/ac). Bass are stocked the following spring at a rate of 250/ha (100/ac). Once stocked, fish ultimately reproduce and restocking is not necessary.

Common Carp-- Seed requirements for common carp (*Cyprinus carpio*) vary greatly because carp are cultured in a variety of systems throughout the world. In the Philippines, 28 g (1 oz) or larger fingerlings are stocked into rice fields at rates of 3,000 to 4,000/ha (1,200 to 1,600/ac). Grow-out is 80 to 100 days. In Europe, fingerlings are stocked into ponds at rates varying from 300 to 10,000/ha (120 to 4,000/ac), depending on the level of management. In certain countries, such as Austria, it may require 2 to 3 years for grow-out because of a relatively short growing season and because large 2 to 3 kg (4.5 to 7 lb) fish are desired. The Japanese and Israelis have grown carp in intensive culture with very high stocking and turnover rates.

Tilapia-- Various species of tilapia are cultured worldwide in a variety of systems. In subsistence farming, which is used in Liberia, tilapia may be stocked into ponds at 1 to 2 fingerlings/m^2 (1.2 to 2.4/yd^2) and fed agricultural by-products. In cages, 500 to 700 fish/m^3 (654 to 916/yd^3) is a common stocking rate. In intensive culture systems, tilapia have been stocked at 20,000 to even 100,000/ha (8,000 to 40,000/ac). In Jamaica, red tilapia fingerlings are stocked at a rate of 12,500 to 20,000/ha (5,000 to 8,000/ac). This is with daily feeding and no aeration. Fish reach market size of 240 to 250 g (8 to 9 oz) in 140 days. With aeration, the stocking rate can be increased significantly. Warm weather allows year-round production.

Milkfish-- Seed requirements for milkfish in the Philippines and Indonesia may vary from 2,000 to 10,000 fingerlings per ha (800 to 4,000/ac). Fish are often not fed but subsist on cultured pond organisms. In Taiwan, where feeding is the rule, the seed requirement may be double. In most countries, milkfish can be grown year-round, and so the need for seed is continuous. When seed is plentiful in natural waters, it is caught and surplus is stored in holding or nursery ponds.

Crustaceans
Crawfish-- The red swamp crawfish (*Procambarus clarkii*) is usually stocked into ponds at a rate of approximately 56 kg/ha (50 lb/ac). Instead of stocking crawfish by numbers, they are stocked by weight of adult animals. Once stocked, ponds do not require further stocking in subsequent years. In Australia, juveniles

of the native crawfish species may be stocked at approximately 5/m² (6/yd²). Restocking after harvest is necessary because of low or no reproduction in ponds.

Shrimp-- Shrimp (*Penaeus* spp.) are cultured in intensive, semi-intensive, and extensive pond systems. In Japan and Taiwan, seed requirements have reached 160 juveniles/m² (191/yd²) for intensive culture (Lawrence et al. 1985). Semi-intensive stocking rates range from 20 to 40 juveniles/m² (24 to 48/yd²), and extensive only 2.5 to 5 juveniles/m² (3 to 6/yd²). The size and age of larval shrimp stocked vary. Generally, postlarval shrimp 1-day-old (PL-1) up to PL-60 are used. A PL-20 is a popular age for many culture strategies. In tropical countries, up to two and a half crops of shrimp can be produced a year if seed is available.

Prawns-- Prawns (*Macrobrachium* spp.) are similar to shrimp regarding seed requirements. Stocking densities of postlarvae (20 to 30 days old) or nursed juveniles (60 + days old) vary from 25,000 to 250,000/ha (10,000 to 100,000/ac), with 125,000/ha (50,000/ac) a common rate. In tropical countries, up to two and a half crops can be obtained per year. One crop is the rule in temperate countries.

Mollusks

The quantity of seed required for most molluskan culture systems is far less exacting than that for finfish or crustaceans. Rather than using known numbers, seed quantity is estimated by weight, by bushels or other volumetric measures, and by visual observation. Use of cultchless seed oysters and clams is more exact, since it is possible to get a more accurate count before stocking.

Oysters-- Oyster (*Crassostrea* spp. and *Ostrea* spp.) seed attached to cultch may be spread on growing grounds at densities of 31,250 to 60,000 kg/ha (27,906 to 53,580 lb/ac). If *Crassostrea gigas* seed is used, requirements may range from 25,000 to 35,000 spat per ha (10,000 to 14,000/ac) (Burrell 1985). In Louisiana, approximately 500 to 750 sacks (one sack equals 1.25 to 1.5 bushels) of oysters attached to cultch are planted per hectare (200 to 300 sacks/ac).

Oysters may reach market size in less than a year in warm-growing regions, such as Louisiana. It may take as long as 5 years in New England. Use of cultchless oyster seed greatly reduces the bulk handled. Where 1 million spat would equal about 167 bushels of seed on cultch, the same amount of cultchless seed is equal to about 1 liter (0.3 gal) (Clark and Langmo 1979). If grown in trays stacked in columns of three, up to 625,000 individual seed oysters can be used for each hectare (250,000/ac).

Mussels-- Seed for mussel (primarily *Mytilus edulis*) culture is typically collected from the wild (Lutz and Darling 1980). The quantity of seed required varies with the method of culture. When using the French bouchot culture method, an unknown quantity of larvae is attached to poles or to ropes which are later wrapped around poles. In bottom culture, as practiced in the Netherlands, mussel seed is dredged from natural populations of juveniles 8 to 13 mm (0.3 to 0.5 in) long, and seed is transported to culture plots. Rafts are used to culture mussels in Spain. Each raft may support 700 ropes. In the fall, young seed mussels, 5 to 8 mm long (0.2 to 0.3 in), are gathered wild from the shoreline and wrapped onto ropes. In Sweden and elsewhere, long-line culture is practiced. A series of buoyed horizontal lines has vertical lines suspended on which natural seed is collected directly.

Clams-- Clam seed is typically produced in hatcheries. In South Carolina, clam (*Mercenaria mercenaria*) seed 8 to 13 mm (0.3 to 0.5 in) long is spread on water bottoms at densities of 4,304 to 10,760 clams per square meter (400 to 1,000/ft^2) (Manzi and Whetstone 1981). In Washington state, Manila clam (*Venerupis japonica*) seed 3 to 4 mm (0.1 to 0.15 in) long is planted on water bottoms at experimental rates ranging from 200 to 1,700/m^2 (19 to 158/ft^2) (Anderson et al. 1982).

METHODS OF OBTAINING SEED
Purchasing Seed
Seed of finfish, crustaceans, and mollusks may be bought from commercial hatcheries or collectors. The seed may be in the form of eggs, larvae and fry, or juveniles and fingerlings. Some aquaculturists produce their own seed. However, seed production or collection of certain culture species is rather complex, and aquaculturists usually rely on specialized hatcheries or collectors.

Finfish-- Most channel catfish farmers who buy seed buy fingerlings. The cost for years has been about 1 to 1.5 cents for each 2.5 cm (1 in) in length. Most farmers prefer a 15- to 20-cm (6- to 8-in) long fingerling. Larger fingerlings are usually more expensive because it costs more for hatcheries to produce them. Smaller fingerlings may require two growing seasons to reach market size. During shortages of fingerlings, farmers may buy fry and grow them to fingerling size in nursery ponds. Experienced farmers often produce their own seed.

Most rainbow trout farmers usually buy eyed eggs for 1 to 1.5 cents per egg plus shipping costs. They hatch the eggs themselves. The ideal water temperature for maturation, spawning, and incubation up to the eyed stage is around 9° to 12°C (48° to 54°F). Trout farmers in Idaho have 15°C (59°F) water, a temperature at which eyed eggs incubate well. Trout farmers in North Carolina and elsewhere in the East also purchase eyed eggs. A few specialize in fingerling production. Because some trout hatcheries have a long history, improved strains such as the Kamloops can be offered to farmers. Eyed eggs of Atlantic salmon may cost 6 to 12 cents each.

Seed of milkfish and eel is usually bought. Eel juveniles, called elvers, are collected from the wild. Some countries such as Japan place quotas on the number that can be harvested. Various tilapia species spawn readily in captivity with no special attention. Nevertheless in certain areas such as Sukabumi, Indonesian farmers often buy seed. Some farmers may buy fry, grow them to fingerling size, and then sell the fingerlings.

Crustaceans-- Brood stock of the red swamp crawfish is usually bought by the kilogram from other farmers and stocked directly into grow-out ponds. In essence these ponds serve for reproduction, rearing, and grow-out. The going price for marketable crawfish is used for purchase of brood stock. Farmers often purchase brood stock toward the end of the harvesting season when supply is greatest and prices are lowest. Prices overall have been around $1.00 per kg (45 cents lb). Near Blentarp, Sweden, one hatchery has sold larval crawfish (*Pacifastacus leniusculus*) for about 50 cents each.

Prawns (*Macrobrachium rosenbergii*) are usually sold while in the postlarval stage. Prices have ranged from less than $18 to $25 per 1,000. Some commercial hatcheries also sell nursed juveniles. These are young that are grown for a month or so after first reaching the postlarval stage. Penaeid shrimps, too, are usually sold by the thousand. *Penaeus monodon*, for example, is often sold as PL-20. The price varies based on demand and availability, and it has run from less than $15 to $20 per 1,000. Hatcheries specialize in production of prawns and shrimp. Since the spawning and seed production of *Macrobrachium* are far less complex than that for penaeid shrimp, prawn farmers are more apt to produce their own seed than are shrimp farmers.

Mollusks-- Oyster seed may be sold attached to cultch or sold cultchless. In Japan, oyster seed (*Crassostrea gigas*) is collected on oyster shell cultch. The cultch may be cut into several pieces and packed into wooden boxes 90 x 45 x 30 cm (35 x 18 x 12 in). The numbers of oyster larvae per box are estimated to determine price. For years, oyster farmers on the west coast of the United States have bought seed oysters from Japan. In Louisiana, oyster seed has been provided free to farmers by the Louisiana Department of Wildlife and Fisheries (LDWF). Beginning 1 September, for 2 to 3 months, farmers can harvest seed oysters at no cost from spawning grounds maintained by the LDWF.

Obtaining wild oyster seed is sometimes unpredictable, and hatcheries have developed to fill the shortfall of oyster seed. New techniques for seed production include production of cultchless oysters, seed not attached to substrate (cultch). Cultchless seed is easier to handle and ship. When oyster larvae reach the eyed stage, they are easy to transport. Numbers can be estimated volumetrically. Larvae in plastic bags are put into Styrofoam boxes and cooled with ice. They can be mailed for up to 48 hours.

Like oysters, seed of mussels and clams is sometimes in short supply. Collectors provide mussel seed, and hatcheries produce clam seed for sale and distribution. Clams do not require cultch as oysters and mussels do in nature, so their larvae are always sold cultchless.

Collecting Wild Seed

Finfish-- Milkfish aquaculture is a classic example of collecting wild seed, and it is described in detail by Villaluz (1986). Spawning occurs in the sea not far from the coastline. The pelagic larvae are concentrated by eddies. After 2 to 3 weeks fry migrate to shore where they enter coastal wetlands. They remain here for about 1 month until they reach the juvenile stage. Seed collectors exploit this migration to catch milkfish fry and fingerlings in great numbers. Most fry are caught just before and after the new and full moon periods. Other factors affecting capture include tidal flow, water turbidity, and availability of shelter. The catch is better during flood tides. In clear water, fry see better and can avoid capture. They often gather near structures or shelters.

Fry are captured by using devices to concentrate them, and nets and seines are used to scoop them up (Figure 13.1).

Figure 13.1 Fry collecting device for milkfish fry used in the Philippines.

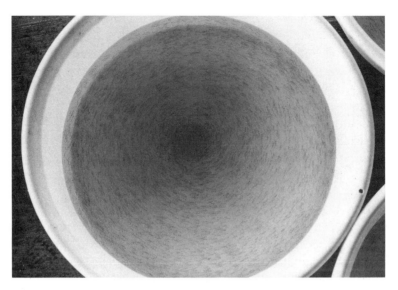

Figure 13.2 Pan used to estimate fry numbers.

Figure 13.3 Fry being poured from pan into earthen jar.

Fry barriers or fences made of fine-mesh nylon attached to poles may be set perpendicular to the shore. They extend 10 to 50 m (33 to 164 ft) into the water. Skimming nets or double-stick nets are used to catch the fish. In Indonesia, a rope is used to concentrate fry that swim near the surface. A 20 m (66 ft) rope is laid in a wide circle, and fry are caught with skimming nets. Once captured, milkfish fry are placed into pans to estimate numbers (Figure 13.2) and then poured into earthen jars or water-tight bamboo baskets (Figure 13.3). Seawater is diluted gradually with fresh water. Fry may be fed yolk of hard-boiled eggs, pulverized rice, or dried wheat flour. Dealers who buy from collectors may store fry in containers for several days or even weeks. Numbers are reduced in holding containers; clean water is periodically added to replace old water, and feeding is continued.

Eel culture has historically relied on wild-caught elvers. Usui (1974) described the procedure. Elvers of all eel species from temperate zones generally enter rivers in the spring when water temperatures reach 8°C (46°F). Elvers do not, however, arrive at all river mouths at the same time. The areas nearest to spawning grounds receive elvers earlier than more distant areas. Some large rivers receive huge numbers. The Loire in France has received between 50 million to 100 million each year. The River Bann in Northern England has produced up to 23 million elvers a year.

There are specialists who capture and sell wild elvers. Some serve as brokers and purchase live elvers from local dip-net fishermen. More elaborate capture methods include setting a fine-mesh net across a river mouth or constructing an elver trap at a weir or waterfall. Once captured, elvers are usually held in tanks of circulating water to await distribution.

Fry of certain riverine finfish historically were captured from flooded rivers with large conical bag-nets during the monsoon months (Chaudhuri and Tripathi 1979). The Indian and Chinese carps normally spawn in large flowing rivers, and for years the only source of these fry was from capture. Today, availability of freeze-dried pituitary for hormone injection allows seed from these species to be produced in hatcheries.

Crustaceans-- Penaeid shrimp farming has depended for years almost entirely on wild seed. India, and later Ecuador and a number of other shrimp-growing countries, allowed wild larval shrimp to enter grow-out ponds with the tides. In Louisiana, de la Bretonne and Avault (1971) stocked natural impoundments with wild postlarvae brown (*Penaeus aztecus*) and white shrimp (*P. setiferus*). The concentration of postlarval shrimp was monitored with a plankton net during high tides. When the concentration appeared the highest, postlarvae were allowed to enter the impoundment over the crest of the weir. As the tide ebbed, a screen was placed across the weir to prevent exit of shrimp. This tide-exchange method was repeated with each high tide throughout the spring and summer.

Mollusks-- The oyster industry throughout the world was developed by collection of wild seed. Oyster culture along the Gulf of Mexico involved transplanting seed oysters from natural spawning beds in brackish water to private or leased growing areas in more saline waters. Oyster reefs in brackish water produce many young, but only infrequently do they produce marketable oysters. In the Gulf of Mexico, the American oyster (*Crassostrea virginica*) has two spawning peaks -- in the spring when water temperatures reach about 20° to 21°C (68° to 70°F) and again in the fall when temperatures drop back to 21°C. Just prior to the spawning peak, cultch in the form of oyster or clam shell is planted in the setting area.

If cultch is put out too soon, barnacles may set on the cultch and compete for space with the spat oysters. If cultch is planted too late, spat fall could be missed. Sometimes wire bags containing shells are set out to capture seed. After spawning, veliger larvae are free swimming for 10 to 20 days and are part of the plankton system. Generally, by the 12th day the larvae get heavy from shell development, settle to the bottom, and attach to cultch. When oyster seed grows to 2.5 to 5.0 cm in length (1 to 2 in), it is removed from beds with tongs or dredges and moved to growing grounds. Spawning and seed collection of tropical oysters are discussed by Angell (1986).

Although mussels have been spawned in hatcheries, production of spat is expensive. Wherever mussels are grown throughout the world, it is based on the collection of wild seed. Numerous collecting materials have been set out for mussel spat and include poles, ropes, polyethylene mesh, and natural grass. Once collected, the density of spat may be reduced on collectors and spat moved to growing waters. Lutz (1980) summarized spat collection.

Commercial clam fisheries in the United States have relied almost entirely on wild populations. Clams produced naturally were harvested. No management was involved. As various clam species were investigated for aquaculture, clam hatcheries were developed.

Producing Seed in Captivity

There are two basic methods to produce seed in captivity. Natural spawning involves the stocking or pairing of culture species in a natural habitat and later harvesting the seed produced. The brood stock must be of a suitable age and size; and environmental conditions, such as water temperature and day length, must be within a proper range. The second method, induced spawning, involves use of techniques normally not required for natural spawning. These might include manipulation of water temperature, photoperiod, or salinity to induce spawning (Figure 13.4). Eye stalk ablation of shrimp and hormone injection of finfish are commonly used to induce spawning (Figures 13.5, 13.6).

Figure 13.4 Mike Pursley of the LSU Agricultural Center checks for eggs of red drum (*Sciaenops occellatus*) in a room where temperature, photoperiod, and salinity are controlled.

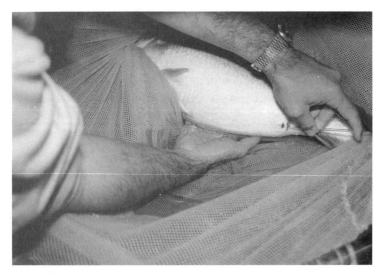

Figure 13.5 Taking an egg sample of the striped bass (*Morone saxatilis*).

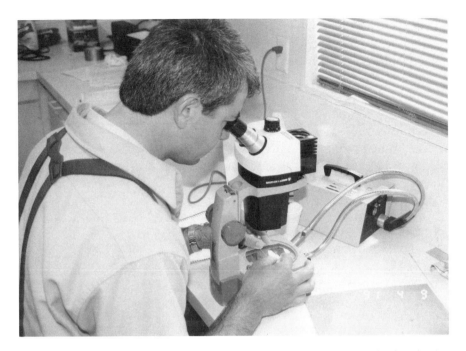

Figure 13.6 Biologist of the Louisiana Department of Wildlife and Fisheries checks egg development of striped bass to predict time of ovulation prior to hormone injection.

SPAWNING TYPES

As aquaculture continues to expand, much attention has focused on propagation of seed in captivity. This is particularly true for new culture species considered for aquaculture (Avault 1988). To spawn a culture species, you must first understand how it reproduces in nature. In this section, we discuss different spawning types and in the next section factors affecting reproduction.

Riverine Spawners

The Chinese carps, Indian major carps, and striped bass (*Morone saxatilis*) are examples of riverine spawners. The grass carp (*Ctenopharyngodon idella*) is a typical riverine spawner. Its spawning season in China extends from April to about mid-August (Lin 1935). Spawning fish congregate when conditions are suitable. Requirements include a sudden rise of water exceeding 1.2 m (4 ft) within 12 hours, caused by a heavy rain upstream, a water temperature of 26° to 30°C (79° to 86°F), a current of 3.7 to 6.1 km (2.3 to 3.8 miles) per hour, and extensive rapids at the upper end of the spawning ground. Spawning fish release eggs, about 100,000 per female, and sperm into the current. Fertilized eggs drift with the current and hatch in about 34 hours. Thus, the current must be maintained during this period or eggs will sink and perish. Moreover the river must be long enough. If we assume a current of 3.7 km/hour and hatching in 34 hours, the river should be at least 126 km (78 miles) long. That is why only large rivers, such as the West River in China and Amur River in Russia, are suitable for reproduction.

Pelagic or Open Seas Spawners

Pelagic spawners are somewhat similar to riverine spawners; that is eggs and milt are released into open water. The word pelagic pertains to open oceans rather than water next to land or inland waters. Shrimp spawn in offshore waters where eggs and sperm are released into the open ocean. One female may produce from 100,000 up to 1 million eggs. Motoh (1981) noted that *Penaeus monodon* females produced from 248,000 to 811,000 eggs. Floating fertilized eggs usually hatch within 18 to 24 hours, and larvae drift toward the shore. Oysters, too, spawn in ocean waters. The cupped oysters (*Crassostrea* spp.) and flat oysters (*Ostrea* spp.) differ, though, in their reproduction. *Crassostrea* releases sex products directly into the water where fertilization occurs. A single female may release 1 million eggs. *Ostrea* males expel sperm that are drawn in by females. Eggs are retained in the pallial cavity where fertilization and early development occur. After 8 to 10 days, larvae are expelled as free-swimming veligers.

Adhesive Spawners

Some culture species have adhesive eggs that attach to vegetation or other substrate. Goldfish (*Carassius auratus*) and common carp, like riverine and pelagic spawners, provide no parental care. The common carp differs from Chinese and Indian major carps in that it can breed naturally in ponds, provided that aquatic vegetation is available for attachment of adhesive eggs. When the water temperature reaches 23° to 24°C (73° to 75°F) and the water level is rising, breeding fish congregate. Several males may chase a female who expels eggs onto vegetation, and males release sperm. One female may produce several hundred thousand eggs.

In the absence of vegetation, hay or other substrate can be placed along the water's edge (Figure 13.7). The golden shiner (*Notemigonus crysoleucas*) spawns on grass mats, and the fathead minnow (*Pimephales promelas*) will spawn on the undersides of boards.

Nest Builders

Nest builders, such as the bluegill and largemouth bass, make depressions on the pond bottom by sweeping away debris. Bluegill are gregarious, and you normally find numerous bluegill nests side by side in a bed. Largemouth bass are territorial, so nests are spaced out. After egg laying, nests are guarded. Bluegill may produce 20,000 or more eggs per spawn, whereas largemouth bass produce

5,000 to 10,000. Bluegill may spawn up to three times per year, whereas largemouth bass spawn only once.

Figure 13.7 Jay Stander of the LSU Agricultural Center puts hay along the pond edge as spawning substrate for koi.

Trout and salmon make a nest, called a redd, on stream bottoms. The female prepares a nest by sweeping the bottom with her tail. Males respond to her actions. After spawning, the redd is covered with gravel but is not guarded. The species making up the Pacific salmon group typically die after spawning. Trout species and the Atlantic salmon may spawn again the next year. The number of eggs per female is relatively low. Leitritz and Lewis (1980) noted that one domesticated rainbow trout strain produced about 1,553 eggs per fish when 2 years old and 2,210 eggs when 3 years old.

Some species of fish produce specialized nests. An example is the sepat siam (*Trichogaster pectoralis*) that lives in rivers and swamps. The male prepares a frothy bubble nest. Fertilized eggs are collected in his mouth and spit into the nest.

Cavity Spawners

The channel catfish, found in streams and ponds, requires a cavity to spawn. The cavity may be a hollow log or a hole in the bank. In ponds, spawning containers, such as cans, may be used (Figure 13.8). Fish spawn once a year. A female produces 6,615 to 8,820 eggs per kilogram of body weight (3,000 to 4,000/lb). Eggs are held together in a jelly-like mass.

Figure 13.8 Spawning containers used for channel catfish.

Mouth Brooders

Tilapia are typical mouth brooders. Fertilized eggs are held in a parent's mouth until they hatch. After eggs hatch, the parent broods fry in the mouth for approximately 5 days. *Tilapia melanopleura* and *T. zilli* are exceptions. They make nests on the bottom of the pond (Figure 13.9). Eggs are deposited in the nest and fertilized. Hatching takes place about 5 days after spawning.

Figure 13.9 Nests of *Tilapia melanopluera*.

Livebearers

Some fish species produce live young. Members of the families Poeciliidae (livebearer family) and Cyprinodontidae retain fertilized ova within their bodies, and young are born alive. (Note: a name ending in idae denotes a family name.) Males of some species have intromittent organs for introducing the spermatozoa into the body of the female. The sperm may be in lumps rather than liquid to avoid loss before fertilization.

Bodily Attachment

Females of some crustaceans hold eggs on the underside of the tail after fertilization. Prawns (*Macrobrachium*) may hold from 10,000 to 100,000 eggs in this manner until they hatch. Lobsters and crabs also hold eggs on their bodies until hatching. Crawfish, such as the red swamp crawfish, typically mate during the summer. The female stores the sperm in a seminal receptacle. In the fall of the year, several hundred eggs are produced. These are fertilized with stored sperm. Eggs attach to the underside of the tail with a sticky substance called glair. After hatching in 2 to 3 weeks, young remain attached for a few days and ultimately drop off. Figure 13.10 shows a female redclaw crawfish (*Cherax quadricarinatus*) in berry with eggs.

Figure 13. 10 Female redclaw crawfish with bodily attachment of eggs.

FACTORS AFFECTING REPRODUCTION OF CULTURE SPECIES
Size and Age at Maturity

We must know the size and age of a culture species when it first reaches sexual maturity, the optimum range in size and age for reproduction, and when fecundity begins to wane. This knowledge will allow us to plan production of an estimated number of fry or larvae each year. It would be folly to anticipate seed production from brood stock if the stock is too young. Similarly, fecundity diminishes as brood stock becomes too old. To plan, younger age groups should be grown so that there is an orderly replacement of brood stock each year or as needed.

Finfish-- Channel catfish become sexually mature as early as 2 years of age and as small as 340 g (12 oz) (Tucker 1985). The size and age at maturity are influenced by the length of the growing season and food supply. For reliable spawning of brood stock, fish should be at least 3 years old and weigh at least 1.4 kg (3 lb). In the northern part of the United States, where there is a shorter growing season, even older fish may be required. Channel catfish are usually productive spawners for 3 to 4 years at which time fecundity drops and fish become too large to handle.

Rainbow trout may become sexually mature when 2 years old if they are raised in relatively warm water (16°C or 61°F) to induce fast growth. Salmon spend several years at sea before returning to fresh water to spawn. Each species and each strain of each species has rather exacting prerequisites for spawning (Childerhose and Trim 1979).

Bait minnows become sexually mature at various ages and sizes, depending on the species. The golden shiner reaches sexual maturity at 1 year of age and at a length of about 6 cm (2.5 in). Brood stock 10 to 15 cm (4 to 6 in) long is preferred. Fathead minnows more than 5 cm (2 in) in length and 1 year old are usually mature. Goldfish (*Carassius auratus*) approximately 20 to 30 cm (8 to 12 in) long and weighing 113 to 340 g (0.25 to 0.75 lb) are desirable as brood fish, although fish 10 cm (4 in) long can be used.

The many species of sunfishes (family Centrarchidae) reach sexual maturity at various sizes and ages. Swingle and Smith (1950) gave detailed information for bluegill and largemouth bass. Bluegill may spawn when they are less than 1 year of age. In Alabama, bluegill hatched in June in ponds with abundant food reproduced the following September. They weighed from 28 to 56 g (1 to 2 oz) and were approximately 4 months old. This was unusual. Most bluegill spawn when about 1 year old, if at that time they weigh 43 g (1.5 oz) or more. Largemouth bass must be at least 10 to 12 months of age, and the smallest bass to spawn was between 142 to 170 g (5 and 6 oz). Year-old bass weighing less than 113 g (4 oz) failed to spawn.

The common carp in temperate countries usually reaches sexual maturity when 2 years old. Note, however, that four subspecies have been recognized (Kirpichnikov 1966). Jhingran and Pullin (1988) listed the size and age at first maturity of common carp under different climatic conditions. Here are examples: Europe 3 to 4 years at 1,500 to 2,500 g (3.3 to 5.5 lb), Japan 0.2 to 0.3 years at 500 to 900 g (1.1 to 2 lb), and Indonesia 1 to 1.5 years at 1,000 to 2,000 g (2.2 to

4.4 lb). The grass carp may reach sexual maturity in 2 years for males and 3 years for females if growth is rapid. In ponds at Auburn University, Alabama, young grass carp have grown as much as 454 g (1 lb) a month.

Tilapia reach sexual maturity rapidly. The Java tilapia (*Oreochromis mossambicus*) may reproduce when only 2 to 3 months old and less than 28 to 56 g (1 to 2 oz) in size. Other less fecund species, such as *O. niloticus*, are older and larger at maturity.

The milkfish has been spawned in captivity using wild brood fish or brood stock raised in captivity. Generally, female milkfish are able to reach sexual maturation in natural or artificial environments at 5 years of age; males may reach maturity around 4 years of age (Kuo 1985).

Crustaceans-- The red swamp crawfish reaches sexual maturity when about 6 to 12 months of age and 10 to 20 g (0.4 to 0.8 oz) in size. If hatched in the fall or winter, crawfish usually become sexually mature 1 year later. If hatched in the spring, crawfish growth is uninterrupted and they may reproduce the following fall. Hooks on the walking legs of males (form 1 crawfish) indicate sexually mature crawfish. The life span of this species is 1 to 2 years. In Europe, the native crawfish, *Astacus astacus*, may require 2 to 3 years to reach sexual maturity because of the short growing season.

The size and age when penaeid shrimp first reach sexual maturity vary with the species and whether the species occurs in tropical or temperate waters. Motoh (1981) gave specific data for *Penaeus monodon*. As a criterion, he defined sexual maturity as the minimum size of *P. monodon* possessing spermatozoa inside the terminal ampoule in males and inside the thelycum in females. From the wild, most males 37 mm (1.5 in) carapace length (CL) and most females 47 mm (1.9 in) CL possessed spermatozoa. Brood stock from brackishwater ponds reached sexual maturity at smaller sizes, 31 and 39 mm (1.2 and 1.5 in) CL for males and females, respectively.

The prawn, *Macrobrachium rosenbergii*, will reach sexual maturity in less than 1 year in temperate countries. In Louisiana, some postlarval prawns stocked into grow-out ponds in mid-May reached sexual maturity by mid October. Females carried eggs on the underside of the abdomen. In males, when an individual reached the blue claw stage, it was assumed to be sexually mature. Sexually mature females ranged in size from 15 to 20 g (0.5 to 0.7 oz) and males 20 to 30 g (0.7 to 1 oz).

Mollusks-- Because most oyster and mussel seed are derived from nature, there is less known when sexual maturity is first reached. Clams (*Mercenaria mercenaria*) reach sexual maturity in less than a year and under 20 mm (0.8 in) in anterior-posterior length (Menzel 1971). *Mya arenaria* and *Tapes japonica* appear to reach sexual maturity at relatively small sizes, whereas *Spisula* *solidissima* and *Arctica islandica* are considerably larger (and older) at sexual maturity (Manzi 1985).

Growth and Condition

Brood stock of all culture species that are in healthy condition will reproduce if sexually mature and other factors are satisfactory. The healthy condition must occur not only just before reproduction but also during maturation. For example, the largemouth bass in the southern United States begins egg development around September and spawns beginning in April. Thus egg development takes 7 months. Bluegill require 4 to 6 weeks for egg formation. In one study, bluegill averaging 90 g (0.2 lb) were stocked into several different spawning ponds (Swingle 1962). Although all bluegill weighed about the same at stocking, some had lost weight, some had gained weight, and others remained their original weight. Those that lost 50% of their original weight (from 180 to 90 g) produced no eggs. Those bluegill that neither lost nor gained weight produced 708 young per female. Those doubling their weight produced an average of 1,766 young.

Temperature

The water temperature has a profound effect on the growth and well-being of a culture species and whether or not it reproduces. You must know the minimum water temperature at which a species will spawn. It is also important to know the maximum water temperature and the optimum temperature. Refer to Chapter 6 and Table 6.1 for a review.

Season of the Year

The season of the year may affect reproduction of a culture species. In temperate countries, such as the United States, four seasons are noted: spring, summer, fall, and winter. Some species, such as the largemouth bass, spawn in the spring as daylight becomes increasingly longer each day. They are sometimes referred to as long-day spawners. Others, such as trout, spawn naturally in the fall as daylight decreases each day. They are sometimes referred to as short-day spawners. The water temperature interacts with the photoperiod as a factor in reproduction, temperature being the dominant factor of the two. Figures 13.11a and b show a building used to control photoperiod for trout reproduction.

In tropical countries, seasons are marked by the rainy season, dry season, monsoons, typhoons, and other major climatic occurrences. Flooding during certain times of the year stimulates the common carp, Chinese carps, and Indian major carps, and it triggers the onset of spawning. Riverine spawners often react to a rapid rise or fall of water as a stimulus. To duplicate this, a spawning pond can be built with a deeper sump (Figure 13.12). The shallower parts of the pond remain dry. Vegetative growth is encouraged if the culture species being spawned has adhesive eggs. When spawning is desired, water is flooded into the pond so that the water rises rapidly and floods the shallower area of the pond. Brood fish leave the sump and spawn in the shallows. Schuster (1949) described this technique for *Puntius javanicus*.

a   b

Figure 13.11a Building used by a United States commercial trout-egg producer to vary photoperiod to effect maturation any time of the year. Note no windows. **b** Inside of building showing tanks where brood stock are held.

Figure 13.12 Pond showing sump in Java, Indonesia.

Sometimes a culture species grown under ideal conditions will not reproduce. In one instance, the channel catfish was introduced from the United States (temperate country) into the Philippines (tropical) for study. After several years, the fish failed to reproduce, although the water temperature was ideal for growth. It is possible that the channel catfish must have a period when cool waters are a requirement for the maturation cycle. In the Philippines, there is no cool or cold season. One catfish farmer in Idaho had the same problem. Fish grew well in heated artesian water, but failed to reproduce when held in the warm water year-round.

Sometimes the season of the year is distinguished as wet or dry, or it may be marked by adverse environmental conditions. These factors may affect reproduction. The onset of dry summer months triggers the red swamp crawfish to mate and burrow underground. *Artemia* living in the Great Salt Lake in Utah often produce eggs (cysts) at the onset of extreme cold weather.

Physical Properties of Water

Physical properties of water affect reproduction of many species. Various culture species, such as riverine carps, must have flowing water; others, such as fishes in the sunfish family (Centrarchidae), reproduce best in standing water. Limnologists often refer to flowing water as a lotic environment and standing water as a lentic environment. Pelagic spawners live in a more stable environment.

Muddy or silty water may adversely affect reproduction by clogging gills and smothering eggs. Suspended silt resulting in turbidity greater than 100 ppm interferes with largemouth bass reproduction. Most sunfish will not reproduce at a turbidity of 150 to 170 ppm. Muddy water may be caused by such factors as cattle wading in the pond or by wind. High winds may result in wave action that causes an impediment to spawning. The unintentional lowering of the water level in a spawning pond may adversely affect nest builders. Many such species often make nests near the levee. If the water level drops suddenly, nest building and mating may discontinue.

Chemical Properties of Water

Salinity, dissolved oxygen, pH, and other water quality parameters have an effect on reproduction. Generally, if the water quality is suitable for growth and general well-being of a culture species, it will be suitable for reproduction. Salinity, however, needs some discussion and the reader is referred to Chapters 6 and 7 and Table 6.3.

Social Factors and Stimuli

Certain riverine species, such as the grass carp, seem to require a critical mass for optimum natural spawning. The congregation of a number of spawning fish acts as a stimulus. The release of sperm into the water by the American oyster stimulates other oysters nearby. Certain nest builders, such as the bluegill and tilapia, appear to be stimulated by the presence of nearby spawning fish.

Sometimes a species may become too crowded for optimum reproduction. When very crowded, trout or salmon may destroy the redds of other spawning fish while in the process of preparing their own nests. Bluegill, if overcrowded in a pond, may resort to eating eggs of other species, such as the largemouth bass. Swingle (1953) reported on a "repressive factor" that inhibited the spawning of overcrowded goldfish. He postulated that the repressive factor was a secretion or excretion from the goldfish themselves that exerted a hormone-like repressive effect on maturation of eggs, or at least prevented egg-laying. When a few pairs of goldfish were taken from a crowded pond and restocked into a pond with fresh water, spawning occurred. When all but a few pair of fish were removed from the pond containing the repressive factor, fish still would not spawn. Swingle (1953) reported this phenomenon with the bigmouth buffalo (*Ictiobus cyprinellus*), the common carp, and the bluegill.

Nesting Sites and Substrate

Suitable nesting sites and substrate are prerequisites for natural reproduction of various species. Trout and salmon require gravel stream bottoms. If bottoms are clay or silt, fertilized eggs would smother. This is of no consequence when salmonids are spawned in captivity. As already noted, channel catfish require cavities to spawn, and common carp and other species with adhesive eggs require vegetation or similar substrate. The red swamp crawfish typically burrows underground as part of its natural biological cycle. This would be difficult if the substrate was sand. The burrow or hole would keep filling up. Prawns (*Macrobrachium rosenbergii*) may mate in ponds, and egg-bearing females are often collected from grow-out ponds. The presence of structure or hiding places facilitates mating for this highly pugnacious species. Penaeid shrimp, which are pelagic spawners, do not have specific requirements for nesting sites or substrate. Oysters and other mollusks require a firm bottom for an optimum spawning site. Cultch or substrate must be present for oyster and mussel larvae attachment.

SEED PRODUCTION
Finfish

Channel Catfish-- Production of fingerling catfish was reviewed by Jensen et al. (1983), Tucker (1985), and Jensen (1987).

There are several methods for selecting brood stock. Some culturists obtain brood stock from the wild, but this is not the preferred source. Wild channel catfish are often unreliable spawners the first year or two. Moreover, fingerlings produced may be slow growers and less adaptable to crowded conditions, disease, and poor water quality (Burnside et al. 1975). The best source of brood stock is from a hatchery that can document the origin, age, and history of its fish. Brood stock is sometimes taken from grow-out ponds, with larger fish being selected. This is not always a good practice. Many farmers harvest marketable fish from grow-out ponds by topping off; fingerlings are restocked to replace those removed. Therefore, it is not always possible to obtain the true age, origin, or history of individual fish. Moreover, you might unknowingly select slower growing fish that were good seine evaders, rather than select the fastest growing fish.

A long-term program for brood stock development is to obtain fry or fingerlings of an improved strain. These fish should be the same age and originate from many females to avoid inbreeding. When the fish become large enough to be identified by sex, the fastest growing fish can be selected (Figure 13.13). A ratio of three females for every two males is suggested because one male can mate with two or three females in a single spawning season.

Figure 13.13 James W. Avault, Jr. of the LSU Agricultural Center with healthy brood channel catfish.

Brood stock should be maintained in holding ponds at weights not exceeding 672 to 896 kg/ha (600 to 800 lb/ac). This allows space for fish to grow. A convenient size pond is from 0.4 to 2 ha (1 to 5 ac). Regardless, not all brood fish should be held in one pond in case of a disease outbreak. Some fish farmers separate females and males to avoid fighting just before the spawning season.

There are several strategies for spawning catfish. Brood stock can be stocked loose in open ponds, or fish can be paired and stocked in spawning pens. After spawning, there are several options for handling eggs and fry.

In open pond spawning, brood stock is introduced into ponds at a rate not exceeding 1,344 kg/ha (1,200 lb/ac). When the water temperature reaches 24°C (75°F), spawning containers such as milk cans, nail kegs, ammunition cans, and wooden boxes are placed 1 to 9 m (approximately 1 to 10 yd) apart in shallow water. The open end faces the center of the pond. Each container should be marked with a numbered float. Spawning containers should be provided for 50% to 90% of breeding pairs. If at any time spawning begins to diminish, water can be flushed through the pond. Older and larger fish usually spawn first.

In pen spawning, individual fish are paired and stocked into pens secured to the pond bottom (Figure 13.14). Pens are usually constructed of wire mesh that restricts brood fish from escaping and allows water circulation. A pen 122 to 244 cm (4 to 8 ft) is adequate.

Figure 13.14 Spawning pens for channel catfish. Photo by the U.S. Department of Agriculture, R.W. Oertel, photographer.

Check spawning containers for eggs every 2 to 3 days (Figure 13.15). If eggs are found, leave them in the container for the male to hatch, or bring them into the hatchery. If hatched by the male, fry can be allowed to swim out into the pond. This method is easy, but it is hard to keep track of fry produced, and survival of fry is sometimes poor because of insect and other predation.

636

Figure 13.15 Ken Rust of the LSU Agricultural Center removes eggs from spawining container.

Another choice is to remove fry from the spawning container after hatching. To do this, you must be able to predict the approximate number of days for eggs to hatch. At 25.5°C (78°F) it takes about 7 to 8 days for eggs to hatch, and for each 1°C (approximately 2°F) above or below 25.5°C subtract or add 1 day, respectively, to hatching time. There is some room for error because newly hatched fry remain in the spawning container as sac fry for approximately 3 days. Once fry are found, they can be stocked directly into rearing ponds or brought into the nursery. When stocked directly in ponds, fry can be held in a wire mesh cage to avoid predation, fed for 10 to 14 days, and released into the open pond.

Most fish culturists remove eggs from spawning containers and bring them inside a hatchery. With this method, spawning containers need to be checked only every 2 to 4 days. Late morning is the best time, since spawning usually occurs at night or in the early morning. Egg masses are removed, placed in an aerated tub or bucket of water, shaded from direct sunlight, and brought to the hatchery. Eggs held in wire-mesh baskets are incubated in aluminum, fiberglass, or wooden troughs approximately 244 cm long by 46 cm wide by 25 to 30 cm deep (8 ft by 18 in by 10 to 12 in) (Figure 13.16). Paddles spaced between baskets are turned with a 30 rpm electric motor. Water flows through each trough at 19 liters/minute (5 gpm). As eggs hatch, sac fry drop through the wire-mesh basket.

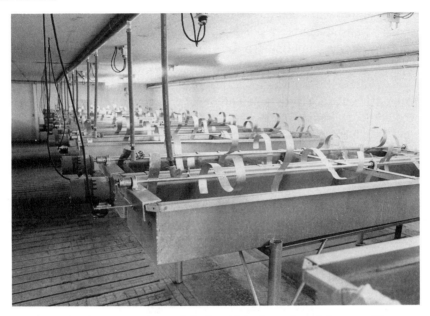

Figure 13.16 Aluminum troughs used for hatching channel catfish eggs. Photo courtesy of John Wozniak, LSU Agricultural Center.

Table 13.1 Estimated fingerling size after 120- to 150-day growing season at different stocking densities.

Fry Stocking Density		Average	Length
per hectare	per acre	centimeters	inches
25,000	10,000	18 - 25	7 - 10
75,000	30,000	15 - 20	6 - 8
132,500	53,000	13 -18	5 - 7
182,000	73,000	10 - 15	4 - 6
237,500	95,000	7 - 13	3 - 5
300,000	120,000	7 - 13	3 - 5
350,000	140,000	7 - 10	3 - 4
500,000	200,000	5 - 7	2 - 3
750,000	300,000	3 - 5	1 - 2
1,250,000	500,000	3	1

Source: Jensen et al., 1983.

For approximately the first 3 days, sac fry crowd into the corners on the bottom of the trough. Around the 4th day, fry swim to the top in search of food. These swim-up fry are darker than sac fry. Fry are typically fed for 1 to 2 weeks and then stocked into nursery ponds at rates up to 1,250,000/ha (500,000/ac). The stocking rate has an effect on the growth and size of fingerlings produced (Table 13.1).

Rainbow Trout-- Spawning and production of rainbow trout fingerlings were reviewed by Sedgwick (1976), Leitritz and Lewis (1980), Piper et al. (1983), and Laird and Needham (1988).

Rainbow trout brood stock are typically grown and held in concrete raceways or small earthen ponds. In most instances, they were originally selected from the fastest growing fish in grow-out units, or they were grown from fingerlings and selected specifically as brooders (Figure 13.17). Established hatcheries usually develop their own strain of fish.

Figure 13.17 Terry Patterson of the College of Southern Idaho examines brood rainbow trout.

Unlike channel catfish, which is allowed to spawn naturally in ponds, the rainbow trout is spawned artificially. The artificial spawning method involves the manual stripping of sex products from fish, mixing them in a container, and placing fertilized eggs in an incubator. This procedure should be performed with a minimum of stress. Some hatcheries use an anesthetic, such as MS-222, when handling brood fish.

To hand-strip eggs from a ripe female, grasp the fish near the head with the right hand; the left hand grasps the body just above the tail (Figure 13.18). The fish is then held with the belly downward over a pan. Eggs are stroked out gently by massaging, beginning forward of the vent and working toward it. Milt is obtained from males in a similar manner. If eggs or milt do not flow freely, the fish is not ripe and is returned to the holding unit. Such fish should be examined about twice a week to determine when they are ripe.

Figure 13.18 Hatchery workers at a United States commercial trout hatchery stripping eggs from rainbow trout.

Two procedures are used for fertilizing eggs, the wet method and the dry method. In the wet method, a pan is partially filled with water, then eggs are collected. Milt is added next. Because sperm live less than a couple of minutes in water, speed is required in taking eggs and milt. Most hatcheries prefer the dry method of fertilization in which no water is added first. This method allows the collection of eggs from a number of females and milt from males before both need to be mixed. The whole operation can be accelerated, reducing stress to brood fish being held. After eggs and milt are combined, they are mixed by hand.

The sperm enters the egg through an opening called a micropyle. Eggs are now rinsed with water for about a minute, and then the water is poured off. Next, eggs can be disinfected with 100 ppm of an iodine solution, such as argentine, for about 10 minutes. When eggs are water hardened, move them into incubators.

Water-hardening is the absorption of water by eggs until eggs become turgid. Avoid exposure to bright light.

Newly fertilized or green eggs may be handled safely for about 48 hours after water hardening. After that, they become progressively fragile until they become eyed. The numbers of eggs are estimated by one of several methods (Leitritz and Lewis 1980). The volumetric method is one such method. A sample of eggs is added to a graduated cylinder containing water until a known volume of water has been displaced. The numbers of eggs are counted. From this you can extrapolate the total numbers from the total volume of the water displaced.

Eggs are typically incubated in upwelling units (Figure 13.19) or in trays that pull out like a drawer in a dresser (Figure 13.20).

Figure 13.19 Michelle Baer with Fish Breeders of Idaho, Inc. shows upwelling unit and trough that receives fry as they hatch.

One upwelling incubator used by a commercial farm in Idaho consists of PVC pipe that is 25 cm (10 in) in diameter and 76 cm (2.5 ft) tall. A screen fits inside the pipe 10 cm (4 in) off the bottom to avoid contact with waste products. Marbles are stacked for 13 cm (5 in) on top of the screen. This aids in an even flow of water that enters the bottom at 76 liters/minute (20 gpm). About 100,000 eggs can be hatched in each unit. As eggs hatch, sac fry, called alevins, swim over the lip of the upwelling unit into a trough.

Pull-out incubator trays, described by Leitritz and Lewis (1980), are of two types: drip, and continuous or vertical flow. In drip incubators, water drips onto the top tray of eggs and filters down through remaining trays. In vertical flow incubators, water introduced to the bottom of each tray wells up through the eggs. In the drip incubator, eggs are transferred to troughs when they are ready to hatch. In the vertical flow incubator, eggs are allowed to hatch, and fry remain until ready for feed. The number of eggs to put into each incubator tray depends on the type of tray system (drip or vertical), water flow rate, and stage of egg development. Generally from 10,000 up to 45,000 eggs can be held per tray. The flow rate of water through a 16-tray incubator varies from 11 to 38 liters/min (3 to 10 gpm) (Leitritz and Lewis 1980). Flows are sometimes increased for eyed eggs and alevins; they require more oxygen than green eggs. Sedgwick (1976) suggested a flow rate of 1 liter/minute for 1,500 to 3,000 eggs (1 gpm for 5,678 to 11,355/eggs). Ingram (1988) used a minimum of about 10 liters/minute (2.6 gpm) for 100,000 eggs at 10°C (50°F).

Figure 13.20 Trays used to incubate trout eggs.

The number of days required for hatching depends mostly on the water temperature. Ingram (1988) found that rainbow trout eggs have about a 300 degree-day hatch duration. This means that from fertilization to hatching requires about 30 days if water remains a constant 10°C.

Trout eggs should be physically shocked after they have developed to the eyed stage. This kills any weak or infertile eggs. Shocking ruptures the yolk membrane of infertile eggs and causes the eggs to turn white. Shocking may be

642

done by striking the trays sharply, pouring eggs from one container to another, or siphoning eggs to another container.

Dead eggs are usually attacked by fungus and must be removed to prevent fungal infection from spreading to viable eggs. There are numerous methods for removing dead eggs. An old method involved picking out dead eggs with a pair of metal or wooden tweezers. A glass tube with a bulb on one end can be used to suck up dead eggs. The flotation method calls for addition of salt or sugar to water containing eggs until dead eggs float and live eggs slowly sink to the bottom. Dead eggs float because of their lower density. Dead eggs are then skimmed off with a net and discarded. Mechanical egg sorters can sort eggs at a rate of 100,000 eggs per minute (Figure 13.21).

Figure 13.21 Mechanical egg sorter. Dead eggs are whitish in color.

Once eggs hatch, alevins receive nourishment from the yolk sac for 1 to 2 weeks, depending on water temperature (Figure 13.22). Many trout farmers in Idaho and elsewhere buy eyed eggs from hatcheries and continue the hatching process. At 15°C (59°F), eyed eggs start hatching in about 5 to 6 days; once hatching begins, it takes about 3 days for all eggs to hatch. About 10 days after hatching, fry swim up to the surface in search of food. Aluminum and fiberglass troughs are normally used to stock newly hatched alevins or fry. The number of fry to stock into each trough depends mainly on the water temperature and flow rate. One trout hatchery in Idaho stocks 10,000 to 15,000 fry into each fiberglass trough that receives 76 liters/minute (20 gpm) of water. Fry are fed for 2 to 3 weeks until they reach approximately 1,544 fry/kg (700/lb). Then about 50,000 fry are stocked into each concrete raceway; raceways are each 18 m^3 (625 ft^3) and receive 1,136 to 1,703 liters/minute (300 to 450 gpm). They are grown here for 3 to 4 months until they reach 55 or 66 fish/kg (25 or 30/lb), at which time they are ready for stocking grow-out raceways.

Figure 13.22 Yolk-sac trout fry.

Salmon-- Spawning and production of salmon fingerlings were reviewed by McNeil and Bailey (1975), Smoker and Kerns (1977), Leitritz and Lewis (1980), Sedgwick (1982), Piper et al. (1983), and Laird and Needham (1988).

Brood salmon (*Salmo salar* and *Oncorhynchus* spp.) are caught during spawning runs from seawater to freshwater streams. Commercial operations seine or trap fish near the mouth of the stream, whereas government operations rely on fish ladders or fish ways. Once caught, adults are kept in floating holding pens until ripe; fish caught with fish ladders are usually held in ponds. If progeny ultimately produced are used for salmon ranching, it is important that not all brood stock be taken from just one time period in the run. Instead brood stock should be taken during the early portion of the run, most during the height of the run, and few during the latter part of the run. This is to prevent the gene pool from becoming too narrow, since not all salmon young ultimately released to ocean waters are later recaptured. Each stream and river has its own sub-population of salmon with its particular gene pool. If fish are scheduled for pen culture, this is of less consequence.

Eggs or progeny of one sub-population should be kept separate from those of another sub-population of the same species. This is because there may be nuances between sub-populations in growth and development that affect culture techniques. This is especially so during smolting when young salmon undergo physiological changes.

Females of all species should be checked every few days for ripeness. A female is dip-netted from a pen and cradled against the worker's chest or stomach. With her tail up, apply a gentle pressure to her belly. If eggs extrude readily, the fish should be moved belly up to avoid further loss of eggs. Sometimes green females may void a few loose eggs and, on occasion, ripe females may hold their eggs. Experienced hatchery workers learn to select ripe females by feeling the anterior abdomen. When eggs are loose in the body cavity, the abdomen has a characteristic texture. Green females, not ready to spawn, are sorted into a separate pen. Males are held in still another pen. They can be identified by a pronounced hook or kype at the end of the jaw; some males, such as the pink salmon (*O. gorbuscha*), develop a hump on the back.

Unlike trout, species of Pacific salmon die after spawning so they are first killed before egg taking to make the task easier. The Atlantic salmon may live after natural spawning, so they may be kept alive after egg taking.

To prepare her for egg taking, a ripe female is killed by a blow behind her eyes, or the head is cut halfway through with a clipper device. She is then bled to prevent blood from contaminating eggs. To bleed the fish, cut the lower part of the tail to sever the caudal artery. The fish is then wiped clean and held head up with the belly toward the collecting basin or bucket. The anal fin is draped over the container. A knife splits the fish open from vent to throat. If the fish is ripe, eggs readily spill out. If she is just barely ripe, only a few eggs fall. A second person then tears away the egg membranes from the body cavity. Eggs that do not readily fall from the sac are green and will not fertilize.

To prepare for milt taking, males may or may not be killed, but it is usually convenient to do so. Milt can be stripped directly into containers of eggs. Sperm and eggs are mixed by hand and left undisturbed for a few minutes before water is added to wash the eggs. Fertilized eggs are then disinfected and placed in incubators, the same as used for trout.

If egg and milt taking are done at the site where brood stock is captured, it may be necessary to transport unfertilized eggs and sperm to the hatchery. The fertilization of salmon eggs can be delayed if eggs and milt are kept cool (below 4.5°C or 40°F) and dry in separate containers and shielded from direct sunlight. Eggs can be stored for up to 3 days, but milt only 20 hours (McNeil and Bailey 1975). This time can be extended by using a container with a good surface area-to-volume ratio and adding oxygen. At the hatchery, eggs and milt are allowed to reach room temperature. Smoker and Kerns (1977) reported that the success of dry fertilization of transported eggs and milt is much lower than wet fertilization.

Incubation of salmon eggs and alevins is similar to that of trout, with some modifications. Eggs and alevins should be held in total darkness. Gravel may be used in some incubators to mimic natural conditions, and it is considered important in alevin troughs. Dissolved oxygen should be at saturation or at least 6 ppm. Incubation temperatures between 4° and 8°C (39° and 46°F) give best hatching success. Green eggs can be incubated at 6° to 8°C (43° to 46°F), eyed eggs at 10°C (50°F), and alevins to swim-up fry at 12°C (54°F) (Laird and Needham 1988). Elevated temperatures speed the hatching process. Water flow should range between 15 to 20 liters/minute (4 to 5 gpm) for each 10,000 eggs.

The alevin stage requires 2 to 4 months, depending on the water temperature and species. Laird and Needham (1988) recommended that alevins should begin receiving feed while 20% of the yolk sac remains. Pacific salmon swim up for feed, but the Atlantic salmon do not. Fry are reared in tanks or troughs much like trout. They are known as parr during the freshwater phase of their growth. Vertical bars or parr marks often distinguish this stage. Sedgwick (1982) suggested that salmon parr be grown in tanks at densities of 10 to 15 kg/m^3 (16 to 25 lb/yd^3).

The smolting of salmon is a critical time. Young salmon change from parr to smolt when they are ready to migrate to sea (Laird and Needham 1988). The word smolt refers to the silvery coating that develops on their scales. Salmon ranchers release smolts to the sea, and net-pen farmers also stock smolts into salt water. The blood of fish must change constantly to maintain a balance between salt in body fluid and salt in surrounding water. Body fluid of fish in fresh water is more saline than the environment. The gills, gut, and skin are semi-permeable membranes. Water enters the bloodstream through these membranes, a process called osmosis. It must be discharged continuously through the kidney to maintain correct osmotic balance. On the other hand, in a marine environment sea water has a higher concentration of salt than does the body fluid of the fish. Water is lost from fish through its semi-permeable membrane. Fish must drink water to compensate for this loss.

Fish must be fully smolted to survive transfer from fresh water to sea water. Laird and Needham (1988) listed factors that can impede sea water adaptation. They suggested transferring small batches of smolts and then measuring blood sodium after 48 hours to see if it is stabilized. Various methods can ease the initial stress from transferring. Salmon have been fed a diet containing 10% salt for 2 weeks before transfer. Smolts can be readied for transfer by gradually acclimating them to low salinity water at first then gradually increasing the salinity before transfer.

Bait Fish-- Production of bait fish was reviewed by Prather et al. (1954), Altman and Irwin (1956), Forney (1957, 58), Prather (1956), Flickinger (1971), Eeckhout (1978), Guidice et al. (1981), Piper et al. (1983), and Dupree and Huner (1984). Seed production is capsuled in Chapter 3. Four species of fish are commonly cultured as bait for sportfish. What follows is taken primarily from Piper et al. (1983).

Golden shiner brood stock should be at least 1 year old and 76 to 203 mm (3 to 8 in) long. About half should be less than 127 mm (5 in) to avoid selecting mostly females since males are smaller than females. Brood fish are stocked into ponds at rates of 5,000 to 7,500/ha (2,000 to 3,000/ac) if fry remain with adults after spawning or 10,000 to 20,000/ha (4,000 to 8,000/ac) if eggs or fry are removed to nursery ponds. Onset of spawning occurs at a water temperature of 18°C (64.5°F) and ceases above 27°C (81°F). Females deposit eggs on submerged plants or on spawning mats placed in the pond. Spawning normally occurs early in the morning, and at least four or five spawns take place during the spawning season. If spawning mats are used, they can be removed, the number of eggs estimated, and mats placed into nursery ponds. Otherwise eggs hatch in spawning ponds in about 4 days at water temperatures of 24° to 27°C (75° to 81°F). Fry are collected with a seine and transferred to nursery ponds at a rate of 500,000 to 750,000/ha (200,000 to 300,000/ac) where they are fed daily. Ultimately, a yield of 187,500 to 375,000/ha (75,000 to 150,000/ac) of 5 to 7.5 cm (2 to 3 in) fish can be expected. If fry are left with adults, about 150,000/ha (60,000/ac) can be obtained. The lower production is because of cannibalism from adults.

Fathead minnow brood stock should range in length from 4 to 10 cm (1.5 to 4 in), males being larger than females. The life span of fathead minnows is only 12 to 15 months. Thus spawning ponds should be stocked with about 60% adults and 40% immature fish. This will allow a continuous supply of newly hatched fry. Spawning ponds are stocked at a rate of 37,500 to 62,500/ha (15,000 to 25,000/ac). Since adhesive eggs are laid on the undersides of objects in a pond, boards are sometimes suspended in the water. Spawning begins when water temperature reaches about 19°C (66°F) and ceases when temperature rises to 29°C (84°F). Fry that congregate near shore are seined and transferred to nursery ponds. They are stocked at 750,000 to 1,500,000/ha (300,000 to 600,000/ac). Like golden shiners, fathead minnows take feed well. Ultimately a harvest of 375,000/ha (150,000/ac) can be expected. Fathead minnows mature rapidly. In only 4 to 8 weeks after transfer to nursery ponds, many fish are sexually mature and may spawn.

White sucker (*Catostomus commersoni*) brood stock is usually taken from streams during natural spawning. Fish are hand stripped, and eggs hatched in jars. After hatching, fry are stocked into ponds containing a good production of zooplankton. Stocking rates vary, depending on the size of fingerlings desired: 100,000 to 150,000/ha (40,000 to 60,000/ac) to obtain 2.5 to 5.0 cm (1 to 2 in) fish, 50,000 to 100,000/ha (20,000 to 40,000/ac) to obtain 5 to 10 cm (2 to 4 in) fish, and 12,500 to 50,000/ha (5,000 to 20,000/ac) to obtain 10 to 15 cm (4 to 6 in) fish. Suckers will accept formulated feeds, but ponds are usually fertilized with organic materials like manure to enhance growth of natural food organisms such as chironomid larvae (bloodworms).

Goldfish averaging 113 to 340 g (0.25 to 0.75 lb) make good brood stock. When the last danger of spring frost is past, adults are stocked into spawning ponds at a rate of 250 to 500/ha (100 to 200/ac). Spawning begins when the water temperature reaches 16°C (61°F). Most spawning occurs just after sunrise. One female may produce 2,000 to 4,000 eggs at a time, and may spawn several times during the season. Adhesive eggs stick to vegetation, hay, or spawning mats placed in the pond. Eggs or fry can be removed and stocked into nursery ponds or left in with adults. If left with adults, up to 250,000 fingerlings can be produced per ha (100,000/ac). In intensive culture, from 500,000 to 750,000 fingerlings can be produced per hectare (200,000 to 300,000/ac). Goldfish take formulated feeds. A phytoplankton bloom should be maintained with fertilization.

Largemouth Bass and Other Sunfishes-- Largemouth bass brood stock should be a minimum of 1 year old in the South and 3 years old in the North to be reliable spawners. In the spring, when water temperature exceeds 19°C (66°F), between 100 and 212 adult bass are stocked per hectare (40 to 85/ac) (Piper et al. 1983). Pond water should remain clear to see bass fry that are removed by seining schools. Do not use inorganic fertilizer to produce a phytoplankton bloom. Organic fertilizer is often used, though, to encourage growth of zooplankton. Bass may begin spawning within 72 hours, and eggs hatch in 72 to 96 hours.

If a cold front lowers the water temperature below 19°C, adult bass may abandon the nest, and eggs often become infected with fungus. To avoid this, some hatchery workers delay stocking until the water temperature reaches at least 21°C (70°F) and holds. Delayed stocking has another advantage. Bass are more apt to spawn all at once, thus producing same-age fry. This lowers the possibility of cannibalism.

Once hatched, fry leave the nest in 8 to 10 days in a school. Individual schools of fry are spotted from a small boat. A clear oil is sometimes cast on the water surface to calm waters for better viewing. Fry are seined from waters and moved to nursery ponds. It is important to seine schools well before fry reach 2.5 cm (1 in) because they disperse, making harvest more difficult.

Nursery ponds are prepared by planting a terrestrial grass for green manure or by using inorganic fertilizer. Fry numbers are estimated, and fry are stocked into ponds at rates varying from 125,000 to 187,500/ha (50,000 to 75,000/ac). The goal is usually to produce a 5 cm (2 in) fish for stocking sportfishing ponds. If a 7.5 to 15 cm (3 to 6 in) fish is desired, reduce the number of fry stocked by 75% to 90%. Fish longer than 10 cm (4 in) require forage fish for maximum growth. Fathead minnows stocked at 5,000/ha (2,000/ac) several weeks before bass fry are introduced will reproduce, and the resulting young provide forage for the bass fry.

Seed production of bluegill is relatively easy. Brood stock 1 to 3 years old is stocked into fertilized spawning ponds at 75 to 100 pairs per hectare (30 to 40 pairs/ac) when the water temperature reaches approximately 27°C (80°F). Adults make nests in communities. Bluegill are capable of reproducing monthly if the food supply is adequate and water temperature exceeds 27°C. This usually results in a variety of sizes of young fish, but this is of no consequence. Bluegill are not carnivorous and can be sorted to size after harvest.

Although fry can be transferred to nursery ponds, most hatchery workers leave fry in spawning ponds until they reach a desirable size of about 5 cm (2 in) for stocking sportfishing ponds. Redear sunfish (*Lepomis microlophus*), black and white crappie (*Pomoxis nigromaculatus* and *P. annularis*), and other sunfish species can be spawned naturally like bluegill.

Common Carp and Chinese and Indian Carps-- Seed production of common carp, Indian carps, and Chinese carps was reviewed by Hora and Pillay (1962), Woynarovich and Horvath (1980), and Jhingran and Pullin (1988). There are numerous sub-species with local varieties of common carp throughout much of the world. In nature, common carp are capable of spawning year round in tropical countries. However, in most regions common carp typically spawn twice a year, in the spring and again in the autumn. Spawning is usually associated with rising waters. Shoreline vegetation becomes inundated and provides substrate for adhesive eggs.

In captivity, common carp are spawned by one of three basic methods -- uncontrolled, semi-controlled, and controlled (Jhingran and Pullin 1988). In uncontrolled spawning, brood stock reproduces naturally in ponds, and fry remain and grow in the pond. Mortality of fry is usually high.

Semi-controlled spawning is further subdivided into two systems, Indonesian and European. Most other systems are minor modifications of these two. In the Indonesian system, brood fish care, spawning, and egg hatching are carried out in separate ponds. When it is time to spawn fish, optimal water temperatures range from 18° to 22°C (64° to 72°F). Water is released into the spawning pond in the morning. Brood stock as well as spawn collectors called kakabans are added to the pond in the afternoon. Kakabans made of plant fibers are kept floating just under the water surface. Spawning fish attach eggs on the underside of kakabans. The kakaban is turned over when one side is egg-laden. When both sides are covered with eggs, the spawning raft is transferred to hatching ponds. When fry are 3 weeks old, they are seined and transferred to nursery ponds at stocking rates up to 10 million per hectare (4,000,000/ac).

Natural food organisms are produced through use of green manure and application of manure and other organic fertilizers. After a few days zooplankton is virtually exhausted, and artificial feeds, along with continued manuring, are used. Fry attain a length of 2.5 cm (1 in) in about 15 days. At this time they are harvested and restocked into rearing ponds at a rate of 125,000 to 250,000/ha (50,000 to 100,000/ac). Fry feed on natural food organisms as well as feedstuffs such as oilcake, mustard, or rice bran. Fingerling size is reached at a length of 10 to 17 cm (4 to 7 in) in about 3 months.

The semi-controlled method for spawning common carp in Europe has several modifications. In central Europe, grasses are grown on the pond bottom as substrate for adhesive eggs. Ponds have peripheral ditches about 40 to 50 cm (16 to 20 in) deep which serve as a haven for brood fish and fry. After spawning, brood stock is removed. The Chinese system uses aquatic plants such as *Eichornia, Ceratophyllum*, and *Myriophyllum* as egg collectors. Floating bamboo frames keep vegetation from drifting away. In India, hapas are used to breed fish, hatch eggs, and grow fry before transfer to nursery ponds. The hapa is a porous, double-cloth sack suspended in water with four poles on the corners stuck into the pond bottom. Aquatic vegetation, such as *Hydrilla* and *Najas*, serves as egg collectors. Brood stock is placed inside the hapas. After spawning, brood fish are removed, and hatching fish pass through the holes of the inner sack and collect in the outer sack of the hapa.

Controlled breeding of common carp involves hypophysation. The pituitary gland (hypophysis) is removed from the brain of a donor fish, usually a carp species, preserved in absolute alcohol, and later homogenized before injection. Ripe female common carp are first anesthetized with MS 222, and the vent is sutured with waxed cotton thread to prevent inadvertent discharge of eggs when operators are not ready. Pituitary extract in a normal saline medium and thickened with glycerine is injected into fish at 2.5 to 3.7 mg/kg weight of female spawner. Ovulation may occur 8 hours after injection at 28°C (82°F), and fish can be hand stripped. A solution of 10 liters (2.6 gal) of hatchery water, 30 g (1 oz) of urea, and 40 g (1.4 oz) of sodium chloride is added to the egg-milt mixture to remove the adhesive substance. A final solution of tannin is used in water to further remove the adhesive substance. Fertilized eggs are placed into incubating jars or hapas for hatching. After hatching, sac fry may be transferred to larval tanks or kept in cloth hapas for about 4 days and then stocked into nursery ponds.

The Chinese carps and Indian major carps breed naturally only in flowing rivers in association with monsoon floods. Induced breeding, however, allows seed production in captivity. Jhingrin and Pullin (1988) described the process in detail. A glass tube called a catheter is inserted into the genital aperture of the female thought to be ripe, and a sample of eggs is removed for examination. Peripheral location of nuclei means the fish is ripe for spawning. In gametogensis, the nucleus of the ovum migrates to the periphery before release of the first polar body in meiosis. If the ova nuclei are centrally located, the fish will not respond to hormonal injection. Ripe females receive intramuscular or intraperitoneal injection. A second injection is given 6 hours later. Generally, one female fish plus two males are placed in a breeding tank with flowing water. Spawning generally occurs within 6 hours after the second injection. If not, fish are hand stripped of their sex products.

Tilapia-- The tilapia group, consisting of about 100 species, is easy to reproduce. Tilapia can be bred in net enclosures or hapas, rice fields, or ponds (Guerrero et al. 1976). In hapas, three to five females for every male are stocked per square meter (4 females/yd^2) of bottom area. Fry are collected once a month and transferred into another hapa or nursery pond. In rice fields containing peripheral trenches, tilapia brood fish are stocked at a ratio of three females per one male for every 2 m^2. Fry are later netted out. In ponds, a mixed population of male and female tilapia is stocked at a rate of 10,000 to 20,000/ha (4,000 to 8,000/ac). Young may be collected after 3 to 4 months.

Tilapia are very prolific, and some species such as the Java tilapia may reproduce when only a few months old. They may spawn every 30 days if conditions are favorable. Most tilapia species prepare depressions on the pond bottom. From 100 to 500 eggs are produced. After spawning and fertilization, a parent picks the eggs up and broods them in the mouth until hatching. Two species, *Tilapia zilli* and *T. melanopleura*, do not pick up the eggs for mouth brooding. They may produce as many as 5,000 eggs per spawn.

Milkfish-- The reproduction and spawning of milkfish were reviewed by Lee and Liao (1985) and Lee et al. (1986). Mature brood stock is captured from the wild or grown and maintained in captivity. Sexual maturity is reached at approximately 5 years of age. Fish are held in earthen ponds, concrete tanks, and floating cages. They have been spawned naturally and have been induced to spawn with hormone injections.

Proper care of brood stock and environmental conditions are important factors for successful reproduction. Brood stock should be handled carefully and stress avoided. Formulated eel diets containing 45% crude protein and trash fish have been fed to brood stock. Ideal environmental conditions include water temperatures ranging between 25° to 32°C (77° to 90°F) and increasing photo-period from 11 to 14 hours of light. Salinity is not as important since milkfish can mature in salinities ranging from 8 to 36 ppt. Before you induce spawning, use a catheter to take an egg sample. The oocyte must be a minimum of 0.72 mm in diameter before fish can be successfully induced to spawn. Optimum conditions for induced breeding include use of 8- to 10-year-old brood stock and females with an oocyte diameter of 0.8 mm. A single injection of human chorionic gonadotropin (HCG) ranging between 1,000 and 1,429 IU (international units) per kg of fish is effective (Figure 13.23). Eggs can be fertilized artificially after stripping of sex products.

Spontaneous spawning without hormone injection also has been achieved by a few farmers. In one case, 30 and 50 milkfish 10 to 11 years of age were stocked into 750 m^2 (897 yd^2) and 1,500 m^2 (1,794 yd^2) ponds, respectively (Kuo 1985). Fish began to school, and a chasing courtship was observed for 2 to 3 days before spawning. Most spawning occurred between midnight and 0300 hours. Water temperature was 27° to 29°C (81° to 84°F) and salinity 34 ppt.

Figure 13.23 Researcher at the Tungkang Marine Laboratory in Taiwan injects milkfish with hormone. Note plastic tube (catheter) used for checking egg development.

Crustaceans

Crawfish-- Reproduction and seed production of crawfish were summarized by Avault and Huner (1985). Although there are well over 280 species of crawfishes in North and Central America, the red swamp crawfish is by far the most important species for aquaculture. The white river crawfish (*P. zonangulus*) is often found in the same pond with the red swamp crawfish. The sexes of crawfish are distinct. Sexually mature males, called form 1, have inflated claws, hooks at the bases of walking legs, and cornified gonopodia. The first two pairs of abdominal appendages or swimmerets are modified into gonopodia; they transfer sperm to a seminal receptacle located between walking legs of the female. Gonopodia and seminal receptacles have distinct morphology, and gonopodia are the principal taxonomic characteristic for distinguishing species (Figure 13.24).

The red swamp crawfish may mate at any time and produce young, but typically it mates during the summer. After mating, egg laying and fertilization are usually not immediate. Females lay from 100 to 500 eggs in the fall while in underground burrows. Eggs fertilized with stored sperm attach to the abdomen with a sticky substance called glair. At temperatures of 20° to 25°C (68° to 77°F), hatching occurs in 2 to 3 weeks. Newly hatched young, resembling young adults, remain attached to the female's tail until they undergo two molts in about 2 weeks. Then they drop off.

Figure 13.24 Male red swamp crawfish (bottom) with gonopodia; female (top) with seminal receptacles.

Producing seed of red swamp crawfish for grow-out is simple. Adult crawfish are stocked into ponds in the spring or early summer at a rate of about 50 kg/ha (45 lb/ac). Crawfish mate and burrow underground. In the fall, when ponds are flooded, females emerge from burrows and release young. The spawning pond, nursery pond, and grow-out pond are all one and the same. There is no special nursery or rearing phase.

The redclaw crawfish breeds year-round in the Northern Territory of Australia where it occurs naturally. Because of its potential as an aquaculture species, methods have been developed to reproduce it in captivity (Medley 1994). Redclaw crawfish usually become sexually mature at 6 months of age. Brood stock is introduced into tanks with flowing water. A temperature of 26°C (79°F) and day length of 14 hours induces breeding (Merrick and Lambert 1991). After mating, the female releases eggs over the next 12 to 24 hours into a temporary brood chamber formed by the tightly curled tail (Jones 1990). Fecundity varies from approximately 300 to 1,000 eggs, depending on the size of the female. Incubation of eggs lasts 4 to 6 weeks. Newly hatched crawfish begin to make forays from the female of gradually increasing distance and duration, returning to the female for refuge. Within a week or two they become entirely independent. Immediately after young leave the female, she is capable of mating again to produce another batch of eggs.

In some parts of Europe, such as Blentarp, Sweden, the signal crawfish (*Pacifastacus leniusculus*) is bred in captivity. Adult crawfish, which ripen in outdoor ponds, are brought inside a hatchery where they are held in tanks with flowing water. Newly hatched young are stocked directly into natural waters or culture ponds without undergoing a nursery phase.

Shrimp-- Maturation, spawning, and larval rearing of penaeid shrimp were reviewed by Mistakidis (1967), Hanson and Goodwin (1977), Motoh (1981), McVey and Moore (1983), Liao (1985), Lawrence et al. (1985), Chamberlain et al. (1985), and Fast and Lester (1992).

It is important to understand that there are two general groups of shrimp based on reproduction, the grooved brown and white shrimps with closed thelyca, and the nongrooved white shrimps with open thelyca. Grooved shrimps have parallel grooves on each side of the rostrum that continue to the back of the carapace. In shrimp with a closed thelyca, such as *P. japonicus, P. monodon,* and *P. aztecus,* mating occurs just after females molt. The ovaries then are underdeveloped, and the chitinous thelyca is soft enough to allow spermatophore insertion for internal storage. In shrimp with an open thelyca, such as *P. vannamei, P. stylirostris,* and *P. setiferus,* the spermatophore is attached to the exterior of the thelyca of a hard-shelled, fully mature female just hours before spawning. Spawning is the discharge of recently ovulated oocytes. This is preceded by the release of sperm stored in closed-thelyca shrimp or from external spermatophores of open-thelyca shrimp. As oocytes are discharged into water, they contact setae around the gonopores that are coated with sperm.

Brood stock can be handled by one of two methods. Female shrimp in advanced reproductive stages and already mated are captured from the wild and brought into the hatchery where they are placed into tanks. Shrimp often spawn on the same day as captured. A second method is to rear and maintain brood stock in captivity. Here they reach maturation, mate, and are induced to spawn by manipulation of the environment, eyestalk ablation (removal), or both.

Certain species of shrimp are relatively easy to collect in the wild; examples include *P. japonicus, P. merguiensis, P. orientalis, P. aztecus, P. duorarum,* and *P. setiferus.* On the other hand, only a limited number of *P. monodon* spawners can be collected from the wild at any one time. Some countries have placed collecting restrictions on capture and transport of scarce mother shrimp (female brood stock). Methods for obtaining mother shrimp are well discussed by Hanson and Goodwin (1977).

Each species has its own biological requirements. Experience teaches the best location, water depth, time of day, and time of year for maximizing capture of mother shrimp. Short drags of about 30 minutes are done with a trawl. The catch is emptied on deck, and shrimp that appear to be possible spawners are put into a container of water with bubbling oxygen. A second culling separates all females that appear ready to spawn. Criteria used are olive green ovarian color for white shrimp, presence of a spermatophore or part of one between the 3rd and 4th walking legs for open-thelyca shrimp, and healthy condition. With some species, such as *P. setiferus*, the developing stage of ovaries somewhat resembles the mature stage. The presence or absence of a sperm packet is the best indicator for shrimp species with an open thelyca. Those shrimp selected as spawners are then placed in chilled, aerated water for transport to the shore-based hatchery.

Some workers found that mother shrimp, if not restricted in movement during transfer, may arrive dead. Restricting movement of spawners can be done by placing individuals in clear plastic tubes about 15 cm (6 in) long or enclosing them in a soft plastic screen. Moreover, restricting shrimp movement lessens the chance of the spermatophore being lost.

Two methods have been used once spawners are brought into a hatchery, extensive and intensive. The extensive method, also known as the Japanese or community method, uses relatively large tanks of 100 to 250 mt (100,000 to 250,000 liters or 26,420 to 66,050 gal). (Hatchery workers often refer to the volume of water in terms of so many metric tons. Note: one mt of water equals 1,000 liters.) The intensive, or Galveston method, uses smaller tanks of about 2 mt (2,000 liters or 528 gal). There are many variations in between.

The extensive method is often chosen when it is easy to capture large numbers of spawners. Seawater maintained at a temperature of about 28° to 30°C (82° to 86°F) and salinity of 25 to 35 ppt is filtered into tanks through a 1 micron screen to exclude zooplankton. Mother shrimp are stocked into a tank at a density resulting in production of 30 to 60 shrimp nauplii per liter (113 to 227/gal). After spawning, females are netted out. Fertilizer is added into the spawning tank daily to produce a phytoplankton bloom for zoea (Some workers use the word protozoea), the first feeding stage. Other foods, such as soybean meal or yeast, may supplement phytoplankton. As shrimp begin metamorphosing from the zoea stage to the mysis stage, the nauplii of brine shrimp are added as food.

The intensive method is usually chosen for those hard-to-capture mother shrimp such as *P. monodon*. Each spawner may be stocked into an individual tank. Food for resulting shrimp larvae is produced in separate tanks and usually consists of monocultures of selected algae, such as *Skeletonema sp.*, and zoo-plankton of *Artemia* nauplii. All food is introduced into nursery tanks containing larval shrimp to maintain a certain density. Algae fed to zoea are maintained at about 100,000 cells/ml. *Artemia* nauplii fed to mysis and post-larval stages are maintained at 2 to 4/ml. Formulated feeds that are micro-encapsulated, powdered microparticulated, or flake forms are also used.

Ali (1978), Ali et al. (1982), and Ali and Alikunhi (1991, 1993) described a third method for spawning, hatching, and feeding shrimp larvae. Their method, developed in India, differs primarily in the way the larvae are fed. Instead of feeding phytoplankton and *Artemia*, they feed the flesh of locally available crustaceans for all stages of shrimp larvae. This dispenses with the need to culture phytoplankton and *Artemia* as food. Crustacean tissue is processed into particles of specified sizes to simulate zooplankton. They reported a survival of 50% from nauplius-6 to harvested postlarvae and a significant reduction in cost. This method has been successfully used with 10 species of penaeid shrimp.

Penaeid shrimps are often divided into three groups based on the ease of mating and spawning in captivity (Lawrence et al. 1985). First, there are those species such as *P. merguiensis* and *P. japonicus*, that spawn freely in response to controlled environmental conditions; those such as *P. monodon*, that require unilateral eyestalk ablation for maturation; and those such as *P. setiferus, P. stylirostris* and *P. vannamei*, which usually respond best to a combination of controlled environmental conditions and ablation.

In nature, penaeid shrimp respond to their environment. Water quality, water depth, day length, and many other factors comingle to produce optimal mating and spawning conditions in the wild. When shrimp are brought in or reared under hatchery conditions, the environment changes. Shrimp are confined in ponds or tanks instead of the open ocean. On the other hand, certain environmental conditions can be controlled or even manipulated. When optimal environmental conditions are closely emulated in the hatchery, shrimp are more apt to spawn. Some environmental conditions studied to date include tank size and shape, water quality, photoperiod, and diet.

Though shrimp have mated and spawned in a variety of tanks, there are some limitations and requirements. Small glass aquaria seem to be unsuitable. For courtship of brood stock, shrimp must be able to swim unimpeded for 50 to 100 cm (20 to 40 in). Emmerson (1983) found that tanks most frequently used for successful maturation were circular with a bottom area of 6 to 13 m^2 (64 to 140 ft^2). In some instances, tanks with black interiors are more effective than those with white interiors. *P. japonicus* requires a sandy bottom in the tanks; most others do not. Structures such as aeration devices should not impede swimming. Most are placed in the center of the tank.

The water quality (temperature, salinity et al.) for optimal conditions is fairly well known. Nuances exist for each species. Light intensity and photoperiod affect various shrimp species differently, depending on the natural geographic location of shrimp. A light period of 14 hours followed by 10 hours of darkness suits the requirements of *P. stylirostris*. Some hatcheries manipulate the photoperiod so that darkness occurs during their normal working hours, when spawning is more apt to occur.

Diet plays an important role in maturation of shrimp. Lawrence et al. (1980) found that long-chain fatty acids are needed for proper egg development. Long-chain fatty acids are often destroyed in preparation of pelleted diets, so it may be necessary to provide fresh natural foods such as marine polychaetes, worms, squid, clams, and mussels.

656

As the shrimp farming industry continues to expand worldwide, more and more pressure will be put on the capture of wild brood stock. The ability to induce maturation, mating, and spawning in captivity with hatchery grown brood stock greatly enhances larval production. Much research with *P. monodon* has been conducted at the Tungkang Marine Laboratory in Taiwan, Republic of China, by I Chiu Liao and his co-workers (Figure 13.25). A generalized account follows.

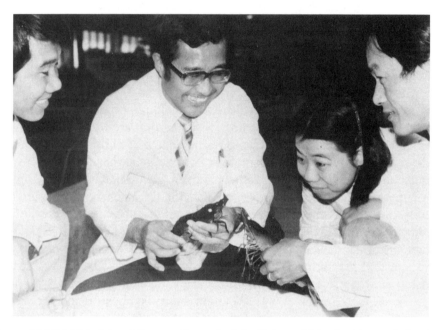

Figure 13.25 I Chiu Liao, Director General of the Taiwan Fisheries Research Institute, (shown center) and co-workers examine brood *Penaeus monodon*.

Brood stock reared and maintained in captivity are used in eyestalk ablation. One eyestalk is ablated (severed) on the female at the base with a heated forceps. This removes the gonad-inhibiting hormone (GIH) found in the eyestalk. Chamberlain et al. (1985) noted that the amount of GIH produced within the eyestalk varies with the season. High levels were reported just after the breeding season, low levels before the breeding season, and no GIH during the breeding season. GIH is presumed to inhibit release of gonad-stimulating hormone (GSH). Ablation also removes the molt-inhibiting hormone (MIH).

After ablation, females are placed into indoor tanks or outdoor concrete ponds with no bottom substrate. The maturation diet may consist of squid, chopped fish, trash shrimp, live marine worms, and oyster meats. Generally, first maturation is observed approximately 2 weeks after eyestalk ablation. Spawning occurs about 18 days after ablation. Before spawning, ablated females are examined at night or in the dark with a light. Color and shape of the ovaries are viewed through the exoskeleton.

Four stages of development are noted. In stage 1, ovaries are translucent and undeveloped; in stage 2, they are light yellow, brown or yellowish green; in stage 3, they are light green; and in stage 4, dark green. Ripe females are removed and placed into spawning tanks. One to two individuals are placed in one 0.5 mt (500 liters or 132 gal) tank or one to three in a 1 mt tank. Water depth is about 60 to 70 cm (24 to 28 in), temperature 26° to 29°C (79° to 84°F), and salinity 28 to 33 ppt. An air stone aerates water. Spawning typically occurs at night, and eggs hatch into spider-like nauplii in 12 to 13 hours.

Nauplii are usually transferred into other tanks. After six molts, which take about 50 hours, nauplii become zoea, the first feeding stage. Survival of nauplii is about 90%.

The zoea, which shuns light, feeds on algae such as *Chlorella* and *Skeletonema*. This stage has paired eyes and a body divided into two parts. The anterior part is covered by a loose-fitting carapace. The narrow posterior part is divided into a six-segmented thorax and an unsegmented abdomen. The zoea molts three times in 3 to 4 days; after this it becomes a mysis. The survival rate of zoea is low, about 30% to 70%. Just as zoea are metamorphosing into mysis, nauplii of *Artemia* are introduced as food.

The mysis stage begins to look like a shrimp, and stalked compound eyes are evident. This stage is also noted for the unique way shrimp swim. Mysis move through the water by leaping backward. The survival of mysis is about 70% to 80%. In 3 to 4 days, after three molts, mysis become postlarval.

Postlarvae, after molting four to five times, move to the bottom of the tank and along the walls. Postlarvae are referred to as PL-1, PL-2, PL-3, and so on. Each day corresponds to the number of days an individual has been in the postlarval stage. For example, a PL-3 is a larval shrimp that has been a postlarva for 3 days. After the PL-5 stage, larvae no longer shun light, and they are sometimes moved to outdoor concrete ponds with earth or sand on the bottom. Air stones provide aeration. At PL-20, larvae are harvested again and stocked into grow-out ponds. Overall, survival from egg to PL-20 is about 20% to 30%.

Prawn-- A breakthrough in production and rearing of prawn (*Macrobrachium rosenbergii*) larvae was made when S.W. Ling discovered that brackish water was required (Ling 1962, 1969a, b). Production and rearing of larval prawns were further reviewed by Goodwin and Hanson (1977), Hanson and Goodwin (1977), New (1982), McVey and Moore (1983), Sandifer and Smith (1985), and Cange et al. (1987).

Brood stock is obtained in one of three ways. It is captured from the wild, seined from production ponds, or maintained in tanks. In the wild, traps are made of bamboo splints and baited with fish or coconut. Brush traps (large bundles of branches), baited barbless hook and line, and cast nets have all been used to attract and capture prawns. In tropical countries with year-round prawn production, brood stock is usually not maintained. Gravid females are simply sorted out during harvest from production ponds. In temperate countries, brood stock, usually selected from production ponds, is moved to indoor heated tanks at fall harvest.

Maturation, spawning, and rearing of prawn larvae are relatively easy when compared with penaeid shrimp. Many farms make no conscious effort to mate prawns, and manipulation of the environment or eyestalk ablation is not necessary. In tropical and temperate countries, prawns mate freely in production ponds, and gravid females are easily obtained. In the southeastern United States, it is possible to stock larval prawns (< 0.5 g) in production ponds in mid May and produce gravid females by mid October. However, in temperate countries, brood stock must be maintained in heated tanks during cool months.

Techniques are relatively easy when mating and spawning prawns in a hatchery. Cange et al. (1987) described a closed-loop indoor hatchery system involving a saltwater mixing tank (for synthetic sea salts), bio-filter tanks, cone-bottom culture tanks, and aeration (Figure 13.26). Use of synthetic sea salts is usually necessary for hatcheries not located near the coastline. Some hatchery systems in tropical countries use large outdoor concrete tanks up to 30 m^3 (39 yd^3) in volume. Brood stock with mixed males and females can be held in community tanks, and gravid females removed as they become available. No attempt is made to pair prawns initially.

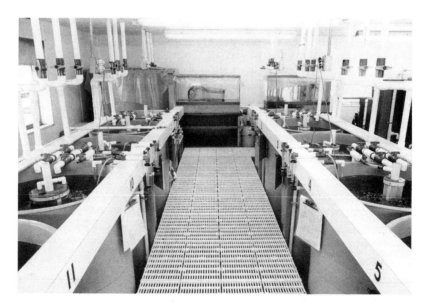

Figure 13.26 Tanks used to spawn prawns, Ben Hur Farm, LSU Agricultural Center.

A more precise method involves selection of individual male and female prawns for pairing and mating. Sexually mature female prawns have ripe ovaries that can be seen through the carapace as large orange masses. Several mature females may be kept together in one large tank, but when a ripe female molts she must be removed or screened off from other females to avoid cannibalism. Two to three hours after molting, when the new shell is fairly hardened, the female can be introduced into a tank containing a sexually mature blueclaw male. Mating will take place within a few hours, followed by egg laying within 24 hours.

Another option is to introduce four to five mature females into a tank for each male present. One male can protect a harem of four to five females after they molt. Gravid females are removed as they appear, and several are placed into a hatching tank. Once eggs hatch in 19 to 20 days, larvae are attracted to one end of the tank with a light while the other end is shaded. Larvae are removed by siphoning and stocked into outdoor nursery tanks containing blooms of green algae water at densities of 30 to 160 larvae per liter (114 to 606/gal) or stocked into indoor tanks at densities of 100 to 200 larvae per liter (379 to 758/gal). Each larvae prawn-rearing system uses brine shrimp nauplii (*Artemia* spp.) as the principal food. Crow (1987) recommended that nauplii of brine shrimp be stocked at 10/ml when prawn larvae are present at 200/liter. Eventually, a paste mixture of steamed egg, fish eggs, and minced fish flesh is fed in addition to supplement *Artemia* nauplii.

Larvae swim tail first, ventral side up, with the head lower than the tail. Individuals of early larval stages tend to swim close together in large groups near the surface. The gregarious habit gradually disappears after larvae are about 10 days old. Larvae undergo 11 molts, but only eight morphological stages can be recognized distinctly. Larvae begin to metamorphose into postlarvae as early as 17 to 18 days at a water temperature of 29°C (84°F) and a salinity of 12 ppt. Once prawns reach this stage, they can be grown to nursed juveniles in tanks or earthen ponds, or they can be stocked directly into freshwater grow-out ponds. There is no clear morphological distinction when larvae change from postlarvae to juveniles. Juveniles lose all pelagic tendencies and become active crawlers; some hatchery workers go by size of larvae (0.5 to 2 g) and days past hatching (30 to 60).

Mollusks

Oyster-- Seed production of oysters involves the planting of substrate (cultch) in natural waters to collect oyster spat. The seed is then moved to growing waters. The unpredictability of this method, however, has led to interest in hatchery-produced seed. The advantages of hatchery-produced seed include: (1) seed production on a year-round basis, (2) production of genetically superior oysters, and (3) production of cultch-free oysters.

Hatchery techniques have been reviewed by Breese and Malouf (1975) and Quayle (1988) for Pacific oysters (*Crassostrea gigas* and *Ostrea lurida*), by Dupuy et al. (1977) for the American oyster, by Hidu et al. (1981) and Burrell (1985) for American and European oysters (*Ostrea edulis*), and by Walne (1974) for the European oyster.

Development of hatchery methods for commercial production of the American oyster began with the successful production of oyster larvae in the laboratory (Brooks 1879). It was not until the 1940s, however, that serious attention was given to hatchery production. The critical limiting factor at that time was suitable larval food.

Today there are three methods used for producing algae as food for larval oysters.

The first, called the Wells-Glancy (Wells 1927) method, uses natural bay water containing algae. The water is centrifuged to remove zooplankton and large alga cells, then incubated for 12 to 24 hours to produce a bloom of small algae species, which is fed to larvae.

The second method (Hidu et al. 1969) also uses natural water, but after removal of zooplankton and other animals, algae is fed directly to larval oysters.

The third method involves growing pure cultures of selected alga cells such as *Isochrysis galbana*, *Phaeudactylum sp.*, *Platymonas sp.*, *Pavlova lutheri*, and *Dunaliella terctiolecta* (Burrell 1985). Most hatcheries today use the last method for producing larval food. A pure strain of alga is added to a small flask that contains nutrients and sterilized seawater. Carbon dioxide may be added in the presence of light. The alga is allowed to multiply and grow to provide inoculant for a larger container and so on until, ultimately, large tanks contain pure cultures of algae.

Animals in peak condition should be selected for brood stock. Burrell (1985) noted that young Pacific oysters (1.5 to 2 years old) produced mostly males; he suggested that about 30% of the brood stock should be males. Older brood stock (over 2.5 years) produced females. Brood stock can be conditioned to prepare them for spawning. This may include placing them in a flume (trough) where they are fed algae, while elevating or lowering water temperatures, and introducing sex products from other oysters into water for stimulation. For Pacific oysters, spawning temperatures are 18° to 20°C (64° to 68°F). For the American oyster in the Chesapeake Bay, 19° to 22°C (66° to 72°F) is optimum for sperm and egg formation, with the onset of spawning occurring at 25°C (77°F).

As soon as oysters begin to spawn, they are isolated in individual containers. Dupuy et al. (1977) placed oysters into jars with 3.8 liters (1 gal) of water, with one oyster per jar. When spawning ceases, brood oysters are removed. Eggs and sperm are then removed from containers, and eggs are poured over a sieve with an 80-micron mesh to remove extraneous materials. Fertilization is accomplished by mixing several ml of sperm for each one million eggs. Oysters in the genus *Ostrea* brood eggs in the pallial cavity of the female, and larvae are released in swarms several days after spawning.

Larvae are grown in tanks with controlled temperature, salinity, and stocking density. Quayle (1988) recommended that Pacific oyster larvae should be reared at concentrations of about 10,000/liter (37,850/gal), at a temperature of 24°C (75°F), and a salinity of 20 to 30 ppt. Initially algae are fed to provide about 25,000 cells per ml of water. As larvae grow, this feeding rate is tripled. In 2 to 3 weeks after a period as free-swimmers, larvae lose their velum used in locomotion and develop a pigmented spot or eyespot. They are now ready to set by attaching to substrate or cultch.

At this time, three options are available: (1) Mesh bags of oyster shell cultch are placed into tanks to which eyed larvae are introduced (Figure 13.27). Aeration bubbling through the water column helps to distribute larvae. After larvae set, the cultch is moved to growing grounds. (2) Eyed oyster larvae are shipped to growers. After receiving the larvae, the grower places them in tanks containing cultch for setting. (3) Small sand-sized particles such as marble chips are placed into setting troughs so that individual oysters set on individual particles. This produces cultchless oysters. There is another method to produce cultchless oysters. Eyed larvae are introduced into tanks with mylar sheets. Once oysters set, they are removed by scrapping them off or by flexing the sheets.

Figure 13.27 Bags of oyster shells used for cultch.

Clam-- Seed production of clams was reviewed by Castagna and Kraeuter (1981), Manzi (1985), and Manzi and Castagna (1989). Manzi listed six species of clams as candidates for commercial aquaculture in the United States, yet hatchery production and grow-out are predominantly with the hard clam (*Mercenaria mercenaria*).

Clam hatcheries closely follow the methodology of oyster hatcheries. Hatcheries should have access to water with 20 to 38 ppt salinity. Growth occurs at water temperatures of 8° to 28°C (46° to 82°F). Gonadal development begins at 8° to 10°C (46° to 50°F), and spawning at 20° to 31°C (68° to 88°F) (Castagna and Kraeuter 1981). Hatcheries usually obtain brood stock from the wild. However, operations that have both a hatchery and grow-out system often select fast-growing clams from their own farms. Preferred brood stock has sharp growing edges on the outer shell, wide spaces between shell annuli, and an overall clean appearance.

Once selected, brood stock is usually held in trays with flowing water until needed for conditioning or spawning. Gonadal development can be stimulated by elevating water to 22°C (72°F) and by providing ample food for 1 to 3 weeks. Because natural water is sometimes lacking in food, supplemental alga is added. Algae production is similar to that described for oysters.

It may be desirable to delay spawning of some brood stock to extend the spawning season. This is accomplished by holding brood stock in slow-flowing or even static water at temperatures of 16° to 19°C (61° to 66°F). Supplemental alga is added once a day. Brood stock held in this manner can be maintained for as long as 8 months, or they can be stimulated to spawn in 1 or 2 days by elevating water temperature to 22°C (72°F) (Manzi and Castagna 1989).

Clams can be spawned by one of two methods, mass spawning or individual spawning. The first method is used by most hatcheries where large numbers of larvae are desired. Individual spawning allows for selective breeding. In mass spawning, 25 to 100 spawners are placed in a trough with flowing water. The water temperature is elevated rapidly. Adding a sperm suspension or phytoplankton increases stimulation. In individual spawning, a single clam is placed in a glass container and stimulated as before. Eggs and sperm are collected and mixed for fertilization.

Twenty-four to 48 hours after fertilization the embryos reach the shelled veliger larval stage, sometimes called straight hinge stage. At this stage larvae obtain their sustenance by feeding and by absorbing dissolved organic material. Larvae are reared in containers as small as 1 liter (0.26 gal) to as large as 30,000 liters (7,926 gal). They are stocked at densities of 1 to 15/ml and fed algae at densities of 10,000 to 100,000 cells/ml/day (Manzi 1985). The larvae are usually grown for 6 to 8 days at which time they begin to metamorphose. At this stage of development, larvae are called pediveligers, and they now have a functional foot and velum. They spend part of their time swimming and part attached to the bottom and sides of the tank.

Once larvae reach the post-set stage and are attached to a surface, they are moved to nursery systems for intermediate growth between hatcheries and field grow-out. Here they are grown until they reach a size of 4 to 10 mm (0.2 to 0.4 in). At this time they are ready to stock into grow-out facilities (Figure 13.28). Nurseries are of two basic types, field systems in which larvae are placed into protected natural waters and onshore systems in which seawater is pumped to land-based units. In field systems, larvae can be placed in trays or racks, with plastic mesh covers to protect against predation. Trays are either placed on the bottom or stacked in tiers. Onshore systems use raceways with shallow trays containing larvae or they use upflow units. Upflow units move water vertically across trays of young clams rather than horizontally as in raceways.

Manzi and Castagna (1989) compared field nursery systems with onshore systems. Field systems offer low cost but they have high maintenance requirements, incomplete predator control, and susceptibility to theft and vandalism. Onshore systems are more expensive, but they provide maximum protection and easy access.

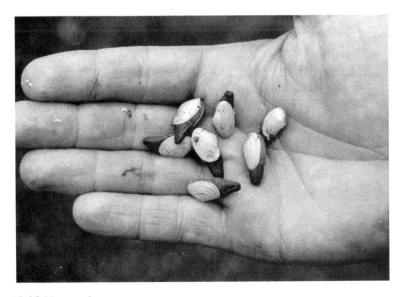

Figure 13.28 Young clams.

SEED TRANSPORTATION

Seed of finfish, crustaceans, and mollusks are transported by several means. Green trout eggs may be shipped for up to 48 hours after being taken. If the eggs have not been fertilized, eggs and sperm are sealed separately in plastic bags without water and with the air removed. The bags are placed in a Styrofoam box with crushed ice. Most salmonid eggs are shipped when in the eyed stage, when an eyespot develops in the embryo. Eggs must be kept moist and cold. They are placed in trays, surrounded by a wet cloth, stacked one on top of the other. Crushed ice is placed above the top tray so that the melted ice water percolates through each tray. The trays are placed in an insulated box and sealed. Leitritz and Lewis (1980) described the procedure.

Busch (1985) reviewed the transportation of eggs, fry, and fingerlings of channel catfish. Recently fertilized egg masses have been transported in aerated coolers, transport tanks, or oxygenated bags with water. Fry and fingerlings are transported in hauling tanks that fit in the back of a pickup truck or in tanks on trucks specifically designed to haul fish. Aerators and bottled oxygen maintain oxygen levels above 5 ppm. Fry and fingerlings are not fed 24 to 48 hours before transportation to clean feed out of the gut for waste reduction. Dupree and Huner (1984) gave additional details on hauling eggs, fry, and catfish fingerlings in plastic bags (Table 13.2). Plastic bags are filled with a liter or two of water; eggs, fry, or fingerlings are introduced, and the air is squeezed out. Pure oxygen is added through a tube to inflate the bags that are then sealed. The bags are then placed into insulated boxes. Ice may be packed around the outside of the bag to keep the fish cool.

Table 13.2 Estimated carrying capacities of fish or eggs in grams per liter of water at 18.5°C (65°F) for plastic bag transport.

Stage of Fish	Transport time in hours			
	1	12	24	48
Egg	60-180	60-150	60-120	30-60
Yolk-sac fry	120-360	84-300	48-240	12-120
Swim-up fry	60-240	54-192	48-150	24-78
1.3 cm fingerlings	108-360	90-300	72-240	36-120
2.5 cm fingerlings	120-420	102-360	78-300	42-150
5.0 cm fingerlings	120-480	108-420	90-360	42-180
7.6 cm fingerlings	120-480	108-420	90-360	42-180
fingerlings >7.6 cm	240-600	180-450	120-300	60-150

Source: Dupree and Huner 1984 Note: 1 inch = 2.54 cm.

Seed of many finfish and crustacean species are shipped in oxygenated bags (Figure 13.29) and hauling tanks. Postlarvae shrimp and prawns are often transported in oxygen-filled bags, sometimes by airplane. In Indonesia, milkfish and tilapia seed are often transported in tarred bamboo baskets containing water.

The shuffling step of the fish culturist gently agitates the water, which adds oxygen (Figure 13.30).

Figure 13.29 Bags of oxygenated water used to transport tilapia seed, Philippines.

Figure 13.30 Fish farmer purchases tilapia seed, Sukabumi, Indonesia.

Eyed oyster larvae can be transported to growers in a damp cloth wrapped in wet paper towels for up to 48 hours. The larvae are placed in a Styrofoam box with artificial ice. Several million larvae can be shipped in a container the size of a match box. Larvae can be held for up to 1 week in this condition at 5°C (41°F). Clam seed can be transported in a similar manner.

STOCK IMPROVEMENT

The goal of stock improvement is to produce a more valuable and profitable culture species. This usually includes fast growth, high dressing percentage (more meat and less waste), disease resistance, tolerance to poor water quality and stressful conditions, and high feed efficiency. To accomplish this goal, a number of husbandry tools are available, such as selective breeding, hybridization, and polyploidy. Moav (1979) and Tave (1993a) reviewed the basics for genetic improvement of culture species.

Selective Breeding

Selective breeding offers two routes. First, in mass selection or individual selection, the fastest growing, largest, or best looking individuals are selected as brood stock. For example, assume that a production pond is stocked with same-age fingerling channel catfish. At harvest, fish average 0.5 kg (1.1 lb) each. Some fish, though, may reach only 0.25 kg (0.55 lb), whereas a few individuals, perhaps 5% of the population, may reach close to 1 kg (2.2 lb). These large fish are retained for brood stock. This practice of mass selection can be carried on with each succeeding generation. Be sure that the brood stock selected consists of truly fast growers and not older fish that are good seine evaders.

Family selection is another type of selective breeding. Here, instead of making selections from individuals, entire families are selected. In this case, progeny of each pair of fish are considered a "family." Mass selection can improve the culture species for those desirable traits with a relatively high heritability, that is $H^2 > 0.3$, whereas traits with a relatively low heritability, that is H^2 is 0.1 to 0.3, are best enhanced through family selection. Heritability, H^2, may range from 0 to 1, with 1 giving the highest heritability. Most fish farmers who produce their own seed and have grow-out units unconsciously practice mass selection. Family selection requires more culture units and record keeping. Both mass selection and family selection may take many years for development of improved stocks.

Of all the culture species, the common carp and trout have the longest histories of selective breeding. Carp farmers in Europe have been selecting the fastest growing fish for centuries, and as a result distinctive strains have evolved. Scientists in Germany have standard procedures for sequential mass selection. The largest individuals are selected, but they also need to have proper body conformation. In the United States, university, governmental, and private hatcheries have practiced selective breeding in trout for high fecundity, large egg size, high hatching percentage, rapid growth, and early maturity. From this effort, there has been a 100% increase in the number of rainbow trout spawning at 2 years of age, a doubling of growth, and a fourfold increase in egg production of 2-year-old females. Tave (1993a) offered guidelines for setting up a selective breeding program for culture species.

Breeding programs have produced disease resistance and modified behavior patterns. Selective breeding has focused on producing common carp resistant to infectious dropsy, Atlantic salmon resistant to vibrio disease, trout resistant to furunculosis, and channel catfish resistant to channel catfish virus disease (CCVD). Plumb et al. (1975) tested a number of channel catfish strains and found significant differences in susceptibility to CCVD. Certain strains of common carp, such as the Chinese big-belly and wild European carp, are able to escape seines much better than domestic European carp. *Oreochromis aureus* is known for escaping capture by seine, whereas *O. niloticus* is easily caught.

The prawn, *Macrobrachium rosenbergii,* is notorious for its aggressiveness. This contributes to skewed sizes of prawns at pond harvest. Different strains of *M. rosenbergii* from the Indo-Pacific Region have different degrees of aggressiveness (Sarver et al. 1979). It appears, then, that a docile strain is best suited for pond grow-out, provided it is a fast grower. Sarver et al. (1979) and Malecha (1977) further noted that different strains of prawns exhibited different growth rates and different responses to water pH, salinity, and temperature. Dunham and Smitherman (1984) documented the various strains of channel catfish known in the United States and gave their performance records.

The beginning aquaculturist faces the decision of which stock of seed to obtain for grow-out or which stock of brood stock to use as a foundation for a breeding program. Learn which strain grows best in your area. This information can be obtained from the literature, extension agents, and word of mouth. If there is a choice between wild and hatchery stocks, hatchery stocks should be chosen because of better performance. If a particular disease such as CCVD has been a problem, opt for a strain of channel catfish that shows the most resistance to this viral disease. Tave (1993a) cautioned when obtaining breeder stock. Not all individuals should originate from a few pairs, to avoid inbreeding depression.

Genotype/environment Interaction

A genetic stock that grows well under one set of environmental conditions may not grow well under another set of conditions. That is why when various stocks are being evaluated, they should be grown under the same conditions as those used for commercial production. Moav (1979) listed several types of genotype x environment interactions:

(1) The genotype x pond interactions include water quality, soil type, and related conditions. For example, the Chinese big-belly carp (*Cyprinus carpio*) and the European common carp respond differently to the same environment.

The European carp is a much faster growing fish, but it cannot compete with the big-belly carp when grown under harsh pond conditions found in China. In China, crowded pond conditions and poor water quality are the rule.

(2) Genotype x age interactions. Sometimes a strain may exhibit superior growth initially, but growth may later wane. That is why when two or more strains are being compared, they must be grown out to market size. It may be misleading to draw conclusions on half-grown fish.

(3) Genotype x culture system. Green et al. (1979) grew eight different groups of channel catfish in aquaria, cages, and ponds, and they found that various strains responded differently under the three systems (Table 13.3).

Table 13.3 Mean net yield (g) per experimental units for eight groups of channel catfish (six strains and two crossbreeds) reared in aquaria, cages, and ponds.

Group	Aquaria		Cages		Ponds	
	Yield	Rank	Yield	Rank	Yield	Rank
Marion	779	1	2,681	1	19,733	1
Warrior x Yazoo	486	4	2,542	2	18,383	2
Rio Grande	600	2	2,271	5	14,779	3
Yazoo	554	3	2,418	4	13,961	4
Warrior	457	5	2,498	3	10,315	6
Kentucky	414	6	1,784	6	8,222	7
Tennessee	294	8	1,484	8	7,920	8
Tennessee x Yazoo	334	7	1,613	7	12,589	5

Mean survival (Percent)

Group	Aquaria	Cages	Ponds	Combined	Rank
Warrior x Yazoo	94.5	89.8	96.6	93.4	1
Tennessee x Yazoo	99.5	80.8	94.0	89.1	2
Warrior	91.5	81.3	91.8	87.3	3
Tennessee	95.5	78.7	92.4	87.0	4
Rio Grande	99.0	77.3	92.0	86.7	5
Marion	94.5	78.8	87.8	84.9	6
Yazoo	98.5	76.0	77.8	80.0	7
Kentucky	92.0	78.8	65.5	75.0	8

Source: Green et al. 1979, Food and Agriculture Organization.

(4) Genotype x competition. Some strains grow well under very crowded conditions; others do not. In nature, aquatic species have a density corresponding to natural limiting factors, such as food. In culture systems, food is usually no longer a limiting factor, and culture species can be densely stocked. Thus, the strain or species must perform well under more stressful conditions.

Crossbreeding

Crossbreeding, as defined here, is the mating or crossing of two different strains of the same species. Whereas selective breeding may take several generations and many years to produce an improved strain, crossbreeding may sometimes produce improved progeny with one mating. Not all crosses, however, produce improved progeny.

A classic example of successful crossbreeding is the mating between the Chinese big-belly strain and the domesticated European strain of the common carp. The big-belly carp, while hardy, has several negative characteristics including slow growth, high fecundity, early sexual maturity, and the ability to evade seining. The European common carp historically had been grown under a different set of conditions. It received grain feeding, protection against predators and diseases, and was harvested by pond draining. These conditions gave rise to a fast-growing, late maturing carp, which is easily caught by seining. On the negative side, it is poorly adapted to harsh environmental conditions such as those found in traditional Chinese carp ponds. Crossing these two strains of common carp produced fish that inherited the positive qualities of the European parents while retaining the hardiness of the Chinese parents. Such a combination gave a strong heterosis of economic value.

Smitherman and Dunham (1985) evaluated eight different crosses of channel catfish strains in an attempt to produce heterosis (Table 13.4). Some crosses produced heterosis; others did not. They also noted a genotype x environment interaction under three culture systems, aquaria, cages, and ponds.

Hybridization

Hybridization, as defined here, is the mating of two different species. It has the same goal as selective breeding and cross breeding, to produce a more valuable culture species. Like crossbreeding, hybridization sometimes may result in heterosis in one generation. The striped bass (*Morone saxatilis*) exhibits fast growth, but it is not a good pond fish and will not readily accept pelleted feed. The white bass (*Morone chrysops*) is hardy and will accept pelleted feed, but it is a slow grower. The female striped bass x male white bass produces a hybrid that will accept pelleted feed, tolerate stressful conditions, and grow well under culture conditions (Kerby et al. 1983; Woods et al. 1983; Hodsen et al. 1987).

Table 13.4 Production of eight genetic groups of channel catfish in three different environments -- ponds, cages, and aquaria -- during 1971 (Adapted from Green et al., 1979).

	Production (g)		
Cross	Ponds	Cages	Aquaria
Marion x Marion	19,733 a	2,686 a	799 a
Warrior x Yazoo	18,383 b	2,542 a	486 c
Rio Grande x Rio Grande	14,779 bc	2,271 a	600 b
Yazoo x Yazoo	13,961 cd	2,418 a	554 b
Tennessee x Yazoo	12,590 de	1,613 b	334 e
Warrior x Warrior	10,381 f	2,498 a	457 cd
Kentucky x Kentucky	8,222 g	1,784 b	414 d
Tennessee x Tennessee	7,920 g	1,484 b	294 e

Means in each column followed by the same letter are not significantly different (P > 0.05).
Source: Smitherman and Durham 1985, with permission from Elsevier Science.

Brood stock of both species is obtained from natural waters. Sex products are stripped after hormone injection. Eggs are fertilized and hatched. Because female striped bass could become in short supply, scientists have experimented with the reciprocal cross, since female white bass are sometimes more available than female striped bass. The yellow bass (*Morone mississippiensis*) x striped bass also shows promise as a pond fish. Ultimately domesticated stocks of striped bass, white bass, and yellow bass must be maintained.

Various catfish species have been mated to produce 28 different hybrids (Guidice 1966; Dupree and Green 1969; Smitherman and Dunham 1985). One hybrid, female channel catfish x male blue catfish (*Ictalurus furcatus*), stands out as an excellent fish to grow commercially. The reciprocal mating does not produce an equally superior fish.

Each parent of the hybrid has positive and negative traits. The channel catfish is hardy, easy to handle, can be grown under a variety of conditions, and has a fair dressout percentage. On the negative side, the channel catfish is difficult to seine, does not grow uniformly, and is prone to the channel catfish virus disease (CCVD) and enteric septicemia of catfish (ESC). The blue catfish is resistant to CCVD and ESC, grows uniformly, has a high dressout percentage, and is easy to seine. On the negative side, it is not easy to handle and is prone to other diseases. The hybrid between the two species appears to combine most of the good traits of both parents without the negative traits.

The husbandry to produce the channel catfish x blue catfish hybrid on a commercial scale needs to be worked out. In nature, the reproductive behavior of the channel catfish is sufficiently different from that of the blue catfish so that natural hybridization is uncommon. In research, female channel catfish that have received hormone injections are placed into spawning tanks with male channel catfish. When eggs are first extruded, the female is removed and remaining eggs are stripped. Sperm from blue catfish is obtained by sacrificing the fish; sperm cannot be stripped because the testes are branch-like rather than lobes.

Tave (1993b) discussed various ways to improve the success of crossing channel and blue catfish, including "recurrent selection." Fish that produce hybrids are isolated and spawned with their own species. The offspring are then evaluated to find F_1 generation fish that readily produce hybrid offspring.

Creating a Synthetic Strain

The crossing of two strains of the same species (crossbreeding) and the mating of two different species (hybridization) has been discussed as possibly bringing about progeny of superior growth in a single F_1 generation. Progeny from the mating of female striped bass x male white bass and from the mating of female channel catfish x male blue catfish, as we have seen, are robust and fast growing. Yet there are husbandry problems. White bass and striped bass brood stock are caught wild from natural waters. Channel catfish do not readily mate with blue catfish on a commercial scale.

If an F_1 generation could be produced and backcrossed with a parent, or if F_1 could be mated to F_1 producing F_2 progeny, perhaps a synthetic strain could be ultimately created. Such might lead to the development of domesticated brood stock that would readily reproduce in captivity and which would still maintain superior culture characteristics.

This is easier said than done. First, certain hybrids produced may be sterile or, in some instances, all one sex. Second, it may take several to many generations to get a synthetic strain, and results are not assured. Third, crossing F_1 x F_1 and F_1 x a parent gives progeny of mixed characteristics. Fourth, there is a danger of developing a narrow gene pool, resulting in inbreeding depression. Nevertheless, creation of a synthetic strain piques the imagination. The various tilapia species probably offer one of the easiest groups of fishes to produce a new breed from a husbandry standpoint. Different species of tilapia readily mate without hormonal injections or other special treatment (Avault and Shell 1968).

Tave (1994) discussed the creation of synthetic strains. In one instance, a red-bodied tilapia was crossed with *Oreochromis aureus*, a cold-tolerant tilapia, to produce F_1 hybrids. Then the F_1 hybrids were backcrossed to the cold-tolerant *Oreochromis aureus*. Some of the backcrossed hybrids were red, while others were normally pigmented. The red backcross hybrids were saved for further backcrossing, while the normally pigmented fish were culled. The process was repeated for two generations and resulted in the creation of a cold-tolerant red strain of tilapia.

Dunham and Smitherman (1985) crossed two strains of channel catfish, the Marion strain and the Kansas strain. Both strains possess outstanding traits. Resulting F_1 fish were mated to produce F_2-generation fish. Outstanding F_2-generation fish were mated to produce an F_3 generation, which was the beginning of the synthetic line. This process was repeated until the fish bred true. They also produced a synthetic hybrid strain by mating female channel catfish with male blue catfish. These two species have similar karyotypes, that is they have the same number of chromosomes, and the shapes and sizes of the chromosomes are similar. This suggested that the hybrids probably would be fertile. The F_1 generation hybrids were mated to produce F_2-generation fish, and so on. Eventually, you hope to produce a fish that breeds true and does not require special treatment such as hormone injection.

Perhaps one of the best examples is the Santa Gertrudis cattle. This was the first distinct breed of cattle produced in the United States and resulted from the mating of the Shorthorn and the Brahman. Santa Gertrudis cattle are about 5/8 Shorthorn and 3/8 Brahman. This breed is raised in Texas and elsewhere in arid areas of the Southwest. Calves grow rapidly and mature into large cattle. The breed has been exported to Latin American countries.

Breeding Aids

Monosex Culture Species-- Sometimes a culture species can be made more valuable by development of all-male or all-female populations. Male tilapia grow much faster than females. Moreover, if all male fish are stocked into grow-out, unwanted spawns can be controlled. Guerrero (1979) produced 98% male *Oreochromis mossambicus* by feeding fry 30 µg of methyltestosterone per gram of feed for 4 weeks. Certain tilapia hybrids result in all-male populations or in skewed populations containing mostly males. Hickling (1962) first reported this phenomenon. Several theories exist and are based on different sex chromosome complements for various species. One hybrid known to give 100% males is a female *O. mossambicus* x male *O. hornorum*.

Male channel catfish outperform females in rapid growth, so growing all male fish could increase production and profit. Simco et al. (1989) reported from their research that males were as much as 37% heavier than females at 26 months of age. Davis et al. (1990, 1992) took an interesting approach for production of all-male channel catfish. Sexually undifferentiated fry were fed male hormone to produce sex-reversed XY "females." These fish were males genetically but females phenotypically. When mated with normal XY males, offspring resulted in a ratio of 3 male: 1 female. Some males were XY and some were YY. Those males that were YY were supermales, and when mated to normal females they produced all-male fish. Note that channel catfish do not possess morphologically distinct sex chromosomes. Sex determination follows a system of male heterogamety or the "XX/YY" system found in mammals (Tiersch et al. 1992).

Sometimes it is desirable to have all-female populations in grow-out (Galbreath and Thorgaard 1993). In raceway culture of rainbow trout, precocious males reach maturity before market size is reached, and energy (feed) is put into production of sex products rather than flesh.

In fish such as salmonids, there are two hormonal methods for production of all-female stocks (Donaldson and Benfey 1987). These are direct feminization using estrogen treatment and indirect feminization using female sperm produced by fish that are genotypic female/phenotypic males. Direct feminization has been accomplished in salmonids during the eyed stage, the alevin stage, and the early feeding stage by immersion in estradiol. One of the most effective periods for successful feminization is just before hatching. Immersion of embryos in 400 µg/liter estradiol at the time of hatching followed by a second immersion 1 week later has been tried at commercial hatcheries. Female fish are masculinized by feeding of androgen. These fish are genetically female but produce sperm. They are phenotypically male. This sperm, when used to fertilize normal female ova, results in production of all female progeny. Donaldson and Benfey (1987) described the process.

Polyploidy-- Polyploidy is the development of individuals with more than the normal two sets of chromosomes (2N), usually three sets (3N or triploidy). Wolters et al. (1981, 1982) reported production of triploid channel catfish and on growth and reproductive development. One method to produce 3N individuals is to cold shock eggs at the second meiotic division. The polar body from the female is retained. (Cold shock at the first mitotic cleavage will produce tetraploidy.) Often triploid individuals are sterile, or their reproductivity is greatly reduced. This is an advantage when a meat individual for market is sought.

Triploid oysters (*Crassostrea gigas*) have been produced by addition of cytochalasin B to water containing newly fertilized eggs (Allen and Downing 1986). The extra polar body, normally lost, is retained. Triploids are good for grow-out during seasons when normal reproduction occurs. Instead of developing sex products and poor flesh, oysters continue to grow and produce good flesh.

Sperm Preservation-- The livestock industry, such as the dairy industry, has benefited greatly from the cryopreservation and use of stored sperm. This allows for preservation of desirable genes for selective breeding, crossbreeding, and hybridization, as well as in the standardization of broodstock quality. Use of stored sperm presents the opportunity for predictability in the quality of offspring. Further, it eliminates the need for the care and maintenance of a large number of brood stock. In commercial aquaculture, preservation and use of stored sperm is still in the research stage, but if we emulate the livestock industry, it could become common practice (Figure 13.31). The preservation and storage of channel catfish sperm have been reported by Guest et al. (1976a, b) and Jaspers et al. (1976). Cryopreservation of striped bass sperm was reported by Kerby (1983), salmonid sperm by Cloud et al. (1990), and sperm of aquatic organisms including shrimp by Grout et al. (1992).

Figure 13.31 Terry Tiersch of the LSU Agricultural Center preserves sperm of channel catfish.

Transgenic Culture Species-- There is a great deal of interest in transgenic production of the plants and animals we use for food and fiber. You may hear such terms as biotechnology, gene splicing, gene transfer, or genetic engineering. A gene is transferred into a species to effect some desirable trait such as fast growth or disease resistance (Fischetti 1991). One method of gene transfer is to microinject the egg of a culture species with cloned DNA shortly after fertilization. If the transfer is successful, the gene fixes itself in the animal. This new genetic material is passed on to subsequent offspring. Transgenic culture species could have a profound beneficial effect on the aquaculture industry. On the other hand, genetically altered cultured species could have a detrimental effect on the gene pool, and great care must be exercised until more is known about the process. Since 1987, the United States Department of Agriculture has issued more than 375 permits to field-test genetically engineered crops such as tomatoes, and an additional 100 more were pending at that time (Marsa 1993).

STUDY QUESTIONS

1. Assume that you farm channel catfish in ponds totaling 100 ha of water. How many fingerlings are needed to stock ponds for one crop? Qualify your answer by giving the number of fingerlings you stock per hectare. What size fingerlings will you use? What is the time required to produce a crop if you grow the fish to an average weight of 570 grams?

2. You have a raceway system that has a total flow rate of 10 cubic feet per second. How many rainbow trout fingerlings will you need to produce one crop? What size fingerlings will you use? How large will you grow the fish for market? How long will it take?

3. You have a total of 100 ha of shrimp ponds. If you stock these ponds at a rate of $25/m^2$, how many postlarval shrimp will be needed? What is this in terms of numbers per hectare? What is this in terms of numbers per acre? If you grow two crops per year, how many postlarvae will be needed for the 100 ha?

4. List factors affecting reproduction of culture species. Give examples for each factor with two species each of finfish, crustaceans, and mollusks.

5. In outline form, give the chronology of seed production for channel catfish, rainbow trout, largemouth bass, *Penaeus monodon*, and the American oyster.

6. How are rainbow trout eggs, channel catfish fingerlings, and postlarval shrimp transported?

7. How would you develop a program for improving channel catfish brood stock through mass selection?

8. What is genotype/environmental interaction?

9. Give a procedure for producing monosex tilapia.

10. Choose one or more culture species you wish to develop into a synthetic strain. List the steps you would take.

REFERENCES

Ali, K.H. 1978. A new system of mass rearing of penaeid shrimp larvae. pp. 254-262. In Proceedings First National Symposium on Shrimp Farming, Bombay, India. Marine Production Export Development Authority, Cochin.

Ali, K.H., S.N. Dwivedi and K.H. Alikunhi. 1982. A new hatchery system for commercial rearing of penaeid prawn larvae. Central Institute of Fisheries Education. Indian Council of Agricultural Research, Versova, Bombay. CIFE Bulletin 2-3(82).

Ali, K.H. and K.H. Alikunhi. 1991. Crustacean tissue suspension for commercial production of marine prawn seed. pp. 133-156. In Proceedings of the Symposium on Aquaculture Productivity, New Delhi, India.

Ali, K.H. and K.H. Alikunhi. 1993. A new simple system of penaeid shrimp larval rearing. pp. 285-294. In Proceedings Aquaculture Symposium Technology and

Investment Opportunities, Riyadh, Saudi Arabia. Ministry of Agriculture and Water. 627 pp.

Allee, B.J. 1982. Oregon and Washington perspectives in salmon ranching. pp. 67-74. In Proceedings 3rd Alaska Aquaculture Conference. Alaska Sea Grant Report 82-8.

Allen, S.K. and S.L. Downing. 1986. Performance of Pacific oysters, *Crassostrea gigas*, (Thunberg). I. Survival, growth, glycogen content and sexual maturation in yearlings. Journal Experimental Biological Ecology 102:197-208.

Altman, R.W. and W.H. Irwin. 1956. Minnow farming in the Southwest. Oklahoma Department of Wildlife Conservation. Oklahoma City, Oklahoma. 35 pp.

Anderson, G.J., M.B. Miller and K. Chew. 1982. A guide to Manila clam aquaculture in Puget Sound. Washington Sea Grant Program, College of Ocean and Fishery Sciences, University of Washington. HG-30, Seattle, Washington.

Angell, C.L. 1986. The biology and culture of tropical oysters. International Center for Living Aquatic Resources Management, Manila, Philippines.

Avault, J.W., Jr. 1988. "New" species for aquaculture. Aquaculture Magazine 14(2):53-55.

Avault, J.W., Jr. 1989. How will fish be grown in the future? Aquaculture Magazine 15(1):57-59.

Avault, J.W., Jr. and E.W. Shell. 1968. Preliminary studies with hybrid tilapia, *Tilapia aurea X T. mossambica*. Proceedings of the World Symposium on Warm-Water Pond Fish Culture. FAO Fisheries Report No. 44, 4:237-242.

Avault, J.W., Jr. and J.V. Huner. 1985. Crawfish culture in the United States. pp. 1-61. In Crustacean and Mollusk Aquaculture in the United States. Westport, Connecticut: Avi Publishing Company Inc. 476 pp.

Bondari, K. 1990. Reproduction and genetics of the channel catfish (*Ictalurus punctatus*). Reviews in Aquatic Sciences 2:357-374.

Breese, W.P. and R.E. Malouf. 1975. Hatchery manual for the Pacific oyster. Oregon State University, Corvallis, Oregon. Sea Grant Program Publication No. ORESU-H-75-002.

Brooks, W.K. 1879. Abstract of observations upon artificial fertilization of oyster eggs and embryology of American oyster. American Journal of Science, New Haven, XVIII:425-527.

Burnside, M.C., J.W. Avault, Jr. and W.G. Perry, Jr.. 1975. Comparison of a wild and a domestic strain of channel catfish grown in brackish water. Progressive Fish-Culturist 37:52-54.

Burrell, V.G. 1985. Oyster culture. pp. 235-273. In Crustacean and Mollusk Aquaculture in the United States. Westport, Connecticut: Avi Publishing Company Inc. 476 pp.

Busch, R.L. 1985. Harvesting, grading and transporting. pp. 543-567. In Channel Catfish Culture. Amsterdam-Oxford-New York-Tokyo: Elsevier Science Publishing Company Inc. 657 pp.

Cange, S.W., D.L. Pavel, M.S. Lamon and J.W. Avault, Jr. 1987. Development of larval rearing systems for the Malaysian prawn, *Macrobrachium rosenbergii*, in Southern Louisiana. pp. 43-49. In Reproduction, Maturation and Seed Production of Cultured Species. U.S. Department of Commerce NOAA Technical Report NMFS 47.

Castagna, M. and J.N. Kraeuter. 1981. Manual for growing the hard clam *Mercenaria*. Special Report in Applied Marine Science and Ocean Engineering No. 249. Virginia Institute of Marine Science, Gloucester Point, Virginia. 110 pp.

Chamberlain, G.W., M.G. Haby and R.J. Miget (editors). 1985. Texas shrimp farming manual, an update on current technology. Proceedings of Texas Shrimp Farming Workshop. Texas A & M Research and Extension Center, Corpus Christi, Texas.

Chaudhuri, H. and S.D. Tripathi. 1979. Problems of warmwater seed production. pp. 127-133. In Advances in Aquaculture. FAO Technical Conference on Aquaculture, Kyoto, Japan. 653 pp.

Childerhose, R.S. and M. Trim. 1979. Pacific salmon and steelhead trout. Seattle, Washington: University of Washington Press. 158 pp.

Clark, J.E. and D. Langmo. 1979. Oyster seed hatcheries on the U.S. West Coast: an overview. Marine Fisheries Review, December 1979:10-16.

Cloud, J.G., W.H. Miller and M.J. Levanduski. 1990. Crypreservation of sperm as a means to store salmonid germ plasm and to transfer genes from wild fish to hatchery populations. Progressive Fish-Culturist 52:51-53.

Collins, C.M. (no date). Catfish cage culture, fingerlings to food fish. Bulletin by Kerr Foundation Agricultural Division, Poteau, Oklahoma. 22 pp.

Crow, C.W. 1987. Effects of brine shrimp (*Artemia salina*) density on development and survival of two densities of larval Malaysian prawns (*Macrobrachium rosenbergii*). M.S. Thesis, Louisiana State University. 34 pp.

Davis, K.B., B.A. Simco, C.A. Goudie, N.C. Parker, W. Cauldwell and R. Snellgrove. 1990. Hormonal sex manipulation and evidence for female homogamety in channel catfish. General and Comparative Endocrinology 78:218-223.

Davis, K.B., C.A. Goudie, B.A. Simco, T.R. Tiersch and G.J. Carmichael. 1992. Influence of dihydrotestosterone on sex determination in channel and blue catfish: period of developmental sensitivity. General and Comparative Endocrinology 86: 147-151.

de la Bretonne, L.W., Jr. and J.W. Avault, Jr. 1971. Movements of brown shrimp, *Penaeus aztecus*, and white shrimp, *Penaeus setiferus*, over weirs in marshes of south Louisiana. Proceedings Southeastern Association of Game and Fish Commissioners 25:651-654.

Donaldson, E.M. 1977. Bibliography of fish reproduction 1963-1974. Part 1 of 3 parts. general, non-teleostean species and teleostei, Abramis to Clinostomus. Fisheries and Marine Service Canada. Technical Report No. 732.

Donaldson, E.M. and T.J. Benfey. 1987. Current status of induced sex manipulation. pp. 108-119. Proceedings Third International Symposium on Reproductive Physiology of Fish, St. John's Newfoundland, Canada.

Dunham, R.A. and R.O. Smitherman. 1984. Ancestry and breeding of catfish in the United States. Alabama Agricultural Experiment Station, Auburn University, Alabama. Circular 273, 93 pp.

Dunham, R.A. and R.O. Smitherman. 1985. Improved growth rate, reproductive performance, and disease resistance of crossbred and selected catfish from AU-M and AU-K lines. Alabama Agricultural Experiment Station, Auburn, Alabama. Circular 279.

Dupree, H.K. and O.L. Green. 1969. Comparison of feed conversion and growth rate of six catfish species and their hybrids. Southeastern Fish Cultural Laboratory, Marion, Alabama. 13 pp.

Dupree, H.K. and J.V. Huner (editors). 1984. Third report to the fish farmers. U.S. Fish and Wildlife Service, Washington, D.C. 270 pp.

Dupuy, J.L., N.T. Windsor and C.E. Sutton. 1977. Manual for design and operation of an oyster seed hatchery. Special Report No. 142 in Applied Marine Science and Ocean Engineering of the Virginia Institute of Marine Science Gloucester Point, Virginia. 104 pp.

Eeckhout, G.V. 1978. Bait vendors handbook. North Dakota Game and Fish Department. 60 pp.

Eipper, A. 1959. Trout for farm ponds. Information Leaflet. New York State Conservation Department.

Emmerson, W.D. 1983. Maturation and growth of ablated and unablated *Peneaus monodon* Fabricius. Aquaculture 32:235-241.

Fast, A.W. and L.J. Lester. 1992. Marine Shrimp Culture: Principles and Practices. Amsterdam-London-New York-Tokyo: Elsevier Publishing Company Inc. 862 pp.

Fischetti, M. 1991. A feast of gene-splicing down on the fish farm. Science 253:512-513.

Flickinger, S.A. 1971. Pond culture of bait fishes. Cooperative Extension Service, Colorado State University, Fort Collins. Bulletin 478 A.

Forney, J.L. 1957. Bait fish production in New York ponds. Department of Conservation, Cornell University. Reprinted from New York Fish and Game Journal.

Forney, J.L. 1958. Raising bait fish and crayfish in New York ponds. Cornell Extension Bulletin 986.

Galbreath, P.F. and G.H. Thorgaard. 1993. Sex reversal, chromosomes set manipulation, and hybridization of salmonids. Parts I, II, III. Spring, summer, and'fall issues of Salmonid.

Goodwin, H.A. and J.A. Hanson. 1977. The aquaculture of freshwater prawns (*Macrobrachium* spp.). The Oceanic Institute of Hawaii. 94 pp.

Goudie, C.A., B.D. Rednes, B.A. Simco and K.B. Davis. 1983. Fertilization of channel catfish by oral administration of steroid sex hormones. Transactions American Fisheries Society 112: 670-672.

Green, O.L., R.O. Smitherman and G.B. Pardue. 1979. Comparisons of growth and survival of channel catfish, *Ictalurus punctatus*, from distinct populations. pp. 626-628. In Advances in Aquaculture. FAO Technical Conference on Aquaculture, Kyoto, Japan. 653 pp.

Grout, B.W., G.J. Morris and M.R. McLellan. 1992. Cryopreservation of gametes and embryos of aquatic organisms. Symposium Zoological Society of London 64: 63-71.

Guerrero, R.D. 1979. Culture of male *Tilapia mossambica* produced through artificial sex reversal. pp. 166-168. In Advances in Aquaculture. FAO Technical Conference on Aquaculture, Kyoto, Japan. 653 pp.

Guerrero, R.D., A.A. Augustines, Jr., R.D. Fortes, P.A. Acosta and G. Guevara. 1976. The Philippines recommendations for tilapia 1976. Philippine Council for Agriculture and Resources Research. 28 pp.

Guest, W.C., J.W. Avault, Jr. and J.D. Roussel. 1976a. A spermatology study of channel catfish (*Ictalurus punctatus*). Transactions American Fisheries Society 105(3):463-468.

Guest, W.C., J.W. Avault, Jr. and J.D. Roussel. 1976b. Preservation of channel catfish sperm. Transactions American Fisheries Society 105(3):469-474.

Guidice, J. 1966. Growth of blue x channel hybrid as compared to its parent species. Progressive Fish-Culturist 28:142-145.

Guidice, J.J., D.L. Gray and J.M. Martin. 1981. Manual for bait fish culture in the South. University of Arkansas Cooperative Extension Service and U.S. Fish and Wildlife Service EC 550-5M-5-81.

Hanson, J.A. and H.L. Goodwin (editors). 1977. Shrimp and prawn farming in the Western Hemisphere. Pennsylvania: Dowden, Hutchinson and Ross Inc. 439 pp.

Harbell, S.C. and R. Carkner. 1981. Trout farming in Washington. Cooperative Extension Service, Washington State University. Sea Grant WSG DP 81-5.

Hickling, C.F. 1962. Fish Culture. London: Faber and Faber. 296 pp.

Hidu, H., K.G. Drobeck, E.A. Dunnington, Jr., W.H. Rossenberg and R.L. Beckett. 1969. Oyster hatcheries for the Chesapeake Bay Region. NRI Special Report No. 2. Natural Resources Institute, University of Maryland, College Park, Maryland.

Hidu, H., S.R. Chapman and D. Dean. 1981. Oyster mariculture in subboreal (Maine, United States of America) waters: Cultchless setting and nursery culture of European and American oysters. Journal Shellfish Research 1(1):57-67.

Hill, T.K., J.L. Chesness and E.E. Brown. 1973. Growing channel catfish, *Ictalurus punctatus*, in raceways. Proceedings Southeastern Association of Game and Fish Commissioners 27:488-499.

Hodson, R., T. Smith, J. McVey, R. Harrell and N. Davis (editors). 1987. Hybrid striped bass culture: status and perspective. University of North Carolina Sea Grant College Publication Inc. UNC-SG-87-03.

Hora, S.L. and T.V.R. Pillay. 1962. Handbook on Fish Culture in the Indo-Pacific Region. FAO Fisheries Biology Technical Paper No. 14.

Huner, J.V. 1983. Trout farming in Finland. Farm Pond Harvest 17(2):12-14 & 29.

Ingram, M. 1988. Farming rainbow trout in fresh water tanks. pp. 155-201. In Salmon and Trout Farming. New York-Chichester-Brisbane-Toronto: John Wiley & Sons Inc. 271 pp.

Jaspers, E.J., J.W. Avault, Jr. and J.D. Roussel. 1976. Spermatozoal morphology and ultrastructure of channel catfish, *Ictalurus punctatus*. Transactions American Fisheries Society 105(3):475-480.

Jensen, G. (editor). 1987. Louisiana aquaculture, catfish fingerling production workshop. Louisiana Cooperative Extension Service.

Jensen, J., R. Dunham and J. Flynn. 1983. Producing channel catfish fingerlings. Alabama Cooperative Extension Service, Auburn University. Circular ANR-327.

Jhingran, V.G. and R.S. V. Pullin. 1988. A hatchery manual for the common, Chinese and Indian major carps. Asian Development Bank, International Center for Living Aquatic Resources Management. 191 pp.

680

Jones, C.M. 1990. The biology and aquaculture potential of the tropical freshwater crayfish *Cherax quadricarinatus*. Queensland Department of Primary Industries GPO Box 46 Brisbane Q4001 Australia.

Kerby, J.H. 1983. Cryogenic preservation of sperm from striped bass. Transactions American Fisheries Society 112:86-94.

Kerby, J.H., L.C. Woods III and M. Huish. 1983. Pond culture of striped bass x white bass hybrids. Journal of the World Mariculture Society 14:613-623.

Kirpichnikov, V.S. 1968. Efficiency of mass selection and selection of relatives in fish culture. Proceedings of the World Symposium on Warm-Water Pond Fish Culture. FAO Fisheries Report No. 44, 4:179-194.

Kuo, C.M. 1985. A review of induced breeding of milkfish. pp. 57-77. In Reproduction and culture of milkfish. Proceedings for a Workshop held at Tungkang Marine Laboratory, Taiwan, Oceanic Institute and Tungkang Marine Laboratory.

Laird, L. and T. Needham (editors). 1988. Salmon and Trout Farming. New York-Chichester-Brisbane-Toronto: John Wiley & Sons Inc. 271 pp.

Landforce, A.S. 1972. Managing Oregon trout ponds. Cooperative Extension Service, Oregon State University. Extension Bulletin 792.

Lawrence, A.L., Y. Akamine, B.S. Middleditch, G.W. Chamberlain and D.L. Hutchins. 1980. Maturation and reproduction of *Penaeus setiferus* in captivity. Proceedings of the World Mariculture Society 11:481-487.

Lawrence, A.L., J.P. McVey and J.V. Huner. 1985. Penaeid shrimp culture. pp. 127-157. In Crustacean and Mollusk Aquaculture in the United States. Westport, Connecticut: Avi Publishing Company Inc. 476 pp.

Lee, C.S. and I.C. Liao (editors). 1985. Reproduction and culture of milkfish. Oceanic Institute Makapuu Point, Waimanalo, Hawaii and Tungkang Marine Laboratory Tungkang, Pingtung, Taiwan. 226 pp.

Lee, C.S., M.S. Gordon and W.O. Watanabe (editors). 1986. Aquaculture of milkfish (*Chanos chanos*): state of the art. Oceanic Institute Makapuu Point Waimanalo, Hawaii. 284 pp.

Leitritz, E. and R.C. Lewis. 1980. Trout and salmon culture. University of California at Berkley. California Fish Bulletin 164.

Liao, I.C. 1985. A brief review on the larval rearing techniques of penaeid prawns. pp. 65-78. In Proceedings First International Conference on the Culture of Penaeid Prawns/Shrimps. Aquaculture Department, Southeast Asian Fisheries Development Center, Iloilo City, Philippines.

Lin, S.Y. 1935. Life History of waan ue, *Ctenopharyngodon idellus* (Cuv. & Val.) Lingnan Science Journal 14(1):129-135 and 14(2):271-274.

Ling, S.W. 1962. Studies on the rearing of larvae and juveniles and culturing of adults of *Macrobrachium rosenbergii* (de Man). Indo-Pacific Fisheries Council Affairs Bulletin No. 35. 11 pp.

Ling, S.W. 1969a. The general biology and development of *Macrobrachium rosenbergii* (de Man). FAO UN Fisheries Report 57(3):589-606.

Ling, S.W. 1969b. Methods of rearing and culturing *Macrobrachium rosenbergii* (de Man). FAO UN Fisheries Report (57)3:607-619.

Lutz, R.A. 1980. Mussel culture: an East Coast Perspective. pp. 99-140. In Mussel Culture and Harvest: A North American Perspective. Amsterdam-Oxford-New York: Elsevier Science Publishing Company Inc. 350 pp.

Lutz, R.A. and I.C. Darling (editors). 1980. Mussel Culture and Harvest: A North American Perspective. Amsterdam-Oxford-New York: Elsevier Science Publishing Company Inc. 350 pp.

Malecha, S. 1977. Genetics and selective breeding. pp. 328-355. In Shrimp and Prawn Farming in the Western Hemisphere. Stroudsburg, Pennsylvania: Dowden, Hutchinson and Ross Inc. 439 pp.

Manzi, J.J. 1985. Clam aquaculture. pp. 275-310. In Crustacean and Mollusk Aquaculture in the United States. Westport, Connecticut: Avi Publishing Company Inc. 476 pp.

Manzi, J.J. and J.M. Whetstone. 1981. Intensive hard clam mariculture: A primer for South Carolina watermen. South Carolina Sea Grant Consortium Marine Advisory Publication 81-01.

Manzi, J.J. and M. Castagna (editors). 1989. Clam Mariculture in North America. Amsterdam-Oxford-New York-Tokyo: Elsevier Science Publishing Company Inc. 461 pp.

Marriage, L.D., A.E. Borell and P.M. Scheffer. 1971. Trout ponds for recreation. U.S. Department of Agriculture. Farmer's Bulletin No. 2249.

Marsa, L. 1993. On the 8th day. Eating Well July/August 41-47 &100.

McNeil, W.J. and J.E. Bailey. 1975. Salmon ranchers manual. Northwest Fisheries Center Auke Bay Fisheries Laboratory, National Marine Fisheries Service, NOAA, P. O. Box 155, Auke Bay, Alaska 99821.

McVey, J.P. and J.R. Moore (editors). 1983. CRC Handbook of Mariculture, Volume I. Crustacean Aquaculture. Boca Raton, Florida: CRC Press Inc. 442 pp.

Medley, P.B. 1994. Production capabilities and economic potential of an Australian redclaw crayfish (*Cherax quadricarinatus*) hatchery in the United States. Ph.D Dissertation, Louisiana State University. 73 pp.

Menzel, R.W. 1971. Quahog clams and their possible mariculture. Proceedings of the World Mariculture Society 2:23-36.

Merrick, J.R. and C.N. Lambert. 1991. The yabby, marron and red claw production and marketing. J.R. Merrick Publications P.O. Box 490 Artarmon, N.S.W. Australia 2064. 180 pp.

Mistakidis, M.N. (editor). 1967. Proceedings of the World Scientific Conference on the Biology and Culture of Shrimps and Prawns. Food and Agriculture Organization Fisheries Reports No. 57, volumes 1, 2, 3,4.

Moav, R. 1979. Genetics and genetic improvements of fish. pp. 610-622. In Advances in Aquaculture. FAO Technical Conference on Aquaculture, Kyoto, Japan. 653 pp.

Motoh, H. 1981. Studies on the fisheries biology of the giant tiger prawn, *Penaeus monodon*, in the Philippines. Seafdec Aquaculture Department Tigbauan, Iloilo, Philippines. Technical Report No. 7. 128 pp.

New, M.B. (editor). 1982. Giant prawn farming. Amsterdam-Oxford-New-York: Elsevier Science Publishing Company Inc. 532 pp.

Piper, R.G., I. McElwain, L.E. Orme, J. McCraren, L.G. Fowler and J.R. Leonard. 1983. Fish Hatchery Management. United States Department of Interior Fish and Wildlife Service, Washington, D.C. 517 pp.

Plemmons, B. and J.W. Avault, Jr. 1980. Six tons of catfish per acre with constant aeration. Louisiana Agriculture 23(4):6, 7 & 9.

Plumb, J.A., O.L. Green, R.O. Smitherman and G.B. Pardue. 1975. Channel catfish virus experiments with different strains of channel catfish. Transactions American Fisheries Society 104:140-143.

Prather, E.E. 1956. Experiments on the commercial production of golden shiners. Proceedings Southeastern Association of Game and Fish Commissioners 10:150-155.

Prather, E.E., J.R. Fielding, M.C. Johnson and H.S. Swingle. 1954. Production of bait minnows in the Southeast. Alabama Agricultural Experiment Station of the Polytechnic Institute. Circular No. 112.

Quayle, D.B. 1988. Pacific oyster culture in British Columbia. Canadian Bulletin of Fisheries and Aquatic Sciences 218. 241 pp.

Sandifer, P.A. and T.I.J. Smith. 1985. Freshwater prawns. pp. 63-126. In Crustacean and Mollusk Aquaculture in the United States. Westport, Connecticut: Avi Publishing Company Inc. 476 pp.

Sarver, D., S. Malecha and D. Onizuka. 1979. Development and characterization of genetic stocks and their hybrids in *Macrobrachium rosenbergii*: physiological responses and larval development rates. Proceedings of the World Mariculture Society 10:880-892.

Schmittou, H.R. 1970. The culture of channel catfish, *Ictalurus punctatus* (Rafinesque), in cages suspended in ponds. Proceedings Southeastern Association of Game and Fish Commissioners 23:226-244.

Schreck, C.B. 1974. Control of sexes in fish. Sea Grant Extension Division. Virginia Polytechnic Institute & State University, Blacksburg, Virginia. UPI-SG-74-01.

Schuster, W. 1949. Fish culture in brackish water ponds of Java. Indo-Pacific Fisheries Publication No. 1 FAO.

Sedgwick, S.D. 1976. Trout farming handbook. London: Seeley Service & Company. 163 pp.

Sedgwick, S.D. 1982. The Salmon Handbook. London: Andre Deutsch 105 Great Russel Street, London WCI. 209 pp.

Simco, B.A., C.A. Goudie, G.T. Klar and N.C. Parker. 1989. Influence of sex on growth of channel catfish. Transactions American Fisheries Society 118:147-151.

Smitherman, R.O. and R.A. Dunham. 1985. Genetics and breeding. pp. 283-321. In Channel Catfish Culture. Amsterdam-Netherlands: Elsevier Publishing Company Inc. 657 pp.

Smoker, W.W. and C.L. Kerns. 1977. Artificial salmon spawning, a manual. University of Alaska Sea Grant Marine Advisory. Bulletin No. 7.

Swingle, H.S. 1953. A repressive factor controlling reproduction in fishes. Proceedings 8th Pacific Science Congress Oceanography and Zoology 8:865-871.

Swingle, H.S. 1956. Determination of balance in farm fish ponds. Transactions North American Wildlife Conference 21:298-322.

Swingle, H.S. 1962. Management of impounded waters. Unpublished Lecture Notes.

Swingle, H.S. and EV. Smith. 1950. Management of farm fish ponds. Agricultural Experiment Station of the Alabama Polytechnic Institute. Bulletin No. 254.

Tave, D. 1989. All-male catfish could improve yield. Aquaculture Magazine 15(4):67-69.

Tave, D. 1993a. Genetics for Fish Hatchery Managers. 2nd edition. Westport, Connecticut: Avi Publishing Company Inc. 415 pp.

Tave, D. 1993b. Improving channel catfish x blue catfish spawning success. Aquaculture Magazine 19(2):83-86.

Tave, D. 1994. Creating a synthetic strain. Aquaculture Magazine 18(5):72-74.

Thomas, C.H., J.C. Bush, E.D. Norwood, E.E. Prather and S.F. Baima. 1982. Catfish farming. U.S. Department of Agriculture, Soil Conservation Service. Farmers Bulletin 2260.

Tiersch, T.R., B.A. Simco, K.B. Davis and S.S. Wachtel. 1992. Molecular genetics of sex determination in channel catfish; Studies on SRY, ZFY, Bkm, and Human Repeats.

Tucker, C.S. (editor). 1985. Channel Catfish Culture. Amsterdam-Oxford-New-York-Tokyo: Elsevier Science Publishing Company Inc. 657 pp.

Usui, A. 1974. Eel Culture. Surrey, England: Fishing News (Books) Ltd. 186 pp.

Villaluz, A.C. 1986. Fry and fingerling collection and handling. pp. 153-180. In Aquaculture of milkfish (*Chanos chanos*). State of the Art. Oceanic Institute Makapuu Point Waimanalo, Hawaii 96795, U.S.A.

Walne, P.R. 1974. Culture of Bivalve Mollusks. Surrey, England: Fishing News (Books) Ltd. 173 pp.

Wells, W.F. 1927. Report of the experimental shellfish station. New York, State Conservation Department. Report No. 16, 22 pp.

Wolters, W.R., G.S. Libey and C.L. Chrisman. 1981. Induction of triploidy in channel catfish. Transactions American Fisheries Society 110: 312-314.

Wolters, W.R., G.S. Libey and C.L. Chrisman. 1982. The effect of triploidy on the growth and reproductive development of channel catfish. Transactions American Fisheries Society 111:102-105.

Woods, L.C. III, J.H. Kerby and M.T. Huish. 1983. Estuarine cage culture of hybrid striped bass. Journal of theWorld Mariculture Society 14:595-612.

Woynarovich, E. and L. Horvath. 1980. The artificial propagation of warm-water finfishes -- a manual for extension. FAO Fisheries Technical Paper No. 201.

CHAPTER 14
MAXIMIZING PRODUCTION AND PROFIT

A major goal in aquaculture is to maximize production and therefore profit. Regardless of the level of production, fixed costs remain the same. It benefits you to increase inputs and variable costs to maximize production and profit. This quantitative production, however, may not always yield the best economic production. For example, in Indonesia and Africa high yields of tilapia can be obtained because people will accept very small fish as food, but in many countries small fish are not marketable. By stocking less tilapia and controlling reproduction in grow-out ponds, production is lower, but the larger fish produced are of more economic value. Either way, a point is reached when the cost of inputs such as feed, fertilizer, and labor exceeds the additional revenue obtained from increased production. Regardless, to increase profit strive to maximize production.

There are two general ways to maximize production. First, an aquaculturist can employ good culture practices including water management, disease and weed control, fertilization and liming, feeding, and pond maintenance. Good culture practices have been well covered and will not be discussed here. Second, production can be increased by optimizing the way in which we grow culture species.

In this chapter, we discuss methods for maximizing production and profit by carefully manipulating the way in which we grow culture species. This involves choice of species cultured, stock manipulation, increasing space for culture species and natural food organisms, polyculture, multiple cropping of culture species, multiple cropping of culture species and plants, multiple cropping of culture species and other animals, and use of thermal waters. Good reviews are given by Hickling (1961, 1962), Huet (1968, 1970), Rabanal (1968), Swingle (1968), Yashouv (1966), and Hepher and Pruginin (1981).

CHOICE OF CULTURE SPECIES
Efficient Species

The highest production, using natural food organisms, is obtained with culture species having the shortest food chain. Mollusks are therefore very efficient species. As filter feeders of plankton, they have short food chains. Swingle (1968) reported production of finfish species with varying food habits in fertilized ponds as follows:

Species	Feeding Habit	Maximizing Production kg/ha	lb/ac
Largemouth bass, *Micropterus salmoides*	piscivorous	196	175
Channel catfish, *Ictalurus punctatus*	insectivorous	370	330
Bluegill, *Lepomis macrochirus*	insectivorous	560	500
Java tilapia, *Tilapia mossambica* (*Oreochromis mossambicus*)	plankton-feeder	1,612	1,440

In this example, the tilapia had the shortest food chain, going from plankton to fish. The channel catfish and bluegill added one more link to the food chain (insects), whereas the largemouth bass added two more links (insects plus forage fish). In fertilized waters, the bluegill was more efficient than the channel catfish. Yet when stocked in ponds receiving supplemental feeding, the order was reversed. Catfish yielded 2,688 kg/ha (2,400 lb/ac) and bluegill 896 kg/ha (800 lb/ac). Swingle concluded that the smaller mouth size of bluegill made it more efficient in harvesting natural food organisms, but this was no advantage when supplemental feed was used.

Swingle pointed out that a particular species may be highly efficient when cultured under one system but less efficient under another system. The Congo tilapia (*Tilapia melanopleura*), for example, feeds extensively on submersed aquatic plants. However, when placed in a pond with fertilized water and plankton, it gives relatively low production because its gill rakers are too widely spaced to use plankton efficiently. When supplemental feed was used, Swingle (1968) reported that maximum production was 2,240 kg/ha (2,000 lb/ac) with Congo tilapia and 6,048 kg/ha (5,400 lb/ac) with Java tilapia.

Yashouv (1968) reviewed choice of culture species for various countries based on particular culture systems. In the Far East, fish farming has developed in small family ponds. Ponds are part of an ecological complex. A latrine, bath house, and pigsty are erected on the bank to supply nutrients to pond waters. Refuse materials, such as grass, banana leaves, silk worm pupae, cow dung, and night soil, are added to ponds. Various Chinese carps, including silver carp (*Hypophthalmichthys molitrix*), bighead carp (*Aristichthys nobilis*), grass carp (*Ctenopharyngodon idella*), and common carp (*Cyprinus carpio*), adapt well to this system. In Europe, fish culture is characterized by large ponds. Feeding is practiced and common carp is a major species. The demand is for large fish, particularly at Christmas. In Israel both land and water are scarce, so culture techniques are intensive, involving high stocking and feeding rates. Fish cultured under these conditions must be efficient. Rabanal (1968) reviewed the most efficient species for culture under particular conditions in India, Pakistan, Japan, China, Indonesia, Taiwan, and elsewhere.

Genetically Improved Culture Species

Use of genetically improved culture species or hybrids can maximize production (Moav 1976a). When two strains of common carp, European carp and big-belly carp of China, were crossed, the progeny outperformed either parent. Moav (1979b), however, pointed out that when a wide range of culture systems is involved, powerful genotype-environment interactions may occur. This is particularly true in finfish aquaculture. Culture systems may range from raising fish in ponds without fertilization or feeding to crowding them in cages where protein-rich feeds are used. You cannot take the view that genetics and husbandry are two separate approaches to increased production. Moav (1979b) made a strong case that genetic improvement and husbandry are inseparable. Green et al. (1979) compared six strains of channel catfish and two of their hybrids in aquaria, cages, and ponds. Their results clearly corroborated Moav's. Growth and survival varied, depending on the culture system, strain, and hybrid.

Fast Growing Culture Species

A fast growing culture species should be chosen for grow-out. The less time required for grow-out, the sooner the product can be sold. The milkfish (*Chanos chanos*) grown in Indonesia, the Philippines, Taiwan, and elsewhere grows extremely fast, reaching market size of about 350 g (0.8 lb) in a few short months (Figure 14.1).

Figure 14.1 Milkfish is a fast growing fish.

Beyond 0.5 kg (1.1 lb), growth slows considerably, but this is of no consequence since market size for most outlets has been reached. Thus two or even three crops of fish can be produced in one year. In the southern United States, the channel catfish outgrows the blue-catfish (*Ictalurus furcatus*) the first year in grow-out ponds. The market calls for a 454 to 680 g (1 to 1.5 lb) fish. The blue catfish usually surpasses the channel catfish in growth the second and third year. If the market calls for a much larger fish, the blue catfish might be the better choice based solely on growth rate.

Sometimes it is wise to choose a fish for economic reasons even if it is not a fast grower. In Yugoslavia, the slow growing tench (*Tinca tinca*) is cultured even though production is relatively low. Greater production can be reached with common carp, but the value of tench is so high that the loss in fish production is offset in economic gain.

Reproduction of Culture Species

Ideally, culture species should spawn in captivity to provide seed for grow-out (Chaudhuri and Tripathi 1976). Some culture species spawn readily in captivity, and techniques are well documented. On the other hand, it is usually desirable that they do not reproduce in grow-out ponds.

Culture of certain species has been affected by lack of seed for stocking grow-out ponds. Pompano (*Trachinotus carolinus*) may have potential for culture in the southeastern United States, but fingerlings had to be seined from ocean bays. The channel catfish, native to rivers, has adapted well to reproducing in ponds. Grass carp require flowing water to complete the natural reproductive cycle. Fertilized eggs float down river currents until they hatch. Now grass carp and other Chinese carps are spawned artificially with injections of carp pituitary or hormones. Milkfish seed is still collected wild from ocean bays, although seed is being produced in captivity. Penaeid shrimp farming was originally based on wild spawning. Either gravid females were caught offshore and brought into hatcheries to spawn, or wild postlarvae were allowed to drift with the tide into coastal ponds or were caught in estuaries.

In grow-out ponds, it is usually best if the culture species does not spawn. Otherwise, the ponds will become overpopulated with undersized, non-marketable fish. This problem is particularly serious with some species such as Java tilapia. It attains sexual maturity when about 2 to 3 months old. The female produces up to 300 young and may breed every 30 to 40 days. This can expand the fish population so greatly that stunting of fish occurs.

Unwanted spawning of any species can be controlled by culturing those species that reach market size before they are capable of spawning, rearing monosex populations, controlling environmental conditions, or using carnivorous species to control excess young.

Harvest Before Sexual Maturity Reached-- Some culture species are typically harvested before they are capable of reproducing. Swingle (1968) stocked 2 to 5 cm (0.8 to 2 in) fingerling brown bullheads (*Ameiurus nebulosus*) in June to obtain rapid growth. Fish were harvested the next May before reproduction could occur. Channel catfish are capable of spawning at 2 to 3 years of age. It is therefore possible to grow a 500 g (1.1 lb) fish before it reaches the minimum spawning age. Blue catfish become sexually mature later than channel catfish, and easily can be harvested for market before they reach maturity. Though the Java tilapia spawns at an early age, *O. niloticus* and *O. aureus* are larger and older before they spawn. Thus it is possible to grow these two species to market size with a minimum of unwanted reproduction.

Use of Monosex Species-- Stocking a monosex culture species avoids reproduction. A monosex population of tilapia may be obtained by: (1) hand sexing males and females, (2) using hormones for sex reversal, and (3) crossing various *Oreochromis* species to get all-male hybrids. Hand sexing involves rearing tilapia to a suitable size and then examining the genital papilla that contains one orifice in males and two in females. Dyes have been used to delineate orifices. Faster growing males are kept; females are discarded. Pruginin and Shell (1962) sexed tilapia, based on body thickness, with a mechanical grader. When same-age fish were used, males had thicker bodies. This method was faster than hand sexing. Hepher and Pruginin (1981) reviewed techniques of sex reversal in tilapia by feeding fry ethyltestosterone or methyltestosterone. Certain species of tilapia when crossed with other species produce all males. Male *O. hornorum* crossed with female *O. niloticus* produces all males. Hepher and Pruginin (1981) discussed other tilapia crosses.

Control of Environmental Conditions-- Control of environmental conditions usually involves temperature or salinity control, culture of riverine species in ponds, or use of a repressive factor. By maintaining temperature above or below spawning temperatures, reproduction can be controlled. This may be feasible in tank or raceway culture or when thermal effluents are used. Milkfish, which spawns in oceans, does not ordinarily spawn in brackishwater ponds. Channel catfish grow well in brackishwater ponds up to 8 ppt salinity, but seldom reproduce in salinities over 1.8 ppt. Chinese and Indian carps that spawn naturally in rivers do not spawn in grow-out ponds. Swingle (1968) reported a repressive factor that controlled reproduction of common carp and buffalo (*Ictiobus* spp.). When they were stocked at very high rates, they excreted substances into water that inhibited reproduction. *O. niloticus* stocked at 20,000 or more per ha (8,000/ac) grew well but failed to reproduce. However, *O. mossambicus* still reproduced at stocking rates of 50,000 per hectare (20,000/ac).

Use of Carnivorous Species-- Carnivorous species used to control unwanted reproduction include largemouth bass in catfish culture and pike (*Esox lucius*) in European carp culture. The snakehead (*Channa* spp.) has controlled unwanted tilapia reproduction.

STOCK MANIPULATION
Stocking Rates
The goal in choosing a stocking rate is to produce the largest percentage of marketable individuals at harvest and, at the same time, obtain the highest production. If too few are stocked, large fish can be produced but production is low. If too many are stocked, production may be high but fish are often too small to market. To increase production of marketable fish, consider species cultured, the size desired, and culture system employed. Strive for maximum production of marketable culture species within the shortest period. Swingle (1968) illustrated this with a 4-month experiment with Java tilapia in fertilized ponds:

Number Stocked		Fish Production kg/ha (lb/ac)				Percentage
Nos./ha	Nos./ac	Total		Marketable		Marketable
5,000	2,023	316	(282)	309	(276)	98
10,000	4,046	403	(360)	203	(181)	50

In this study, at the higher stocking rate of 10,000/ha production was higher than at the 5,000/ha stocking rate but the weight of marketable fish was less. In a 6-month study with bigmouth buffalofish (*Ictiobus cyprinellus*) in fertilized ponds, Swingle (1968) reported:

Number Stocked		Production		Average Size	
Nos./ha	Nos./ac	kg/ha	lb/ac	grams	lb
300	121	152	136	636	1.4
600	242	274	245	603	1.3
1,080	437	656	586	590	1.3

In this study, the final size of buffalofish was approximately the same at all stocking rates. It may have been possible to increase the stocking rate past 1,080/ha and still produce a marketable fish.

Most stocking rates of finfish in fertilized waters are based on trial and error studies. Tang and Chen (1968), however, calculated stocking rates of milkfish in ponds based on the amount of pasture algae, consisting mostly of filamentous blue-greens and diatoms. They determined that in Taiwanese ponds, the production of algae during the growing season amounted to 25,000 kg/ha (22,325 lb/ac), This amount can maintain an average fish production of 2,000 kg/ha (1,786 lb/ac).

The stocking rate of channel catfish has varied over time and with changes in culture systems. In fertilized waters at low stocking rates, catfish yielded 370 kg/ha (330 lb/ac) (Swingle 1968). Swingle later stocked 560 catfish per hectare (227/ac) and provided supplemental feed. He dismissed the fish as of little commercial value because production was only 302 kg/ha (270 lb/ac), but later he pointed out that his stocking rate was far too low.

When the catfish farming industry was in its infancy in the 1960s, many farmers stocked 3,700 fingerlings per ha (1,497/ac) in grow-out ponds and provided supplemental feed. Catfish subsisted on both natural food organisms and pelleted feeds. Later, stocking rates were increased to 5,000 per hectare (2,023/ac), and it was felt for a time that 7,500 per hectare (3,035/ac) was the ultimate maximum stocking rate. Then farmers shifted from a supplemental feed to a complete feed, and began to use aeration routinely. Now the common stocking rate became 14,826 per hectare (6,000/ac) and higher. In a study by Plemmons and Avault (1980), catfish stocked at 30,888 per hectare (12,500/ac) and grown with continuous aeration and heavy feeding produced up to 5.7 mt/ha (6.25 tons/ac) of marketable fish. These ever-increasing stocking rates have resulted in higher production and a higher percentage of marketable fish. Currently, the practice of topping off has affected the strategy for choosing stocking rates. (See topping off later this chapter.)

Trout are typically grown in raceways with flowing water. Stocking rates and production are based on flow rate such as cubic meters per second or cubic feet per second. Stocking rates and production also are presented as volume of water present in a raceway at any given time. Though stocking rates and production methods vary, rainbow trout (*Oncorhynchus mykiss*) farmers in Idaho can produce 160,085 kg of marketable trout per m^3 per second water flow (10,000 lb/ft^3/second). This production is possible by reuse of water in connecting raceways. When the trout farming industry first developed in Idaho, availability of source water was not a major limiting factor. Now water is becoming scarcer, and some trout farmers inject pure oxygen into water. This allows increased stocking rates and production.

Regarding prawns (*Macrobrachium rosenbergii*), up to and over 125,000 postlarval prawns have been stocked per hectare (50,587/ac) in tropical ponds. Large marketable prawns are produced. In south Louisiana and in other temperate climates, prawns stocked at this rate produced a very low number of acceptable size. Cange et al. (1983) reported that the percentage of marketable prawns (12 cm total length or 4.5 in) produced for stocking densities of 1.2, 2.5, 5.0, and 6.5/m^2 (1, 2, 4, and 6/yd^2) was 90%, 56%, 54%, and 56% respectively. In tropical countries, the growing season is longer, whereas in Louisiana it has run from about mid May to mid October. Moreover, prawns must often compete in the marketplace with penaeid shrimp. Prawns that run 20 to 30 g (0.7 to 1 oz) each may not look much different to most consumers than wild-caught shrimp and may not be economical to culture. Miltner et al. (1983), by stocking only 2,500 prawns per hectare (1,000/ac) in polyculture with channel catfish, had low production (200 kg/ha or 179 lb/ac), but the large prawns were more marketable. Females grew 15 to 18 per kg (7 to 8/lb) and males 9 to 11 per kg (4 to 5/lb). Since catfish was the major species, production of prawns was considered a bonus.

For years, the red swamp crawfish (*Procambarus clarkii*) was stocked into Louisiana ponds at rates to give the highest production. The price paid for live crawfish at the processing plants was for pond run. There was no grading to size. The major size-grading at the time was done in the pond by using traps with a certain mesh size. Processing plants recognized two general sizes, the largest crawfish for the boiling market (restaurant trade and home use) and the smaller crawfish for the peeling market (tail meat). Then the export market to Europe escalated for jumbo crawfish (30/kg or larger or 14/lb or larger). This was caused partly by the collapse of the wild crawfish crop from Turkey. Turkey had been supplying Sweden and other countries until a fungal disease devastated the native population of crawfish. This rather sudden demand placed a premium price on large crawfish. Moreover, the domestic markets in the United States became more sophisticated for a graded product, and a number of grades emerged.

Now researchers and farmers are searching for the optimum stocking rate in which to produce a larger, more valuable, crawfish while at the same time obtaining acceptable production. Use of manufactured feeds, while augmenting production, does not seem to increase the percentage of large crawfish. Production of large individual crawfish seems to be density dependent, much as it is with prawns. Both groups, crawfish and prawns, are very aggressive and have a strong pecking order.

Stocking Sizes

Production and profit are not only affected by stocking rates but also by stocking sizes. Fish farmers often gauge the success of their culture method by production obtained for a growing season. What is sometimes overlooked is the time required to produce a crop. A more accurate measure for efficiency of a culture method is weight gain of a culture species per unit area per per day.

Assume, for example, that a pond is stocked with 13-cm long (5 in) channel catfish fingerlings at a rate of 12,500/ha (5,000/ac). Thus a weight of about 78 kg (70 lb/ac) of fish would be stocked. If fish are fed at 3% of body weight per day, a total of 2.3 kg (2 lb/ac) of feed would be required daily. At a feed conversion of 1.5, the weight gain of fish is only 1.5 kg (1.3 lb/ac) the first day.

Now assume that 25-cm (10-in) fish are stocked weighing a total of 745 kg/ha (665 lb/ac). If fish are fed at 3% of body weight per day, a total of 22 kg (20 lb/ac) of feed would be required daily, and at a conversion rate of 1.5, the gain is 15 kg/ha (13 lb/ac) the first day.

For each culture system there is a maximum weight that can be produced. When the weight is near this maximum, space is used efficiently. Conversely, when the weight of a culture species is low, less efficient use is made of available space. Use of small fingerlings or larvae for stocking grow-out ponds lengthens the period when pond space is underutilized.

Snow (1976) suggested use of ponds of unequal size but proportionate to expected growth rate in four growing phases (Table 14.1).

Table 14.1 Multiple cropping system for unequal size pond units proportioned for four growth phases.

Pond 1 1-acre	20,000[a] 5-inch	Phase 1[b]	Stock 667 pounds. Remove 2,000 pounds. Restock immediately with 20,000 5-inch fingerlings.
Pond 2 2-acres	20,000[a] 7-inch	Phase 2[b]	Stock 2,000 pounds. Remove 4,000 pounds.
Pond 3 4-acres	20,000[a] 9-inch	Phase 3[b]	Stock 4,000 pounds. Remove 8,000 pounds.
Pond 4 8-acres	20,000[a] 11-in	Phase 4[b]	Stock 8,000 pounds. Remove 16,000 - 20,000 pounds.

[a] Less mortality, a total of 10-20 percent estimated for four phases
[b] Phase 1 - 212 days, October 16- May 15; Phase 2 - 51 days, May 16-July 5; Phase 3 - 51 days, July 6-August 25; Phase 4 - 51 days, August 26 -- October 15.
Source: Snow 1976.

In this hypothetical example, 20,000 5-in catfish fingerlings weighing 667 lb, were stocked into a 1-ac pond. When fish reached a total of 2,000 lb, they were harvested and restocked into a still larger pond, and so on. Snow (1976) pointed out that this scheme must be tempered by extra labor for harvesting and fish stress from handling. Martin (1983) demonstrated that stocking size of channel catfish and time of stocking (spring vs. fall) affected both days required for fish to reach market size and cost of production.

Both Rabanal (1968) and Tang (1979) discussed use of transition ponds in milkfish culture for maximizing daily fish gain (Figure 14.2). With this system, a series of ever larger ponds are interconnected. When fry in the first pond reach a certain weight, and when the natural food organisms are used fully, the resulting fingerlings are allowed to enter the next larger pond. Meanwhile, the first fry pond is restocked after natural food organisms become replenished. Rabanal (1968) reported that a hectare of pond area is capable of yielding 70 to 120 kg (62 to 107 lb/ac) of fish food each day, and so careful stock manipulation must be used to use this food fully.

Figure 14.2 Transition ponds for milkfish in the Philippines. Nursery pond in the foreground is interconnected to a larger intermediate size pond which is interconnected to a final grow-out pond.

A segment of the milkfish farming industry specializes in rearing milkfish fry to the fingerling stage. Fish are then stunted by reduced feeding and crowding, and maintained in good health. These fingerlings provide continuous stock for ponds when fry are no longer available. In large grow-out ponds, the frequency in which marketable fish are harvested determines profit. Frequent cropping is done by making use of a series of transition ponds that provide stock of increasingly larger sizes. By using large fish to stock grow-out ponds, the intervals between harvests are reduced to 15 to 45 days instead of the usual 90 to 180 days. Rabanal (1968) estimated that, by this system, production was increased by 200 to 900 kg/ha/year (179 to 804 lb/ac/year).

Transition ponds have been used in growing shrimp (Figure 14.3). Early postlarvae are grown in a nursery pond, allowed to move into an intermediate pond, and then a final grow-out pond.

This concept of fully using grow-out area applies to other culture systems besides ponds. Raceways, cages, floating net-pens, and tanks all can be used to maximum efficiency by keeping culture units at or near carrying capacity.

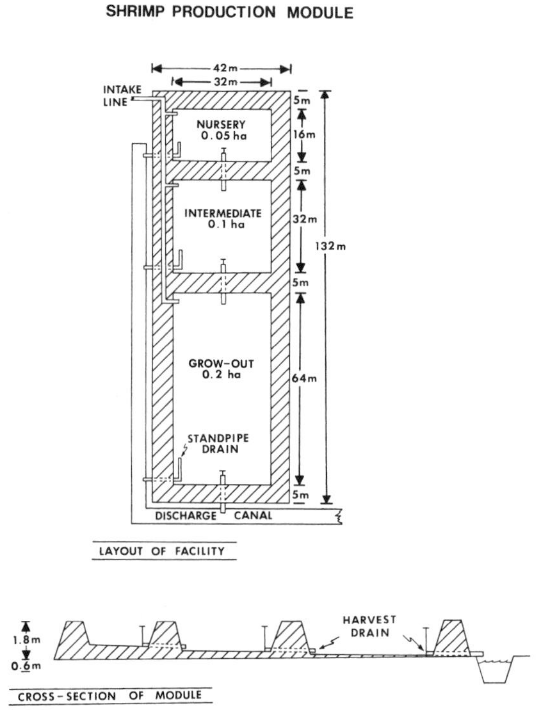

SHRIMP PRODUCTION MODULE

Figure 14.3 Transition ponds used in shrimp farming. Photo courtesy of Food and Agriculture Organization.

Size of Culture Species at Harvest

The smaller the culture species grown for market, the more efficient the system based on use of natural food organisms, time between stocking and harvest, growth rate, and feed conversion. If one market accepts a 0.5 kg (1.1 lb) fish and another requires a 1 kg (2.2 lb) fish, you may be wise to sell the smaller fish.

Growing smaller fish for market allows you to increase stocking rates. This allows better use of natural food organisms in ponds because there are more fish to find them. Moreover, small fish of the same species are more apt to feed lower on the food chain than are larger fish. In intensive culture systems, such as tanks, cages, and raceways, this would be of no advantage since all food is ordinarily from commercial diets.

By growing smaller market fish, less time is required. Depending on the species cultured and other factors, it may be possible to grow two or more crops a year. The initial cost of seed, however, must be factored into the grow-out strategy.

Growth rate and feed conversion are major considerations in maximizing efficient production. Growth rate of fish has been expressed in terms of absolute growth and relative growth. Absolute growth is simply the actual increase in size per unit of time. If a fish is 1 kg and grows to 2 kg, the absolute growth is 1 kg. Relative growth is expressed as a percentage increase in size relative to initial size, or:

$$\frac{\text{final weight - initial weight}}{\text{initial weight}}$$

If a fish initially weighs 2 kg and is grown to 3 kg, relative growth rate is: 3 - 2 ÷ 2 = 0.5 or 50%. The larger the fish, the higher its absolute potential growth. However, the absolute potential growth does not increase in direct proportion to increase in fish weight, but instead slows down. Moreover, the relative growth rate also decreases with increase in fish size.

Hepher and Pruginin (1981) gave this example: A fish of 500 g can grow 10.6 g/day, but a fish of 250 g can grow only 6.7 g/day, and a 100-g fish 3.6 g/day. However, two 250-g fish will grow more than one 500-g fish (2 x 6.7 = 13.4 g), and five 100-g fish will grow more than the larger fish (5 x 3.6 = 18 g). The larger the fish, the more food required for maintenance (no gain or loss in weight). Since small fish have less body mass, less food is required for maintenance and more is left over for growth. This fact can be used to maximize economic production.

Problem and Solution. Assume that the feed conversion to grow a fish to 2 kg is 3 and that to grow a fish to 0.5 kg is 1.5. Further assume, that net production for both is 2,000 kg/ha. What is the feed requirement for each size? For the 2 kg fish, 3 kg of feed are required for each kg of growth, requiring a total of 6,000 kg of feed. Since the 0.5 kg fish has a more efficient feed conversion of 1.5, only half as much feed is required, yet fish production is the same, 2,000 kg.

If large fish are cultured in grow-out ponds, they may reach sexual maturity before harvest. Dressing percentage will be lower, because more food goes toward production of sex products and less toward production of flesh. Further, male secondary sexual characteristics, such as large heads in catfish and large claws in crawfish, reduce dressing percentage.

Topping Off

Topping off, cull harvesting, skimming, or intermediate harvesting is the partial harvest of a fish crop. Repeated topping off may be made at regular intervals. Fingerlings or larvae stocked into ponds or other culture systems seldom grow at the same rate. By partial harvesting with seines and nets, the larger fish can be periodically removed and sold. Faster growing and larger fish often become dominant and may suppress the growth of smaller fish even though food is not a limiting factor. This was reported for channel catfish in cage culture (Schmittou 1969) and pond culture of prawns (Malecha et al. 1981). By removing larger fish, smaller fish move up in size. This allows for more efficient use of natural food and space, and shortens the time required to produce a fish crop.

Topping off is practiced with several variations. In Taiwan, milkfish fingerlings of several graded sizes are stocked into the same pond. Marketable fish are periodically removed and replaced with an equal number of fingerlings. Stocking rates and harvesting are carefully monitored to match the production of natural food organisms. Thus a series of fish crops are harvested at spaced intervals. Rabanal (1968) presented a detailed flow chart showing stocking/harvesting schedules of milkfish. He noted that the first topping off with seines may begin 2 to 4 weeks after initial stocking and at about 2-week intervals thereafter. From 10 to 13 harvests are made from April to October. In spite of the short growing season of 7 months, Taiwanese fish farmers, by stock manipulation, have produced about 2 mt/ha (0.9 tons/ac).

Channel catfish farmers in the southern United States may top off catfish, then restock with the same number of fingerlings as those fish removed, or restock with one fingerling for each 0.5 kg (1 lb) of marketable fish harvested. Seines used in harvesting have a mesh size that captures marketable fish, about 0.5 kg and larger; smaller fish pass through.

Some farmers have not drained ponds in more than 5 years. This has advantages and disadvantages. Advantages include: (1) efficient use of natural food and pond space, (2) removal of large individuals that allows smaller animals to increase in size more quickly, (3) no production time lost from harvest, (pond not drained), (4) better control over market needs, (5) conservation of water since none is lost at harvest, and (6) no discharge of effluents containing wastes to the environment. Disadvantages include: (1) metabolites accumulate, compounding problems with water quality (ammonia, low DO) and disease (brown blood disease), and (2) less opportunity for pond repairs.

Trout farmers in Idaho routinely top off fish grown in raceways. Trout, 4-cm (1.5 in) long , are stocked into production raceways. After 5 to 6 months, fish are graded as to tops (large) and bottoms (small) and then stocked back into separate production raceways. This may be repeated several times during the growing season (Figure 14.4).

Figure 14.4 Grading trout to size.

Fujimura (1974) and Malecha (1977) discussed continuous stocking and harvesting of *M. rosenbergii*. Malecha et al. (1981) later called attention to the drawbacks of continuous stocking and harvesting. They suggested instead that larvae of the same size be stocked, later divided and graded, then restocked and so on. They pointed out that severe suppression exists with prawns of mixed sizes. Moreover, female prawns are smaller and subordinate to male prawns. They further suggested a possible advantage of stocking only one sex in grow-out ponds. In research at the University of Hawaii, the Hebrew University, and the LSU Agricultural Center, the pecking order and dominance were clearly demonstrated. Blue claw males are dominant over all other prawns. For practical purposes, their growth has stopped because they are sexually mature. Orange claw males are still in the growth stage, and though they may be as large as blue claw males, they are subordinate to them. The other remaining prawns are juveniles or females. By removing blue claw males with topping off, other individuals are allowed to move up in size.

In Louisiana and elsewhere in the South, crawfish (*Procambarus spp.*) farming is based on constant topping off. Brood crawfish are stocked into ponds at about 50 kg/ha (45 lb/ac) between May and July. They mate and burrow underground for the summer. In the fall ponds are flooded, and females emerge from the ground and release young. About 61% of the females release young shortly after flooding. A smaller peak of about 15% occurs in December and

January (de la Bretonne and Avault 1976). Sporadic spawning occurs throughout the growing season, September through June. Harvesting may begin in late November. Chicken wire traps with 2-cm (0.75-in) mesh are baited with fish or manufactured baits and fished several times a week at 25 to 74 traps per ha (10 to 30/ac). Crawfish ≥ 75 mm total length (3 in) are trapped and retained. Smaller non-marketable crawfish can move in and out of the trap. Later, as they grow, they are retained in the traps.

INCREASE OF SPACE

Space can be increased by expanding the substrate area and by using the water column fully. Additional substrate provides hiding places for culture species, especially molting crustaceans, and attachment space for natural food organisms (Figure 14.5). Substrate area can be increased in ponds by adding brush piles, aquatic vegetation, and other materials. In tanks and other intensive culture systems gravel, screening, and a variety of materials have been used. Increasing the available living area of the water column can be accomplished by having adequate levels of dissolved oxygen and only low levels of toxic substances throughout the water column. This can be accomplished by circulating water from top to bottom.

Figure 14.5 Filipino pond planted with aquatic vegetation to increase substrate for natural food organisms.

Crustaceans require protection from cannibalism during molting. Goyert and Avault (1978) studied growth and survival of crawfish *Procambarus clarkii* in tanks at two stocking densities, 10/m² and 40/m² (12/yd² and 48/yd²), and with various substrate configurations. The control tanks had a gravel filter medium only. Hiding places with additional substrate were beneficial to crawfish, and survival was high. When relatively uncrowded and with low substrate area, crawfish were antagonistic, and high mortality occurred because of cannibalism during their intermolt phase. In pond production of crawfish, rice and other forages planted as food also serve as a substrate. This should also apply to culture of prawns and other crustaceans.

Limnologists refer to natural food organisms which cling to substrate as aufwuchs or periphyton. Swingle (1968) noted that in many fertilized ponds almost the entire bottom contained individual natural food organisms in proximity. He surmised that "floor space" was a limiting factor, and that providing various materials would increase surface attachment and fish production. In fertilized ponds, he concluded that brush piles greatly increased natural food organisms and freshwater shrimp (*Palaemontes kadiakensis*), and in turn increased the harvestable crop of bluegills.

In a second study, Swingle (1968) added brush to bass/bluegill ponds. Total production per ha was 283 kg (253 lb/ac) without cover and 493 kg (440 lb/ac) with cover. Hickling (1961) wrote that aufwuchs may be the primary source of food in lakes deficient in phytoplankton. In one instance, an area of rock 510 cm² (79 in²) was scraped clean of aufwuchs and the organisms counted. There were 3,500 chironomid larvae, more than 10,000 ostracods, and more than 1,000 copepods, plus other organisms.

In some pond culture systems, the water column is not used fully. In summer, water stratifies, with nonproductive dead water near the bottom. This water is typically low in dissolved oxygen and temperature and high in waste metabolites. If this stratification can be broken up, fish now have more living space. This allows for higher stocking rates and increased production. Plemmons and Avault (1980) noted that the benefits of constant aeration included the breaking up of stratification.

During pond construction, pond depth is sometimes limited. It is assumed that bottom water will stagnate during summer, and so to limit the percentage of dead water, ponds are built relatively shallow. If stratification can be controlled with water circulation, it might be wise to build deeper ponds, assuming it is economically feasible. In oyster and other mollusk culture, living space can be increased by switching from bottom culture to off-bottom culture where mollusks more fully use available plankton in the water column.

POLYCULTURE

To obtain the greatest production in ponds, grow several compatible culture species together that have various feeding habits. In Chapter 8, food chains and food webs were discussed. It was noted that a pond has a number of food niches. Figure 14.6 illustrates various food niches that may be present in a pond, but not all may be present in abundance at once. For example, channel catfish grow-out ponds may lack filamentous algae and higher plants. Milkfish ponds may have an abundance of filamentous algae and zooplankton but be deficient in phytoplankton. In designing a polyculture scheme, you must consider a number of factors.

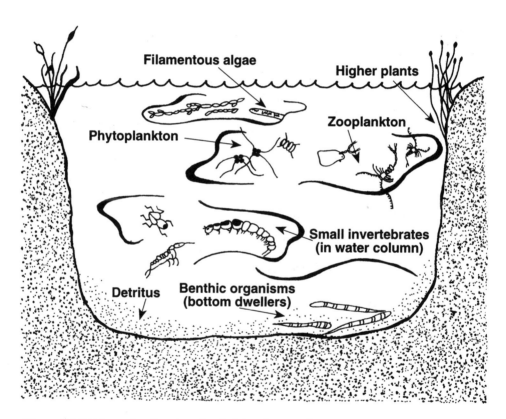

Figure 14.6 Schematic of various food niches in a pond.

Structuring the Polyculture Scheme

You must choose culture species that are marketable while filling as many food niches as possible. Tuten and Avault (1981) developed a polyculture scheme for Louisiana with this in mind. They stocked channel catfish in floating cages and fed them daily. Stocked free in the same ponds were bigmouth buffalo, paddlefish (*Polyodon spathula*), and red swamp crawfish. They were not fed but subsisted on natural food organisms and on waste catfish feed. Total net production approached 6,000 kg/ha (5,358 lb/ac). In control ponds without catfish, total net production was approximately 1,200 kg/ha (1,072 lb/ac). Production in the first set of ponds was modest when compared with that obtained in China, Israel, and elsewhere. The bigmouth buffalo and paddlefish present consumed primarily zooplankton. Crawfish used bacteria, detritus, and waste feed. Production could have been increased by stocking additional culture species. If common carp were stocked they would have used benthic organisms and silver carp phytoplankton. However, there is virtually no market for common carp in Louisiana, and silver carp is not native and illegal to grow.

As socio-economic conditions change new culture species can be added to the polyculture scheme. Such a change did occur within the channel catfish farming industry at one point. The price of producing channel catfish was above the break-even point. Farmers were losing money. A number of options were considered. One that paid off for some farmers, where legal, was addition of the bighead carp to the monoculture system of channel catfish (Stone 1994). The bighead carp added extra production without additional cost. Catfish production was not affected. The bighead was marketed to oriental communities as a fresh product, and the flesh was canned. The canned product compared favorably with salmon (*Oncorhynchus* spp.) and tuna (*Thunnus* spp.).

Each country or region must develop its polyculture scheme to reflect the market and environmental pond conditions. China has the longest history of polyculture, particularly in Kwangtung Province. Fishes usually cultured together in China include: (1) the grass carp, that feeds on coarse plants either present in the pond or added, (2) black carp (*Mylopharyngodon piceus*), that feeds on snails and other mollusks, (3) bighead carp, that consumes zooplankton, (4) silver carp, that feeds on phytoplankton, (5) mud carp (*Cirrhinus molitorella*), a bottom feeder of benthos and detritus, and (6) common carp, an omnivore and scavenger. With such a species combination, when ponds receive fertilizer and supplemental feed, a farmer can gross about 4,480 kg/ha/year (4,000 lb/ac/year) (Hickling 1962).

In the Pearl River Delta of China, the number of each species stocked per hectare varies, depending on which species is considered the major one. In one combination, the grass carp is the major species, comprising 55% of the total number of all fish species stocked. In a second, black carp comprises 42%, and in a third, silver carp comprises 65%.

In Hong Kong, gray mullet (*Mugil cephalus*) and bream (*Parabramis pekinensis*) are included in polyculture ponds. The gray mullet feeds on organic debris, algae, diatoms, rice bran, and ground cereals. The bream is an omnivore. Lin (1940) gave four stocking combinations for Hong Kong.

Stocking systems in Malaya are based on the Chinese system with modifications (Hora and Pillay 1962). Fry other than common carp are not always readily available. Moreover, returns from mud carp are not attractive. On the other hand, plants suitable for grass carp are readily available, so fish farmers in Malaya stock a proportionately larger number of grass carp.

In Israel, the common carp was formerly the main species cultured, and for years approximately 85% of all fish produced was the carp. Culture practices included heavy feeding. Now polyculture is the rule with the use of cow manure and other wastes. A typical polyculture system includes 3,000 to 6,000 common carp, 3,000 to 4,000 tilapia, 500 to 1,500 silver carp, about 1,000 mullet, and about 300 grass carp/ha. This gives a total stocking density of from 7,000 to 9,500 fish/ha (2,800 to 3,800/ac) (Hepher and Pruginin 1981).

Compatible Species

Culture species stocked in polyculture should not only fill various food niches but also be compatible with one another. In the study by Tuten and Avault (1981), channel catfish may have eaten crawfish had catfish not been cultured in floating cages. Miltner et al. (1983) stocked channel catfish fingerlings and juvenile prawns (*M. rosenbergii*) in one set of ponds and catfish fry and juvenile prawns in a second set of ponds. At harvest, the first set of ponds yielded marketable sizes of both catfish and prawns. You might surmise that catfish would have eaten the prawns, but this did not happen. Survival of prawns from 16 ponds averaged 96%. Females were 15 to 17 to the kg (7 to 8/lb) and males 8 to 11 to the kg (4 to 5/lb).

In the second set of ponds, fingerling catfish and marketable prawns were harvested, but it was very difficult to separate the two. This combination may not be feasible because of the sorting problem at harvest. Further, most channel catfish farmers harvest marketable fish by topping off. Ponds are not drained. This would pose a problem for harvesting prawns stocked with catfish. Prawns must be harvested before the onset of winter or they will perish.

W. Lorio formerly of the LSU Agricultural Center (personnel communication 1995) developed the technique of growing channel catfish and crawfish in polyculture but in separate ponds. In ponds containing crawfish, rice is planted as forage. In adjacent ponds channel catfish are grown with formulated feeds. Water is circulated from catfish ponds through crawfish ponds and back to catfish ponds. Nutrients produced from catfish wastes are filtered by growing rice plants.

Swingle (1968) wrote of stocking fathead minnows (*Pimephales promelas*) in channel catfish grow-out ponds. Minnows fed on unutilized natural food organisms and were in turn fed upon by catfish. Other polyculture systems incorporate predators. The snakehead, for example, is stocked into tilapia ponds in Africa to reduce excess reproduction. Stocking bluegill, redear (*Lepomis microlophus*), and largemouth bass in combination for sportfishing has been well worked out (Swingle 1949, 1950).

The common carp grows well with other fish species, yet if stocked at rates more than 240 per ha (96/ac) in fertilized ponds it often muddies the water (Swingle 1968). This interferes with phytoplankton production and would affect silver carp adversely. Yashouv (1968) discussed compatibility in polyculture schemes where the common carp is the principal species. The tench was added to carp ponds to control trash fish and to eat food not used by carp. Even though fish were fed, competition existed between the two species and carp production dropped. Yashouv (1968) reviewed research of others to find compatible species for carp.

Production of some culture species is sometimes greater in polyculture than in monoculture. The prawn (*M. rosenbergii*) grows well with certain fish species, such as tilapia, by feeding on bacterial enriched feces. Some fish feed on excreta of other fish, and it seems that tilapia feed on excreta of common carp, which feed on excreta of silver carp. Grass carp feed on higher plants, and their excreta is fed upon by other species. Excreta not eaten is mineralized. Released nutrients encourage growth of phytoplankton.

Herbivorous fish have been stocked into ponds containing other fish species with the sole purpose of controlling weeds. Overall production also may be increased as a result of weed control. Avault et al. (1968) reported that grass carp controlled a wide variety of weeds when stocked into ponds at 50 to 100/ha (20 to 40/ac). *Tilapia melanopleura* controlled filamentous algae and a variety of plants when stocked at 2,500 to 5,000/ha (1,000 to 2,000/ac). At this stocking rate *T. melanopleura* did not affect other fish species adversely. *Oreochromis niloticus* and *O. mossambicus* showed little promise for weed control except for control of filamentous algae. Common carp controlled filamentous algae and some higher plants when stocked at 125/ha (50/ac). Carp controlled weeds by rooting along the bottom and muddying the water. *T. zilli* is also a herbivorous species that controls weeds.

Some culture species are stocked into polyculture schemes with the intention of improving water quality. Swingle (1968) cultured the mussel (*Lampsilis* spp.) in bass/bluegill ponds. He noted that the mussel, by filtering out wastes, improved water.quality and fish production. Yashouv (1971) demonstrated that the yield of silver and common carp cultured in polyculture was higher than that of either species cultured alone. The same effect occurs when culturing common carp and tilapia. Hepher and Pruginin (1981) explained that dissolved oxygen levels improve. Silver carp consume excess algae that reduce an imbalance between oxygen production and consumption. Tilapia feed on the ooze of the pond bottom. This ooze increases oxygen consumption when decomposed by bacteria. Cohen and Ra'anan (personal communication 1982) of the Hebrew

University suggested stocking silver carp, grass carp, and common carp in all culture ponds to act as "sanitary" species for improvement of water quality.

MULTIPLE CROPPING OF CULTURE SPECIES

To obtain maximum production and profit, a culture species should be grown year-round. It is not enough that a culture species merely tolerates winter conditions; if it is not adding weight, production and profit are at a standstill. The water temperature, as we have seen in Chapter 6, has a profound effect on the growth of a culture species.

In tropical countries with a year-round growing season, more than one crop can be produced each year. In Indonesia, for example, some people prefer small fish of about 200 g (0.4 lb) so that each family member can have an individual fish at meal time. This preference and the tropical climate allow for continuous stocking and harvesting of the same species on a year-round basis.

The Philippines and Taiwan also practice constant stocking and harvesting on a year-round basis. In the Philippines, *Penaeus monodon* can be grown to market size in about 120 days. Thus it is possible to grow two or more crops per year in that country. In the southern part of Taiwan, it has been possible to grow up to two and a half crops of *P. monodon* per year. In the northern part of that country the climate becomes a bit cooler during part of the year Other shrimp species such as *P. japonicus* and *P. penicillatus* have been tested.

In temperate countries, a different strategy must be used. Typically in Europe and North America there is a distinct winter period when little or no growth occurs for warmwater species, but conditions may be suitable for culturing cool or coldwater species. In studies in Georgia (Hill et al. 1972, 1973; Brown et al. 1974), channel catfish were grown in earthen raceways during warm months and rainbow trout during cold months. The strategy was that channel catfish growth is virtually nil when water temperatures drop below 13° to 16°C (55° to 60°F), so rainbow trout were grown when temperatures were below 60°F.

In preliminary studies, the LSU Agricultural Center has alternated prawns (*Macrobrachium rosenbergii*) and red swamp crawfish (Granados et al. 1991). Crawfish were grown from October through mid May and prawns from mid May to October. Thus ponds produced a crop on a year-round basis. This not only gave higher overall annual yields, but it also spread fixed costs over two crops instead of one. Caffey et al. (1993) noted that the soft-shell crawfish industry in Louisiana is without product for 5 to 6 months of the year. This is because the native red swamp crawfish burrows underground during summer months and is therefore not available for shedding tanks. The prawn, however, is available during summer. It was possible to grow newly hatched young to 17 g (0.6 oz) in 93 days, an ideal size for the shedding tanks. Under commercial conditions, Caffey et al. (1993) reported that it was as easy to produce soft-shell prawns as it was crawfish.

There is more to it, however, than water temperature when choosing an alternative species for culture to complement the primary species. Culturing a "new" species may require major adjustments, and a number of questions should be addressed. Here are a few. Is seed readily available? Obtaining rainbow trout fingerlings may require shipping them in from other than local sources. Is this economically feasible? Culturing a different shrimp species may require entirely different hatchery techniques for obtaining seed, as noted in Chapter 13. Will the same harvesting gear be suitable for the new species? Is the new species legal to grow? In Louisiana, the prawn, *M. rosenbergii*, is not native and therefore not legal to farm without a special permit. Then there are questions regarding the market. For example, *P. monodon* is a major species for culture throughout much of the world. This shrimp has gray-colored flesh and is grown to about 30 to 40 g (1 to 1.4 oz). If a white shrimp which normally reaches a smaller size is substituted, it could require major adjustments to marketing strategy.

In spite of all these considerations, it is an advantage to seek out an alternative species for growth during winter. In reality, most farmers stay with a single species as long as they make money. It is only when profits drop below production costs that they search for an additional culture species.

MULTIPLE CROPPING OF CULTURE SPECIES WITH PLANTS

Fish can be grown simultaneously or in rotation with rice (*Oryza sativa*) by three basic methods. First, the captural method allows native fish to enter rice fields with irrigation water. Fish are trapped either on a day-to-day basis or just before rice harvest. Second, fish may be deliberately stocked into fields, a practice referred to as rice-cum-fish or rizipisciculture. The third method is the rotation of rice and fish, a practice called double cropping. Rice/fish culture is reviewed by Chen (1954), Anonymous (1957), Ardinawata (1958), Hora and Pillay (1962), Coche (1967), and Avault (1980a).

Captural

The captural system has been practiced in India, Vietnam, Malaya, Indonesia, and elsewhere. Pillay and Bose (1957) described methods used in India. Rice fields are located along the tidal rivers of Ichamati and Raimangal. The fields are surrounded by strong embankments to protect against tidal flooding. Each field has a canal system meant mainly for drainage of excess rainwater. The mouth of each canal leading to the river is provided with bamboo fencing to prevent escape of fish when water is let out.

Rice is harvested from November to January when fields and canals are dry. From February to March onward, tidal waters are taken into canals at high tides. During spring tides, young of estuarine species gain access to canals. Tidal flow into canals stops around June when the monsoon begins. Fields are planted with salt-resistant rice seedlings in July. By August, the water level in canals increases mainly because of rainwater. Bunds along canals are cut, which allows canal water to merge with water in fields. By October or November, when the rainy season is over, water in fields drops appreciably, and fields may dry up. Fish move back into canals where they may be harvested over time. Tidal water is let into canals, and fish are caught in traps as they concentrate at the bamboo fencing. Fish also are harvested by allowing them to enter ditches and then draining the ditches. A number of species is captured, including three species of mullet (*Mugil spp.*), bhekt (*Lates calcarifer*), tengra (*Mystus gulio*), and five species of prawns. Total production is estimated at 100 to 200 kg/ha (89 to 178 lb/ac).

Malaya has practiced the captural method of rice/fish culture that has been of considerable economic importance, with fish adding 25% to 50% additional income (Chua et al. 1973). Fish species of importance include sepat siam (*Trichogaster pectoralis*), catfish (*Ikan keli*), snakehead, puyu (*Anabas testudineus*), and sepat ronggeng (*T. trichopterus*). Of these, the sepat siam is most important. The fish, introduced from Thailand in the mid 1930s, adapts well to rice fields and swampy conditions. During spawning, the male builds a frothy bubble nest. After mating with a female, the male collects the eggs in his mouth and blows them into the bubble nest where they are kept afloat. Hatching takes place within 48 hours.

Major requirements for the sepat siam and other species include rice fields that hold 15 to 16 cm ($\approx$ 6 in) of water for 6 to 7 months and fields where use of insecticides is moderate to low. Fish are harvested by draining sump pits or "telaga" and scooping them out, using gill nets "pukat sepat," using hook and line "pancing," using fish traps "bubu" or "tempang," and using lift nets "tangkol" and throw nets "jala."

Rice-Cum-Fish

Species deliberately stocked and cultured in rice fields must meet certain requirements. They must: (1) be able to thrive in shallow water, (2) tolerate high water temperatures, high turbidity, and low dissolved oxygen, and in some instances brackish water, (3) not interfere with rice, (4) be adept at escaping predators, (5) grow to suitable size in a few months, and (6) be marketable. Though rice fields are normally used to grow marketable fish, they also may be used in fry and fingerling production.

Coche (1967) presented detailed information on candidate species throughout the world. The tilapia species are widely cultured in rice fields. *O. mossambicus* is very hardy and thrives in rice fields, but it reproduces readily and is therefore considered undesirable by some. In the Philippines, *O. aureus* and *niloticus* are preferred. They grow well in rice fields and are less prolific. Stocked fish reach market size of about 80 g (3 oz) in 80 days. The few young produced are restocked in other fields. Monosex *O. mossambicus* or tilapia hybrids adapt well to rice fields. The common carp is of particular importance and is widely cultured in rice fields. Dark-colored carp are preferred in some countries because they escape detection and predation better.

In Japan and elsewhere, carp may be harvested from rice fields held in wintering ponds, then restocked a second year into rice fields. Some fish may even be raised for a third year in rice fields. The milkfish meets all the requirements for culture in rice fields and thrives in brackish water. Rice fields may be used to raise milkfish fingerlings that are sold to fish farmers. The sepat siam, a highly preferred species in Malaya, is an air breather and can tolerate poor water quality. The catfish *Clarias* spp. is an air breather, too, and thrives in rice fields.

The following is a general account of rice-cum-fish culture with emphasis on methods used in the Philippines. Rice fields chosen for rice-cum-fish should use irrigation water, since water from rainfall is unpredictable. Water should be free of wild fish, insecticides, and excess silt. Weld wire screens aid in keeping out most unwanted fish. Though the size of each field may vary, most range from 200 to 2,500 m^2 (239 to 2,990 yd^2).

Fields contain trenches that serve as refuges for fish during an unexpected drop in water level, as a passageway for movement around the field, and as a catch basin for harvest. Trenches, which measure 1 m wide (3.3 ft) and 0.5 m (1.6 ft) deep, may be peripheral on all four sides (Figure 14.7), or a single trench may go through the center (Figure 14.8).

Figure 14.7 Peripheral trenches in rice field, the Philippines.

Figure 14.8 Center trench to lessen theft, the Philippines. Note sticks in middle of trench. If a thief steals fish, sticks will be knocked over to warn rice farmer.

Peripheral and center trenches may take up 25% to 10% of the total area depending on the size of the rice field. In the Philippines, center trenches are preferred because they reduce the rice area by only 10%. Moreover, both poaching and predation are less than that in fields with peripheral trenches. Levees should be larger than when rice monoculture is practiced. They should be 50 cm (20 in) wide at the base, 30 to 40 cm (12 to 16 in) top width, and 40 cm high.

Rice used in rice-cum-fish ideally should be insect and disease resistant. The International Rice Research Institute located in the Philippines has developed several useful varieties. Direct seeding is possible, but many farmers still prefer to transplant seedlings. Usually two to three seedlings per hill are set out with 20 to 25 cm (8 to 10 in) between hills and 30 cm (12 in) between rows. Rice is fertilized as usual except that acid-forming fertilizers, such as ammonium sulfate, should be avoided. At transplanting, seedlings may be soaked in a solution of 3% Carbofuran (Furadan) for 24 hours to provide temporary protection against insects. Furadan also can be incorporated into the soil at the time of fertilization and before planting. Rice plants take up the chemical by translocation with little harm to fish. If Furadan must be used later, water can be drawn off fields to allow fish to enter trenches. A 0.01% concentration of Furadan is then sprayed at the base of rice plants.

Fish fingerlings are stocked about 10 days after rice seedlings are planted. In the Philippines, common carp and tilapia fingerlings have been stocked at about 3,000 and 5,000/ha (1,200 to 2,000/ac), respectively. In polyculture, 3,000 *O. niloticus* and 2,000 common carp per hectare have been stocked. When fish and rice are small, water is kept at 5 to 8 cm (2 to 3 in). As rice grows, water depth is increased to 8 to 20 cm. Some farmers use supplemental feeds for fish, such as rice bran, fish meal, ipilipil meal, or corn meal. Fish are fed at a rate of 5% body weight daily, divided into two equal feedings. At harvest, water is drawn off the fields, and fish are collected in trenches. Fish are harvested first, then rice. A 25 g (1 oz) tilapia at stocking should grow to 50 g (2 oz) or more in 80 days. A 25 g or larger carp at stocking should grow to about 170 g (6 oz). Production reaches about 200 kg/ha (179 lb/ac), depending on species stocked and whether fish are fed.

In some countries, such as Japan, fish may be restocked to achieve larger size. In Indonesia, farmers stock up to 64,000 carp fry per ha (25,600/ac). Water is eventually drawn off fields for weeding of rice. At this time, fry are 3 to 5 cm (1 to 2 in) long and have suffered 50% mortality. Fish are harvested and restocked at rates of 16,000/ha (6,400/ac) and reach 5 to 8 cm (2 to 3 in) during the next month. At the second weeding, fish are harvested again and restocked at rates of 2,000/ha (809 ac).

Major concerns of rice-cum-fish include: poaching problems, adverse effect of pesticides on fish, requirement for higher levees and more water, and social adjustments of farmers to different farm practices. In the Philippines, some farmers who practice rice-cum-fish eventually switch to monoculture of fish because it is more lucrative.

Double Cropping

Fish are sometimes alternated or double cropped with rice. In certain areas of West Java, which have a continuous water supply, short-term fish production may be practiced between rice harvest and the next planting. Fish produced are not always grown to market size but instead may be grown to intermediate size for restocking grow-out ponds.

In Louisiana and elsewhere in the southern United States, crawfish and rice are double cropped (Avault 1980a). Rice is typically planted in March or April. Fertilization and weed control are practiced as usual; use of insecticides such as Furadan should be avoided since most insecticides are highly toxic to crawfish. In May or June, brood red swamp crawfish are stocked along the inside of levees at rates of about 40 kg/ha (45 lb/ac). Crawfish typically burrow underground where they may mate. Females also may mate before burrowing. Rice is harvested in August or September, and fields are reflooded in October. Crawfish emerge from under-ground burrows, and females release young. Crawfish begin feeding on bacteria and other microorganisms which coat decomposing rice stubble. Harvest begins in late November and is continuous until next April when rice is replanted. Crawfish yields should easily reach 1,000 kg/ha (893 lb/ac), and up to 2,000 kg/ha (1,784 lb/ac) are possible without use of commercial feeds (Day and Avault 1984).

Sometimes the market price for crawfish is very good and farmers may opt to continue harvest until June. In this case, it may be too late to plant rice but not soybeans (*Glycine max*) which have a shorter growing season. The second year that rice and crawfish are rotated, seed crawfish need not be stocked since some always remain after harvest. They produce next year's crop of young.

Besides income from two crops, rice and crawfish, there are other benefits to the farmer. (1) Since the fields stay leveed year round, there is no soil erosion. (2) Winter rains are used, thus lessening the need for pumping water. (3) Since water remains on the field throughout the winter and early spring, all terrestrial weeds are controlled, and crawfish control any aquatic weeds. Thus the need for herbicides in rice production is virtually eliminated the second year. (4) Crawfish till the soil with their activities. There is no need to disc the soil to prepare a seed bed for rice planting.

When water is drawn down after crawfish harvest, remaining crawfish burrow underground. When about 7.5 cm (3 in) of water remain, rice is wet planted. Eliminating the need to dry out and disc soils saves time, labor, and fuel. Soybeans have also been broadcasted much like rice, only they are planted immediately after all water is removed. The moist, weed-free soil allows for quick germination and growth.

Other Plant Crops
Although rice is the major plant crop grown with fish, a host of other plants has been grown in combination with fish. In the Philippines and other developing nations, family fish farms are often only 1 to 2 ha (2.5 to 5 ac) in size. They must therefore squeeze as much production from the land and water as possible. In Figure 14.9, a Filipino pond is planted with rice and tilapia. Gabi grows along the water's edge. Papaya trees produce fruit, and garden vegetables on the levee help provide family needs. In Jamaica coconut trees are a common sight along tilapia ponds (Figure 14.10). Sometimes plants are added for purposes other than food. In the Philippines pond banks have been planted with ipilipil for fire wood. After cutting, the tree puts on new growth and the tree is later reharvested.

Figure 14.9 Filipino pond showing combination of plant crops being grown with fish.

Figure 14.10 Coconut trees growing along the banks of tilapia ponds in Jamaica.

MULTIPLE CROPPING OF FISH AND FARM ANIMALS

In Asia, Africa, and elsewhere, where land holdings are typically small, farmers sustain themselves by integrating a variety of crops including principally pigs, cattle, ducks, chickens, and fish (Figure 14.11). Rice and garden crops are also a part of the production scheme. In China, this system is ancient. Animals, principally ducks and pigs, are sources of animal protein in addition to fish protein. Pigs are fed aquatic plants and kitchen leftovers. The animal manure serves as fertilizer for crops, vegetables, and fish ponds. The Chinese consider a pig a "costless fertilizer factory moving on hooves" (FAO 1977). A number of researchers have reported on integrated agriculture-aquaculture farming systems. Particularly good reviews are those by Delmendo (1980), Schroeder (1980a, 1980b), and Nash and Brown (1980). Pullin and Shehadeh (1980) edited conference proceedings on the subject.

Figure 14.11 Ducks grown in combination with fish in the Philippines.

The Food Web

Understanding how manure leads to fish production is essential in determining species to use, stocking densities, and stocking ratios between species. Manure may enter the food web in one of several ways: (1) as a food consumed directly by fish, (2) as a source of minerals used in photosynthesis, and (3) as a source of organic substrate and minerals for heterotrophic micro-organisms which in turn may be consumed directly by fish or zooplankton (Schroeder 1980a) (Figure 14.12).

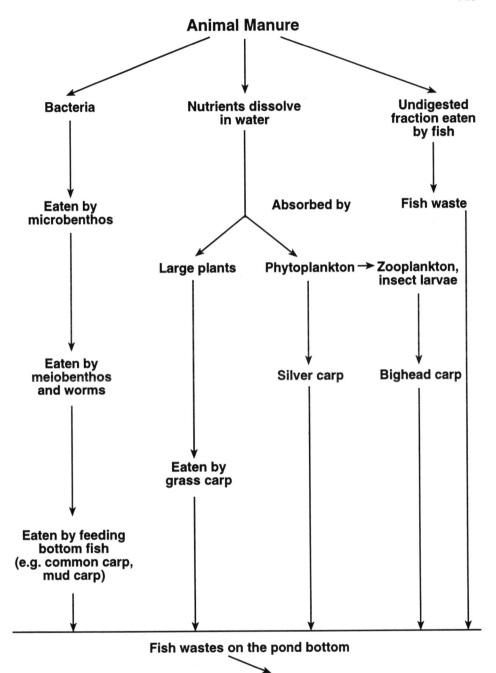

Figure 14.12 A diagrammatic representation of the breakdown of animal manure in fish ponds and its nutrient pathways in the polyculture of Chinese and common carps. Source: Delmendo 1980.

Manure has been fed directly to fish. Dried manure, when incorporated into a pellet and fed to various fish species, generally gave poor results in intensive culture systems. In open ponds, however, Schroeder (1980b) reported that where fish had access to products from decay of pellets, feeds containing as high as 30% manure produced fish growth equal to growth obtained with conventional fish-feed pellets. Metabolizable energy in cow and chicken manure ranges from 600 to 800 and from 900 to 1,200 kcal/kg, respectively; whereas energy from conventional pellets is about 3,000 kcal/kg (Shiloh and Viola 1973). Schroeder (1980b) concluded that cow and chicken manure in themselves are poor sources of energy and protein and that microbial enrichment and resulting zooplankton are the primary sources of energy and protein.

Most animal-fish systems do not use pelleted manure but rather use the manure as is. Coillis and Smitherman (1978) reported that hybrid tilapia (female *Tilapia nilotica* x male *T. hornorum*) fed cattle manure ingested manure directly, according to stomach analysis. Fish fed only manure grew 62% as well as those fed a high protein diet. Sin (1980) reported that in Hong Kong studies, goose droppings were readily eaten directly by common carp, tilapia, and grass carp, more so than duck droppings.

Manure serves as fertilizer for photosynthetic production. When manure enters a pond, bacteria digest the material, and minerals and carbon dioxide released become available for primary production, that is photosynthesis. The average mineral composition of several manures is listed in Table 14.2.

Table 14.2 Average composition (%) of several manures (figures in brackets are based on estimates of the organic matter in the manure as originally reported).

	Water	N	P	K	Organic matter	C-N-P
Dairy cows [a]	79	0.5	0.1	0.5	(17)	17:1:0.2
Fattening cattle[a]	78	0.7	0.2	0.5		
Sheep [a]	64	1.1	0.3	1.1		
Sheep [b]	-	0.7	0.3	0.3		
Pig [a]	74	0.5	0.2	0.4		
Pig [b]	-	0.6	0.2	0.4	15	13:1:0.3
Hen [a]	76	1.1	0.4	0.4	(19)	9:1:0.4
Poultry [a]	-	1.6	0.7	0.7		

[a]Morrison 1959 [b]Food and Agriculture Organization 1977 Source: Schroeder 1980b.

A quantitative measure of primary production is expressed in grams of carbon produced per meter squared per day or g $C/m^2/day$. This value may vary according to the quality and quantity of nutrients present, water temperature, solar energy, and other factors. Minerals resulting from breakdown of manure are readily used in primary production. Schroeder (1980a) noted that 90% of the phytoplankton produced was the very small nannoplankton and that only a small fraction was directly harvested by fish. Thus an additional link(s) in the food chain is required before fish benefit. Certain fish species, such as *O. niloticus* and silver carp, however, appear to use nannoplankton directly.

Manure serves directly as a food substrate for bacteria and other microorganisms. Microorganisms flourish on manure, and flocs of bacteria may form. Bacteria may in turn be fed upon by fish. Dense populations of protozoans are often associated with a matrix of organic matter and bacteria. They appear to be actively grazing the coat of bacteria. Schroeder (1980b) concluded that microbial production is the key to high fish yields. In Louisiana, crawfish farming is based on microbial production. Rice straw and other plant material serve as food substrate for microorganisms, and in research yields have exceeded 2 mt per ha (0.9 tons/ac) without use of supplemental feed pellets (Day and Avault 1984).

Polyculture is often practiced in manured ponds to use all food niches and to maximize fish production. Various carps, tilapias, and the mullet are frequently used. Stocking ratios between species have been determined by years of trial and error and may vary according to local market demands. With low stocking densities, this idea works well, but Schroeder (1980b) noted that at high stocking densities the demand for food in a given niche may exceed supply. This forces the fish to exploit other trophic niches. Usually fish begin feeding on a lower trophic level. Some species are more flexible than others in adjusting to other trophic levels. Common carp are less able to adjust than those fish accustomed to feeding on lower trophic levels such as detritus.

Stocking a mixture of fish species increases production in another way. One fish species may benefit another in a synergistic manner. Yashouv (1971) reported that common carp stirred benthic detritus into the water column, making it available for silver carp. Feces from silver carp became available as bottom manure. Each species thus increased the growth potential of the other. The grass carp that feeds on aquatic plants produces fecal pellets that are readily consumed by other species. In our research, *M. rosenbergii* thrived in ponds with channel catfish by feeding on bacterial-enriched catfish feces and waste feed.

Quantity and Quality of Animal Wastes

Estimated annual tonnage of manure production per animal is as follows: cow 6.0, pig 3.0, goat or sheep 0.8, and poultry 0.025 (Delmendo 1980). The quantity and quality of fertilizer vary according to species, size, age, feed and water intake, and environmental factors. Their availability is also influenced by waste management practices. Nitrogen (N) in animal wastes may be in the form of ammonia, ammonium, nitrite, or nitrate. Gaseous nitrogen can be lost easily to the atmosphere, and handling can affect other losses of various N species. With solid wastes, N loss may vary from 20% in deep pits to 55% in open feedlots; in liquid handling, N losses range from 25% for anaerobic systems to 80% under aerobic conditions (Taiganides 1978). According to Taiganides, 30 pigs excrete daily wastes comprising 58.5 kg (129 lb) N, 10.5 kg (23 lb) P, and 12.0 kg (26 lb) K. By comparison, 2,500 laying hens excrete daily wastes comprising 495 kg (1,091 lb) N, 170 kg (375 lb) P, and 145 kg (320 lb) K.

The value of manure as a substrate for microbial growth is directly related to the quality of feed the animal received. If the feed is of high quality, the manure will be an excellent substrate. If low quality feed is used, say primarily crude fiber, the manure will be of lower value. Generally, the value of manures in increasing order is cow and sheep, followed by pig, chicken, and duck (Schroeder 1980b).

APPLICATION OF MANURES

Manures can be applied (1) as a compost, (2) to pond bottoms, (3) directly into pond waters, and (4) as a liquid. In composting, animal manure is collected and placed in pits that may measure 1.5 m (5 ft) deep and 2.5 to 3 m (8 to 10 ft) in diameter. In China and elsewhere, each pit is filled by layering 7.5 mt (8.3 tons) of river silt mixed with rice straw, 1 mt (1.1 tons) of pig or cow manure, and 0.75 mt (0.8 tons) of aquatic plants or green manure crops in 15-cm (6-in) layers (Delmendo 1980). The top is covered with mud, and a water depth of 3 to 4 cm (1 to 1.5 in) is maintained. The contents of the pit are turned over after 1, 2, and 2.5 months. At the first turning, 0.02 mt (0.02 tons) of superphosphate are added because most compost is used for crops. Each pit produced about 8 mt (8.8 tons) of compost. Compost is applied to fish ponds in China at rates ranging from 5 to more than 10 mt/ha (2.2 to 4.4 tons/ac) during the 6- to 8-month growing period.

In the Philippines, dry chicken manure is added to dry pond bottoms along with inorganic fertilizer to cultivate lab-lab for milkfish (See Chapter 8). This is costly because most milkfish farmers must buy the manure from others. Moreover, it is not always readily available. By contrast, the Chinese system is integrated; the right number and kind of animals are grown by the farmer to provide all manure needs for crops and fish.

The application of untreated animal wastes to fish ponds is common to Asia, where pigsties and chicken coops are sited over ponds. Droppings fall directly into ponds through a slat floor, or they must be washed from the animal pen into pond waters. With ducks, droppings may enter the water directly. In Israel, cow manure is brought in and added to ponds.

Liquid manure is obtained after production of bio-gas from anaerobic fermentation. Animal wastes enter fermentation pits or vats, and the resulting effluent is washed into ponds. In China, a 10 m^3 (13 yd^3) capacity bio-gas plant is a standard household size (Delmendo 1980). It produces about 10 m^3 of sludge and 14 m^3 (18 yd^3) of effluent per year. The effluent is called "fertile water" and is used in fish production; sludge is also used as a base manure.

Fish Yields From Manured Ponds

Thailand practices integrated poultry-pig-fish farming. A three-tier system is applied where poultry are raised above the pigsty that is over the fish pond. Chicken manure is eaten by pigs and whatever is left is washed into the pond along with pig manure. Production from 1.5 rai (1 rai = 1,600 m^2) is 4,000 kg (8,820 lb) of catfish (*Pangasius pangasius*), 8,000 kg (17,640 lb) of pigs, and 15,330 chicken eggs (Delmendo 1980). Vegetables also are produced.

In the Philippines, Cruz and Shehadeh (1980) reported on experiments using 40 or 60 pigs/ha (16 or 24/ac) and 750 or 1,250 ducks/ha (300 or 500/ac) with total fish stocking densities of 10,000 or 20,000/ha (4,000 or 8,000/ac) (85% *O. niloticus*, 14% *C. carpio*, and 1% *Ophicephalus striatus*). The highest net yields were obtained with the 60 pigs/20,000 fish and 750 ducks/20,000 fish combinations: 1,950 kg/ha (1,741 lb/ac) and 1,690 kg/ha (1,509 lb/ac), respectively, over a 90-day period.

In India, fish yields of 7,300 kg/ha/year (6,519 lb/ac) and 4,323 kg/ha/year (3,860 lb/ac) were achieved for pig-fish and duck-fish farming, respectively (Jhingram and Sharma 1980). A mixture of major Indian carps and Chinese carps were used.

In Hong Kong, 58% of the integrated fish farms raise ducks and about 8% raise geese (Sin 1980). The number of ducks used ranges from 2,500 to 3,500/ha/year (1,000 to 1,400/ac), yielding 5 to 6 mt/ha (2.2 to 2.6 tons/ac) of duck meat and 2,750 to 5,640 kg/ha (2,456 to 5,036 lb/ac) of fish.

In Vietnam, the raising of 1,000 to 2,000 ducks/ha (400 to 800/ac) on ponds increased average fish yield to 5.0 mt/ha/year compared to 1 mt/ha/year (0.5 tons/ac) without ducks.

In Taiwan, the most important integrated farming systems are duck-fish and pig-fish. From 2,000 to 4,000 ducks are used per ha (800 to 1,600/ac) and 150 to 300 pigs per ha (60 to 120/ac). This is a very high stocking rate for both. The ducks used are either the meat-producing mule duck or the native egg-producing duck. Pigs are grown to 90 kg (198 lb) finished weight. When less than 100 pigs/ha (40/ac) are used, supplemental fish feeds are required.

In Illinois, Buck et al. (1978) used a polyculture system with various Chinese carps, channel catfish and largemouth bass and 39 to 85 pigs per ha (16 to 34/ac). Fish yields ranged from 20 to 33 kg/ha/day (18 to 29 lb/ac/day) over a 120-day growing season. Similar yields were obtained in Israel using a polyculture system of common carp, tilapia hybrids and silver carp. Cow or chicken manure was applied daily at 2 to approximately 4% dry organic matter of fish biomass (Schroeder 1980a).

In Hungary, use of pig-fish and duck-fish culture is well established. From 40 to 80 pig/ha (16 to 32/ac) are used, with Chinese carps yielding approximately 2.5 mt of fish/ha (1.1 tons/ac) over a 150- to 180-day growing season (Woynarovich 1980a). From 300 to 500 ducks/ha (120 to 200/ac) are used, which can increase common carp production by 140 to 175 kg/ha (125 to 156 lb/ac) (Woynarovich 1980b).

Health Aspects

Diseases communicable or potentially communicable to people by fish or the water of integrated animal-fish farming must be considered (Velasquez 1980). A number of bacteria have been identified in such systems, and a partial list includes *Escherichia coli, Shigella* spp., *Salmonella* spp., *Leptospira* spp., and *Erysipelothrix* spp. *E. coli* and *Shigella* spp. may be carried by fish with no harm to them. Erysipelas is a communicable disease of swine and poultry. Infected fish show no symptoms. People obtain the infection through cuts on the hands while handling fish. The disease in people is often called "fish handler's disease" and produces a condition called "fish rose." Severe inflammation may result when wounds are infected with mucus of dead fish, causing a burning, itching skin sensation.

Leptospirosis may occur in people who are exposed to water contaminated by the urine or feces of animals. The disease is referred to as Weil's disease, Canicola fever, hemorrhagic jaundice, or swine's head disease. Salmonellosis is a disease that has been transmitted to people from fish and shellfish. About 45 species are known in the Philippines. In Louisiana, it has posed a problem to farmers of small pet turtles. Protozoa infections may cause amoebic and balantidail dysentery in people. These two diseases occur in areas of poor environmental sanitation, particularly where hog manure is used.

A number of helminth infections may occur in humans. Velasquez (1980) listed 17 species of fish in the Philippines known to carry helminth parasites that may affect humans. Infection usually occurs by eating fish that are raw or not well cooked. Schistosomiasis is a particularly serious threat to people. Infection is acquired through skin penetration of cercariae released from a snail host. Nematode infection in people may be caused by *Ascaris lumbricoides*. This species in people and pig are morphologically identical but serologically and physiologically different. In some instances cross-infestations may occur.

Fish farmers who use animal manures must maintain sanitation and hygiene. Farm animals can be immunized. Government regulations must be followed. Fish and shellfish can be purged by methods already established, and fish should be well cooked before eating.

USE OF HEATED WATER

Use of heated water for aquaculture in temperate countries extends the growing season. There are two major sources of heated water, ground water and thermal effluents from power plants. Heated ground water has been used both in hatcheries and in grow-out systems. A commercial catfish hatchery near Yazoo City, Mississippi, blends water from two wells, one hot and one cool, to maintain a near constant 27°C (81°F) water supply to hatching troughs. Ray (1978) described use of artesian wells in a grow-out system for catfish and tilapia. He has access to artesian wells that produce 20,000 liters (5,284 gal) of 32°C (90°F) water per minute. Cold water springs supply water to cool the hot water to the desired 26° to 27°C (79° to 81°F). Raceways are located below the wells on a hill. They are in pairs with a common center wall. Channel catfish are raised in upper sections and tilapia below. Catfish are fed, and wastes from fish and feed flow to the tilapia. For each kg of catfish produced, 1 kg of tilapia is produced from the wastes.

As the world population and standard of living increase, there will be greater demands for electricity. Electricity is produced from both fossil and nuclear fuel plants. Some nuclear plants can generate more than one million kilowatts of energy to the environment. This implies a water-cooling flow of over 28 m^3/second (1,000 ft^3/second), with a water temperature rise of -9° to -1°C (15° to 30°F) (Kildow and Huguenin 1974). Thermal effluent can be dissipated from electric generating plants from one of three basic modes -- cooling towers, cooling ponds, and once-through cooling. Some aquaculturists see thermal effluents as having potential for culturing fish and shellfish, and reviews include Luebke (1973), Kildow and Huguenin (1974), Peterson and Seo (1977), Shimbun (1977), Kawaratani (1978), and FAO (1980). The subject is well referenced in the Index of the Proceedings World Mariculture Society (Avault 1980b, 1985).

The obvious advantage of using thermal effluents for aquaculture is that fish and shellfish could be cultured year-round in temperate climates. Moreover, the time required to grow certain species to market size can be reduced. For example, in nature 8 years are required for lobsters to reach market size. With constant warm water this time may be reduced to 2 years (Hughes and Sullivan 1972). Other advantages include: (1) optimization of the nuclear power plant to produce two commercial sources of revenue instead of one, (2) production of commercial species near major marketing sites, (3) ability to culture tropical organisms in temperate climates, and (4) ability to speed up maturation and metamorphosis of culture species.

720

STUDY QUESTIONS

1. List factors that should be considered when choosing an "efficient species" to culture. Illustrate with examples.

2. To maximize production of marketable culture species, what are the ideal stocking rates for channel catfish in ponds, rainbow trout in raceways, shrimp in ponds, and prawns in ponds? Qualify your answer regarding aeration, feeding rates, and other factors affecting production.

3. Discuss strategies for maximizing "daily production" per hectare for channel catfish and milkfish, and per cubic feet per second water flow for rainbow trout.

4. Assume that you have the opportunity to market to one of two places. The first place wants a 0.5 kg fish and the second wants a 1 kg fish. Assume that feed costs $300 per ton and that the feed conversion is 1.5 to produce the 0.5 kg fish and 2.0 to produce the 1 kg fish. On the basis of feed cost, which is the most economical market for you? Show math.

5. List advantages and disadvantages of topping off channel catfish?

6. How are red swamp crawfish topped off?

7. List ways in which to increase the living area (space) for crustaceans in a pond.

8. Choose a number of culture species you wish to grow in polyculture. Explain your strategy for structuring this particular polyculture scheme.

9. Give two examples of multiple cropping culture species.

10. List the steps for double cropping rice and crawfish as practiced in Louisiana. What are the advantages of this strategy?

11. How does manure enter the food web?

12. List the advantages and disadvantages of using heated effluent for aquaculture.

REFERENCES

Anonymous. 1957. Fish culture in rice fields -- a preliminary review and annotated bibliography. Proceedings Indo-Pacific Fisheries Council 7(2-3):193-206.

Ardinawata, R.O. 1958. Fish culture on paddy fields in Indonesia. Proceedings Indo-Pacific Fisheries Council 7(2-3):119-218.

Avault, J.W., Jr. 1980a. Double cropping rice and crawfish. Aquaculture Magazine 7(2):40-41.

Avault, J.W., Jr. (editor). 1980b. Index of Proceedings of the World Mariculture Society. Volumes 1-11.

Avault, J.W., Jr. (editor). 1985. Index of Proceedings of the World Mariculture Society. Volumes 12-16.

Avault, J.W., Jr., R.O. Smitherman and E.W. Shell. 1968. Evaluation of eight species of fish for aquatic weed control. Proceedings of the World Symposium on Warm-Water Pond Fish Culture. FAO Fisheries Report No. 44, 5:109-122.

Boubjerg, R. and S. Stephen. 1974. Behavioral changes with increased density in the crawfish (*Orconectes virilis*). In International Symposium on Freshwater Crayfish, Baton Rouge, Louisiana 2:429-442.

Brown, E.E., T.K. Hill and J.L. Chesness. 1974. Rainbow trout and channel catfish, a double cropping system. Department of Agricultural Economics, College Station, Athens, Georgia 30602. Research Report 196.

Buck, H., R.J. Baur and C.R. Rose. 1978. Polyculture of Chinese carps in ponds with swine wastes. In Symposium on Culture of Exotic Fishes, Auburn, Alabama. Fish Culture Section, American Fisheries Society 1978:144-155.

Caffey, R.H., G. Lutz, J.W. Avault, Jr. and K.K. Higgins. (1993. Observations on production of soft-shell freshwater prawns, *Macrobrachium rosenbergii* (Demann) in commercial crawfish shedding facilities. Journal of Applied Aquaculture 2(2):93-102.

Cange, S.W., J.W. Avault, Jr. and W.G. Perry, Jr. 1982. Culture of the giant Malaysian prawn in southern Louisiana. Proceedings Catfish Farmers of America 4:41-42.

Cange, S.W., J.W. Avault, Jr. and W.G. Perry, Jr. 1983. *Macrobrachium rosenbergii* culture in southwest Louisiana in brackish water ponds. In Proceedings First International Crustacean Meeting, Laie, Hawaii 1:148-156.

Chamberlain, G. and K. Strawn. 1977. Submerged cage culture of fish in supersaturated thermal effluent. Proceedings of the World Mariculture Society 8:625-646.

Chaudhuri, H. and S.D. Tripathi. 1979. Problems of warmwater fish seed production. pp. 127-134. In Advances in Aquaculture. FAO Technical Conference on Aquaculture, Kyoto, Japan. 653 pp.

Chen, T.P. 1934. A preliminary study on association of species in Kwangtung fish ponds. Lingnan Science Journal 13(2):275-283.

Chen, T.P. 1954. The culture of tilapia in rice paddies in Taiwan. Chinese-American Joint Commission of Rural Construction Fisheries Series: No. 2, Taipei, Taiwan.

Chua, T.E., C.B. Jock, S.H. Koon and T. Moulton. 1973. A report on paddy and paddy-fish production in Krian, Perak. Ministry of Agriculture and Fisheries, Kuala Lumpur, Malaysia. 57 pp.

Coche, A.G. 1967. Fish culture in rice fields, a world-wide synthesis. Hydrobiologia 30:1-44.

Collis, W.J. and R.O. Smitherman. 1978. Production of tilapia hybrids with cattle manure or commercial diet. In Symposium on Culture of Exotic Fishes, Auburn, Alabama. Fish Culture Section, American Fisheries Society 1978:43-54.

Cruz, E.M. and Z.H. Shehadeh. 1980. Preliminary results of integrated pig-fish and duck-fish production tests. Proceedings ICLARM-SEARCA Conference on Integrated Agriculture-Aquaculture Farming Systems, Manila, Philippines 1980:225-238.

Day, C.H. and J.W. Avault, Jr. 1984. Crayfish production in ponds receiving varying amounts of soybean stubble and rice straw as forage. In International Symposium on Freshwater Crayfish, Lund, Sweden 6:247-265.

de la Bretonne, L. and J.W. Avault, Jr. 1976. Egg development and management of *Procambarus clarkii* (Girard) in a south Louisiana commercial crayfish pond. In International Symposium on Freshwater Crayfish, Kuopio, Finland 3:133-140.

722

Delmendo, M.N. 1980. A review of integrated livestock-fowl-fish farming systems. Proceedings ICLARM-SEARCA Conference on Integrated Agriculture-Aquaculture Farming Systems, Manila, Philippines 1980:59-72.

FAO. 1977. China: Recycling of organic wastes in agriculture. Report of the FAO study tour to the People's Republic of China. 28 April 24 May 1977. FAO Soils Bulletin 40. 107 pp.

FAO. 1980. Symposium on New Developments in the Utilization of Heated Effluents and of Recirculation Systems for Intensive Aquaculture. EIFAC/80/Symposium.

Fujimura, T. 1974. Development of a prawn culture industry in Hawaii. National Marine Fisheries Service, N.O.A.A., Department of Commerce.

Goyert, J.C. and J.W. Avault, Jr. 1978. Effect of stocking density and substrate on growth and survival of crawfish (*Procambarus clarkii*) grown in a recirculating system. Proceedings of the World Mariculture Society 9:731-735.

Granados, A.E., J.W. Avault, Jr. and S.W. Cange. 1991. Double cropping Malaysian prawns, *Macrobrachium rosenbergii,* and red swamp crawfish, *Procambarus clarkii.* Journal of Applied Aquaculture 1(1):65-77.

Green, O.L., R.O. Smitherman and G.B. Pardue. 1979. Comparisons of growth and survival of channel catfish, *Ictalurus punctatus*, from distinct populations. pp. 626-628. In Advances in Aquaculture. FAO Technical Conference on Aquaculture, Kyoto, Japan. 653 pp.

Hepher, B. and Y. Pruginin. 1981. Commercial Fish Farming. New York-Chichester-Bribane-Toronto: John Wiley & Sons Inc. 261 pp.

Hickling, C.F. 1961. Tropical Inland Fisheries. New York: John Wiley & Sons Inc. 287 pp.

Hickling, C.F. 1962. Fish Culture. London: Faber and Faber. 295 pp.

Hill, T.K., J.L. Chesness and E.E. Brown. 1972. Utilization of rainbow trout, *Salmo gairdneri*: Richardson, in a double-crop fish culture system in South Georgia. Proceedings Southeastern Association of Game and Fish Commissioners 26:368-375.

Hill, T.K., J.L. Chesness and E.E. Brown. 1973. A two-crop fish production system. Transactions American Society of Agricultural Engineers 16(5):930-933.

Hora, S.L. and T.V.R. Pillay. 1962. Handbook on fish culture in the Indo-Pacific Region, FAO Fisheries Biology Technical Paper No. 14. 204 pp.

Huet, M. 1968. Methodes biologiques d'accroissement de la production piscicole (Europe et Afrique). Proceedings of the World Symposium on Warm-Water Pond Fish Culture. FAO Fisheries Report No. 44, 4:289-327.

Huet, M. 1970. (Translated by Henry Kahn). Textbook of Fish Culture, Breeding and Cultivation of Fish. Surrey, England: Fishing New (Books) Ltd. 436 pp.

Hughes, J.T. and J.J. Sullivan. 1972. Enhancement of lobster growth. Science 177:1,110-1,111.

Jhingran, V.G. and B.K. Sharma. 1980. Integrated livestock-fish farming in India. Proceedings ICLARM-SEARCA Conference on Integrated Agriculture-Aquaculture Farming Systems, Manila, Philippines 1980:135-142.

Kawaratani, R.K. 1978. State-of-the-art waste heat utilization for agriculture and aquaculture. Tennessee Valley Authority. Technical Report B-12.

Kildow, J. and J.E. Huguenin. 1974. Problems and potentials of recycling wastes for aquaculture. Massachusetts Institute of Technology. Report No. MITSG 74-27.

Korringa, P. 1976a. Farming Cupped Oysters of the Genus *Crassostrea*. Amsterdam-Oxford-New York: Elsevier Science Publishing Company Inc. 224 pp.

Korringa, P. 1976b. Farming Flat Oysters of the Genus *Ostrea*. Amsterdam-Oxford-New York: Elsevier Science Publishing Company Inc. 238 pp.

Leitritz, E. and R.C. Lewis. 1980. Trout and salmon culture. University of California. California Fish Bulletin 164. 197 pp.

Liao, I.C. 1985. A brief review on the larval rearing techniques of penaeid shrimp. pp. 65-78. In First International Conference on the Culture of Penaeid Prawns/Shrimps. Aquaculture Department, Southeast Asian Fisheries Development Center, Iloilo City, Philippines.

Lin, S.Y. 1940. Fish culture in ponds in the New Territories of Hong Kong. Journal Hong Kong Fisheries Research Station Volume 1, No. 2.

Luebke, R.W. 1973. The culture of some marine fishes in ponds receiving heated discharge water from a power plant. M.S. Thesis, Texas A&M. 213 pp.

Lutz, R.A. (editor). 1980. Mussel Culture and Harvest: A North American Perspective. Amsterdam-Oxford-New York: Elsevier Science Publishing Company Inc. 350 pp.

Malecha, S.R. 1977. Genetics and selective breeding. Chapter XIV. In Shrimp and Prawn Farming in the Western Hemisphere. Pennsylvania: Dowden, Hutchinson and Ross Inc. 439 pp.

Malecha, S.R., J. Polovina and R. Moav. 1981. Multi-stage rotational stocking and harvesting system for year-round culture of the freshwater prawn, *Macrobrachium rosenbergii*. Sea Grant Technical Report UNIHI - Sea Grant-TR-81-01.

Martin, R.J. 1983. A comparison of three sizes of fingerlings for stocking catfish ponds. For Fish Farmers Mississippi Cooperative Extension Service 83:5.

Miltner, M.R., A. Granados, R. Romaire, J.W. Avault, Jr., Z. Ra'anan and D. Cohn. 1983. Polyculture of the prawn, *Macrobrachium rosenbergii*, with fingerlings and adult catfish and Chinese carps in earthen ponds in south Louisiana. Journal of the World Mariculture Society 14:127-134.

Moav, R. 1979a. Genetic aspects of the transition from traditional to modern fish farming. Theoretical Applied Genetics 47:285-290.

Moav, R. 1976b. Genetics and genetic improvement of fish. pp. 610-622. In Advances in Aquaculture. FAO Technical Conference on Aquaculture, Kyoto, Japan. 653 pp.

Morrison, F. 1959. Feeds and feeding. Iowa: Morrison Publishing Company Inc.

Nash, C.E., and C.M. Brown. 1980. A theoretical comparison of waste treatment processing ponds and fish production ponds receiving animal wastes. Proceedings ICLARM-SEARCA Conference on Integrated Agriculture-Aquaculture Farming Systems, Manila, Philippines 1980:87-98.

New, M.B. (editor). 1982. Giant Prawn Farming. Amsterdam-Oxford-New York: Elsevier Science Publishing Company Inc. 532 pp.

Peterson, R.E. and K.K. Seo. 1977. Thermal aquaculture. Proceedings of the World Mariculture Society 8:491-503.

724

Pillay, T.V.R. and B. Bose. 1957. Observations on the culture of brackishwater fishes in paddy fields of West Bengal (India). Proceedings Indo-Pacific Fisheries Council 7(2-3):187-192.

Piper, G.R., I.B. McElwain, L.E. Orme, J.P. McCraren, L.G. Fowler and J.R. Leonard. 1982. Fish Hatchery Management. Washington, D.C.: Superintendent of Documents, U.S. Government Printing Office. 517 pp.

Plemmons, B. and J.W. Avault, Jr. 1980. Six tons of catfish per acre with constant aeration. Louisiana Agriculture 23(4):6, 7 & 9.

Pruginin, Y. and E.W. Shell. 1962. Separation of the sexes of *Tilapia nilotica* with a mechanical grader. Progressive Fish-Culturist 24(1):37-40.

Pullin, R.S.V. and Z.H. Shehadeh (editors). 1980. Proceedings ICLARM-SEARCA Conference on Integrated Agriculture-Aquaculture Farming Systems, Manila, Philippines. 258 pp.

Rabanal, H.R. 1968. Stock manipulation and other biological methods of increasing production of fish through pond fish culture in Asia and the Far East. Proceedings of the World Symposium on Warm-Water Pond Fish Culture. FAO Fisheries Report No. 44, 4:274-288.

Ray, L. 1978. Production of tilapia in catfish raceways using geothermal water. In Symposium on Culture of Exotic Fishes, Auburn, Alabama. Fish Culture Section, American Fisheries Society 1978:86-89.

Schmittou, H.R. 1969. The culture of channel catfish, *Ictalurus punctatus*, (Rafinesque) in cages suspended in ponds. Proceedings Southeastern Association Game and Fish Commissioners 23:226-244.

Schroeder, G.L. 1980a. Autotrophic and heterotrophic production of microorganisms in intensively manured fish ponds and related fish yields. Aquaculture 14:303-325.

Schroeder, G.L. 1980b. Fish farming in manure-loaded ponds. Proceedings ICLARM-SEARCA Conference on Integrated Agriculture-Aquaculture Farming Systems, Manila, Philippines 1980:73-86.

Sea Grant Technical Report UNIHI-SEAGRANT-TR-81-01.

Sedgwick, S.D. 1976. Trout Farming handbook. 2nd edition. London: Seeley Service and Company. 163 pp.

Sedgwick, S.D. 1982. The Salmon Handbook. London: Andre Deutsch Limited 209 pp.

Shigueno, K. 1975. Shrimp Culture in Japan. Tokyo: Association for International Technical Promotion. 153 pp.

Shiloh, S. and S. Viola. 1973. Experiments in the nutrition of carp growing in cages. Bamidgeh 25:17-31.

Shimbun, M. 1977. Aquaculture using thermal effluents. Translated from Japanese by National Marine Fisheries Service NOAA.

Sin, A.W.C. 1980. Integrated animal-fish husbandry systems in Hong Kong with case studies on duck-fish and goose-fish systems. Proceedings ICLARM-SEARCA Conference on Integrated Agriculture-Aquaculture Farming Systems, Manila, Philippines 1980:113-124.

Snow, J.R. 1976. Increasing the yield of channel catfish rearing ponds by periodic division of the stock. Proceedings Southeastern Association of Fish and Wildlife Agencies 30:239-245.

Squires, H.J. 1970. Lobster (*Homarus americanus*) fishery and ecology in Port au Port Bay, Newfoundland, 1960-65. Proceedings National Shellfish Association 60:23-29.

Stone, N. 1994. Mixing bighead carp culture with catfish farming. The Catfish Journal 9(2):10-23.

Swingle, H.S. 1949. Experiments with combinations of largemouth bass, bluegill and minnows in ponds. Transactions American Fisheries Society 76(1946):46-62.

Swingle, H.S. 1950. Relationships and dynamics of balanced and unbalanced fish populations. Alabama Agricultural Experiment Station Bulletin No. 274.

Swingle, H.S. 1968. Biological means of increasing productivity in ponds. Proceedings of the World Symposium on Warm-Water Pond Fish Culture. FAO Fisheries Report No. 44, 4:243-257.

Taiganides, E.P. 1978. Principles and techniques of animal waste management and utilization. FAO Soils Bulletin 36:341-362.

Tang, Y.A. 1979. Planning design and construction of a coastal milkfish farm. pp. 104-117. In Advances in Aquaculture. FAO Technical Conference on Aquaculture, Kyoto, Japan. 653 pp.

Tang, Y. and S. H. Chen. 1968. A survey of the algal pasture soils of milkfish ponds in Taiwan. Proceedings of the World Symposium on Warm-Water Pond Fish Culture. FAO Fisheries Report No. 44, 3:198-209.

Tiemeier, O.W. and C.W. Deyoe. 1968. Growth obtained by stocking various size combinations of channel catfish (*Ictalurus punctatus*) and efficiencies of utilized pelleted feed. Southwestern Naturalists 13(2):167-174.

Tuten, J.S. and J.W. Avault, Jr. 1981. Growing red swamp crawfish (*Procambarus clarkii*) and several North American fish species together. Progressive Fish-Culturist 43(2):97-99.

Velasquez, C. 1980. Health constraints of integrated animal-fish farming in the Philippines. Proceedings ICLARM-SEARCA Conference on Integrated Agriculture-Aquaculture Farming Systems, Manila, Philippines 1980:103-111.

Woynarovich, E. 1980a. Utilization of piggery wastes in fish ponds. Proceedings ICLARM-SEARCA Conference on Integrated Agriculture-Aquaculture Farming Systems, Manila, Philippines 1980:125-128.

Woynarovich, E. 1980b. Raising ducks on fish ponds. Proceedings ICLARM-SEARCA Conference on Integrated Agriculture-Aquaculture Farming Systems, Manila, Philippines 1980:129-134.

Woynarovich, E. and L. Horvath. 1980. The artificial propagation of warm-water finfishes -- a manual for extension. FAO Fisheries Technical Paper No. 201. 183 pp.

Yashouv, A. 1968. Mixed fixed culture, an ecological approach to increase pond productivity. Proceedings of the World Symposium on Warm-Water Pond Fish Culture. FAO Fisheries Report No. 44, 4:258-273.

Yashouv, A. 1971. Interaction between the common carp (*Cyprinus carpio*) and the silver carp (*Hypophthalmichthys molitrix*) in fish ponds. Bamidgeh 23(3):85-92.

CHAPTER 15
HARVESTING AND PROCESSING

Most culture species are harvested and processed for consumption. You can harvest when the culture species is an acceptable market size and in robust condition. Proper handling at harvest and good processing technology ensure a quality product.

In this chapter, we follow the chronology of harvesting and processing starting with harvesting and handling, transportation to the plant, and the processing operation. Sanitation and quality assurance are discussed, as are byproduct use and waste management.

HARVESTING AND HANDLING

You may spend many months growing a culture species to market size. Often the culture species is fed a formulated diet, and water quality and fish health are monitored. This special care must continue at harvest and during transportation to the processing plant.

Finfish

Methods of harvesting and handling finfish may vary with the species grown, culture system employed, and with the tradition and resources of a particular region or country. Regardless of the method, certain precautions and preparations should be taken before harvest (Collins 1993). First, certain finfish such as channel catfish (*Ictalurus punctatus*) should be checked for off-flavor. Second, feeding if practiced should be discontinued 1 to 3 days before harvest. This allows fish to clean out their system of waste. Coldwater fish require more time for this than warmwater species. If fish have been fed medicated feed, a proper withdrawal time should pass before harvest. Third, if possible fish should be harvested during cool weather to lessen stress. For warmwater species, this is a water temperature below approximately 26°C (79°F). Finally, all harvesting, grading, and transportation equipment should be set up in advance to ensure a smooth operation.

A seine is used in many instances to harvest fish in ponds. It is a net pulled through the water, mechanically or by hand, to capture fish. It consists of a lead line or mud line to hold the bottom down and a float line that holds the net upright in the water. The seine is usually made of nylon or polyethylene. A nylon seine may be coated with asphalt or plastic if it is used to harvest fish with spines, such as catfish. A polyethylene seine requires no coating. A knotted net is suitable for carp (*Cyprinus carpio*), buffalo fish (*Ictiobus* spp.), and catfish, but some scaled fish require a soft, uncoated, knotless seine. A seine should be about 1.5 times as long and deep as the width and water depth of the pond, respectively.

Fish may be seined with the pond full of water, or the pond may be partially drained. After several seinings, the pond may be completely drained and the remaining fish captured by hand, or the pond may be left full and partially harvested periodically by topping off.

The harvest of channel catfish depends on use of seines. The seine is stored on a hydraulically operated seine reel mounted on a two-wheel trailer and pulled by a tractor (Figure 15.1). A standard reel stores seines up to 366 m (1,200 ft) long.

Figure 15.1 Seine stored on reel. Notice boat that follows behind seine.

The loose seine end is attached to a second tractor on the opposite levee of the first tractor (Figure 15.2). Together both tractors slowly pull the seine from one end of the pond to the other (Huner et al. 1984; Busch 1985). A boat with a tongue or seine catcher mounted on the bow follows behind the seine as it is pulled through the water. If a portion of the seine fills up with mud, the bow of the boat nudges the seine and rolls the mud out without letting too many fish escape. When the seine nears the other end of the pond, one of two methods may be employed.

Figure 15.2 Tractors pull seine through pond.

The first method uses a live car or fish-holding bag (Figure 15.3). A typical live car is 12 m (39 ft) x 3 m (10 ft) x 1.4 m (4.5 ft). It contains a mesh size that retains marketable fish but allows escape of smaller fish (Table 15.1).

Figure 15.3 The live car has been separated from the large seine.

Table 15.1 Approximate sizes of channel catfish retained by nets of different meshes.

Mesh Size (bar measure)		Weight of smallest fish held	
millimeter	inches	grams	pounds
25	1	227	1/2
34	1 3/8	340	3/4
41	1 5/8	454	1
44	1 3/4	680	1 1/2
50	2	907	2

Source: Huner et al. 1984.

One end of the bag has a throat supported by a metal frame. It is attached by a drawstring to the harvesting seine. The harvesting seine is closed up gradually and beached by the two moving tractors. Fish are funneled through the drawstring opening into the live car. Up to 9,000 kg (19,845 lb) of fish can be held. Once filled, the live car can be detached and another set in place. Because fish are crowded, you must make certain that dissolved oxygen levels are adequate (approximately 5 ppm) by adding fresh water or using aeration. Further, avoid stirring up bottom sediments in the harvest area. Hydrogen sulphide can be a problem, especially in ponds that have not been drained for several years. Potassium permanganate has been used to detoxify this gas.

Fish can be left in a live car for several hours or until the next day. This allows the fish to further clean out their gut before transport to the processing plant. A brailing bag is lowered into the crowded fish and scoops them up (Figure 15.4). It is then lifted with a power-boom winch positioned over an opening in the truck hauling tank and opened by a drawstring (Figure 15.5).

The second method of harvest excludes use of live cars. The pond is seined as before, and fish are crowded at one end of the pond. The harvesting seine is then staked in place with metal rods. Next, a smaller seine, called a cutting seine, is pulled by hand through the enclosed area, crowding the fish even more for removal to the hauling tank (Figure 15.6).

A seine can be used for trapping catfish; the method was described by Smitherman et al. (1979) and Jensen (1981). A corral seine is stretched almost all the way across near one end of the pond. Fish are able to swim freely around both ends of the seine. Feed is introduced behind the seine, and fish grow accustomed to swimming around. Both ends of the seine are pulled to the bank to trap fish.

Figure 15.4 Brailing bag scoops up fish from live car. Notice scale on end of boom.

Figure 15.5 Operator prepares to open drawstring to release fish into tank of water.

Figure 15.6 Cutting seine is used to concentrate fish that are hand dipped from pond.

In Europe, fish often are harvested on the outside of the pond levee (Huet 1970). This works well when the pond is completely drained. A concrete drain structure called a monk is situated on the inside of the pond levee. A drain pipe originating at the monk leads through the levee to the outside. Two sets of grooves in the monk hold sluice boards to retain the water. The boards are removed one at a time to drain a pond. To prevent fish from leaving, a screen is placed in the groove where boards are being removed. Two grooves with two sets of boards allow you to manipulate whether water is drained off the bottom or top. Additionally, two sets of screens can be used so that one can be lifted for cleaning while one is left in place. When fish begin to gather at the monk, the screens can be lifted. Fish go through the drain pipe into a screened box where they can be dip-netted out. In some instances, a shear-gate valve on the drain pipe replaces the sluice boards. Grooves, however, are still present on the monk for screens that can be raised or lowered to control entry of fish through the drain pipe to the outside.

Some ponds, such as watershed ponds, do not have a level bottom, and they may be deep. Conventional seining does not work well. Lift nets, slat traps, hoop nets, electrical shocking devices, and angling have been used.

A lift net is a square or rectangular net that sits on the bottom of a pond. Risers attached to each corner connect to a fulcrum that provides leverage to lift the net out of the water. Fish are baited with feed on top of the net that is raised periodically for capture of culture species.

A slat trap consists of wooden slats that form a box. The spacing between slats grades for the desired size. On each end of the box is a slatted funnel-like throat through which fish enter. Bait is placed in the center of the box to entice the fish.

A hoop net consists of decreasing smaller hoops connected with netting to form a cylindrical trap. The throat end has the largest hoop, and wings may be attached on each side to funnel fish into the throat. The opposite end of the hoop net has a drawstring to empty the catch. Hoop nets operate best in streams with a current, and they are not always effective in production ponds.

Electrical shocking devices, like hoop nets, work best on wild fish in streams. Angling in fee fishing lakes is an effective method of harvesting fish.

Small floating cages used to grow fish can be towed alongside the levee by boat and then lifted with a power boom to a hauling tank. Fish grown in floating pens are usually harvested by first crowding and then netting out.

Fish such as rainbow trout (*Oncorhynchus mykiss*) that are grown in raceways are easier to harvest because they are concentrated. In concrete raceways, a crowder is pushed mechanically or by hand from one end of the raceway to the other end. This concentrates fish even more. The crowder usually consists of a series of pipes spaced a specified distance apart for grading fish to size. Once crowded to one end, fish may be dip-netted out or removed with a fish pump that works like a vacuum cleaner (Figure 15.7).

Figure 15.7 Fish pump used to harvest trout from raceway.

Crustaceans

Crawfish-- Crawfish, principally the red swamp crawfish (*Procambarus clarkii*) and white river crawfish (*P. zonangulus*), are harvested in ponds with wire-mesh traps containing bait (Avault et al. 1984; Romaire 1989) (Figure 15.8). The three-funnel pyramid trap is commonly used by farmers. It is made of plastic-coated chicken wire with 19 mm (0.75 in) mesh, thus grading crawfish to size at capture. The funnels located on three sides at the bottom allow crawfish to enter the trap. A plastic throat made of PVC pipe prevents crawfish from crawling out over the top once trapped.

Figure 15.8 Vernon Pfister (with trap) and Robert Romaire of the LSU Agricultural Center harvest crawfish.

From 50 to 75 traps per hectare (20 to 30/ac) are placed in rows to allow harvest by boat. Fish, principally gizzard shad (*Dorosoma cepedianum*) or a formulated bait consisting of an attractant, plant and animal ingredients, and a binder are used as bait.

Trapping in Louisiana usually begins in November, but this depends on a number of factors, such as the availability of marketable crawfish and the market price. Traps typically are run several times a week. During cold months, principally December and January, the catch may drop off, less than 454 g (1 lb) per trap, and trapping may be temporarily discontinued. Once trapping resumes, it may continue until around the middle of May.

In southern Spain, small unbaited hoop nets placed in rice-field irrigation ditches are used to harvest red swamp crawfish (Figure 15.9). Crawfish respond to the movement of water. Cain and Avault (1983) reported on a boat-mounted electro-trawl for harvesting crawfish (Figure 15.10).

Figure 15.9 Hoop net used in southern Spain to harvest crawfish.

Figure 15.10 Boat-mounted electro-trawl. Trawl is in raised position.

After harvest, some crawfish farmers purge or depurate the catch. In other instances, the processing plants may do the purging. Crawfish are purged by one of two methods. In the first method, crawfish are held in floating baskets or pens within the pond for approximately 24 to 48 hours (Figure 15.11). This allows the crawfish to clean out its gut (vein) of undigested materials. Moreover, it allows the crawfish shell to cleanse itself of attached debris. In the second method, crawfish are held in tanks with flowing water. After purging, crawfish often look shiny-clean. Grading of crawfish to size is now common practice, with larger sizes bringing the most money. However, size groupings vary. Some processors recognize five sizes, others three.

Figure 15.11 Purging crawfish in pens held in pond water.

Prawns-- Prawns (*Macrobrachium rosenbergii*) are either batch harvested or cull harvested. In batch harvesting, prawns are harvested all at once by seining and draining the pond. In cull harvesting, prawns are usually seined with the pond full of water. Marketable prawns are removed; the others are returned for further growth. Batch harvesting is practiced in temperate countries, whereas cull harvesting is usually practiced in tropical countries.

Shrimp-- Shrimp are harvested a number of ways. Seining by hand is commonly practiced in some countries. *Penaeus monodon* and certain other shrimp species swim parallel to and around the pond bank. A seine similar to a corral seine used for channel catfish can be set in place. The seine is pulled in the day after setting. Once concentrated, shrimp can be removed with a brailing bag operated with a power-boom winch, or they can be harvested with a pump, similar to the kind used for trout harvest.

Shrimp also are harvested by placing a pound net on the drain pipe outside the levee (Figure 15.12). As water drains from the pond, shrimp move through the drain pipe into the net.

Figure 15.12 Net being set in place outside drain pipe to harvest shrimp, Indonesia.

Some shrimp farmers still use a cast net, especially if only a small quantity of shrimp is required at one time. An area in the pond is first baited with feed to concentrate shrimp. When shrimp are polycultured with other species, a set net has been used. A set net operates much like a hoop net. It consists of a net-covering over three rectangular stainless steel rings in reducing sizes, two wing screens, and one center guide screen. A funnel is located near the tail. The set net is placed in the pond to take advantage of the shrimp's habit of swimming around the pond edge.

In Taiwan and certain other countries, shrimp have been harvested with the use of electricity (Chien et al. 1988). An electro-trawl constructed like a beam trawl is pulled through the bottom by walking (Figure 15.13). The electrodes across the bottom of the trawl's mouth transmit a low level shock, 8 to 12 volts. This stimulates shrimp to jump up for easy capture in the net. An electrifier, consisting of a voltage regulator and battery, is housed in a box. This is placed on a floating Styrofoam raft. During operation of the trawl, the person harvesting uses one hand to push the raft ahead while dragging the trawl with a rope and body harness. When trawling is completed, the horizontal bamboo pole across the top of the trawl's mouth is hung on forked iron poles. Several strings connected between the bamboo pole and bottom lead-line are used to close off the opening. The shrimp are worked back into the tail of the bag and collected in a basket. About 85% to 90% of the shrimp can be harvested in this manner. Remaining shrimp are collected with effluent during complete draining.

Pond owners usually contract with people who specialize in harvesting shrimp. Shrimp may be harvested any time during day or night. The idea is to get the shrimp to the buyer at a specified time.

Figure 15.13 Electro-trawl for harvesting shrimp. Paddlewheel aerator shown top right.

Mollusks

Oysters, clams, mussels, and other mollusks are cultured in a variety of ways throughout the world. Harvesting methods vary.

Oysters-- Bottom culture of oysters offers several options for harvest. An original method for gathering oysters is to wade along shallow reefs and pick them up by hand. In deeper waters, oysters can be gathered by diving. Oyster tongs were among the first implements used to harvest oysters (Figure 15.14). They consist of two long wooden handles joined like a pair of scissors. At the end of each handle is a metal rake that forms a basket when the tongs are closed off. The tongs are lowered to the bottom, usually from a boat, and the handles are opened and closed. Teeth on the rakes dig under the oysters and forces them into baskets.

Figure 15.14 Hand tongs for harvesting oysters.

The oyster dredge is an efficient method to harvest large quantities of oysters. It is a metal basket with teeth. The dredge is pulled by boat over the oyster bed. When full, it is hauled aboard by hand or by winch. A dredge commonly used in the Gulf of Mexico holds 35 to 175 liters (1 to 5 bu). Once on board, marketable oysters are separated from young oysters with a hand hatchet (Figure 15.15). After separating, oysters are placed in porous sacks and stacked on deck (Figure 15.16). Immature oysters and trash are scattered over the oyster reef. Along the Atlantic Coast, suction dredges, which act like vacuum cleaners, harvest oysters from the bottom. Oysters grown on floating rafts, as practiced in Australia, are easily harvested by hand. Quayle (1988) reviewed other culture and harvesting methods for oysters.

Oysters and other mollusks, being filter feeders, may take up pathogens that are harmful to humans when raw or partially cooked meats are consumed. Viruses, bacteria, and other organisms frequent polluted waters, especially waters that receive domestic sewage. As an example, paralytic shellfish poison caused by dinoflagellates of the genus *Gonyaulax* has resulted in serious illness and even death when contaminated oyster meats are consumed.

Figure 15.15 Tom Hymel of the LSU Agricultural Center with select oysters after culling. Top left chain pulls in dredge from boat.

Figure 15. 16 Sacks of oysters on board boat.

Two methods have been used to cleanse oysters. Relaying is the moving of mollusks from culture grounds that are polluted to grounds that are not. When oysters are filter feeding in clean water, the contents of the digestive system are cleansed of pathogens. Relaying may require 2 to 3 days or up to 2 weeks and may not be economical because of additional labor and handling. Further, relaying waters must remain uncontaminated during the cleansing process. Depuration involves the transfer of oysters from culture waters to on-shore purging tanks. Quayle (1988) described a depuration process for Pacific oysters. Purified water, from use of ultraviolet light, flows at a rate of 90 liters/min (24 gpm) through four 2,000-liter (528 gal) tanks. Each tank holds 1,000 kg (2,205 lb) of oysters in baskets. Depuration requires 48 hours.

Clams-- Clams are typically grown on the bottom without cultch. Raking, tonging, and dredging are a few of the common harvest practices. The oldest methods are by hand and treading. Treading involves the feeling of clams with one's feet when wading. Some clam farmers are experimenting with on-bottom basket culture. The basket protects clams from predators. In this instance, clams are removed from baskets at harvest. Clams, like oysters, may require relaying and depuration. Techniques are similar to those used for oysters (Blogoslawski 1989).

Mussels-- Mussels are grown a number of ways, and harvest methods vary from country to country (Lutz 1980). In France, mussels are harvested on foot or by boat from poles (bouchots). The clumps are broken apart, washed, and graded for size. The marketable mussels are placed in 20 kg (44 lb) burlap sacks. Depuration is not normally practiced. In the Netherlands, mussels are dredged from the bottom, depurated, and cleansed in on-shore tanks. Then they are machine scrubbed to remove debris. Finally, they are conveyed to a weighing and bagging area.

In Spain, where mussels are grown by rope or raft culture, marketable mussels are thinned from growing units by hand. Depuration is practiced by pumping seawater into holding tanks with chlorine. In Sweden, mussels are grown on long-lines. Harvesting and processing techniques are similar to those practiced in Spain. Chalfant et al. (1980) gave an overview of harvest mechanization with ample instructions.

TRANSPORTING TO THE PROCESSING PLANT

Once harvested, a culture species should continue to receive careful handling during transportation to the processing plant. Some people may reason that no special care is required since the culture species will soon be processed. A processing plant, however, cannot produce a quality product from poor quality raw materials.

Finfish

Finfish are transported to the processing plant live in tanks of water or packed in ice. Tanks usually are insulated and made of fiberglass or aluminum. Supplemental aeration to tanks is supplied by agitators, blowers, compressed air, or gaseous bottled oxygen.

Transport tanks should be disinfected for disease control before fish delivery. A good disinfecting agent is HTH (calcium hypochloride). Collins (1990) recommended that if a 65% chlorine formulation is used, then 34 ml of HTH should be used per 100 liters (1 oz/26 gal) of water. The disinfectant is left in for 1 hour before draining. During transport of warmwater fish, bacteria can be held in check with Acriflavine at 1 to 2 ppm, Furacin at 5.0 ppm, or Combiotic at 15 ppm (Piper et al. 1983). If chemicals are used, they must be approved by the Food and Drug Administration. Common salt, without iodine, frequently is used at 500 to 10,000 ppm to transport fish. Salt reduces the osmotic difference between the tank water and fish blood, thus reducing stress. The anesthetic MS-222 has been used at 10 to 20 ppm in transport water.

The weight of fish that can be transported safely in a live-hauling truck depends on efficiency of the aeration system, duration of the haul, water temperature, fish size, and fish species. General guidelines for channel catfish were given by Piper et al. (1983):
(1) 1.8 kg (4 lb) of 40-cm long (16-in) catfish can be transported for each 3.8 liters (1 gal) of water at 19°C (66°F).
(2) Loading rates can be increased by 25% for each 7°C (10°F) decrease in water temperature and reduced proportionately for an increase in temperature.
(3) If transportation time exceeds 12 hours, loading rates should be decreased by 25% and by 50% for 16 hours, or a complete water change should be given.
(4) During winter, hauling temperatures of 7° to 10°C (45° to 50°F) are preferred whereas during summer 16° to 21°C (60° to 70°F) are preferred.
(5) As fish length increases, the weight of fish per unit volume of water can be increased.

Once live-hauled fish reach the processing plant, they are unloaded into aerated tanks of dechlorinated water to await processing (Figure 15.17).

For live-hauling rainbow trout that are 20 to 28 cm long (8 to 11 in), 1 to 1.6 kg can be hauled for each 3.8 liters of water (2.5 to 3.5 lb/gal) for 8 to 10 hours.

Fish can be hauled to the processing plant packed in ice. Ice cools fish to a temperature just above freezing. This retards bacterial and enzymatic spoilage. Crushed ice should surround each fish. Cubed ice may bruise flesh. The amount of ice required depends on the initial temperature of fish, efficiency of insulation, and time required for hauling. Lovell and Ammerman (1974) gave guidelines for hauling channel catfish on ice:
(1) With good ice-to-fish contact, 150 g (0.33 lb) of ice lowers the temperature of 454 g (1 lb) of fish from 27° to 2°C (80° to 35°F) within 4 to 6 hours.

742

(2) If hauling conditions are not ideal and hauling time is longer than 12 hours, triple the amount of ice to give a 1:1 ratio of fish to ice if fish are near 27°C when loaded.
(3) If fish flesh at loading is near 10°C (50°F), then a fish-to-ice ratio of 2:1 is adequate. Wheaton and Lawson (1985) discussed in detail ice-hauling of various species.

Figure 15.17 Holding tanks for channel catfish to be processed. Photo courtesy of John Wozniak, LSU Agricultural Center.

Crustaceans

Like finfish, crustaceans too must be handled with great care during transport to the processing plant. In some instances, processing plants serve mainly as distribution centers. A live product is marketed. The red swamp crawfish, for example, is often sold live to consumers for social crawfish boils. In Japan, Hong Kong, and elsewhere, live prawns and shrimp may be featured in restaurants.

The red swamp crawfish, farmed primarily in Louisiana, is transported live to the processing plant in porous onion sacks (Figure 15.18). Crawfish need not be hauled in water. Each sack holds about 18 to 20 kg (40 to 44 lb) of crawfish. Before transportation, crawfish should be cleaned and washed of all mud and debris. At all times, keep sacks of crawfish moist and cool and out of direct sunlight. They should be stored on their sides no more than two sacks deep. Air should circulate around all sacks. If they are hauled in an open truck, a strong wind could dry out crawfish, and they will die. As long as their gills are moist, crawfish can respire by moving air across gill filaments. Sprinkling a little dechlorinated crushed ice on the top layer of sacks helps to cool crawfish and keep them moist. Once crawfish reach the processing plant, they are stored in a walk-in cooler to await processing. At temperatures of 3° to 4°C (37° to 39°F), they can be held for 2 to 3 days.

Figure 15.18 Sacks of live crawfish ready for processing.

Prawns and shrimp usually are hauled live to the processing plant in tanks of water or packed in ice. Similar precautions and procedures are used as those for finfish. The quality of prawn flesh deteriorates rapidly, so prawns require extra attention. Upon death of prawns, enzymes in the musculature and in the hepato-pancreas activate rapidly and may result in mushy flesh. For this reason, some farmers opt to chill-kill prawns in an ice slurry immediately after harvest. This is followed by freezing and packing in airtight containers or glazing with ice and then storing at a low temperature.

In some instances, prawns are blanched in boiling water after chill-killing, and then frozen or packed in ice. Blanching is thought to deactivate enzymes. Further, the hepatopancreas may be removed after chill-killing to prevent softening of the flesh.

Mollusks

At the harvest site, oysters if attached to cultch are usually separated from clusters into singles and doubles. Undersized oysters are replanted to the growing area. Remaining oysters are graded at the harvest site into those suitable for the half-shell trade and those selected for shucking. Oysters transport easily in burlap sacks or porous containers as long as they are kept cool, moist, and out of the sun.

Two methods have been used to store oysters at the processing plant, wet storage and dry storage (Quayle 1988). Wet storage involves placing oysters in a beach-receiving area floored with clean, firm gravel or concrete. An alternative is to use a floating platform submerged to a depth of 30 to 40 cm (12 to 16 in). The platform is anchored near the shucking house so that oysters are available at all times. A wet storage area allows oysters to cleanse themselves of accumulated mud and debris.

Use dry storage if there is pollution or the threat of pollution in wet storage areas. Optimum storage temperature for Pacific oysters (principally *Crassostrea gigas*) is about 1°C (34°F), but up to 5°C (41°F) is acceptable. At these temperatures, oysters may be stored 4 months or longer in walk-in coolers.

Clams, like oysters, also may be stored on floating platforms. They may be stored in layers to a depth of about five times the extent to which they can extend the siphons. Mussels, upon harvesting, can be washed with a high pressure hose. Grading is based on size and the amount of fouling, particularly from barnacles.

Mussels may be stored with either the wet or dry method. Dry storage at 2° to 5°C (36° to 41°F) keeps mussels in good condition for 2 more weeks.

Scallops do not possess the ability to close their shells tightly, and they may dehydrate soon after harvesting. Because of this, they must be transported to the processing plant soon after harvest and processed quickly.

THE PLANT DESIGN AND OPERATION

Development of a processing plant first involves the establishment of goals. You should determine the type of products to be handled, desired volume of output, and marketing and distribution. After this, a systematic plan should be organized around: site selection, plant layout, employee working conditions, receiving the raw material, processing operation, packaging, in-process storage, sanitation and safety, and distribution and marketing.

Site Selection

A plant sometimes is located in the hometown of the owner. This has some advantages in that the owner is known, and this may facilitate financing from local sources. Being in familiar surroundings also aids in efficient monitoring of plant operations. This does not mean necessarily that the plant is located at the most advantageous site.

Site selection involves a feasibility study of two parts (Wheaton and Lawson 1985). The first part involves selection of a general area, and the second a specific parcel of land. Selection of a general area involves finding enough raw material to process, market locations, volume of product needed for each market, and transportation costs. Each incipient processing operation must fine-tune these general guidelines. For example, at one time processors of channel catfish in the southeastern United States perceived that they could draw on raw material within an 80 km (50 miles) radius. Beyond that distance transportation was too costly. Further, some plants perceived that they needed a base of 800 ha (2,000 ac) for enough raw material to operate. This assumes that the annual production of catfish was approximately 5,600 kg/ha (5,000 lb/ac).

Choice of a specific site involves the evaluation of many factors, including intangibles. A partial checklist includes: availability of labor, skilled, semi-skilled, and unskilled; background of the community; history and success of other local industries; utilities, electrical, natural gas, water supply; waste disposal; transportation, rail, truck, air; commercial services, postal, professional, such as legal and accounting; specific site considerations, drainage, availability of utilities; employee requirements, schools, health services, culture and recreation, housing, stores, fire and police protection, trash and garbage pickup; physical climate; and availability of raw material. For detail treatment see Wheaton and Lawson (1985).

Plant Layout

The plant size is determined by the species and type of product(s) processed and by the volume of desired production. The processing methods used, equipment required, and other factors also influence the size of plant required. As the processing operation gets under way and marketing efforts increase, a time may come when the plant seems too small for the volume of product required. Addition of a second or even third work shift can double or even triple output. However, enough downtime must be allocated to allow for cleanup, maintenance, and safety.

Development of a flow chart helps you visualize each operation including the equipment, space, and number and type of workers required. Each operation can be termed a work center. A collection of related work centers forms a work block. Lovell et al. (1981) presented a flow diagram for a small catfish processing plant (Figure 15.19). The plant was designed to process 22,676 kg (50,000 lb) per week. Notice that work centers are grouped together to form work blocks. The holding area, or first work block, contains three work centers.

In addition to work blocks for the processing operation, space should be provided for an employee restroom and lounge, office, dry storage for supplies, a mechanical room for power, and temporary storage for wastes. By convenience and by law, certain work blocks must be separated from others. Restrooms, for

746

example, must be isolated from the processing operations. Follow guidelines and regulations of local and federal agencies.

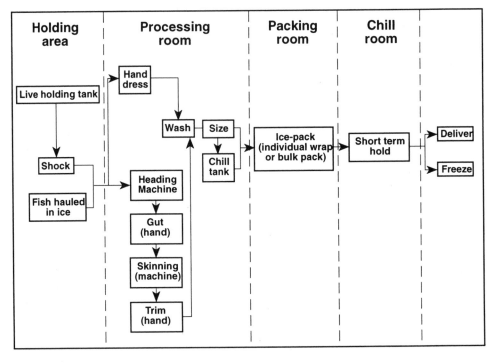

Figure 15.19 Flow diagram for processing channel catfish. Source Tom Lovell et al. 1981.

Employee Working Conditions

A plant must be designed to take into consideration employee needs and comfort; some obvious items such as restrooms are required by law. Food service facilities, restroom and locker room, recreational needs, medical services, safety, lighting, noise control, temperature/humidity control, and working space are integral parts of the planning process for plant design (Wheaton and Lawson 1985).

The food service provided depends on plant location and number of employees. A plant located near fast-food outlets will not have the same requirements as a plant with no nearby restaurants. Plants with 10 or fewer employees hardly can justify providing a cafeteria, whereas a plant employing 200 people may. All plants could provide vending machines, a microwave for warming homemade lunches, and tables and chairs for lunch breaks.

Restrooms should be in convenient locations within the plant to avoid wasting time going back and forth. A plant should have one water closet for each 20 male employees and one for each 12 female employees, and one urinal per 35 male employees. Locker rooms are often combined with restrooms.

Plants that have space should consider a recreational area. One trout processing plant in Idaho has outdoor space for a volleyball court. Employees use this during the lunch break.

Every plant should make provisions for emergency medical assistance. First aid kits located in strategic areas should be available to handle minor cuts, burns, and related injuries. A record should be kept on file of all employees who may have disabilities and special needs. This should be considered when such an employee is assigned to a work center.

Proper lighting reduces employee fatigue and provides a pleasant, safe environment. Moreover, error can be reduced because employees can distinguish better between blemished and unblemished products. Fluorescent lamps that are cool-white are widely used and are preferred over incandescent lamps.

Noise control is essential. Prolonged exposure to 85 to 90 decibels or above may impair hearing. Temperature and humidity, along with physical activity, affect physical comfort of employees. In the workplace, the desirable temperature and humidity for processing operations are often different from that for human comfort; compromise is needed. Working under crowded conditions can be aggravating, as are work centers requiring a lot of unnecessary walking back and forth.

Receiving Raw Material

The first work block involves receiving and unloading. Here the culture species is unloaded, tallied by weight, and temporarily stored in tanks of water, walk-in coolers, or other appropriate storage to await processing. There must be space for trucks to drive up, a mechanism to weigh the shipment, electricity, and a storage facility. A water supply will be needed if the culture species is stored in tanks. This first work block should be outside of the processing building and separated from the processing operation. Careful scheduling with producers is also required to assure a steady supply. Contracts describing the date of delivery, total weight, and average size per animal help to keep an orderly flow of raw materials.

The next work block for some species involves stunning with electricity. This is a normal procedure for channel catfish. Yet not all culture species, such as mollusks, require this work center. Moreover, some catfish and trout processing plants allow fish to die by suffocation; they are held out of water until they expire. Each processing plant must have work centers tailored for specific requirements.

Processing Operation

The processing operation is the next work block in the chronology of events. The plant design will vary with the culture species processed, types of products processed, volume of products produced, and even from plant to plant. Following are generalized accounts for the processing of finfish, crustaceans, and mollusks. For a detailed account see Avault (1980) and Wheaton and Lawson (1985).

Finfish-- Finfish are processed and marketed in various forms (Figure 15.20). Fish come out of the water whole. Drawn fish have entrails removed. Dressed fish have scales (if any), head, and entrails removed. The tail and fins may be removed. The fish may be filleted or cut into steaks. Fish further can be smoked, canned, or made into sticks or patties. For a more detailed classification, see Chapter 16.

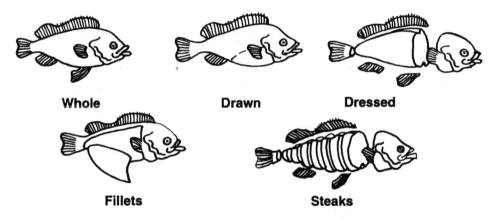

Figure 15.20 Some common forms of processed finfish. Courtesy of the Louisiana Sea Grant Office.

The channel catfish will be used as our example to follow the chronology of processing. Channel catfish ranging from 0.6 to 0.7 kg (1.25 to 1.5 lb) are removed from holding tanks in wire baskets with a power winch. Fish are stunned with electricity and moved by conveyer belt (Figure 15.21) to a ban saw where they are beheaded. The body cavity is cut open, and entrails are removed with a vacuum tube and conveyed outside of the processing plant wall. Fish are then rinsed. It is best if beheading, gutting, and rinsing operations are separated from the remainder of the processing plant by a wall. The skin is removed next by hand, with membrane skinners such as the Townsend, or by use of sodium hydroxide. Most plants use membrane skinners.

Figure 15.21 Channel catfish after stunning being loaded onto conveyor belt. Photo courtesy of John Wozniak, LSU Agricultural Center.

Next the fish are conveyed to a chill tank to rinse off blood and to cool them. Chilling fish firms the flesh and makes it easier for filleting and other operations. After chilling, fish are conveyed to the weighing station (Figure 15.22). In some plants, the conveyor automatically monitors fish weight and bumps them off at the proper station. The belly flap, called the nugget, is removed and the fish can be left whole, cut into steaks, or filleted. Filleting is done by hand or by machine (Figure 15.23). After filleting, the product is inspected (Figure 15. 24) and may be individually quick frozen (Figure 15. 25). Other finfish species are processed in a similar manner, although there are many nuances (Figures 15.26, 15.27). After processing, finfish products are usually held fresh on ice, in refrigeration without ice, or frozen.

Figure 15.22 Dressed fish after cleaning are segregated by weight for further processing. Photo courtesy of John Wozniak, LSU Agricultural Center.

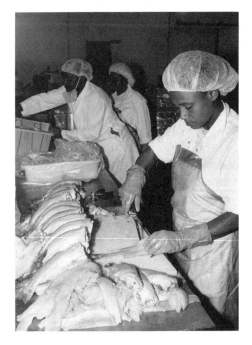

Figure 15.23 Hand filleting. Photo courtesy of John Wozniak, LSU Agricultural Center.

Figure 15.24 Catfish being checked one last time for off-flavor. Photo courtesy of John Wozniak.

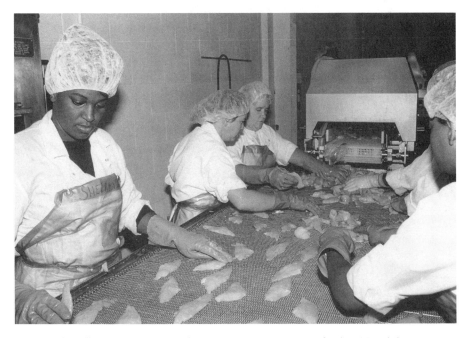

Figure 15.25 Fillets being readied for IQF. Photo courtesy of John Wozniak,

Figure 15.26 These particular rainbow trout have had entrails removed. The head and skin were left on. The fish will be packaged and marketed in this form.

Figure 15.27 Processed eels filleted to portion sizes near Kyoto, Japan.

Crustaceans-- In Louisiana, crawfish typically are processed into one of three products: whole and live, cooked and whole, and peeled tail meat. The first steps in crawfish processing are washing and inspecting. Washing removes debris, such as old bait and mud. Sacks of live crawfish are removed from a walk-in cooler, opened, and poured into a vat of water. A conveyor belt scoops up the crawfish from the vat and carries them past an inspector who removes any debris or dead crawfish. After this, crawfish are graded to size. Crawfish that are 33 or fewer/kg (15/lb) are considered large and select, and may be further processed for European and other specialty markets. Claws and other body parts should not be missing. Crawfish that are 33/kg up to 50/kg (22/lb) are considered medium in size and have a live market locally. Crawfish smaller than this are used for the peeled tail meat market (Figure 15.28). This size classification, however, may vary, depending on the processor.

Figure 15.28 Crawfish tail meat being removed by hand.

Once crawfish are cleaned and inspected, crawfish for peeling and the export market are dropped into cooking baskets with a capacity of about 45 to 68 kg (100 to 150 lb). If for the European market, dill and other seasonings may be added; otherwise, no seasonings are added. Cooking accomplishes several things. It kills the crawfish, kills the bacteria and enzymes, and it facilitates peeling of tail meat. Blanching time (cooking) is important and normally ranges from 6 to 8 minutes. Crawfish underblanched will often develop a mushy texture several days after storage. This textural change is attributed to enzyme activity of the hepatopancreas (locally called fat). Conversely, overcooking will make hand peeling more difficult. The undesirable black vein running the length of the tail meat loses strength and is likely to break during peeling.

After blanching, crawfish for tail meat markets are emptied through a chute to cooling tables. The chute is mounted in the wall between the blanching room and peeling room. Workers remove tail meat by hand from shells. A skillful worker normally can peel from 3.6 to 4.5 kg (8 to 10 lb) of crawfish tail meat per hour. Peeled tail meat is placed in a colander; the fat is placed in a separate container if the product is to be sold fresh locally. Otherwise, the fat is washed off since it may result in rancidity during frozen storage. Just before tail meat is packaged for freezing, it should be dipped in a weak lemon solution consisting of 1 part lemon juice to 10 parts water. Lemon juice prevents crawfish tails from turning blue or gray.

Crawfish for the European market after blanching are again graded to size, general appearance, and color (Figure 15.29). Crawfish from different farms may color differently upon blanching, and it is important not to mix different colored crawfish in the same shipping container. Once inspected, crawfish are individually quick frozen (IQF), packaged, and stored in a freezer.

Figure 15.29 Select crawfish being readied for Swedish market.

Chill-killed prawns are brought to the processing table. An experienced worker can behead 54 kg (120 lb) of prawns per hour, peel 18 kg (40 lb) per hour, and peel and devein 5 kg to 6 kg (11 to 13 lb) per hour when prawns are 57 to 88 count per kg (26 to 40/lb) (Silva et al. 1989). Beheaded prawns can be graded to size: jumbo, 14.5 count/kg (6.6/lb); large, 18.7/kg (8.5/lb); medium, 38.8/kg (17.6/lb); small, 100/kg (45.5/lb); and berried or egg-containing females, 34.6/kg (15.7/lb). After the processing operation, prawns are stored fresh on ice or frozen.

Shrimp are handled much like prawns for processing. Upon arrival at the plant, shrimp are washed and inspected. Any debris and cull shrimp are discarded. The shrimp next are conveyed to an automatic weighing machine. The shrimp are then beheaded, peeled, and deveined, usually with automatic machinery.

Like most other crustaceans, the price paid to producers depends on the size or count of shrimp. The count is the number of shrimp per kilogram. Designations such as jumbo, large, medium, and small have been used. The biggest shrimp often bring the best prices. Price may also be based on color, such as white shrimp, brown shrimp, pink shrimp, and so on. Though most shrimp are sold live, fresh, or frozen, some may be canned. Shrimp are precooked for about 4 minutes, inspected again, and graded to size. Shrimp are packed into cans containing hot salt. Each can is sealed before retorting.

Mollusks-- Oysters are processed either in the shell, termed half shell (Figure 15.30), or as shucked meats. Sacks of oysters are removed from cold storage and emptied onto shucking tables. Oyster shells are pried open by hand with an oyster knife at the hinge where the adductor muscle is found (Figure 15.31). Shuckers at one plant in Louisiana can each process 14 to 15 sacks in 5.5 hours. Each sack contains 15 to 18 dozen oysters and produces approximately 3.3 liters (7 pints) of meat. This particular plant processes up to 500 sacks per day. Empty oyster shells are shoveled onto a conveyor belt and trucked away.

Figure 15.30 Oysters on the half shell.

Figure 15.31 Oyster shuckers. Photo at Guedry's oyster plant, Cut Off, Louisiana.

Figure 15.32 Washed oyster meats.

There have been attempts to pry open oysters mechanically, but generally this has been unsuccessful. Brown (1982) suggested steam-shocking oysters before hand shucking. Steam shocking exposes oysters, still in their shells, to live steam long enough to raise the temperature of meat to about 49°C (120°F). This takes about 90 to 150 seconds. Oysters relax the adductor muscle, which causes the shells to gap just enough to allow easy access with a shucking knife. Quayle and Newkirk (1989) discussed a method whereby oysters are given a 2-to 3-minute dip in water with a temperature of 60° to 65°C (140° to 150°F).

After the oyster is shucked, meats are washed (Figure 15.32). Air is bubbled from the bottom of the container with oyster meats. This washes without bruising. In small operations, a rubber-gloved hand gently stirs oyster meats. After washing, oysters are poured into colanders and washed with a spray.

In Maine, the blue mussel (*Mytilus edulis*) is washed with water spray for about 5 minutes in a rotating drum cage with at least 11 revolutions per minute. The drum cage is 2 m (6.5 ft) long with an inside diameter of 0.8 m (2.6 ft) (Slabyj 1980). Mussels are tumbled for about 5 minutes to break up aggregates. At the lower end of the washer, empty shells and debris are removed. Cleaned mussels are packed in baskets. Most mussels are sold fresh, either whole or as shucked meats. Steaming releases meats from shells without the need for individual shucking. Meats can be canned in a light brine or in the juice collected in the steaming process. Mussel meats also can be smoked or canned in light oil.

Scallops are shucked by hand. A knife is used to slice between the adductor mussel and shell to free meat from the shell. A skilled shucker can process 400 to 500 kg (882 to 1,102 lb) of whole scallops in an 8-hour shift (Swann 1989). Mechanical shucking can be done by first heating scallops long enough to relax the adductor muscle. The shell opens easily for removal of meat. In Japan, scallops are blanched before processing. A net bag containing about 150 kg (330 lb) of live scallops is dipped into a vat of boiling water for 1 minute, then dropped into a vat of cold water. Once shucked, the meat can be kept fresh, frozen, or sundried.

Packaging and Value Added Products

After the processing operation, the next work block is the packaging room. Packaging may be in bulk for distribution to wholesalers or it may be for direct distribution to consumers. Some processed products may undergo further processing, such as breading of fish fillets or canning of products to produce a more valuable commodity.

Packaging of aquaculture products serves four functions: (1) containment, (2) protection, (3) utility, and (4) communication (Raphael and Olsson 1978).

Containment facilitates handling, transportation, and storage. The container must have physical strength and be easy to open and close.

Protection must be provided for the product from its surroundings and to safeguard the environment from the product. Protection involves ease of handling, transportation, storage, marketing, and use of the product by consumers.

The package must be convenient for consumers to use and may have boil-in-bag packages, tear tape to open, bake-and-serve packages, portion-size packages, and twist-off caps (Wheaton and Lawson 1985).

Communication of packaged products must convey information of importance to consumers, such as date packaged, weight, number of servings, nutritional content, how to prepare, and related information. Recipes are helpful, especially for new products or products that have been enhanced by value added. Communication also involves providing an appealing package for consumers. The package must look good, because eye appeal is buy appeal.

Selection of package materials and package appearance depends on product characteristics and on consumer preferences. Glass has been used as a container for aquatic products, but plastic is more commonplace. Certain products, such as oyster meats, are packaged in their own liquid. Metal cans are sometimes used for salmon, and metal foils are versatile for use in packaging. Paper and plastic products are commonly used for a variety of finfish and crustacean products. A common package consists of a foam plastic tray with transparent plastic film overwraps. For products that may drip, an absorbent paper is placed under the product. Individually wrapped packages are often transported in insulated waxed cardboard boxes.

The package must not only be functional, but it also must be attractive. The colors used provoke certain reactions from people. For example, light green does not elicit much of a reaction, but dark green induces a feeling of calmness. Blue, combined with white, conveys a refreshing and antiseptic feeling (Griffin and Sacharow 1972). Product identity can be enhanced by choosing a particular package design and sticking with it. A logo or certain symbols become familiar to consumers, and they feel comfortable buying the product.

Value added products are becoming more popular with consumers. They take many forms. Certain markets, such as restaurants, require strict portion size. An entree might consist of a single fillet. For household consumption, the size and weight of the product need not be as exact. A breaded product might be more appealing, especially if it can be cooked by placing the package directly in an oven or microwave. Breading is done by coating the raw product with a viscous batter followed by breading. A good batter should coat the product uniformly, not distract from product flavor, and retain a desirable amount of breading. Batter materials are available from companies specializing in preparation of batter and breading material. Breading, applied after the batter, is usually a dry granular material that acts as an extender. Since breading is less costly than the raw product itself, the value added product becomes more cost efficient.

Value added products can be made with soups, gumbos, and stews. Clam chowder soup, seafood gumbo, and oyster stew are familiar to many of us. In some instances the product, like crawfish etouffee, may come in a container with recipe, and mixed seasonings may come in a companion container.

One trout processing plant in North Carolina makes trout pate (Figure 15.33). Smoked trout fillets are made into a paste. Creamed cheese, sour cream, cultured skim milk, other ingredients, and spices are blended with the pate.

Figure 15.33 Preparing trout pate. Photo at Blankenship-Cherokee trout farm, Cherokee, North Carolina.

Canning is a method of increasing the value of a product and its shelf life. The raw product is usually cooked before it is put in cans. Substances then may be added to enhance flavor and keeping qualities. Once cans are sealed, they are heated with steam to sterilize contents. The procedure is called retorting. The volume of product in the can determines retort time, but contents must be heated for at least 4 minutes at 120°C (248°F) or 10 minutes at 115°C (239°F) to kill heat-resistant strains of bacteria (Ball 1955). General principles for canning food are reviewed by the Food Processors Institute (1988). Wheaton and Lawson (1985) discussed canning of salmon, crustaceans, and mollusks.

In-Process Storage

In-process storage is a work block for temporary storage of processed products before distribution. Separate storage may be set up for byproducts such as oyster shells and fish offal.

Finished products usually require refrigeration or frozen storage. The plant design should flow from the packaging work block directly to storage. From storage, products are taken to the distribution area.

Distribution and Shipping
This work block should be designed for getting a final weight and tally of finished products leaving the plant. Ample parking and turn-around room must be provided for trucks.

SANITATION
Up to this point, we have discussed the flow of raw materials from the holding and receiving area, through the processing room, packaging room, in-process storage, and distribution area. Sanitation, though not a work block, must be part of the total processing operation and is important in plant design. Sanitation is designed to: (1) protect the health of the consumer, (2) prevent any offense to the aesthetic sense of the consumer, and (3) minimize economic loss from spoilage. The Food and Drug Administration (FDA) established criteria for food plant sanitation. It promulgated good manufacturing practice regulations, known as the umbrella GMPs, for manufacturing, packaging, or holding human foods. Food plant sanitation was summarized by Nickerson and Ronsivalli (1980) and by the Food Processors Institute (1988).

Plant Grounds
The plant surroundings should be neat, clean, orderly, well landscaped, and free from weeds, rubbish, and unused equipment. Dusty roads, yards, and parking lots must be eliminated. Poorly drained areas encourage flies, mosquitoes, and odor-producing microorganisms. Beautiful surroundings have a good psychological effect on plant workers who are more apt to keep things neat and clean inside the plant. Moreover, customers will perceive that beautiful surroundings mean quality products.

The Building
The processing building should be constructed of brick or concrete. Walls and floors must be constructed with easily cleaned non-porous materials. Concrete, plastic tile, and similar materials are recommended for floors and walls where hosing down is a routine procedure. Floors must be sloped toward drains. Electrical systems must be watertight to allow cleanup. Equipment benches and machinery should allow easy cleaning. All floors, walls, benches, tables, conveyors, hoppers, kettles, and utensils used in processing food should be thoroughly cleaned and sanitized with appropriate materials at least once, preferably twice, per 8-hour shift. Large plants should consider a cleaning crew with a supervisor. Detergents should clean but not be corrosive. Sanitizing treats

food-contact surfaces and destroys vegetative cells of microorganisms of public health significance. Common sanitizers used in food processing plants are: (1) chlorine compounds, (2) iodine compounds, and (3) quaternary ammonium compounds (Food Processors Institute 1988).

Personal Hygiene

Rules of personal hygiene by plant workers must be concomitant with sanitation policies of the physical plant. Nickerson and Ronsivalli (1980) summarized:

(1) Persons with communicable diseases should not handle food.

(2) Physical cleanliness should be observed. Workers should wear clean (preferably white) work uniforms. Jewelry should be removed. Heads should be covered and fingernails kept short with no polish.

(3) Hands should be washed and dipped in a disinfectant before and periodically thereafter when handling food.

(4) When handling foods, the hands should not touch the nose, mouth, or other body parts since these are potential sources of contamination. Sneezing and coughing should be into a handkerchief, or better yet the person should leave the work area.

(5) During work, food handlers should not eat, drink, nor smoke in the area.

(6) Pets should be kept out.

(7) Cloths should not be used for cleaning.

(8) Foods that appear to be unwholesome should not be handled.

QUALITY ASSURANCE

Quality control involves activities within the processing plant to maximize quality of products. Quality assurance goes beyond the processing plant. It guarantees quality from the producer and processor to the consumer and from all operations in between (Gorga and Ronsivalli 1988).

Processing plants typically serve a role in both marketing and distribution. Restaurants that buy directly from a plant normally practice good handling and storage procedures. Supermarkets do not always store and handle fishery products properly. When the consumer is unhappy with the package, the processor whose name is identified with the package often receives blame. This translates into quality control at the plant but not quality assurance overall.

In some countries, such as Iceland, Japan, and Norway, quality assurance is guaranteed at the national level. The United States has not had a history of national quality assurance for fishery products. Mandatory inspection and grading of red meat and poultry by the U.S. Department of Agriculture has not been extended to aquaculture and capture fisheries products. The National Marine Fisheries Service and the Food and Drug Administration will, upon request, inspect products for a fee. Inspections are made at various key points, beginning with the point of capture (harvest) to the point of display. Inspections are based on a plan known as Hazard Analysis Critical Control Point (HACCP).

Hazard Analysis Critical Control Point

HACCP is an inspection technique that focuses on problem prevention by industry (Johnson 1994). Industry and the U.S. Department of Commerce (USDC) work together to develop a plan. Specific plans may vary from plant to plant. The basic idea of HACCP is to identify hazards to products during processing at certain critical points. An example of a critical control point might be when the product reaches the end of the conveyor belt and must be moved to a new work block. Other critical control points are identified, and a plan is developed. The plan focuses on critical control points that can be controlled, monitored, and recorded.

The U.S. Department of Commerce HACCP-based program focuses on three general areas: food safety, food and plant hygiene, and economic integrity (Anonymous 1994). The seven basic principles of HACCP are: (1) determine product hazards and how they can be prevented, (2) identify the control points and determine which are critical, (3) establish the limits that must be met at each critical control point (CCP), (4) establish procedures to control and monitor each CCP, (5) establish corrective actions when critical limits are exceeded, (6) establish record keeping systems, (7) establish procedures for monitoring and verification of the HACCP-based system (U.S. Department of Commerce, National Marine Fisheries Service Inspection Services Division, 1335 East-West Highway, Silver Spring, MD 20910). Plants that have an accepted plan for HACCP may put a logo on their products stating that they are HACCP approved.

Some people will argue against further government intervention. Yet quality assurance without national standards would be difficult. Processing plants can muster some influence over quality assurance up to and including marketing and distribution, but they can only suggest proper handling and storage beyond that point.

Chain of Events for Quality Assurance

There is a chain of events that collectively goes into quality assurance, namely: the condition and quality of the culture species grown, harvesting and handling, processing, preservation and storage, distribution to brokers or wholesalers, distribution to retailer, sale to consumer, and consumption by consumer.

Growing the Culture Species-- Condition and quality of the culture species grown can be controlled to a degree by the culturist. Attention to water management, proper feeding, and good culture practices in general should assure a robust animal at harvest. Some aquaculture farms do not consciously try to produce a quality fish. Goals at the farm level may center more around keeping the culture species alive, growing as many kg per unit area as quickly as possible, and doing it cost efficient. Processing plants are more inclined to consider size of the culture species and general appearance. State and federal regulations determine whether or not oysters and other mollusks are safe to eat by making bacterial counts. Quality assurance must go beyond these measures.

Management practices during grow-out must have quality assurance in mind. Feed additives and finishing formulations need development to produce a higher quality flesh. In some instances, crawfish meal containing the pigment astaxanthin can be added to feed to promote a pink or red flesh in salmon, red sea bream (*Pagrus major*), and certain other culture species. Several days before harvest, culture species should be taken off feed to allow them to clean out the gut and firm the flesh. At certain seasons, a culture species may be in poor flesh, and should not be harvested for processing. The mouth-brooding tilapia is in poor flesh after egg incubation. The red swamp crawfish, in Louisiana, toughens up before burrowing underground in summer, and it may be hollow-tailed upon emergence in the fall. The American oyster (*Crassostrea virginica*) has soft, watery flesh during the spawning season.

Harvesting-- Harvesting and handling mechanics have been discussed earlier, but there is much room for improving quality assurance. Harvest techniques must minimize stress. Picking up finfish and crustaceans from a muddy pond bottom is not the way to do it. Channel catfish farmers normally remove fish from harvesting nets in a brailing bag with the aid of a power boom. Fish are stacked one on top of another. If catfish farmers used fish pumps to remove fish along with the water, as do many trout farmers, fish would bruise less. Transportation to the processing plant allows further opportunity for quality assurance. Fish hauled live should be stressed as little as possible. Buildup of lactic acid and other products of stress do not enhance the quality of the flesh. Some species, such as hybrid striped bass (striped bass *Morone saxatilis* x white bass, *M. chrysops*), are hard to handle when transporting, and they die easily. It is best to haul this fish on ice.

Processing-- Processing, the next link in the chain of quality assurance, has two objectives. The first is to procure only those culture species that have the necessary reserve quality to last up to the moment of consumption. The second is to minimize the deterioration of quality that the product undergoes during processing (Gorga and Ronsivalli 1988). In aquaculture, unlike capture fisheries, most culture species can be brought to the processing plant live. If culture species are on ice, careful planning can ensure a minimum lag time between harvest, transportation to the plant, and processing. Bringing in a culture species alive, however, does not guarantee quality. Stress in handling, as we have seen, may charge the flesh with lactic acid and other undesirable substances. Careless handling can occur in other ways as well. A harvest boat with a leaky gas can does no good to sacks of live crawfish lying on the bottom of the boat. The manager of a processing plant should visit the aquaculture operations where raw material is bought and observe methods of harvest. Suggested guidelines may be developed for harvesting and transportation to obtain quality assurance.

Three factors involved in maximizing quality assurance in the processing plant are time, temperature, and spoilage enzymes and microorganisms. Minimizing the processing time is crucial. Every effort must be made to move the product quickly through the processing work blocks to in-process storage. Generally, the shelf life of most fresh fish lasts only 2 weeks at 0°C (32°F). Thus, quality is high for about a week. The time required during handling reduces its reserve time to the consumer. Bacteria, under ideal conditions, are capable of doubling their numbers every 20 minutes. Reduce processing time, and you reduce bacterial numbers. Every effort should be made to process raw materials at reduced temperatures, because as temperatures increase, bacterial activity increases. The processing plant should be kept at a comfortable temperature for the workers. This is not always easy. Some processors maintain a processing temperature of 10°C (50°F), others of 4.5°C (40°F). A system called the Friotube confines refrigeration only to the space immediately surrounding the product (Gorga 1983). Spoilage enzymes and microorganisms can be reduced by sanitary handling as reviewed earlier.

Preservation-- Preservation practices must continue to maximize quality assurance. Preservation is usually accompanied by lowering the temperature of the product. Low temperatures reduce bacterial and enzymatic activity. Other means of preservation include canning, salting, drying, smoking, irradiating, and fermenting. Fishery products destined for the fresh markets are preserved with ice or refrigeration. Products on ice should not be allowed to sit in water. They should be kept from direct contact with ice by wrapping them in cellophane or similar materials, yet they should be surrounded by ice. Refrigerated products should be held at temperatures just above freezing. Freezing is becoming a more common method to preserve fishery products. Depending on the culture species, fish contains approximately 60% to 80% water. The preservative effect of freezing is caused mainly by making water unavailable for bacterial and enzymatic activities and slowing the rate of chemical reactions.

As water begins freezing in tissues, enzymes and other compounds in the muscle tend to concentrate in the unfrozen water remaining. They speed denaturation of protein (Wheaton and Lawson 1985). Therefore, the quicker the freezing process, the less protein denaturation that takes place. Further, when products are allowed to freeze slowly, water molecules tend to migrate to seed-crystals and freeze into large ice crystals (Nicherson and Ronsivalli 1980). Fast freezing results in the more desirable small ice crystals. Several methods are used to quick freeze fishery products. Air-blast freezing and use of liquid freezers are two. Air-blast freezing entails the movement of processed fish on a conveyor through an insulated tunnel. Supercooled air is blown over the product. Liquid nitrogen tunnels are used more and more in processing to individually quick freeze (IQF) processed products. Individual fish fillets, individual shrimp and crawfish, and other processed products move through liquid nitrogen tunnels on stainless steel belts.

Salting is a form of preservation. Salt added to fishery products lowers the water activity that, in turn, reduces growth of spoilage bacteria. Gorga and Rosivalli (1988) described a hard cure and a light cure. In the light-cure method, fish are layered in tubs with salt at a ratio of 12 kg fish to 1 kg salt. After 24 hours, brine forms and fish may float. A weighted cover holds the product down. Two to 3 days later fish are removed and drained. The hard-cure method is similar to the light-cure method, but the fish to salt ratio is 3:1. Water leaving the fish is drained off, and brine is not allowed to form.

Other forms of preservation are practiced out of necessity or choice in certain countries. Sun drying is practiced in areas suited to tradition. Small shrimp or fish, with a large surface area relative to volume, are spread out under the sun. Loss of water reduces bacteria and enzymatic activity. Smoking is a process whereby fish is dehydrated and saturated with aromatic smoke (Doré 1993). Irradiation is accomplished with gamma rays, x-rays, or high energy electrons. The irradiation must penetrate the product completely to kill all microorganisms. Government regulations have allowed its use. Fermented fishery products are prepared by first salting and fermenting the salted product. Fermentation is accomplished in a closed container. Fish sauces and pastes are often used as food condiments.

Storage-- In-process storage is the next link in quality assurance. Usually, this is a temporary storage of only a few hours up to several days. Refrigeration products, or products on ice, should be moved out within hours to ensure freshness. Frozen products can be stored longer. Nevertheless, the deterioration rate depends on the temperature at which the product is stored. If the product was initially processed as IQF, it was frozen at extremely low temperatures. However, it is uneconomical to store at such low temperatures. On the other hand, higher storage temperatures allow an increase in water activity within the frozen product. Bacteria need higher water activities than do yeasts and molds. There is a trade-off, then, in choosing the proper storage temperature. If economical, Gorga and Ronsivalli (1988) suggested that fish fillets be stored at -29°C (-20°F). Temperatures of -23° to -18°C (-10° to 0°F) are acceptable, but they should not be higher than this.

Distribution-- There are several times when the product is distributed after in-process storage, namely to the wholesaler, the retailer, and when the consumer takes the product home. Every effort should be taken to keep the product cold in transit and to minimize time in transit. Using common sense helps. Leaving a shipment of processed fish on the loading dock in the sun will not enhance its quality.

The retailer, such as the supermarket, is usually the last link in the chain of quality assurance before the consumer. The portion of the product not displayed immediately should be held in storage. Store fresh products at about -1°C (30°F) and frozen products at -29°C (-20°F) (Gorga and Rosivalli 1988). In no instances should display cases be higher than 0°C (32°F) for fresh products and -18°C (0°F) for frozen products. Display cases often have inadequate temperature controls, and rotation of products may be ineffective. The first product stocked in the display case should be the first sold.

The consumer is the final link in quality assurance. There is a time lag between purchase and storing in the home freezer or refrigerator. Shorten the time, and you help maintain quality. Thawing the product before cooking is important. Placing a frozen product in hot water does little to maintain quality. Thawing is best done in a microwave or by placing the product in the refrigerator beforehand. Simple instructions on the package help.

As we have seen, quality assurance goes beyond the processor. National seafood inspection programs, however, will no doubt continue to focus at the processor level. Therefore, it is suggested that the aquaculture industry design its own guidelines (not regulations) to develop the highest possible product quality from the farmer to the consumer. In the United States, the Catfish Farmers of America (Brunson 1993), U.S. Trout Farmers Association (Anonymous 1994a), and like organizations have developed quality assurance guidelines, while working in concert with the National Aquaculture Association.

BYPRODUCT USE

Processing plants have materials left over after processing. The dressing percentage of channel catfish is about 60%, leaving 40% as waste. This waste consists of heads, entrails, and skin. If the fish are filleted, the dressing percentage drops, and fish frames are added to the waste. When crawfish are peeled, tail meat is removed, and up to 85% waste is left behind. Shrimp and prawns, too, when beheaded and peeled, produce wastes. Oysters and other mollusks leave behind huge quantities of shells (Figure 15.34). These wastes, or preferably byproducts, can be put to good use.

Instead of costing money for waste disposal, they may bring added income. Many good uses have been found for byproducts from processing plants. To be feasible, a large enough volume of material must be readily available and it must be cost efficient to produce a usable product. In some instances, such as production of minced fish, further processing is necessary to produce a usable product. In others, no further processing is required, such as use of clam shells for road fill. Stansby (1963), Green and Kramer (1979), Windsor and Barlow (1981), and Wheaton and Lawson (1985) reviewed various uses of byproducts.

Figure 15.34 Oyster shells being removed for further use. Photo at Guedry's oyster plant, Cut Off, Louisiana.

Minced Fish

Minced fish has been produced in Japan for many decades. It is produced by passing whole gutted and headed fish, fillets, or fish frames with the fillets removed over a drum with small perforations, typically 1 to 7 mm (1 in = 25.4 mm) in diameter. Pressure forces the soft meat through the perforations. Bones, skin, fins, and scales remain in the exterior of the perforated drum. These machines are called meat-bone separators, and they are particularly useful in processing plants that have fish frames left over from filleting.

Minced fish is washed with cold water; the pH is adjusted, and excess water is removed by centrifuging. The minced fish is then refrigerated during grinding. Salt, starch sugar, sodium glutamate, and other materials are mixed with the minced fish. The product is formed after mixing into various shapes, such as loaves.

From minced fish, a variety of products can be produced including kamaboko, fish blocks, and surimi (Aquanotes 1984; Wheaton and Lawson 1985). Kamaboko is an elastic fish cake eaten in Japan; it may vary in shape, color, size, and flavor. Minced fish can be made into frozen fish blocks that, in turn, are cut into fish sticks. Surimi can be made to look and taste like more expensive seafoods such as lobster or crab. Rust (1993) reviewed the process.

Fish Meals and Oils

Production of fish meal and oils is principally from menhaden (*Brevoortia* spp.) in North America and anchovy (*Anchoa spp.*) from South America. Wheaton and Lawson (1985) outlined the process. These fish are small, present in large numbers, and not desirable for human consumption. Fish meals are used principally in animal feed, including those used for culture species grown in aquaculture. In the Philippines and elsewhere, fish processing waste may be fed directly to hogs without first processing to meal. Oils have a variety of uses including cooking oils, cosmetics, paints, and lubricants. Fish wastes produced in processing plants can be reduced to fish meal and oil.

Lovell (1980) concluded that channel catfish processing waste can be processed by conventional fish meal reduction or by enzyme hydrolysis with subsequent drying into meal. He fed wet diets containing pasteurized catfish waste (70%) and corn (30%) to pigs with satisfactory results. Oil produced from catfish wastes is an excellent attractant in crawfish baits (Avault et al. 1984-85). Walker et al. (1967) studied use of crawfish waste as a feed ingredient for channel catfish. Meyers (1981) reduced shrimp and crawfish waste to meals. The meals contain a carotenoid pigment called astaxanthin, which imparts a pink or red color when incorporated into diets for salmonids. Crawfish meal also has been tested as an attractant in crawfish baits (Burns and Avault 1991).

Chitin

Crustacean shells contain chitin. Chitin, or its derivative chitosan, has properties similar to cellulose, with the same kinds of uses. A partial list of uses includes: a paper-making additive to improve strength, a flocculant for waste water, an additive to baby food formulations, as a substance for controlled long-term releases of pesticides, in textile finishes, shoe polish, and water-based paint, as a synthetic fiber, a food thickener, for biodegradable moisture-proof packaging, for making gels, and for use in manufacture of films (Anonymous 1973). Commercial production of chitin is under way in Japan and the United States. Processing of chitin is a rather complex process, involving a number of steps (Anonymous 1973). Major problems are the logistics of getting a sufficient volume of crustacean waste, transferring it to the processing plant, and having a year-round supply.

Shells and Pearls

Oyster and other molluskan shells have been used to replace gravel on roads, in cesspools, as poultry grit, as a source of lime, as cultch material, and for decorative purposes. Mother-of-pearl shells, such as abalone shells, are used for button making and decorative items. Certain oyster species may contain an occasional pearl.

Fish Roe

The eggs, called roe, of many fish species are used as high-value food. Most people are familiar with caviar, which is lightly salted sturgeon (*Acipenser* spp.) roe. Paddlefish (*Polyodon spathula*) and bowfin (*Amia calva*) also make good caviar. The general procedure for producing caviar is to first remove the ovaries of gravid females. The membrane and fatty tissue are separated from the eggs. Eggs are rinsed several times in cold water containing a light salt solution. After draining, eggs are salted with 142 g (5 oz) of very fine-grained salt to each 4.5 kg (10 lb) of eggs. Following this, caviar is placed in a slip-lid tin or jar with no air left in the container. The caviar can be refrigerated at -3.5° to -1°C (26° to 30°F) for up to 6 months. The peak of quality is reached in about 1 week. Besides caviar, finfish eggs offer good potential for other foods. The Japanese eat salmon eggs in a dish called ikura (Figure 15.35). Eggs from channel catfish, common carp, and other finfish are often discarded during processing, although they could be used.

Figure 15.35 Salmon eggs to be used for a dish called ikura in Japan.

Other Uses

Wheaton and Lawson (1985) listed other uses for fish byproducts. Insulin can be extracted from yellowtail (*Seriola quinqueradiata*), salmon and certain other finfish species. Fish oils, especially from the liver, are rich in vitamins. Leather has been made from salmon, catfish, and other finfish. Fish glue can be manufactured from skins and fish heads.

WASTE MANAGEMENT

Processing plants produce solid waste such as bones, shells, entrails, heads, and similar materials, and they produce liquid wastes. Solids in liquid wastes can be categorized into total, settleable, suspended or filterable, and dissolved or nonfilterable. Total solids in wastewater include a combination of all solids. Settleable solids settle out to the bottom of a container when quiescent for a time. They also settle out in a settling basin. Suspended or filterable solids are those that do not readily settle out, but can be caught on a filter. Dissolved or nonfilterable solids consist of very fine particles that pass through a filter.

Solid Waste Disposal

Processing plants do not have as much trouble handling solid wastes as they do handling wastes found in processing water. Generally, useful byproducts can be produced from solid wastes as already discussed. Certain wastes can be fed directly to hogs and other livestock or used as fertilizer on cropland. When used as fertilizer, they should be incorporated into the soil.

One trout processing plant in North Carolina makes compost from processing wastes. A layer of sawdust is put down then a layer of fish processing wastes, then another layer of sawdust. Air is injected periodically through PVC pipe that runs underneath (Figure 15.36). Compost is ready for use by plant nurseries in about 12 weeks. Processing wastes from the blue crab (*Callinectes sapidus*) also has been composted (Cathcart et al. 1984).

Figure 15.36 Composting trout processing wastes. Photo at Jennings-Sunburst Trout Farm, Sunburst, North Carolina.

Dumping solid wastes into a stream, lake, other body of water, or on top of the ground should never be done. Small processing plants may simply use a landfill for wastes. Various government regulations must be checked for whatever method is used for waste disposal.

Liquid Effluent Disposal

There are three ways to disposal of liquid effluent from processing plants: to a public sewer system, land application, or discharge to receiving waters. The type of disposal system used depends on the nature and volume of the effluent, degree of effluent clarity required by regulatory agencies, land requirements, and other factors. To use the public sewer system, you must have permission from the local sewer authority. A permit is needed, and some pretreatment may be required. Land application has several options: use of effluent for irrigation, use of injection wells, or use of treatment ponds. Regardless of the type of disposal system, pretreatment is necessary. Various stages of effluent treatment are usually called primary treatment, secondary treatment, and tertiary treatment.

Primary Treatment-- This involves removal of insoluble suspended material by screening, flow equalization, and/or sedimentation (Wheaton and Lawson 1985). Screens used may have openings larger than 6.3 mm (coarse) or 0.8 mm (most common opening). The EPA has recommended a 20-mesh-per-inch screen as a minimum for most seafood processing effluents. However, this mesh size plugs up easily, and it may be more practical to have a larger mesh screen ahead of the 20-mesh screen, or even a series of screens. Flow equalization follows screening. This consists of a holding tank with pumping system to reduce shock loadings. In other words, effluent discharge is spread out over time. Sedimentation or settling is a common primary treatment method. It is a quiescent basin where settleable coarse material can settle out. Sedimentation is reviewed by Loehr (1977) and Green and Kramer (1979).

Secondary Treatment This treatment system may consist of dissolved air floatation, biological filters, or lagoons. Dissolved air floatation is based on the principle of floating fats, oils, and grease with the aid of air bubbles. Floating material is skimmed off. The air is dissolved in the liquid waste as it flows through a pressure tank. Biological filters are not filters *per se*. Rather they consist of substrate or media containing bacteria. As effluent flows over the filter, bacteria break down organic material to nutrients (Chapter 7). Substrate may be in the form of shells, koch rings, rotating disks, and the like. Lagoons are commonly used by processing plants with available land. Lagoons may be aerobic, anaerobic, or facultative, a combination of the two. Effluent entering the lagoon is oxidized or reduced with subsequent release of CO_2 and other compounds (nutrients). Nutrients in turn can be removed with phytoplankton, such as *Chlorella* sp. and *Scenedesmus* sp., or higher plants, such as duckweed (*Lemna* spp. and *Spirodela polyrhiza*). Duckweed in turn has been harvested, dried, and incorporated into animal rations (Culley et al. 1981). Phelps and Stiebel (1991) cautioned that wastewater could be contaminated with *Salmonella*.

In some instances fish low on the food chain, such as tilapia, can be introduced into lagoons to harvest flora and fauna produced. Mechanical aeration is often used to enhance aerobic decomposition and to ensure enough oxygen for fish.

Tertiary Treatment-- Also known as advanced wastewater treatment, it includes such processes as chemical precipitation, sand filtration, carbon adsorption, ion exchange, ozone oxidation, and others (Wheaton and Lawson 1985). Most plants do not use tertiary treatment.

STUDY QUESTIONS
1. Describe methods for harvesting channel catfish.
2. Describe methods for harvesting crawfish.
3. Describe methods for harvesting shrimp.
4. Describe methods for harvesting mussels.
5. How are finfish transported to the processing plant?
6. How are prawns and shrimp transported to the processing plant?
7. How are oysters stored before processing?
8. List factors that must be considered when selecting a site for a processing plant.
9. Choose any culture species. In outline form, list the work centers and work blocks you need for processing.
10. With the culture species you chose above, describe a value-added product you will produce.
11. What is the purpose of sanitation in a processing plant?
12. Develop a quality assurance plan for the culture species you chose in questions 9 and 10.
13. What are the seven basic principles of HACCP?
14. List as many byproducts and their uses as you can for finfish, crustaceans, and mollusks.
15. How are wastes handled at processing plants?

REFERENCES
Anonymous. 1973. Pilot plant could develop into new industry for converting waste shells into chitin and chitosan. Pacific Northwest Sea 6(1):6-12 & 15.
Anonymous. 1994. Food Safety Law. Summary of FDA warning letters, 1993 food safety violations. Thompson Publishing Group 1725 K Street N.W. Washington, D.C.

Anonymous. 1994a. Trout producers quality assurance program. U.S. Trout Farmers Association. 28 pp.

Aquanotes. 1984. Surimi: high tech seafood. Louisiana Sea Grant, Louisiana State University. Volume 13, No. 1.

Avault, J.W. Jr. 1980. Fisheries products from aquaculture and capture fisheries. pp. 142-155. In Animal Agriculture. 2nd edition. San Francisco: W.H. Freeman and Company. 739 pp.

Avault, J.W., Jr., B. Pollock, J.A. Collazo, R.P. Romaire and S.W. Cange. 1984-85. Evaluating experimental crawfish baits. Louisiana Agriculture 28(2):4-5.

Ball, C.O. 1955. Food sterilization methods: the future. Food Technology 9:588-590.

Blogoslawski, W. J. 1989. Depuration and clam culture. pp. 415-426. In Clam Mariculture in North America. Amsterdam-Oxford-New York-Tokyo: Elsevier Science Publishing Company Inc. 461 pp.

Brown, J.W. 1982. Economic analysis of "steam-shock" and "pasteurization" processes for oyster shucking. Marine Fisheries Review 44(5):21-25.

Brunson, M. (editor). 1993. Catfish quality assurance. Mississippi Cooperative Extension Service. Mississippi State University Publication 1873.

Burns, C.M. and J.W. Avault, Jr. 1991. Effects of bait composition and of water temperature on harvestability of crawfish baits. Journal of Applied Aquaculture 1(1): 57-64.

Busch, R.L. 1985. Harvesting, grading and transporting. pp. 543-567. In Channel Catfish Culture. Amsterdam, Oxford, New York, Tokyo: Elsevier Science Publishing Company Inc. 657 pp.

Cain, C.D., Jr. and J.W. Avault, Jr. 1983. Evaluation of a boat-mounted electro-trawl as a commercial harvesting system for crawfish. Aquacultural Engineering 2(2):135-152.

Cathcart, T P., D.W. Lipton, F.W. Wheaton, R.B. Brinsfield, D.G. Swartz and I.E. Strand. 1984. Composting blue crab processing waste. A Maryland Sea Grant Publication, University of Maryland. Publication Number UM-SG-TS-84-01.

Chalfant, J.S., Jr., T. Archambault and A.E. West. 1980. Natural stocks of mussels: growth, recruitment and harvest potential. pp. 38-39. In Mussel Culture and Harvest: A North American Perspective. Amsterdam-Oxford-New York: Elsevier Science Publishing Company Inc. 350 pp.

Chien, Y.H., I.C. Liao and C.M. Young. 1988. The evolution of prawn grow-out systems and their management in Taiwan. IChemE Symposium Series 111: 143-(EFCE Publication Series 66, Institute Chemical Engineering, United Kingdom).

Collins, C.B. 1990. Live hauling warmwater fish. Aquaculture Magazine 16(4):70-76.

Collins, C.B. 1993. Preparing pond fish for harvest. Aquaculture Magazine 19(4):76-79.

Culley, D.D., E. Rejmánková, J. Kuët and J.B. Frye. 1981. Production, chemical quality and use of duckweeds (Lemnaceae) in aquaculture, waste management, and animal feeds. Journal of the World Mariculture Society 12(2):27-49.

Doré, I. 1993. The Smoked and Cured Seafood Guide. Toms River, New Jersey: Urner Barry Publications Inc. 251 pp.

Food Processors Institute. 1988. Canned Foods- Principles of Thermal Process Control, Acidification and Container Closure Evaluation. 5th edition. The Food Processors Institute, 1401 New York Avenue, N.W. Washington, D.C. 20005.

Gorga, C. 1983. A proposal for a feasibility study for the R & D of a new concept to maintain quality control at minimal cost through a cold chain system within processing plants. A proposal submitted to the NE Regional Office of the National Marine Fisheries Service.

Gorga, C. and L.J. Ronsivalli. 1988. Quality Assurance of Seafood. New York: An Avi Book published by Van Nostrand Reinhold Company Inc. 245 pp.

Green, J.H. and A. Kramer. 1979. Food Processing Waste Management. Westport, Connecticut: Avi Publishing Company Inc.

Griffin, R.C. and S. Sacharow. 1972. Principles of Package Development. Westport, Connecticut: Avi Publishing Company Inc.

Huet, M. 1970. Textbook of Fish Culture Breeding and Cultivation of Fish. Surrey, England: Fishing News (Books) Ltd. 436 pp.

Huner, J.V., H.K. Dupree and D.C. Greenland. 1984. Harvesting, grading and holding fish. pp. 158-164. In Third Report to the Fish Farmers. U.S. Fish and Wildlife Service, Washington, D.C. 270 pp.

Jensen, J. 1981. Corral seine for trapping catfish. Alabama Cooperative Extension Service, Auburn University. Circular ANR-257.

Johnson, D.R. 1994. Guide to Food Safety Law. Thompson Publishing Group. 1725 K Street, N.W. Washington, D.C.

Loehr, R.C. 1977. Pollution Control for Agriculture. New York: Academic Press. 383 pp.

Love, R.M. 1988. The Food Fishes. New York: An Avi Book Published by Van Nostrand Reinhold Company Inc. 276 pp.

Lovell, R.T. 1980. Utilization of catfish processing waste. Alabama Agricultural Experiment Station, Auburn University. Bulletin 521.

Lovell, R.T. and G.R. Ammerman (editors). 1974. Processing farm-raised catfish. Southern Cooperative Series. Bulletin 193.

Lovell, R.T., W.G. Mustin and J.W. Jensen. 1981. Design of small-scale catfish processing plants in Alabama. Alabama Agricultural Experiment Station, Auburn University. Circular 255.

Lutz, R.A. (editor). 1980. Mussel Culture and Harvest: A North American Perspective. Oxford, New York, Tokyo: Elsevier Science Publishing Company Inc. 350 pp.

Meyers, S.P. 1981. Using wastes for aquaculture feeds. Aquanotes, Sea Grant College Program, Louisiana State University. Volume 9, Issue 6.

Moody, M.W. 1980. Louisiana seafood delight- the crawfish. Louisiana Cooperative Extension Service. Sea Grant Publication, LSU-TL-80-002.

Nickerson, J.T.R. and L.J. Ronsivalli. 1980. Elementary Food Science. 2nd edition. Westport, Connecticut: Avi Publishing Company Inc. 436 pp.

Phelps, R.P. and C.L. Stiebel. 1991. Salmonella in wastewater-aquaculture system. Bioresource Technology 37(1991):205-210.

Pigott, G.M. and B.W. Tucker. 1990. Seafood Effects of Technology on Nutrition. New York, N.Y.: Marcel Dekker Inc., 270 Madison Ave., New York, N.Y. 10016. 362 pp.

Piper, R.G., I.B. McElwain, L. Orme, J.P. McCraren, L.G. Fowler and J.R. Leonard. 1983. Fish Hatchery Management. American Fisheries Society and Fish and Wildlife Service, United States Department of Interior, Washington, D.C. 517 pp.

Quayle, D.B. 1988. Pacific Oyster Culture in British Columbia. Canadian Bulletin of Fisheries and Aquatic Sciences 218. Department of Fisheries and Oceans, Ottawa, Canada. 241 pp.

Quayle, D.B. and G.F. Newkirk. 1989. Farming Bivalve Mollusks: Methods for Study and Development. Baton Rouge, Louisiana: World Aquaculture Society in Association with the International Development Research Centre. 294 pp.

Raphael, H.J. and D.L. Olsson. 1978. Package Production Management. 2nd edition. Westport, Connecticut: Avi Publishing Company Inc.

Romaire, R.P. 1989. Overview of harvest technology used in commercial crawfish aquaculture. Journal of Shellfish Research 8(1): 281-286.

Rust, K.S. 1993. Surimi processing. LSU Agricultural Center. Mimeograph 18 pp.

Silva, J.L., J.O. Hearnsberger, F. Hagan and G.R. Ammerman (editors). 1989. A summary of processing research on freshwater prawns at Mississippi State University 1984-1988. Department of Information Services, Division of Agriculture, Forestry and Veterinary Medicine, Mississippi State University.

Slabyj, B.M. 1980. Storage and processing of mussels. pp. 247-265. In Mussel Culture and Harvest: A North American Perspective. Amsterdam, Oxford, New York: Elsevier Science Publishing Company Inc. 350 pp.

Smitherman, R.O., M.C. Mohead, W.G. Mustin and R.K. Goodman. 1979. Trapping channel catfish from upland ponds. Alabama Agricultural Experiment Station, Auburn University. Highlights of Agricultural Research 26:6.

Soderquist, M.R., K.J. Williamson, G.I. Blanton, D.C. Phillips, D.K. Law and D.L. Crawford. 1970. Current practice in seafoods processing waste treatment. Waste Pollution Control Series 12060 ECF 04/70. Environmental Protection Agency, Corvallis, Oregon.

Stansby, M. 1963. Industrial Fishery Technology. New York: Van Nostrand Reinhold.

Swann, C.S. 1989. An introduction to scallop farming. Vancouver, British Columbia, Canada: Keugor Aquasystems. 56 pp.

Walker, W.H., Jr., R.O. Smitherman and J.W. Avault, Jr. 1967. Crawfish waste- a potential feed for channel crawfish. Louisiana Agriculture 10(2):14-15.

Wheaton, F.W. and T.B. Lawson. 1985. Processing Aquatic Food Products. New York-Chichester-Brisbane-Toronto, Singapore: John Wiley & Sons Inc. 518 pp.

Windsor, M. and S. Barlow. 1981. Introduction to Fishery By-Products. Surrey, England: Fishing News (Books) Ltd. 220 pp.

CHAPTER 16
MARKETING

Marketing is defined as the physical and economic flow of products from the producer through intermediaries to the consumer. Through the marketing channel, products may undergo change that adds value. Though this chapter on marketing follows those on growing and harvesting a culture species, you should make a marketing study before investing the first dollar or stocking the first fish.

In this chapter, we discuss three broad areas you must understand about marketing. First, you must understand the marketing climate and how products are marketed. Next, you must analyze the market to determine the demand for your product and the degree of competition. Finally, you must develop a plan to sell your product. The sale will involve certain business transactions that you must understand.

MANAGEMENT APPROACHES, WHICH SPECIES TO GROW
Market-oriented Approach

The starting point for some people and companies is to identify potential customers and their needs. This is the market-oriented approach (Chaston 1983). This information is used to develop a strategy for marketing a product. Product type, price, promotion, distribution, and other variables are all part of the marketing strategy.

Sometimes a marketing study identifies a culture species with a large market demand but with insufficient culture techniques. For example, in 1965 in the southern United States, the pompano (*Trachinotus carolinus*) and shrimp (*Penaeus* spp.) were identified as excellent culture species based on their being great tablefare. A number of big-name companies began attempts to culture these species. At the time, seed for both pompano and shrimp were difficult to obtain, and even less was known about culture techniques. Early attempts at culture failed. More recently, the red drum (*Sciaenops ocellatus*) has been heralded as a potential culture species because of its popularity as a new dish. A marketing study revealed a great demand for this species but a very limited supply. Culture techniques are being worked out. This species has spawned in captivity and diets are being developed, but it will die during extreme cold weather even in the southern United States.

The market-oriented approach is the best approach for choosing a particular species for culture. Be sure, however, that enough is known about the biology of the culture species chosen. Refer to Chapter 3 for a critique of candidate species for aquaculture.

Production-oriented Approach

Aquaculturists who produce a crop of fish before looking for a market are production oriented. In the southern United States during the 1960s, some entrepreneurs learned from incipient channel catfish (*Ictalurus punctatus*) farmers that there was such a demand for catfish people would buy fish at the pond bank. In some instances this was true. Eventually pond bank sales ceased, and farmers growing catfish had to search for a place to sell fish. Many who did not have ready access to a processing plant sold fish to individuals, to grocery stores, or to restaurants. A number of catfish farmers opened restaurants to move their product.

Environmental-oriented Approach

Some people search for a suitable culture species that will adapt to environmental conditions in a particular geographical location. Often these people have family roots in the area or they wish to pursue economic development in a given area. The environment along the northeast coast of North America is well suited for culture of the blue mussel (*Mytilus edulis*). Technology transferred from Europe works well. Companies that began growing mussels, however, failed to evaluate the market. This mollusk is relatively unknown in the United States. Moreover, the oyster is a more traditional mollusk consumed. Chaston (1983) suggested that entrepreneurs should have imported European mussels first to develop a market demand before farms were established.

Species-oriented Approach

Occasionally someone will become enamored with a particular culture species and vow to culture it. The lobster (*Homarus americanus*) and the prawn (*Macrobrachium rosenbergii*) are good examples. The eating qualities of the lobster are well known, and yet most attempts to culture it have failed economically. The prawn is cultured successfully in the Indo-Pacific Region and elsewhere. Culture success in temperate countries has been marginal because of the relatively short growing season.

Sometimes a culture species may not have a broad-range potential, but there may be a narrow window of opportunity. It is difficult, for example, to grow prawns economically in the southeastern United States. In Louisiana, prawns must be stocked around mid May and harvested by mid October because of possible low temperatures (below 14°C or 57°F) before and after these dates. Since most markets require a relatively large (28 g+ or 1 oz +) prawn, it is difficult to compete on a year-round basis with tropical countries.

Granados et al. (1991) suggested that there may be both biological and market niches for prawns in Louisiana by rotating them with red swamp crawfish (*Procambarus clarkii*) in the same ponds. Crawfish are typically grown from mid October to mid May. Ponds are drained in mid May, and the remaining crawfish burrow underground. Prawns can be cultured from mid May to mid October in the crawfish ponds. Perhaps the best market niche is for the soft-shell trade. During warm months, crawfish are seldom available for shedding troughs, but prawns can be harvested during this period. The ideal size of prawns for molting troughs is about 17 g (0.6 oz). Granados et al. (1991) grew 0.02 g postlarval prawns to 17 g in only 93 days. Caffey et al. (1993) reported that prawns performed well (molted) in crawfish shedding troughs.

UNDERSTANDING THE MARKETING CLIMATE

You must produce a product that is in demand or stimulate demand through a promotional campaign. Regardless, you must grasp national and world events that help shape demand for aquaculture products. This goes beyond just finding a buyer for your product. In the short run, buyer and producer may develop a mutually beneficial relationship, but certain national and international events may affect this relationship in the long run.

Demand for Fishery Products

To grasp the overall demand for fishery products, look at such things as trends in population growth and eating habits, and sources of fisheries products. Chapter 2 reviews this subject, so we will summarize only. Approximately 86 million people are added to the world's population each year. These additional humans will increase the demand for food. Animal protein can be supplied by beef, chicken, pork, fish, and certain other animals. The type of animal protein chosen depends on cost and availability, tastes and preferences of the consumer, and other factors. In some developing countries, people without means will do little to increase demand for animal products.

Aside from increasing population, demand for fishery products is increasing because of increased per capita consumption. Consumers these days are more health conscious and look for animal protein low in cholesterol and saturated fats and high in nutritional value. Most fishery products also are relatively low in calories, a bonus for weight-conscious dieters.

The simple conclusion is that demand for fishery products is increasing because of increased population growth, increased per capita consumption, and changes in diet. Historically, this demand has been met with increased harvests from our oceans, but this catch has leveled off for more than a decade. The trend is clear; the increased demand for fishery products must be met from aquaculture.

Economics

Mention economics, and a producer is apt to think in terms of a cash flow schedule, costs and returns of the operation, and similar economic projections. All are important. Nevertheless, economics on a national and international scale may shape events that directly affect a producer who wishes to market aquaculture products. For example, if a merchant who markets aquaculture products lives in a country where the currency has appreciated relative to that of other nations, there may be a problem selling products internationally. The product now costs more on world markets. Countries or regions within a country that gain in affluence often increase consumption of animal products; this happened in oil-producing countries of the Middle East. Such countries sometimes opt for high-value aquaculture products. On the other hand, countries that drop in affluence may switch from high-value species to less expensive species.

Sometimes intangibles occur that are hard to predict, but which can have a profound impact on the sale of aquaculture products (Avault 1990a, b). In the fall of 1988, it was difficult for U.S. citizens to buy salmon (*Oncorhynchus* spp. and *Salmo salar*) in the marketplace. The Japanese paid high prices and bought much of the product. This changed dramatically during the illness and passing of Japan's Emperor, Hirohito. The Japanese, in tribute to their emperor during mourning, discontinued eating certain high-value species, including salmon and shrimp. With a dramatic drop in consumption of salmon and shrimp, prices plunged and some aquaculturists lost money.

Events occur in capture fisheries that may have a positive or negative effect on aquaculture products. In August of 1990, Iraq attempted to annex Kuwait. This event, which sent oil prices sharply upwards, made it difficult for commercial fishermen to harvest ocean species at a profit. Diesel fuel is a major expense. Those aquaculture products less dependent on the cost of diesel fuel gained an economic edge.

Legal, Social, and Political Factors

Chapter 4 reviewed this topic and we will summarize only. If your aquaculture products are marketed nationally or internationally, be aware of the legal, social, and political factors. Some states and countries have particular labeling requirements and quality standards. Certain countries may impose trade barriers to protect domestic production. A classic example has been Japan's past trade barrier against imported rice.

Problems may arise between capture fisheries and culture fisheries. Net-pen culture of salmon and commercial fishing of salmon in Washington's Puget Sound have caused strained relations between the two entities. Stickney (1988) suggested that the two groups can complement one another in the marketplace.

Farm-grown salmon can be marketed when wild-caught salmon are not readily available.

Sometimes an incipient fish farmer misreads the social climate. In one instance, a catfish farming newcomer had trouble marketing locally. People had a tradition of eating channel catfish caught from a nearby river, but they were reluctant to eat a farm-grown fish that had no access to natural food.

These random examples illustrate the importance of checking factors affecting the marketing of aquaculture products. Though laws may be promulgated, certain political and social factors are often only understood. This is particularly true when you wish to market to another country. It may be necessary to have a partner from that country who knows how to get things done. Setting up a test market is a safe alternative to an all-at-once marketing program. Learn from your mistakes when they don't cost too much.

Technological

New technology in aquaculture is increasing at an almost exponential rate. When new technology is introduced that lowers production costs or increases production, there is a decided advantage in the marketplace. One example of such technology is the use of the paddlewheel and other aeration devices in ponds. Oxygen injection into raceways also shows promise for increasing production and lowering production costs. When such an advantage is gained, a producer can market at a competitive price. Some of the new profit can be used in promotion to solidify the market position.

Sometimes technological advantages occur outside the aquaculture industry but which affect the marketing of aquaculture products. The manufacture of surimi makes it possible to take low-value finfish and produce an imitation high-value product such as crab meat (Chapter 15).

Product Life Cycle

Products go through cycles from introduction, to growth, to maturity, and then to decline in popularity. When a product first enters the introductory phase, sales are limited and the company tries to get the consumer familiar with the product. If the product is not successful, it will die out. However, if the product gains consumer acceptance, it will enter the growth phase. Sales begin to increase rapidly in the growth stage, and consumer acceptance increases. Companies are attracted to the product and begin further development of the product for sales. From the growth stage, products enter into the maturity stage. Sales of the product have about peaked, and the market is saturated. From the maturity stage comes the decline stage where sales begin to decrease, and companies begin looking for other products to sell as consumers shift their preferences to other products. An example of the product life cycle showing how sales and profits interact with the product life cycle is given in Figure 16.1.

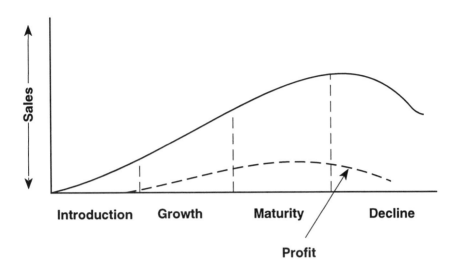

Figure 16.1 Product life cycle.

Four culture species will illustrate product life cycle. Note in the examples that the form undergoes change in the product life cycle. In the mid 1960s when farm-grown channel catfish became a force in the marketplace, the product was a dressed fish. The head, skin, and entrails were removed. As the industry matured, consumer demand for the dressed product began to wane; consumers now showed preference for other forms of products, such as fillets. One new product, the "nugget," is of particular interest. This product comes from the belly flap of the fish and had been perceived as a less desirable part. However, with value-added processing, such as breading, and with a promotional blitz, this new product has found a niche in the marketplace.

The traditional method for processing and eating rainbow trout (*Oncorhynchus mykiss*) has been as a dressed product, but with the head and skin left on. As the market for trout expanded outside the traditional trout-eating areas, consumers showed preference for fillets and other forms. Today, there are many nuances to each product form. For example, fillets may be separated from each side of the fish. The fish may be split down the middle and spread apart butterflied. The bones may be left in or removed. The head may be left on or removed. Thus the product life cycle rose and fell for the dressed product in non-traditional areas for eating trout. New product forms replaced the original form.

The tilapia has been perceived as a fish to feed people from Third World countries, perhaps because the tilapia is native to Africa and is relatively easy to culture in ponds. The product form traditionally has been as a whole or dressed fish. When the tilapia first was introduced to consumers in developed nations, there was little consumer demand. Then producers began to practice quality assurance in culture methods, such as intensive culture in recirculating systems. Processors began to promote and market portion-size fillets, and in some instances a breaded product. Consumer demand has increased significantly.

Figure 16.2 Grading of crawfish to size and quality at the Louisiana Premium Seafood Company in Palmetto, Louisiana.

Figure 16.3 Preparing dill as a seasoning for crawfish at Louisiana Premium Seafood.

Our last example deals with the red swamp crawfish (*Procambarus clarkii*). For years, the crawfish has been marketed as a whole, live product in Louisiana. Then markets opened up in Europe for a particular niche vacated by the loss of wild-caught Turkish crawfish. At first, ungraded crawfish were exported. The product life cycle was short indeed. The product was not accepted. Then processors began to grade crawfish to size and to appearance. They were boiled in dill water to the specifications of Swedish chefs (Figures 16.2, 16.3). This form of product should enjoy a longer product life cycle.

THE MARKETING MIX

The major variables involved in marketing a product are referred to as the four Ps of the marketing mix, namely: (1) product, (2) price, (3) promotion, and (4) place or distribution. For example, assume that a company decides to produce a breaded soft-shell crawfish as its product and that the product will be of premium quality. Rigid quality control in processing results in added costs that reflect in above-average price. The strategy of promotion is to advertise introductory reduced prices. Further, information will be given about product quality that sets the product apart from competitor's product. Because it is a high-value product, the ultimate purchaser targeted will be the white-tablecloth trade. The product must be delivered to the place in a timely manner.

Product

Form, size, and quality all go into the makeup of a product. There are a number of forms possible for finfish, crustaceans, and mollusks. The classification may vary within the processing industry.

Finfish Product Forms--   Some common forms of finfish include:

(1)   Live fish are sold to live haulers who stock fee fishing lakes.

(2)   Whole fish or fish in the round are sold just as they come out of the water.

(3)   Drawn fish have entrails removed. Since entrails spoil rapidly, drawn fish have a longer storage life than fish in the round.

(4)   Dressed fish are sold completely cleaned but with head on. Some classify a dressed fish with head off. This was a common form of trout for years. Oriental markets also like a dressed fish. A peek at gill filaments indicates the freshness of the product. Pink gills mean freshness; bleached-looking gills indicate lower quality. With salmon, gills are first severed then removed to bleed the fish.

(5)   Headed and gutted fish have head and entrails removed. Fins and tails may be removed or left on. With some species, such as channel catfish, the skin is removed. For trout and other salmonids, the skin and scales are left on.

(6)   Chunks are cross sections of large dressed fish that have a cross section of backbone as the only bone. They are similar to beef and pork roasts.

(7)   Steaks are slices of dressed fish smaller than chunks. Salmon, buffalofish (*Ictiobus* spp.), and often large channel catfish are processed this way.

(8)   Fillets can be obtained in one of two ways. Flank fillets are the two sides of the fish cut away from the backbone. They usually have no bones or waste. A butterflied fillet includes the two flank fillets held together by the belly flap. In processing channel catfish, the belly flap is usually cut free and called the nugget.

(9)   Deboned fish are those with the bones removed but the body is left intact. Milkfish (*Chanos chanos*) have many small bones that can be removed by hand. Trout may be butterflied lengthwise down the middle and the two strips of backbone removed.

(10) Fish sticks may be produced from frozen minced fish, or they may be pieces of fish flesh cut into a uniform width and length.

(11) Fish strips are smaller pieces of fish cut from fillets. If cut lengthwise, they may be referred to as fingers.

(12) Breaded fish are usually filleted products that are battered, breaded, and ready for cooking.

(13) Canned fish usually contain only edible flesh plus seasonings and preservatives.

(14) Fish sausage is from flesh taken primarily from frames (Figure 16.4).

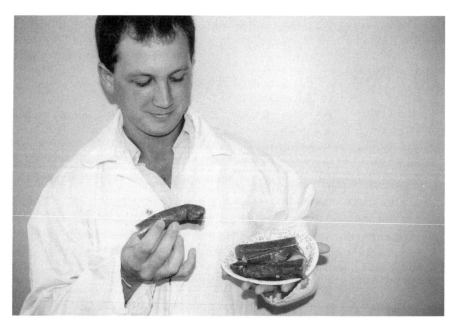

Figure 16.4 Ken Rust, formerly of the LSU Agricultural Center, with fish sausage.

Crustacean Product Forms-- Some common forms of crustaceans include:

(1) Live crawfish, prawns, and shrimp may be marketed. In Louisiana, more than 50% of the crawfish grown are marketed live. In Japan, Hong Kong, and elsewhere, shrimp and prawns are kept live in restaurant aquaria. Patrons choose the animals before preparation.

(2) Whole on ice is a product form mostly for local distribution.

(3) Headed is a common product form for crawfish, prawns, and shrimp. The crustaceans may be blanched in boiling water or left uncooked. They may be peeled, deveined, and frozen. Deveining is a process whereby the digestive tube that runs along the tail is removed. Freezing may be in block form or individually quick frozen (IQF).

(4) Butterflied and breaded is a value-added product often placed in the grocery store.

(5) Crawfish may be blanched in seasoned water and frozen. Later they are thawed and prepared in restaurants.

(6) Crustaceans can be sun dried. This lessens spoilage (Figure 16.5).

Figure 16.5 Sun drying shrimp in Tungkang, Taiwan.

Molluskan Product Forms-- Some common forms of mollusks include:

(1) Live is a common form for all molluskan species. Oysters (*Crassostrea* spp. and *Ostrea edulis*) on the half shell are very popular.

(2) Shucked meats are the meats removed from mollusks. They are usually sold fresh and refrigerated, but the frozen product is also available.

(3) Smoked mussels and oysters are often sold in cans or jars.

(4) Soups, stews, and gumbos are value-added products of mollusks.

The size of the product must be precise for some markets and less exacting for others. Consumers shopping at a seafood market are usually less demanding of product size. Restaurants want a specific size. Whole fish, fillets, or steaks must be in portion size. Various restaurants have their own requirements. Some restaurants in Louisiana may serve two whole medium catfish as an entree, whereas restaurants in Florida may serve six small fish. Crustacean sizes are usually noted by the count, number of individuals to the kilogram or pound. The lower the count, the larger the size. The count may be for heads on or heads off. Oysters and other mollusks also have a size gradation. Large meats that are cut in the shucking process may be chopped into smaller pieces for canning or for soups, stews, and gumbos. Other size gradations depend on the specific market targeted.

The quality of the product depends on the culture species chosen to process and market and on quality assurance practices. The common carp (*Cyprinus carpio*) is normally not considered in the same class as the Atlantic salmon (*Salmo salar*). Each culture species has a certain status in the marketplace. The culture species you choose to produce and market will dictate to some degree markets open to your product. The carp may be best targeted for everyday consumption by the working class, whereas the Atlantic salmon could be marketed to the white-tablecloth trade. However, some people who relish carp will disagree with this.

Price

Pricing is a critical marketing decision affected by type of product, consumer demand, competition, and other factors. Pricing compromises have been developed between buyer and seller to achieve equilibrium. As unit price falls, buyers usually are willing to buy more product, whereas as price increases buyers may buy less. Conversely, producers usually are willing to supply more product with increased prices but less apt to do so with declining prices. There is a mid-point between supply and demand when an equilibrium is met.

Forward contracting is an option that allows you to lock in a predetermined price with your buyer before or during production. This method of marketing avoids some risk. You may lose money, however, if the value of your product increases later. In some instances, some producers willingly accept the marginally lower price because the contract provides a stable market for their production stream. In Louisiana, many soft-shell crab producers forward contract their annual production to a single restaurant.

Price elasticity is another concept you must understand when setting or increasing prices.

Chaston (1983) used the following equation to define elasticity:

$$\text{Elasticity} = (Q_1 - Q_0)/Q_0 \text{ divided by } (P_1 - P_0)/P_0$$

where, Q_1 = quantity sold per period after price change
Q_0 = quantity sold per period before price change
P_1 = new price
P_0 = old price.

An elasticity of one means that sales increase or decrease by the same percentage as the price increases or decreases. An elasticity greater than one means sales increase or decrease by more than the percentage price increases or decreases. This is called elastic demand. An elasticity less than one means sales increase or decrease by less than the percentage price increases or decreases. This is called inelastic demand. Calculating price elasticity does not produce an absolute number to guide price setting because there are so many factors involved. Yet monitoring price elasticity over time will provide a general understanding.

There are a number of systems to consider when setting prices including: (1) cost-plus pricing, (2) return on investment, (3) competitive pricing, (4) penetration pricing, (5) skimming the market, (6) what the market will bear, (7) discount pricing, (8) loss-leader pricing, (9) psychological pricing, and (10) prestige pricing (Chaston 1983; Downey and Erickson 1987).

Cost-plus Pricing-- This simply adds a constant margin of profit above the cost of producing a product. If, for example, it costs $1.00 to produce 1 kg of product and the product is sold for $1.20, the markup (profit) is 20%. The problem with cost-plus pricing is that it is sometimes difficult to assess costs accurately unless total costs, including fixed as well as variable costs, are calculated.

Return on Investment (ROI)-- This is similar to cost-plus pricing. It also begins with the cost of manufacturing the product, but rather than adding fixed or overhead costs, it adds an amount to earn a specified ROI. For example, a firm calculates profit needed to earn a 15% ROI. The ROI system has similar problems to the cost-plus system.

Competitive Pricing-- This is probably the easiest system to use. You simply set the price at the going rate. Usually, a lead company establishes the price; others follow. Sometimes a company or companies will offer a product at break-even, or lower, prices to force out some of the competition. Usually these companies have the financial means to allow losses for a period of time. Smaller or under-financed companies may go under. This happened to the catfish farming industry in the South around the mid-1980s. Prices fluctuated wildly in the marketplace, making things unstable for both producers and processors. A Catfish Bargaining Association was formed which consisted of volunteer producers and processors. Both groups agreed on a pricing structure.

If a producer, through new technology or other means, develops methods to lower production costs, it appears logical that the selling price could be lowered to increase sales. Chaston (1983), however, suggested that extra profits be put into improved marketing and promotion to solidify customer loyalty, or used to develop new and unique products. The day may come when competitors also have the same technology to lower production costs. If a company markets mainly on low price, the edge could be lost.

Penetration Pricing-- This offers a product at a relatively low price to gain wide acceptance in the marketplace quickly. This strategy often introduces a new product. After the product gains consumer acceptance, the price is gradually raised to a more profitable level.

Skimming-- This is the opposite of penetration pricing. It introduces a product at a higher price for more affluent customers. Then, as this market becomes saturated, the price is gradually lowered. This system works best on new products of high value. Introduction of soft-shell crawfish in Louisiana was at relatively high prices. Producers received $18 to $20/kg ($8 to $9/lb) initially. Prices later were lowered to $13/kg ($6/lb). In this case, however, the market did not become saturated. Rather, problems developed in the marketing channel (Gillespie 1990).

What the Market Will Bear-- This involves varying prices to determine what consumers are willing to pay. For example, the USDA conducted a test in 1972 to determine what people would pay for farm-raised channel catfish (Raulerson and Trotter 1973). The test was conducted in Atlanta, Georgia, involving six supermarkets. The optimum retail price was $2.62/kg ($1.19/lb). At this price, only one of every 150 or more shoppers bought. Sales increased by 70% when the price was dropped to $2.18/kg ($.99/lb).

Discount Pricing-- This offers customers a reduction from advertised prices for a specified reason. Volume buyers may get discounts. Dealers in the marketing channel, brokers, wholesalers, and the like may get special prices. Prompt payment also may be rewarded with discounts.

Loss-leader Pricing-- This offers a product at a specially reduced price for a limited time. The idea is to encourage long-term adoption of the product and to pull customers in to look at other products. This system is common in supermarkets and may have less application for aquaculture products.

Psychological Pricing-- This involves establishing prices that sound better and that are more palatable to purchasers. Instead of charging $2.00 for a kilogram of product, the price might be $1.99/kg.

Prestige Pricing-- This appeals to the elite who feel that "you get what you pay for." Some purchasers may automatically reach for the higher-priced product, assuming it is the top of the line. A particular shrimp processing plant in the Philippines has produced a quality product for a number of customers. The same product went for different prices, depending on the packaging, brand name used, and customer.

Promotion

Promotion has one goal, to create a customer. This is accomplished by (1) advertising, (2) personal selling, (3) general publicity, and (4) by a sales promotion program (Downey and Erickson 1987).

Advertising-- The four components of advertising are the communicator or source of information, the channel or route through which information is moved, the message or information given, and the audience the message is intended for (Chaston 1983). To illustrate, the Louisiana Crawfish Promotion and Marketing Board (communicator) through brochures (channel) wishes to communicate about a crawfish tasting and trade show in Lafayette, Louisiana (message), to both local and out-of-town seafood business people (audience). This kind of advertisement is generic because it represents the industry rather than an individual or company.

The communicator may be an individual, company, cooperative, trade association, or government agency. Trade associations, such as the Catfish Farmers of America and U.S. Trout Farmers Association, may advertise generically about the qualities of catfish and trout and why the fish is a good buy. You have no doubt seen such advertisements for oranges, milk, beef, and other agricultural products. When producers pool their resources through trade organizations, television advertisements and other costly media may serve as the channel. Other common channels for advertising include radio, newspaper ads, magazines, handbills, fliers, and posters.

Advertisement is usually aimed at the consumer. The idea is to pull the product through the marketing channel of intermediaries. Though advertising is a common promotional tool, it is often difficult to assess its effectiveness. Some advertisements give incentives to customers to determine what ad caught their attention. "Bring in the coupon accompanying the advertisement," or "be sure to say Harry sent you," are tip-offs that the ad was successful.

The message must be clear, succinct, and have focus. For example, farm-grown trout raised in pristine waters are highly nutritious and are available at an everyday price anyone can afford. This simple message has three points. First, the audience can visualize that trout are clean and safe to eat, having been grown in such pristine waters. Second, "nutritious" denotes good for you, and third, "everyday price" means that the average household can enjoy trout.

If this advertisement was a generic television commercial, these three points could be enforced even more. Scenes could include clear spring water, trout being fed a high-protein diet, a couple shopping in a grocery store, and the same couple (looking fit and trim) serving trout to their children at the supper table. The audience targeted above was somewhat broad. Certain products are targeted for a narrow audience that may be based on sex, age, ethnic origin, family income, or geographical location.

Personal Selling-- This means one-on-one selling. A salesperson calls on a potential customer and informs the customer about the merits of the product(s) with the intention of making a sale. This is what most small aquaculture operations do. Larger operations may have a sales force which concentrates on just selling the product. When a sales force is used, a salesperson can be given a specified area of responsibility. This may be based on geographical location, type of product, or type of customer. Most companies pay sales representatives a base salary plus a performance bonus.

General Publicity-- This form of promotion is not necessarily intended to make a specific sale, but rather to inform the public or a specific audience. In past years, the Catfish Farmers of America has cooked catfish for the U.S. House and Senate. The Louisiana Crawfish Farmers Association has sponsored meals for various events and groups, including the Symposium of the International Association of Astacology held in April 1990 in Baton Rouge, Louisiana.

Sales Promotions-- These are programs intended to spark interested customers into buying. Giving away T-shirts, caps, pens, note pads, and other gifts with the company logo are commonplace. Well-organized companies may show videos at trade shows and scientific meetings on how to combat oxygen depletion, feed fish properly, and the like. The sales pitch by the company for its product may be subtle and in the background. A company representative may take a potential customer on a hunting or fishing trip or just treat the individual to an evening meal and entertainment. On big deals involving a lot of money, potential buyers must first be sold on the salesperson, then the product.

Place

Every producer must determine the best physical system to move raw material to the processor, and the processor must determine the best marketing system to move product to the consumer. The simplest system is for producers to process their own raw material at the farm and then move the product directly to the consumer. Because fishery products are perishable, a dependable transportation system is critical. Sometimes the processor may have an excess of product for immediate needs. Adequate storage space must be available. Besides physical distribution of product, there is market distribution, called marketing channels, that may involve one or more intermediaries.

Physical transportation is usually by truck, rail, or air. If by truck, good highways must be available and conveniently located near the processing plant. Lawson and Brown (1988), conducting a study in Louisiana, mapped existing processing plants and their proximity to interstate highways, railroads, and airports. Though some trucking firms specialize in contracting shipment for fishery products, most aquaculture operations provide their own transportation. Refrigerated, insulated trucks are capable of handling up to 4,762 kg (10,500 lb) of product (Lawson and Brown 1988). When live animals, such as crawfish and oysters, are transported, they must be kept cool, moist, and stacked properly to avoid crushing and suffocation.

Rail transport is used less to transport perishable products because federal deregulation of rail shipments and freight charges fluctuate. The cost to rent and transport a refrigerated car from New Orleans to Chicago was about $3,500; capacity of the car was about 59 mt (65 tons) (Lawson and Brown 1988).

Use of air transportation for moving aquaculture products is increasing, particularly as international markets expand. Some airlines use special metal containers that fit into the fuselage of cargo jets. The LD-3 container has a volume of 4.2 m^3 (150 ft^3) and will carry 1,587 kg (3,500 lb) of product (Anonymous 1989a). The Air Transportation Association of America, in cooperation with the National Fisheries Institute, promulgated guidelines for shipping fishery products, and these guidelines were reviewed by Lawson and Brown (1988).

As a producer's operation expands, it no longer may be cost efficient to market directly to the consumer. This is particularly true when the product is marketed to new geographical locations and if new products and new customers with differing wants and needs are added. One or more people, called intermediaries, may be added to the marketing channel.

The flow of product through the marketing channel may take a number of paths, depending on many factors. It starts with the producer who cultures the finfish, crustacean, or mollusk. A processor converts the raw material to product form.

A broker is an intermediary whose main talent is an ability to bring buyer and seller together. A broker acts as an agent for others in negotiating contracts, purchases, or sales in return for a fee. A broker obtains orders but does not physically handle or store product.

A distributor, sometimes called a dealer or wholesaler, markets or sells the product to other distributors or retailers. A distributor takes orders for a product. The distributor handles, stores, and repackages the products, if called for.

A retailer sells to the final consumer. Retail outlets may include specialty stores, restaurants, and supermarkets. A few examples of product flow through market channels are:

(1) Producer → Consumer. A carp farmer holds live fish in a tank. People pick out the fish they want to eat, take it home, and cook and eat it.

(2) Producer → Processor → Retailer → Consumer. A crawfish farmer sells live crawfish to a processing plant, is paid, and goes home. The processor washes, grades to size, and resacks the crawfish. The processor in turn sells to a supermarket which in turn sells to a customer for a weekend crawfish boil.

(3) Producer → Processor → Broker → Distributor → Retailer → Consumer. Rainbow trout produced and processed in Idaho are contracted by a broker to distributors in San Francisco, Los Angeles, Chicago, Denver, Kansas City, and New York. The distributors move product to restaurants and other retail outlets. The consumer dining on trout is the final customer.

The efficiency of market supply is usually best when there are few links in the marketing channel, such as Producer → Consumer or Producer → Restaurant → Consumer. As the links in the marketing channel increase, the producer (first link) has less influence on form and price of the product that ultimately reaches the consumer. Not all channel intermediaries may agree on the product form or price. Sometimes a channel captain emerges who manages the product flow to the mutual benefit of all. Moreover, the question may arise, who will promote the product to increase sales. Usually promotion activities are funded by the producer rather than by an intermediary. These are commonly known as "pull" strategies designed to pull the product through the marketing channel. Distributors and brokers who do emphasize promotion are using "push" strategies to push the product through the marketing channel.

RESEARCHING YOUR MARKET
Selecting a Product

In a previous discussion of understanding the marketing climate, we looked at aquaculture in a broad sense. If you are satisfied that aquaculture is a good business, then you must narrow the fact-finding to a select group of culture species or even to a single species. This should be reduced even further to type of products you anticipate marketing. Usually an incipient aquaculturist has a particular culture species in mind. Sometimes this may be a candidate species for which little is known. Unless you have unlimited funds and are satisfied with being a hobby farmer, it is best to pass up such a species. Questions must be asked and answered (Laumer et al. no date).

Your Competition

You must determine if there are other producers, or sources, of the product(s) you wish to market. Learn your competition.

Native Wild-- Competition sometimes exists between a cultured product and a native wild product. You must determine if there is a season for the wild product and what price is paid. In Louisiana, crawfish are farmed in ponds. Crawfish are also trapped in natural waters, particularly the Atchafalaya Basin. Pond crawfish are usually available for market beginning in the fall of the year and extending to mid May of the following year. The best profit is made at the beginning of the season. In the spring and summer, when the wild crop is available, the price drops. This is usually of no consequence to the farmer who typically ends the harvesting season before the wild crop reaches its peak. There are occasions, however, when the two harvesting seasons overlap for a period, and the price may collapse. The wild crop is not predictable. One year a good crop may be produced if environmental requirements are met; the next year may be a failure.

There are other culture species for which there is competition between farm-raised and native wild. A notable example is the salmon in the Pacific Northwest of the United States. Wild-caught salmon must be captured when they are available. Farm-raised salmon grown in floating net-pens can be harvested and marketed when wild-caught salmon are not available. Thus one can complement the other in the marketplace.

Foreign Wild-- Foreign imports of wild-caught fishery products may pose competition to a domestic farmed product. In the 1960s and again in the mid-1970s, this was a major problem facing the industry, according to the Catfish Farmers of America organization. Initially, farm-raised channel catfish were introduced to restaurants in the southern United States. Patrons packed restaurants to eat this delicious fish. Some restaurant owners later switched to a lower-priced catfish that was caught wild, mainly from Brazil. Proper promotion and marketing later distinguished the quality difference between the two sources of catfish.

Farm Domestic-- Local competition comes from your fellow fish farmers who are farming the same species you wish to culture. You should determine their output, price received for the product, and overall market demand. Can you put out a quality product at a price competitive with your neighbor's? In the short term, competition from your neighbors may be perceived as a problem. In the long term though, competition could be beneficial. It creates an expanded demand for the product. In effect, your competitors advertise not just their product but the product in general.

Farmed International-- Sometimes your domestically farmed product will receive competition from other countries. In Texas, South Carolina, and Hawaii, there is modest production of farm-raised shrimp. However, it is difficult for prices of U.S. shrimp to compete with shrimp prices in China, Ecuador, Indonesia, and elsewhere. To even the odds, shrimp farmers in the United States must find a market niche that gives them an economic advantage over shrimp farmers in other countries.

Cultured trout (*Oncorhynchus mykiss*) have been imported into the United States from Denmark and Japan. Trout farmers in Idaho, North Carolina, and other trout-producing states have been able to compete with these foreign imports.

Other Species-- Competition may exist between culture species of a similar class. Examples might include mussels vs. oysters, channel catfish vs. tilapia, salmon vs. trout, prawns vs. shrimp, and golden shiners (*Notemigonus crysoleucas*) vs. fathead minnow (*Pimephales promelas*).

It is important to position your product properly in the marketplace. For example, the soft-shell crawfish (*Procambarus clarkii*) is a gourmet value-added product. Positioning this product against the hard-shell crawfish market implies that the buyer perceives soft-shell crawfish as a close substitute for hard-shell crawfish. Positioning soft-shell crawfish against the soft-shell blue crab (*Callinectes sapidus*) implies that the buyer perceives soft-shell crawfish as a close substitute for soft-shell blue crab. In regard to product positioning, it is important to determine which has the greatest opportunity.

Other Animal Products-- Beef, chicken, and pork are sources of animal products that may compete with your farm-raised culture species. The consumer buys animal products based on a mixture of price, health, and taste. Seafoods generally are perceived as health foods, and per capita consumption has steadily increased. However, hog and cattle farmers are breeding and feeding animals to produce products lower in fat content.

Sometimes consumers confuse fishery products from aquaculture (culture fisheries) with those from our oceans (capture fisheries). In 1988, per capita consumption of fishery products in the United States actually dropped. The Alaskan oil spill and medical wastes washing up on the Atlantic Coast had consumers questioning the safety of seafoods harvested from our oceans. Some consumers do not differentiate between aquaculture products and products derived from our oceans. Generic promotion by producers and processors, such as the U.S. Trout Farmers Association and the Catfish Farmers of America, will go a long way in educating the public as to the wholesomeness of cultured products.

Determining Market Demand

The elements for analyzing market demand center around: (1) who will buy your product and (2) those factors affecting their willingness to buy (Anonymous 1989a). Potential buyers can be categorized according to location, demographics, ethnic origin, and lifestyle. Determining the market demand for your product is reviewed by Chaston (1983), Anonymous (1989), Shang (1990), and Shaw (1990).

Location-- Certain geographic locations are known for preference of particular aquaculture products. This often is because of the tradition for consuming native wild products. People living near the Chesapeake Bay on the Atlantic Coast have a history of eating wild striped bass (*Morone saxatilis*). Farm-raised hybrid striped bass (female striped bass x male white bass, *M. chrysops*) are readily accepted in this area. The channel catfish is known as a southern fish, but northern markets are being developed. Crawfish markets in the United States are concentrated in Louisiana and neighboring states. For years, the market was limited to southern Louisiana. With promotion and marketing efforts, this market base has been extended to other parts of the country and to certain European countries. The edible blue mussel is readily accepted in coastal communities of New England states, but not so outside of this region. Some culture species, such as salmon and shrimp, have a much broader geographic appeal. Every region has its preferences for certain aquaculture products, and when a new product is introduced, it must struggle to get on the menu. Only through promotion and education can new products be marketed successfully in regions where they do not normally occur.

Demographics-- Age, sex, education, occupation, family size, and overall population must be taken into account when targeting your marketing program. In the United States, middle-aged people are more apt to try new products than teen-agers. Some teen-agers are content to have a limited diet of hamburgers and french fries. Working women often prefer pre-cooked or microwaveable products. Educated people are more apt to try new products. Large families, unless affluent, often prefer a no-frills, low-cost product.

Individuals go through a family life cycle from birth until death, and each stage affects what types of products they will buy. If you graduate from college, you may take a position with a firm and have few responsibilities other than to yourself. Your discretionary income will be high, and you will probably buy convenience items. When you get married, your discretionary income will probably decrease and you will likely buy more durable goods such as a washer and dryer and refrigerator. You will think about buying a house. When the first child comes along, your discretionary income will further decrease as you spend money on the child's needs. As the child grows older, the needs of the family and the child will change, and household consumption patterns will change. When the child grows up and leaves home, this is called the empty nest stage. Your purchasing power will increase as you have fewer demands on your money, and your lifestyle will change. As time goes on, you will retire and go on a fixed income that will affect your purchasing ability. Death of a spouse will also influence the consumption of products.

Consumption of channel catfish, for example, is influenced by the family life cycle. Catfish consumption is high among single and newly married couples and then decreases when children are introduced into the home. As the child increases in age, the likelihood that the household will consume catfish increases. When the children have left home, catfish consumption is at its highest among households. The family life cycle can affect marketing strategies.

Ethnic Origin-- Different ethnic groups have different preferences. Some Asians enjoy eating various scaled fish such as carp species. Bighead carp (*Aristichthys nobilis*) and grass carp (*Ctenopharyngodon idella*), polycultured with channel catfish, have been marketed to Asian communities within the United States. On the other hand, Caucasians in the United States usually disdain scaled fish with so many small bones. Chinese communities in San Francisco prefer tilapia to channel catfish, and in certain areas of the Philippines the tilapia is replacing the milkfish as the preferred fish. Yet in certain regions of the Philippines, tilapia is not consumed for cultural reasons. Japanese relish species such as salmon and the red seabream (*Pagrus major*) partly because of their pink flesh.

It is a mistake to think that just because you like to eat a particular culture species prepared a particular way that everyone else should. In south Louisiana, crawfish tail meat is used in preparing various dishes, such as etouffée. In Europe, however, the whole animal is boiled a certain way. You must determine then what your potential buyers want, not what you think they ought to like.

Lifestyle-- Two trends are evident. North American consumers are becoming more health conscious, preferring foods low in saturated fats and cholesterol but high in nutritional value. Another trend is toward fast foods found at drive-through restaurants and foods easy to prepare. In both cases, this usually entails processing of a value-added product.

Willingness To Buy

Once you have targeted your potential customers, you must determine those factors affecting their willingness to buy. Key factors include availability, quality, and price.

Availability-- When channel catfish farming in the United States was in its infancy around the early 1960s, farmers typically stocked grow-out ponds in spring and harvested in the fall or winter by draining ponds. There was a glut of fish all at once, and it was difficult to establish sustained markets. Eventually, management techniques such as harvesting by topping off were developed, so fish are available year-round.

Quality-- Consumers need to be confident that the farm-grown products they buy are of the highest quality. The producer and processor must strive for quality assurance at all levels. Further, the consumer must be educated about the wholesomeness of your product. Protein-fed and grain-fed are two slogans that have been used in describing farm-raised channel catfish.

Price-- If your product is available and is perceived as wholesome, price is the next major factor determining demand. Will your product be priced so that it is bought mainly during a special season or will it be priced so that it becomes normal tablefare? In parts of Europe, common carp is especially enjoyed during Christmas holidays.

Other factors determine demand (Anonymous 1989a). Packaging affects demand and buying. Hotels and other large institutions may prefer boxes with 4.5 kg (10 lb) of product. Individual customers shopping in a seafood market may buy enough for one family meal. Freezer storage may be necessary if the customer does not plan to eat the product shortly after purchase. Some potential customers shy away from buying fishery products simply because they are not experienced in cooking fish. Such people eat seafood in restaurants. A simple recipe on the package and cooking demonstrations in the seafood store or supermarket reassure the customer that it is really easy to prepare seafood at home.

Gathering Data

Now that we have a basic understanding of factors that determine market demand, it is necessary to gather data to quantify demand. This can be accomplished by gathering existing information and by conducting your own survey.

Existing Information-- Published information on fish consumption and demand can be obtained from newsletters; trade magazines, such as Aquaculture Magazine; government statistics, such as those promulgated by the Food and Agriculture Organization of the United Nations, the U.S. Department of Agriculture, and the U.S. Department of Commerce; publications put out by academia; and the articles and papers published in various journals and professional society media, such as World Aquaculture, promulgated by the World Aquaculture Society. Information also can be gathered from banks, chambers of commerce, and business feasibility studies. Regardless of the source of information, you must scrutinize the method by which the data were gathered. In other words, are the data reliable? Note also the trend in consumption and demand for the fishery product(s) of interest to you. Absolute figures are really meaningless unless you can tell whether market demand is going up or down.

Surveys-- Sometimes it also becomes necessary to gather your own information to fit your particular requirements. General observation of shoppers in a seafood market may give you a hint of their preferences, and talking with them helps. This causal approach can be improved by designing an experiment to carefully take into consideration age, sex, ethnic background, geographical location, and other variables that affect purchase of a product. Shang (1990) outlined a general step-by-step procedure. An example of such an experiment (survey) was described by Engle et al. (1990). They conducted a survey to determine market demand for channel catfish in the United States. National telephone surveys were conducted of 3,600 households, 1,800 retail restaurant managers, and 1,800 retail grocery store managers. Specific questions were asked to determine awareness and availability of product, attitudes, preferences, and consumption patterns. Overall, the study indicated that consumer attitudes toward catfish have changed in nontraditional consumption areas. Consumers perceived catfish as a nutritious, high-quality product that is easy to prepare. As long as the catfish farming industry continues to produce a consistently high-quality product, potential consumer demand will continue to support further growth of U.S. farm-raised catfish.

Another form of experimentation is to set up a display case with your product in a seafood outlet and observe and record customer purchases. This method is used to estimate market potential for new products and to forecast consumer response to advertising, price changes, and new packaging. Shang (1990) outlined the steps: (1) the test locations (retail stores, restaurants, and wholesalers) selected should be located in low-, medium-, and high-income districts. (2) Enough product must be available for the duration of the test. (3) Variables tested can include such things as sizes of fish, forms of the product, prices, and packaging. For best results, a limited number of variables should be introduced at any one time. (4) Record the sales and information on the buyers such as age, sex, race, etc. A simple questionnaire may be distributed at time of purchase to gather more information. (5) Results of the sales are analyzed. The number of buyers relative to the entire household population in the testing area, plus the amount of sale, can be used to get an approximate market demand for the area.

Market Segmentation

By now you should understand those factors that influence customers to buy a product. Two strategies are available for marketing your product(s). The first assumes that the market is composed of homogenous needs, and a single product is introduced which appeals to the largest number of buyers. This is often called mass or undifferentiated marketing (Chaston 1983). When the channel catfish farming industry began development in the early 1960s, one product was processed, a dressed fish. This product was marketed to a variety to customers. The second strategy acknowledges that sales can be increased by producing a range of products for specific segments of the market. This is termed market segmentation and involves (1) type of product, (2) type of market, and (3) geographical location and demographics.

Type of Product-- By producing a broad range of products, such as whole dressed fish, fillets, and breaded fish fillets, you can meet buyer demand. However, such an approach is usually accompanied by higher operation costs. With more than one product, new work blocks may have to be set up in the processing plant or existing work blocks modified when there is a change-over in processing a new product. To avoid depletion of a given product, inventories must be maintained. The greater the number of products, the greater the inventory and cost. Finally, added products require additional promotional effort and expense.

Perhaps the most effective approach initially would be to divide any market into segments and select a specific segment for exploitation. Instead of going after a small share of a large market, you can target a specific market segment. By specializing with one product type, you can maximize efficiency. This lowers processing costs for increased profits. As confidence and profits build, other product types can be added. The implication is that all product types will ultimately decline in sales. An example of new product development would be to change from packaging bulk fish fillets that are ungraded, to graded fillets of strict portion sizes for restaurants. A fast-food outlet may want the fillets cut into finger-shaped portions. Such a change-over may require only minor adjustments in the processing work blocks. However, marketing and promotional efforts could be considerable.

Type of Market-- The type of product(s) produced will depend on your prospective buyers. Market segmentation divides buyers into groups based on similar needs and usage. Each buyer is sensitive to certain product variables. Expensive seafood restaurants, the so-called "white-tablecloth" restaurant segment, is most sensitive to quality and portion control, but less sensitive to price increase. Other restaurants not specializing in seafood will have more emphasis on price. Supermarkets are concerned with consistency of supply and price. While quality and portion size are important, they are emphasized less. Brokers, wholesalers, specialty fish markets, fast-food outlets, and other outlets all have their requirements.

Geographical Location and Demographics-- As discussed earlier, different regions of the United States have different preferences, and this in turn is affected by demographics. Bjorndal (1990) discussed market segmentation with salmon on a global scale. In Japan, salted salmon is the main product, but salmon is now used in sashimi. The United States has a tradition of eating canned salmon, but this demand is decreasing relative to increasing demand for fresh and frozen products. In France, about 70% of the salmon are consumed as a smoked product, especially during the Christmas season. In the United Kingdom, canned salmon is traditional, but fresh salmon consumption has increased considerably.

Summing It Up

To sum up, a potential market should be segmented into its parts that include type of product, type of market or buyer, geographical location, demographics, and other variables. You may then exploit a specific segment of the market. Regardless of the market segment you pursue, it must be of sufficient size, have potential for further growth, not be over-occupied by competition, and have an identified need that your company is uniquely capable of satisfying (Chaston 1983). Further, the marketing mix of product, price, promotion, and place must serve as the framework for your marketing plan.

YOUR MARKET POSITION

After you analyze the market, you are ready to establish your market position. You should know the market segment(s) you will serve, the product forms you will provide, and how you will introduce your product in a way that distinguishes it from its competition.

Your Market Niche

You must decide through what channel you will market your product, such as restaurants, cooperatives, and seafood specialty outlets, and you should list the reasons. For example, assume that you plan to produce hybrid striped bass and that few farmers are growing this fish. Since so little product is available, it would be difficult to establish a relationship with a distributor. Instead you might target a select number of white-tablecloth restaurants in your immediate vicinity or even a single restaurant. Here are some advantages, using our example above. You can eliminate the intermediaries in the marketing channel. You can determine weekly quantity of product required and develop grow-out and management strategies to meet this demand. You know who your competition is, perhaps none initially.

There is another approach to marketing a relatively new, low-volume product. Join forces with another producer(s) to have enough product to interest buyers. Rex Caffey (personal communication, 1995) found it difficult to market soft-shell crawfish because of the low volume his company produced. He joined with two other producers and was able to meet an international order for 3,000 dozen soft-shell crawfish. A more long-term approach is to form a cooperative. Ideally, producer cooperatives stabilize demand and price while providing additional market penetration. You must be careful, however, that all producers who contribute product to a common market adhere to strict quality assurance. It takes only one producer with bad product to ruin the market.

New products often have differences in how they are graded, processed, and packaged. These differences make it difficult for buyers to become familiar with the product. For example, buyers of soft-shell crawfish were once faced with choosing among processed, non-processed, breaded, non-breaded, stuffed, fresh, frozen, vacuum packed, and block-frozen products. This variety confused buyers who did not know what soft-shell crawfish were. Educational material was eventually made available by the Louisiana Seafood Promotion and Marketing Board.

Many buyers have little patience with new products. For example, a chef in a fine restaurant is not likely to stop serving shrimp because of problems with one shipment or supplier; however, the chef is less likely to be patient when the product involved is less established and accounts for a small portion of sales.

Type of Product

Once you target your buyer, you will be able to concentrate on providing a specific product type discussed earlier (Figure 16.6). Moreover, you will be able to calculate your cost of production.

Product Distinction

Once you concentrate on a product type, you will want to distinguish it from all incipient competition. This can be done with packaging and promotion, development of a logo, and a statement about the product. Having a HACCP logo accompany your company logo will show that your product is of the highest quality. Quality assurance and top notch service should always be a part of product distribution.

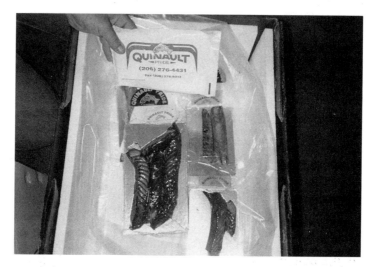

Figure 16.6 Quinault Pride of Washington State developed a smoked salmon product that is targeted for a particular market niche.

Estimating Sales

If you are dealing exclusively with a single restaurant, estimating sales is easy. If, however, you market to more than one outlet or if you have competition, you will need to determine your market share and potential sales. Sales forecasting involves estimating sales in dollars and in physical units as accurately as possible for a specific period. It involves forecasting sales for the total market and determining what share of the market you can capture. Expansion of your production or processing operation is predicted on sales projections.

Economic forecasting considers broader factors affecting the economy such as inflation, interest rate, and international affairs. In some instances, market forecasts are "guesstimates" at best. Sales forecasting, then, is based on the general economic forecast and the market forecast. It involves projecting from past trends and takes into account expected economic and market pressures.

Buying trends have been well established for some culture species in certain regions and countries. In Austria and certain other European countries, citizens like to have their Christmas carp. Turkey is the choice in the United States during the Thanksgiving and Christmas season. Sales for fish during this period may drop. On the other hand, sales for fish strengthen during the Lenten season. Crawfish sales in Louisiana are strong up to Easter, but historically sales drop off after Easter. Farmers hope for a late Easter. By understanding nuances in market demand, you can plan accordingly.

Pricing Strategy

Most aquaculture products have established prices based on supply and demand. Competition is usually such that if you ask too high a price buyers will look elsewhere. If you sell too low, you will be bought out quickly and not make a profit. Thus, you will most likely be constrained to sell at the going price.

Sometimes a new species or product is offered for which there is no history of a pricing structure. When the soft-shell crawfish was first introduced, here is how the pricing structure developed, according to Gillespie (1990): Producers received $18.74/kg ($8.50/lb). If you assume a 6% selling cost, then you must add $1.10/kg ($0.50/lb). The distributor adds 25% to 35% to the purchase price and in turn sells the soft-shell crawfish to a food service firm for about $25.35 to $27.56/kg ($11.50 to $12.50/lb). The food service firm calculates the cost per serving and multiplies by about 3 to get the menu price. If there are 55 crawfish/kg (25/lb) and each crawfish costs $0.50, a three-piece serving as an appetizer costs $1.50 and sells retail for $3.50. Gillespie (1990) suggested that producers should discuss with food brokers and food service firms the impact of a producer price of $18.74/kg. The need is to identify restaurants that have a product-mix on their menus that can accommodate an unbreaded soft-shell crawfish dish with a unit food cost of 40 to 50 cents. This means the appetizer menu can accommodate a $1.50 per unit item at retail.

Promotion and Advertising

Your promotional and advertising strategy should be developed to target the market segment you choose. Promotion targeted at end consumers should require more educational effort than promotion aimed at wholesalers. Promotional efforts can be initiated by individual firms, cooperatives, by industrywide groups, and by government sponsors. The industrywide approach is more suited to educating and is termed generic.

Producers in a generic group promote standards of quality, product form, and availability. Individual company promotion is developed to produce brand identification and is often associated with value-added products. Methods of advertising may include brochures, slide-show talks, videos, trade shows, and use of seafood trade journals, such as Seafood Leader. Sending mailouts to all restaurants in a geographic area, termed "junk mail approach," is one form of advertising. A letter lists all bottom-line information about your company, its products, and how you can be reached.

CHECKLIST OF QUESTIONS

Meyer and Burzell (1988) presented a checklist of marketing questions that should be addressed by those considering commercial aquaculture. Their checklist, modified here, is based on their experience in Hawaii.

Marketing Checklist

To whom will you sell your product?
>Who buys it now?
>How much do they buy now?
>How much are they paying for it now?
>Why will they buy it from you?
>How much will they buy from you?
>How much will they pay you?
>Are you sure what you will sell is what they now buy?
>If not, how long will it take to build customer demand?

What exactly are you going to sell?
>What product form?
>What product presentation?
>What choices do you have?
>Are you the first to try what you are going to do? Why?

How will you process your product for sale?
>How will you process it at the production site?
>How will you process it for shipment?
>What materials will you need for processing?
>Will you require more than one processing step and site?
>Who will do the processing?
>When will the processing have to be done?
>What losses will you incur in handling and processing?
>How will you store the product as it is processed?
>What will the unit processing cost be?

How will you get the product to the buyers?
>Where are the buyers?
>Where are the actual points of sale?
>What transport methods will you use?
>Will transporters firmly schedule your product?
>What losses will you incur during transport?
>Who will handle and coordinate transport?
>What will be the unit cost of transport and delivery?

How will you sell your product?
>Look again at all the questions under "to whom will you sell your product."
>What will you do to differentiate your product?
>What price will you receive for your product?
>Why not more, or less?
>Who will handle sales promotion?
>Who will handle selling, billing, collections?
>What is the unit cost to sell your product?

What will you do with product you cannot sell immediately?

Can you store your product?

How long can your store your product?

Where can you store your product?

Can you process excess product differently to sell it?

At what price?

What is the unit cost to store or to process into another form?

What are the overall economics now?

What is the unit cost of production?

What is the unit cost of processing?

What is the unit cost of transportation?

What is the unit cost of selling?

What is the unit cost of storing or further processing?

What other marketing costs must be considered?

What is the total unit cost for each product form you offer for sale?

What is the price buyers will pay for each product form?

Now add your own questions to this list.

Do You Build or Not?

Stop, if you have to develop a consumer preference for the product, unless you have a very generous working-capital budget and enjoy being a pioneer.

Stop, if you cannot be sure you can deliver a high quality product to your market points on a regular basis.

Stop, if existing producers are supplying current market demands and you cannot offer a significantly lower price with higher quality.

Stop, if you will not budget for promotion, marketing, and sales costs efforts.

Go, if your profit margins provide a sufficient return on equity to attract bank financing, if you have located an immediate market for your specific product, if you have working capital to carry you 6 months beyond the point when you anticipate making your first sales collection, if you are prepared to treat marketing and sales efforts equally with production, if you are prepared to put together a team of people with the diverse talents necessary to operate and manage a business, and if you are prepared to work twice as hard as you have ever imagined, physically and mentally!

Now add to this list.

INTERNATIONAL MARKETING

What may start off as a small company that markets domestically could lead to market expansion to other states or even other countries. The basics of marketing still apply, but new strategies must be understood. The U.S. Department of Commerce listed the 12 most common mistakes and pitfalls made by new exporters (Albins 1990). They are condensed here:

(1) Failure to obtain qualified export expertise and to develop a master plan before you start. A firm must have clearly defined goals and a plan to meet these goals.

(2) Insufficient commitment by management to stick to it and overcome initial difficulties. It will usually take more effort and time than you think it will.

(3) Insufficient care in selecting international distributors. It is crucial that an experienced distributor be obtained, especially one who can cut through a maze of governmental red tape and who can promote a new product (yours). Some distributors can market new products on the basis of their reputation.

(4) Chasing orders from around the world instead of targeting a specific area. As sales increase, an executive from the firm could be located in the distributor's geographical region to increase communication and efficiency.

(5) Neglecting export business when the U.S. market booms. Some U.S. companies turn to international markets when domestic markets sag but neglect them when domestic markets strengthen again.

(6) Failure to treat international distributors on an equal basis with domestic counterparts. Companies may carry out domestic advertising campaigns, special discount offers, sales incentive programs, and the like, but fail to give similar assistance to their international distributors.

(7) Assuming that a given market technique or product worked in one country so it will work the same in other countries.

(8) Unwillingness to modify products to meet regulations or cultural preferences of other countries.

(9) Failure to print service, sale, and other messages in locally understood language. Although a distributor's top management may speak English, sales personnel may not. Further, containers with product should have writing and pictures that are understood by the customers. One Louisiana crawfish processing plant that markets to Sweden has a picture of boiled crawfish surrounded by dill on its container (box) (Figure 16.7). The box, which holds 1 kg, has a message in Swedish.

(10) Failure to consider use of an export management company.

(11) Failure to consider licensing or joint-venture agreements. Import restrictions and political difficulties in some countries may make international marketing seem unfeasible. Having a partner from the country targeted for marketing often helps solve such problems.

(12) Failure to provide readily available service for the product. After sale of the product, an exporting firm must be able to advise on storage, handling, and use of product.

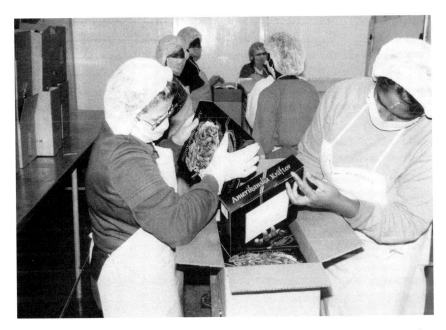

Figure 16.7 Packaging crawfish at Louisiana Premium Seafood for European markets .

SALES TERMS

A crawfish producer markets live crawfish to a buyer out of country. The buyer accepts the shipment but fails to pay the bill. A shrimp farmer in the Philippines purchases feed from a firm in another country. The feed is infested with weevils, and the farmer wants his money back. The seller refuses. These two problems may have been avoided if a "letter of credit" was established before the sale was made.

Letter of Credit

A letter of credit, or L/C, is a document that lends the credit of the issuing bank to that of the buyer. The letter is issued on behalf of the buyer in favor of an exporter. It states that the bank agrees to honor the exporter's draft when presented if terms of the credit are complied with. A confirmed L/C has the confirmation of a domestic bank. This gives the credit prestige and responsibility since the issuing foreign bank may not be well known to the buyer.

There are other terms you must be familiar with. We list some of those most commonly used. Albins (1990) presented a comprehensive list.

Purchase Order

Often a buyer will talk with a seller over the telephone about buying a particular quantity of product at a given price. This is followed up with a written purchase order, usually by FAX. The purchase order (P.O.) describes the product type, quantity required, date to be received, price, and method of payment.

Terms and Conditions

The first transaction between buyer and seller needs to be written out. Often it is on a cash basis. The new customer pays cash in advance or on delivery (C.O.D). After a relationship develops between buyer and seller, customers may be extended payment terms of 15 to 30 days. Some firms continue to use the L/C as a means of doing business, especially when large orders or foreign sales are involved.

F.O.B.

This stands for free on board. It means that if a seller quotes a price, for example $10/kg F.O.B. Baton Rouge, Louisiana airport, the seller is responsible for all handling and shipping costs to the Baton Rouge airport. The buyer must pay all shipping costs beyond that point.

C.I.F.

This stands for cost, insurance, and freight. The price includes the cost of the product and container, insurance, and freight up to a specified designation. The insurance is protection against damage or spoilage of the product. The importance of insurance cannot be overemphasized because you are dealing with perishable products. Delays in shipping, damage to packaging, and spoilage can cause a shipment to be refused, and without insurance the producer faces the possibility of loss.

Bill of Lading

The bill of lading is a shipping contract issued to the shipper of the product by the producer or their agent. It lists the product shipped, to whom it is shipped, shipping dates, and other relevant information. A clean bill of lading acknowledges that the goods were received in "apparent good order and condition" and without qualification.

Invoice

The invoice is the bill the seller sends the buyer. If there was a purchase order, the invoice lists the P.O. number. The invoice lists what was sold, the quantity, unit price, total cost, and terms of payment.

Accounts Receivable

If you sell to a customer on credit, certain steps should be taken. A credit application form should be filled out by the buyer similar to that used by a bank. Describe in detail the terms of agreement. When the application is complete, have it scrutinized by a credit checking agency. If the agreement calls for payment within 30 days, and payment has not been received within 45 days, a polite past-due notice should be sent out. Other follow-up notices should be sent. If payment is not forthcoming, send a final letter stating that legal action will follow. If the matter is settled amicably, conduct new business transactions on a cash basis.

Ad Valorem

"According to value" is a tax imposed on imports based on a percentage of the product value from the port of shipment.

Consignment

This is a physical transfer of product from an exporter (consignor) to an importer (consignee) for the importer to sell. The consignor retains title to the product until the consignee sells it. The consignee sells for a commission and remits the net proceeds to the consignor.

Forwarder

This is an independent business that handles shipments for exporters. Individuals may be referred to as freight forwarders.

FOR MORE INFORMATION

Many sources can provide information on marketing. Here are a few.

Federal Level

The U.S. Department of Commerce has two sources of information under its auspices, the National Oceanic and Atmospheric Administration (NOAA), which administers the National Marine Fisheries Service (NMFS), and the Bureau of Census.

NMFS publishes statistics on commercial and sport fishery production including volume, imports, export, and prices. The address is National Marine Fisheries Service, U.S. Department of Commerce, Silver Spring Metro Center 1, 1335 East-West Highway, Silver Spring, MD 20910.

The Bureau of Census, through its Census of Agriculture, provides information on domestic aquaculture production, methods of production, product sales, and supply and demand. The address is Bureau of the Census, U.S. Department of Commerce, Washington, D.C. 20233.

The U.S. Department of Agriculture (USDA), with its Agricultural Marketing Service, provides assistance to aquaculturists. The address is Federal-State Marketing Improvement Program, Market Research and Development Division, Agricultural Marketing Service, U.S. Department of Agriculture, Room 3524, South Building, Washington, D.C., 20250.

The USDA publishes a report called "Aquaculture Situation and Outlook." It provides statistics and easy-to-read write-ups on production, marketing, prices, and trends with domestic species. For information, write USDA 1301 New York Avenue, NW Washington, D.C. 20005-4789.

The Foreign Agricultural Service (FAS) with headquarters in Washington, D.C., has field offices in 76 U.S. embassies around the world. FAS has the leading government role in developing foreign agricultural markets to promote American exports, including farmed fish (Anonymous 1986). Federal addresses are subject to change. For current addresses refer to the Conservation Directory (National Wildlife Federation 1995). It is published annually.

State Level

Many state departments of agriculture offer assistance. An example is the Louisiana Department of Agriculture and Forestry. This state also has the Louisiana Seafood Promotion and Marketing Board and other marketing boards. The land-grant universities, with their cooperative extension services, are sources of information.

Private Sources

Four private sources are of note (Anonymous 1989a):

(1) National Fisheries Institute (NFI), 2000 M Street NW Suite 580, Washington, D.C. 20036. The NFI, a national trade association, has served the U.S. commercial seafood industry since 1945. It helps producers, processors, brokers, wholesalers, and exporters.

(2) The National Restaurant Association, 150 North Michigan, Suite 2000, Chicago, IL 60601.

(3) The Food Marketing Institute, 1750 K Street, NW, Washington, D. C. 20006.

(4) Urner Barry Publications, P.O. Box 389, Toms River, NJ 08754-0389. Urner Barry produces two weekly seafood price reports.

Trade Journals

Many trade journals publish marketing information. Here are five: (1) Seafood Leader, 1115 NW 46th Street, Seattle, WA 98107, (2) Seafood Business, 120 Tillson Avenue, Box 908, Rockland, ME 04841-0908, (3) Water Farming Journal, 3400 Neyrey Drive, Metairie, LA 70002, (4) Aquaculture Magazine, Post Office Box 2329, Asheville, NC 28802, and (5) The Catfish Journal, Post Office Box 34, 550 High Street, Jackson, MS 39205.

STUDY QUESTIONS

1. What are the various management approaches for growing culture species? Give examples for each.

2. What is product life cycle? Give an example.

3. Define, explain, or identify in three to five sentences cost-plus pricing, competitive pricing, penetration pricing, skimming, what the market will bear, psychological pricing, and prestige pricing.

4. Choose any culture species and product(s) you wish to market. Address the following:

    a) Develop a promotional plan for the product(s).

    b) Discuss potential competition.

    c) Develop a plan for determining market demand.

    d) What product distinction will you develop?

    e) How will you estimate sales?

    f) Develop a plan for marketing overseas.

    g) List sources of information you will use for gathering data.

5. Define, explain, or identify letter of credit, purchase order, F.O.B., bill of lading, invoice, accounts receivable, consignment, and forwarder.

REFERENCES

Albins, J.H. (editor). 1990. Louisiana International Trade Directory 1989-90. World Trade Center of New Orleans, LA 70130.

Anonymous. 1986. Seafood marketing, opportunities to improve the U.S. position. Briefing report to the Honorable Ted Stevens, United States Senate. GAO/RCED-87-11BR.

Anonymous. 1989. Fish and seafood made easy. U.S. Department of Commerce, National Fish and Seafood Promotional Council. Booklet 28.

Anonymous. 1989a. Marketing your aquaculture product. Kevgor Aquasystems, P.O. Box 48851, 595 Burrand Street, Vancouver, BC U7X1A8 Canada.

Avault, J.W., Jr. 1989. Social/political aspects of aquaculture. Aquaculture Magazine 15(4):70-73.

Avault, J.W., Jr. 1990a. Aquaculture in the United States, the signs for the future. Aquaculture Magazine 16(2):26-38.

Avault, J.W., Jr. 1990b. Culture species for aquaculture, why some succeed and others fail. Aquaculture Magazine 16(4):77-79.

Bjorndal, T. 1990. The Economics of Salmon Aquaculture. Oxford, London, Edinburgh, Boston, Melbourne: Blackwell Science Publications Ltd. 119 pp.

Caffey, R.H., C.G. Lutz, J.W. Avault, Jr. and K.K. Higgins. 1993. Preliminary observations on production of soft-shell prawns, *Macrobrachium rosenbergii*, (deMann) in commercial shedding facilities. Journal of Applied Aquaculture 2(2):93-102.

Chaston, I. 1983. Marketing in Fisheries and Aquaculture. Surrey, England: Fishing News (Books) Ltd. 144 pp.

Dellenbarger, L.E. and A.R. Schupp. 1988. Household consumption patterns for Louisiana aquaculture species. Louisiana State University Agricultural Center. 11 pp.

Downey, W.D. and S.P. Erickson. 1987. Agribusiness Management. New York-St. Louis-San Francisco: McGraw-Hill Book Company Inc. 428 pp.

Engle, C.R., U. Hatch, S. Swinton and T. Thorpe. 1989. Marketing alternatives for past Alabama catfish producers. Auburn University, Alabama Agricultural Experiment Station. Bulletin 596.

Engle, C., O. Capps, Jr., L. Dellenbarger, J. Dillard, U. Hatch, H. Kinnucan and R. Pomeroy. 1990. The U.S. market for farm-raised catfish. University of Arkansas, Arkansas Agricultural Experiment Station, Division of Agriculture. Bulletin 925.

Gillespie, S.M., B. Schwartz and M.A. Stuffs. 1973. Selling seafood successfully. Marine Advisory Bulletin, Texas A & M Sea Grant College, College of Business Administration. Seafood TAMU-SG-73-505.

Gillespie, S.M. 1990. Marketing soft-shelled crawfish. Louisiana Sea Grant College Program for Wetland Resources, Louisiana State University, Baton Rouge, La 70803.

Granados, A.E., J.W. Avault, Jr. and S.W. Cange. 1991 Double cropping Malaysian prawns, *Macrobrachium rosenbergii* and red swamp crawfish *Procambarus clarkii*. Journal of Applied Aquaculture 1(1):65-78.

Laumer, J.F., J.R. Harris, H.J. Guffey, Jr. and R.C. Erffmeyer. no date. Researching your market. U.S. Small Business Administration Office of Business Development, Business Development Publication MT 8.

Lawson, T.B. and L.Y. Brown. 1988. Transportation of Louisiana seafood products. Louisiana State University Agricultural Center 15 pp.

Lee, C.S. 1983. Production and marketing of milkfish in Taiwan: an economic analysis. International Center for Living Aquatic Resources Management, Manila, Philippines. ICLARM Technical Reports 6.

Meyer, P.L. and L.A. Burzell. 1988. Know your market potential and problems before you build your farm -- the Amorient aquafarm experience in Hawaii. Presented Annual Meeting of the World Aquaculture Society, Honolulu, Hawaii, January 6, 1988.

National Wildlife Federation. 1990. Conservation Directory. Published by National Wildlife Federation 1400 Sixteenth Street, N.W. Washington, D.C. 20036-2266.

Raulerson, R.C. and W.K. Trotter. 1973. Demand for farm-raised channel catfish in supermarkets: Analysis of a selected market. U.S. Department of Agriculture. Economic Research Service. Marketing Report No. 993. 21 pp.

Roberts, K.J. and C.D. Harper. 1988. Seafood market trends. Louisiana State University Agricultural Center 19 pp.

Roberts, K.J. and L. Dellenbarger. 1989. Louisiana crawfish markets and marketing. Journal of Shellfish Research 8(1):303-307.

Sevilleja, R.C. and E.C. McCoy. 1979. Fish marketing in central Luzon, Philippines. Auburn University, International Center for Aquaculture, Alabama Agricultural Experiment Station. Research and Development Series No. 21.

Shang, Y.C. 1981. Aquaculture Economics: Basic Concepts and Methods of Analysis. Boulder, Colorado, Croom Helm, London, England: Westview Press. 153 pp.

Shang, Y.C. 1990. Aquaculture Economic Analysis: An Introduction. Baton Rouge, Louisiana: The World Aquaculture Society. 211 pp.

Shaw, S.A. 1990. Marketing, a practical guide for fish farmers. Cambridge, Massachusetts: Blackwell Science Publications Ltd. 96 pp.

Slavin, J.W. and Associates. 1982. Fish facts. Food Marketing Institute, 1750 K Street, NW Washington, D.C. 20006.

Stickney, R.R. 1988. Commercial fishing and net-pen salmon aquaculture: turning conceptual antagonism toward a common purpose. Fisheries, a Bulletin of the American Fisheries Society 13 (4):9-13.

CHAPTER 17
YOUR BUSINESS PLAN

Your business plan is the written document that serves as a blueprint to guide your aquaculture operation. In this chapter, we first introduce you to a few basics such as forming a business, your management team, financial planning, borrowing money, and where to get help. The rest of the chapter involves preparation of your business plan.

IS AQUACULTURE FOR YOU?

People become involved in commercial aquaculture for various reasons. Many become involved for strictly business reasons. For example, in the mid 1960s a number of well-known companies embraced shrimp farming in the United States. They noted that the United States seemed to have an insatiable appetite for shrimp and that much of the product was imported. These companies failed to note that we did not, at the time, have the knowledge to mass produce seed, to feed larval shrimp, and in general to grow shrimp. They reasoned that surely it can't be that difficult to farm shrimp. We farm other culture species, don't we?

At the other end of the spectrum, some biologists feel that they have the fundamental knowledge for growing a particular culture species. They forge ahead, knowing that surely someone will want their product once it has been grown and harvested. They reason that since this is a great-tasting fish, there is really no need to worry about markets. People will find out about the product and come to buy it. In reality, an aquaculturist must focus attention on both business matters and on farming, plus a host of other areas, to be successful. By successful, we mean making a profit.

Perhaps the best place to start is by thinking it through. Do you have the temperament for commercial aquaculture (Gebhart and Williams no date; Lindbergh and Pryor 1984; Beem 1991; Garling 1992; Lichtkoppler 1993)?

Frank Taylor (1991) discussed what he had to go through to start a commercial shrimp farming operation in South Carolina (based on an oral presentation at the annual meeting of the World Aquaculture Society in Puerto Rico June 16-20, 1991). He loved to grow shrimp. Feeding them, checking the water quality, and all the work that goes into growing shrimp were enjoyable. But he noted that he had to become involved in many facets of the business before he could even begin farming.

To start, he had to be a land purchaser. This meant preparing a business plan to obtain a loan. Before the actual purchase it was necessary to check the soil. Did it have enough clay to hold water, and what about the possibility of pesticide residues and heavy metals? A good water supply was next. Once the land and water supply were in place, he had to become an engineer and contractor. It was necessary to work with the Soil Conservation Service and other agencies on the pond layout.

Then came preparation of the specifications so the job could be bid. Next he had to become a permit specialist. Permits were needed from the EPA, Corps of Engineers, and various state, county, and city agencies. When all the permits were in place, the budding shrimp farmer had to turn his attention to becoming a purchasing agent. Equipment, such as pumps, aerators, tractors, and feeders, had to be bought. Storage buildings were needed. Then there were office supplies, and supplies needed for the actual growing of shrimp.

At long last he came to that part of shrimp farming that he liked best of all. He became an aquaculturist. This involved stocking postlarvae, feeding, checking the water quality, bird control, and the ultimate harvest of the shrimp. While growing the shrimp, he had to spend time on maintenance. This involved such things as repair of motors, seines, nets, pumps, tractors, feeders, and other equipment. While all this was going on he could not forget to pay those monthly bills and record sales. So he became an office manager. When the shrimp finally were harvested, they had to be processed and marketed. A decision had to be made. Should the shrimp be individually quick frozen, processed fresh, or processed in other forms? This, of course, depends on the requirements of the customer. So a promotional effort had to be made just to find out what the customer wanted. And the list of tasks lengthens.

A farmer of traditional agricultural crops, such as cotton or soybeans, has an infrastructure in place for farming and doing business. Further, a farmer usually has the temperament for dealing with so many diverse groups and tasks. A large company that wishes to enter aquaculture may have much of the necessary infrastructure in place. However, to a newcomer, commercial aquaculture may seem overwhelming. Some people opt to have partners, with each partner responsible for a particular segment of the operation. Decide the form of business you wish to set up. This will be affected by the decision to go it alone or to form partnerships.

FORMING A BUSINESS

There are three forms of business: sole proprietorship, partnership, and corporation. Each has advantages and disadvantages.

Sole Proprietorship

The sole proprietorship is usually defined as a business owned and operated by one person. Your spouse may be involved, as well as any children. Some sole proprietorships also hire employees. This is the simplest form of a business operation. To form a sole proprietorship, you need only to obtain the necessary licenses and begin operation. It needs little or no government approval and is usually less expensive than a partnership or corporation. The owner has complete control over the operation and does not have to share profits with anyone. The profit or loss of the business is included with the owner's individual federal or state tax returns.

A sole proprietorship has disadvantages. The owner has unlimited liability. He or she is responsible for the full amount of business debts, and they may exceed the total investment. This liability extends to all of the proprietor's assets, such as the house and car. Problems of liability, such as physical loss or personal injury, may be reduced with insurance. It is more difficult to raise capital, and the business ends when the owner dies.

The Partnership

This is a business wherein two or more people own the business jointly. It is necessary to put into writing what each partner will contribute in cash or other assets. Salaries, profit and loss, and what part of the assets each partner will get if the business is dissolved, also should be put into writing. It should be determined beforehand, what will be done if a partner dies, withdraws, or goes bankrupt.

This business is relatively simple to form. You are still in command, but you will have to share. By forming a partnership, you combine the strengths of each person, be they assets or be they skills needed to run the operation. Partnerships have a definite legal status and must be registered with the secretary of state. Partnerships are not taxable entities. Each partner records his or her profit or loss on their individual tax returns.

There are some disadvantages. You still have unlimited liability. The partnership can develop into a difficult situation because of different personalities, and it can be difficult to dissolve.

Corporation

The corporation is the most complex of the three business structures. The corporation is a distinct legal entity, distinct from the individuals or stockholders who own it. It pays taxes on the profits of the corporation.

There are advantages to forming a corporation. The corporation continues to exist regardless of what happens to management. Stockholders have limited liability. Ownership can be easily transferred. It is easier to raise capital and to expand. You can hire specialized management and change management without affecting the structure of the corporation. This allows you to obtain people with specialized skills. A corporation is adaptable to small and large businesses.

There are several disadvantages. It is more difficult and expensive to organize. A written articles of incorporation must be developed and registered with the secretary of state. Bylaws must be drafted. Stock certificates must be issued. There are extensive government regulations to deal with. A corporation requires extensive bookkeeping. A corporation is taxed on its profits, and the stockholders are taxed. This is true for a C corporation that is the regular type of corporation. However, you can form an S corporation and avoid this double taxation. In an S corporation, profits are taken out of the corporation and taxed only once by individuals receiving the profit.

MANAGEMENT TEAM

As seen earlier, a commercial aquaculture operation involves many tasks, each requiring different skills. Some small aquaculture operations hire a manager to run the farm while the owner attends to business matters. Large firms may have responsibilities spread out among many managers. Chaston (1988) and Meade (1989) discussed the role of management in aquaculture.

Core Managerial Positions

In general, a core of managerial positions includes: (1) operations, (2) finance, (3) marketing, and (4) research and development (Kevgor Aquasystems no date; Kevgor Aquasystems 1990). You, as the owner or boss, have each of the managers answer to you. If you have a family-run business and do not bring in outside managers, then the tasks and responsibilities should also be broken down into the same core areas. Various responsibilities should be assigned to appropriate family members. On the other hand, if you are part of a large corporation, these core areas can be subdivided further to meet the needs of the company.

Operations-- This involves the day-to-day activities of running the farm. The manager assigned to this position should be someone who can work outside, accept harsh weather, be able to repair equipment, and do what it takes to get the job done. Operations involve such tasks as feeding and caring for the fish, checking the water quality, harvesting, and transporting to the processing plant. It also involves operation and maintenance of all farm equipment.

Finance-- In some instances, this person is the key figure in obtaining start-up capital. Later as the operation gets under way, they keep the books on money matters. The person hired for this position should have a background in accounting or a closely related field. In some instances, a Certified Public Accountant (CPA) is brought into the organization, either as a full-time or part-time manager. The finance manager records sales and expenditures. This person must also make predictions as to financial trends. Pro forma cash flow and cost and returns are examples of two financial records that must be kept. Records are needed for profit and loss statements and for income tax purposes.

Marketing-- This involves finding customers, finding out what they want, and making the sale. Follow-up service is necessary. (See also Chapter 16 on marketing.) The marketing manager must be able to meet people, be willing to travel, and have the ability to sell product.

Research and Development-- This area cuts across the others. The manager of R & D must be innovative and have the knack of determining which new trends, equipment, methods, or products can be incorporated into the operation.

Finding and Keeping the Best People

Once the core areas and responsibilities have been identified, it is necessary to develop criteria to find the best people for the positions. According to Bangs (1992), managerial weakness is a major reason for the failure of small businesses. The job description for each position must be explained in writing, listing the duties and responsibilities of each person. It must be clear who does what, who reports to whom, and who makes the final decisions. Further, the salary and benefits package should be detailed.

There are several ways to find the best people for the positions. Advertising in aquaculture newsletters, talking with experienced fish farmers, attending aquaculture meetings, visiting with the cooperative extension services at land-grant institutions, and word of mouth are but a few sources for finding the right people.

Each applicant for a managerial position should submit his or her resume. Among other things, the resume should include personal data such as name, address, phone number, age, health, education, work experience, and references. It is difficult to determine from a written resume if an applicant is enthusiastic about the position. An interview, however, will reveal this.

Once you have the managerial team in place, you must keep them happy and productive. After the base salary, the benefits package should be carefully thought out. Health care, vacation with pay, workers' compensation, and such benefits are standard. After this, consider an incentive package whereby the managers can receive bonuses or share in the profits.

Managers should be made to feel that they have a part of the business and not that they are just there to follow your orders. Give them responsibility and respect their advice. When dissolved oxygen becomes low in a particular pond at 2:30 in the morning, the operations manager will be there to correct the problem. After all, the manager has to save "their fish." There are other incentives, and each manager will have personal interests. For example, working outdoors is not enough incentive to keep a good operations manager, but hunting rights on the farm and having a pickup truck may mean a lot to the manager. Provision of on-farm housing with utilities paid and the chance to attend an aquaculture meeting with expenses paid are other examples of incentives.

FINANCIAL PLANNING

Various analyses have been used to predict and to monitor the financial viability of an aquaculture operation. Of these, the costs and returns estimation, cash flow projection, balance sheet, break-even analysis, and profit and loss statement are especially useful. You need to know if you are making or losing money. The size and design of the physical operation affect profitability, and thought must be given to its planning.

Costs and Returns

Costs are expenditures incurred in production of the aquatic crop. Some costs may be overlooked. For example, if a trout farmer is asked what it costs to grow a crop a fish, the farmer may think in terms of feed, fuel, labor, and chemicals. Money for insurance, property taxes, and depreciation may be overlooked. Nevertheless, the latter costs are necessary and must be taken into account to determine total production costs.

Returns from aquaculture may be gross return or net return. Gross return is simply the amount of money received for the aquatic crop. Net return, or profit, is the amount left over after total costs have been subtracted.

Initial Investments-- The purchasing of land and a water supply system are major initial investments for many aquaculture operations. Initial investments also may include such items as storage buildings, feed silos, tanks, vats, hauling truck, tractor, and the like. Generally, such items are bought once, at the outset, rather than yearly. Certain equipment, such as a tractor, is replaced periodically as it wears out.

Fixed Costs-- These costs, normally computed annually, are those that must be paid regardless of the level of production. Fixed costs include land, property taxes, depreciation, and interest on capital investment, such as pond construction. Fixed costs do not change as production increases or decreases. Moreover, if no crop is produced at all, fixed costs still must be paid.

Property tax and insurance are fairly straightforward and are quickly determined by the land assessor and insurance agent.

Interest on all borrowed money can be a major item, particularly on land and other big items such as a water well. Expenditures for land are amortized for 10 to 30 years. A loan is amortized by repaying a portion of it at regular intervals, usually annually. Most homeowners who finance a house are familiar with amortization.

Ponds, equipment, and other facilities depreciate or become obsolete with time. This depreciation is considered a fixed cost and must be computed to determine costs and returns. Land *per se* does not depreciate; rather it appreciates or goes up in value. To calculate depreciation, a straight-line method is often used where depreciation equals initial cost divided by the expected life in years.

Problem and Solution. Assume that a tractor costs $48,000 and its expected life is 12 years. What is the annual depreciation?

The solution is we simply depreciate the tractor $4,000 a year for 12 years. In this example, we assume no salvage value. However, we sometimes use a salvage value of 10% to 15%, depending on the item being depreciated. If the salvage value is 10%, then 10% x $48,000 = $4,800. We therefore subtract $4,800 from, $48,000, which gives us $43, 200 to depreciate. We now depreciate $3,600 a year for 12 years. Generally, it is desirable to depreciate ponds, equipment, and facilities as quickly as possible but within guidelines of the Internal Revenue Service (Table 17.1).

Table 17.1 Expected life of selected items.

Item	Expected Life (years)
Ponds	15 to 20
Water well	15 to 20
Tractor and mower	12
Storage buildings	10
Truck	5 to 10
Motor and pump	6
Boat and motor	5
Agitators	3

Variable Costs-- These costs include payments for items used in production. If there is no production, variable costs are zero, but as production increases variable costs also increase. Variable costs often are thought of as out-of-pocket expenditures and may be for such items as feed, fertilizer, fuel, transportation, and other everyday costs. Most of these costs are simply recorded as they are incurred. Gasoline costs can be calculated. One method is to divide total mileage accumulated by miles per gallon you obtain on the vehicle(s) and multiply this times the cost of gasoline per unit volume.

Total Cost-- The total cost of production, then, combines fixed costs and variable costs. Total cost may be figured one of two ways: on an annual basis or on a production basis. For the latter, total costs can be determined on a per hectare basis or on what it costs to produce a kilogram of fish, regardless of the time involved. This is known as average total cost and is more meaningful than annual total cost when making management decisions. You can also calculate average fixed costs and variable costs on a per hectare basis or on a per kilogram of fish produced. You can quickly determine where the big-cost items are. Examples will be given later in this chapter.

Returns-- Gross return is simply the total amount of money received for the crop. If, for example, a farmer sells 10,000 kilograms of tilapia at $2.50 a kilogram, the gross return is $25,000.

Net profit must be calculated. To determine, we add fixed costs to variable costs and get total cost. Total cost is subtracted from gross return to obtain returns to land and management. This is the money left over to pay on the cost of owning land and to pay management. Some economists calculate returns to land, labor, and management.

Problem and Solution. Assume, for example, that on a per acre basis gross return is $750, fixed cost is $80, and variable cost is $500. Calculate net profit.

The solution is total cost is then $580 ($80 + $500) and returns to land and management is $170 ($750 - $580). If land costs $200 an acre and the cost of owning land is 8%, then the annual investment in land per acre is $16 ($200 x 8%). The return to management then becomes $154 ($170 - $16). This return to management is net profit.

Return on Investment-- An aquaculture operation is an investment just as stocks or bonds are an investment. When you buy bonds, you know what percentage will be received on money invested. An aquaculture operation should also return a percentage on money invested.

To determine the return on investment (ROI), calculate the average annual investment (excluding fixed costs and variable costs) on land, equipment, and facilities. Average annual investment equals initial costs less salvage value divided by 2 for all but land that is valued at initial cost. This answer is multiplied by the interest paid. This calculation must be done separately for each piece of equipment and for general facilities.

Problem and Solution. Assume that the initial cost of a pickup truck is $12,000, the estimated life of the truck is 5 years, salvage value is $1,200, and that interest on investment is 8%. What is the average annual investment on the truck?

The solution is: $12,000 - $1,200 = $10,800 ÷ 2 = $5,400. And, $5,400 x 8% = $432. The average annual investment on the truck is $432.

This method of calculation is used to determine average annual investment for each and every piece of equipment, facility such as ponds, and for land. As mentioned earlier, only land *per se* is calculated slightly differently. The total investment, then, is the sum of the average annual investment for each item. To determine percentage return on investment, we divide net profit by total investment.

Problem and Solution. Assume that our total investment in a fish farming operation is $500,000 and that net profit (returns to management) is $40,000. What is the percentage return on investment?
The solution is $40,000 ÷ $500,000 = 8%.

So far we have explained how costs and returns are computed, and in our discussion the cost of land has been a major consideration. For a number of aquaculture operations this is so. For some operations, such as net-pen culture of salmon and raft culture of oysters, land may not be an expense. Nevertheless, the fundamentals of costs and returns apply.
Costs and returns should be studied before entering aquaculture and should be computed on a regular basis once the operation begins. This will help in making management decisions. Some aquaculture businesses may have more than one operation. For example, those operations that are vertically integrated may involve fingerling production, grow-out for the food market, processing, and even feed manufacturing. In this instance, separate costs and returns should be tabulated for each endeavor. The fingerling operation may make money whereas the grow-out operation may lose money. By keeping separate records, it is easy to determine.

Costs and Returns, an Example
Here is an example of costs and returns for channel catfish (*Ictalurus punctatus*) (Adrian and McCoy 1971) (Tables 17.2, 17.3).
You will quickly note that figures in these tables are out of date. We have chosen this particular example because the authors have put forth clearly in simple terms the fundamentals we wish to illustrate. Further, we wish to focus on the mechanics of calculating costs and returns, and their interpretation, rather than on the actual figures. Costs and returns will vary from operation to operation, depending on management and other factors. The important points are the various cost items involved, the cost of each item relative to total cost, and the mechanics of calculating return to land and management, average annual investment, and percentage return on investment. If you understand these

principles, it will be easy to calculate for an incipient operation or for an operation under way.

Table 17.2 Average costs per acre in catfish production and per pound of catfish produced, 58 commercial catfish producers, Alabama, 1970.

Item	Per acre Dollars	Per pound Dollars
Variable costs		
Feed[a]	132.81	.108
Fingerlings	104.64	.085
Electricity	10.47	.009
Maintenance	8.56	.007
Transportation costs	4.87	.004
Harvest labor	8.95	.007
Fertilizer	6.11	.005
Chemicals	2.62	.002
Miscellaneous	2.35	.002
Interest on operating capital	12.66	.010
Total	294.04	.239
Fixed costs		
Pond depreciation	24.60	.020
Equipment and facilities depreciation	17.30	.014
Interest on and taxes	5.06	.004
Total	46.96	.038
Other costs		
Land[b]	6.00	.005
Labor[c]	30.00	.024
Total	36.00	.029
Total all costs	377.00	.306

[a] Feed conversion: 1.92:1

[b] Land was valued at $100 per acre. Land investment was charged at 6%.

[c] Labor was charged at a rate of $1.50 per hour. Average labor requirement per acre for Alabama producers was approximately 20 hours.

Source: Adrian and McCoy 1971. Alabama Agricultural Experiment Station Bulletin 421.

Table 17.3 Average costs and returns per acre in catfish production and per pound of catfish produced, 58 commercial catfish producers, Alabama, 1970.

Item	Per acre Dollars	Per pound Dollars
Gross receipts[a]	508.39	.414
Costs		
Variable	294.04	.239
Fixed	46.96	.038
Total	341.00	.277
Returns		
Returns to land and management	167.39	.137
Cost of land	6.00	.005
Return to labor and management	161.39	.132
Cost of labor	30.00	.024
Return to management	131.39	.108
Average investment	771.65	.629
Return to investment , Percentage	17.00	17.00

[a]Average catfish production was 1,228 pounds per acre. The figure included 16 pounds of catfish consumed by the producer.
Source: Adrian and McCoy 1971. Alabama Agricultural Experiment Station Bulletin 421.

Adrian and McCoy (1971) obtained data from 58 channel catfish farmers in Alabama. Data on costs are given in Table 17.2. Data are given on a per acre basis and on a per pound basis. From this table you can see the various items involved in a channel catfish farming operation and their relative cost. Note also that the authors have distinguished between harvest labor (a variable cost) and labor for day-to-day work.

Major variable cost items were feed, fingerlings, electricity, maintenance, transportation, harvest labor, fertilizer, and chemicals. Fixed costs included pond depreciation, equipment and facility depreciation, interest, and taxes.

Feed and fingerling outlays represented 81% of total variable costs. Feed was the single most expensive item, comprising 45% of the total variable cost. This is still the case for most aquaculture operations that use hatchery-produced seed and formulated feed. Since fingerlings and feed are such expensive items, you should be able to estimate needs.

Problem and Solution. Assume that a channel catfish farmer wishes to stock four 10-acre ponds with 8-inch fingerlings at a rate of 6,000 per acre. Assume that feed costs $250 a ton, and that it will take 2 pounds of feed to grow each pound of fish. When fish reach an average weight of 1.5 pounds each, the fish will be harvested and sold. In our example, we will assume no fish mortality.

Determine how many fingerlings will be required and the total cost if fingerlings are bought at one cent an inch. Further, determine the tons of feed required and the total cost.

The solution is: the total number of fingerlings needed would be 240,000 (6,000 x 10 x 4). The total cost would be $19,200 (240,000 x $0.08).

Assume that each fingerling weighed 0.1 of a pound at stocking. Therefore, a total weight of 24,000 pounds of fingerlings was stocked (240,000 x 0.1). If you grow each fish to 1.5 pounds, you produce a total weight of 360,000 pounds minus the weight of fish at stocking. This gives 336,000 pounds of fish flesh to grow (240,000 x 1.5 = 360,000 - 24,000 =336,000).

If it takes 2 pounds of feed to produce 1 pound of fish, a total of 672,000 pounds of feed will be needed (336,000 x 2). This comes to 336 tons, and at a cost of $250 a ton it will cost a total of $84,000 (336 x $250).

Now let's go back to Table 17.2 and look at other figures. Electricity ranged from $0.54 to $31.50, with an average of $10.47. The largest electrical expense was for pumping. Various other operating costs are itemized. Variable costs totaled $294.04 per acre or $0.239 to produce each pound of fish.

Regarding fixed costs, pond depreciation represented 52% of total fixed costs. Calculating the cost of pond construction was covered in Chapter 5. Equipment and facility depreciation comprised 37% of total fixed costs, and interest and tax charges made up the rest. Total fixed costs came to $46.96 per acre or $0.038 per pound.

The average gross receipts per acre were $508.39 based on a production of 1,228 pounds of fish produced at $0.414 per pound (Table 17.3). Average net return to land, labor, and management was $167.39. After charging land at 6% of its estimated value, net returns to labor and management were $161.39 per acre. Labor was set at a rate of $1.50 per hour. The cost of labor is subtracted from returns to labor and management, leaving a residual return to management of $131.39.

Average total investment was $771.65 per acre (Table 17.4) and percentage return to investment was 17% (Table 17.3).

Table 17.4 Average investment in capital assets and average labor requirements per acre in catfish production and per pound catfish produced, 58 commercial catfish producers, Alabama, 1970.

Item	Per acre Dollars	Per pound Dollars
Equipment and facilities		
Boat and motor	11.16	.009
Truck	51.38	.042
Tractor and mower	15.38	.013
Fish hauling tanks	36.83	.030
Storage shelter	53.72	.044
Motor and pump	34.66	.028
Well	72.29	.059
Miscellaneous	3.73	.003
Total	279.65	.228
Other investment		
Ponds	492.00	.401
Total investment	771.65	.629
Labor requirements	Hours	Hours
Operators	20.0	.016
Harvest labor	6.0	.005
Total	26.0	.021

Source: Adrian and McCoy 1971. Alabama Agricultural Experiment Station Bulletin 421.

Cash Flow Projection

The cash flow projection is one of the most important documents in a formal business plan (Bangs 1992; Strombom and Tweed 1992). The cash flow statement reveals how much money you need to run the business, when you need it, and how much money you bring in and when.

Basic Structure of Cash Flow-- The cash flow statement shows money being spent monthly and money coming in monthly (Table 17.5). Cash flows into the business from sales, collection of receivables, and capital injection. It flows out through cash payments for expenses of all kinds. This is essential information because many aquaculture operations may take 12 to 18 months before income is realized. The lending agency will want to know when payment for the loan can begin.

Table 17.5 Cash flow for one year.   Month

Beginning cash balance	1	2	3	4	5	6	7	8	9	10	11	12
Add: Cash sales												
Collection of Receivables												
Loans												
Additional investment												
Total cash receipts												
Deduct: Start-up costs[a]												
Seed or juveniles expense												
Feed												
Chemicals												
On-site fuel and oil												
Electricity-utilities												
Variable labor costs												
Advertising												
Insurance												
Legal and accounting												
Delivery Expense												
Fixed cash disbursements[b]												
Loan payment												
Mortgage or rent												
Taxes												
Total Cash Disbursements												
Net Cash Flow												
Cumulative Cash Flow												
Ending Cash Balance												

[a] Start-up costs: site development, buildings, production facilities, equipment, and vehicles.
[b] Fixed cash disbursements: salaries, payroll taxes and benefits, office supplies, boxes, licenses, telephone, miscellaneous, total per month.
Source: Strombom and Tweed 1992.

In hard clam (*Mercenaria mercenaria*) culture, for example, revenues do not come in until year 2 or 3, and profitability may not be achieved for another year or two. For some finfish operations, it may take 6 to 8 months to grow the fry to fingerling size, and it may take another 8 months to grow fingerlings to market size. That is a long time to be in a business without net cash flow. The time can be shortened by starting off with fingerlings.

The cash flow structure records data monthly for a year. It deals only with actual cash transactions. Depreciation, a non-cash expense, does not appear on a cash flow. Loan repayments, including interest, do represent a cash disbursement. This monthly accountability should be continued for at least 3 years or until the business is definitely making money. Thereafter, cash flow data can be maintained quarterly.

Monthly accountability has several advantages. In the beginning, start-up capital may be needed to construct ponds, put down a water well, and get storage facilities in place. Money can be borrowed to begin this work. Though money eventually will be needed to buy fingerlings and feed, there is no need to borrow money initially because you are not ready; there is no need to pay interest on money you cannot use at the time. By carefully analyzing the needs of the operation and the chronology of events, you can borrow money for specific needs only when ready.

The cash flow statement begins with the cash on hand the day you start business. Do not wait until you stock out and begin feeding. You will be spending money long before this. To the initial balance, receipts are added and disbursements are subtracted for a prescribed period. The end balance then becomes the start balance for the next period.

Use your cash flow as a budget. If the cash outlays for a given item increase over the amount allocated for a given month, find out why and take measures to correct it.

What if-- The most careful planning cannot always anticipate the unexpected. When the cash flow (budget) is prepared in the beginning, the cost of each item or material is estimated. Costs may go up. Feed and other items used in production may increase in price. What if you are growing channel catfish, and you discover that your fish have off-flavor. This could mean harvest will have to be delayed, and more feed will be required. Fortunately, cash flow projections lend themselves to computerization. Spreadsheet programs, such as Lotus 1-2-^{TM} or Excel^{TM}, to name two, allow you to make "what if" statements without starting calculations over from the beginning. It is probably a good idea to make "what if" calculations to give flexibility in preparing the cash flow budget.

Budget Deviation Analysis-- Budgets are made to be revised and updated. Budget deviation analysis (BDA) is a direct control on your business operations. It records what you have budgeted for a given month (B) on your cash flow statement, what you actually spent (A), and the deviation (B-A) (Bangs 1992). It will help you hold down costs and increase profits. BDA should be performed monthly. For example, suppose utilities you budgeted for $400 in January actually cost $600. Why? Perhaps a windstorm damaged windows and doors and allowed winter air to enter the poorly insulated buildings. If careful attention was not paid to the utility bill, the added expense could have gotten out of hand. On the other hand, suppose you budgeted a modest net income for the sale of fish in March but the income was much higher. Again, why? In this case, an investigation revealed there is a strong seasonal demand for the product at this time. With experience, you can become more exact in budgeting, giving you more control over your business and profits.

Other Financial Statements

Other useful financial statements include the balance sheet, break-even analysis, and profit and loss statement (Bangs 1992).

Balance Sheet-- The balance sheet is a summary of what the business owns, what it owes, and what investment the owners have in the business. Balance sheets for all companies contain the same categories in the same order (Table 17.6). The possessions that have monetary value are called assets. The amounts the business owes to creditors are called liabilities. The value of the assets over and above the liabilities is called the owner's claim against the assets, or owner's equity. Owner's equity also is called net worth.

Table 17.6. Abbreviated balance sheet.

John and Jane Doe Fish Farm		
May 20, 1995		
Assets		
Current Assets --	$300,000	
Fixed Assets --	$190,000	
Other Assets -·-------------------------------------	$10,000	
Total Assets -------------------------------------		$500,000
Liabilities		
Current Liabilities -------------------------------	$150,000	
Long-term Liabilities ---------------------------	$50,000	
Total Liabilities -------------------------------		$200,000
Net Worth (total assets minus total liabilities) or ----------- $300,000		
Owner's Equity		
Total Liabilities and Net Worth ---------------------------		$500,000

A brief description of the categories follows: Current assets include such items as cash, government securities, marketable securities, notes receivable, accounts receivable, inventories, prepaid expenses, or any other item that could be converted into cash in a given business year. Fixed assets include such items as land, water well, equipment, and other items that have an expected useful business life measured in years. Depreciation is applied to those fixed assets that, unlike land, will wear out. Other assets might include such items as intangible assets such as patents, exclusive use contracts, and notes receivable from officers and employees.

Current liabilities include accounts payable, notes payable, accrued expenses, (wage, salaries, withholding tax, FICA), taxes payable, current portion of long-term debt, and other obligations that will come due within a year. Long-term liabilities include such items as mortgages, trust deeds, long-term loans, and equipment loans.

Net worth includes the owner's equity, retained earnings, and other equity. See Downey and Erikson (1987) for a complete explanation.

The balance sheet is set up to portray two aspects of each entry or event recorded on it. For each item of value, or asset, there is an offsetting claim against that asset. This leads to the formula: Assets = liabilities + owner's equity. For example, assume that a fish farmer deposits $20,000 in the bank. This sum may include an investment of $10,000 from the farmer's own funds and $10,000 borrowed from the bank. If a balance sheet is drawn up for this transaction, it would show assets of $20,000 balanced against a liability claim of $10,000 and an owner's claim of $10,000. Using the balance sheet formula, we find:

Assets = liabilities + owner's equity
$20,000 = $10,000 + $10,000

Break-even Analysis-- A break-even analysis tells when your business will break even, that is when you are neither making money nor losing money. It also will show how much product must be sold to break even.

Problem and Solution. Assume that a tilapia farm has fixed costs of $10,000. For each unit (by weight) of tilapia sold, variable costs are $75. Assume that the sale of one unit brings in $100. How many units of tilapia must be sold to break even?

If the tilapia farm is open for business but grows no tilapia (no variable costs) and sells no tilapia, it incurs its fixed costs of $10,000; so the entire $10,000 is a net loss. If the farm manages to sell one unit ($100) of product, it incurs the fixed cost of $10,000 and the variable cost of $75 for that unit. The total cost of production is $10,075 against an income of $100. The loss is $9,975 ($10,075 - $100). If two units are sold, the fixed cost remains at $10,000, and the variable cost becomes $150 (2 x $75). The loss is reduced to $9,950 ($10,150 - $200). Each time another unit of tilapia is sold, the income derived is used first to cover its own variable cost of $75. The remaining $25 is to help cover the fixed cost or contribution to overhead (CTO). The basic formula for the break-even point is then: BE = FC ÷ CTO. At this CTO rate, the sales volume necessary to cover all costs (the break-even point) is simply: $10,000 ÷ $25 = 400 units of tilapia.

Profit and Loss Statement-- The primary purpose of the profit and loss statement is to establish the profit or loss that results from the combination of income and expenses. It is a key financial statement for operating managers. For most farms, profit and loss statements cover from January 1 to December 31. As a budget tool, the actual progress of your business should be compared against projections every month. Profit and loss statements are standardized to facilitate comparison and analysis (Table 17.7).

Sales represent the dollar value of all the products and services sold from January 1 through December 31, 1995. These may be cash sales or credit sales. Cost of goods represents the total cost of goods sold. These costs may be for such items as channel catfish fingerlings bought by the farmer from a hatchery. (If a processing plant was involved, it would pay for fish produced by farmers.) Gross margin is net sales minus cost of goods sold. Cash operating expenses include such things as feed, chemicals, gasoline, and other variable-cost items. Non-cash expenses include depreciation of machinery, ponds or other facilities, and buildings. Total operating expenses is the sum of the two. Profit (loss) before tax is gross margin minus total operating expenses. Net profit is what is left over after taxes. For a detailed treatment of profit and loss statements, refer to Jolly and Clonts (1993).

Table 17.7 Abbreviated profit and loss statement.

John and Jane Doe		
Fish Farm		
January 1 through December 31, 1995		
(1) Net sales		$1,000,000
(2) Less cost of goods sold		$750,000
(3) Equals gross margin		$250,000
(4) Operating Expenses		
Cash expenses	$125,00	
Non-cash expenses	$25,000	
(5) Total operating expenses	$150,000	
(6) Profit (Loss) Pre-Tax		$100,000
(7) Taxes		$40,000
(8) Net profit after taxes		$60,000

Size of Operation and Efficiency

The size and design of the operation have an effect on production costs and profit. For example, a person can feed fish on a 40-ha (100 acre) operation as easily as on a 20-ha (50 acre) operation. Thus cost of labor is reduced on a per hectare basis. Feed can be bought in bulk for large operations, whereas small operations may rely on more expensive feed in bags. As still another example, one tractor can maintain or mow grass on levees for 40 ha as well as for 20 ha. If you buy a tractor to maintain levees on a 20-ha operation, the tractor is not being used to full capacity. Fixed costs, depreciation for the tractor, will be higher on a per hectare basis.

Production costs can be lowered and profit increased by improving the efficiency of design on a given operation. A case in point was given by Foster and Waldrop (1972). They studied costs and returns on six pond sizes involving a land base of 160 acres as follows: (1) a simulated farm consisting of 32 5-acre ponds, (2) 16 10-acre ponds, (3) 8 20-acre ponds, (4) 4 40-acre ponds, (5) 2 80-acre ponds, and (6) 1 160-acre pond. The estimated initial investment decreased significantly on a per acre basis as the pond size was increased, from roughly $1,730 per acre for the 5-acre pond system to about $947 per acre for one 160-acre pond. Most of the economics of investment associated with size were attributed to pond construction costs. Smaller ponds cost more to construct than larger ponds on a per acre basis. Investment in harvesting equipment was the only investment item that increased as pond size increased. Costs per pound of fish produced were highest, 30.55 cents in the 32 5-acre pond and lowest, 26.2 cents in the 8 20-acre ponds. Put another way, net profit was lowest in the 5-acre ponds and highest in the 20-acre ponds. Obviously these figures will differ over time, since the way in which we grow and market fish is changing constantly. The point to establish is the concept that the size and design of the aquaculture operation affect production costs and profit.

BORROWING MONEY

A few aquaculturists do not borrow money. Rather they "grow as they go." Farmers of traditional agricultural crops, such as soybeans and cotton, already have their business infrastructure in place. They may build a pond or two with revenues from their existing operation and pay for feed and other items with cash on hand. However, most beginning fish farmers and companies borrow money to finance their aquaculture operations.

Types of Credit

Loans may be secured or unsecured. A secured loan is backed by collateral such as a lien against your property, savings account, or investments like certificates of deposit. An unsecured loan, sometimes called a signature loan, is one not backed by any collateral. These are almost always short-term loans and available only to the most credit-worthy individuals and companies. There are three general types of credit based on life of the loan.

Short-term-- This type of loan is usually for 1 year. Credit is used for costs to produce a crop, for short-run construction, and for short-term liquidity problems. In crop production, it is intended for such items as feed, maintenance, labor, and other operating expenses. When the crop is sold, the loan is usually paid off in a lump sum. If loans for production are financed longer than 1 year, the result is deepening debt and the erosion of business assets. Your cash flow may look good, since payments are stretched out. However, you would violate a cardinal rule of borrowing: paying for a benefit after it has been exhausted (Bangs 1992).

Intermediate-term-- This type of credit is for 1 to 7 years. It is used to buy machinery and equipment, and for working capital of businesses undergoing rapid growth. Repayment is made from profits over several production periods.

Long-term-- This type of credit is provided for more than 5 years involving major purchases of fixed assets such as land. Payments are amortized (spread out) for up to 30 years.

Debt Versus Equity

A new company with no "track record" may have difficulty obtaining a loan. Although site property, buildings, and equipment can and do serve as collateral, lending agencies usually require some form of funding to handle the "lead-in" or "start-up" period. Getting the operation off to a start, and harvesting and marketing that first crop, usually take longer than anyone anticipates. Therefore your beginning aquaculture operation will need a certain amount of equity investment. Equity comes from your own money that you put into the business. It also comes from money of people you take into the company. These people do not lend money to you that must be paid back. Rather, they now have a piece of the company. They are looking for potential income instead of an immediate return on their investment.

Lending agencies like to see a debt/equity (D/E) ratio of less than 50%; that is debt is 50% or less of the capital used to finance the aquaculture operation. Although it may be possible to obtain a loan with a higher D/E ratio, there are associated problems. New businesses that are highly leveraged never seem to have enough capital to pay bills, and cash flow problems never seem to end. It is necessary, then, to obtain adequate equity financing. This type of financing is termed venture capital.

Venture Capital

Venture capital is used: (1) during start-up when the operation has not begun and is still in the late planning or pilot stage, (2) during early operations when the culture species is being grown, but the first crop has not been harvested, and (3) where harvests have been realized with positive cash flow, but expansion or new facilities are needed (Kevgor Aquasystems no date).

People interested in investing venture capital are called venture capitalists. They are looking for capital gain of about three to five times or more of their original investment in 5 to 7 years (U.S. Small Business Administration no date). Venture capitalists are usually wealthy individuals, family, friends, and those from venture capital firms. There are more than 400 venture capital firms throughout the United States and Canada (Kevgor Aquasystems no date). They consist of a diverse group of investors with various investment interests. The National Venture Capital Association includes names and addresses of all NVCA members.

Lending Agencies

A borrower should shop carefully for credit. He or she should not only obtain the right type of credit and interest rate but should consider other factors such as repayment schedules, services provided with the loan, and the willingness of a lender to stand by the borrower in emergencies. Once a good source of credit is established, a borrower should stick with that source. McVey (no date) reviewed various financial sources and consultation services available for commercial aquaculture.

The appropriate lending agency will depend on the type of loan desired. A few sources of loans include: (1) private industry, (2) commercial banks, (3) insurance companies, (4) Farm Credit System, and (5) Farmers Home Administration. Private industry, as discussed before, will sometimes invest a certain amount of venture or "risk capital." High-risk ventures, such as culture of a new species, are usually financed by industry rather than by conventional lending agencies. Commercial banks have played a major role in financing channel catfish operations. In one Alabama study (Adrian and McCoy 1972), 65% of catfish farmers who borrowed money did so from commercial banks. Banks, in addition to lending money, also provide checking accounts and other banking services. Insurance companies have been a source of long-term mortgage credit.

The Farm Credit System is owned by American farmers and is designed to provide credit tailored to fit highly specialized needs. In each of the 12 Farm Credit districts throughout the United States, there is a Federal Land Bank, a Federal Intermediate Credit Bank, and a Bank for Cooperatives. Federal Land Banks make long-term loans secured by first mortgagees on farm real estate through local Federal Land Bank Associations. Federal Intermediate Credit

Banks discount farmers' notes for local Production Credit Associations (PCAs) and other financing institutions. They also make direct loans to the local farmer-owned PCAs. The 12 district Banks for Cooperatives make loans to farmer cooperatives in their respective districts, while the Central Bank for Cooperatives participates with them on larger loans. Of the various "banks" within the Farm Credit System, PCAs have been most active in making loans for fish farming.

The Farmers Home Administration (FHA) was created as a result of the Farmers Home Administration Act of 1946. The FHA provides federal government loans directly to farmers. The major responsibility of FHA is to provide supervised agricultural credit for farmers who are unable to obtain credit from any other source on reasonable terms. The FHA, an agency of the U.S. Department Agriculture, has branches throughout the United States.

The International Finance Corporation (IFC) is the largest source of direct project financing in the form of loan and equity for private investment in developing countries. IFC, an affiliate of the World Bank, operates independently with separate staff and funding. IFC's purpose is to promote economic development of its developing member countries by supporting the private sector. Since it began operation in 1956, IFC has supported more than 1,000 business ventures in more than 90 developing countries. IFC acts as a catalyst by encouraging other investors and lenders, inside and outside the host country, to share in the risks of private sector projects. IFC finances only a portion, usually up to 25%, of the cost of the project.

Where to Get Advice For Starting Your Business

There are a number of sources for help. Each state has a land-grant university. The Cooperative Extension Service at land-grant universities can usually offer help in the organization of financial statements, such as costs and returns and pro forma cash flow. For example, in the early 1990s there was much interest in the farming of red drum (*Sciaenops ocellatus*) in Gulf Coast states. However, little was known of the economics of production. Baldridge et al. (1991) and Huffman et al. (1991) analyzed the economic potential for commercial-scale red drum production. Moreover, they factored a number of "what if" scenarios into their analysis. Some universities have federal sea grant offices that can help. Many are involved in aquaculture research and extension.

There are agencies that are particularly helpful. The local chamber of commerce is geared to advise budding new businesses. Check the phone book for the number. The Small Business Administration (SBA) and the Service Corps of Retired Executives (SCORE) are geared to advise entrepreneurs. The SBA has many publications that should be of help. Several were consulted in preparation of this chapter. You can write them at SBA P.O. Box 30, Denver, CO 80201-0030 or call toll free for information at 1-800 225-5722. SCORE is an organization that consists of retired men and women who give free advice on starting a business. There are several hundred SCORE chapters around the country. This author has met with a representative of SCORE and was impressed with the interest in helping newcomers to the business world. SCORE hosts workshops from time to time, and once you get on the mailing list you will be kept informed. The SBA can help you find a SCORE member to assist you in business matters, or check your local phone book.

The services of an attorney and accountant should be obtained. By setting up your business correctly at the outset, you can save headaches later. Certainly it is advisable to obtain the services of professionals who have experience in aquaculture. When getting professional help, however, do not feel that you can turn over all of the legal and accounting tasks to them, and have little involvement. This is especially true in the preparation of your business plan. You must be completely involved in the process. After all, it is your aquaculture business.

PREPARATION OF YOUR BUSINESS PLAN
Purpose of the Business Plan

A business plan is needed to give your aquaculture enterprise direction. It is the blueprint you will follow to run your business. It is better to make mistakes on paper and correct them, than to plunge into production with no plan or direction. It costs you nothing to make mistakes on paper. If you are thinking about a loan or if you are seeking investors, you will need a business plan. The first thing a lender or investor will ask for is a copy of your business plan.

Some beginning aquaculturists may think a business plan is not really necessary because not all of the answers are known. These people may feel that they can develop something as they go along. Some feel they don't have time. There is too much to do, ponds to build, and a water supply to put in place. To others, it may seem like an impossible mountain to climb. It is not, however, if it is approached in the right way.

First, an outline of your business plan should be prepared, then revised, and revised again. Now you can work on it in small chunks, one section at a time. Years ago, a geologist discovered a mountain from the air in Irian Jaya (New Guinea) that had signs of holding copper. He put together an expedition to reach the mountain by foot. The climb through the rain forest seemed impossible. He survived the ordeal by not thinking of the climb to the top, but rather he focused on reaching a nearby landmark, such as a dead tree. When this was reached, another landmark was picked out to reach. The business plan, too, can be approached in the same manner, one landmark at a time. To start, you need an outline (Table 17.8).

The Outline

Development of a business plan, with an outline, was presented by O'Hara (1993), McVey (no date), Kevgor Aquasystems (no date), and Bangs (1992). Engle and Stone (1991) developed eleven steps for obtaining an aquaculture loan. Though aquaculture business plans may vary, certain information should be included. Table 17.8 presents a generic outline for a business plan. You can modify it to suit your particular need. Moreover, some lending agencies may have a particular format that they prefer you use.

Table 17.8 Outline of a business plan for aquaculture.

Cover Page	III Management Team
Statement of Purpose	Operations
Table of Contents	Finance
	Marketing
I Description of Business	Research and development
Permits and licenses	
Hiring of crew	IV Critical Risks
Site selection	Construction and production
Development of water supply	Marketing
Construction of facilities	
Procurement of equipment	V Financial Information
Procurement of supplies	Estimated costs and returns
Growing the crop	Pro forma cash flow
Harvesting	Budget deviation analysis
	Balance sheet
II Marketing Strategy	Break-even analysis
Marketing analysis	Profit and loss statement
The product	Equity
Competition	Personal financial statement
Market demand	
Market segment	VI Supporting Documents
Market position	Letters of reference
Market niche	Letters of intent
Type of product	Letters of credit
Product distinction	Contracts
Estimating sales	Credit reports
Pricing strategy	Legal documents
Promotion and advertising	Trip reports
	Blueprints and photographs
	Resumes

Cover Page

The cover page should include: (1) identification of the business plan, (2) to whom submitted, (3) name address, phone number, and FAX number of person(s) involved, and (4) date prepared or submitted. This information should be spaced on a single sheet of paper to cover the whole page. It might look something like this (without complete spacing):

(Cover Page)

Business Plan of Spring-fed Trout Farm Inc.

submitted to
the Big Bank and Trust Company

by
John and Jane Doe
1234 Main Street
Spring Falls, Idaho 80000
Phone (---) --- ----
FAX (---) --- ----

January 1, 1995

Statement of Purpose

The first page should state your objectives and goals as simply as possible. This page is sometimes called an executive summary. If the plan is for your sole use, the statement can be a brief description of how you intend to put the plan into effect. For example: This plan will be used as an operations manual for the business of Spring-fed Trout Farm Inc.

Next, short-term and long-term goals should be stated. For example, the short-term goal is to produce ___ kilograms of trout per year with an annual profit of ___dollars. Within 5 years, it is anticipated that production will reach ___ kilograms with a net profit of ___dollars.

If the plan also will be used as a financial proposal, the statement of purpose is more descriptive and should address these points (Bangs 1992): (1) Who is asking for the loan? (2) What is the business structure? For example, sole proprietorship, partnership, C corporation, S corporation? (3) How much money do you want to borrow? (4) How will the money be used? (5) How will the money benefit the business? (6) Why does this loan or investment make good business sense? (7) How will the loan be repaid?

Here is a sample of statement of purpose: The Spring-fed Trout Farm Inc., of Spring Falls, ID, seeks loans totaling ___ dollars to: construct raceways, develop a water supply system, and to construct feed storage facilities and ancillary buildings. The sum of ___ dollars in equity from the principals will be used for production costs, fixed costs, and for the hiring of labor and management personnel. Spring-fed Trout Farm Inc., has contracts for the sale of ___ kilograms of trout. It is anticipated that the first crop of trout will be sold (give date), and that payment on the loan will begin (give date). Notice that this statement of purpose addresses the points listed above. The last two statements are intended to ensure the bank that the company has a market for the trout and that the loan will be repaid.

Table of Contents

The Table of Contents follows your Statement of Purpose. Your business plan contains six main sections: description of business, marketing strategy, management team, critical risks, financial information, and supporting documents. These sections are further broken down (Table 17.8).

Description of Business

Permits and Licenses-- List all of the permits and licenses you have obtained and those still pending, if any. List them in order of importance or in chronological order. Copies of permits and licenses can be placed in the Supporting Documents section. Also in the Supporting Documents section, list the names of contact persons, their agencies, addresses, and phone numbers regarding permits and licenses.

Hiring of Crew-- List the names of the work crew you have hired, their responsibilities, and who answers to whom. If such personnel have not been hired, briefly describe the jobs you need to fill.

Site Selection-- Describe the site location of your farm. Include a map and photographs. Show the transportation routes to and from the farm. Indicate the proximity to a processing plant or customers. Discuss taxes and utility costs.

Discuss the environmental and physical features of the location. Refer to Chapter 5 for site selection for other pertinent information.

Development of Water Supply-- Describe the source, its dependability, quality, and volume. Discuss future expansion. Will the supply be adequate?

Construction of Facilities-- Discuss the chronology of events for construction of culture facilities. Show a flow chart, based on monthly time, for each of the major phases of development. For example, the proposed area for trout raceways will be developed in stages. First, the land will be cleared during January and February. The land will be graded during March to allow gravity flow water from one raceway to another. Forms will be set in place and concrete poured by the end of March, and so on.

Do not forget to discuss ancillary culture facilities, such as a facility for holding brood stock, hatchery and nursery, and sorting and grading area. Blueprints can be appended in the Support Documents section. Certainly more detail can be given than indicated here. Refer to Chapter 5 for site selection and culture facilities.

Discuss also facilities other than the culture system itself. These might include feed storage, buildings to store tractors and equipment, shop for repairs, and general storage.

Procurement of Equipment-- List all the equipment you need. Organize it by categories such as equipment used for pond maintenance (tractors, small bulldozer), for feeding, harvesting equipment, vehicles, and office. Record when they will be bought and the cost. For example, you will need to buy vehicles for transportation as soon as possible. Equipment for feeding should be bought before harvesting equipment.

Procurement of Supplies-- A list for supplies should be developed in the same manner as that for equipment. Broad categories might include office supplies, supplies for crop production, and supplies for processing.

Growing the Crop-- Discuss the way in which you will grow a crop. For example, 4 cm (1.5 in) trout will be stocked into raceways at such and such a rate. Five to 6 months after stocking, the fish will be graded to size and restocked into raceways with similar-size fish. At a water temperature of 13°C (55°F), it is anticipated that a 340 g (12 oz) trout will be produced in 15 to 18 months. Production is expected to be 160 to 240 kg of trout/liter/second of water flow (10,000 to 15,000 lb/ft^3/second or 22 to 33 lb/gpm). Brief statements can be made about the feeding schedule, water management, and other management techniques required. Give more detail if the culture species is relatively new.

Harvesting-- Describe the method of harvest and the anticipated date of harvest. How will the fish be transported to the processing plant? Or, will you process the fish yourself? If so, describe the procedure.

Marketing Strategy

In the previous chapter, we discussed marketing strategy as it could be applied to your business plan. It is necessary to show that you have a market for your product. Moreover, the anticipated date(s) of the sale(s) is important to determine when you will have a positive cash flow. This means you can start paying off the loan. Certainly letters of credit, contracts, and letters of intent are important to show that you have a market. The lending agency will be reluctant if you plan to look for a market just before harvest.

Management Team

Describe the management team, duties of each, and the chain of command. Place resumes in the Supporting Documents section.

Critical Risks

Any business venture has risks. Certainly, your aquaculture operation is no exception. The risks should be clearly pointed out in your business plan. Do not plan to omit listing the risks, thinking that they may jeopardize your chances for the loan.

There are two areas of risk common to many beginning operations. First, you almost always seem to fall behind in your schedule. If you estimate that it will take two months to perform a particular task, then it will probably take three. The second common mistake is that you never seem to have enough money to handle contingencies. In your cash flow statement, you list the amount of money required. Invariably, something is overlooked, and naturally it costs money, money that you did not expect to spend. Some loan applications take this into consideration by including 10% contingency funds to handle such unexpected expenses.

Risks can be categorized into construction and production, and marketing.

Construction and Production-- List the risks for construction if any. Examples might include shortage of certain materials, strike by construction workers, and bad weather. All result in delays. It is assumed that all appropriate permits and licenses are in place and that this is not a risk at this point.

Production risks might include such problems as diseases, poor water quality, bird predation, and off-flavor. Be specific. For example, instead of simply listing diseases, name the diseases you are most concerned with. If you are growing channel catfish (*Ictalurus punctatus*), you might list ESC, ICH, brown-blood disease, channel catfish virus disease, and so on. For water quality, oxygen depletion and high ammonia levels may be listed. You should not only list the specific problems, but tell what you plan to do about it. How will you prevent the problem from occurring? If the problem does occur, how will you control it?

Marketing-- Several common problems may arise here. You have a delay in the harvest and in the sale of your crop; the price drops for your product; your buyers no longer purchase from you, and you have trouble collecting money from a customer. All of these possibilities, and any others you perceive, should be addressed. A delay of one or two months may occur because your fish are off-flavor. What are you going to do about it? If you continue feeding your fish at 3%, they may become too large for your buyer. The buyer may want a 0.5 kg (1.1 lb) rainbow trout, but your fish are now 1 kg (2.2 lb).

Some new businesses start off with a limited number of buyers. If only one buyer fails to pay on time or refuses to pay, it may devastate a positive cash flow. A letter of credit may avoid this problem.

To sum up, make a list of everything that can go wrong. Then determine how you will prevent the problem from happening and what you will do if it does happen. Think ahead! Plan ahead! Certainly, your "complete" list need not be included in your business plan. Include only those items that are major and have some chance of occurring.

Financial Information

This section includes various financial statements already discussed. Include all in your business plan.

Supporting Documents

This is an appendix where you can include various materials pertinent to your business plan. The trip reports listed would include all the people with whom you visited and the places where you sought information. In other words, it shows the lender that you did your homework. Another useful compilation is to include the business cards of all the people you talked with, particularly those whom you will have business dealings with.

STUDY QUESTIONS

1. From your viewpoint, list reasons for and against for starting a commercial aquaculture operation.
2. What are the three forms of businesses and what are advantages and disadvantages of each?
3. What are four core management positions? Define responsibilities of each.

4. What is the function of a costs and returns estimation? What are fixed costs, variable costs, and total costs? Set up an abbreviated costs and returns schedule for a culture species you wish to produce.

5. How is return on investment calculated? Illustrate with an example showing math.

6. What is the purpose of a cash flow projection? How is it set up?

7. How is a budget deviation analysis related to a cash flow projection?

8. Define, explain, or identify balance sheet, break-even analysis, and profit and loss statement.

9. What are the different types of credit based on repayment time?

10. What does debt versus equity mean? How does this affect obtaining a loan?

11. What is venture capital and how is it used to finance an aquaculture operation?

12. Name agencies that lend to aquaculture operations.

13. List sources that provide advice for a beginning aquaculture business.

14. Choose a culture species you wish to farm. Prepare a business plan for it.

REFERENCES

Adrian, J.L. and E.W. McCoy. 1971. Costs and returns of commercial catfish production in Alabama. Auburn University, Alabama Agricultural Experiment Station. Bulletin 421. 23 pp.

Adrian, J.L. and E.W. McCoy. 1972. Experience and location as factors influencing income from commercial catfish enterprises. Auburn University, Agricultural Experiment Station. Bulletin 437. 28 pp.

Anonymous. 1987. Marine shrimp farming: a guide to feasibility study preparation. International Finance Corporation, Washington, D.C. Edited and published by Aquafood Business Associates P.O. Box 16190 Charleston, S.C. 29412.

Baldridge, T., L. Dellenbarger and D. Huffman. 1991. Economics of commercial redfish production in Louisiana. Department of Agricultural Economics and Agribusiness, Louisiana Agricultural Experiment Station, LSU Agricultural Center. D.A.E. Research Report No. 688.

Bangs, D.H., Jr. 1992. The Business Planning Guide. Dover, New Hampshire: Upstart Publishing Company Inc., a division of Dearborn Publishing Group Inc. 184 pp.

Beem, M. 1991. Aquaculture: realities and potentials when getting started. Southern Regional Aquaculture Center. SRAC Publication No. 441.

Chaston, I. 1988. Managerial Effectiveness in Fisheries and Aquaculture. Surrey, England: Fishing News (Books) Ltd. 132 pp.

Downey, W.D. and S.P. Erickson. 1987. Agribusiness Management. New York, St. Louis, San Francisco: McGraw-Hill Book Company Inc. 477 pp.

Engle, C. and N.M. Stone. 1991. Preparing a business proposal for aquaculture loans. University of Arkansas, Arkansas Cooperative Extension Service. MP-334.

844

Foster, T.H. and J.E. Waldrop. 1972. Cost-size relationships in the production of pond-raised catfish for food. Mississippi State University, Mississippi Agricultural and Forestry Experiment Station. Bulletin 792. 69 pp.

Garling, D.L. 1992. Making plans for commercial aquaculture in the North Central Region. North Central Regional Aquaculture Center. Fact Sheet Series No. 101.

Gebhart, G. and K. Williams. (no date). "Is fish farming for me." Langston University Extension Facts. P.O. Box 730 Langston, Oklahoma 73050.

Huffman, D., T.R. Baldridge and L.E. Dellenbarger. 1991. Estimated economic potential for commercial redfish production. Louisiana Agriculture 35(2):8-9 & 17.

Jolly, C.M. and H.A. Clonts. 1993. Economics of Aquaculture. New York-London-Norwood (Australia): Food Products Press. 319 pp.

Kevgor Aquasystems. no date. How to write an aquaculture business plan. P.O. Box 48851-595 Burrard Street, Vancouver, British Columbia V7X1A8, Canada. 29 pp.

Kevgor Aquasystems. no date. Financing your aquaculture business. P.O. Box 48851-595 Burrard Street, Vancouver, British Columbia V7X1A8, Canada. 31 pp.

Kevgor Aquasystems. 1990. Starting an aquaculture business. P.O. Box 48851-595 Burrard Street, Vancouver, British Columbia V7X1A8, Canada. 56 pp.

Lichtkoppler, F.R. 1993. Factors to consider in establishing a successful aquaculture business in the North Central Region. North Central Regional Aquaculture Center. Michigan State University 13 Natural Resources Building, East Lansing, Michigan 48824-1222. Technical Bulletin Series No. 106.

Lindbergh, J. and K. Pryor. 1984. Six ways to lose money in aquaculture. Aquaculture Magazine 10(4):24-25.

McVey, E. (no date). Financial sources for aquaculture. U.S. Department of Agriculture, National Agricultural Library. 25 pp.

Meade, J.W. 1989. Aquaculture Management. New York: Avi, Published by Van Nostrand Reinhold Company Inc. 175 pp.

O'Hara, P.D. 1993. The Total Business Plan, How to Write, Rewrite, and Revise. New York, Chichester, Brisbane, Toronto, Singapore: John Wiley & Sons Inc. 143 pp.

Rhodes, R.J. 1983. Primer on aquaculture finances, planning for success. Part I. Aquaculture Magazine November/December. pp. 16-20.

Rhodes, R.J. 1984. Primer on aquaculture finances, capital for startup ventures. Part II. Aquaculture Magazine January/February. pp. 21-25.

Rhodes, R.J. 1984. Primer on aquaculture finances, taxes, time and investors. Part III. Aquaculture Magazine March/April. pp. 22-25.

Rhodes, R.J. 1984. Primer on aquaculture finances, avoiding a cash crisis. Part IV. Aquaculture Magazine May/June. pp. 32-35.

Strombom, D.B. and S.M. Tweed. 1992. Business planning for aquaculture--is it feasible? Northeastern Regional Aquaculture Center. NRAC Fact Sheet No. 150.

U.S. Small Business Administration. no date. The ABCs of borrowing. Business Development Publication FM 1.

U.S. Small Business Administration. no date. Understanding cash flow. Business Development Publication FM 4.

U.S. Business Administration. no date. A venture capital primer for small business, financial management. Business Development Publication FM 5.

EPILOG-- how to be successful in commercial aquaculture

In this book, we have taken you step-by-step through the development of commercial aquaculture. In the last chapter, we discussed preparation of your business plan. Why is it that some people are successful and others are not?

After World War II some developing nations concentrated on farming culture species for animal protein. Various carp and tilapia species were often cultured. In the decade of the 1980s many nations, both developed and developing, began shifting attention to culture of high-value species such as penaeid shrimp. Developed nations saw demand for high-value species escalate because capture fisheries could not keep pace. Demand also increased because of increasing population and per capita consumption. Developing nations saw the possibility of foreign exchange.

Aquaculture became big business, and with it came both success and failure. While there is a myriad of factors responsible for success or failure, there are prerequisites for successful aquaculture. We can arbitrarily lump them into six broad areas: Can you produce it? Can you market for a profit? Can you adapt to the intangibles or changing events? Do you have the managerial and financial resources? Do you have the infrastructure? Do you have the desire?

Can You Produce it?

Sometimes an entrepreneur picks a culture species to farm for which information is lacking. In the early 1970s, there was a great deal of interest in shrimp (*Penaeus* spp.) farming. Well-known companies invested money. All pointed to reports that the United States was importing more and more shrimp. The market was there. It couldn't be too hard to grow shrimp, or could it? At that time, shrimp were grown as a secondary crop, primarily in the Indo-Pacific Region. Some milkfish (*Chanos chanos*) farms grew shrimp in polyculture. Most farms allowed the tides to carry wild postlarvae into coastal marsh impoundments. Many such extensive operations did not feed, and management consisted of capturing adults as they attempted to return to sea. This seemed to work well. There was virtually no investment involved. When attempts to spawn shrimp were tried, it was realized that it was not easy. In fact, years of research with millions of dollars invested were needed before shrimp could be spawned in captivity. Further, more research revealed that each larval stage had different requirements. The nauplius stage was the first stage, and it did not feed; the zoea stage needed phytoplankton, and the mysis stage grew well on *Artemia*. All this translated into a need for even more research. After a while the ardor for shrimp farming cooled, and some companies now turned attention to prawns (*Macrobrachium rosenbergii*). Eventually, the farming of marine shrimp became a reality, and production from ponds has escalated in many parts of the world. This is because the industry is market driven, and because research has closed the cycle on this crustacean.

About the same time that interest in shrimp farming began, a similar interest was developing with pompano (*Trachinotus carolinus*). It was interest in pompano and shrimp farming that led to the eventual formation of the World Mariculture (later changed to Aquaculture) Society. Overnight, companies were formed for culturing pompano. There was only one small matter. We did not know how to spawn this fish at the time or how to grow it in ponds. To obtain seed, permits had to be obtained from the state for seining wild fingerlings. Then we learned our next lesson. Pompano die when it gets cold, so they had to be harvested early enough in the year to avoid the problem. Some people felt that there was a way around this problem. We will grow them in recirculating systems with heated water. This author still remembers talking with a beginning pompano farmer who said his only problem was what to do with all the feces produced. As it turned out, we learned a lot about the pompano; now we had to learn how recirculating systems work.

The farming of salmon (*Salmo salar* and *Oncorhynchus* spp.) started differently than that of shrimp or pompano. We had decades of research on production of young to restock natural waters. So we knew how to spawn salmon and produce smolts. Every major salmon stream in the United States has a government hatchery. The technology for farming salmon in floating net-pens was developed with far less trouble than that for farming shrimp. Disease problems developed, but research developed vaccines. When the question can you produce it is asked, the center of attention shifts from the biological arena to the legal-socio-cultural arena. It appeared that the legality of leasing public waters posed a major hurdle. Various states and countries have regulations. Some allow it, others do not. Commercial salmon fishers and environmentalists have voiced concern. The fishers are concerned about competition from farm-raised salmon in public waters Environmentalists point to contamination of gene stocks, to pollution, and to aesthetic alteration of the pristine environment.

Let us look at a more recent example, the red drum (*Sciaenops ocellatus*). The popularity of this fish exploded overnight, because of a dish called blackened red fish, created by a world-renowned chef. In no time, fish stocks in the Gulf of Mexico became depleted, and a moratorium was placed on commercial harvest of red drum. The high market demand for this species seemed to make it an ideal candidate for aquaculture. However, we did not know much about its farming attributes. We did know at the time that it had a high market demand based on a single dish. Researchers and the private sector learned to spawn this fish, and it was stocked into grow-out ponds. Then one winter the temperature dropped to -12°C (10°F), and fish in many ponds were lost. Now some red drum farmers switched to the farming of another new and promising culture species, the hybrid striped bass (female *Morone saxitalis* x male *M. chrysops*). Meanwhile, restaurants did not wait for researchers and farmers to figure out how to grow red drum. They substituted other fish, such as tuna (*Thunnus* spp.), for the blackened dish.

What can be learned from these examples? It is wise to not be the first one to farm a "new" culture species until its life cycle has been closed. Let someone else make the mistakes, and you learn from them. It is tempting, however, to be the first one to get into the culture of a new species. This is fine, if you are a hobby farmer and do not risk too much capital, or if you are a researcher whose job it is to conduct visionary research with government dollars. This attitude of waiting until something is proven may seem to hold back the pioneering spirit. If some forge ahead without all the answers, they are to be admired, but it may cost much time and money. In the beginning it is probably best to seek help from research and extension agencies such as land-grant institutions. Some people in the private sector are not willing to wait until all the answers are obtained, and there is no clear-cut time when best to venture into a commercial operation. This is what makes commercial aquaculture so exciting and exasperating at times.

Can You Market for a Profit?

The market should be in place for your product before the first pond is dug or the first fish is stocked. Yet some aquaculture companies seek a market a few weeks before harvest. The author is reminded of Louisiana around the mid 1960s when channel catfish (*Ictalurus punctatus*) farming began to develop. Pioneering farmers told of selling catfish at the pond bank. There was no need to look for a market. The market would come to you. This was true for a while, but it did not last long. Some catfish farmers opened seafood restaurants in Louisiana to sell their own product.

Successful aquaculture industries worldwide are market driven. There is no better example than the shrimp farming industry. The shrimp is perhaps one of the most difficult of all species to culture, and yet the tremendous expansion in shrimp farming is testimony to its worldwide market appeal. Even so, some entrepreneurs culture various species for other reasons. The biology student may choose the ideal species from a culture standpoint. For example, some years ago there was an interest in polyculturing tilapia with channel catfish. Total production in weight per unit area was increased significantly, and catfish production was not lowered. At harvest, tons of tilapia were on hand with nowhere to go. There was no market. Now, however, tilapia has received much promotion and marketing effort, and it has reached up-scale restaurants.

Some people may choose a culture species suitable to the particular climate where they live. In the New England area, the edible blue mussel (*Mytilus edulis*) grows naturally. This would appear to be the ideal species to farm for this area, and it is. Yet the marketing of this species is another story. It may have been better to ship in the mussel from Europe to prospective markets, develop a taste for it, then pursue its culture. Some individuals choose a culture species because they are enamored with it. The freshwater prawn is a good example. This is an excellent species to farm from many standpoints. Yet it does not have the worldwide market appeal that shrimp has. With promotion and marketing, this species too can be expanded in culture.

Marketing a product and marketing for a profit are not always the same. There are three ways in which to increase profit: increase production in terms of weight per unit area, lower production costs, and market your product for more money.

In states where allowed, catfish farmers are adding exotic species, such as the bighead carp (*Aristichthys nobilis*), to ponds for increased production. Bighead carp are finding markets in Asian communities. The fish is also being canned, and some say it rivals canned salmon and tuna (*Thunnus* spp.). Other species could be added, from a biological standpoint, but this must go hand-in-hand with market development.

One way to lower production costs is to examine big-cost items. Certainly feed is one of the major variable costs for most operations. There are two ways to lower feed costs: pay less for the feed and have improved management techniques. In other words, do not waste feed. There are of course many other ways to lower production costs. Various computer programs can help you track daily progress and expenses. The Cooperative Extension Service and other technology-transfer groups can help you develop a program suited to your needs.

To sell your product for more seems straightforward. One way is to add value to your product. When channel catfish were first processed, fish were sold dressed whole. Now there are nuggets, fillets, and a host of products. Value added also applies to shrimp and other culture species. Block-frozen shrimp bring a relatively low price, but butterfly and bread the product and you immediately add value. The classic example of capitalizing on the value-added concept is the economic success story of Japan. This country does not have the natural resources of many countries. They must import petroleum products, logs and timber, steel, and other resources. They add value to these raw materials by manufacturing products of high value.

To sum up marketing, there are several prerequisites. Get a market before you venture into commercial aquaculture. Check out the going price of the product that you contemplate marketing. Can you compete? How can you get your production costs down, increase production in terms of weight per unit area, and get more money for your product through such strategies as value-added processing?

Can You Deal with the Intangibles?

Another way of expressing this is can you deal with the unexpected? While some control is possible over production and marketing of a product, the intangibles are difficult to anticipate. Let us use the salmon and catfish farming industries as our examples.

In the fall of 1988, Dr. Ken Chew of the University of Washington took this author to a restaurant in Seattle, Washington, to eat broiled salmon. The salmon was excellent. We were told that some of the restaurants featuring salmon were having problems. At that time, Japan was paying a high price for salmon. The price that restaurants in the United States had to pay for the fish was so high that the menu price went up significantly. It was so high that customers began balking at the elevated prices. Then Japan went through a period of mourning at the loss of its beloved emperor. Happy foods, including shrimp and salmon, were not eaten for one year. Meanwhile, the salmon farming industry was expanding at a great rate. Andrew Davlin (The Aquaculture Industry Newsletter Volume. 3 No. 3, April 1, 1992) reviewed the expansion of the salmon farming industry. He noted that the industry had been expanding at 15% a year. In the late 1970s, farm-raised salmon was less than 2% of world production; 98% came from commercial fisheries. In 1992, it approached 32%. The result has been a glut in salmon inventories, both live and processed. This has resulted in a sharp decline in prices. The price of pink salmon (*O. gorbuscha*) offered by processors to Alaskan fishers was 18 cents per pound, according to Davlin. While pink salmon is the lower-priced species among the six salmon species normally consumed, its pricing influences the demand for other salmon species. As a result, farm-raised salmon, largely the Atlantic salmon (*Salmo salar*), were selling below production costs.

Catfish farming has been expanding, and area devoted to production has increased. Davlin noted in his newsletter that in 1990 the Catfish Bargaining Association (CBA) was formed to stabilize prices and to get producers and processors to work together on pricing the product. Many of the large producers and major processors became members of the CBA, so this organization had the clout to affect prices. Prices at the time were about $0.65 a pound to the producer; this price moved to $0.69 and ultimately to $0.80 for live pond-side fish. This high price spurred expansion in the area devoted to catfish farming. Along with expansion of food-fish production came an increasing demand for fingerlings. It takes approximately 18 to 24 months for the expansion in food fish production to reach the market, one growing season for fingerling production and one for food fish production.

In 1992 the price paid for food fish plummeted because of a temporary glut. The price was below the break-even level for many producers. Fortunately, the price later climbed to levels that were profitable. However, because of cash flow problems, coupled with a poor 1992 hatch, producer inventories plummeted.

To sum up the intangibles in aquaculture, you never know what may happen. In most instances, you can deal with the problems associated with production and marketing, but how do you prepare for the intangibles? You can probably learn from farmers of traditional crops, such as rice, soybeans, and cotton. Unexpected problems are a way of life for them. To prepare for the intangibles, spread your production over more than one crop (species of fish), prepare financially to survive lean years when crops (fish) are below the break-even price, and invest in new but proven technology (visionary research).

Do you have the managerial and financial resources?

Bangs (1992), reviewing businesses in general, stated that "managerial weakness is a major reason for failure of small business."

Aquaculture companies often are initiated by someone with a biology or farm background or by someone with a business background. Regardless, you should realize that a successful aquaculture business must give equal attention to the four core managerial positions: (1) operations, (2) finance, (3) marketing, and (4) research and development. There must not be a weak link. Moreover, all people must work together in a synergistic manner.

You must have more than adequate financial resources at hand. You must have financial resources in reserve. When you prepare your business plan, you determine how much money you need to get started and to run the operation. If everything goes well you will have a positive cash flow.

Delays, however, may adversely affect a positive cash flow. Further, the intangibles, or an unexpected event, may have a negative impact on your operation making money. We discussed earlier price drops for salmon and channel catfish. Sometimes low prices last for more than a year. Can you hold out for that long? This is one reason large companies seem to get larger. They have the financial deep pockets to take a loss for an extended time. If you are not only to survive but also prosper, you must be prepared to weather bad times. Having a lending agency stand behind you helps.

To sum up, the bottom line is you must put together a solid managerial team that works together. You must not only have adequate funds to operate your aquaculture business, but you also must have funds in reserve to handle difficult financial times.

Do you have the infrastructure?

Think of infrastructure as a chain containing a series of links. Each link contributes to production of the crop, harvesting of the crop, transporting it to processing, and marketing and distributing. One weak link can jepardize the whole operation.

Here are a few examples: In the mid 1960s, a large company had access to land and water to farm channel catfish in southern Louisiana. Everything seemed to be in place, except for one thing. The company could not get a loan because there was no history of catfish farming in southern Louisiana. Lending institutions were reluctant to loan money to an unproved business.

Crawfish farming is well established in southern Louisiana, but has had difficulties developing in the northern part of the state. This is partly because the infrastructure was not in place. The industry has been too small for much development of ancillary businesses. Crawfish farmers had to buy traps and bait from dealers in south Louisiana. Processing plants were not available.

You can expect to have problems with infrastructure when locating in a new region or country. You may have low-cost land, excellent water, and warm temperatures, but the logistics of getting supplies in and product out may offset these advantages. Many companies locating in remote areas become vertically integrated out of necessity.

Bean et al. (1988) made a parish by parish assessment of the infrastructure for aquaculture development in Louisiana. Among other things, they recorded the miles of paved highways, the number of seafood processors, and the distance to air transportation.

To sum up, make a list of the links needed for your infrastructure chain. You might put "knowledge base" as the first link. Even though you may have a good managerial team, no one has all the answers. Remember, a smart person does not necessarily have all the answers, but a smart person knows where to get the answers. Having close access to a land-grant college, or other knowledge base, helps. From there, you might list lending agencies, transportation system, power source, and so on.

Do you have the desire and determination?

Hill (1971) was commissioned by Andrew Carnegie to study rich and successful people to see how they became so. After spending much of his adult life pursuing this task, he drew several conclusions. Hill noted that not all successful people were exceptionally gifted or talented, but all had exceptional desire and determination. This holds true for commercial aquaculture. If you are looking for quick profits, aquaculture may not be for you. If, however, you have desire, determination, dedication, and perseverance, commercial aquaculture can be very rewarding.

852

REFERENCES

Bangs, D.H. 1992. 6th edition. The Business Planning Guide. Dover, New
 Hampshire: Upstart Publishing Company Inc. 184 pp.

Bean, R.A., T. Baum, M. Lamon, J.W. Avault, Jr., M.W. Moody, L.W. de la Bretonne,
 Jr. and G.L. Jensen. 1988. Louisiana aquaculture potential: a parish-by-parish
 assessment. Louisiana State University Agricultural Center, Louisiana Agricultural
Experiment Station, Louisiana Cooperative Extension Service. 323 pp.

Hill, N. 1971. Think and Grow Rich. Hollywood, California: Wilshire Book
 Company Inc. 296 pp.

APPENDIX
Conversion Tables

Degrees Celsius ($^{\circ}$C) to Fahrenheit ($^{\circ}$F)

$^{\circ}$C	$^{\circ}$F	$^{\circ}$C	$^{\circ}$F	$^{\circ}$C	$^{\circ}$F
-18	-0.4	9	48.2	31	87.8
-16	+3.2	10	50.0	32	89.6
-14	+6.8	11	51.8	33	91.4
-12	+10.4	12	53.6	34	93.2
-10	+14.0	13	55.4	35	95.0
-8	+17.6	14	57.2	36	96.8
-7	+19.4	15	59.0	37	98.6
-6	+21.2	16	60.8	38	100.4
-5	+23.0	17	62.6	39	102.2
-4	+24.8	18	64.4	40	104.0
-3	+26.6	19	66.2	41	105.8
-2	+28.4	20	68.0	42	107.6
-1	+30.2	21	69.8	43	109.4
0	+32.0	22	71.6	44	111.2
1	33.8	23	73.4	45	113.0
2	35.6	24	75.2	46	114.8
3	37.4	25	77.0	47	116.6
4	39.2	26	78.8	48	118.4
5	41.0	27	80.6	49	120.2
6	42.8	28	82.4	50	122.0
7	44.6	29	84.2		
8	46.4	30	86.0		

Celsius to Fahrenheit = (C x 9/5) + 32
Fahrenheit to Celsius = (F - 32) x 5/9

Example:

Convert 10°C to Fahrenheit
(10 x 1.8) + 32 = 50°F

Convert 50°F to Celsius
(50 - 32) x 0.5555 = 10°C

Length

1 micron (µ) = 10^{-6} meter (m)
1 millimeter (mm) = 0.1 centimeter (cm)
1 centimeter = 10 millimeters
1 centimeter = 0.01 meter

1 millimeter = 0.04 inch (in)
1 centimeter (cm) = 0.3937 inches
1 meter (m) = 3.281 feet (ft)
1 meter = 1.094 yards (yd)
1 kilometer = 0.621 statute mile
1 kilometer = 0.5396 nautical mile

1 meter = 1,000 mm
1 meter = 100 cm
1 kilometer (km) =1,000 meters

1 inch = 25.4 mm
1 inch = 2.54 cm
1 foot = 0.305 meter
1 yard = 0.914 meter
1 statute mile = 1.61 km
1 nautical mile = 1.853 km

Weights

1 milligram = 0.001 grams (g)
1 kilogram (water) = 1 liter
1 metric ton (water) = 1,000 liters

1 gram = 15.43 grains
1 gram = 0.0353 ounce
1 kilogram = 2.205 pounds (lb)
1 metric ton = 2,205 pounds
1 metric ton = 1.1025 short tons

1 kilogram (kg) = 1,000 grams
1 metric ton (mt) = 1,000 kg

1 pound = 453.6 grams
1 ounce = 28.35 grams
1 gallon = 3.785 kilograms
1 cubic foot (water) = 28.3 kg
1 short ton = 0.9070294 metric ton

1 cubic foot (water) = 62.4 pounds
1 gallon = 8.34 pounds
1 acre foot (water) = 2,718,144 pounds

1 short ton = 2,000 pounds
1 long ton = 2,240 pounds

Area

1 hectare = 10,000 square meters

1 acre = 43,560 square feet

1 square centimeter = 0.155 square inch
1 square meter = 10.76 square feet
1 square meter = 1.196 square yards
1 hectare (ha) = 2.471 acres (ac)
1 hectare = 107,593 square feet

1 square inch = 6.45 square cm
1 square foot = 0.0929 square meter
1 square yard = 0.836 square meter
1 acre = 0.405 hectare

Volume and Capacity

1 cubic meter = 1,000 liters

1 metric ton (water) = 1,000 liters

1 cubic centimeter = 0.0610 cubic inch
1 cubic meter = 35.3 cubic feet
1 cubic meter = 1.308 cubic yards
1 milliliter = 0.0338 liquid ounce (oz)
1 liter = 0.2642 liquid gallons
1 liter = 1.057 liquid quarts
1 liter = 61.03 cubic inches

1 cubic inch = 16.39 cm^3
1 cubic foot = 28.3 liters
1 cubic yard = 0.765 cubic meter
1 liquid ounce = 29.57 milliliters
1 liquid quart (qt) = 0.946 liters
1 liquid gallon = 3.785 liters
1 pint = 0.473 liters
1 acre foot = 1,233.5 cubic meters

1 cubic foot = 7.48 liquid gallons
1 liquid gallon = 231 cubic inches
1 acre slice = 0.55 acre foot

1 liquid gallon = 128 liquid oz
1 acre foot = 325,850 gallons

Fish Production

1 kilogram per hectare (kg/ha) = 1.12 pounds per acre (lb/ac)
1 pound per acre = 0.893 kilogram per hectare

Flow Rate of Water

1 cubic meter per minute = 265 gallon per minute (gpm)
1 liter per minute = 0.2642 gallons per minute

1 cubic foot per second (cfs) ≈ 1,703 liters per minute
1 cubic foot per second ≈ 1.7 cubic meters per minute
1 cubic foot per second ≈ 450 gallons per minute

Stocking Rate of Culture Species

1 per square meter = 10,000 per hectare
1 per square meter ≈ 4,000 per acre
1 per hectare ≈ 0.4 per acre
1 per acre ≈ 2.5 per hectare

Concentrations of Chemicals

1 milligram per liter (mg/L) = 1 part per million (ppm) *
2.72 pounds = 1 ppm per acre foot of water
1 gram per cubic meter = 1 mg/L

* For solutions in fresh water, 1 mg of chemical per 1 liter of water equals 1 ppm. Therefore, 1 mg/L = 1 ppm. This is because 1 liter of fresh water weighs 1,000,000 milligrams. Salt water is heavier than fresh water, and 1 ppm and 1 mg/L are not exactly interchangeable.

Index

866